Big Ideas Learning, LLC
1762 Norcross Road
Erie, PA 16510-3838
USA

For product information and customer support, contact Big Ideas Learning
at **1-877-552-7766** or visit us at ***BigIdeasLearning.com***.

Printed in the U.S.A.

ISBN 13: 978-1-60840-172-7
ISBN 10: 1-60840-172-3

1 2 3 4 5 6 7 8 9 10 WEB 14 13 12 11 10

BIG IDEAS
MATH 8 ®

VIRGINIA TEACHING EDITION

Ron Larson
Laurie Boswell

Erie, Pennsylvania
BigIdeasLearning.com

AUTHORS

Ron Larson is a professor of mathematics at Penn State Erie, The Behrend College, where he has taught since receiving his Ph.D. in mathematics from the University of Colorado in 1970. Dr. Larson is well known as the lead author of a comprehensive program for mathematics that spans middle school, high school, and college courses. His high school and Advanced Placement books are published by Holt McDougal. Ron's numerous professional activities keep him in constant touch with the needs of students, teachers, and supervisors. Ron and Laurie Boswell began writing together in 1992. Since that time, they have authored over two dozen textbooks. In their collaboration, Ron is primarily responsible for the pupil edition and Laurie is primarily responsible for the teaching edition of the text.

Laurie Boswell is the Head of School and a mathematics teacher at the Riverside School in Lyndonville, Vermont. Dr. Boswell received her Ed.D. from the University of Vermont in 2010. She is a recipient of the Presidential Award for Excellence in Mathematics Teaching. Laurie has taught math to students at all levels, elementary through college. In addition, Laurie was a Tandy Technology Scholar, and served on the NCTM Board of Directors from 2002 to 2005. She currently serves on the board of NCSM, and is a popular national speaker. Along with Ron, Laurie has co-authored numerous math programs.

ABOUT THE BOOK

This book is brand new! It is not a revision of a previously published book.

When the NCTM released its new *Curriculum Focal Points* for mathematics for grades 6–8, we were delighted. The traditional mile-wide and inch-deep programs that have been followed for years have clearly not worked. Middle school students need something new . . . fewer topics with deeper coverage.

- **DEEPER** Each section is designed for 2–3 day coverage.
- **DYNAMIC** Each section begins with a full class period of active learning.
- **DOABLE** Each section is accompanied by full student and teacher support.
- **DAZZLING** How else can we say this? This book puts the dazzle back in math!

Ron Larson

Laurie Boswell

TEACHER REVIEWERS

- Gail Englert
  Math Department Chairperson
  Norfolk Public Schools
  Norfolk, VA

- J. Patrick Lintner
  Mathematics Supervisor
  Harrisonburg City Public Schools
  Harrisonburg, VA

- Jamie Rosati Perkins
  Middle School Mathematics Coach
  Henrico County Public Schools
  Richmond, VA

- Dianne Schoonover
  Secondary Math Teacher Specialist
  Hampton City Schools
  Hampton, VA

- Bill Setzer
  Retired Mathematics Supervisor
  Roanoke County Schools
  Salem, VA

- Beth Swain
  Mathematics Coordinator
  Salem City Schools
  Salem, VA

- Denise Walston
  Mathematics Coordinator
  Norfolk Public Schools
  Norfolk, VA

STUDENT REVIEWERS

- Ashley Benovic

- Vanessa Bowser

- Sara Chinsky

- Kaitlyn Grimm

- Lakota Noble

- Norhan Omar

- Jack Puckett

- Abby Quinn

- Victoria Royal

- Madeline Su

- Lance Williams

CONSULTANTS

● Patsy Davis
Educational Consultant
Knoxville, Tennessee

● Ryan Keating
Special Education Advisor
Gilbert, Arizona

● Bob Fulenwider
Mathematics Consultant
Bakersfield, California

● Michael McDowell
Project-Based Instruction Specialist
Scottsdale, Arizona

● Deb Johnson
Differentiated Instruction Consultant
Missoula, Montana

● Sean McKeighan
Interdisciplinary Advisor
Midland, Texas

● Mark Johnson
Mathematics Assessment Consultant
Raymond, New Hampshire

● Bonnie Spence
Differentiated Instruction Consultant
Missoula, Montana

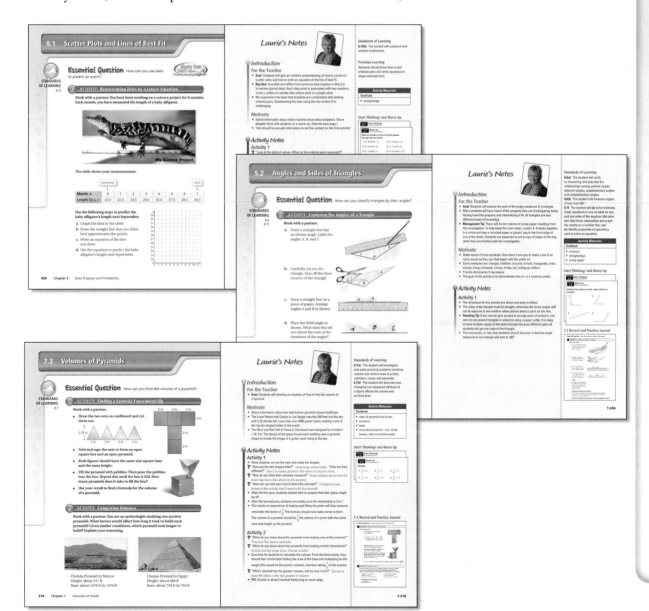

Solving Equations and Inequalities

"I love my math book. It has so many interesting examples and homework problems. I have always liked math, but I didn't know how it could be used. Now I have lots of ideas."

BIG IDEAS MATH 8
Ron Larson
Laurie Boswell

Graphing and Writing Linear Equations

"I like starting each new lesson with a partner activity. I just moved to this school and the activities helped me make friends."

Functions

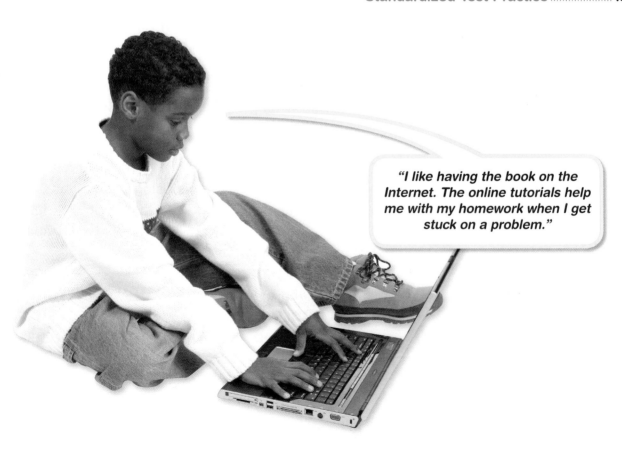

"I like having the book on the Internet. The online tutorials help me with my homework when I get stuck on a problem."

Percents

"I love the cartoons. They are funny and they help me remember the math. I want to be a cartoonist some day."

Angles and Polygons

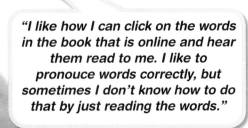

"I like how I can click on the words in the book that is online and hear them read to me. I like to pronouce words correctly, but sometimes I don't know how to do that by just reading the words."

Surface Areas of Solids

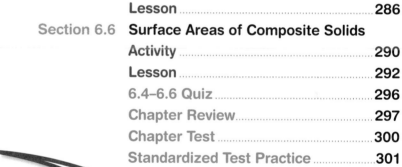

"I really liked the projects at the end of the book. The history project on ancient Egypt was my favorite. Someday I would like to visit Egypt and go to the pyramids."

Volumes of Solids

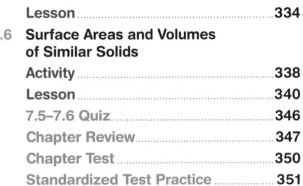

"I like how the glossary in the book is part of the index. When I couldn't remember how a vocabulary word was defined, I could go to the index and find where the word was defined in the book."

Square Roots and the Pythagorean Theorem

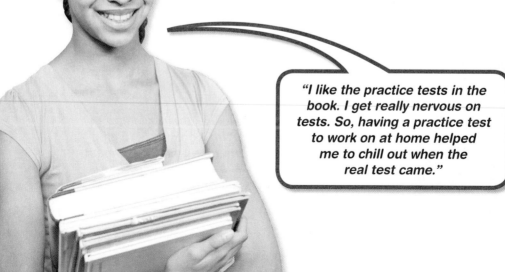

"*I like the practice tests in the book. I get really nervous on tests. So, having a practice test to work on at home helped me to chill out when the real test came.*"

Data Displays and Probability

"I like the review at the beginning of each chapter. This book has examples to help me remember things from last year. I don't like it when the review is just a list of questions."

Exponents and Scientific Notation

"I like the workbook (Record and Practice Journal). It saved me a lot of work to not have to copy all the questions and graphs."

Appendix A: My Big Ideas Projects

PROGRAM OVERVIEW
Print

Available in print, online, and in digital format

- **Pupil Edition**

- **Teaching Edition**

- **Record and Practice Journal**

- **Assessment Book**
  - Pre-Course Test
  - Quizzes
  - Chapter Tests
  - Standardized Test Practice
  - Alternative Assessment
  - End-of-Course Tests

- **Resources by Chapter**
  - Start Thinking! and Warm Up
  - Family and Community Involvement: English and Spanish
  - School-to-Work
  - Graphic Organizers/Study Help
  - Financial Literacy
  - Technology Connection
  - Life Connections
  - Stories in History
  - Extra Practice
  - Enrichment and Extension
  - Puzzle Time
  - Projects with Rubrics
  - Cumulative Practice

- **Differentiating the Lesson**
- **Skills Review Handbook**
- **Basic Skills Handbook**
- **Worked-Out Solutions**
- **Lesson Plans**
- **Teacher Tools**

Skills Review Handbook

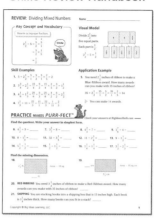

Basic Skills Handbook

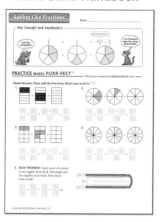

Technology

- Big Ideas **Exam**_View_® Assessment Suite
  Includes
  - Test Generator
  - Test Player
  - Test Manager

- **Lesson**_View_® Dynamic Planning Tool

- **Puzzle**_View_® Vocabulary Puzzle Builder

- **Mind**_Point_® Quiz_Show_

- Interactive Glossary: English and Spanish

- Dynamic Classroom

- Answer Presentation Tool

- _BigIdeasMath.com_
  - Student Companion Website
  - Teacher Companion Website

- Lesson Tutorials

- Online Pupil Edition

VIRGINIA STANDARDS OF LEARNING TO BOOK CORRELATION

After a standard is introduced, it is revisited many times in subsequent activities, lessons, and exercises.

STRAND: Number and Number Sense
Focus: Relationships within the Real Number System

Standards of Learning	
8.1	The student will **(a)** simplify numerical expressions involving positive exponents, using rational numbers, order of operations, and properties of operations with real numbers; and **(b)** compare and order decimals, fractions, percents, and numbers written in scientific notation.
8.2	The student will describe orally and in writing the relationships between the subsets of the real number system.

Section 8.3 Approximating Square Roots
Essential Question: How can you find decimal approximations of square roots that are irrational?

Section 8.4 Simplifying Square Roots
Essential Question: How can you use a square root to describe the golden ratio?

Section 10.1 Properties of Exponents
Essential Question: How can you use carbon dating to estimate the age of an object?

Section 10.2 Product of Powers Property
Essential Question: How can you multiply two powers that have the same base?

Section 10.3 Quotient of Powers Property
Essential Question: How can you divide two powers that have the same base?

Section 10.4 Scientific Notation
Essential Question: How did people in ancient cultures represent large numbers?

STRAND: Computation and Estimation
Focus: Practical Applications of Operations with Real Numbers

Standards of Learning	
8.3	The student will **(a)** solve practical problems involving rational numbers, percents, ratios, and proportions; and **(b)** determine the percent increase or decrease for a given situation.
8.4	The student will apply the order of operations to evaluate algebraic expressions for given replacement values of the variables.
8.5	The student will **(a)** determine whether a given number is a perfect square; and **(b)** find the two consecutive whole numbers between which a square root lies.

Section 2.2 Slope of a Line
Essential Question: How can the slope of a line be used to describe the line?

Section 4.1 The Percent Equation
Essential Question: How can you use models to estimate percent questions?

Section 4.2 Percents of Increase and Decrease
Essential Question: What is a percent of decrease? What is a percent of increase?

Section 4.3 Discounts and Markups
Essential Question: How can you find discounts and markups efficiently?

Section 4.4 Simple Interest
Essential Question: How can you find the amount of simple interest earned on a savings account? How can you find the amount of interest owed on a loan?

Section 5.4 Using Similar Triangles
Essential Question: Which properties of triangles make them special among all other types of polygons?

Section 8.1 Finding Square Roots
Essential Question: How can you find the dimensions of a square or circle when you are given its area?

Section 8.3 Approximating Square Roots
Essential Question: How can you find decimal approximations of square roots that are irrational?

STRAND: Measurement
Focus: Problem Solving

Standards of Learning	
8.6	The student will **(a)** verify by measuring and describe the relationships among vertical angles, adjacent angles, supplementary angles, and complementary angles; and **(b)** measure angles of less than 360°.
8.7	The student will **(a)** investigate and solve practical problems involving volume and surface area of prisms, cylinders, cones, and pyramids; and **(b)** describe how changing one measured attribute of a figure affects the volume and surface area.

Section 5.1   Classifying Angles
Essential Question: How can you classify two angles as complementary or supplementary?

Section 5.2   Angles and Sides of Triangles
Essential Question: How can you classify triangles by their angles?

Section 5.3   Angles of Polygons
Essential Question: How can you find a formula for the sum of the angle measures of any polygon?

Section 6.2   Surface Areas of Prisms
Essential Question: How can you use a formula to find the surface area of a prism?

Section 6.3   Surface Areas of Cylinders
Essential Question: How can you derive a formula for the surface area of a cylinder?

Section 6.4   Surface Areas of Pyramids
Essential Question: How can you find the surface area of a pyramid?

Section 6.5   Surface Areas of Cones
Essential Question: How can you find the surface area of a cone?

Section 6.6   Surface Areas of Composite Solids
Essential Question: How can you find the surface area of a composite solid?

Section 7.1   Volumes of Prisms
Essential Question: How can you find the volume of any prism?

Section 7.2   Volumes of Cylinders
Essential Question: How can you find a pattern for changes in volume that occur in nature?

Section 7.3   Volumes of Pyramids
Essential Question: How can you find the volume of a pyramid?

Section 7.4 Volumes of Cones
Essential Question: How can you remember the formulas for surface area and volume?

Section 7.5 Volumes of Composite Solids
Essential Question: How can you estimate the volume of a composite solid?

Section 7.6 Surface Areas and Volumes of Similar Solids
Essential Question: When the dimensions of a solid increase by a factor of k, how does the surface area change? How does the volume change?

STRAND: Geometry
Focus: Problem Solving with 2- and 3-Dimensional Figures

Standards of Learning	
8.8	The student will (a) apply transformations to plane figures; and (b) identify applications of transformations.
8.9	The student will construct a three-dimensional model, given the top or bottom, side, and front views.
8.10	The student will (a) verify the Pythagorean Theorem; and (b) apply the Pythagorean Theorem.
8.11	The student will solve practical area and perimeter problems involving composite plane figures.

Section 5.5 Polygons and Transformations
Essential Question: How can transformations be used in calligraphy?

Section 5.6 Perimeters of Composite Figures
Essential Question: How can you find the perimeter of a composite figure?

Section 5.7 Areas of Composite Figures
Essential Question: How can you find the area of a composite figure?

Section 6.1 Drawing 3-Dimensional Figures
Essential Question: How can you draw three-dimensional figures?

Section 8.2 The Pythagorean Theorem
Essential Question: How are the lengths of the sides of a right triangle related?

Section 8.5 Using the Pythagorean Theorem
Essential Question: How can you use the Pythagorean Theorem to solve real-life problems?

STRAND: Probability and Statistics
Focus: Statistical Analysis of Graphs and Problem Situations

Standards of Learning	
8.12	The student will determine the probability of independent and dependent events with and without replacement.
8.13	The student will **(a)** make comparisons, predictions, and inferences, using information displayed in graphs; and **(b)** construct and analyze scatterplots.

Section 3.4 Comparing Linear and Nonlinear Functions
Essential Question: How can you recognize when a pattern in real life is linear or nonlinear?

Section 9.1 Scatter Plots and Lines of Best Fit
Essential Question: How can you use data to predict an event?

Section 9.2 Choosing a Data Display
Essential Question: How can you display data in a way that helps you make decisions?

Section 9.3 Probability
Essential Question: How is probability used in the "mark-recapture" method?

Section 9.4 Independent and Dependent Events
Essential Question: How can you use probability to help you win a game show?

STRAND: Patterns, Functions, and Algebra
Focus: Linear Relationships

Standards of Learning	
8.14	The student will make connections between any two representations (tables, graphs, words, and rules) of a given relationship.
8.15	The student will **(a)** solve multistep linear equations in one variable with the variable on one and two sides of the equation; **(b)** solve two-step linear inequalities and graph the results on a number line; and **(c)** identify properties of operations used to solve an equation.
8.16	The student will graph a linear equation in two variables.
8.17	The student will identify the domain, range, independent variable, or dependent variable in a given situation.

Section 1.1   Solving Simple Equations
Essential Question: How can you use inductive reasoning to discover rules in mathematics? How can you test a rule?

Section 1.2   Solving Multi-Step Equations
Essential Question: How can you solve a multi-step equation? How can you check the reasonableness of your solution?

Section 1.3   Solving Equations with Variables on Both Sides
Essential Question: How can you solve an equation that has variables on both sides?

Section 1.4   Rewriting Equations and Formulas
Essential Question: How can you use a formula for one measurement to write a formula for a different measurement?

Section 1.5   Writing and Graphing Inequalities
Essential Question: How can you use an inequality to describe a real-life statement?

Section 1.6   Solving One-Step Inequalities
Essential Question: How can you use addition or subtraction to solve an inequality?

Section 1.7   Solving Two-Step Inequalities
Essential Question: How can you solve a two-step inequality?

Section 2.1   Graphing Linear Equations
Essential Question: How can you recognize a linear equation? How can you draw its graph?

Section 2.2   Slope of a Line
Essential Question: How can the slope of a line be used to describe the line?

Section 2.3   Graphing Linear Equations in Slope-Intercept Form
Essential Question: How can you describe the graph of the equation $y = mx + b$?

Section 2.4   Graphing Linear Equations in Standard Form
Essential Question: How can you describe the graph of the equation $ax + by = c$?

Section 2.5   Writing Equations in Slope-Intercept Form
Essential Question: How can you write an equation of a line when you are given the slope and y-intercept of the line?

Section 2.6   Writing Equations Using a Slope and a Point
Essential Question: How can you write an equation of a line when you are given the slope and a point on the line?

Section 2.7   Writing Equations Using Two Points
Essential Question: How can you write an equation of a line when you are given two points on the line?

Section 2.8   Solving Real-Life Problems
Essential Question: How can you use a linear equation in two variables to model and solve a real-life problem?

Section 3.1   Domain and Range of a Function
Essential Question: How can you find the domain and range of a function?

Section 3.2   Discrete and Continuous Domains
Essential Question: How can you decide whether the domain of a function is discrete or continuous?

Section 3.3   Linear Function Patterns
Essential Question: How can you use a linear function to describe a linear pattern?

Section 5.2   Angles and Sides of Triangles
Essential Question: How can you classify triangles by their angles?

BOOK TO VIRGINIA STANDARDS OF LEARNING CORRELATION

Chapter 5 Angles and Polygons

5.1 Classifying Angles

8.6(a) The student will verify by measuring and describe the relationships among vertical angles, adjacent angles, supplementary angles, and complementary angles.

5.2 Angles and Sides of Triangles

8.6(a) The student will verify by measuring and describe the relationships among vertical angles, adjacent angles, supplementary angles, and complementary angles.

8.6(b) The student will measure angles of less than 360°.

8.15(a) The student will solve multistep linear equations in one variable with the variable on one and two sides of the equation.

8.15(b) The student will solve two-step linear inequalities and graph the results on a number line.

8.15(c) The student will identify properties of operations used to solve an equation.

5.3 Angles of Polygons

8.6(b) The student will measure angles of less than 360°.

5.4 Using Similar Triangles

8.3(a) The student will solve practical problems involving rational numbers, percents, ratios, and proportions.

5.5 Polygons and Transformations

8.8(a) The student will apply transformations to plane figures.

8.8(b) The student will identify applications of transformations.

5.6 Perimeters of Composite Figures

8.11 The student will solve practical area and perimeter problems involving composite plane figures.

5.7 Areas of Composite Figures

8.11 The student will solve practical area and perimeter problems involving composite plane figures.

Chapter 8 Square Roots and the Pythagorean Theorem

NARROWER AND DEEPER™

Middle school students need a new approach to learning mathematics. Big Ideas Math's *Narrower and Deeper*™ program is a revolutionary combination of the discovery and direct instruction approaches. Students gain a deeper understanding of math concepts by narrowing their focus to fewer topics. They master concepts through fun and engaging activities, stepped-out, concise examples, and rich, thought-provoking exercises.

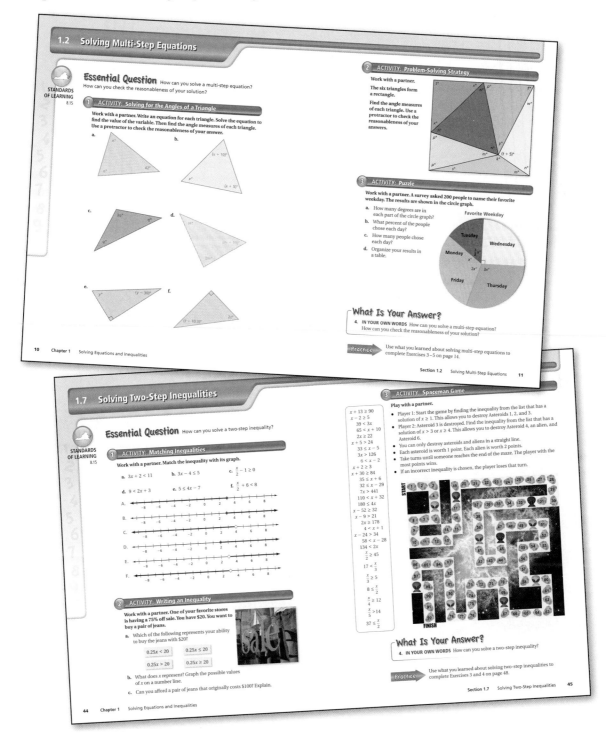

A BALANCED APPROACH

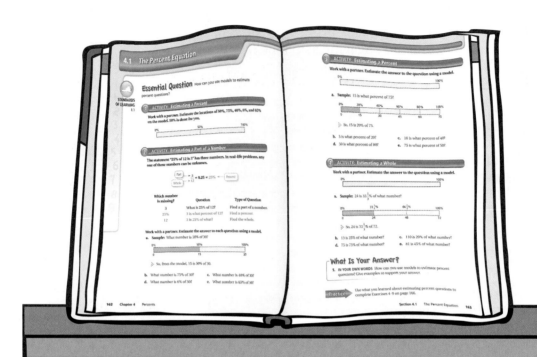

DISCOVERY

*Each section begins with a 2-page **Activity** that is introduced by an Essential Question.*

- **Deeper**
- **Dynamic**
- **Doable**
- **Dazzling**

TO INSTRUCTION

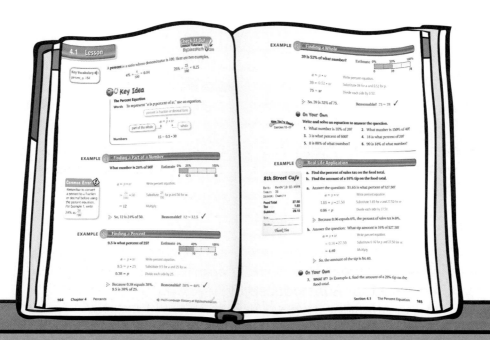

DIRECT INSTRUCTION

*After the concept has been introduced with a full-class period **Activity**, it is extended the following day through the **Lesson**.*

- **Key Ideas**
- **Examples**
- **"On Your Own" Questions**

ENGAGING PUPIL BOOKS

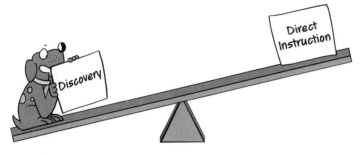

ACTIVITY

Each section begins with a 2-page
Activity *that is introduced by*
an Essential Question.

- ● **Deeper**
- ● **Dynamic**
- ● **Doable**
- ● **Dazzling**

Students gain a deeper
understanding of topics
through inductive
reasoning and exploration.

Students develop
communication and
problem-solving skills
by answering Essential
Questions.

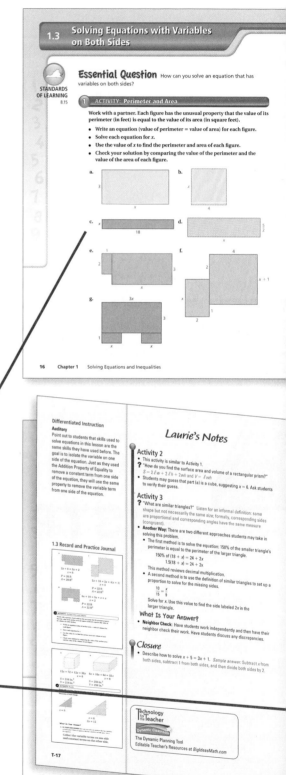

INSPIRING TEACHER BOOKS

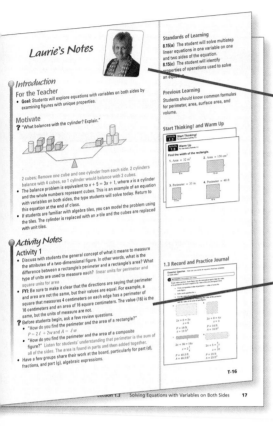

Teachers have the benefit of **Laurie Boswell's** 20-plus years of classroom experience reflected in her lively and informative notes.

Teachers are offered suggestions for questioning that help guide students toward better understanding.

"Laurie's Notes"

COMPLETE ACTIVITY AND TIME MANAGEMENT SUPPORT FROM A MASTER CLASSROOM TEACHER

2 ACTIVITY: Surface Area and Volume

Work with a partner. Each solid has the unusual property that the value of its surface area (in square inches) is equal to the value of its volume (in cubic inches).

- Write an equation (value of surface area = value of volume) for each figure.
- Solve each equation for x.
- Use the value of x to find the surface area and volume of each figure.
- Check your solution by comparing the value of the surface area and the value of the volume of each figure.

3 ACTIVITY: Puzzle

Work with a partner. The two triangles are similar. The perimeter of the larger triangle is 150% of the perimeter of the smaller triangle. Find the dimensions of each triangle.

What Is Your Answer?

4. **IN YOUR OWN WORDS** How can you solve an equation that has variables on both sides? Write an equation that has variables on both sides. Solve the equation.

 Practice Use what you learned about solving equations with variables on both sides to complete Exercises 3–5 on page 20.

Section 1.3   Solving Equations with Variables on Both Sides   **17**

CLEAR PUPIL BOOKS

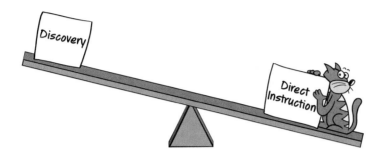

LESSON

After the concept has been introduced with a full-class period **Activity***, it is extended the following day through the* **Lesson***.*

- ● **Key Ideas**
- ● **Examples**
- ● **"On Your Own" Questions**

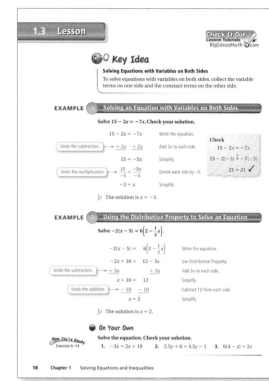

Each concept is accompanied by clear, stepped-out examples.

Each example in the pupil edition is accompanied by teaching suggestions from Laurie.

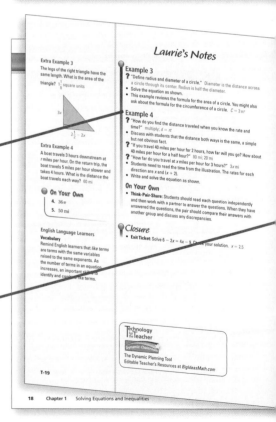

INSIGHTFUL TEACHER BOOKS

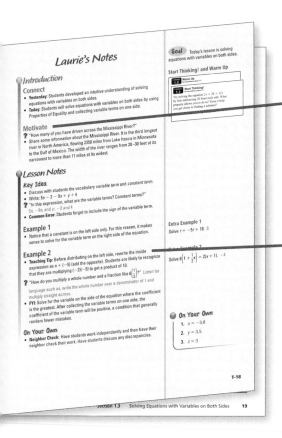

Student-friendly and teacher-tested motivation activities start each lesson.

Laurie shares insights she has gained through years of teaching experience.

"Laurie's Notes"
COMPREHENSIVE TEACHING SUPPORT FROM A MASTER CLASSROOM TEACHER

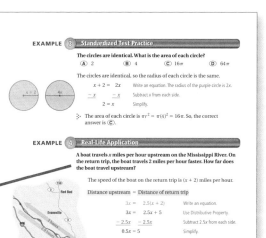

SKILLS REVIEW HANDBOOK

The Skills Review Handbook provides complete coverage of pre-course skills. Each of the 85 lessons includes Key Concepts and Vocabulary, Visual Models, Skill Examples, Application Examples, and practice.

This complete, full color handbook was authored and designed by Ron Larson, ensuring consistency and thoroughness in coverage of the content.

BigIdeasMath.com

BASIC SKILLS HANDBOOK

The Basic Skills Handbook covers basic skills needed for success in middle school mathematics. This handbook is designed for students who are working two or more grades below grade level. This colorful, highly visual handbook uses few words, making it ideal for students with reading difficulties or students learning English.

The Basic Skills Handbook was also authored and designed by Ron Larson.

BigIdeasMath.com

PACING GUIDE

Each page in the book is in the *Pacing Guide*.
- Chapters 1–10:   157 days
- With Appendix A: 167 days

Chapter 1   (21 Days)

Chapter Opener	1 Day
Activity 1.1	1 Day
Lesson 1.1	2 Days
Activity 1.2	1 Day
Lesson 1.2	1 Day
Activity 1.3	1 Day
Lesson 1.3	1 Day
Activity 1.4	2 Days
Lesson 1.4	1 Day
Study Help/Quiz	1 Day
Activity 1.5	1 Day
Lesson 1.5	1 Day
Activity 1.6	1 Day
Lesson 1.6	1 Day
Activity 1.7	2 Days
Lesson 1.7	1 Day
Chapter Review/Tests	2 Days

Chapter 2   (21 Days)

Chapter Opener	1 Day
Activity 2.1	1 Day
Lesson 2.1	1 Day
Activity 2.2	1 Day
Lesson 2.2	1 Day
Activity 2.3	1 Day
Lesson 2.3	1 Day
Activity 2.4	1 Day
Lesson 2.4	1 Day
Study Help/Quiz	1 Day
Activity 2.5	1 Day
Lesson 2.5	1 Day
Activity 2.6	1 Day
Lesson 2.6	1 Day
Activity 2.7	1 Day
Lesson 2.7	1 Day
Activity 2.8	2 Days
Lesson 2.8	1 Day
Chapter Review/Tests	2 Days

Chapter 3   (12 Days)

Chapter Opener	1 Day
Activity 3.1	1 Day
Lesson 3.1	1 Day
Activity 3.2	1 Day
Lesson 3.2	1 Day
Study Help/Quiz	1 Day
Activity 3.3	1 Day
Lesson 3.3	1 Day
Activity 3.4	1 Day
Lesson 3.4	1 Day
Chapter Review/Tests	2 Days

Chapter 4   (12 Days)

Chapter Opener	1 Day
Activity 4.1	1 Day
Lesson 4.1	1 Day
Activity 4.2	1 Day
Lesson 4.2	1 Day
Study Help/Quiz	1 Day
Activity 4.3	1 Day
Lesson 4.3	1 Day
Activity 4.4	1 Day
Lesson 4.4	1 Day
Chapter Review/Tests	2 Days

Chapter 5   (18 Days)

Chapter Opener	1 Day
Activity 5.1	1 Day
Lesson 5.1	1 Day
Activity 5.2	1 Day
Lesson 5.2	1 Day
Activity 5.3	1 Day
Lesson 5.3	1 Day
Study Help/Quiz	1 Day
Activity 5.4	1 Day
Lesson 5.4	1 Day
Activity 5.5	1 Day
Lesson 5.5	1 Day
Activity 5.6	1 Day
Lesson 5.6	1 Day
Activity 5.7	1 Day
Lesson 5.7	1 Day
Chapter Review/Tests	2 Days

PROFESSIONAL DEVELOPMENT

Big Ideas Learning, LLC is a professional development and publishing company founded by Dr. Ron Larson. We are dedicated to providing 21st century teaching and learning in the area of mathematics. We work with middle schools across the country as they implement world-class standards for mathematics.

As teachers and school districts move forward in implementing new standards, the fundamental ideas of rigor and relevance and big ideas that are deep and focused take on new meaning. Big Ideas Learning provides a rich, hands-on experience that allows for astute understanding and practice, not only of the challenging world-class standards, but of the underlying mathematics pedagogy as well.

WORKSHOPS

- Creating Highly Motivating Classrooms
- Implementing the NCTM Curriculum Focal Points

Activities for the Mathematics Classroom:

- Teaching More with Less
- Best Practices in the Mathematics Classroom
- Questioning in the Mathematics Classroom
- The Three R's: Rigor, Relevance and Reality
- Reading in the Content Areas
- Games for Numerical Fluency
- Engaging the Tech Natives

Our professional staff of experienced instructors can also assist you in creating customized training sessions tailored to achieving your desired outcome.

Virginia Standards of Learning for Grade 8

Chapter Coverage for Content Strands

Strand — Number and Number Sense
Focus: Relationships within the Real Number System

Standards of Learning

8.1 The student will **(a)** simplify numerical expressions involving positive exponents, using rational numbers, order of operations, and properties of operations with real numbers; and **(b)** compare and order decimals, fractions, percents, and numbers written in scientific notation.

8.2 The student will describe orally and in writing the relationships between the subsets of the real number system.

Strand — Computation and Estimation
Focus: Practical Applications of Operations with Rational Numbers

Standards of Learning

8.3 The student will **(a)** solve practical problems involving rational numbers, percents, ratios, and proportions; and **(b)** determine the percent increase or decrease for a given situation.

8.4 The student will apply the order of operations to evaluate algebraic expressions for given replacement values of the variables.

8.5 The student will **(a)** determine whether a given number is a perfect square; and **(b)** find the two consecutive whole numbers between which a square root lies.

Strand — Measurement
Focus: Problem Solving

Standards of Learning

8.6 The student will **(a)** verify by measuring and describe the relationships among vertical angles, adjacent angles, supplementary angles, and complementary angles; and **(b)** measure angles of less than 360°.

8.7 The student will **(a)** investigate and solve practical problems involving volume and surface area of prisms, cylinders, cones, and pyramids; and **(b)** describe how changing one measured attribute of a figure affects the volume and surface area.

Strand   Geometry
Focus: Problem Solving with 2- and 3-Dimensional Figures

Standards of Learning

8.8   The student will **(a)** apply transformations to plane figures; and **(b)** identify applications of transformations.

8.9   The student will construct a three-dimensional model, given the top or bottom, side, and front views.

8.10   The student will **(a)** verify the Pythagorean Theorem; and **(b)** apply the Pythagorean Theorem.

8.11   The student will solve practical area and perimeter problems involving composite plane figures.

Strand   Probability and Statistics
Focus: Statistical Analysis of Graphs and Problem Situations

Standards of Learning

8.12   The student will determine the probability of independent and dependent events with and without replacement.

8.13   The student will **(a)** make comparisons, predictions, and inferences, using information displayed in graphs; and **(b)** construct and analyze scatterplots.

Strand   Patterns, Functions, and Algebra
Focus: Linear Relationships

Standards of Learning

8.14   The student will make connections between any two representations (tables, graphs, words, and rules) of a given relationship.

8.15   The student will **(a)** solve multistep linear equations in one variable with the variable on one and two sides of the equation; **(b)** solve two-step linear inequalities and graph the results on a number line; and **(c)** identify properties of operations used to solve an equation.

8.16   The student will graph a linear equation in two variables.

8.17   The student will identify the domain, range, independent variable, or dependent variable in a given situation.

How to Use Your Math Book

- Read the **Essential Question** in the activity.

  Work with a partner to decide **What Is Your Answer?**

  Now you are ready to do the  problems.

- Find the **Key Vocabulary** words, **highlighted in yellow**.

  Read their definitions. Study the concepts in each **Key Idea**.

  If you forget a definition, you can look it up online in the

  Multi-Language Glossary at BigIdeasMath.com.

- After you study each **EXAMPLE**, do the exercises in the ● **On Your Own**.

  Now You're Ready to do the exercises that correspond to the example.

  As you study, look for a **Study Tip** or a **Common Error**.

- The exercises are divided into 3 parts.

   Vocabulary and Concept Check

   Practice and Problem Solving

   Fair Game Review

  If an exercise has a ① next to it, look back at Example 1 for help with that exercise.

  More help is available at  **Check It Out** Lesson Tutorials BigIdeasMath.com.

- To help study for your test, use the following.

   Quiz    **Study Help**

  Chapter Review   **Chapter Test**

SCAVENGER HUNT

Use this *Scavenger Hunt* to find where things are in **Chapter 1**.

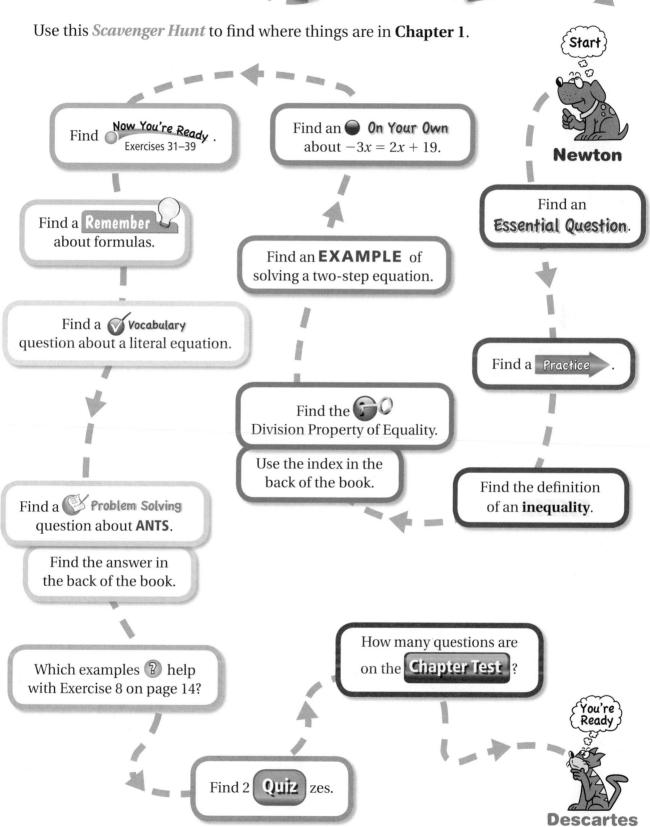

Find **Now You're Ready** Exercises 31–39.

Find an ● **On Your Own** about $-3x = 2x + 19$.

Start

Newton

Find an **Essential Question**.

Find a **Remember** about formulas.

Find an **EXAMPLE** of solving a two-step equation.

Find a ✓ **Vocabulary** question about a literal equation.

Find a **Practice** ➡.

Find the ⚷ Division Property of Equality.

Use the index in the back of the book.

Find the definition of an **inequality**.

Find a ✎ **Problem Solving** question about **ANTS**.

Find the answer in the back of the book.

Which examples ❓ help with Exercise 8 on page 14?

How many questions are on the **Chapter Test**?

Find 2 **Quiz** zes.

You're Ready

Descartes

1 Solving Equations and Inequalities

"Here is a math quiz, Descartes. Tell me about these symbols."

That's easy. One just means I am happy.

The other means that I have a piece of spaghetti stuck between my fangs.

"Just think of the Addition Property of Inequality in this way. If Fluffy has more cat treats than you have ..."

This guy really knows how to hurt a cat, doesn't he?

"... and you each get 2 more cat treats, then Fluffy will STILL have more cat treats than you have!"

Strands Development

6th Grade
• Solve one-step linear equations in one variable (whole number coefficients and positive rational solutions). • Graph inequalities on a number line.

7th Grade
• Write verbal sentences as equations and vice versa. • Solve one-step and two-step linear equations in one variable. • Solve one-step inequalities in one variable and graph the solutions on a number line.

8th Grade
• Identify properties of operations used to solve an equation. • Solve multi-step linear equations in one variable (with the variable on one or both sides of the equation). • Solve two-step linear inequalities and graph the solutions on a number line.

Math in History

The concept of writing all numbers by using only ten different symbols appears to have originated in India.

★ Here are some of the symbols that were used in the Brahmi system in India until around 400 A.D.

1	2	3	4	5	6	7	8	9
—	=	≡	+	Ⴙ	Ⴙ	?	ら	?

Notice that there is no symbol for 0. That concept was not yet devised. Also notice that the symbols for 2 and 3 are related to our modern symbols for 2 and 3.

Draw two horizontal bars quickly

Draw three horizontal bars quickly

★ By comparing the Brahmi symbols to another culture's symbols (such as the Chinese), you can see that our modern symbols are more closely related to the ancient Brahmi symbols.

1	2	3	4	5	6	7	8	9
一	二	三	四	五	六	七	八	九

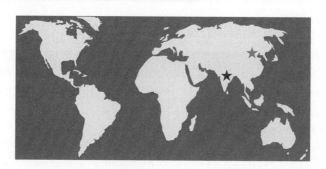

Pacing Guide for Chapter 1

Chapter Opener	1 Day
Section 1 Activity Lesson	 1 Day 2 Days
Section 2 Activity Lesson	 1 Day 1 Day
Section 3 Activity Lesson	 1 Day 1 Day
Section 4 Activity Lesson	 2 Days 1 Day
Study Help / Quiz	1 Day
Section 5 Activity Lesson	 1 Day 1 Day
Section 6 Activity Lesson	 1 Day 1 Day
Section 7 Activity Lesson	 2 Days 1 Day
Chapter Review / Tests	2 Days
Total Chapter 1	21 Days
Year-to-Date	21 Days

Check Your Resources

- Record and Practice Journal
- Resources by Chapter
- Skills Review Handbook
- Assessment Book
- Worked-Out Solutions

Technology For the Teacher

The Dynamic Planning Tool Editable Teacher's Resources at *BigIdeasMath.com*

7.16 The student will apply the following properties of operations with real numbers: **(a)** the commutative and associative properties for addition and multiplication; **(b)** the distributive property; **(c)** the additive and multiplicative identity properties; **(d)** the additive and multiplicative inverse properties; and **(e)** the multiplicative property of zero.

Additional Topics for Review
- Order of operations
- Multiplying and dividing fractions
- Multiplying and dividing decimals

Try It Yourself

1. $4m$ 2. $14g - 30$
3. $18 - 6y$ 4. $12a - 48$
5. $7n - 1.3$ 6. $7k + 88$
7. $\dfrac{7}{3}$ 8. $\dfrac{1}{4}$
9. $\dfrac{21}{11}$ 10. $-\dfrac{13}{4}$

Record and Practice Journal

1. $14x$ 2. $-11b - 4$
3. $2n + 6.8$ 4. $8k + 24$
5. $90 - 15g$ 6. $2y - 42$
7. $5m + 48$ 8. $13a - 2$
9. $1.5p + 3p + 2.5p; 7p$
10. 7 11. $\dfrac{1}{4}$ 12. $\dfrac{6}{5}$
13. $-\dfrac{9}{2}$ 14. $\dfrac{1}{12}$ 15. 16
16. $\dfrac{13}{7}$ 17. $\dfrac{5}{4}$ 18. $-\dfrac{11}{2}$
19. -40 20. $\dfrac{23}{6}$ 21. $\dfrac{50}{3}$
22. $\dfrac{15}{29}$ 23. $-\dfrac{3}{8}$ 24. $\dfrac{18}{31}$
25. $-\dfrac{5}{17}$ 26. $\dfrac{12}{47}$ 27. $\dfrac{77}{100}$
28. $\dfrac{8}{21}$ inch

Math Background Notes

Vocabulary Review
- Expression
- Like Terms
- Coefficient
- Simplest Form
- Distributive Property
- Commutative Property of Addition
- Numerator
- Denominator

Simplifying Algebraic Expressions
- Students should know how to simplify algebraic expressions.
- Remind students that an algebraic expression contains numbers, operations, and variables.
- Remind students that like terms are terms that have the same variables raised to the same exponents. A term without a variable, such as 5, is a constant. Constant terms are also like terms.
- **Common Error:** When identifying terms, make sure students include the sign of the term.
- An algebraic expression is in simplest form if it has no like terms and no parentheses. To combine like terms that have variables, use the Distributive Property to add or subtract the coefficients.

Writing Reciprocals
- Students should know how to write reciprocals.
- Remind students that two numbers whose product is 1 are reciprocals.
- To write a reciprocal of a number, first write the number as a fraction.
- The numerator of the original number becomes the denominator of the reciprocal and the denominator of the original number becomes the numerator of the reciprocal.
- **Common Error:** When you ask students to write a number and its reciprocal, they often write: $\frac{3}{4} = \frac{4}{3}$. Reciprocals are not equal (except for 1). Students should write $\frac{3}{4}, \frac{4}{3}$.

Reteaching and Enrichment Strategies

If students need help. . .	If students got it. . .
Record and Practice Journal • Fair Game Review Skills Review Handbook Lesson Tutorials	Game Closet at *BigIdeasMath.com* Start the next section

What You Learned Before

"Some people remember which is bigger by thinking that < is the mouth of a hungry alligator who is trying to eat the LARGER number."

Simplifying Algebraic Expressions

Example 1 Simplify $10b + 13 - 6b + 4$.

$$10b + 13 - 6b + 4 = 10b - 6b + 13 + 4 \quad \text{Commutative Property of Addition}$$
$$= (10 - 6)b + 13 + 4 \quad \text{Distributive Property}$$
$$= 4b + 17 \quad \text{Simplify.}$$

Example 2 Simplify $5(x + 4) + 2x$.

$$5(x + 4) + 2x = 5(x) + 5(4) + 2x \quad \text{Distributive Property}$$
$$= 5x + 20 + 2x \quad \text{Multiply.}$$
$$= 5x + 2x + 20 \quad \text{Commutative Property of Addition}$$
$$= (5 + 2)x + 20 \quad \text{Distributive Property}$$
$$= 7x + 20 \quad \text{Add coefficients.}$$

Try It Yourself
Simplify the expression.

1. $9m - 7m + 2m$

2. $3g - 9 + 11g - 21$

3. $6(3 - y)$

4. $12(a - 4)$

5. $22.5 + 7(n - 3.4)$

6. $15k + 8(11 - k)$

Writing Reciprocals

Example 3 Write the reciprocal of the number.

Original Number	*Fraction*	*Reciprocal*	*Check*
a. $\dfrac{2}{3}$	$\dfrac{2}{3}$	$\dfrac{3}{2}$	$\dfrac{2}{3} \times \dfrac{3}{2} = 1$
b. 6	$\dfrac{6}{1}$	$\dfrac{1}{6}$	$\dfrac{6}{1} \times \dfrac{1}{6} = 1$
c. $-\dfrac{5}{7}$	$-\dfrac{5}{7}$	$-\dfrac{7}{5}$	$-\dfrac{5}{7} \times \left(-\dfrac{7}{5}\right) = 1$

Try It Yourself
Write the reciprocal of the number.

7. $\dfrac{3}{7}$

8. 4

9. $\dfrac{11}{21}$

10. $-\dfrac{4}{13}$

1.1 Solving Simple Equations

STANDARDS OF LEARNING
8.15

Essential Question How can you use inductive reasoning to discover rules in mathematics? How can you test a rule?

1 ACTIVITY: Sum of the Angles of a Triangle

Work with a partner. Copy the triangles. Use a protractor to measure the angles of each triangle. Copy and complete the table to organize your results.

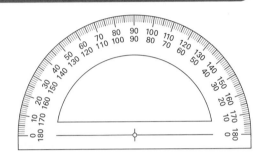

a.

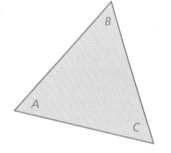

b.

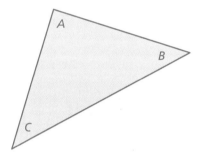

c.

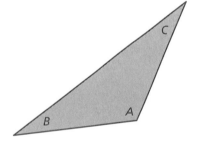

d.

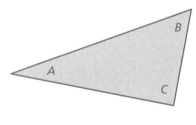

Triangle	Angle A (degrees)	Angle B (degrees)	Angle C (degrees)	A + B + C
a.				
b.				
c.				
d.				

Laurie's Notes

Introduction

For the Teacher

- **Goal:** Students will explore the sum of the angle measures of a triangle to develop an understanding of writing and solving simple equations.
- Note that the triangles drawn in the activities are not shown in the standard orientation, with a side parallel to the horizontal edge. You do not want students to believe, by repeated example, that triangles must have a horizontal base.

Motivate

- **?** "What do Tony Hawk, Shaun White, and Rodney Mullen have in common?" All are famous skateboarders. Shaun White is also a snowboarder.
- Today's activity is about angle measures. Boarders know a lot about angle measure, in particular the multiples of 180°, because of the different tricks they perform.

Activity Notes

Words of Wisdom

- **?** "What does it mean to measure an angle?" Listen for an understanding of the rotation from one ray to a second ray. Both angles shown have the same measure, although some students would say the angle on the left is greater.

- Review with students how to place the protractor on the angle, and how to read the protractor.
- **Common Error:** Notice that 0° does not always align with the bottom edge of some protractors, nor does the vertex of the angle always align with the bottom edge. It is common for students to align the bottom edge of the protractor with one ray of the angle, producing an error of more than 5°.

Activity 1

- **?** "Do you see any pattern(s) in the table? Describe the pattern(s)." The sum of the angle measures is 180°, or close to 180°. Students might also mention that in part (a), all of the angles are congruent (same measure) and in parts (b) and (c), two of the angles are congruent.
- **FYI:** If a sum is significantly different from 180°, the student may have read the protractor incorrectly (i.e., they recorded 150° instead of 30°).

Standards of Learning

8.15(c) The student will identify properties of operations used to solve an equation.

Previous Learning

Students should know the vocabulary of angles, such as ray, vertex, acute, obtuse, right, and straight.

Activity Materials
Textbook
• protractors

Start Thinking! and Warm Up

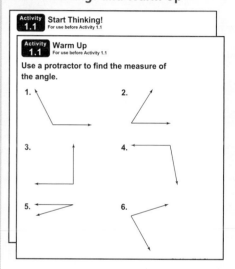

Activity 1.1 Start Thinking! For use before Activity 1.1

Activity 1.1 Warm Up For use before Activity 1.1

Use a protractor to find the measure of the angle.

1. 2.

3. 4.

5. 6.

1.1 Record and Practice Journal

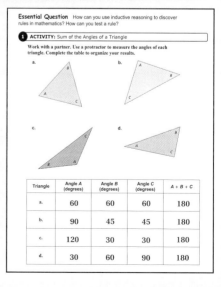

Essential Question How can you use inductive reasoning to discover rules in mathematics? How can you test a rule?

1 ACTIVITY: Sum of the Angles of a Triangle

Work with a partner. Use a protractor to measure the angles of each triangle. Complete the table to organize your results.

Triangle	Angle A (degrees)	Angle B (degrees)	Angle C (degrees)	A + B + C
a.	60	60	60	180
b.	90	45	45	180
c.	120	30	30	180
d.	30	60	90	180

Differentiated Instruction

Kinesthetic

Ask two students to assist you at the board or overhead when solving equations. Assign one student to the left side of the equation and the other student to the right side. Each student is responsible for performing the operations on his or her side. Emphasize that to keep the equality, both students must perform the same operation to solve the equation.

1.1 Record and Practice Journal

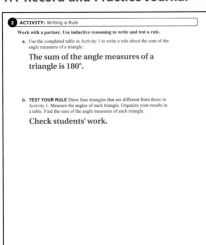

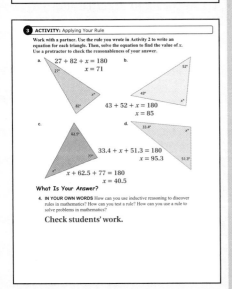

Laurie's Notes

Activity 2

? "What rule did you write for the sum of the angle measures of a triangle?" Students should write that the sum of the angle measures of a triangle equals 180°.

- Suggest to students that they make their triangles larger so that it is easier to measure the angles. They should also use a straight edge to make straight lines.

? "Did you measure all three angles for each triangle?" Some students will not measure all three angles! They will only measure two and do a quick computation to find the third.

Activity 3

- You should model the first problem and write the equation. Otherwise, students will do a computation to find the missing angle.
- **Write:** $27 + 82 + x = 180$. Students have solved equations previously and may simply write the answer as the second step: $x = 71$. Focus on the representation of equation solving instead of the intuitive sense of how to solve this addition equation. Model the second step by showing 109 subtracted from each side of the equation.
- Note that parts (c) and (d) integrate decimal review. Their answers should be exact.
- Have students share their answers.

What Is Your Answer?

? "What is inductive reasoning and how was it used in the activities today?" *Sample answer:* Inductive reasoning is writing a general rule based on examples. Today I found that the sum of the angle measures of several triangles equals 180°, so I wrote a rule for triangles in general.

- Have students discuss their ideas to the questions posed in Question 4.

Closure

- **Exit Ticket:** Two angles of a triangle measure 48.2° and 63.8°. Make a reasonable sketch of the triangle. Write and solve an equation to find the measure of the third angle. $48.2 + 63.8 + x = 180$; $x = 68$

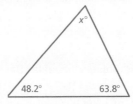

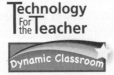

Technology For the Teacher

Dynamic Classroom

The Dynamic Planning Tool
Editable Teacher's Resources at *BigIdeasMath.com*

ACTIVITY: Writing a Rule

Work with a partner. Use inductive reasoning to write and test a rule.

a. Use the completed table in Activity 1 to write a rule about the sum of the angle measures of a triangle.

b. **TEST YOUR RULE** Draw four triangles that are different from those in Activity 1. Measure the angles of each triangle. Organize your results in a table. Find the sum of the angle measures of each triangle.

3 **ACTIVITY: Applying Your Rule**

Work with a partner. Use the rule you wrote in Activity 2 to write an equation for each triangle. Then, solve the equation to find the value of x. Use a protractor to check the reasonableness of your answer.

a.
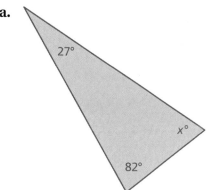

b.
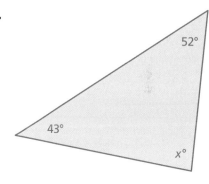

c.
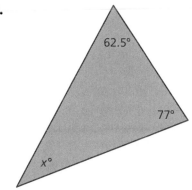

d.
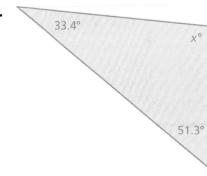

What Is Your Answer?

4. **IN YOUR OWN WORDS** How can you use inductive reasoning to discover rules in mathematics? How can you test a rule? How can you use a rule to solve problems in mathematics?

Practice

Use what you learned about solving simple equations to complete Exercises 4–6 on page 7.

Check It Out
Lesson Tutorials
BigIdeasMath .com

 **Key Ideas**

Remember

Addition and subtraction are inverse operations.

Addition Property of Equality

Words Adding the same number to each side of an equation produces an equivalent equation.

Algebra If $a = b$, then $a + c = b + c$.

Subtraction Property of Equality

Words Subtracting the same number from each side of an equation produces an equivalent equation.

Algebra If $a = b$, then $a - c = b - c$.

EXAMPLE 1 **Solving Equations Using Addition or Subtraction**

a. Solve $x - 7 = -6$.

$$x - 7 = -6 \qquad \text{Write the equation.}$$

Undo the subtraction. $\longrightarrow$
$$\underline{+ 7 \qquad + 7} \qquad \text{Add 7 to each side.}$$
$$x = \quad 1 \qquad \text{Simplify.}$$

∴ The solution is $x = 1$.

Check
$$x - 7 = -6$$
$$1 - 7 \stackrel{?}{=} -6$$
$$-6 = -6 \checkmark$$

b. Solve $y + 3.4 = 0.5$.

$$y + 3.4 = \quad 0.5 \qquad \text{Write the equation.}$$

Undo the addition. $\longrightarrow$
$$\underline{- 3.4 \qquad - 3.4} \qquad \text{Subtract 3.4 from each side.}$$
$$y = \quad -2.9 \qquad \text{Simplify.}$$

∴ The solution is $y = -2.9$.

Check
$$y + 3.4 = 0.5$$
$$-2.9 + 3.4 \stackrel{?}{=} 0.5$$
$$0.5 = 0.5 \checkmark$$

c. Solve $h + 2\pi = 3\pi$.

$$h + 2\pi = \quad 3\pi \qquad \text{Write the equation.}$$

Undo the addition. $\longrightarrow$
$$\underline{- 2\pi \qquad - 2\pi} \qquad \text{Subtract } 2\pi \text{ from each side.}$$
$$h = \quad \pi \qquad \text{Simplify.}$$

∴ The solution is $h = \pi$.

Laurie's Notes

Introduction

Connect

- **Yesterday:** Students used the sum of the angle measures of a triangle to explore simple equation solving.
- **Today:** Students will use Properties of Equality to solve one-step equations.

Motivate

- Tell students that you are going to play a quick game of *REVERSO*. The directions are simple: you give a command to a student and your opponent must give the reverse (inverse) command to undo your command. For example, you say, "take 3 steps forward " and your opponent would say "take 3 steps backward."
- Sample commands: turn lights on; step up on a chair; turn to your right; fold 2 sheets of paper; draw a square; open the door
- The goal is for students to think about inverse operations.

Lesson Notes

Key Ideas

- Write the Key Ideas.
- Redefine *equivalent equations*. Two equations that have the same solution are *equivalent equations.*
- **Teaching Tip:** Use an alternate color to show adding (subtracting) c to (from) each side of the equation.
- Remind students of the big idea. Whatever you do to one side of the equation, you must do to the other side of the equation.

Example 1

- Work through each part. Note that the vertical format of equation solving is used. The number being added to or subtracted from each side of the equation is written vertically below the number with which it will be combined.
- **?** "What is the approximate value of π?" 3.14 "of 2π?" 6.28
- Remind students that 2π and 3π are (irrational) numbers, so you can treat these numbers as you would integers. It is common for students to think of π as a variable and they will say that there are two variables in $h + 2\pi$.

Start Thinking! and Warm Up

Lesson 1.1 **Warm Up** For use before Lesson 1.1

Lesson 1.1 **Start Thinking!** For use before Lesson 1.1

The Addition Property of Equality states that adding the same number to each side of an equation produces an equivalent equation. What do you think the Subtraction, Multiplication, and Division Properties of Equality state?

Describe a real-life situation that you can relate to one of the properties of equality.

Extra Example 1

a. Solve $d - \dfrac{1}{4} = -\dfrac{1}{2}$. $-\dfrac{1}{4}$

b. Solve $m + 4.8 = 9.2$ 4.4

c. Solve $r - 6\pi = 2\pi$. 8π

On Your Own

1. $b = -7$ 2. $g = 0.8$

3. $k = -6$ 4. $r = 2\pi$

5. $t = -\dfrac{1}{2}$ 6. $z = -13.6$

Extra Example 2

a. Solve $\dfrac{2}{5}m = -4$. -10

b. Solve $3p = -\dfrac{2}{3}$. $-\dfrac{2}{9}$

On Your Own

7. $y = -28$ 8. $x = 6$

9. $w = 20$

English Language Learners

Vocabulary

In this section, students will learn to use inverse (or opposite) operations to solve equations. Students will use addition to solve a subtraction equation and use subtraction to solve an addition equation. Review these pairs of words that are essential to understanding mathematics. Give students one word of a pair and ask them to provide the opposite.

Examples:

odd, even   positive, negative
add, subtract   sum, difference
multiply, divide   product, quotient
plus, minus

Laurie's Notes

On Your Own

- Circulate as students work on these six questions. Remind them that it is the practice of *representing* their work that is important in these questions.

Key Ideas

- Write the Key Ideas.
- **Representation:** Review different ways in which multiplication is represented.

$$a(c) = b(c) \qquad ac = bc \qquad a \times c = b \times c \qquad a \cdot c = b \cdot c$$

- Generally, when there are variables in equations, you do not want to use $\times$ to represent multiplication because it can be mistaken for a variable.
- **Representation:** Review different ways in which division is represented.

$$a \div c = b \div c \qquad \dfrac{a}{c} = \dfrac{b}{c} \qquad a/c = b/c$$

Example 2

- Work through each part.
- Remind students that the goal is to solve for the variable so that it has a coefficient of 1.
- Remind students that the Multiplicative Inverse Property states that the product of a number and its reciprocal is 1. In this case, $-\dfrac{4}{3} \cdot -\dfrac{3}{4} = 1$.
- The purpose of part (b) is to practice working with π in an algebraic expression.

On Your Own

- Circulate as students work on these three questions. Stress representation with students. Do not let them short-cut the process and simply record the answer. They should show what operation is being performed on each side of the equation.
- **Common Error:** Students may try to subtract 6π from πx or subtract πx from 6π. Remind them that the variable they are solving for is x.

On Your Own

Now You're Ready
Exercises 7–15

Solve the equation. Check your solution.

1. $b + 2 = -5$ **2.** $g - 1.7 = -0.9$ **3.** $-3 = k + 3$

4. $r - \pi = \pi$ **5.** $t - \dfrac{1}{4} = -\dfrac{3}{4}$ **6.** $5.6 + z = -8$

Remember

Multiplication and division are inverse operations.

Key Ideas

Multiplication Property of Equality

Words   Multiplying each side of an equation by the same number produces an equivalent equation.

Algebra   If $a = b$, then $a \cdot c = b \cdot c$.

Division Property of Equality

Words   Dividing each side of an equation by the same number produces an equivalent equation.

Algebra   If $a = b$, then $a \div c = b \div c$, $c \neq 0$.

EXAMPLE 2   **Solving Equations Using Multiplication or Division**

a. Solve $-\dfrac{3}{4}n = -2$.

$$-\frac{3}{4}n = -2 \qquad \text{Write the equation.}$$

(Use the reciprocal.) $\longrightarrow -\dfrac{4}{3} \cdot \left(-\dfrac{3}{4}n\right) = -\dfrac{4}{3} \cdot (-2)$ Multiply each side by $-\dfrac{4}{3}$, the reciprocal of $-\dfrac{3}{4}$.

$$n = \frac{8}{3} \qquad \text{Simplify.}$$

∴ The solution is $n = \dfrac{8}{3}$.

b. Solve $\pi x = 3\pi$.

$$\pi x = 3\pi \qquad \text{Write the equation.}$$

(Undo the multiplication.) $\longrightarrow \dfrac{\pi x}{\pi} = \dfrac{3\pi}{\pi}$ Divide each side by π.

$$x = 3 \qquad \text{Simplify.}$$

∴ The solution is $x = 3$.

Check

$$\pi x = 3\pi$$

$$\pi(3) \stackrel{?}{=} 3\pi$$

$$3\pi = 3\pi \checkmark$$

On Your Own

Now You're Ready
Exercises 18–26

Solve the equation. Check your solution.

7. $\dfrac{y}{4} = -7$ **8.** $6\pi = \pi x$ **9.** $0.09w = 1.8$

Section 1.1   Solving Simple Equations   **5**

What value of k makes the equation $k + 4 \div 0.2 = 5$ true?

Ⓐ -15 Ⓑ -5 Ⓒ -3 Ⓓ 1.5

$k + 4 \div 0.2 =$	5	Write the equation.
$k + 20 =$	5	Divide 4 by 0.2.
-20	-20	Subtract 20 from each side.
$k = -15$		Simplify.

∴ The correct answer is Ⓐ.

EXAMPLE ④ **Real-Life Application**

The melting point of bromine is $-7°C$.

The *melting point* of a solid is the temperature at which the solid becomes a liquid. The melting point of bromine is $\frac{1}{30}$ of the melting point of nitrogen. Write and solve an equation to find the melting point of nitrogen.

Words   The melting point of bromine   is $\frac{1}{30}$ of   the melting point of nitrogen.

Variable   Let n be the melting point of nitrogen.

Equation -7 $=$ $\frac{1}{30}$ n

$$-7 = \frac{1}{30}n \qquad \text{Write the equation.}$$

$$30 \cdot (-7) = 30 \cdot \left(\frac{1}{30}n\right) \qquad \text{Multiply each side by 30.}$$

$$-210 = n \qquad \text{Simplify.}$$

∴ The melting point of nitrogen is $-210°C$.

● **On Your Own**

Now You're Ready
Exercises 33–38

10. Solve $p - 8 \div \frac{1}{2} = -3$.   **11.** Solve $q + |-10| = 2$.

12. The melting point of mercury is about $\frac{1}{4}$ of the melting point of krypton. The melting point of mercury is $-39°C$. Write and solve an equation to find the melting point of krypton.

Laurie's Notes

Lesson Notes

Example 3

? "What is $10 + 4 \div 2$?" Listen for order of operations; Answer is 12, *not* 7.

- Students could use *Guess, Check, and Revise*. However, it is more efficient to use order of operations and then solve the equation.

Example 4

- Note the color-coding of the words and symbols. Discuss this feature with students. Students find it difficult to read a word problem and translate it into symbols. This skill is practiced throughout the text.
- **Representation:** The term $\frac{1}{30}n$ could also have been written as $\frac{n}{30}$. Make sure students understand why. It is how a fraction and number are multiplied.
- **FYI:** The final answer $-210 = n$ can also be written as $n = -210$.

On Your Own

- Remind students to perform the operations following the order of operations.
- **Common Error:** $8 \div \frac{1}{2} \neq 4$; $8 \div \frac{1}{2} = 16$
- **?** "For Question 11, what does $\left| -10 \right|$ mean?" absolute value of -10, which equals 10

Closure

- Describe in words how to solve a one-step equation.
- Write and solve a one-step equation.

Extra Example 3

Solve $w - 4 \div \frac{1}{2} = 5$. $w = 13$

Extra Example 4

The melting point of ice is $\frac{2}{9}$ of the melting point of candle wax. The melting point of ice is 32°F. Write and solve an equation to find the melting point of candle wax. $\frac{2}{9}x = 32$; 144°F

On Your Own

10. $p = 1$

11. $q = -8$

12. $-39 = \frac{1}{4}k$; -156°C

Technology
For
the **T**eacher

Dynamic Classroom

The Dynamic Planning Tool
Editable Teacher's Resources at *BigIdeasMath.com*

Vocabulary and Concept Check

1. $+$ and $-$ are inverses. $\times$ and $\div$ are inverses.

2. yes; The solution of each equation is $x = -3$.

3. $x - 3 = 6$; It is the only equation that does not have $x = 6$ as a solution.

Practice and Problem Solving

4. $x = 32$

5. $x = 57$

6. $x = 111$

7. $x = -5$

8. $g = 24$

9. $p = 21$

10. $y = -2.04$

11. $x = 9\pi$

12. $w = 10\pi$

13. $d = \dfrac{1}{2}$

14. $r = -\dfrac{7}{24}$

15. $n = -4.9$

16. $p - 14.50 = 53$; $67.50

17. **a.** $105 = x + 14$; $x = 91$

   b. no; Because $82 + 9 = 91$, you did not knock down the last pin with the second ball of the frame.

Assignment Guide and Homework Check

Level	Day 1 Activity Assignment	Day 2 Lesson Assignment	Homework Check
Basic	4–6, 45–48	1–3, 7–15 odd, 16, 19–33 odd, 28, 37	7, 11, 16, 19, 21, 33
Average	4–6, 45–48	1–3, 10–14, 17, 21–24, 27–37 odd, 41	10, 11, 17, 21, 22, 33
Advanced	4–6, 45–48	1–3, 17, 24–27, 30–38 even, 39–44	17, 24, 30, 34, 39, 42

For Your Information

- **Exercise 17** Students may not know what a spare is in bowling. A spare means that all of the pins were knocked down after the second ball of a frame was thrown. To calculate the score after a spare, you add the number of pins knocked down on your next ball to 10. For example, if you got a spare in the first frame and then knocked down 6 pins on your next ball, your score for the first frame would be 16.
- **Exercise 31** Simple interest will be covered in a later chapter.

Common Errors

- **Exercises 4–6** Students may struggle using the protractor to find the missing angle. Encourage them to trace the triangle and extend the sides so they can get a more accurate reading.
- **Exercises 7–15** Students may perform the same operation on both sides instead of the opposite operation. Remind them that to solve for the variable, they must *undo* the operation by using the opposite (or inverse) operation.
- **Exercise 16** Students may write the wrong equation for the problem. Encourage them to rewrite the problem so that it is clear what equation they should write. Remind them that subtraction is not commutative.

1.1 Record and Practice Journal

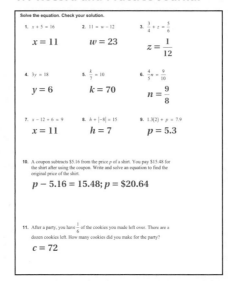

 ## Vocabulary and Concept Check

1. **VOCABULARY** Which of the operations $+$, $-$, $\times$, and $\div$ are inverses of each other?

2. **VOCABULARY** Are the equations $3x = -9$ and $4x = -12$ equivalent? Explain.

3. **WHICH ONE DOESN'T BELONG?** Which equation does *not* belong with the other three? Explain your reasoning.

$$x - 2 = 4 \qquad x - 3 = 6 \qquad x - 5 = 1 \qquad x - 6 = 0$$

 ## Practice and Problem Solving

Find the value of x. Use a protractor to check the reasonableness of your answer.

4.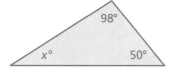

5.

6.

Solve the equation. Check your solution.

1 **7.** $x + 12 = 7$ **8.** $g - 16 = 8$ **9.** $-9 + p = 12$

10. $0.7 + y = -1.34$ **11.** $x - 8\pi = \pi$ **12.** $4\pi = w - 6\pi$

13. $\dfrac{5}{6} = \dfrac{1}{3} + d$ **14.** $\dfrac{3}{8} = r + \dfrac{2}{3}$ **15.** $n - 1.4 = -6.3$

16. **CONCERT** A discounted concert ticket is $14.50 less than the original price p. You pay $53 for a discounted ticket. Write and solve an equation to find the original price.

17. **BOWLING** Your friend's final bowling score is 105. Your final bowling score is 14 pins less than your friend's final score.

   a. Write and solve an equation to find your final score.

   b. Your friend made a spare in the tenth frame. Did you? Explain.

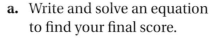

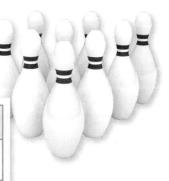

	9	10	FINAL SCORE
	8 − 7 / 6		
	89	105	105
	6 3 9		
	82		?

Solve the equation. Check your solution.

② **18.** $7x = 35$

19. $4 = -0.8n$

20. $6 = -\dfrac{w}{8}$

21. $\dfrac{m}{\pi} = 7.3$

22. $-4.3g = 25.8$

23. $\dfrac{3}{2} = \dfrac{9}{10}k$

24. $-7.8x = -1.56$

25. $-2 = \dfrac{6}{7}p$

26. $3\pi d = 12\pi$

27. ERROR ANALYSIS Describe and correct the error in solving the equation.

$$\times \quad \begin{array}{l} -1.5 + k = 8.2 \\ \quad k = 8.2 + (-1.5) \\ \quad k = 6.7 \end{array}$$

28. TENNIS A gym teacher orders 42 tennis balls. Each package contains 3 tennis balls. Which of the following equations represents the number x of packages?

$$x + 3 = 42 \qquad 3x = 42 \qquad \dfrac{x}{3} = 42 \qquad x = \dfrac{3}{42}$$

In Exercises 29–32, write and solve an equation to answer the question.

29. PARK You clean a community park for 6.5 hours. You earn $42.25. How much do you earn per hour?

Launch Time 11:20 A.M.

30. SPACE SHUTTLE A space shuttle is scheduled to launch from Kennedy Space Center in 3.75 hours. What time is it now?

31. BANKING After earning interest, the balance of an account is $420. The new balance is $\dfrac{7}{6}$ of the original balance. How much interest was earned?

Tallest Coasters at Cedar Point	
Roller Coaster	Height (feet)
Top Thrill Dragster	420
Millennium Force	310
Magnum XL-200	205
Mantis	?

32. ROLLER COASTER Cedar Point amusement park has some of the tallest roller coasters in the United States. The Mantis is 165 feet shorter than the Millennium Force. What is the height of the Mantis?

Common Errors

- **Exercises 18–26** Students may use the same operation instead of the opposite operation to get the variable by itself. Remind them that to *undo* the operation, they must use the opposite (or inverse) operation. Demonstrate that using the same operation will not work. For example:

Incorrect	Correct
$7x = 35$	$7x = 35$
$7 \cdot 7x = 35 \cdot 7$	$\dfrac{7x}{7} = \dfrac{35}{7}$
$49x = 245$	$x = 5$

- **Exercise 32** Students may skip the step of writing the equation and just subtract the difference in height from the height of the Millennium Force. Encourage them to develop the problem solving technique of writing the equation before solving. This skill will be useful later in mathematics.

- **Exercises 33–38** Students may forget to use the order of operations when solving for the variable. Remind them of the order of operations and encourage them to simplify both sides of the equation before solving.

Practice and Problem Solving

18. $x = 5$ **19.** $n = -5$

20. $w = -48$ **21.** $m = 7.3\pi$

22. $g = -6$ **23.** $k = 1\dfrac{2}{3}$

24. $x = 0.2$ **25.** $p = -2\dfrac{1}{3}$

26. $d = 4$

27. They should have added 1.5 to each side.
$$-1.5 + k = 8.2$$
$$k = 8.2 + 1.5$$
$$k = 9.7$$

28. $3x = 42$

29. $6.5x = 42.25$; $6.50 per hour

30. $x + 3\dfrac{3}{4} = 11\dfrac{1}{3}$; 7:35 A.M.

31. $420 = \dfrac{7}{6}b$, $b = 360$; $60

32. $x + 165 = 310$; 145 ft

Practice and Problem Solving

33. $h = -7$ **34.** $w = 19$

35. $q = 3.2$ **36.** $d = 0$

37. $x = -1\frac{4}{9}$ **38.** $p = -\frac{1}{12}$

39. greater than; Because a negative number divided by a negative number is a positive number.

40. *Sample answer:* $x - 2 = -4$, $\frac{x}{2} = -1$

41. 3 mg

42. See *Taking Math Deeper.*

43. 8 in.

44. a. $18, $27, $45

   b. *Sample answer:* Everyone did not do an equal amount of painting.

Fair Game Review

45. $7x - 4$ **46.** $1.6b - 3.2$

47. $\frac{25}{4}g - \frac{2}{3}$

48. A

Mini-Assessment

Solve the equation.

1. $t + 17 = 3$ $t = -14$

2. $-2\pi + d = -3\pi$ $d = -\pi$

3. $-13.5 = 2.7s$ $s = -5$

4. $\frac{2}{3}j = 8$ $j = 12$

5. You earn $9.65 per hour. This week, you earned $308.80 before taxes. Write and solve an equation to find the number of hours you worked this week. $9.65x = 308.8$; You worked 32 hours this week.

Taking Math Deeper

Exercise 42

A nice way to organize the given information is to put it into a table.

 Use a table to organize the information.

	Total	Retake
Girls	x	$\frac{1}{4}x = 16$
Boys	y	$\frac{1}{8}y = 7$

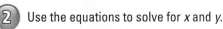 Use the equations to solve for x and y.

Girls: $\frac{1}{4}x = 16$

$x = 64$

Boys: $\frac{1}{8}y = 7$

$y = 56$

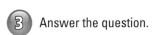 Answer the question.

There are $64 + 56 = 120$ students in the eighth grade.

Project

Find out how many retakes were done at your school last year. Do the given ratios work for your school? What do you think are some of the reasons students have retakes?

Reteaching and Enrichment Strategies

If students need help...	If students got it...
Resources by Chapter • Practice A and Practice B • Puzzle Time Record and Practice Journal Practice Differentiating the Lesson Lesson Tutorials Skills Review Handbook	Resources by Chapter • Enrichment and Extension Start the next section

Solve the equation. Check your solution.

33. $-3 = h + 8 \div 2$

34. $12 = w - \left| -7 \right|$

35. $q + \left| 6.4 \right| = 9.6$

36. $d - 2.8 \div 0.2 = -14$

37. $\dfrac{8}{9} = x + \dfrac{1}{3}(7)$

38. $p - \dfrac{1}{4} \cdot 3 = -\dfrac{5}{6}$

39. CRITICAL THINKING Is the solution of $-2x = -15$ *greater than* or *less than* -15? Explain.

40. OPEN-ENDED Write a subtraction equation and a division equation that each has a solution of -2.

41. ANTS Some ant species can carry 50 times their body weight. It takes 32 ants to carry the cherry. About how much does each ant weigh?

42. PICTURES One-fourth of the girls and one-eighth of the boys in an eighth grade retake their school pictures. The photographer retakes pictures for 16 girls and 7 boys. How many students are in the eighth grade?

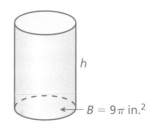

43. VOLUME The volume V of the cylinder is 72π cubic inches. Use the formula $V = Bh$ to find the height h of the cylinder.

44. **Critical Thinking** A neighbor pays you and two friends $90 to paint her garage. The money is divided three ways in the ratio $2:3:5$.

   a. How much is each share?

   b. What is one possible reason the money is not divided evenly?

Fair Game Review What you learned in previous grades & lessons

Simplify the expression. *(Skills Review Handbook)*

45. $2(x - 2) + 5x$

46. $0.4b - 3.2 + 1.2b$

47. $\dfrac{1}{4}g + 6g - \dfrac{2}{3}$

48. MULTIPLE CHOICE The temperature at 4 P.M. was $-12\,°\text{C}$. By 11 P.M. the temperature had dropped 14 degrees. What was the temperature at 11 P.M.? *(Skills Review Handbook)*

   (A) $-26\,°\text{C}$
   (B) $-2\,°\text{C}$
   (C) $2\,°\text{C}$
   (D) $26\,°\text{C}$

STANDARDS
OF LEARNING
8.15

Essential Question How can you solve a multi-step equation?
How can you check the reasonableness of your solution?

1 ACTIVITY: Solving for the Angles of a Triangle

Work with a partner. Write an equation for each triangle. Solve the equation to find the value of the variable. Then find the angle measures of each triangle. Use a protractor to check the reasonableness of your answer.

a.

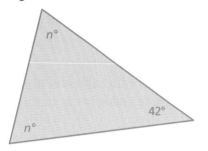

b.

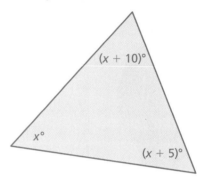

c.

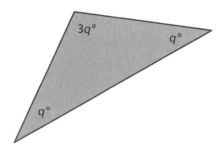

d.

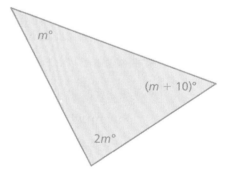

e.

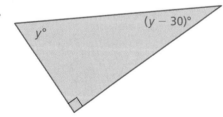

f.

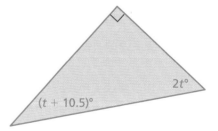

Laurie's Notes

Introduction

For the Teacher

- **Goal:** Students will develop an understanding of solving multi-step equations using the sum of the angle measures of a triangle.
- Have an informal discussion of the vocabulary associated with the triangles shown.

Motivate

- Make a card for each student in your class. Write a variable term on each card. Students will walk around to find others with a card containing a *like term* to the one they are holding.

  Samples: $5x$, $-13x$, $5y$, $6xy$, x, $3.8x$, $\frac{1}{2}y$, $-3.8y$

- Ask students to explain what it means for terms to be *like* terms.

Activity Notes

Activity 1

? Ask a few questions to prepare students for the activity.
- "In the previous lesson, what did you conclude about the sum of the angle measures of a triangle?" sum = 180°
- "So if two angles measure 65° and 75°, what does the third angle measure?" 40°
- "If the angles of a triangle measure $x°$, $2x°$, and $3x°$, could you determine the measure of each angle?" Students should say yes.

- Model how to write and solve the equation $x + 2x + 3x = 180$. Be sure to mention like terms when solving. Ask about the coefficient of x.
- **Common Error:** After solving the equation, you still need to substitute the value into each angle expression to solve for each angle measure. Students sometimes forget this step.
- **FYI:** The triangles are drawn to scale, so the angle measures can be checked using a protractor.
- Ask for volunteers to show a few of the solutions at the board.

? "Why are there only two angles with variable expressions written in parts (e) and (f)?" The third angle in each is a right angle.

Standards of Learning

8.15(a) The student will solve multistep linear equations in one variable on one and two sides of the equation.
8.15(c) The student will identify properties of operations used to solve an equation.

Previous Learning

Students should know how to use inverse operations to solve one-step equations.

Activity Materials
Introduction
• index cards

Start Thinking! and Warm Up

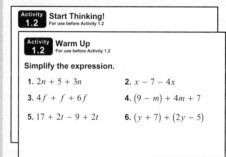

1.2 Record and Practice Journal

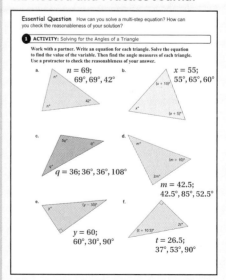

Auditory

Remind students that in order to solve an equation, the variable must be isolated on one side of the equation. The operations on the same side as the variable are those that need to be undone.

Laurie's Notes

Activity 2

- Students will have different strategies for solving this puzzle.
- **?** "Define a straight angle." An angle that measures 180°.
- Remind students to look for a variety of ways to check their answers.
- Discuss results and strategies for finding the angle measures. Listen for: right angles at the vertices of the rectangle; sum of angle measures forming a straight angle equals 180°; sum of angle measures about a point equals 360°; sum of the angle measures of a triangle equals 180°.
- Most students will not write a formal equation, but the thinking involved is an equation. For example, $k + m + s = 180$. If you know k and m, you can use mental math to solve for s.

Activity 3

- This example reviews fraction addition, mixed numbers, fraction division, and percents.
- **?** Ask a few questions to help students begin the activity.
    - "How many people were surveyed?" 200
    - "What is the sum of the five central angle measures?" 360°
    - "What is the angle measure of the sector labeled Wednesday?" 90°
- Some students may use all five angles and set the expression equal to 360, while other students may only consider the four angles represented by a variable expression and set it equal to 270.
- **?** "How do you find the percent each angle measure represents?"

  Convert $\dfrac{\text{angle measure}}{360}$ to a percent.

Words of Wisdom

- There are many steps in Activity 3, but it is possible to solve. This problem takes time and students will feel a sense of accomplishment when they finish.

Closure

- Find the angle measures in the right triangle. $x = 60$, $y = 30$, $z = 120$

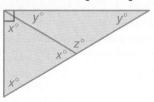

1.2 Record and Practice Journal

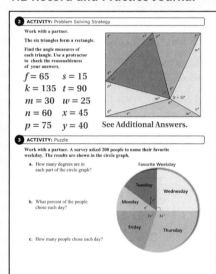

2 ACTIVITY: Problem Solving Strategy

Work with a partner.

The six triangles form a rectangle.

Find the angle measures of each triangle. Use a protractor to check the reasonableness of your answers.

$f = 65$ $s = 15$
$k = 135$ $t = 90$
$m = 30$ $w = 25$
$n = 60$ $x = 45$
$p = 75$ $y = 40$ **See Additional Answers.**

3 ACTIVITY: Puzzle

Work with a partner. A survey asked 200 people to name their favorite weekday. The results are shown in the circle graph.

a. How many degrees are in each part of the circle graph?

b. What percent of the people chose each day?

c. How many people chose each day?

d. Organize your results in a table.

a–d.

	Mon.	Tues.	Wed.	Thurs.	Fri.
Degrees	36°	54°	90°	108°	72°
Percent	10%	15%	25%	30%	20%
People	20	30	50	60	40

What Is Your Answer?

4. **IN YOUR OWN WORDS** How can you solve a multi-step equation? How can you check the reasonableness of your solution?

Use inverse operations.

Check by substituting solution back into original equation.

2 ACTIVITY: Problem-Solving Strategy

Work with a partner.

The six triangles form a rectangle.

Find the angle measures of each triangle. Use a protractor to check the reasonableness of your answers.

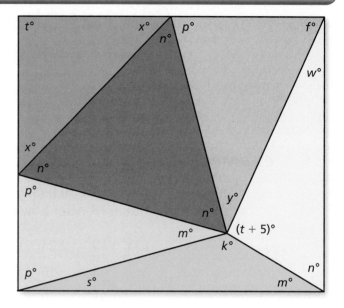

3 ACTIVITY: Puzzle

Work with a partner. A survey asked 200 people to name their favorite weekday. The results are shown in the circle graph.

  a. How many degrees are in each part of the circle graph?

  b. What percent of the people chose each day?

  c. How many people chose each day?

  d. Organize your results in a table.

Favorite Weekday

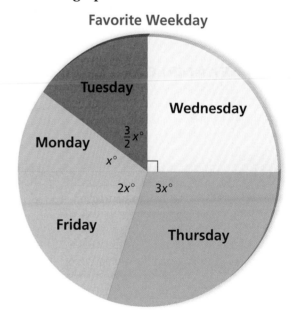

What Is Your Answer?

4. **IN YOUR OWN WORDS** How can you solve a multi-step equation? How can you check the reasonableness of your solution?

Practice Use what you learned about solving multi-step equations to complete Exercises 3–5 on page 14.

Key Idea

Solving Multi-Step Equations

To solve multi-step equations, use inverse operations to isolate the variable.

EXAMPLE 1 Solving a Two-Step Equation

The height (in feet) of a tree after x years is $1.5x + 15$. After how many years is the tree 24 feet tall?

$$1.5x + 15 = 24 \quad \text{Write an equation.}$$

Undo the addition. → $\underline{ -15 \quad -15} \quad$ Subtract 15 from each side.

$$1.5x = 9 \quad \text{Simplify.}$$

Undo the multiplication. → $\dfrac{1.5x}{1.5} = \dfrac{9}{1.5} \quad$ Divide each side by 1.5.

$$x = 6 \quad \text{Simplify.}$$

The tree is 24 feet tall after 6 years.

EXAMPLE 2 Combining Like Terms to Solve an Equation

Solve $8x - 6x - 25 = -35$.

$$8x - 6x - 25 = -35 \quad \text{Write the equation.}$$

$$2x - 25 = -35 \quad \text{Combine like terms.}$$

Undo the subtraction. → $\underline{ +25 \quad +25} \quad$ Add 25 to each side.

$$2x = -10 \quad \text{Simplify.}$$

Undo the multiplication. → $\dfrac{2x}{2} = \dfrac{-10}{2} \quad$ Divide each side by 2.

$$x = -5 \quad \text{Simplify.}$$

The solution is $x = -5$.

On Your Own

Solve the equation. Check your solution.

Now You're Ready
Exercises 6–9

1. $-3z + 1 = 7$

2. $\dfrac{1}{2}x - 9 = -25$

3. $-4n - 8n + 17 = 23$

Laurie's Notes

Introduction

Connect

- **Yesterday:** Students developed an intuitive understanding about solving multi-step equations.
- **Today:** Students will solve multi-step equations by using inverse operations to isolate the variable.

Motivate

- Share information with students about the three man-made, palm-shaped islands built in Dubai, the self-proclaimed "Eighth Wonder of the World!"

  - Each of the islands is being built in the shape of a palm tree consisting of a trunk and a crown with fronds. Each of the palm-shaped islands is surrounded by a crescent island that acts as a breakwater.
- There will be over 100 luxury hotels, exclusive residential beachside villas and apartments, marinas, water theme parks, restaurants, shopping malls, sports facilities, and health spas on the islands.

Lesson Notes

Key Idea

- **Connection:** When you evaluate an expression, you follow the order of operations. Solving an equation undoes the evaluating, in reverse order. The goal is to isolate the variable term and then solve for the variable.

Example 1

- One way to explain the equation is to think of the tree as being 15 feet tall when being planted. It then grows 1.5 feet each year.
- **Extension:** Make a table to show the height of the tree from the first year to the sixth year.

Example 2

- **?** "Why is $8x - 6x = 2x$?" Use the Distributive Property to subtract the terms; $8x - 6x = (8 - 6)x = 2x$.

On Your Own

- In Question 2, students may divide both sides by $\frac{1}{2}$ and get $x = -8$. Remind students that dividing by $\frac{1}{2}$ is the same as multiplying by 2.

 Goal Today's lesson is solving multi-step equations.

Start Thinking! and Warm Up

> **Lesson 1.2** Warm Up
> For use before Lesson 1.2

> **Lesson 1.2** Start Thinking!
> For use before Lesson 1.2
>
> A multi-step equation requires two or more operations to solve the equation. Explain why the following situation can be modeled by a multi-step equation.
>
> A plumber charges $80 per hour for labor plus $60 for parts.
>
> Come up with your own scenario that can be modeled by a multi-step equation.

Extra Example 1

The height (in inches) of a plant after t days is $\frac{1}{2}t + 6$. After how many days is the plant 21 inches tall? 30 days

Extra Example 2

Solve $-2m + 4m + 5 = -3$. $m = -4$

 On Your Own

1. $z = -2$ 2. $x = -32$

3. $n = -0.5$

Laurie's Notes

Extra Example 3

Solve $-4(3g - 5) + 10g = 19$. 0.5

Example 3

- Ask students to identify the operations involved in this equation. from left to right: multiplication (by 2), subtraction, multiplication ($5x$), addition
- **Note:** Combining like terms in the third step is not obvious to students. When the like terms are not adjacent, students are unsure of how to combine them. Rewrite the left side of the equation as $2 + (-10)x + 4$.

Words of Wisdom

- Take time to work through the Study Tip and discuss the steps. Instead of using the Distributive Property, both sides of the equation are divided by 2 in the third step. This will not be obvious to students, nor will they know why it is okay to do this.
- Explain to students that the left side of the equation is 2 times an expression. When the expression $2(1 - 5x)$ is divided by 2, it leaves the expression $1 - 5x$. In the next step, students want to add 1 to each side because of the subtraction operation shown. Again, it is helpful to write $1 - 5x$ as $1 + (-5)x$ so that it makes sense to students why 1 is subtracted from each side.

Extra Example 4

You have scored 7, 10, 8, and 9 on four quizzes. Write and solve an equation to find the score you need on the fifth quiz so that your mean score is 8.
$$\frac{x + 7 + 10 + 8 + 9}{5} = 8; \; 6$$

Example 4

- You may need to review *mean* with the students.
- Discuss the information displayed in the table and write the equation.
- ? "Is it equivalent to write $\frac{x + 3.5}{5} = 1.5$ instead of $\frac{3.5 + x}{5} = 1.5$? Explain." yes; Commutative Property of Addition
- **FYI:** It may be helpful to write the third step with parentheses: $5\left(\frac{3.5 + x}{5}\right)$.
- **Note:** This is a classic question. When all of the data are known except for one, what is needed in order to achieve a particular average? Students often ask this in the context of wanting to know what they have to score on a test in order to achieve a certain average.

On Your Own

4. $x = -1.5$ **5.** $d = -1$

6. $\dfrac{88 + 92 + 87 + x}{4} = 90$;

$x = 93$

On Your Own

- Encourage students to work with a partner. Students need to be careful with multi-step equations and it is helpful to have a partner check each step.

Closure

- **Exit Ticket:** Solve $8x + 9 - 4x = 25$. Check your solution. $x = 4$

English Language Learners

Vocabulary

English learners will benefit from understanding that a *term* is a number, a variable, or the product of a number and variable. *Like terms* are terms that have identical variable parts.

3 and 16 are like terms because they contain no variable.

$4x$ and $7x$ are like terms because they have the same variable x.

$5a$ and $5b$ are *not* like terms because they have different variables.

EXAMPLE 3 Using the Distributive Property to Solve an Equation

Solve $2(1 - 5x) + 4 = -8$.

$2(1 - 5x) + 4 = -8$	Write the equation.
$2(1) - 2(5x) + 4 = -8$	Use Distributive Property.
$2 - 10x + 4 = -8$	Multiply.
$-10x + 6 = -8$	Combine like terms.
$\underline{\quad -6 \quad -6}$	Subtract 6 from each side.
$-10x = -14$	Simplify.
$\dfrac{-10x}{-10} = \dfrac{-14}{-10}$	Divide each side by −10.
$x = 1.4$	Simplify.

Study Tip

Here is another way to solve the equation in Example 3.
$$2(1 - 5x) + 4 = -8$$
$$2(1 - 5x) = -12$$
$$1 - 5x = -6$$
$$-5x = -7$$
$$x = 1.4$$

EXAMPLE 4 Real-Life Application

Use the table to find the number of miles x you need to run on Friday so that the mean number of miles run per day is 1.5.

Day	Miles
Monday	2
Tuesday	0
Wednesday	1.5
Thursday	0
Friday	x

Write an equation using the definition of mean.

sum of the data →
number of values →

$\dfrac{2 + 0 + 1.5 + 0 + x}{5} = 1.5$	Write the equation.
$\dfrac{3.5 + x}{5} = 1.5$	Combine like terms.
Undo the division. → $5 \cdot \dfrac{3.5 + x}{5} = 5 \cdot 1.5$	Multiply each side by 5.
$3.5 + x = 7.5$	Simplify.
Undo the addition. → $\underline{\quad -3.5 \qquad -3.5}$	Subtract 3.5 from each side.
$x = 4$	Simplify.

⋰ You need to run 4 miles on Friday.

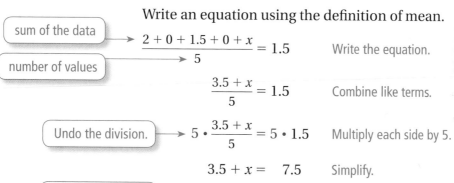

● **On Your Own**

Now You're Ready
Exercises 10 and 11

Solve the equation. Check your solution.

4. $-3(x + 2) + 5x = -9$ **5.** $5 + 1.5(2d - 1) = 0.5$

6. You scored 88, 92, and 87 on three tests. Write and solve an equation to find the score you need on the fourth test so that your mean test score is 90.

 Vocabulary and Concept Check

1. **WRITING** Write the word sentence as an equation. Then solve.

   2 more than 3 times a number is 17.

2. **OPEN-ENDED** Explain how to solve the equation $2(4x - 11) + 9 = 19$.

 Practice and Problem Solving

Find the value of the variable. Then find the angle measures of the polygon. Use a protractor to check the reasonableness of your answer.

3.

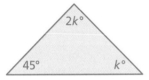

Sum of angle
measures: 180°

4.

Sum of angle
measures: 360°

5.

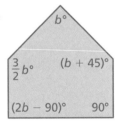

Sum of angle
measures: 540°

Solve the equation. Check your solution.

① ② 6. $10x + 2 = 32$

7. $19 - 4c = 17$

8. $1.1x + 1.2x - 5.4 = -10$

9. $\dfrac{2}{3}h - \dfrac{1}{3}h + 11 = 8$

③ 10. $6(5 - 8v) + 12 = -54$

11. $21(2 - x) + 12x = 44$

12. **ERROR ANALYSIS** Describe and correct the error in solving the equation.

$$
\begin{aligned}
\mathbf{X} \quad -2(7 - y) + 4 &= -4 \\
-14 - 2y + 4 &= -4 \\
-10 - 2y &= -4 \\
-2y &= 6 \\
y &= -3
\end{aligned}
$$

13. **WATCHES** The cost (in dollars) of making n watches is represented by $C = 15n + 85$. How many watches are made when the cost is $385?

14. **HOUSE** The height of the house is 26 feet. What is the height x of each story?

Assignment Guide and Homework Check

Level	Day 1 Activity Assignment	Day 2 Lesson Assignment	Homework Check
Basic	3–5, 19–22	1, 2, 6–14	6, 8, 10, 12, 14
Average	3–5, 19–22	1, 2, 7, 9, 11, 12–17	7, 9, 11, 14, 16
Advanced	3–5, 19–22	1, 2, 6–14 even, 15–18	10, 12, 14, 16

Common Errors

- **Exercises 8 and 9** When combining like terms, students may square the variable. Remind them that $x^2 = x \cdot x$, and in these exercises they are not multiplying the variables. Remind them that when adding and subtracting variables, they perform the addition or subtraction on the coefficient of the variable.
- **Exercises 10 and 11** When using the Distributive Property, students may forget to distribute to all the values within the parentheses. Remind them that they need to distribute to all the values and encourage them to draw arrows showing the distribution, if needed.
- **Exercise 16** Students may struggle with writing the equation for this problem because of the tip that is added to the total. Encourage them to write an expression for the cost of the food and then add on the tip.

1.2 Record and Practice Journal

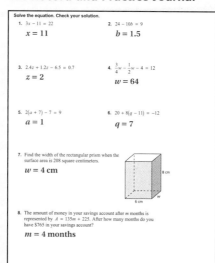

Solve the equation. Check your solution.

1. $3x - 11 = 22$
   $x = 11$

2. $24 - 10b = 9$
   $b = 1.5$

3. $2.4z + 1.2z - 6.5 = 0.7$
   $z = 2$

4. $\frac{3}{4}w - \frac{1}{2}w - 4 = 12$
   $w = 64$

5. $2(a + 7) - 7 = 9$
   $a = 1$

6. $20 + 8(q - 11) = -12$
   $q = 7$

7. Find the width of the rectangular prism when the surface area is 208 square centimeters.
   $w = 4 \text{ cm}$

8. The amount of money in your savings account after m months is represented by $A = 135m + 225$. After how many months do you have $765 in your savings account?
   $m = 4 \text{ months}$

Technology **F**or **T**he **T**eacher

Answer Presentation Tool
QuizShow

Vocabulary and Concept Check

1. $2 + 3x = 17$; $x = 5$

2. *Sample answer:* Subtract 9 from each side. Divide each side by 2. Add 11 to each side. Divide each side by 4.

Practice and Problem Solving

3. $k = 45$; $45°, 45°, 90°$

4. $a = 60$; $60°, 120°, 60°, 120°$

5. $b = 90$; $90°, 135°, 90°, 90°, 135°$

6. $x = 3$

7. $c = 0.5$

8. $x = -2$

9. $h = -9$

10. $v = 2$

11. $x = -\dfrac{2}{9}$

12. They did not distribute the -2 properly.
$$-2(7 - y) + 4 = -4$$
$$-14 + 2y + 4 = -4$$
$$2y - 10 = -4$$
$$2y = 6$$
$$y = 3$$

13. 20 watches

14. 10 ft

15. $4(b + 3) = 24$; 3 in.

16. $1.15(2p + 1.5) = 11.5$; $4.25

17. $\dfrac{2580 + 2920 + x}{3} = 3000$;
3500 people

18. See *Taking Math Deeper*.

Fair Game Review

19. <

20. =

21. >

22. D

Mini-Assessment

Solve the equation.

1. $18 = 5a - 2a + 3$ $a = 5$

2. $2(4 - 2w) - 8 = -4$ $w = 1$

3. $2.3y + 4.4y - 3.7 = 16.4$ $y = 3$

4. $\dfrac{3}{4}z + \dfrac{1}{4}z - 6 = -5$ $z = 1$

5. The perimeter of the picture is 36 inches. What is the height of the picture? 10 in.

x

8 in.

Taking Math Deeper

Exercise 18

This problem points out that mathematics and algebra are used in many different fields.

 Begin by translating the scoring system into a mathematical formula.

minus the highest and lowest

Score = 0.6(degree of difficulty)(sum of countries' scores)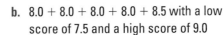

 Substitute the given information.

Let x = the degree of difficulty.

$77.7 = 0.6(x)(7.5 + 8.0 + 7.0 + 7.5 + 7.0)$
$77.7 = 0.6x(37)$
$77.7 = 22.2x$
$3.5 = x$

a. The degree of difficulty is 3.5.

 This question has many answers.

Let x = sum of the five countries' scores.

$97.2 = 0.6(4)(x)$
$97.2 = 2.4x$
$40.5 = x$

One possibility is the following:

b. $8.0 + 8.0 + 8.0 + 8.0 + 8.5$ with a low score of 7.5 and a high score of 9.0

High score

Project

Use the Internet or school library to find all the different dives that are scored in a diving competition. Find the degree of difficulty that goes with each dive.

Reteaching and Enrichment Strategies

If students need help. . .	If students got it. . .
Resources by Chapter • Practice A and Practice B • Puzzle Time Record and Practice Journal Practice Differentiating the Lesson Lesson Tutorials Skills Review Handbook	Resources by Chapter • Enrichment and Extension Start the next section

In Exercises 15–17, write and solve an equation to answer the question.

15. **POSTCARD** The area of the postcard is 24 square inches. What is the width b of the message (in inches)?

16. **BREAKFAST** You order two servings of pancakes and a fruit cup. The cost of the fruit cup is $1.50. You leave a 15% tip. Your total bill is $11.50. How much does one serving of pancakes cost?

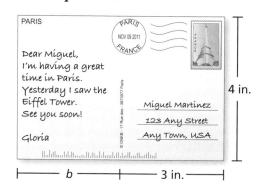

4 in.

$\vdash$ b $\dashv\vdash$ 3 in. $\dashv$

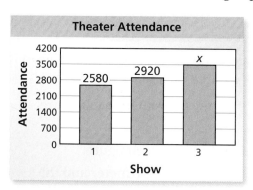

17. **THEATER** How many people must attend the third show so that the average attendance for the three shows is 3000?

18. **DIVING** Olympic divers are scored by an international panel of judges. The highest and lowest scores are dropped. The total of the remaining scores is multiplied by the degree of difficulty of the dive. This product is multiplied by 0.6 to determine the final score.

a. A diver's final score is 77.7. What is the degree of difficulty of the dive?

Judge	Russia	China	Mexico	Germany	Italy	Japan	Brazil
Score	7.5	8.0	6.5	8.5	7.0	7.5	7.0

b. **Critical Thinking** The degree of difficulty of a dive is 4.0. The diver's final score is 97.2. Judges award half or whole points from 0 to 10. What scores could the judges have given the diver?

© Paul Slaughter, www.slaughterphoto.com
Greg Louganis diving at the 1984 Olympics

 Fair Game Review What you learned in previous grades & lessons

Let $a = 3$ and $b = -2$. Copy and complete the statement using <, >, or =.
(Skills Review Handbook)

19. $-5a$ ▧ 4

20. 5 ▧ $b + 7$

21. $a - 4$ ▧ $10b + 8$

22. **MULTIPLE CHOICE** What value of x makes the equation $x + 5 = 2x$ true?
(Skills Review Handbook)

Ⓐ -1 Ⓑ 0 Ⓒ 3 Ⓓ 5

STANDARDS OF LEARNING

8.15

Essential Question How can you solve an equation that has variables on both sides?

1 **ACTIVITY: Perimeter and Area**

Work with a partner. Each figure has the unusual property that the value of its perimeter (in feet) is equal to the value of its area (in square feet).

- Write an equation (value of perimeter = value of area) for each figure.
- Solve each equation for x.
- Use the value of x to find the perimeter and area of each figure.
- Check your solution by comparing the value of the perimeter and the value of the area of each figure.

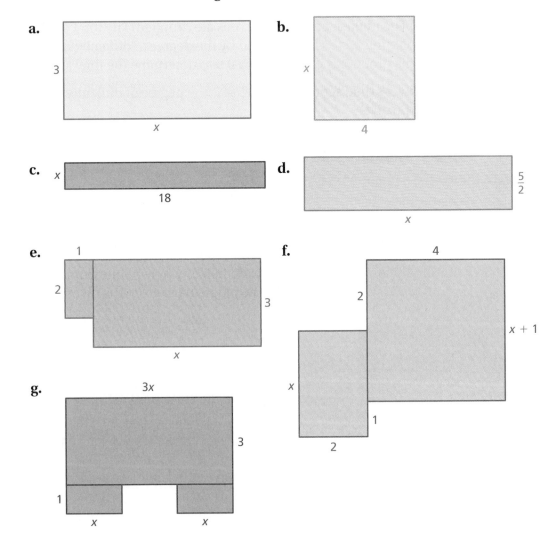

Laurie's Notes

Introduction

For the Teacher

- **Goal:** Students will explore equations with variables on both sides by examining figures with unique properties.

Motivate

❓ "What balances with the cylinder? Explain."

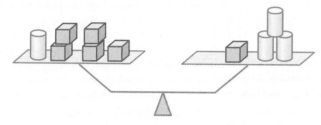

2 cubes; Remove one cube and one cylinder from each side. 2 cylinders balance with 4 cubes, so 1 cylinder would balance with 2 cubes.

- The balance problem is equivalent to $x + 5 = 3x + 1$, where x is a cylinder and the whole numbers represent cubes. This is an example of an equation with variables on both sides, the type students will solve today. Return to this equation at the end of class.
- If students are familiar with algebra tiles, you can model the problem using the tiles. The cylinder is replaced with an x-tile and the cubes are replaced with unit tiles.

Activity Notes

Activity 1

- Discuss with students the general concept of what it means to measure the attributes of a two-dimensional figure. In other words, what is the difference between a rectangle's perimeter and a rectangle's area? What type of units are used to measure each? linear units for perimeter and square units for area
- **FYI:** Be sure to make it clear that the directions are saying that perimeter and area are not the same, but their values are equal. For example, a square that measures 4 centimeters on each edge has a perimeter of 16 centimeters and an area of 16 square centimeters. The value (16) is the same, but the units of measure are not.

❓ Before students begin, ask a few review questions.
  - "How do you find the perimeter and the area of a rectangle?"
    $P = 2\ell + 2w$ and $A = \ell w$
  - "How do you find the perimeter and the area of a composite figure?" Listen for students' understanding that perimeter is the sum of all the sides. The area is found in parts and then added together.
- Have a few groups share their work at the board, particularly for part (d), fractions, and part (g), algebraic expressions.

Standards of Learning

8.15(a) The student will solve multistep linear equations in one variable on one and two sides of the equation.
8.15(c) The student will identify properties of operations used to solve an equation.

Previous Learning

Students should know common formulas for perimeter, area, surface area, and volume.

Start Thinking! and Warm Up

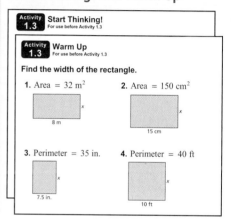

1.3 Record and Practice Journal

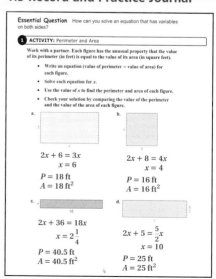

Differentiated Instruction

Auditory

Point out to students that skills used to solve equations in this lesson are the same skills they have used before. The goal is to isolate the variable on one side of the equation. Just as they used the Addition Property of Equality to remove a constant term from one side of the equation, they will use the same property to remove the variable term from one side of the equation.

1.3 Record and Practice Journal

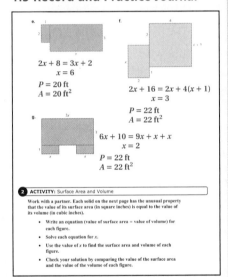

$2x + 8 = 3x + 2$
$x = 6$

$P = 20\,\text{ft}$
$A = 20\,\text{ft}^2$

$2x + 16 = 2x + 4(x + 1)$
$x = 3$

$P = 22\,\text{ft}$
$A = 22\,\text{ft}^2$

$6x + 10 = 9x + x + x$
$x = 2$

$P = 22\,\text{ft}$
$A = 22\,\text{ft}^2$

2 ACTIVITY: Surface Area and Volume

Work with a partner. Each solid on the next page has the unusual property that the value of its surface area (in square inches) is equal to the value of its volume (in cubic inches).

- Write an equation (value of surface area = value of volume) for each figure.
- Solve each equation for x.
- Use the value of x to find the surface area and volume of each figure.
- Check your solution by comparing the value of the surface area and the value of the volume of each figure.

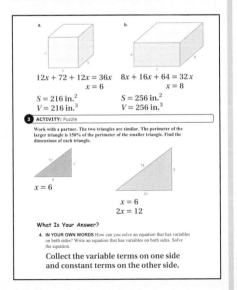

$12x + 72 + 12x = 36x$
$x = 6$

$S = 216\,\text{in.}^2$
$V = 216\,\text{in.}^3$

$8x + 16x + 64 = 32x$
$x = 8$

$S = 256\,\text{in.}^2$
$V = 256\,\text{in.}^3$

3 ACTIVITY: Puzzle

Work with a partner. The two triangles are similar. The perimeter of the larger triangle is 150% of the perimeter of the smaller triangle. Find the dimensions of each triangle.

$x = 6$

$x = 6$
$2x = 12$

What Is Your Answer?

4. **IN YOUR OWN WORDS** How can you solve an equation that has variables on both sides? Write an equation that has variables on both sides. Solve the equation.

Collect the variable terms on one side and constant terms on the other side.

Laurie's Notes

Activity 2

- This activity is similar to Activity 1.
- **?** "How do you find the surface area and volume of a rectangular prism?" $S = 2\ell w + 2\ell h + 2wh$ and $V = \ell wh$
- Students may guess that part (a) is a cube, suggesting $x = 6$. Ask students to verify their guess.

Activity 3

- **?** "What are similar triangles?" Listen for an informal definition: same shape but not necessarily the same size; formally, corresponding sides are proportional and corresponding angles have the same measure (congruent).
- **Another Way:** There are two different approaches students may take in solving this problem.
  - The first method is to solve the equation: 150% of the smaller triangle's perimeter is equal to the perimeter of the larger triangle.

    150% of $(18 + x) = 24 + 2x$
    $1.5(18 + x) = 24 + 2x$

    This method reviews decimal multiplication.
  - A second method is to use the definition of similar triangles to set up a proportion to solve for the missing sides.

    $$\frac{10}{15} = \frac{x}{9}$$

    Solve for x. Use this value to find the side labeled $2x$ in the larger triangle.

What Is Your Answer?

- **Neighbor Check:** Have students work independently and then have their neighbor check their work. Have students discuss any discrepancies.

Closure

- Describe how to solve $x + 5 = 3x + 1$. *Sample answer:* Subtract x from both sides, subtract 1 from both sides, and then divide both sides by 2.

Technology For the Teacher

Dynamic Classroom

The Dynamic Planning Tool
Editable Teacher's Resources at *BigIdeasMath.com*

2 ACTIVITY: Surface Area and Volume

Work with a partner. Each solid has the unusual property that the value of its surface area (in square inches) is equal to the value of its volume (in cubic inches).

- Write an equation (value of surface area = value of volume) for each figure.
- Solve each equation for x.
- Use the value of x to find the surface area and volume of each figure.
- Check your solution by comparing the value of the surface area and the value of the volume of each figure.

a.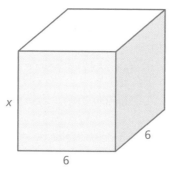

b.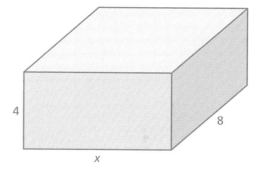

3 ACTIVITY: Puzzle

Work with a partner. The two triangles are similar. The perimeter of the larger triangle is 150% of the perimeter of the smaller triangle. Find the dimensions of each triangle.

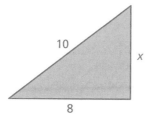

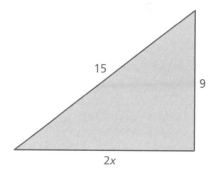

What Is Your Answer?

4. **IN YOUR OWN WORDS** How can you solve an equation that has variables on both sides? Write an equation that has variables on both sides. Solve the equation.

Practice

Use what you learned about solving equations with variables on both sides to complete Exercises 3–5 on page 20.

 **Key Idea**

Solving Equations with Variables on Both Sides

To solve equations with variables on both sides, collect the variable terms on one side and the constant terms on the other side.

EXAMPLE 1 — Solving an Equation with Variables on Both Sides

Solve $15 - 2x = -7x$. Check your solution.

	$15 - 2x = -7x$	Write the equation.
Undo the subtraction. →	$\underline{+\ 2x \quad +\ 2x}$	Add $2x$ to each side.
	$15 = -5x$	Simplify.
Undo the multiplication. →	$\dfrac{15}{-5} = \dfrac{-5x}{-5}$	Divide each side by -5.
	$-3 = x$	Simplify.

Check

$$15 - 2x = -7x$$
$$15 - 2(-3) \overset{?}{=} -7(-3)$$
$$21 = 21 \checkmark$$

∴ The solution is $x = -3$.

EXAMPLE 2 — Using the Distributive Property to Solve an Equation

Solve $-2(x - 5) = 6\left(2 - \dfrac{1}{2}x\right)$.

	$-2(x - 5) = \ \ 6\left(2 - \dfrac{1}{2}x\right)$	Write the equation.
	$-2x + 10 = \ \ 12 - 3x$	Use Distributive Property.
Undo the subtraction. →	$\underline{+\ 3x \qquad\qquad +\ 3x}$	Add $3x$ to each side.
	$x + 10 = \ \ 12$	Simplify.
Undo the addition. →	$\underline{-\ 10 \quad -\ 10}$	Subtract 10 from each side.
	$x = 2$	Simplify.

∴ The solution is $x = 2$.

On Your Own

Now You're Ready
Exercises 6–14

Solve the equation. Check your solution.

1. $-3x = 2x + 19$
2. $2.5y + 6 = 4.5y - 1$
3. $6(4 - z) = 2z$

Laurie's Notes

Introduction

Connect
- **Yesterday:** Students developed an intuitive understanding of solving equations with variables on both sides.
- **Today:** Students will solve equations with variables on both sides by using Properties of Equality and collecting variable terms on one side.

Motivate
- **?** "How many of you have driven across the Mississippi River?"
- Share some information about the Mississippi River. It is the third longest river in North America, flowing 2350 miles from Lake Itasca in Minnesota to the Gulf of Mexico. The width of the river ranges from 20–30 feet at its narrowest to more than 11 miles at its widest.

Lesson Notes

Key Idea
- Discuss with students the vocabulary *variable term* and *constant term*.
- Write: $5x - 2 - 9x + y + 4$
- **?** "In this expression, what are the variable terms? Constant terms?"
  $5x$, $-9x$, and y; -2 and 4
- **Common Error:** Students forget to include the sign of the variable term.

Example 1
- Notice that a constant is on the left side only. For this reason, it makes sense to solve for the variable term on the right side of the equation.

Example 2
- **Teaching Tip:** Before distributing on the left side, rewrite the inside expression as $x + (-5)$ (add the opposite). Students are likely to recognize that they are multiplying $(-2)(-5)$ to get a product of 10.
- **?** "How do you multiply a whole number and a fraction like $6\left(\frac{1}{2}\right)$?" Listen for language such as, write the whole number over a denominator of 1 and multiply straight across.
- **FYI:** Solve for the variable on the side of the equation where the coefficient is the greatest. After collecting the variable terms on one side, the coefficient of the variable term will be positive, a condition that generally renders fewer mistakes.

On Your Own
- **Neighbor Check:** Have students work independently and then have their neighbor check their work. Have students discuss any discrepancies.

Goal Today's lesson is solving equations with variables on both sides.

Start Thinking! and Warm Up

> **Lesson 1.3** Warm Up
> For use before Lesson 1.3
>
> **Lesson 1.3** Start Thinking!
> For use before Lesson 1.3
>
> Try solving the equation $2x + 20 = 12x$ by first subtracting 20 from each side. What property allows you to do so? Does it help you get closer to finding a solution?
>
> What is a better first step? Explain.

Extra Example 1
Solve $r = -5r + 18$. 3

Extra Example 2
Solve $6\left(1 + \frac{1}{2}x\right) = 2(x + 1)$. -4

On Your Own
1. $x = -3.8$
2. $y = 3.5$
3. $z = 3$

Extra Example 3

The legs of the right triangle have the same length. What is the area of the triangle? $1\frac{1}{8}$ square units

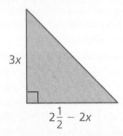

$3x$

$2\frac{1}{2} - 2x$

Extra Example 4

A boat travels 3 hours downstream at r miles per hour. On the return trip, the boat travels 5 miles per hour slower and takes 4 hours. What is the distance the boat travels each way? 60 mi

On Your Own

4. 36π

5. 50 mi

English Language Learners

Vocabulary

Remind English learners that *like terms* are terms with the same variables raised to the same exponents. As the number of terms in an equation increases, an important skill is to identify and combine like terms.

Laurie's Notes

Example 3

❓ "Define radius and diameter of a circle." Diameter is the distance across a circle through its center. Radius is half the diameter.

• Solve the equation as shown.

• This example reviews the formula for the area of a circle. You might also ask about the formula for the circumference of a circle. $C = 2\pi r$

Example 4

❓ "How do you find the distance traveled when you know the rate and time?" multiply; $d = rt$

• Discuss with students that the distance both ways is the same, a simple but not obvious fact.

❓ "If you travel 40 miles per hour for 2 hours, how far will you go? How about 40 miles per hour for a half hour?" 80 mi; 20 mi

❓ "How far do you travel at x miles per hour for 3 hours?" $3x$ mi

• Students need to read the time from the illustration. The rates for each direction are x and $(x + 2)$.

• Write and solve the equation as shown.

On Your Own

• **Think-Pair-Share:** Students should read each question independently and then work with a partner to answer the questions. When they have answered the questions, the pair should compare their answers with another group and discuss any discrepancies.

Closure

• **Exit Ticket:** Solve $6 - 2x = 4x - 9$. Check your solution. $x = 2.5$

Technology For the Teacher

Dynamic Classroom

The Dynamic Planning Tool
Editable Teacher's Resources at *BigIdeasMath.com*

The circles are identical. What is the area of each circle?

(A) 2   (B) 4   (C) 16π (D) 64π

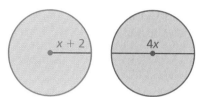

The circles are identical, so the radius of each circle is the same.

$$x + 2 = 2x \qquad \text{Write an equation. The radius of the purple circle is } 2x.$$
$$\underline{-x \qquad\quad -x} \qquad \text{Subtract } x \text{ from each side.}$$
$$2 = x \qquad\qquad \text{Simplify.}$$

∴ The area of each circle is $\pi r^2 = \pi(4)^2 = 16\pi$. So, the correct answer is (C).

EXAMPLE ④ **Real-Life Application**

A boat travels x miles per hour upstream on the Mississippi River. On the return trip, the boat travels 2 miles per hour faster. How far does the boat travel upstream?

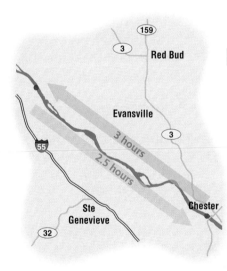

The speed of the boat on the return trip is $(x + 2)$ miles per hour.

Distance upstream = Distance of return trip

$$3x = 2.5(x + 2) \qquad \text{Write an equation.}$$
$$3x = 2.5x + 5 \qquad \text{Use Distributive Property.}$$
$$\underline{-2.5x \quad -2.5x} \qquad \text{Subtract } 2.5x \text{ from each side.}$$
$$0.5x = 5 \qquad\qquad \text{Simplify.}$$
$$\frac{0.5x}{0.5} = \frac{5}{0.5} \qquad\qquad \text{Divide each side by 0.5.}$$
$$x = 10 \qquad\qquad \text{Simplify.}$$

∴ The boat travels 10 miles per hour for 3 hours upstream. So, it travels 30 miles upstream.

● **On Your Own**

4. **WHAT IF?** In Example 3, the diameter of the purple circle is $3x$. What is the area of each circle?

5. A boat travels x miles per hour from one island to another island in 2.5 hours. The boat travels 5 miles per hour faster on the return trip of 2 hours. What is the distance between the islands?

 Vocabulary and Concept Check

1. **WRITING** Is $x = 3$ a solution of the equation $3x - 5 = 4x - 9$? Explain.

2. **OPEN-ENDED** Write an equation that has variables on both sides and has a solution of -3.

 Practice and Problem Solving

The value of the figure's surface area is equal to the value of the figure's volume. Find the value of *x*.

3.

11 in.   3 in.

4.
2.5 cm

x

5.
6 in.

5 in.
x

Solve the equation. Check your solution.

① ② 6. $m - 4 = 2m$

7. $3k - 1 = 7k + 2$

8. $6.7x = 5.2x + 12.3$

9. $-24 - \frac{1}{8}p = \frac{3}{8}p$

10. $12(2w - 3) = 6w$

11. $2(n - 3) = 4n + 1$

12. $2(4z - 1) = 3(z + 2)$

13. $0.1x = 0.2(x + 2)$

14. $\frac{1}{6}d + \frac{2}{3} = \frac{1}{4}(d - 2)$

15. **ERROR ANALYSIS** Describe and correct the error in solving the equation.

✗
$$3x - 4 = 2x + 1$$
$$3x - 4 - 2x = 2x + 1 - 2x$$
$$x - 4 = 1$$
$$x - 4 + 4 = 1 - 4$$
$$x = -3$$

16. **TRAIL MIX** The equation $4.05p + 14.40 = 4.50(p + 3)$ represents the number p of pounds of peanuts you need to make trail mix. How many pounds of peanuts do you need for the trail mix?

17. **CARS** Write and solve an equation to find the number of miles you must drive to have the same cost for each of the car rentals.

$15 plus $0.50 per mile

$25 plus $0.25 per mile

Assignment Guide and Homework Check

Level	Day 1 Activity Assignment	Day 2 Lesson Assignment	Homework Check
Basic	3–5, 26–29	1, 2, 6–12, 15–19	6, 9, 10, 12, 16, 18
Average	3–5, 26–29	1, 2, 9–19, 21	9, 10, 12, 16, 18, 21
Advanced	3–5, 26–29	1, 2, 12–15, 18–25	12, 18, 22, 24

For Your Information

- **Exercise 16** The equation represents a mixture problem in which peanuts are added to other ingredients, making trail mix. The equation shows that p pounds of peanuts that cost \$4.05 per pound are added to other ingredients that cost a total of \$14.40. This mixture creates $(p + 3)$ pounds of trail mix that costs \$4.50 per pound.

Common Errors

- **Exercises 6–14** Students may perform the same operation instead of the opposite operation when trying to get the variable terms on the same side. Remind them that whenever a variable or number is moved from one side of the equal sign to the other, the opposite operation is used.
- **Exercises 6–14** Students may use the opposite operation when combining like terms on the same side of the equal sign. Remind them that the opposite operation is used only when moving the variable or number to the other side of the equation.
- **Exercises 16 and 17** Students may forget to write the units in their answers. Remind them that when units are given, the units need to be included in the answer.

1.3 Record and Practice Journal

Solve the equation. Check your solution.

1. $x + 16 = 9x$
   $x = 2$

2. $4y - 70 = 12y + 2$
   $y = -9$

3. $5(p + 6) = 8p$
   $p = 10$

4. $3(g - 7) = 2(10 + g)$
   $g = 41$

5. $1.8 + 7n = 9.5 - 4n$
   $n = 0.7$

6. $\frac{3}{7}w - 11 = -\frac{4}{7}w$
   $w = 11$

7. One movie club charges a \$100 membership fee and \$10 for each movie. Another club charges no membership fee but movies cost \$15 each. Write and solve an equation to find the number of movies you need to buy for the cost of each movie club to be the same.
   $100 + 10x = 15x; \ x = 20$

8. Thirty percent of all the students in a school are in a play. All students except for 140 are in the play. How many students are in the school?
   200 students

Technology For the Teacher
Answer Presentation Tool
QuizShow

Vocabulary and Concept Check

1. no; When 3 is substituted for x, the left side simplifies to 4 and the right side simplifies to 3.

2. *Sample answer:*
   $4x + 1 = 3x - 2$

Practice and Problem Solving

3. $x = 13.2$ in.

4. $x = 10$ cm

5. $x = 7.5$ in.

6. $m = -4$

7. $k = -0.75$

8. $x = 8.2$

9. $p = -48$

10. $w = 2$

11. $n = -3.5$

12. $z = 1.6$

13. $x = -4$

14. $d = 14$

15. The 4 should have been added to the right side.
$$3x - 4 = 2x + 1$$
$$3x - 2x - 4 = 2x + 1 - 2x$$
$$x - 4 = 1$$
$$x - 4 + 4 = 1 + 4$$
$$x = 5$$

16. 2 lb

17. $15 + 0.5m = 25 + 0.25m$;
    40 mi

18. 3 units   **19.** 7.5 units

20. 232 units

21. See *Taking Math Deeper*.

22. fractions; Because $\frac{1}{3}$ written as a decimal is repeating.

23. 10 mL   **24.** 25 grams

25. square: 12 units
triangle: 10 units, 19 units, 19 units

Fair Game Review

26. 27 cm³

27. 54.6 in.³

28. about 50.24 ft³

29. C

Mini-Assessment

Solve the equation.

1. $n - 4 = 3n + 6$ $n = -5$

2. $0.3(w + 10) = 1.8w$ $w = 2$

3. $3p = 4(-3p + 6)$ $p = 1.6$

4. $\frac{1}{3}v = -\frac{2}{3}\left(\frac{1}{2}v - 1\right)$ $v = 1$

5. The perimeter of the rectangle is equal to the perimeter of the square. What are the side lengths of each figure? rectangle: 4 units by 10 units; square: 7 units by 7 units

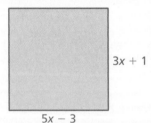

$3x + 1$

$5x - 3$

$2x$

$4x + 2$

Taking Math Deeper

Exercise 21

This problem seems like it is easy, but it can actually be quite challenging.

 Identify the key information in the table.

	Packing Material	Priority	Express
Box	$2.25	$2.50/lb	$8.50/lb
Envelope	$1.10	$2.50/lb	$8.50/lb

 Write and solve an equation.

Let $x =$ the weight of the DVD and packing material.

Cost of Mailing Box: $2.25 + 2.5x$
Cost of Mailing Envelope: $1.10 + 8.5x$

$$2.25 + 2.5x = 1.10 + 8.5x$$
$$1.15 = 6x$$
$$0.19 \approx x$$

Set costs equal.

 Answer the question.

The weight of the DVD and packing material is about 0.19 pound, or about 3 ounces.

Project

Postage for special types of mail, such as priority mail, is determined by the weight of the package and the distance it needs to travel. Find the cost of sending a 15-ounce package from your house to Los Angeles, Washington D.C., and Albuquerque.

Reteaching and Enrichment Strategies

If students need help. . .	If students got it. . .

Resources by Chapter
  • Practice A and Practice B
  • Puzzle Time
Record and Practice Journal Practice
Differentiating the Lesson
Lesson Tutorials
Skills Review Handbook
	Resources by Chapter
	  • Enrichment and Extension
	  • School-to-Work
	Start the next section

A polygon is *regular* if each of its sides has the same length. Find the perimeter of the regular polygon.

18.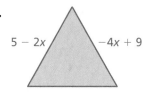

$5 - 2x$ $-4x + 9$

19.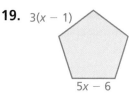

$3(x - 1)$

$5x - 6$

20.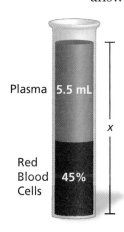

$x + 7$

$\frac{4}{3}x - \frac{1}{3}$

21. POSTAGE The cost of mailing a DVD in an envelope by express mail is equal to the cost of mailing a DVD in a box by priority mail. What is the weight of the DVD with its packing material? Round your answer to the nearest hundredth.

	Packing Material	Priority Mail	Express Mail
Box	$2.25	$2.50 per lb	$8.50 per lb
Envelope	$1.10	$2.50 per lb	$8.50 per lb

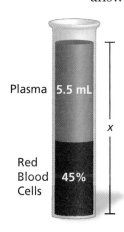

Plasma **5.5 mL**

x

Red Blood Cells **45%**

22. REASONING Would you solve the equation $0.25x + 7 = \frac{1}{3}x - 8$ using fractions or decimals? Explain.

23. BLOOD SAMPLE The amount of red blood cells in a blood sample is equal to the total amount in the sample minus the amount of plasma. What is the total amount x of blood drawn?

24. NUTRITION One serving of oatmeal provides 16% of the fiber you need daily. You must get the remaining 21 grams of fiber from other sources. How many grams of fiber should you consume daily?

25. **Geometry** The perimeter of the square is equal to the perimeter of the triangle. What are the side lengths of each figure?

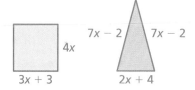

$4x$ $3x + 3$ $7x - 2$ $7x - 2$ $2x + 4$

Fair Game Review What you learned in previous grades & lessons

Find the volume of the figure. Use 3.14 for π. *(Skills Review Handbook)*

26.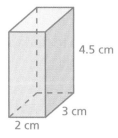

4.5 cm

3 cm

2 cm

27.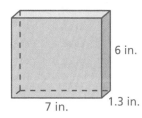

6 in.

7 in.   1.3 in.

28.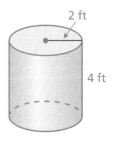

2 ft

4 ft

29. MULTIPLE CHOICE A car travels 480 miles on 15 gallons of gasoline. How many miles does the car travel per gallon? *(Skills Review Handbook)*

Ⓐ 28 mi/gal   Ⓑ 30 mi/gal   Ⓒ 32 mi/gal   Ⓓ 35 mi/gal

Essential Question How can you use a formula for one measurement to write a formula for a different measurement?

STANDARDS
OF LEARNING
8.15

1 ACTIVITY: Using Perimeter and Area Formulas

Work with a partner.

a. • Write a formula for the perimeter P of a rectangle.
   • Solve the formula for w.
   • Use the new formula to find the width of the rectangle.

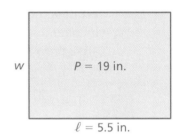

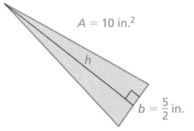

b. • Write a formula for the area A of a triangle.
   • Solve the formula for h.
   • Use the new formula to find the height of the triangle.

c. • Write a formula for the circumference C of a circle.
   • Solve the formula for r.
   • Use the new formula to find the radius of the circle.

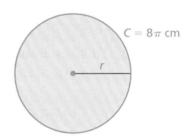

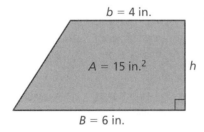

d. • Write a formula for the area A of a trapezoid.
   • Solve the formula for h.
   • Use the new formula to find the height of the trapezoid.

e. • Write a formula for the area A of a parallelogram.
   • Solve the formula for h.
   • Use the new formula to find the height of the parallelogram.

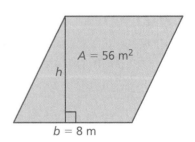

Laurie's Notes

Introduction

For the Teacher

- **Goal:** Students will use common formulas for perimeter, area, and volume to explore rewriting equations.
- **Teaching Tip:** Continually ask students what operations are being performed in each formula.

Motivate

- **Preparation:** Make a set of formula cards. My set is a collection of five cards for each shape: the labeled diagram, the two measurements, and the two formulas being found.

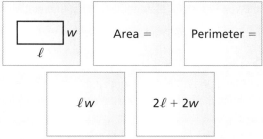

- Depending upon the number of students in your class, use some or all of the cards. Pass out the cards and have students form groups matching all 5 cards for the shape.
- When all of the matches have been made, ask each group to read their formulas aloud.

Activity Notes

Activity 1

- Solving literal equations can be one of the most challenging skills for students. Model a problem, such as solving $A = \ell w$ for width.
- Fractional coefficients can also be a challenge, so model an additional problem, such as solving $A = \frac{1}{2}xy$ for y. First, multiply both sides by 2, then divide both sides by x.
- **Teaching Tip:** You may find that students are substituting the known values of the variables and then solving the equation, instead of solving the equation and then substituting.
- **Connection:** The reason for solving for the variable is that the equation can be used for the width of any rectangle given the perimeter and length, not just the specific example shown. It is a general solution that can be reused.
- **Teaching Tip:** After 2 or more groups have correctly solved part (a), have a volunteer write the solution on the board for the other groups to see.
- For parts (b) and (d), suggest students start by multiplying both sides by the reciprocal of $\frac{1}{2}$. In part (c), 2π is a number and can be manipulated as such, so divide both sides by 2π.

Standards of Learning

8.15(c) The student will identify properties of operations used to solve an equation.

Previous Learning

Students should know the common formulas for area, perimeter, and volume.

Activity Materials
Introduction
• formula cards (index cards)

Start Thinking! and Warm Up

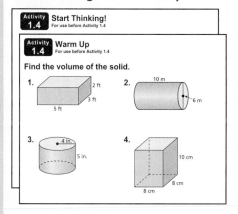

1.4 Record and Practice Journal

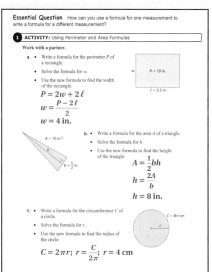

Kinesthetic
Have kinesthetic learners model the areas of the polygons on grid paper. Then compare their answers with the answers found using the area formulas.

1.4 Record and Practice Journal

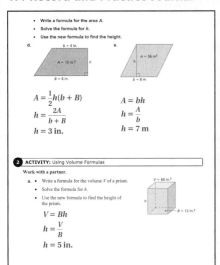

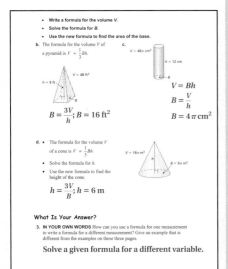

Laurie's Notes

Activity 2

- This activity is similar to Activity 1, where students worked with perimeter and area formulas. In Activity 2, students will work with volume formulas.
- Note that all of the diagrams use *B* for the area of the base instead of having students use specific area formulas. Using this approach, the volume formulas for parts (a) and (c) are the same ($V = Bh$) and the volume formulas for parts (b) and (d) are the same $\left(V = \frac{1}{3}Bh\right)$. This shows that structurally the prism and the cylinder are the same, and that structurally the pyramid and the cone are the same.
- The volume formulas for pyramids and cones are covered in Chapter 7.
- Use the *Teaching Tips* from Activity 1. Have students work in groups of 3 or 4 and post a correct solution on the board after 2 or more groups have been successful.
- **Common Error:** For parts (b) and (d), suggest that students start by multiplying both sides by the reciprocal of $\frac{1}{3}$.

What Is Your Answer?

- **Neighbor Check:** Have students work independently and then have their neighbor check their work. Have students discuss any discrepancies.

Closure

- Describe how to solve $d = rt$ for *t*. *Sample answer:* Divide both sides of the equation by *r*.

Technology
For
the **T**eacher

Dynamic Classroom

The Dynamic Planning Tool
Editable Teacher's Resources at *BigIdeasMath.com*

Work with a partner.

a. • Write a formula for the volume V of a prism.

   • Solve the formula for h.

   • Use the new formula to find the height of the prism.

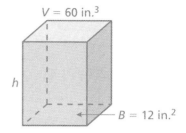

$V = 60$ in.³

h

$B = 12$ in.²

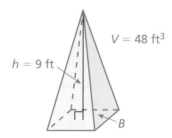

$V = 48$ ft³

$h = 9$ ft

B

b. • The formula for the volume V of a pyramid is $V = \frac{1}{3}Bh$.

   • Solve the formula for B.

   • Use the new formula to find the area of the base of the pyramid.

c. • Write a formula for the volume V of a cylinder.

   • Solve the formula for B.

   • Use the new formula to find the area of the base of the cylinder.

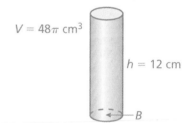

$V = 48\pi$ cm³

$h = 12$ cm

B

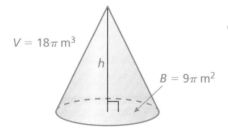

$V = 18\pi$ m³

h

$B = 9\pi$ m²

d. • The formula for the volume V of a cone is $V = \frac{1}{3}Bh$.

   • Solve the formula for h.

   • Use the new formula to find the height of the cone.

What Is Your Answer?

3. IN YOUR OWN WORDS How can you use a formula for one measurement to write a formula for a different measurement? Give an example that is different from the examples on these two pages.

Practice

Use what you learned about rewriting equations and formulas to complete Exercises 3 and 4 on page 26.

Key Vocabulary
literal equation, *p. 24*

An equation that has two or more variables is called a **literal equation**. To rewrite a literal equation, solve for one variable in terms of the other variable(s).

EXAMPLE 1 Rewriting an Equation

Solve the equation $2y + 5x = 6$ for y.

$$2y + 5x = 6 \qquad \text{Write the equation.}$$

Undo the addition. $\longrightarrow \quad 2y + 5x - 5x = 6 - 5x \qquad$ Subtract $5x$ from each side.

$$2y = 6 - 5x \qquad \text{Simplify.}$$

Undo the multiplication. $\longrightarrow \quad \dfrac{2y}{2} = \dfrac{6 - 5x}{2} \qquad$ Divide each side by 2.

$$y = 3 - \frac{5}{2}x \qquad \text{Simplify.}$$

On Your Own

Now You're Ready
Exercises 5–10

Solve the equation for y.

1. $5y - x = 10$
2. $4x - 4y = 1$
3. $12 = 6x + 3y$

EXAMPLE 2 Rewriting a Formula

Remember

A *formula* shows how one variable is related to one or more other variables. A formula is a type of literal equation.

The formula for the surface area S of a cone is $S = \pi r^2 + \pi r \ell$. Solve the formula for the slant height ℓ.

$$S = \pi r^2 + \pi r \ell \qquad \text{Write the formula.}$$

$$S - \pi r^2 = \pi r^2 - \pi r^2 + \pi r \ell \qquad \text{Subtract } \pi r^2 \text{ from each side.}$$

$$S - \pi r^2 = \pi r \ell \qquad \text{Simplify.}$$

$$\frac{S - \pi r^2}{\pi r} = \frac{\pi r \ell}{\pi r} \qquad \text{Divide each side by } \pi r.$$

$$\frac{S - \pi r^2}{\pi r} = \ell \qquad \text{Simplify.}$$

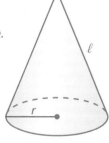

On Your Own

Now You're Ready
Exercises 14–19

Solve the formula for the red variable.

4. Area of rectangle: $A = bh$
5. Simple interest: $I = Prt$
6. Surface area of cylinder: $S = 2\pi r^2 + 2\pi rh$

Laurie's Notes

Introduction

Connect

- **Yesterday:** Students practiced rewriting common geometric formulas.
- **Today:** Students will use the techniques explored yesterday to solve literal equations.

Motivate

- Share with students the following highest and lowest recorded temperatures.

State	Highest Recorded Temperatures		State	Lowest Recorded Temperatures	
NM	122°F	50°C	NM	−50°F	−46°C
NH	106°F	41°C	NH	−47°F	−44°C
PA	111°F	44°C	PA	−42°F	−41°C

- The purpose is to pique interest and have students observe that the temperatures are measured in degrees Fahrenheit or degrees Celsius.

Lesson Notes

Example 1

- Write the definition of literal equation.
- **?** "Can 6 and $5x$ be combined? Explain." no; They are not like terms.
- Simplifying the last step is not obvious to all students. Relate it to fractions. You subtract the numerators and keep the same denominator. For example:

$$\frac{5-3}{7} = \frac{5}{7} - \frac{3}{7} \quad \text{and} \quad \frac{6-5x}{2} = \frac{6}{2} - \frac{5x}{2} = 3 - \frac{5}{2}x.$$

On Your Own

- Notice in Question 2 that the coefficient of y is −4. Suggest students rewrite the equation as $4x + (-4)y = 1$.

Example 2

- **Teaching Tip:** Highlight the variable ℓ in red as shown in the textbook. Discuss the idea that everything except the variable ℓ must be moved to the left side of the equation using Properties of Equality.
- **?** "The term πr^2 is added to the term $\pi r \ell$. How do you move it to the left side of the equation?" Subtract πr^2 from each side of the equation.
- Discuss the technique of dividing by πr in one step, instead of dividing by π and then dividing by r.

On Your Own

- **Think-Pair-Share:** Students should read each question independently and then work with a partner to answer the questions. When they have answered the questions, the pair should compare their answers with another group and discuss any discrepancies.

Start Thinking! and Warm Up

> **Lesson 1.4** Warm Up
> For use before Lesson 1.4
>
> **Lesson 1.4** Start Thinking!
> For use before Lesson 1.4
>
> How does solving the equation $5x + 4y = 14$ for x compare to solving the equation $5x + 20 = 14$ for x? Describe the steps involved in each solution.

Extra Example 1

Solve the equation $-2x - 3y = 6$ for y.

$$y = -\frac{2}{3}x - 2$$

On Your Own

1. $y = 2 + \frac{1}{5}x$

2. $y = x - \frac{1}{4}$

3. $y = 4 - 2x$

Extra Example 2

The formula for the surface area of a square pyramid is $S = x^2 + 2x\ell$. Solve the formula for the slant height ℓ.

$$\ell = \frac{S - x^2}{2x}$$

On Your Own

4. $b = \frac{A}{h}$

5. $P = \frac{I}{rt}$

6. $h = \frac{S - 2\pi r^2}{2\pi r}$

English Language Learners

Vocabulary

Have students start a *Formula* page in their notebooks with the formulas used in this section. Each formula should be accompanied by a description of what each of the variables represents and an example. In the case of area formulas, units of measure should be included with the description (e.g., units and square units). As students progress throughout the year, additional formulas can be added to the *Formula* notebook page.

Extra Example 3

Solve the temperature formula

$F = \frac{9}{5}C + 32$ for C. $C = \frac{5}{9}(F - 32)$

Extra Example 4

Which temperature is greater, 400°F or 200°C? 400°F

 **On Your Own**

7. greater than

Key Idea

- Write the formula for converting from degrees Fahrenheit to degrees Celsius.
- Use this formula if you know the temperature in degrees Fahrenheit and you want to find the temperature in degrees Celsius.

? "You are traveling abroad and the temperature is always stated in degrees Celsius. How can you figure out the temperature in degrees Fahrenheit, with which you are more familiar?" Students may recognize that you will want to have a different conversion formula that allows you to substitute for *C* and calculate *F*.

Example 3

? "What is the reciprocal of $\frac{5}{9}$?" $\frac{9}{5}$

- Remind students that multiplying by the reciprocal $\frac{9}{5}$ is more efficient than dividing by the fraction $\frac{5}{9}$.

Example 4

- **FYI:** The graphic on the left provides information about the temperature of a lightning bolt and the temperature of the surface of the sun. The two temperatures use different scales.

? "How can you compare two temperatures that are in different scales?" Listen for understanding that one of the temperatures must be converted.

? "How do you multiply $\frac{9}{5}$ times 30,000?" Students may recall that you can simplify before multiplying. Five divides into 30,000 six thousand times, so $6000 \times 9 = 54{,}000$.

? "Approximately how many times hotter is a lightning bolt than the surface of the sun?" 5 times This is a *cool* fact for students to know!

On Your Own

- **Neighbor Check:** Have students work independently and then have their neighbor check their work. Have students discuss any discrepancies.

Closure

- **Exit Ticket:** Solve $2x + 4y = 11$ for y. Check your solution. $y = -\frac{1}{2}x + \frac{11}{4}$

Technology For the Teacher

Dynamic Classroom

The Dynamic Planning Tool
Editable Teacher's Resources at *BigIdeasMath.com*

 **Key Idea**

> **Temperature Conversion**
>
> A formula for converting from degrees Fahrenheit F to degrees Celsius C is
>
> $$C = \frac{5}{9}(F - 32).$$

EXAMPLE 3 | **Rewriting the Temperature Formula**

Solve the temperature formula for F.

$C = \dfrac{5}{9}(F - 32)$	Write the temperature formula.

Use the reciprocal. → $\dfrac{9}{5} \cdot C = \dfrac{9}{5} \cdot \dfrac{5}{9}(F - 32)$ Multiply each side by $\dfrac{9}{5}$, the reciprocal of $\dfrac{5}{9}$.

$\dfrac{9}{5}C = F - 32$ Simplify.

Undo the subtraction. → $\dfrac{9}{5}C + 32 = F - 32 + 32$ Add 32 to each side.

$\dfrac{9}{5}C + 32 = F$ Simplify.

∴ The rewritten formula is $F = \dfrac{9}{5}C + 32$.

EXAMPLE 4 | **Real-Life Application**

Sun
11,000°F

Lightning
30,000°C

Which has the greater temperature?

Convert the Celsius temperature of lightning to Fahrenheit.

$F = \dfrac{9}{5}C + 32$ Write the rewritten formula from Example 3.

$= \dfrac{9}{5}(30,000) + 32$ Substitute 30,000 for C.

$= 54,032$ Simplify.

∴ Because 54,032 °F is greater than 11,000 °F, lightning has the greater temperature.

● **On Your Own**

7. Room temperature is considered to be 70 °F. Suppose the temperature is 23 °C. Is this greater than or less than room temperature?

 Vocabulary and Concept Check

1. **VOCABULARY** Is $-2x = \dfrac{3}{8}$ a literal equation? Explain.

2. **DIFFERENT WORDS, SAME QUESTION** Which is different? Find "both" answers.

Solve $4x - 2y = 6$ for y.	Solve $6 = 4x - 2y$ for y.
Solve $4x - 2y = 6$ for y in terms of x.	Solve $4x - 2y = 6$ for x in terms of y.

 Practice and Problem Solving

3. **a.** Write a formula for the area A of a triangle.

    b. Solve the formula for b.

    c. Use the new formula to find the base of the triangle.

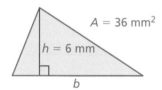

$A = 36$ mm^2
$h = 6$ mm
b

4. **a.** Write a formula for the lateral surface area S of a cylinder.

    b. Solve the formula for h.

    c. Use the new formula to find the height of the cylinder.

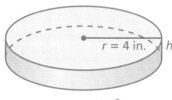

$r = 4$ in. h
$S = 40\pi$ in.^{2}

Solve the equation for y.

5. $\dfrac{1}{3}x + y = 4$

6. $3x + \dfrac{1}{5}y = 7$

7. $6 = 4x + 9y$

8. $\pi = 7x - 2y$

9. $4.2x - 1.4y = 2.1$

10. $6y - 1.5x = 8$

11. **ERROR ANALYSIS** Describe and correct the error in rewriting the equation.

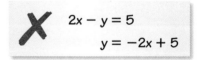

✗ $2x - y = 5$
    $y = -2x + 5$

12. **TEMPERATURE** The formula $K = C + 273.15$ converts temperatures from Celsius C to Kelvin K.

    a. Solve the formula for C.

    b. Convert 300 K to Celsius.

13. **INTEREST** The formula for simple interest is $I = Prt$.

    a. Solve the formula for t.

    b. Use the new formula to find the value of t in the table.

I	$75
P	$500
r	5%
t	

Assignment Guide and Homework Check

Level	Day 1 Activity Assignment	Day 2 Lesson Assignment	Homework Check
Basic	3, 4, 24–28	1, 2, 5–19 odd, 12	7, 12, 13, 17
Average	3, 4, 24–28	1, 2, 8–11, 15–21 odd, 20	8, 10, 17, 20
Advanced	3, 4, 24–28	1, 2, 10, 11, 17–23	10, 17, 20, 22

For Your Information

- **Exercise 2** *Different Words, Same Question* is a new type of exercise. Three of the four choices pose the same question using different words. The remaining choice poses a different question. So there are two answers.

Common Errors

- **Exercises 5–10** Students may solve the equation for the wrong variable. Remind them that they are solving the equation for *y*. Encourage them to make *y* a different color when solving so that it is easy to remember that they are solving for *y*.
- **Exercises 14–19** Each equation has a different step that could confuse students. Remind them to take their time when solving for the red variable. Remind them of the process for solving for a variable. They should start away from the variable and move toward it.

1.4 Record and Practice Journal

Solve the equation for y.

1. $2x + y = -9$
   $y = -2x - 9$

2. $4x - 10y = 12$
   $y = \frac{2}{5}x - \frac{6}{5}$

3. $13 = \frac{1}{6}y + 2x$
   $y = -12x + 78$

Solve the formula for the bold variable.

4. $V = \ell wh$
   $w = \dfrac{V}{\ell h}$

5. $f = \frac{1}{2}(r + 6.5)$
   $r = 2f - 6.5$

6. $S = 2\pi r^2 + 2\pi rh$
   $h = \dfrac{S - 2\pi r^2}{2\pi r}$

7. The formula for the area of a triangle is $A = \frac{1}{2}bh$.

   a. Solve the formula for *h*.
   $h = \dfrac{2A}{b}$

   b. Use the new formula to find the value of *h*.
   $h = 9$ in.

   $A = 54 \text{ in.}^2$

   12 in.

Technology For the Teacher

Answer Presentation Tool
Quiz*Show*

Vocabulary and Concept Check

1. no; The equation only contains one variable.

2. Solve $4x - 2y = 6$ for x in terms of y.;
   $x = \dfrac{3}{2} + \dfrac{1}{2}y$; $y = -3 + 2x$

Practice and Problem Solving

3. **a.** $A = \dfrac{1}{2}bh$

   b. $b = \dfrac{2A}{h}$

   c. $b = 12$ mm

4. **a.** $S = 2\pi rh$

   b. $h = \dfrac{S}{2\pi r}$

   c. $h = 5$ in.

5. $y = 4 - \dfrac{1}{3}x$

6. $y = 35 - 15x$

7. $y = \dfrac{2}{3} - \dfrac{4}{9}x$

8. $y = \dfrac{7}{2}x - \dfrac{\pi}{2}$

9. $y = 3x - 1.5$

10. $y = \dfrac{4}{3} + \dfrac{1}{4}x$

11. The *y* should have a negative sign in front of it.
    $$2x - y = 5$$
    $$-y = -2x + 5$$
    $$y = 2x - 5$$

12. **a.** $C = K - 273.15$

    b. $26.85°C$

13. **a.** $t = \dfrac{I}{Pr}$

    b. $t = 3$ yr

14. $t = \dfrac{d}{r}$

15. $m = \dfrac{e}{c^2}$

16. $C = R - P$

17. $\ell = \dfrac{A - \frac{1}{2}\pi w^2}{2w}$

18. $V = \dfrac{Bh}{3}$

19. $w = 6g - 40$

20. The rewritten formula is a general solution that can be reused.

21. **a.** $F = 32 + \dfrac{9}{5}(K - 273.15)$

   b. 32°F

   c. liquid nitrogen

22. See *Taking Math Deeper*.

23. $r^3 = \dfrac{3V}{4\pi}; r = 4.5$ in.

24. $3\dfrac{3}{4}$ 25. $6\dfrac{2}{5}$

26. $\dfrac{1}{3}$ 27. $1\dfrac{1}{4}$

28. D

Mini-Assessment

Solve the formula for the red variable.

1. Distance Formula: $d = rt$ $r = \dfrac{d}{t}$

2. Area of a triangle: $A = \dfrac{1}{2}bh$ $h = \dfrac{2A}{b}$

3. Circumference of a circle: $C = 2\pi r$

   $r = \dfrac{C}{2\pi}$

4. The temperature in Portland, Oregon is 37°F. The temperature in Mobile, Alabama is 22°C. In which city is the temperature higher? Mobile, Alabama

Taking Math Deeper

Exercise 22

This problem reviews circles and percents, as well as distance, rate, and time. It also has a bit of history related to George Ferris, who designed the first Ferris wheel for the 1893 World's Fair in Chicago.

 Organize the given information.
Circumference (Navy Pier Ferris Wheel): $C = 439.6$ ft
Circumference (first Ferris wheel): x ft
Relationship: $439.6 = 0.56x$

 Find the radius of each wheel.
  a. Radius (Navy Pier Ferris Wheel):
$$C = 2\pi r$$
$$439.6 \approx 2(3.14)r$$
$$70 = r$$
Circumference (first Ferris wheel):
$$439.6 = 0.56x$$
$$785 = x$$

56% smaller

  b. Radius (first Ferris wheel):
$$785 \approx 2(3.14)R$$
$$125 = R$$

③ **c.** The first Ferris wheel made 1 revolution in 9 minutes. How fast was the wheel moving?

$$\text{rate} = \dfrac{785 \text{ ft}}{9 \text{ min}} \approx 87.2 \text{ ft per min}$$

It might be interesting for students to know that the first Ferris wheel had 36 cars, each of which held 60 people!

Project

Use your school's library or the Internet to find how long one revolution takes for the Ferris wheel on the Navy Pier in Chicago and the one in London, England. Which one has the greater circumference? Which one travels faster? How do you know?

Reteaching and Enrichment Strategies

If students need help. . .	If students got it. . .
Resources by Chapter • Practice A and Practice B • Puzzle Time Record and Practice Journal Practice Differentiating the Lesson Lesson Tutorials Skills Review Handbook	Resources by Chapter • Enrichment and Extension • School-to-Work Start the next section

Solve the formula for the red variable.

14. $d = rt$

15. $e = mc^2$

16. $R - C = P$

17. $A = \dfrac{1}{2}\pi w^2 + 2\ell w$

18. $B = 3\dfrac{V}{h}$

19. $g = \dfrac{1}{6}(w + 40)$

20. WRITING Why is it useful to rewrite a formula in terms of another variable?

21. TEMPERATURE The formula $K = \dfrac{5}{9}(F - 32) + 273.15$ converts temperatures from Fahrenheit F to Kelvin K.

   a. Solve the formula for F.

   b. The freezing point of water is 273.15 Kelvin. What is this temperature in Fahrenheit?

   c. The temperature of dry ice is $-78.5\,°C$. Which is colder, dry ice or liquid nitrogen?

Navy Pier Ferris Wheel

C = 439.6 ft

22. FERRIS WHEEL The Navy Pier Ferris Wheel in Chicago has a circumference that is 56% of the circumference of the first Ferris wheel built in 1893.

   a. What is the radius of the Navy Pier Ferris Wheel?

   b. What was the radius of the first Ferris wheel?

   c. The first Ferris wheel took 9 minutes to make a complete revolution. How fast was the wheel moving?

23. Geometry The formula for the volume of a sphere is $V = \dfrac{4}{3}\pi r^3$. Solve the formula for r^3. Use guess, check, and revise to find the radius of the sphere.

$V = 381.51$ in.^{3} $\vdash\!\!-\!\!- r \!-\!\!-\!\!\dashv$

 Fair Game Review What you learned in previous grades & lessons

Multiply. *(Skills Review Handbook)*

24. $5 \times \dfrac{3}{4}$

25. $2.4 \times \dfrac{8}{3}$

26. $\dfrac{1}{4} \times \dfrac{3}{2} \times \dfrac{8}{9}$

27. $25 \times \dfrac{3}{5} \times \dfrac{1}{12}$

28. MULTIPLE CHOICE Which of the following is not equivalent to $\dfrac{3}{4}$? *(Skills Review Handbook)*

   Ⓐ 0.75   Ⓑ 3 : 4   Ⓒ 75%   Ⓓ 4 : 3

You can use a **Y chart** to compare two topics. List differences in the branches and similarities in the base of the Y. Here is an example of a Y chart that compares solving simple equations to solving multi-step equations.

Solving
Simple Equations

Solving
Multi-Step Equations

- You can solve the equation in one step.

- You must use more than one step to solve the equation.
- Undo the operations in the reverse order of the order of operations.

- As necessary, use the Addition, Subtraction, Multiplication, and Division Properties of Equality to solve for the variable.
- The variable can end up on either side of the equation.
- It is always a good idea to check your solution.

On Your Own

Make a Y chart to help you study and compare these topics.

1. solving equations with the variable on one side and solving equations with variables on both sides

2. solving multi-step equations and solving equations with variables on both sides

3. solving multi-step equations and rewriting literal equations

After you complete this chapter, make Y charts for the following topics.

4. solving one-step inequalities and solving two-step inequalities

5. solving equations and solving inequalities

"I made a Y chart to compare and contrast yours and Fluffy's characteristics."

Sample Answers

1.

Solving Equations with the Variable on One Side

- Collect the constant terms on the side that does not have the variable term(s).

Solving Equations with Variables on Both Sides

- Collect the variable terms on one side and the constant terms on the other side.

- Use inverse operations to isolate the variable.
- The variable can end up on either side of the equation.
- It is always a good idea to check your solution.

2.

Solving Multi-Step Equations

- Collect the constant terms on the side that does not have the variable term(s).

Solving Equations with Variables on Both Sides

- Collect the variable terms on one side and the constant terms on the other side.

- Use inverse operations to isolate the variable.
- The variable can end up on either side of the equation.
- It is always a good idea to check your solution.

3.

Solving Multi-Step Equations

- Isolate the variable.
- Solution is numerical.

Rewriting Literal Equations

- Solve for one variable in terms of the other variable(s).

- Use the Addition, Subtraction, Multiplication, and Division Properties of Equality as necessary.
- The variable being isolated or solved for can end up on either side of the equation.

List of Organizers
Available at *BigIdeasMath.com*

Comparison Chart
Concept Circle
Definition (Idea) and Example Chart
Example and Non-Example Chart
Formula Triangle
Four Square
Information Frame
Information Wheel
Notetaking Organizer
Process Diagram
Summary Triangle
Word Magnet
Y Chart

About this Organizer

A **Y Chart** can be used to compare two topics. Students list differences between the two topics in the branches of the Y and similarities in the base of the Y. A Y chart serves as a good tool for assessing students' knowledge of a pair of topics that have subtle but important differences. You can include blank Y charts on tests or quizzes for this purpose.

Technology
For
the **T**eacher

Vocabulary Puzzle Builder

Answers

1. $y = \frac{1}{2}$
2. $w = 5\pi$
3. $m = 0.5$
4. $x = 60$; $55°$, $60°$, $65°$
5. $x = 126$; $63°$, $80°$, $126°$, $91°$
6. $x = -1$
7. $s = 6$
8. $h = \frac{V}{\pi r^2}$
9. $b = \frac{2A}{h} - B$
10. $r = \frac{I}{Pt}$; 30%
11. 50 ft, 150 ft, 75 ft, 180 ft
12. $230x = 1265$; 5.5 hours
13. passing beach: 13 miles
    passing park: 15 miles

Assessment Book

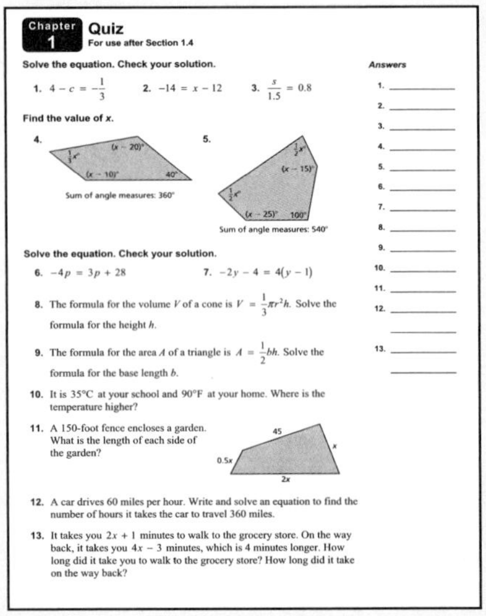
Chapter 1 **Quiz**
For use after Section 1.4

Solve the equation. Check your solution.

1. $4 - c = -\frac{1}{3}$
2. $-14 = x - 12$
3. $\frac{s}{1.5} = 0.8$

Find the value of *x*.

4. Sum of angle measures: 360°
5. Sum of angle measures: 540°

Solve the equation. Check your solution.

6. $-4p = 3p + 28$
7. $-2y - 4 = 4(y - 1)$
8. The formula for the volume V of a cone is $V = \frac{1}{3}\pi r^2 h$. Solve the formula for the height h.
9. The formula for the area A of a triangle is $A = \frac{1}{2}bh$. Solve the formula for the base length b.
10. It is 35°C at your school and 90°F at your home. Where is the temperature higher?
11. A 150-foot fence encloses a garden. What is the length of each side of the garden?
12. A car drives 60 miles per hour. Write and solve an equation to find the number of hours it takes the car to travel 360 miles.
13. It takes you $2x + 1$ minutes to walk to the grocery store. On the way back, it takes you $4x - 3$ minutes, which is 4 minutes longer. How long did it take you to walk to the grocery store? How long did it take on the way back?

Answers

1. ______
2. ______
3. ______
4. ______
5. ______
6. ______
7. ______
8. ______
9. ______
10. ______
11. ______
12. ______
13. ______

Alternative Quiz Ideas

100% Quiz	Math Log
Error Notebook	Notebook Quiz
Group Quiz	**Partner Quiz**
Homework Quiz	Pass the Paper

Partner Quiz

- Partner quizzes are to be completed by students working in pairs. Student pairs can be selected by the teacher, by students, through a random process, or any way that works for your class.
- Students are permitted to use their notebooks and other appropriate materials.
- Each pair submits a draft of the quiz for teacher feedback. Then they revise their work and turn it in for a grade.
- When the pair is finished they can submit one paper, or each can submit their own.
- Teachers can give feedback in a variety of ways. It is important that the teacher does not reteach or provide the solution. The teacher can tell students which questions they have answered correctly, if they are on the right track, or if they need to rethink a problem.

Reteaching and Enrichment Strategies

If students need help...	If students got it...
Resources by Chapter • Study Help • Practice A and Practice B • Puzzle Time Lesson Tutorials *BigIdeasMath.com* Practice Quiz Practice from the Test Generator	Resources by Chapter • Enrichment and Extension • School-to-Work Game Closet at *BigIdeasMath.com* Start the next section

Technology For the Teacher

Answer Presentation Tool
Big Ideas Test Generator

Solve the equation. Check your solution. *(Section 1.1)*

1. $-\dfrac{1}{2} = y - 1$

2. $-3\pi + w = 2\pi$

3. $1.2m = 0.6$

Find the value of x. Then find the angle measures of the polygon. *(Section 1.2)*

4.

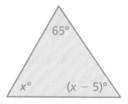

Sum of angle
measures: 180°

5.

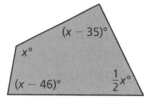

Sum of angle
measures: 360°

Solve the equation. Check your solution. *(Section 1.3)*

6. $2(x + 4) = -5x + 1$

7. $\dfrac{1}{2}s = 4s - 21$

Solve the formula for the red variable. *(Section 1.4)*

8. Volume of a cylinder: $V = \pi r^2 h$

9. Area of a trapezoid: $A = \dfrac{1}{2}h(b + B)$

10. INTEREST The formula for simple interest I is $I = Prt$. Solve the formula for the interest rate r. What is the interest rate r if the principal P is $1500, the time t is 2 years, and the interest earned I is $900? *(Section 1.4)*

11. PASTURE A 455-foot fence encloses a pasture. What is the length of each side of the pasture? *(Section 1.2)*

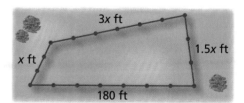

12. POSTERS A machine prints 230 movie posters each hour. Write and solve an equation to find the number of hours it takes the machine to print 1265 posters. *(Section 1.1)*

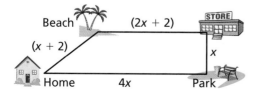

13. ROUTES From your home, the route to the store that passes the beach is 2 miles shorter than the route to the store that passes the park. What is the length of each route? *(Section 1.3)*

1.5 Writing and Graphing Inequalities

STANDARDS OF LEARNING
8.15

Essential Question How can you use an inequality to describe a real-life statement?

1 ACTIVITY: Writing and Graphing Inequalities

Work with a partner. Write an inequality for the statement. Then sketch the graph of all the numbers that make the inequality true.

a. **Statement:** The temperature t in Minot, North Dakota has never been below $-36\,°F$.

   Inequality:

   Graph:
   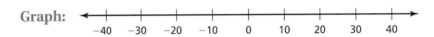

b. **Statement:** The elevation e in Wisconsin is at most 1951.5 feet above sea level.

   Inequality:

   Graph:

TIMM'S HILL
WISCONSIN'S HIGHEST
NATURAL POINT
ELEV. 1951.5 FT

2 ACTIVITY: Writing and Graphing Inequalities

Work with a partner. Write an inequality for the graph. Then, in words, describe all the values of x that make the inequality true.

a.

b.

c.

d.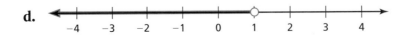

Laurie's Notes

Introduction

For the Teacher

- **Goal:** Students will review how to graph and write an inequality.
- This lesson has an algebraic theme with geometric concepts integrated within.
- Students will be working with inequalities involving integers.

Motivate

- **Preparation:** Write 8 inequalities on index cards. Draw the matching graphs on 8 strips of paper large enough to be seen by students across your room. Tape the 8 graphs in different locations around your room.
- Examples of inequalities to explore: $x > 4$; $x \leq -4$; $x > -4$; $x \leq 4$; $x < -2.5$; $x \leq -2.5$; $x > 3.5$; $x \geq 3.5$
- Select 8 students at random and hand each an index card. Ask students to find their graphs and to go stand next to the graphs.
- **?** After students have matched their cards to the graphs, ask each student to explain how they know their match is correct. What features of the graph did they look for? Listen for: open circle versus closed circle, shading the correct side of the number line.
- After all of the students have made their explanations, collect their cards. Next, ask 8 different students to go to one of the graphs and say aloud the inequality that is shown by the graph.

Activity Notes

Discuss

- Remind students of the symbols used to express inequalities and the open circle/closed circle notation used when graphing an inequality.

Activity 1

- Students should work with their partner on this activity. Caution them to read carefully.
- In part (a), did students graph the temperatures that Minot experienced or did *not* experience?

Activity 2

- Students should be familiar with the direction of the inequality and with the open/closed notation.
- This activity assesses a student's ability to distinguish between $x > 1$ and $x \geq 1$, and between $x \leq 1$ and $x < 1$.

Standards of Learning

8.15(b) The student will solve two-step linear inequalities and graph the results on a number line.

Previous Learning

Students should know how to graph numbers on a number line, solve single variable equations, and solve single variable inequalities using whole numbers.

Activity Materials	
Introduction	**Textbook**
• index cards • paper strips	• spaghetti • metric ruler

Start Thinking! and Warm Up

Activity 1.5 Start Thinking! For use before Activity 1.5

Activity 1.5 Warm Up For use before Activity 1.5

Measure the line segment to the nearest tenth of a centimeter.

1. _____
2. _____
3. _____
4. ___
5. _____
6. _____

1.5 Record and Practice Journal

Essential Question How can you use an inequality to describe a real-life statement?

1 ACTIVITY: Writing and Graphing Inequalities

Work with a partner. Write an inequality for the statement. Then sketch the graph of all the numbers that make the inequality true.

a. **Statement:** The temperature t in Minot, North Dakota has never been below $-36°$F.

Inequality: $t \geq -36$

Graph:
$-40 \; -30 \; -20 \; -10 \quad 0 \quad 10 \quad 20 \quad 30 \quad 40$

TIMM'S HILL WISCONSIN'S HIGHEST NATURAL POINT ELEV. 1951.5 FT

b. **Statement:** The elevation e in Wisconsin is at most 1951.5 feet above sea level.

Inequality: $e \leq 1951.5$

Graph:
$-3000 \quad -1000 \; 0 \; 1000 \quad 3000$

2 ACTIVITY: Writing and Graphing Inequalities

Work with a partner. Write an inequality for the graph. Then, in words, describe all the values of x that make the inequality true.

a.
$-4 \; -3 \; -2 \; -1 \quad 0 \quad 1 \quad 2 \quad 3 \quad 4$
$x \geq 1$; all values of x greater than or equal to 1

b.
$-4 \; -3 \; -2 \; -1 \quad 0 \quad 1 \quad 2 \quad 3 \quad 4$
$x > 1$; all values of x greater than 1

English Language Learners

Vocabulary and Symbols

Students should review the vocabulary and symbols for inequalities. Have students add a table of symbols and what the symbols mean to their notebooks. Students should add to the table as new phrases are used in the chapter.

Symbol	Phrase
$=$	is equal to
$\neq$	is not equal to
$<$	is less than
$\leq$	is less than or equal to
$>$	is greater than
$\geq$	is greater than or equal to

1.5 Record and Practice Journal

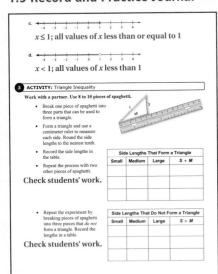

Laurie's Notes

Activity 3

- **Management Tip:** In this activity, students will explore another property of triangles. This investigation uses spaghetti. Tell students your expectation is that the floor will remain spaghetti free.
- Distribute metric rulers and pieces of spaghetti to each pair of students.
- Circulate as students work on the activity. Check to see that they are measuring to the nearest tenth of a centimeter.
- **Whole Class:** Discuss results with the class. Some students may not have observed a pattern for when the three lengths form a triangle.
- **?** "Is there a group that would like to share their observation about when the lengths form a triangle and when they don't? Explain." Sum of the two shorter sides has to be greater than the longest side.
- **FYI:** Even though a triangle is shown for the last three parts of Activity 3, they may not be drawn to scale. In fact, parts (b) and (c) are *not* triangles.

What Is Your Answer?

- **Big Idea:** This is known as the *Triangle Inequality Theorem*. When the sum of the two shorter sides is less than the length of the longest side, a triangle is not formed, that is, the ends do *not* meet.

Closure

- **Exit Ticket:** Write a word description with a real-life context for each inequality. Then graph the inequality.

  $x > 8$ *Sample answer:* You need to work more than 8 hours a day.

  $x \leq -10$ *Sample answer:* The diver will stay at least 10 feet below sea level.

Technology **For** **the** **Teacher**

Dynamic Classroom

The Dynamic Planning Tool
Editable Teacher's Resources at *BigIdeasMath.com*

3 ACTIVITY: Triangle Inequality

Work with a partner. Use 8 to 10 pieces of spaghetti.

- Break one piece of spaghetti into three parts that can be used to form a triangle.

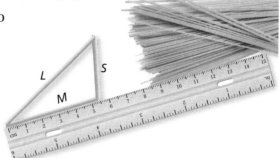

- Form a triangle and use a centimeter ruler to measure each side. Round the side lengths to the nearest tenth.

- Record the side lengths in a table.

Side Lengths That Form a Triangle			
Small	**Medium**	**Large**	**S + M**

- Repeat the process with two other pieces of spaghetti.

- Repeat the experiment by breaking pieces of spaghetti into three pieces that *do not* form a triangle. Record the lengths in a table.

Side Lengths That Do Not Form a Triangle			
Small	**Medium**	**Large**	**S + M**

- **INDUCTIVE REASONING** Write a rule that uses an inequality to compare the lengths of three sides of a triangle.

- Use your rule to decide whether the following triangles are possible. Explain.

a.
4   5   7

b.
4   5   10

c.
2   5   7

What Is Your Answer?

4. **IN YOUR OWN WORDS** How can you use an inequality to describe a real-life statement? Give two examples of real-life statements that can be represented by inequalities.

Practice

Use what you learned about writing and graphing inequalities to complete Exercises 4 and 5 on page 34.

An **inequality** is a mathematical sentence that compares expressions. It contains the symbols <, >, ≤, or ≥. To write an inequality, look for the following phrases to determine where to place the inequality symbol.

Key Vocabulary 🔊
inequality, *p. 32*
solution of an
   inequality, *p. 32*
solution set, *p. 32*
graph of an
   inequality, *p. 33*

	Inequality Symbols			
Symbol	<	>	≤	≥
Key Phrases	• is less than • is fewer than	• is greater than • is more than	• is less than or equal to • is at most • is no more than	• is greater than or equal to • is at least • is no less than

EXAMPLE ① **Writing an Inequality**

A number *w* minus 3.5 is less than or equal to −2. Write this sentence as an inequality.

A number *w* minus 3.5 is less than or equal to −2.

$$w - 3.5 \qquad\qquad \le \qquad\qquad -2$$

∴ An inequality is $w - 3.5 \le -2$.

🔘 **On Your Own**

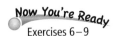

Now You're Ready
Exercises 6−9

Write the word sentence as an inequality.

1. A number *b* is fewer than 30.4.   **2.** Twice a number *k* is at least $-\frac{7}{10}$.

A **solution of an inequality** is a value that makes the inequality true. An inequality can have more than one solution. The set of all solutions of an inequality is called the **solution set**.

Reading

The symbol ≱ means "is not greater than or equal to."

Value of *x*	$x + 5 \ge -2$	Is the inequality true?
−6	$-6 + 5 \overset{?}{\ge} -2$ $-1 \ge -2$ ✓	yes
−7	$-7 + 5 \overset{?}{\ge} -2$ $-2 \ge -2$ ✓	yes
−8	$-8 + 5 \overset{?}{\ge} -2$ $-3 \not\ge -2$ ✗	no

Laurie's Notes

Introduction

Connect

- **Yesterday:** Students reviewed how to graph and write an inequality.
- **Today:** Students will translate inequalities from words to symbols and check to see if a value is a solution of the inequality.

Motivate

- **Story Time:** You are planning to visit several theme parks and notice in doing your research that some of the rides have height restrictions.

Attraction	Restriction	Inequality
Dinosaur	Minimum is now 40 inches	$h \geq 40$
Primeval Whirl	Must be at least 48 inches	$h \geq 48$
Bay Slide	Must be under 60 inches	$h < 60$

- Ask students to write each as an inequality, where h is the rider's height.
- In today's lesson, they will be translating words to symbols.

Lesson Notes

Discuss

- Write the definition of an inequality.
- Review the four inequality symbols and key phrases or words that suggest each inequality.

Example 1

? "Would $3.5 - w \leq -2$ be equivalent to $w - 3.5 \leq -2$? Explain." no; Subtraction is *not* commutative.

? "Is there another way to say $w - 3.5$? Explain." yes; the difference of w and 3.5

On Your Own

- **Think-Pair-Share:** Students should read each question independently and then work with a partner to answer the questions. When they have answered the questions, the pair should compare their answers with another group and discuss any discrepancies.

Discuss

- Discuss what is meant by a solution of an inequality. Inequalities can, and generally do, have more than one solution. All of the solutions are collectively referred to as the **solution set**.
- It is helpful to write the inequality and substitute the value you are checking, as shown in the table.
- **Common Error:** Students will often make the mistake of thinking $-1 \leq -2$, forgetting that relationships are reversed on the negative side of 0; $-1 \geq -2$.

Start Thinking! and Warm Up

Lesson 1.5 **Warm Up** For use before Lesson 1.5

Lesson 1.5 **Start Thinking!** For use before Lesson 1.5

Write a sentence involving a real-life situation that can be modeled using an inequality.

Which inequality symbol applies: $<$, $\leq$, $>$, or $\geq$?

Extra Example 1

A number b plus 2.7 is greater than or equal to 3. Write this sentence as an inequality. $b + 2.7 \geq 3$

On Your Own

1. $b < 30.4$

2. $2k \geq -\dfrac{7}{10}$

Extra Example 2

Tell whether −2 is a solution of the inequality.

a. $x - 4 < -10$ no

b. $2.3x > -5$ yes

 On Your Own

   3. yes

   4. no

   5. yes

Extra Example 3

Graph $y \geq -5$.

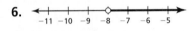

 On Your Own

   6.

   7.

   8.

   9.

Differentiated Instruction

Auditory

Stress to students the importance of reading a statement and translating it into an expression, equation, or inequality. The word "is" plays an important role in the meaning of the statement. For instance, *six less than a number* translates to $x - 6$, while *six is less than a number* translates to $6 < x$.

Laurie's Notes

Example 2

? "How do you determine if −4 is a solution of an inequality?" Substitute −4 for the variable, simplify, and decide if the inequality is true.

- Work through each example as shown. In part (b), students must recall that the product of two negatives is a positive.

On Your Own

- **Common Error:** In Question 4, when students substitute for *m*, the result is $5 - (-6)$ which is 11.
- Ask volunteers to share their work at the board.

Discuss

- Discuss what is meant by the graph of an inequality. Remind students of the difference between the open and closed circles.

Example 3

- A number is tested on each side of the boundary point. This is a technique that demonstrates what it means to have a boundary point. On one side of the boundary point are all of the values which satisfy the inequality, and on the other side are all of the values which do *not* satisfy the inequality.

On Your Own

- In Question 8, check to see that students locate $-\frac{1}{2}$ correctly.
- Ask students to share their graphs at the board.

Closure

- **Writing Prompt:** To decide if a number is a solution of the inequality, you . . .

EXAMPLE ② **Checking Solutions**

Tell whether −4 is a solution of the inequality.

a. $x + 8 < -3$

$x + 8 < -3$	Write the inequality.
$-4 + 8 \overset{?}{<} -3$	Substitute −4 for x.
$4 \not< -3$ ✗	Simplify.

4 is *not* less than −3.

⁘ So, −4 is *not* a solution
of the inequality.

b. $-4.5x > -21$

$-4.5x > -21$

$-4.5(-4) \overset{?}{>} -21$

$18 > -21$ ✓

18 is greater than −21.

⁘ So, −4 is a solution
of the inequality.

On Your Own

Now You're Ready
Exercises 11–16

Tell whether −6 is a solution of the inequality.

3. $c + 4 < -1$ **4.** $5 - m \le 10$ **5.** $21 \div x \ge -3.5$

The **graph of an inequality** shows all of the solutions of the inequality on a number line. An open circle ○ is used when a number is *not* a solution. A closed circle ● is used when a number is a solution. An arrow to the left or right shows that the graph continues in that direction.

EXAMPLE ③ **Graphing an Inequality**

Graph $y \le -3$.

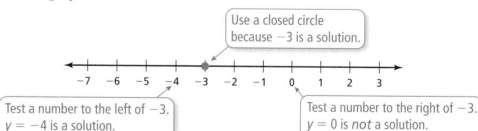

Use a closed circle because −3 is a solution.

Test a number to the left of −3.
$y = -4$ is a solution.

Test a number to the right of −3.
$y = 0$ is *not* a solution.

Shade the number line on the side where you found the solution.

On Your Own

Now You're Ready
Exercises 17–20

Graph the inequality on a number line.

6. $b > -8$ **7.** $g \le 1.4$ **8.** $r < -\dfrac{1}{2}$ **9.** $\dfrac{5}{2} \le v$

Check It Out
Help with Homework
BigIdeasMath ✔com

 Vocabulary and Concept Check

1. **VOCABULARY** Would an open circle or a closed circle be used in the graph of the inequality $k < 250$? Explain.

2. **DIFFERENT WORDS, SAME QUESTION** Which is different? Write "both" inequalities.

w is greater than or equal to -7.	w is no less than -7.
w is no more than -7.	w is at least -7.

3. **REASONING** Do $x \geq -9$ and $-9 \geq x$ represent the same inequality? Explain.

 Practice and Problem Solving

Write an inequality for the graph. Then, in words, describe all the values of x that make the inequality true.

4.

5.

Write the word sentence as an inequality.

6. A number x is no less than -4.

7. A number y added to 5.2 is less than 23.

8. A number b multiplied by -5 is at most $-\dfrac{3}{4}$.

9. A number k minus 8.3 is greater than 48.

10. **ERROR ANALYSIS** Describe and correct the error in writing the word sentence as an inequality.

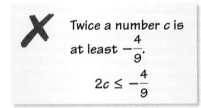

Twice a number c is at least $-\dfrac{4}{9}$.

$2c \leq -\dfrac{4}{9}$

Tell whether the given value is a solution of the inequality.

11. $s + 6 \leq 12;\ s = 4$

12. $15n > -3;\ n = -2$

13. $a - 2.5 \leq 1.6;\ a = 4.1$

14. $-3.3q > -13;\ q = 4.6$

15. $\dfrac{4}{5}h \geq -4;\ h = -15$

16. $\dfrac{1}{12} - p < \dfrac{1}{3};\ p = \dfrac{1}{6}$

Graph the inequality on a number line.

17. $g \geq -6$

18. $q > 1.25$

19. $z < 11\dfrac{1}{4}$

20. $w \leq -2\dfrac{1}{3}$

21. **DRIVING** When you are driving with a learner's license, a licensed driver who is 21 years of age or older must be with you. Write an inequality that represents this situation.

Assignment Guide and Homework Check

Level	Day 1 Activity Assignment	Day 2 Lesson Assignment	Homework Check
Basic	4, 5, 28–31	1–3, 6–10, 11–21 odd	8, 10, 13, 17
Average	4, 5, 28–31	1–3, 7–19 odd, 10, 18, 23–25	9, 10, 13, 17, 24
Advanced	4, 5, 28–31	1–3, 10–20 even, 22–27	10, 12, 20, 22, 24

Common Errors

- **Exercises 6–9** Students may struggle with knowing which inequality symbol to use. Encourage them to put the word sentence into a real-life context and to use the table in the lesson that explains what symbol matches each phrase.
- **Exercises 11–16** Students may try to solve for the variable instead of substituting the given value into the inequality and determining if that value is a solution of the inequality. Remind them that they are not solving inequalities yet, just checking a number to see if it is a solution.
- **Exercises 17–20** Students may use a closed circle instead of an open circle and vice versa. They may also shade the wrong side of the number line. Review how to graph inequalities and encourage students to test a value on each side of the circle.

1.5 Record and Practice Journal

Write the word sentence as an inequality.

1. A number p is no greater than -6.

$p \leq -6$

2. A number n divided by -2 is no less than $\frac{1}{2}$.

$\frac{n}{-2} \geq \frac{1}{2}$

Tell whether the given value is a solution of the inequality.

3. $q + 7 \geq 8$; $q = 10$

solution

4. $-12r < -6$; $r = -2$

not a solution

5. $-2.4k \geq -4$; $k = 0.5$

solution

6. $\frac{x}{4} < x - 9$; $x = 8$

not a solution

Graph the inequality on a number line.

7. $p \leq 4\frac{1}{2}$

8. $z > -8.3$

9. For your birthday, you want to invite some friends to join you at the movies. Movie tickets cost $8. You can spend no more than $35. Write an inequality to represent this situation. Then solve the inequality to find the greatest number of people you can invite.

$8x \leq 35$; 4

1. An open circle would be used because 250 is not a solution.

2. w is no more than -7.; $w \leq -7$; $w \geq -7$

3. no; $x \geq -9$ is all values of x greater than or equal to -9. $-9 \geq x$ is all values of x less than or equal to -9.

Practice and Problem Solving

4. $x \geq 9$; all values of x greater than or equal to 9

5. $x < -3$; all values of x less than -3

6. $x \geq -4$

7. $y + 5.2 < 23$

8. $-5b \leq -\dfrac{3}{4}$

9. $k - 8.3 > 48$

10. The inequality symbol is reversed. $2c \geq -\dfrac{4}{9}$

11. yes   12. no

13. yes   14. no

15. no   16. yes

17.

18.

19.

20.

21. $x \geq 21$

Practice and Problem Solving

22. yes   **23.** yes

24. maybe; If your friend is 10, 11, or 12, then your friend can play "E 10+" games, but is not old enough for "T" games. If your friend is 13 or older, then your friend can play "T" games.

25. See Additional Answers.

26. See *Taking Math Deeper*.

27. a. $m < n$; $n \le p$

   b. $m < p$

   c. no; Because n is no more than p and m is less than n, m cannot be equal to p.

 Fair Game Review

28. $r = 15$ **29.** $p = -1.7$

30. $n = 10\pi$ **31.** B

Mini-Assessment

Write the word sentence as an inequality.

1. A number m multiplied by -4.9 is at most 5. $-4.9m \le 5$

2. A number p minus 1.1 is greater than or equal to $-\frac{2}{3}$. $p - 1.1 \ge -\frac{2}{3}$

3. A number h divided by 4 is less than -7.5. $\frac{h}{4} < -7.5$

Graph the inequality on a number line.

4. $x > -2.9$

5. $a \le -5.25$

Taking Math Deeper

Exercise 26

This is a practical problem for anyone who is planning to fly. This size restriction applies only to carry-on luggage, not to luggage that is checked. For students who have not thought of the differences, it might be interesting for them to think about the advantages of carry-on luggage.

- No chance of luggage not arriving
- No waiting for luggage at destination
- No extra fees for luggage

(1) Draw a diagram showing the length, width, and height of a carry-on bag.

(2) Find some possible combinations for which $\ell + w + h \le 45$.

Bag	ℓ	w	h
A	22 in.	14 in.	9 in.
B	20 in.	14 in.	11 in.
C	18 in.	14 in.	13 in.

Standard size → A

(3) Students might find it interesting to discover which of their three choices has the greatest volume. In the three examples in the table, the volumes are 2272, 3080, and 3276 cubic inches.

In general, the more cube-like the luggage, the greater the volume. So, the maximum volume would be with luggage that is 15 inches by 15 inches by 15 inches, which has a volume of 3375 cubic inches.

Reteaching and Enrichment Strategies

If students need help. . .	If students got it. . .
Resources by Chapter • Practice A and Practice B • Puzzle Time Record and Practice Journal Practice Differentiating the Lesson Lesson Tutorials Skills Review Handbook	Resources by Chapter • Enrichment and Extension • School-to-Work • Financial Literacy Start the next section

Tell whether the given value is a solution of the inequality.

22. $3p > 5 + p; \ p = 4$

23. $\dfrac{y}{2} \geq y - 11; \ y = 18$

24. VIDEO GAME RATINGS Each rating is matched with the inequality that represents the recommended ages of players. Your friend is old enough to play "E 10+" games. Is your friend old enough to play "T" games? Explain.

$x \geq 3$　　　$x \geq 6$　　　$x \geq 10$　　　$x \geq 13$　　　$x \geq 17$

The ESRB rating icons are registered trademarks of the Entertainment Software Association.

25. SCUBA DIVING Three requirements for a scuba diving training course are shown.

   a. Write and graph three inequalities that represent the requirements.

   b. You can swim 10 lengths of a 25-yard pool. Do you satisfy the swimming requirement of the course? Explain.

26. LUGGAGE On an airplane, the maximum sum of the length, width, and height of a carry-on bag is 45 inches. Find three different sets of dimensions that are reasonable for a carry-on bag.

27. A number m is less than another number n. The number n is less than or equal to a third number p.

   a. Write two inequalities representing these relationships.

   b. Describe the relationship between m and p.

   c. Can m be equal to p? Explain.

Fair Game Review　What you learned in previous grades & lessons

Solve the equation. Check your solution.　*(Section 1.1)*

28. $r - 12 = 3$

29. $4.2 + p = 2.5$

30. $n - 3\pi = 7\pi$

31. MULTIPLE CHOICE Which expression has a value less than 1?
(Skills Review Handbook)

   Ⓐ $\dfrac{1}{2^{-2}}$　　　Ⓑ 2^{-2}　　　Ⓒ 2^{0}　　　Ⓓ 2^{2}

1.6 Solving One-Step Inequalities

Essential Question How can you use addition or subtraction to solve an inequality?

1 ACTIVITY: Quarterback Passing Efficiency

Work with a partner. The National Collegiate Athletic Association (NCAA) uses the following formula to rank the passing efficiency P of quarterbacks.

$$P = \frac{8.4Y + 100C + 330T - 200N}{A}$$

Y = total length of all completed passes (in Yards)

C = Completed passes

T = passes resulting in a Touchdown

N = iNtercepted passes

A = Attempted passes

M = incoMplete passes

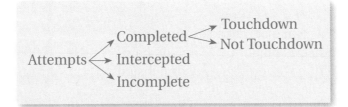

Which of the following equations or inequalities are true relationships among the variables? Explain your reasoning.

a. $C + N < A$ **b.** $C + N \leq A$ **c.** $T < C$ **d.** $T \leq C$

e. $N < A$ **f.** $A > T$ **g.** $A - C \geq M$ **h.** $A = C + N + M$

2 ACTIVITY: Quarterback Passing Efficiency

Work with a partner. Which of the following quarterbacks has a passing efficiency rating that satisfies the inequality $P > 100$? Show your work.

Player	Attempts	Completions	Yards	Touchdowns	Interceptions
A	149	88	1065	7	9
B	400	205	2000	10	3
C	426	244	3105	30	9
D	188	89	1167	6	15

Laurie's Notes

Introduction

For the Teacher

- **Goal:** Students will explore inequalities and solve simple inequalities using mental math.
- Students have solved whole number inequalities and equations. This lesson is a natural extension of familiar content.
- Wear a football related piece of clothing today, if you own one.

Motivate and Discuss

- Set the tone by tossing a few passes in class with a small foam football. Ask a statistician to record your efforts in a table at the board. Use 3 columns: **C**ompleted, I**N**tercepted, and Inco**M**plete.
- I recommend **A**ttempting 10 short passes to students nearby. You may need to give permission to have a pass intercepted.
- ❓ Ask the following questions.
  - "How many passes did I attempt?" 10 Record this next to the table.
  - "Can I complete more passes than I attempt?" no
  - "Are *completed passes* + *incomplete passes* always *less than or equal to attempted passes*?" yes
  - "Are *completed passes* + *incomplete passes* always *less than attempted passes*?" No, they could be equal.

Activity Notes

Activity 1

- The tree diagram should be a helpful aid to students.
- Discuss students' answers and their reasoning when they have finished.
- For parts (c) and (d), point out the need to pay attention to the inequality symbol. It is possible, though unlikely, that $T = C$. In that case, the inequality $T < C$ may *not* be true, while the inequality $T \le C$ is true.
- There will be some heated discussion about the inequalities, but remember to ask, is it *possible* versus is it *probable*.

Activity 2

- You may want to allow calculators to increase speed and accuracy, or you may want to use this as an opportunity to review computation skills.
- **Common Error:** Students may forget order of operations. The computation in the numerator must be completed before dividing by the denominator. On a calculator, this can be done by using parentheses, or simply by pressing the *Enter* key before dividing by the denominator.
- Suggest to students that they write the formula, and then rewrite it substituting the values for the variables.
- ❓ Ask the following questions.
  - "Which player(s) were above average, meaning $P > 100$?" A and C
  - "Which player(s) were average, meaning $P = 100$?" B
  - "So, was player D below average, meaning $P < 100$?" yes

Standards of Learning

8.15(b) The student will solve two-step linear inequalities and graph the results on a number line.

Previous Learning

Students should know how to solve equations. Students should be able to evaluate expressions.

Activity Materials	
Introduction	**Textbook**
• foam football	• calculator

Start Thinking! and Warm Up

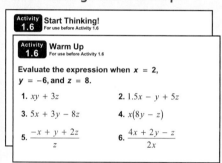

Activity 1.6 Start Thinking!
For use before Activity 1.6

Activity 1.6 Warm Up
For use before Activity 1.6

Evaluate the expression when $x = 2$, $y = -6$, and $z = 8$.

1. $xy + 3z$ 2. $1.5x - y + 5z$

3. $5x + 3y - 8z$ 4. $x(8y - z)$

5. $\dfrac{-x + y + 2z}{z}$ 6. $\dfrac{4x + 2y - z}{2x}$

1.6 Record and Practice Journal

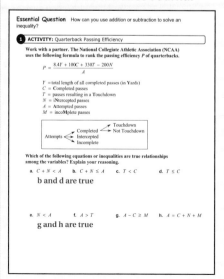

English Language Learners

Vocabulary

It is important that English learners understand the difference between *is less than* and *is less than or equal to*, as well as *is greater than* and *is greater than or equal to*. Give each student a card with one of the numbers −10, −9, −8, −7, −6, . . . , 10. (Include more numbers if your class is larger.) Tell students to stand up if their number *is less than* (say a number), and then *is less than or equal to* that same number. The class should discuss the difference between the two. This can be repeated with *is greater than* and *is greater than or equal to*.

1.6 Record and Practice Journal

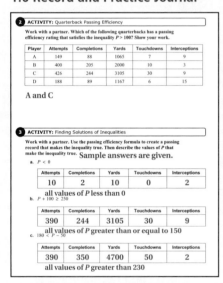

Activity 3

- Now that students have had the opportunity to work with the formula as stated, it is time to put a twist on the problem.
- Notice that four of the inequalities in this activity force students to think about solving the inequality before they begin. In the second problem, if $P + 100 \geq 250$, then it means $P \geq 150$. This should make sense to students.
- Remind students that yards do not count unless the pass is completed.
- Answers will vary for this activity, but suggest to students that they keep the numbers as simple as possible. For instance, one possible answer for the first question is 1, 0, 0, 0, 1, where only 1 pass is attempted and it is intercepted. This is the $P = -200$ result, and so $P < 0$.
- Students will need to do a little trial and error with these problems. They should start to ask themselves, "*what happens when I increase this variable, but decrease another variable.*"

What Is Your Answer?

- **Think-Pair-Share:** Students should read each question independently and then work with a partner to answer the questions. When they have answered the questions, the pair should compare their answers with another group and discuss any discrepancies.

Closure

- **Exit Ticket:**
  If $a < b$ is true, is $a \leq b$ also true? Explain. yes; Because in both cases a is less than b.
  If $a \leq b$ is true, is $a < b$ also true? Explain. no; Because if a equals b, then a cannot be less than b.

Technology For the Teacher

The Dynamic Planning Tool
Editable Teacher's Resources at *BigIdeasMath.com*

3 **ACTIVITY: Finding Solutions of Inequalities**

Work with a partner. Use the passing efficiency formula to create a passing record that makes the inequality true. Then describe the values of P that make the inequality true.

a. $P < 0$

Attempts	Completions	Yards	Touchdowns	Interceptions

b. $P + 100 \geq 250$

Attempts	Completions	Yards	Touchdowns	Interceptions

c. $180 < P - 50$

Attempts	Completions	Yards	Touchdowns	Interceptions

d. $P + 30 \geq 120$

Attempts	Completions	Yards	Touchdowns	Interceptions

e. $P - 250 > -80$

Attempts	Completions	Yards	Touchdowns	Interceptions

What Is Your Answer?

4. Write a rule that describes how to solve inequalities like those in Activity 3. Then use your rule to solve each of the inequalities in Activity 3.

5. **IN YOUR OWN WORDS** How can you use addition or subtraction to solve an inequality?

6. How is solving the inequality $x + 3 < 4$ similar to solving the equation $x + 3 = 4$? How is it different?

Practice

Use what you learned about solving inequalities using addition or subtraction to complete Exercises 5–7 on page 41.

 **Key Ideas**

Addition Property of Inequality

Words If you add the same number to each side of an inequality, the inequality remains true.

Algebra If $a < b$, then $a + c < b + c$.

Subtraction Property of Inequality

Words If you subtract the same number from each side of an inequality, the inequality remains true.

Algebra If $a < b$, then $a - c < b - c$.

These properties are true for $<$, $>$, $\le$, and $\ge$.

Study Tip

You can solve inequalities in much the same way you solve equations. Use inverse operations to get the variable by itself.

EXAMPLE 1 **Solving Inequalities Using Addition or Subtraction**

a. Solve $x - 5 < -3$. Graph the solution.

$$x - 5 < -3 \qquad \text{Write the inequality.}$$

Undo the subtraction. ⟶ $\underline{+5 \quad +5} \qquad$ Add 5 to each side.

$$x < 2 \qquad \text{Simplify.}$$

⠇• The solution is $x < 2$.

Reading

The inequality $-8.3 \le x$ is the same as $x \ge -8.3$.

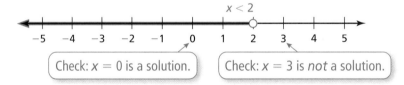

Check: $x = 0$ is a solution.

Check: $x = 3$ is *not* a solution.

b. Solve $-3.5 \le 4.8 + x$.

$$-3.5 \le \quad 4.8 + x \qquad \text{Write the inequality.}$$

Undo the addition. ⟶ $\underline{-4.8 \quad -4.8} \qquad$ Subtract 4.8 from each side.

$$-8.3 \le x \qquad \text{Simplify.}$$

⠇• The solution is $x \ge -8.3$.

On Your Own

Now You're Ready
Exercises 8–16

Solve the inequality. Graph the solution.

1. $n + 7 \ge -4$ **2.** $r - 1.2 > -0.5$ **3.** $\dfrac{3}{5} \ge z + \dfrac{2}{5}$

Laurie's Notes

Introduction

Connect

- **Yesterday:** Students explored inequalities and solved simple inequalities using mental math.
- **Today:** Students will use the Addition, Subtraction, Multiplication, and Division Properties of Inequality to solve inequalities.

Motivate

- ❓ "What does TSA stand for?" Transportation Safety Administration
- The TSA has guidelines for the maximum weight of luggage, depending on whether it is carry-on or checked luggage.
- ❓ "If there is a maximum weight restriction of 50 pounds for a checked bag, what inequality does this suggest?" $w \le 50$
- Suggest different scenarios. "If my bag weighs 40.5 pounds, how much weight can I add? If my bag weighs 56.4 pounds, how much weight must I remove?"
- Today's lesson involves solving inequalities of this type.

Lesson Notes

Key Ideas

- Write the Key Ideas. These properties should look familiar, as they are similar to the Addition and Subtraction Properties of Equality that students have used in solving equations.
- **Teaching Tip:** Summarize these two properties in the following way: George is older than Martha. In two years, George will still be older than Martha.

George's age > Martha's age	If $a > b$,
George's age + 2 > Martha's age + 2	then $a + c > b + c$.

Two years ago, George was older than Martha.

George's age > Martha's age	If $a > b$,
George's age − 2 > Martha's age − 2	then $a - c > b - c$.

Example 1

- ❓ Write the problem in part (a). "How do you isolate the variable, meaning get x by itself?" Add 5 to each side of the inequality.
- Adding 5 is the inverse operation of subtracting 5.
- Solve, graph, and check.
- Part (b) reviews subtraction of rational numbers. The common wrong answer will be -1.3. To help students, write the problem horizontally off to the side: $-3.5 - 4.8 = ?$
- Although $-8.3 \le x$ is a correct answer, it is standard practice to rewrite inequalities so that the variable is read first, left to right. So, the solution is $x \ge -8.3$. The variable changes sides and the direction of the inequality symbol is reversed.

On Your Own

- These problems integrate review of fraction and decimal operations.

Start Thinking! and Warm Up

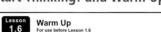

Lesson 1.6 Warm Up
For use before Lesson 1.6

Lesson 1.6 Start Thinking!
For use before Lesson 1.6

Are the solutions to the following inequalities the same? Explain why or why not.

$2x < -12$

$-2x < 12$

Extra Example 1

a. Solve $f - 4 \le 1$. Graph the solution.
$f \le 5$

b. Solve $-7 \ge 2.3 + x$. Graph the solution.
$x \le -9.3$

On Your Own

1. $n \ge -11$;

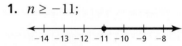

2. $r > 0.7$;

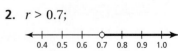

3. $z \le \dfrac{1}{5}$;

Extra Example 2

a. Solve $\dfrac{d}{5} < -7$. Graph the solution.

$d < -35$

b. Solve $2x \geq 12$. Graph the solution.

$x \geq 6$

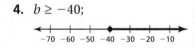

On Your Own

4. $b \geq -40$;

5. $g < -6$;

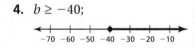

6. $q > 7$;

7. $u > -12$;

Laurie's Notes

Key Idea

- Write the Key Idea. These properties should look familiar, as they are similar to the Multiplication and Division Properties of Equality.
- Note that the properties are restricted to multiplying and dividing by a *positive* number. This is very important.

Example 2

- Write the problem in part (a). Read it aloud: "A number x is divided by 10 and the answer is less than or equal to -2."
- **?** "How do you isolate the variable, meaning get x by itself?" Multiply by 10 on each side of the inequality.
- Multiplying by 10 is the inverse operation of dividing by 10.
- **Representation:** Note that multiplication is represented by the dot notation and that -2 is enclosed in parentheses for clarity only; otherwise students might become confused and think 2 is being subtracted.
- Solve, graph, and check.
- Write the problem in part (b). Read it aloud and solve.

On Your Own

- **Think-Pair-Share:** Students should read each question independently and then work with a partner to answer the questions. When they have answered the questions, the pair should compare their answers with another group and discuss any discrepancies.
- Notice that the variable is on the right side of the inequality in Questions 5 and 6.
- These problems integrate review of decimal operations.

 **Key Idea**

Multiplication and Division Properties of Inequality (Case 1)

Words If you multiply or divide each side of an inequality by the same *positive* number, the inequality remains true.

Algebra If $a < b$, then $a \cdot c < b \cdot c$ for a positive number c.

If $a < b$, then $\dfrac{a}{c} < \dfrac{b}{c}$ for a positive number c.

EXAMPLE ② **Solving Inequalities Using Multiplication or Division**

a. Solve $\dfrac{x}{10} \le -2$. Graph the solution.

$$\dfrac{x}{10} \le -2 \qquad \text{Write the inequality.}$$

Undo the division. ⟶ $10 \cdot \dfrac{x}{10} \le 10 \cdot (-2)$ Multiply each side by 10.

$$x \le -20 \qquad \text{Simplify.}$$

∴ The solution is $x \le -20$.

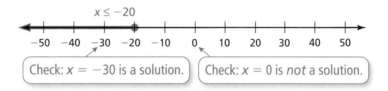

Check: $x = -30$ is a solution. Check: $x = 0$ is *not* a solution.

b. Solve $2.5x > 11.25$. Graph the solution.

$$2.5x > 11.25 \qquad \text{Write the inequality.}$$

Undo the multiplication. ⟶ $\dfrac{2.5x}{2.5} > \dfrac{11.25}{2.5}$ Divide each side by 2.5.

$$x > 4.5 \qquad \text{Simplify.}$$

∴ The solution is $x > 4.5$.

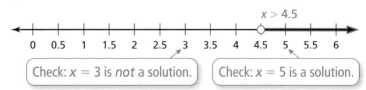

Check: $x = 3$ is *not* a solution. Check: $x = 5$ is a solution.

● **On Your Own**

Now You're Ready
Exercises 21–29

Solve the inequality. Graph the solution.

4. $\dfrac{b}{8} \ge -5$

5. $-0.4 > \dfrac{g}{15}$

6. $63 < 9q$

7. $1.6u > -19.2$

 **Key Idea**

Multiplication and Division Properties of Inequality (Case 2)

Words   If you multiply or divide each side of an inequality by the same *negative* number, the direction of the inequality symbol must be reversed for the inequality to remain true.

Algebra   If $a < b$, then $a \cdot c > b \cdot c$ for a negative number c.

If $a < b$, then $\dfrac{a}{c} > \dfrac{b}{c}$ for a negative number c.

EXAMPLE 3   Solving Inequalities Using Multiplication or Division

a. Solve $\dfrac{y}{-4} > 6$. **Graph the solution.**

$\dfrac{y}{-4} > 6$ Write the inequality.

Undo the division. → $-4 \cdot \dfrac{y}{-4} < -4 \cdot 6$ Multiply each side by -4.
Reverse the inequality symbol.

$y < -24$ Simplify.

⁖ The solution is $y < -24$.

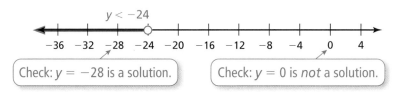

$y < -24$

Check: $y = -28$ is a solution.

Check: $y = 0$ is *not* a solution.

b. Solve $-21 \geq -1.4y$.

$-21 \geq -1.4y$ Write the inequality.

Undo the multiplication. → $\dfrac{-21}{-1.4} \leq \dfrac{-1.4y}{-1.4}$ Divide each side by -1.4.
Reverse the inequality symbol.

$15 \leq y$ Simplify.

⁖ The solution is $y \geq 15$.

● **On Your Own**

Now You're Ready
Exercises 31–39

Solve the inequality. Graph the solution.

8. $7 > \dfrac{j}{-1.5}$

9. $\dfrac{a}{-3} \leq -2$

10. $-2s < 24$

11. $-3.1z \geq 62$

Laurie's Notes

Key Idea
- This Key Idea addresses the negative coefficient.
- Write the Key Idea. These properties look similar to what students have been using in the lesson, *except* now the direction of the inequality symbol must be reversed for the inequality to remain true because they are multiplying or dividing by a *negative* quantity.
- The short version of the property: When you multiply or divide by a negative quantity, reverse the direction of the inequality symbol.
- **Common Error:** When students solve $2x < -4$, they sometimes reverse the inequality symbol because there's a negative number in the problem. The inequality symbol is reversed *only* when both sides of the inequality are multiplied or divided by a negative number.

Example 3
- Write the problem in part (a).
- ❓ "What operation is being performed?" Divide by -4.
- ❓ "How do you undo dividing by -4?" Multiply by -4.
- Solve as usual, reversing the direction of the inequality symbol.
- When graphing, the endpoint is an open circle because the inequality is strictly less than.
- Write the problem in part (b).
- ❓ "What operation is being performed?" Multiply by -1.4.
- ❓ "How do you undo multiplying by -1.4? Divide by -1.4.
- Solve as usual, reversing the direction of the inequality symbol. Also, remember that the quotient of two negatives is positive.
- If you graph the solution, remember the endpoint is a closed circle because the inequality is greater than or equal to.

On Your Own
- **Neighbor Check:** Have students work independently and then have their neighbor check their work. Have students discuss any discrepancies.
- Have volunteers share their work at the board.

Closure
- **Exit Ticket:** Solve and graph:

$$\frac{x}{-3} \leq -9 \quad x \geq 27$$

$$-8 > 4x \quad x < -2$$

Differentiated Instruction

Visual
Use the inequality $6 < 9$ to show students why it is necessary to reverse the inequality symbol when multiplying or dividing by a negative number.

Add -3 to each side. The result is $3 < 6$, a true statement.

Subtract -3 from each side. The result is $9 < 12$, a true statement.

Multiply each side by -3. If the inequality is *not* reversed, the statement $-18 < -27$ is false. By reversing the inequality, the statement $-18 > -27$ is true.

Divide each side by -3. If the inequality is *not* reversed, the statement $-2 < -3$ is false. By reversing the inequality, the statement $-2 > -3$ is true.

Extra Example 3

a. Solve $\frac{c}{-4} \leq 3$. Graph the solution.

$c \geq -12$

b. Solve $-3j > -9$. Graph the solution.

$j < 3$

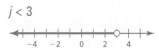

On Your Own

8. $j > -10.5$;

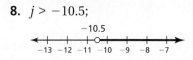

9. $a \geq 6$;

10. $s > -12$;

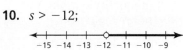

11. $z \leq -20$;

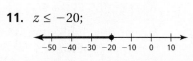

Vocabulary and Concept Check

1. *Sample answer:* Inequalities and equations represent a relationship between two expressions. In an equation, both expressions are equal. In an inequality, one expression is less than the other expression.

2. The first inequality is divided by a positive number. The second inequality is divided by a negative number. Because this inequality is divided by a negative number, the direction of the inequality symbol must be reversed.

3. *Sample answer:* $x + 5 < -3$

4. $10 \geq -2n$; It is the only one whose solution is $n \geq -5$. The solution of the other three inequalities is $n \geq 5$.

Practice and Problem Solving

5. *Sample answer:* $A = 350$, $C = 275$, $Y = 3105$, $T = 50$, $N = 2$

6. *Sample answer:* $A = 500$, $C = 205$, $Y = 1700$, $T = 10$, $N = 17$

7. *Sample answer:* $A = 400$, $C = 380$, $Y = 6510$, $T = 83$, $N = 0$

8–16. See Additional Answers.

17. When the solution was rewritten with the variable on the left side, the inequality symbol was not reversed.
$x < -3.7$

18. **a.** $w + 16 \leq 20$; $w \leq 4$

    b. The dog drank at most 4 quarts of water.

Assignment Guide and Homework Check

Level	Day 1 Activity Assignment	Day 2 Lesson Assignment	Homework Check
Basic	5–7, 54–57	1–4, 9–43 odd, 18, 30, 40	11, 18, 25, 35, 40, 41
Average	5–7, 54–57	1–4, 14–20, 21–47 odd, 30, 40, 48	16, 18, 25, 35, 40, 48
Advanced	5–7, 54–57	1–4, 15–18, 26–40 even, 42–53	16, 26, 36, 44, 48, 50

Common Errors

- **Exercises 8–16** When solving the inequality, students may perform the same operation on both sides instead of the opposite operation. Remind them that solving inequalities is similar to solving equations, so they should use the opposite operation to solve the inequality.
- **Exercises 8–16** Students may reverse the direction of the inequality symbol when adding or subtracting. Remind them that the inequality symbol does not change direction when adding to or subtracting from both sides.

1.6 Record and Practice Journal

Solve the inequality. Graph the solution.

1. $x - 4 < 8$
$x < 12$

2. $16 + p \geq 14$
$p \geq -2$

3. $9 > y + \frac{3}{4}$
$y < 8\frac{1}{4}$

4. $-9.6 \leq z - 2.1$
$z \geq -7.5$

5. $5n < 75$
$n < 15$

6. $\frac{x}{6} \leq -12$
$x \leq -72$

7. $-15t > -60$
$t < 4$

8. $-8p < \frac{4}{5}$
$p > -\frac{1}{10}$

9. $-\frac{t}{6} > 1.2$
$t < -7.2$

10. To win a trivia game, you need at least 60 points. Each question is worth 4 points. Write and solve an inequality that represents the number of questions you need to answer correctly to win the game.
$4x \geq 60$; $x \geq 15$

Technology For the Teacher

Answer Presentation Tool

QuizShow

Check It Out
Help with Homework
BigIdeasMath.com

Vocabulary and Concept Check

1. **REASONING** How are inequalities and equations the same? different?

2. **WRITING** Explain how solving $3m < -9$ is different from solving $-3m < 9$.

3. **OPEN-ENDED** Write an inequality that is solved using the Subtraction Property of Inequality.

4. **WHICH ONE DOESN'T BELONG?** Which inequality does *not* belong with the other three? Explain your reasoning.

| $2n \geq 10$ | $10 \leq 2n$ | $-2n \leq -10$ | $10 \geq -2n$ |

Practice and Problem Solving

Use the formula in Activity 1 to create a passing record that makes the inequality true.

5. $P \geq 180$

6. $P + 40 < 110$

7. $280 \leq P - 20$

Solve the inequality. Graph the solution.

8. $g + 8 > 5$

9. $m - 6 < 4$

10. $-10 \leq x - 3$

11. $k - 2.9 \geq 1.5$

12. $3.6 \leq w + 5.8$

13. $c - \dfrac{1}{4} > -\dfrac{3}{4}$

14. $b + \dfrac{2}{3} \geq -\dfrac{1}{2}$

15. $m - 4.7 < -12.3$

16. $6 \geq x + \dfrac{2}{5}$

17. **ERROR ANALYSIS** Describe and correct the error in solving the inequality.

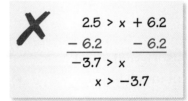

$$2.5 > x + 6.2$$
$$\underline{-6.2 \qquad -6.2}$$
$$-3.7 > x$$
$$x > -3.7$$

18. **WATER** A dog's water container holds at most 20 quarts.

   a. Which inequality shows how much water w your dog has drunk? Solve the inequality.

   | $w + 16 \geq 20$ | $w + 16 \leq 20$ |

   b. Interpret the solution to part (a).

Write and solve an inequality that represents the value of x.

19. The base is less than or equal to the height.

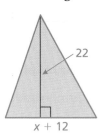

22

$x + 12$

20. The height is greater than the base.

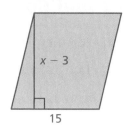

$x - 3$

15

Solve the inequality. Graph the solution.

② 21. $6m > -54$

22. $\dfrac{z}{6} < 8$

23. $\dfrac{v}{2} \le -15$

24. $51 \le 17c$

25. $\dfrac{7}{10}x < -\dfrac{3}{5}$

26. $-12.4 \ge \dfrac{h}{5}$

27. $\dfrac{g}{5.1} > -4$

28. $28.8 < 3.2d$

29. $9.8b \ge -29.4$

30. ERROR ANALYSIS Describe and correct the error in solving the inequality.

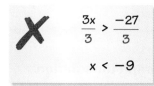

$\dfrac{3x}{3} > \dfrac{-27}{3}$

$x < -9$

Solve the inequality. Graph the solution.

③ 31. $\dfrac{n}{-4} < 5$

32. $0 \ge \dfrac{w}{-8}$

33. $6 > b \div (-3)$

34. $-3p > 72$

35. $-27 \le -5.4a$

36. $\dfrac{u}{-1.8} < -2.5$

37. $-0.5d \ge -3.4$

38. $\dfrac{h}{-8} > \dfrac{3}{4}$

39. $21.6 \le -7.2x$

40. ERROR ANALYSIS Describe and correct the error in solving the inequality.

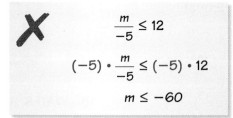

$\dfrac{m}{-5} \le 12$

$(-5) \cdot \dfrac{m}{-5} \le (-5) \cdot 12$

$m \le -60$

41. FUNDRAISER You are selling sandwiches as a fundraiser. Your goal is to raise at least $225.

   a. Write and solve an inequality to determine how many sandwiches you must sell to meet your goal.

   b. How does your answer to part (a) change when the price decreases? increases?

Sandwiches
$4.50 each

Common Errors

- **Exercises 21–29** When solving the inequality, students may perform the same operation on both sides instead of the opposite operation. Remind them that solving inequalities is similar to solving equations, so they should use the opposite operation to solve the inequality.

- **Exercises 21–29** When there is a negative in the inequality, students may reverse the direction of the inequality symbol. Remind them that they only reverse the direction when they are multiplying or dividing by a negative number. All of these exercises keep the same inequality symbol.

- **Exercises 31–39** Students may forget to reverse the inequality symbol when multiplying or dividing by a negative number. Remind them of this rule. Encourage students to substitute values into the original inequality to check that the solution is correct.

- **Exercises 42 and 43** Students may use the wrong formula to solve the inequality. Encourage them to write the formula and then substitute the given values.

19. $x + 12 \leq 22$; $x \leq 10$

20. $x - 3 > 15$; $x > 18$

21. $m > -9$;

22. $z < 48$;

23. $v \leq -30$;

24. $c \geq 3$;

25. $x < -\dfrac{6}{7}$;

26. $h \leq -62$;

27. $g > -20.4$;

28. $d > 9$;

29. $b \geq -3$;

30. The inequality symbol should not have been reversed.
$x > -9$

31. $n > -20$;

32. $w \geq 0$;

33. $b > -18$;

34–39. See Additional Answers.

40. The inequality symbol should have been reversed.
$m \geq -60$

41. See Additional Answers.

T-42

42. $6x < 30$; $x < 5$ m

43. $9x \geq 108$; $x \geq 12$ mm

44. sometimes; If $x > 0$, then $kx > 0$. But if $x \leq 0$, then $kx \leq 0$.

45. always; The product of two positive numbers is positive.

46. sometimes; If $x > 0$, then $kx < 0$. But if $x \leq 0$, then $kx \geq 0$.

47. never; The product of a negative number and a positive number is negative.

48. See *Taking Math Deeper*.

49. at least $1.25

50–53. See Additional Answers.

Fair Game Review

54. $x = -6$

55. $m = 13$

56. $k = -1.75$

57. B

Mini-Assessment

Solve the inequality. Graph the solution.

1. $q - 2.5 \geq 6.3$ $q \geq 8.8$

2. $-\dfrac{2}{3} \geq f + \dfrac{1}{3}$ $f \leq -1$

3. $\dfrac{m}{4} \geq -3$ $m \geq -12$

4. $3 < \dfrac{\ell}{-6}$ $\ell < -18$

5. $-6p < -36$ $p > 6$

Taking Math Deeper

Exercise 48

① One way to solve this problem is to use a table or a spreadsheet.

	A	B	C
	Times you go bowling	Buying	Renting
1			
2	1	$48.00	$2.50
3	2	$48.00	$5.00
4	3	$48.00	$7.50
5	4	$48.00	$10.00
6	5	$48.00	$12.50
7	6	$48.00	$15.00
8	7	$48.00	$17.50
9	8	$48.00	$20.00
10	9	$48.00	$22.50
11	10	$48.00	$25.00
12	11	$48.00	$27.50
13	12	$48.00	$30.00
14	13	$48.00	$32.50
15	14	$48.00	$35.00
16	15	$48.00	$37.50
17	16	$48.00	$40.00
18	17	$48.00	$42.50
19	18	$48.00	$45.00
20	19	$48.00	$47.50
21	20	$48.00	$50.00

② Write an inequality to represent the problem. Let n be the number of times you go bowling.

$48 < 2.5n$ Less expensive to buy than rent

③ Solve the inequality.
$$48 < 2.5n$$
$$19.2 < n$$
$$n > 19.2$$

So, it is less expensive to buy new shoes if you go bowling more than 19 times.

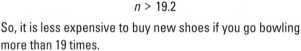

Reteaching and Enrichment Strategies

If students need help...	If students got it...
Resources by Chapter • Practice A and Practice B • Puzzle Time Record and Practice Journal Practice Differentiating the Lesson Lesson Tutorials Skills Review Handbook	Resources by Chapter • Enrichment and Extension • School-to-Work • Financial Literacy • Technology Connection Start the next section

Write and solve an inequality that represents the value of *x*.

42. Area < 30 m²

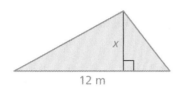

12 m

43. Area ≥ 108 mm²

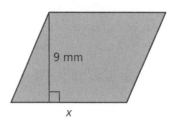

9 mm

x

REASONING Determine whether the statement is *always*, *sometimes*, or *never* true. Explain your reasoning.

44. If *k* is greater than 0, then $kx > 0$.

45. If *k* is greater than 0 and *x* is greater than 0, then $kx > 0$.

46. If *k* is less than 0, then $kx < 0$.

47. If *k* is less than 0 and *x* is greater than 0, then $kx > 0$.

48. BOWLING You can rent bowling shoes each time you bowl or you can buy a new pair for $48. Write and solve an inequality to determine when it is less expensive to buy new bowling shoes than to rent.

Rental fee: $2.50

49. LAUNDROMAT A dryer at a laundromat will run for 10 minutes on one quarter. To dry your clothes, you need to run the dryer for at least 50 minutes. How much will it cost to dry your clothes?

Critical Thinking Let *a* > *b* and *x* > *y*. Tell whether the statement is *always* true. Explain your reasoning.

50. $a + x > b + y$

51. $a - x > b - y$

52. $ax > by$

53. $\dfrac{a}{x} > \dfrac{y}{b}$

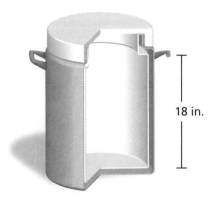

Fair Game Review What you learned in previous grades & lessons

Solve the equation. Check your solution. *(Section 1.2)*

54. $29 = 17 - 2x$

55. $\dfrac{3}{4}m - \dfrac{1}{4}m - 6 = \dfrac{1}{2}$

56. $3(2.5 - k) - k = 14.5$

57. MULTIPLE CHOICE The inside diameter of the cooler is 1 foot. About how many gallons of water does the cooler contain? ($1\ \text{ft}^3 \approx 7.5$ gal) *(Skills Review Handbook)*

Ⓐ 1 gal

Ⓑ 8 gal

Ⓒ 12 gal

Ⓓ 18 gal

18 in.

1.7 Solving Two-Step Inequalities

Essential Question How can you solve a two-step inequality?

STANDARDS
OF LEARNING
8.15

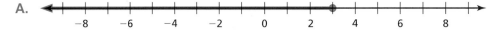

1 ACTIVITY: Matching Inequalities

Work with a partner. Match the inequality with its graph.

a. $3x + 2 < 11$ **b.** $3x - 4 \leq 5$ **c.** $\dfrac{x}{2} - 1 \geq 0$

d. $9 < 2x + 3$ **e.** $5 \leq 4x - 7$ **f.** $\dfrac{x}{2} + 6 < 8$

A.

B.

C.

D.

E.

F.

2 ACTIVITY: Writing an Inequality

Work with a partner. One of your favorite stores is having a 75% off sale. You have $20. You want to buy a pair of jeans.

a. Which of the following represents your ability to buy the jeans with $20?

$0.25x < 20$	$0.25x \leq 20$
$0.25x > 20$	$0.25x \geq 20$

b. What does x represent? Graph the possible values of x on a number line.

c. Can you afford a pair of jeans that originally costs $100? Explain.

Laurie's Notes

Introduction

For the Teacher

- **Goal:** Students will develop an intuitive understanding of solving two-step inequalities.

Motivate

- Pac Man, one of the most famous video games of all time, was released in 1980. Ask how many students have played Pac Man or a similar video game. It is expected that virtually 100% of your students will answer yes.
- Historical facts to share: William Higinbotham created the first video game in 1958. His game, called *Tennis for Two,* was created and played on a Brookhaven National Laboratory oscilloscope. In 1962, Steve Russell invented *SpaceWar!,* the first game intended for computer use. Russell used a MIT PDP-1 mainframe computer to design his game.

Activity Notes

Activity 1

- Students should be able to use *Guess, Check, and Revise* to complete this matching activity. In the process, they should be able to confirm that you solve a two-step inequality in much the same way you solve a two-step equation.
- Caution students to be careful with the inequalities that have the variable on the right side. Also remind them how division is represented $\left(\dfrac{x}{2} \text{ versus } x \div 2\right)$.

- ❓ "What are the inequalities graphed in (A) and (F)? (A) is $x \le 3$ and (F) is $x < 3$.
- ❓ "What are the inequalities graphed in (B) and (E)?" (B) is $x \ge 3$ and (E) is $x > 3$.
- Given the similarity of all 6 solutions, it is important to have students discuss how they completed the matching activity.
- **Extension:** Ask students to name a value of x that would be a solution of (C) but would not be a solution of (F). $x = 3.5$ Name a value of x that would be a solution of (D) but would not be a solution of (E). $x = 2.5$ Name a value of x that is a solution of (A) and (B). $x = 3$

Activity 2

- Make sure students understand that x equals the original purchase price of the jeans.
- ❓ "Why is 0.25 used in this problem when the jeans are 75% off?" 25% is the amount you must pay when there is a 75% off sale; 25% = 0.25.
- **Extension:** Discuss the sales tax that would be added in your state.

Standards of Learning

8.15(b) The student will solve two-step linear inequalities and graph the results on a number line.

Previous Learning

Students should know how to solve two-step equations.

Start Thinking! and Warm Up

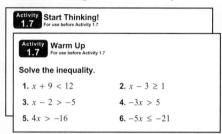

Activity 1.7 Start Thinking! For use before Activity 1.7

Activity 1.7 Warm Up For use before Activity 1.7

Solve the inequality.

1. $x + 9 < 12$
2. $x - 3 \ge 1$
3. $x - 2 > -5$
4. $-3x > 5$
5. $4x > -16$
6. $-5x \le -21$

1.7 Record and Practice Journal

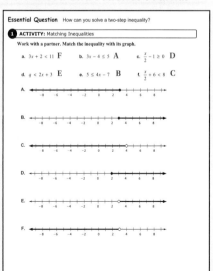

Essential Question How can you solve a two-step inequality?

1 ACTIVITY: Matching Inequalities

Work with a partner. Match the inequality with its graph.

a. $3x + 2 < 11$ F   b. $3x - 4 \le 5$ A   c. $\dfrac{x}{2} - 1 \ge 0$ D

d. $q < 2x + 3$ E   e. $5 \le 4x - 7$ B   f. $\dfrac{x}{2} + 6 < 8$ C

Differentiated Instruction

Kinestetic

Starting with 1, give each student a unique number card. Tell students to stand up if their number is *less than* (say a number) and then *less than or equal to* that same number. Students should discuss the difference between the two. This can be repeated with *greater than* and *greater than or equal to*.

1.7 Record and Practice Journal

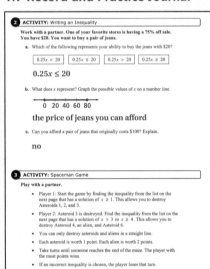

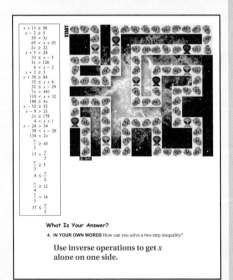

What Is Your Answer?

4. IN YOUR OWN WORDS How can you solve a two-step inequality?

Use inverse operations to get *x* alone on one side.

Laurie's Notes

Activity 3

- Give students time to read through the directions and ask questions.
- This activity provides fun practice with solving inequalities and with practicing mental math strategies!
- Students will be solving many inequalities and should become better at judging which inequalities to skip over as they scan for an appropriate inequality.
- **Big Idea:** The third bullet says that asteroids and aliens can only be destroyed in a straight line. In other words, you cannot turn a 90° angle to destroy additional asteroids or aliens.
- When students have finished, ask volunteers to explain their strategies for locating the next inequality to be solved.

What Is Your Answer?

- **Neighbor Check:** Have students work independently and then have their neighbor check their work. Have students discuss any discrepancies.

Closure

- **Exit Ticket:** Solve each inequality.

  $4x + 5 \geq 21$ $x \geq 4$ and $\dfrac{x}{4} - 3 \geq 13$ $x \geq 64$

Technology
For
the **T**eacher

Dynamic Classroom

The Dynamic Planning Tool
Editable Teacher's Resources at *BigIdeasMath.com*

$x + 13 \geq 90$
$x - 2 \geq 5$
$39 < 3x$
$65 < x + 10$
$2x \geq 22$
$x + 5 > 24$
$33 \leq x - 5$
$3x > 126$
$6 < x - 2$
$x + 2 \geq 3$
$x + 30 \geq 84$
$35 \leq x + 6$
$32 \leq x - 29$
$7x > 441$
$110 < x + 32$
$180 \leq 4x$
$x - 52 \geq 32$
$x - 9 > 21$
$2x \geq 178$
$4 < x + 1$
$x - 24 > 34$
$58 < x - 28$
$134 < 2x$
$\dfrac{x}{2} \geq 45$
$17 < \dfrac{x}{3}$
$\dfrac{x}{3} \geq 5$
$8 \leq \dfrac{x}{2}$
$\dfrac{x}{4} \geq 12$
$\dfrac{x}{5} > 14$
$37 \leq \dfrac{x}{2}$

Play with a partner.

- Player 1: Start the game by finding the inequality from the list that has a solution of $x \geq 1$. This allows you to destroy Asteroids 1, 2, and 3.
- Player 2: Asteroid 3 is destroyed. Find the inequality from the list that has a solution of $x > 3$ or $x \geq 4$. This allows you to destroy Asteroid 4, an alien, and Asteroid 6.
- You can only destroy asteroids and aliens in a straight line.
- Each asteroid is worth 1 point. Each alien is worth 2 points.
- Take turns until someone reaches the end of the maze. The player with the most points wins.
- If an incorrect inequality is chosen, the player loses that turn.

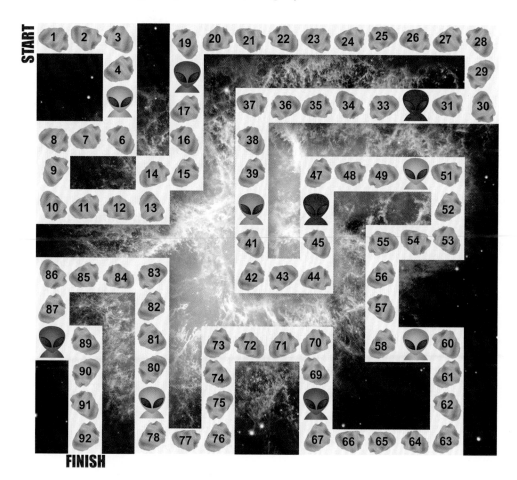

What Is Your Answer?

4. IN YOUR OWN WORDS How can you solve a two-step inequality?

Practice → Use what you learned about solving two-step inequalities to complete Exercises 3 and 4 on page 48.

You can solve two-step inequalities in much the same way you solve two-step equations.

EXAMPLE **1** **Solving Two-Step Inequalities**

a. Solve $5x - 4 \geq 11$. Graph the solution.

$$5x - 4 \geq 11 \qquad \text{Write the inequality.}$$

Step 1: Undo the subtraction. $\longrightarrow$ $\underline{+ 4 \quad + 4}$ Add 4 to each side.

$$5x \geq 15 \qquad \text{Simplify.}$$

Step 2: Undo the multiplication. $\longrightarrow$ $\dfrac{5x}{5} \geq \dfrac{15}{5}$ Divide each side by 5.

$$x \geq 3 \qquad \text{Simplify.}$$

∴ The solution is $x \geq 3$.

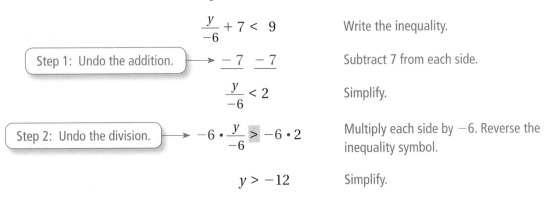

Check: $x = 0$ is *not* a solution.

Check: $x = 4$ is a solution.

b. Solve $\dfrac{y}{-6} + 7 < 9$. Graph the solution.

$$\dfrac{y}{-6} + 7 < 9 \qquad \text{Write the inequality.}$$

Step 1: Undo the addition. $\longrightarrow$ $\underline{- 7 \quad - 7}$ Subtract 7 from each side.

$$\dfrac{y}{-6} < 2 \qquad \text{Simplify.}$$

Step 2: Undo the division. $\longrightarrow$ $-6 \cdot \dfrac{y}{-6} > -6 \cdot 2$ Multiply each side by -6. Reverse the inequality symbol.

$$y > -12 \qquad \text{Simplify.}$$

∴ The solution is $y > -12$.

On Your Own

Solve the inequality. Graph the solution.

Now You're Ready
Exercises 5–10

1. $4b - 1 < 7$ **2.** $8 + 9c \geq -28$ **3.** $\dfrac{n}{-2} + 11 > 12$

Laurie's Notes

Introduction

Connect

- **Yesterday:** Students developed an intuitive understanding of solving two-step inequalities.
- **Today:** Students will solve and graph two-step inequalities.

Motivate

- ❓ "How many of you have played the game *Trivial Pursuit*® or a variation of it?" Answers will vary.
- This popular trivia game was created in 1979 by two friends who had lost some pieces to the game SCRABBLE®. They decided to create a new game. The rest is history. *Trivial Pursuit*® has sold more than 88 million copies in 26 countries, and in 17 languages. There are versions of the game that focus on sports, pop culture, and regional geography.
- In Example 3, students use the context of a trivia game to solve a multi-step inequality.

Lesson Notes

Discuss

- You solve two-step inequalities in much the same way you solve two-step equations. You only need to remember to change the direction of the inequality symbol if you multiply or divide by a negative quantity.
- Recall that solving an equation undoes the evaluating in reverse order. The goal is to isolate the variable.

Example 1

- ❓ "What operations are being performed on the left side of the inequality? multiplication and subtraction
- ❓ "What is the first step in isolating the variable, meaning getting the x-term by itself?" Add 4 to each side of the inequality.
- Notice that subtracting 4 would have been the last step if evaluating the left side, so its inverse operation is the first step in solving the inequality.
- ❓ "To solve for x, what is the last step?" Divide both sides by 5.
- Because you are dividing by a positive quantity, the inequality symbol does not change. The solution is $x \geq 3$. Graph and check.
- Part (b) is solved in a similar fashion.
- ❓ "To solve $\frac{y}{-6} < 2$, what do you need to do?" Multiply both sides by -6 and change the direction of the inequality symbol.
- Graph and check. Remember to use an open circle because the variable cannot equal -12.

On Your Own

- These are all straightforward problems. Students should not be confused by them.
- Ask volunteers to share their solutions at the board.

Goal

 Today's lesson is solving two-step inequalities.

Start Thinking! and Warm Up

> **Lesson 1.7** Warm Up
> For use before Lesson 1.7
>
> **Lesson 1.7** Start Thinking!
> For use before Lesson 1.7
>
> What are your math quiz grades so far this grading period?
>
> What must you earn on the next quiz in order to have at least a C quiz average? a B? an A?

Extra Example 1

Solve $17 \leq 3y - 4$. Graph the solution.

$y \geq 7$

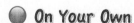

On Your Own

1. $b < 2$;

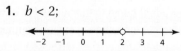

2. $c \geq -4$;

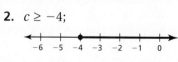

3. $n < -2$;

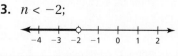

Extra Example 2

Solve $12 > -2(y - 4)$. Graph the solution. $y > -2$

Extra Example 3

In Example 3, suppose you need a mean score of at least 85 to advance to the next round of the trivia game. What score do you need on the fifth game to advance? You need at least 73 points to advance to the next round.

On Your Own

4. $k < 8$;

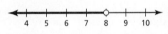

5. $n > 2$;

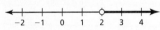

6. $y \geq -14$;

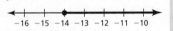

7. at least 88 points

English Language Learners

Vocabulary

Give English learners the opportunity to use precise language to solve an inequality. Write the inequality $-2x + 4 > 8$ on the board. Have one student come to the board. For each step of the solution, call on another student to give the instruction for solving. The instructions should be given in complete sentences. The instructions for the inequality are:

(1) Subtract 4 from each side.

(2) Simplify.

(3) Divide each side by -2. Reverse the inequality symbol.

(4) Simplify.

Example 2

- **Another Way:** The inequality has two factors on the left side: -7 and $(x + 3)$. Instead of distributing, divide both sides by -7. Dividing by a negative number changes the direction of the inequality symbol.

$$-7(x + 3) \leq 28 \qquad \text{Write the inequality.}$$

$$\frac{-7(x + 3)}{-7} \geq \frac{28}{-7} \qquad \begin{array}{l}\text{Divide each side by } -7. \\ \text{Reverse the inequality symbol.}\end{array}$$

$$x + 3 \geq -4 \qquad \text{Simplify.}$$

$$\underline{-3} \quad \underline{-3} \qquad \text{Subtract 3 from each side.}$$

$$x \geq -7 \qquad \text{Simplify.}$$

- Discuss each method with students.

Example 3

- This is a classic problem. Students always want to know what they have to score on a test in order to have a (mean) average of ___. This is the same type of problem.

? "How do you compute a mean?" Sum the data and divide by the number of data values.

- Set up the problem to compute the mean. Because you want your score to be a minimum of 90, you need to set the mean greater than or equal to 90.

- You need at least a 98 to advance to the next level. Hopefully this score is attainable. Often with my students, the score they need to achieve isn't possible on one test!

On Your Own

- **Common Error:** If students solve Question 5 by distributing the -4, it is very possible they will write $-4n - 40$ instead of $-4n + 40$. For the factor $n - 10$, they need to remember to *add the opposite* so that the initial equation could be written as $-4[n + (-10)] < 32$. Then distribute the -4.

- Students may need guidance on Question 6. Distributing 0.5 results in $-3 \leq 4 + 0.5y$.

Closure

- **Writing:** How are these problems alike? How are they different?

$$3n - 4 = -25 \qquad 3n - 4 > -25 \qquad 3n - 4 \leq -25$$

Sample answer: They are alike because they each use the expressions $(3n - 4)$ and (-25). They are different because of the way the expressions are related: equal to, greater than, and less than or equal to.

Technology For the Teacher

Dynamic Classroom

The Dynamic Planning Tool
Editable Teacher's Resources at *BigIdeasMath.com*

EXAMPLE 2 **Standardized Test Practice**

Which graph represents the solution of $-7(x + 3) \le 28$?

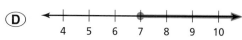

$$-7(x + 3) \le 28 \qquad \text{Write the inequality.}$$

$$-7x - 21 \le 28 \qquad \text{Use Distributive Property.}$$

Step 1: Undo the subtraction. $\longrightarrow \quad \underline{+\,21 \quad +\,21} \qquad \text{Add 21 to each side.}$

$$-7x \le 49 \qquad \text{Simplify.}$$

Step 2: Undo the multiplication. $\longrightarrow \quad \dfrac{-7x}{-7} \ge \dfrac{49}{-7} \qquad$ Divide each side by -7. Reverse the inequality symbol.

$$x \ge -7 \qquad \text{Simplify.}$$

∴ The correct answer is **B**.

EXAMPLE 3 **Real-Life Application**

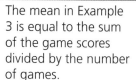

Trivia Challenge

Your Scores

- 95 **Round 1:** Very impressive!
- 91 **Round 2:** Good job!
- 77 **Round 3:** You can do better!
- 89 **Round 4:** Nice work!

You need a mean score of at least 90 to advance to the next round of the trivia game. What score do you need on the fifth game to advance?

Use the definition of mean to write and solve an inequality. Let x be the score on the fifth game.

$$\frac{95 + 91 + 77 + 89 + x}{5} \ge 90$$

> The phrase "at least" means greater than or equal to.

$$\frac{352 + x}{5} \ge 90 \qquad \text{Simplify.}$$

$$5 \cdot \frac{352 + x}{5} \ge 5 \cdot 90 \qquad \text{Multiply each side by 5.}$$

$$352 + x \ge 450 \qquad \text{Simplify.}$$

$$\underline{-\,352 \qquad\qquad -\,352} \qquad \text{Subtract 352 from each side.}$$

$$x \ge 98 \qquad \text{Simplify.}$$

Remember

The mean in Example 3 is equal to the sum of the game scores divided by the number of games.

∴ You need at least 98 points to advance to the next round.

On Your Own

Now You're Ready
Exercises 12–17

Solve the inequality. Graph the solution.

4. $2(k - 5) < 6$　　**5.** $-4(n - 10) < 32$　　**6.** $-3 \le 0.5(8 + y)$

7. WHAT IF? In Example 3, you need a mean score of at least 88 to advance to the next round of the trivia game. What score do you need on the fifth game to advance?

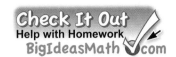

Vocabulary and Concept Check

1. **WRITING** Compare and contrast solving two-step inequalities and solving two-step equations.

2. **OPEN-ENDED** Describe how to solve the inequality $3(a + 5) < 9$.

Practice and Problem Solving

Match the inequality with its graph.

3. $\dfrac{t}{3} - 1 \geq -3$

A.
 number line with open circle at -6, shaded left, marks -9 to -2

B. number line with closed dot at -6, shaded left, marks -9 to -2

C. number line with closed dot at -6, shaded right, marks -9 to -2

4. $5x + 7 \leq 32$

A. number line with closed dot at 5, shaded left, marks 2 to 9

B. number line with open circle at 5, shaded right, marks 2 to 9

C. number line with closed dot at 5, shaded right, marks 2 to 9

Solve the inequality. Graph the solution.

1 5. $7b + 4 \geq 11$

6. $2v - 4 < 8$

7. $1 - \dfrac{m}{3} \leq 6$

8. $\dfrac{4}{5} < 3w - \dfrac{11}{5}$

9. $1.8 < 0.5 - 1.3p$

10. $-2.4r + 9.6 \geq 4.8$

11. **ERROR ANALYSIS** Describe and correct the error in solving the inequality.

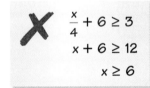

$$\dfrac{x}{4} + 6 \geq 3$$
$$x + 6 \geq 12$$
$$x \geq 6$$

Solve the inequality. Graph the solution.

2 12. $6(g + 2) \leq 18$

13. $2(y - 5) \leq 16$

14. $-10 \geq \dfrac{5}{3}(h - 3)$

15. $-\dfrac{1}{3}(u + 2) > 5$

16. $2.7 > 0.9(n - 1.7)$

17. $10 > -2.5(z - 3.1)$

18. **ATM** Write and solve an inequality that represents the number of $20 bills you can withdraw from the account without going below the minimum balance.

Anytown Savings and Loan
Your current balance is
$320.00
The minimum balance is $100.00.
Would you like to make another transaction?
Yes   No

Assignment Guide and Homework Check

Level	Day 1 Activity Assignment	Day 2 Lesson Assignment	Homework Check
Basic	3, 4, 26–29	1, 2, 5–21 odd, 18	7, 15, 18, 19
Average	3, 4, 26–29	1, 2, 7–21 odd, 18, 22	7, 15, 18, 19
Advanced	3, 4, 26–29	1, 2, 11, 14, 16, 19–25	14, 20, 22, 23

Common Errors

- **Exercises 5–10** Students may incorrectly multiply or divide before adding to or subtracting from both sides. Remind them that they should work backward through the order of operations, or that they should start away from the variable and move toward it.
- **Exercises 5–10, 12–17** Students may forget to reverse the inequality symbol when multiplying or dividing by a negative number. Encourage them to write the inequality symbol that they should have in the solution before solving.
- **Exercises 12–17** If students distribute before solving, they may forget to distribute the number to the second term. Remind them that they need to distribute to everything within the parentheses. Encourage students to draw arrows to represent the multiplication.

1.7 Record and Practice Journal

Solve the inequality. Graph the solution.

1. $9x - 6 > 66$
$x > 8$

2. $\frac{d}{3} + 7 \le -11$
$d \le -54$

3. $14.9 - 5.2n < 20.1$
$n > -1$

4. $\frac{9}{10} \ge 5z + \frac{3}{10}$
$z \le \frac{3}{25}$

5. $8(p + 3) > -24$
$p > -6$

6. $-\frac{1}{2}(y + 8) < -12$
$y > 16$

7. In the United States music industry, an album is awarded gold certification with at least 500,000 albums sold. A recording artist is selling about 1200 albums each day. The artist has already sold 15,000 albums. About how many more days will it take before the album is awarded gold certification?
405 days

Technology
For
the Teacher
Answer Presentation Tool
QuizShow

Practice and Problem Solving

3. C   4. A

5. $b \ge 1$;

6. $v < 6$;
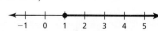

7. $m \ge -15$;
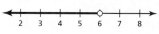

8. $w > 1$;

9. $p < -1$;
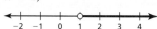

10. $r \le 2$;
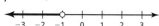

11. They did not perform the operations in proper order.

$$\frac{x}{4} + 6 \ge 3$$

$$\frac{x}{4} \ge -3$$

$$x \ge -12$$

12. $g \le 1$;

13–18. See Additional Answers.

T-48

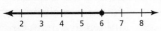

19. $x \le 6$;

(number line: marks 2, 3, 4, 5, 6, 7, 8 with filled dot at 6)

20. $b < 3$;

(number line: marks −2, −1, 0, 1, 2, 3, 4 with open dot at 3)

21. $\dfrac{3}{16}x + 2 \le 11$;
$x \le 48$; at most 48 lines

22. $500 - 20x \ge 100$;
$x \le 20$; at most \$20 per hour

23. See *Taking Math Deeper*.

24–25. See Additional Answers.

 Fair Game Review

26. 100π mm^2

27. 625π in.^{2}

28. 1089π m^2

29. A

Mini-Assessment

Solve the inequality. Graph the solution.

1. $2x + 4 < 10$ $x < 3$

(number line: marks −4, −2, 0, 2, 4 with open dot at 3)

2. $3 \le \dfrac{y}{-5} + 7$ $y \le 20$

(number line: marks 0, 5, 10, 15, 20, 25 with filled dot at 20)

3. $-4.2 - 1.1b \le 2.4$ $b \ge -6$

(number line: marks −8, −6, −4, −2, 0, 2 with filled dot at −6)

4. $\dfrac{2}{3}m + \dfrac{2}{3} \ge -\dfrac{1}{3}$ $m \ge -\dfrac{3}{2}$

(number line: marks −2, −$\frac{3}{2}$, −1, −$\frac{1}{2}$, 0, $\frac{1}{2}$ with filled dot at −$\frac{3}{2}$)

Taking Math Deeper

Exercise 23

Inequality problems can throw students off, simply because of the "inequality." A good way to approach the problem is to imagine that it is an "equality" problem. After the "equation" is written, decide which way the inequality symbol should point.

 Write an equation.

$$75 + 15x = 140$$

| Eaten today | Pounds per bucket | Number of buckets | Total for a day |

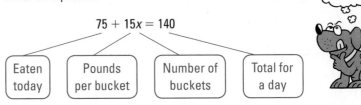
4 or 5 buckets?

2 **a.** Write an inequality and solve it. Recall the whale needs to eat at least 140 pounds of fish each day.

$$75 + 15x \ge 140 \quad \text{Write inequality.}$$
$$15x > 65 \quad \text{Subtract 75 from each side.}$$
$$x \ge 4\tfrac{1}{3} \quad \text{Divide each side by 15.}$$

The whale needs to eat at least $4\tfrac{1}{3}$ more buckets of fish.

3 **b.** If you only have a choice of whole buckets, then the whale should be given 5 more buckets of food. With 4 buckets, the whale would only get $75 + 60 = 135$ pounds of fish.

Project

Select a marine park. Research the amount of fish needed to feed all of the animals at the park. Determine the cost of the fish, not including storage and personnel needed to feed the animals. Using the entrance fee to the park, how many visitors are needed every day to meet the cost? What are some ways that park officials might help offset the daily costs?

Reteaching and Enrichment Strategies

If students need help. . .	If students got it. . .
Resources by Chapter • Practice A and Practice B • Puzzle Time Record and Practice Journal Practice Differentiating the Lesson Lesson Tutorials Skills Review Handbook	Resources by Chapter • Enrichment and Extension • School-to-Work • Financial Literacy • Technology Connection • Life Connections Start the next section

Solve the inequality. Graph the solution.

19. $5x - 2x + 7 \le 15 + 10$

20. $7b - 12b + 1.4 > 8.4 - 22$

21. TYPING One line of text on a page uses about $\frac{3}{16}$ of an inch. There are 1-inch margins at the top and bottom of a page. Write and solve an inequality to find the number of lines that can be typed on a page that is 11 inches long.

22. WOODWORKING A woodworker builds a cabinet in 20 hours. The cabinet is sold at a store for $500. Write and solve an inequality that represents the hourly wage the store can pay the woodworker and still make a profit of at least $100.

23. KILLER WHALES A killer whale has eaten 75 pounds of fish today. It needs to eat at least 140 pounds of fish each day.

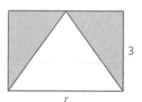

   a. A bucket holds 15 pounds of fish. Write and solve an inequality to represent how many more buckets of fish the whale needs to eat.

   b. Should the whale be given *four* or *five* more buckets of fish? Explain.

24. DRIVE-IN A drive-in movie theater charges $3.50 per car. The drive-in has already admitted 100 cars. Write and solve an inequality to find how many more cars the drive-in needs to admit to earn at least $500.

25. **Challenge** For what values of *r* will the area of the shaded region be greater than or equal to 12?

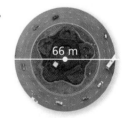

3

r

 Fair Game Review What you learned in previous grades & lessons

Find the area of the circle. *(Skills Review Handbook)*

26.

10 mm

27.

25 in.

28.

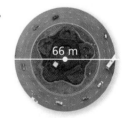

66 m

29. MULTIPLE CHOICE What is the volume of the cube? *(Skills Review Handbook)*

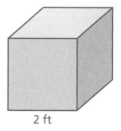

   (A) 8 ft^3 (B) 16 ft^3

   (C) 24 ft^3 (D) 32 ft^3

2 ft

Write the word sentence as an inequality. *(Section 1.5)*

1. A number x plus 1 is less than -13.

2. A number t minus 1.6 is at most 9.

Graph the inequality on a number line. *(Section 1.5)*

3. $x > -10$

4. $y \le \dfrac{3}{5}$

5. $w < 6.8$

Solve the inequality. *(Section 1.6)*

6. $x - 2 < 4$

7. $g + 14 \ge 30$

8. $-2m > 14$

Solve the inequality. Graph the solution. *(Section 1.7)*

9. $2m + 1 \ge 7$

10. $\dfrac{n}{6} - 8 \le 2$

11. $2 - \dfrac{j}{5} > 7$

12. $\dfrac{5}{4} > -3w - \dfrac{7}{4}$

13. MP3 PLAYER Your MP3 player can store up to 160 gigabytes of media. You transfer 8.5 gigabytes of media to the MP3 player. Write and solve an inequality that represents the amount of memory available on the MP3 player. *(Section 1.6)*

14. LIFEGUARD Three requirements for a lifeguard training course are shown. *(Section 1.5)*

    a. Write and graph three inequalities that represent the requirements.

    b. You can swim 350 feet. Do you satisfy the swimming requirement of the course? Explain.

LIFEGUARDS NEEDED
Take Our Training Course NOW!!!
Lifeguard Training Requirements
- Swim at least 100 yards
- Tread water for at least 5 minutes
- Swim 10 yards or more underwater without taking a breath

15. BOOKS You have a gift card worth $50. You want to buy several paperback books that cost $6 each. Write and solve an inequality to find the number of books you can buy and still have at least $20 on the gift card. *(Section 1.7)*

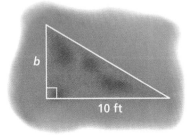
b

10 ft

16. GARDEN The area of the triangular garden must be less than 35 square feet. Write and solve an inequality that represents the value of b. *(Section 1.6)*

Alternative Assessment Options

Math Chat Student Reflective Focus Question
Structured Interview Writing Prompt

Math Chat

- Have students work in pairs. One student describes how to write and graph inequalities, giving examples. The other student probes for more information. Students then switch roles and repeat the process for how to solve one- and two-step inequalities.
- The teacher should walk around the classroom listening to the pairs and asking questions to ensure understanding.

Study Help Sample Answers

Remind students to complete Graphic Organizers for the rest of the chapter.

4.

Solving One-Step Inequalities

- Use one inverse operation to isolate the variable.

Solving Two-Step Inequalities

- Use two inverse operations to isolate the variable.

- Use inverse operations to isolate the variable.
- Collect the variable terms on one side and the constant terms on the other side.
- The variable can end up on either side of the inequality.
- More than one number can be the solution.
- It is always a good idea to check your solution.

5.

Solving Equations

- The sign between two expressions is an equal sign, =.
- One number is the solution.

Solving Inequalities

- The sign between two expressions is an inequality symbol: <, >, ≤, or ≥.
- More than one number can be the solution.

- Use inverse operations to isolate the variable.
- Collect the variable terms on one side and the constant terms on the other side.
- The variable can end up on either side of the equation or inequality.
- It is always a good idea to check your solution.

Reteaching and Enrichment Strategies

If students need help. . .	If students got it. . .
Resources by Chapter • Study Help • Practice A and Practice B • Puzzle Time Lesson Tutorials *BigIdeasMath.com* Practice Quiz Practice from the Test Generator	Resources by Chapter • Enrichment and Extension • School-to-Work Game Closet at *BigIdeasMath.com* Start the Chapter Review

Answers

1. $x + 1 < -13$

2. $t - 1.6 \leq 9$

3. ![number line from -13 to -7, open circle at -10, arrow left]

4. ![number line from -1/5 to 1, closed circle at 3/5, arrow left]

5. ![number line from 6.4 to 7, open circle at 6.8, arrow left]

6. $x < 6$ 7. $g \geq 16$

8. $m < -7$

9. $m \geq 3$;
![number line from 0 to 6, closed circle at 3, arrow right]

10. $n \leq 60$;
![number line from 57 to 63, closed circle at 60, arrow left]

11. $j < -25$;
![number line from -29 to -23, open circle at -25, arrow left]

12. $w > -1$;
![number line from -3 to 3, open circle at -1, arrow right]

13. $8.5 + x \leq 160$; $x \leq 151.5$; at most 151.5 gigabytes

14–16. See Additional Answers.

Technology For the Teacher

Answer Presentation Tool

Assessment Book

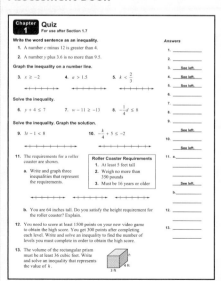

For the Teacher
Additional Review Options
- **Quiz***Show*
- Big Ideas Test Generator
- Game Closet at *BigIdeasMath.com*
- Vocabulary Puzzle Builder
- Resources by Chapter
    Puzzle Time
    Study Help

Answers

1. $y = -19$
2. $n = -8$
3. $t = 12\pi$

Review of Common Errors

Exercises 1–3

- Students may perform the same operation that is in the equation instead of the inverse operation. Remind them that they must use an inverse operation to undo an operation. Also, remind them to check their solution in the original equation.

1 Chapter Review

Check It Out
Vocabulary Help
BigIdeasMath ✓com

Review Key Vocabulary

literal equation, *p. 24*
inequality, *p. 32*

solution of an inequality, *p. 32*

solution set, *p. 32*
graph of an inequality, *p. 33*

Review Examples and Exercises

1.1 Solving Simple Equations (pp. 2–9)

The *boiling point* of a liquid is the temperature at which the liquid becomes a gas. The boiling point of mercury is about $\frac{41}{200}$ of the boiling point of lead. Write and solve an equation to find the boiling point of lead.

Let x be the boiling point of lead.

Mercury 357°C

$$\frac{41}{200}x = 357 \qquad \text{Write the equation.}$$

$$\frac{200}{41} \cdot \left(\frac{41}{200}x\right) = \frac{200}{41} \cdot 357 \qquad \text{Multiply each side by } \tfrac{200}{41}.$$

$$x \approx 1741 \qquad \text{Simplify.}$$

∴ The boiling point of lead is about 1741°C.

Exercises

Solve the equation. Check your solution.

1. $y + 8 = -11$

2. $3.2 = -0.4n$

3. $-\dfrac{t}{4} = -3\pi$

1.2 Solving Multi-Step Equations (pp. 10–15)

Solve $-14x + 28 + 6x = -44$.

$$-14x + 28 + 6x = -44 \qquad \text{Write the equation.}$$

$$-8x + 28 = -44 \qquad \text{Combine like terms.}$$

Step 1: Undo the addition. $\longrightarrow$

$$\underline{\ -28 \quad\ -28} \qquad \text{Subtract 28 from each side.}$$

$$-8x = -72 \qquad \text{Simplify.}$$

Step 2: Undo the multiplication. $\longrightarrow$

$$\frac{-8x}{-8} = \frac{-72}{-8} \qquad \text{Divide each side by } -8.$$

$$x = 9 \qquad \text{Simplify.}$$

∴ The solution is $x = 9$.

Exercises

Find the value of x. Then find the angle measures of the polygon.

4.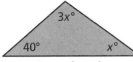

Sum of angle
measures: 180°

5.

Sum of angle
measures: 360°

6.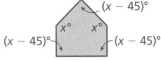

Sum of angle
measures: 540°

1.3 Solving Equations with Variables on Both Sides *(pp. 16–21)*

Solve $3(x - 4) = -2(4 - x)$.

$3(x - 4) = -2(4 - x)$	Write the equation.
$3x - 12 = -8 + 2x$	Use Distributive Property.
Undo the addition. → $\quad - 2x \qquad\qquad - 2x$	Subtract $2x$ from each side.
$x - 12 = -8$	Simplify.
Undo the subtraction. → $\quad + 12 \quad + 12$	Add 12 to each side.
$x = 4$	Simplify.

∴ The solution is $x = 4$.

Exercises

Solve the equation. Check your solution.

7. $5m - 1 = 4m + 5$ **8.** $3(5p - 3) = 5(p - 1)$ **9.** $\dfrac{2}{5}n + \dfrac{1}{10} = \dfrac{1}{2}(n + 4)$

1.4 Rewriting Equations and Formulas *(pp. 22–27)*

The equation for a line in slope-intercept form is $y = mx + b$.

Solve the equation for x.

$y = mx + b$	Write the equation.
$y - b = mx + b - b$	Subtract b from each side.
$y - b = mx$	Simplify.
$\dfrac{y - b}{m} = \dfrac{mx}{m}$	Divide each side by m.
$\dfrac{y - b}{m} = x$	Simplify.

∴ So, $x = \dfrac{y - b}{m}$.

Review of Common Errors (continued)

Exercises 4–6

- Students may change the exponent of the variable when combining like terms. For example, they may write the sum $x + x + \frac{1}{2}x + \frac{1}{2}x$ as $3x^3$. Remind them how to correctly combine like terms that have variables.

Exercise 7

- Students may make mistakes when collecting the variable terms on one side and the constant terms on the other side. Remind them that when a term is moved from one side of an equation to the other, the inverse operation is used. Also, remind them to check their solution in the original equation.

Exercises 8 and 9

- Students may multiply only one of the terms in parentheses by the factor outside the parentheses. Remind them how to correctly use the Distributive Property.

Answers

10. **a.** $K = \frac{5}{9}(F - 32) + 273.15$

   b. about 388.71 K

11. **a.** $A = \frac{1}{2}h(b + B)$

   b. $h = \frac{2A}{b + B}$

   c. $h = 6$ cm

12. $v < -2$

13. $x - \frac{1}{4} \leq -\frac{3}{4}$

14. no

15. yes

16.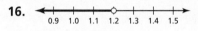

17.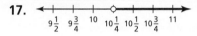

Review of Common Errors (continued)

Exercises 10 and 11

- Students may be unsure about how to solve the formula for the specified variable. Point out that they should work through the order of operations *backwards,* using inverse operations to isolate the variable.

Exercises 12 and 13

- Students may struggle knowing which inequality symbol to use. Encourage them to put the word sentence into a real-life context and to use the table in the lesson that explains what symbol matches each phrase.

Exercises 14 and 15

- Students may try to solve for the variable instead of substituting the given value into the inequality and determining if that value is a solution of the inequality.

Exercises 16 and 17

- Students may use a closed circle instead of an open circle and vice versa. They may shade the wrong side of the number line. Review how to graph inequalities. Encourage them to test a value on each side of the circle.

Exercises 18–21

- Students may reverse the direction of the inequality symbol when adding or subtracting. Remind them that the inequality symbol does not change direction when adding to or subtracting from both sides.
- Students may forget to reverse the inequality symbol when multiplying or dividing by a negative number. Encourage them to write the inequality symbol that they should have in the solution before solving.

Exercises 22–24

- Students may incorrectly multiply or divide before adding to or subtracting from both sides. Remind them that they should work backwards through the order of operations.

Exercises 25–27

- If students distribute before solving, they may forget to distribute the coefficient to the second term. Remind them that they need to distribute to everything within the parentheses. Encourage students to draw arrows to represent the multiplication.

Exercises

10. a. The formula $F = \frac{9}{5}(K - 273.15) + 32$ converts temperatures from Kelvin K to Fahrenheit F. Solve the formula for K.

  b. Convert $240\,°F$ to Kelvin K. Round your answer to the nearest hundredth.

11. a. Write the formula for the area A of a trapezoid.

  b. Solve the formula for h.

  c. Use the new formula to find the height h of the trapezoid.

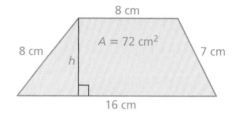

1.5 | **Writing and Graphing Inequalities** *(pp. 30–35)*

a. **Four plus a number w is at least $-\frac{1}{2}$. Write this sentence as an inequality.**

Four plus a number w	is at least	$-\frac{1}{2}$.
$4 + w$	$\geq$	$-\frac{1}{2}$

⫶ An inequality is $4 + w \geq -\frac{1}{2}$.

b. **Graph $m > 4$.**

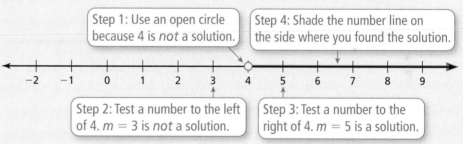

Step 1: Use an open circle because 4 is *not* a solution.

Step 4: Shade the number line on the side where you found the solution.

Step 2: Test a number to the left of 4. $m = 3$ is *not* a solution.

Step 3: Test a number to the right of 4. $m = 5$ is a solution.

Exercises

Write the word sentence as an inequality.

12. A number v is less than -2.

13. A number x minus $\frac{1}{4}$ is no more than $-\frac{3}{4}$.

Tell whether the given value is a solution of the inequality.

14. $10 - q < 3;\ q = 6$

15. $12 \div m \geq -4;\ m = -3$

Graph the inequality on a number line.

16. $p < 1.2$

17. $n > 10\frac{1}{4}$

1.6 **Solving One-Step Inequalities** *(pp. 36–43)*

a. Solve $x - 7 > -15$. Graph the solution.

$$x - 7 > -15$$ Write the inequality.

Undo the subtraction. → $\underline{+7 \quad +7}$ Add 7 to each side.

$$x > -8$$ Simplify.

∴ The solution is $x > -8$.

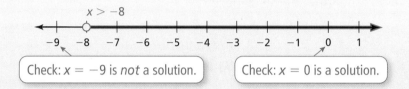

Check: $x = -9$ is *not* a solution. Check: $x = 0$ is a solution.

b. Solve $\dfrac{x}{-2} \le -3$. Graph the solution.

$$\frac{x}{-2} \le -3$$ Write the inequality.

Undo the division. → $-2 \cdot \dfrac{x}{-2} \ge -2 \cdot (-3)$ Multiply each side by -2. Reverse the inequality symbol.

$$x \ge 6$$ Simplify.

∴ The solution is $x \ge 6$.

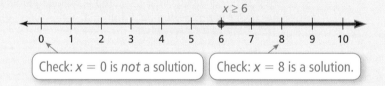

Check: $x = 0$ is *not* a solution. Check: $x = 8$ is a solution.

Exercises

Solve the inequality. Graph the solution.

18. $c + 13 \ge -3.7$ **19.** $8 < \dfrac{j}{-2.1}$ **20.** $\dfrac{1}{3} \le \dfrac{2}{9}m$

21. PARTY You host a party. You can spend no more than $100. Write and solve an inequality to find the number of guests you can invite to the party.

Cost per guest: $7

Review Game

Musical Toss

Big Ideas
Game Closet

For the Student
Additional Practice
- Lesson Tutorials
- Study Help (textbook)
- Student Website
  - Multi-Language Glossary
  - Practice Assessments

Materials
- soft object that can be tossed around
- a device to play music
- old homework, quiz, and test questions

Directions

Divide the class into pairs (groups of two).

Designate one pair of students to play the music and write the problems on the board. Pairs of students should be switched periodically.

The remaining members of the class will stand in a circle with each pair clearly identifiable.

When the music starts, the soft object is tossed to a pair of students and the problem is written on the board. That pair has to solve the problem and toss the object to another pair before the music stops.

Who wins?

The group holding the object when the music stops is eliminated. This will continue until there is one group remaining, the winner.

Answers

18. $c \geq -16.7$;

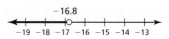

19. $j < -16.8$;

20. $m \geq \dfrac{3}{2}$;

21. $7x \leq 100$; $x \leq 14\dfrac{2}{7}$;

at most 14 guests

22. $x < 2$;

23. $z \geq -16$;

24. $w < -4$;

25. $q < 3$;

26. $p \geq -40$;

27. $k \geq 1.4$;

My Thoughts on the Chapter

What worked. . .

What did not work. . .

What I would do differently. . .

1.7 **Solving Two-Step Inequalities** *(pp. 44–49)*

a. Solve $2x - 3 \le -9$. Graph the solution.

$2x - 3 \le -9$	Write the inequality.

Step 1: Undo the subtraction.

$$\underline{+3 \quad +3}$$ Add 3 to each side.

$$2x \le -6$$ Simplify.

Step 2: Undo the multiplication.

$$\frac{2x}{2} \le \frac{-6}{2}$$ Divide each side by 2.

$$x \le -3$$ Simplify.

∴ The solution is $x \le -3$.

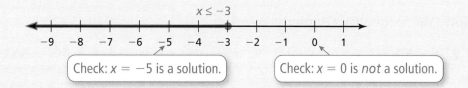

Check: $x = -5$ is a solution. Check: $x = 0$ is *not* a solution.

b. Solve $\dfrac{t}{-3} + 4 > 7$. Graph the solution.

$$\frac{t}{-3} + 4 > 7$$ Write the inequality.

Step 1: Undo the addition.

$$\underline{\phantom{\frac{t}{-3}}-4 \quad -4}$$ Subtract 4 from each side.

$$\frac{t}{-3} > 3$$ Simplify.

Step 2: Undo the division.

$$-3 \cdot \frac{t}{-3} < -3 \cdot 3$$ Multiply each side by -3. Reverse the inequality symbol.

$$t < -9$$ Simplify.

∴ The solution is $t < -9$.

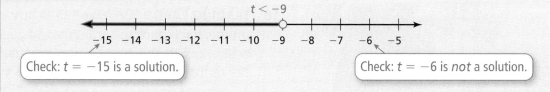

Check: $t = -15$ is a solution. Check: $t = -6$ is *not* a solution.

Exercises

Solve the inequality. Graph the solution.

22. $4x + 3 < 11$

23. $\dfrac{z}{-4} - 3 \le 1$

24. $-3w - 4 > 8$

25. $8(q + 2) < 40$

26. $-\dfrac{1}{2}(p + 4) \le 18$

27. $1.5(k + 3.2) \ge 6.9$

Check It Out
Test Practice
BigIdeasMath √com

Solve the equation. Check your solution.

1. $4 + y = 9.5$

2. $x - 3\pi = 5\pi$

3. $3.8n - 13 = 1.4n + 5$

Solve the formula for the red variable.

4. Perimeter of a rectangle: $P = 2\ell + 2w$

5. Distance formula: $d = rt$

Write the word sentence as an inequality.

6. A number j plus 20.5 is greater than or equal to 50.

7. A number r multiplied by $\frac{1}{7}$ is less than -14.

Solve the inequality. Graph the solution.

8. $n - 3 > -3$

9. $x - \frac{7}{8} \leq \frac{9}{8}$

10. $-6b \geq -30$

11. $\frac{y}{-4} \geq 13$

12. $3v - 7 \geq -13.3$

13. $-5(t + 11) < -60$

14. BASKETBALL Your basketball team wins a game by 13 points. The opposing team scores 72 points. Write and solve an equation to find your team's score.

Summer Care
Lawn Service
$8 per hour

15. JOBS Your profit for mowing lawns this week is $24. You paid $40 for gas for the lawnmower. How many hours did you work this week?

16. TRADING CARDS You have $25 to buy trading cards online. Each pack of cards costs $4.50. Shipping costs $2.95. Write and solve an inequality to find the number of packs of trading cards you can buy.

17. SCIENCE QUIZZES The table shows your scores on four science quizzes. What score do you need on the fifth quiz to have a mean score of at least 80?

Quiz	1	2	3	4	5
Score (%)	76	87	73	72	?

Test Item References

Chapter Test Questions	Section to Review
1, 2, 14	1.1
15	1.2
3	1.3
4, 5	1.4
6, 7	1.5
8–11	1.6
12, 13, 16, 17	1.7

Test-Taking Strategies

Remind students to quickly look over the entire test before they start so that they can budget their time. When working with equations, students need to write all numbers and variables clearly, line up terms in each step, and not crowd their work. When writing word phrases as inequalities, students can get confused by the subtle differences in wording. Encourage students to think carefully about which inequality symbol is implied by the wording. Have students use the **Stop** and **Think** strategy.

Common Assessment Errors

- **Exercises 1–3, 8–13** Students may perform the same operation that is in the equation or inequality instead of the inverse operation. Remind them that they must use an inverse operation to undo an operation.
- **Exercises 4 and 5** Students may be unsure how to solve for the specified variable. Point out that they should work through the order of operations *backwards*, using inverse operations to isolate the variable.
- **Exercises 6 and 7** Students may not use the correct inequality symbol. Remind them to put the word sentence into a real-life context.
- **Exercises 8–13** Remind students that they only reverse the direction of the inequality symbol when they are multiplying or dividing by a negative number.
- **Exercises 8–13** Students may use the wrong circle and/or shade the wrong side of the number line. Remind them to test a value on each side of the circle.

Reteaching and Enrichment Strategies

If students need help. . .	If students got it. . .

Resources by Chapter
  • Practice A and Practice B
  • Puzzle Time
Record and Practice Journal Practice
Differentiating the Lesson
Lesson Tutorials
Practice from the Test Generator
Skills Review Handbook
	Resources by Chapter
	  • Enrichment and Extension
	  • School-to-Work
	  • Financial Literacy
	  • Technology Connection
	  • Life Connections
	Game Closet at *BigIdeasMath.com*
	Start Standardized Test Practice

Answers

1. $y = 5.5$

2. $x = 8\pi$

3. $n = 7.5$

4. $w = \dfrac{P}{2} - \ell$

5. $r = \dfrac{d}{t}$

6. $j + 20.5 \geq 50$

7. $\dfrac{1}{7}r < -14$

8. $n > 0$;

9. $x \leq 2$;

10. $b \leq 5$;

11. $y \leq -52$;

12–13. See Additional Answers.

14. $x - 13 = 72$; $x = 85$ points

15. 8 hours

16. $4.5x + 2.95 \leq 25$; $x \leq 4.9$; at most 4 packs of trading cards

17. at least 92%

Assessment Book

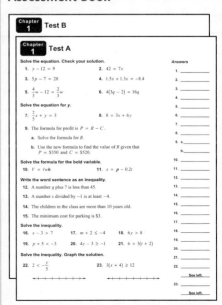

After Answering Easy Questions, Relax
Answer Easy Questions First
Estimate the Answer
Read All Choices before Answering
Read Question before Answering
Solve Directly or Eliminate Choices
Solve Problem before Looking at
   Choices
Use Intelligent Guessing
Work Backwards

About this Strategy

When taking a multiple choice test, be sure to read each question carefully and thoroughly. Before answering a question, determine exactly what is being asked, then eliminate the wrong answers and select the best choice.

Answers

1. A
2. I
3. D
4. 5 yd
5. G

Item Analysis

1. **A.** Correct answer

   B. The student subtracts 4 from 32 instead of dividing 32 by 4.

   C. The student adds 4 to 32 instead of dividing 32 by 4.

   D. The student multiplies 4 and 32 instead of dividing 32 by 4.

2. **F.** The student correctly subtracts 3 from 39, but then multiplies instead of dividing.

   G. The student correctly subtracts 3 from 39, but then subtracts 2 instead of dividing.

   H. The student incorrectly adds 3 and 39 instead of subtracting, then performs division correctly.

   I. Correct answer

3. **A.** The student mishandles the fraction, multiplying by $\frac{1}{4}$ instead of dividing.

   B. The student finds the number of teaspoons instead of quarter-teaspoons in the bottle.

   C. The student adds 6 and 4 instead of multiplying, then works correctly.

   D. Correct answer

4. **Gridded Response:** Correct answer: 5 yd

   Common Error: The student correctly calculates 15 feet as the distance traveled in 1 second, but fails to convert feet to yards.

5. **F.** The student moves r over in the equation instead of dividing both sides by r.

   G. Correct answer

   H. The student subtracts r instead of dividing by r.

   I. The student divides r by d and moves t to the other side of the equal sign instead of dividing d by r.

6. **A.** The student misunderstands that $3x$ and 5 are not like terms.

   B. Correct answer

   C. The student does not realize that the Distributive Property must first be used to multiply 2 by $x + 7$.

   D. The student does not realize that the Distributive Property must first be used to multiply 2 by $x + 7$.

Standardized Test Practice Icons

 Gridded Response

 Short Response (2-point rubric)

 Extended Response (4-point rubric)

1. Which value of x makes the equation true?

$$4x = 32$$

A. 8   **C.** 36

B. 28   **D.** 128

2. A taxi ride costs $3 plus $2 for each mile driven. When you rode in a taxi, the total cost was $39. This can be modeled by the equation below, where m represents the number of miles driven.

$$2m + 3 = 39$$

How long was your taxi ride?

F. 72 mi   **H.** 21 mi

G. 34 mi   **I.** 18 mi

Test-Taking Strategy

Solve Directly or Eliminate Choices

When a cat wakes up, it's grumpy for x hours, where $2x - 5x = x - 4$. What's x?

Ⓐ 0 Ⓑ 1 Ⓒ 2 Ⓓ -3

Don't talk to me until I've had my morning milk.

"You can eliminate A and D. Then, solve directly to determine that the correct answer is B."

3. One fluid ounce (fl oz) contains 6 teaspoons. You add $\frac{1}{4}$ teaspoon of vanilla each time you make hot chocolate. How many times can you make hot chocolate using the bottle of vanilla shown?

A. 6   **C.** 40

B. 24   **D.** 96

4. A bicyclist is riding at a speed of 900 feet per minute. How many yards does the bicyclist ride in 1 second?

5. The formula below relates distance, rate, and time.

$$d = rt$$

Solve this formula for t.

F. $t = dr$ **H.** $t = d - r$

G. $t = \dfrac{d}{r}$ **I.** $t = \dfrac{r}{d}$

6. What could be the first step to solve the equation shown below?

$$3x + 5 = 2(x + 7)$$

A. Combine $3x$ and 5.

C. Subtract x from $3x$.

B. Multiply x by 2 and 7 by 2.

D. Subtract 5 from 7.

7. You work as a sales representative. You earn $400 per week plus 5% of your total sales for the week.

Part A Last week, you had total sales of $5000. Find your total earnings. Show your work.

Part B One week, you earned $1350. Let s represent your total sales that week. Write an equation that could be used to find s.

Part C Using your equation from Part B, find s. Show all steps clearly.

8. In ten years, Maria will be 39 years old. Let m represent Maria's age today. Which equation can be used to find m?

F. $m = 39 + 10$

H. $m + 10 = 39$

G. $m - 10 = 39$

I. $10m = 39$

9. Which value of y makes the equation below true?

$$3y + 8 = 7y + 11$$

A. -4.75

C. 0.75

B. -0.75

D. 4.75

10. The equation below is used to convert a Fahrenheit temperature F to its equivalent Celsius temperature C.

$$C = \frac{5}{9}(F - 32)$$

Which formula can be used to convert a Celsius temperature to its equivalent Fahrenheit temperature?

F. $F = \frac{5}{9}(C - 32)$

H. $F = \frac{9}{5}C + \frac{32}{5}$

G. $F = \frac{9}{5}(C + 32)$

I. $F = \frac{9}{5}C + 32$

Item Analysis (continued)

7. **4 points** The student demonstrates a thorough understanding of evaluating expressions, writing equations, and solving equations, and presents his or her steps clearly. The following answers should be obtained: Part A: $650; Part B: $0.05s + 400 = 1350$; Part C: $19,000.

   3 points The student demonstrates an essential but less than thorough understanding. In particular, the correct equation or its equivalent should be given in Part B, but an arithmetic error may have been performed in Part C.

   2 points The student demonstrates a partial understanding of the processes of writing and solving equations. Part A should be correctly completed, but the equation in Part B may be written incorrectly. Alternatively, the correct equation could be written in Part B, but Part C might display misunderstanding of how to proceed.

   1 point The student demonstrates a limited understanding of equation writing and solving, as well as working with percents. The student's response is incomplete and exhibits many flaws.

   0 points The student provided no response, a completely incorrect or incomprehensible response, or a response that demonstrates insufficient understanding of percents and equations.

8. **F.** The student misunderstands the problem and decides to add the two numbers together.

   G. The student gets the idea that m and 39 are 10 apart, but chose subtraction instead of addition to relate them.

   H. Correct answer

   I. The student mistakes $10m$ for $10 + m$.

9. **A.** The student adds 8 and 11 instead of subtracting, and either misplaces a negative sign when subtracting $3x$ and $7x$ or performs a sign error when dividing.

   B. Correct answer

   C. The student subtracts 8 and 11 correctly, but then misplaces a negative sign when subtracting $3x$ and $7x$ or performs a sign error when dividing.

   D. The student adds 8 and 11 instead of subtracting.

10. **F.** The student simply interchanges the variables.

    G. The student "inverts" the variables, the fraction, and the subtraction.

    H. The student correctly multiplies both sides of the equation by $\frac{9}{5}$, but also incorrectly applies operations to 32.

    I. Correct answer

11. **Gridded Response:** Correct answer: 14 weeks

    Common Error: The student adds 35 and 175 to get 210, then divides by 10 to get 21 as an answer.

Answers

6. B

7. *Part A* $650

   Part B $0.05s + 400 = 1350$

   Part C $19,000

8. H

9. B

10. I

Answers

11. 14 weeks

12. D

13. I

14. A

Answer for Extra Example

1. **A.** The student multiplies 4 by 0.95 but does not carry out the multiplication correctly.

   B. Correct answer

   C. The student divides 4 by 0.95 instead of multiplying.

   D. The student adds 4 and 0.95.

Item Analysis (continued)

12. **A.** The student multiplies by 12 because there are 12 inches in 1 foot.

    B. The student realizes that volume requires accounting for "12 inches = 1 foot" three times, but adds the factors instead of multiplying them.

    C. The student finds the number of square inches in 1 square foot.

    D. Correct answer

13. **F.** The student distributes correctly but then makes a mistake combining the constant terms, yielding $2x = -11$.

    G. The student does not distribute the left side of the equation correctly, yielding $6x - 3$.

    H. The student combines $6x$ and $4x$ incorrectly, yielding $10x$ instead of $2x$.

    I. Correct answer

14. **A.** Correct answer

    B. The student incorrectly uses the fact that there are 4 items on one side and 2 on the other to get the ratio $\frac{2}{4} = \frac{1}{2}$.

    C. The student incorrectly uses the fact that there are 4 items on one side and 2 on the other to get the ratio $\frac{2}{4} = \frac{1}{2}$, and then misuses the order of the ratio.

    D. The student gets the correct ratio of $\frac{1}{3}$, but misuses it.

Extra Example for Standardized Test Practice

1. Which of the following best completes the table below?

1 quart ≈ 0.95 liters	
1 gallon = 4 quarts	
1 gallon ≈ ☐ liters	

   A. 3.6   **C.** 4.21

   B. 3.8   **D.** 4.95

11. You have already saved \$35 for a new cell phone. You need \$175 in all. You think you can save \$10 per week. At this rate, how many more weeks will you need to save money before you can buy the new cell phone?

12. The cube shown below has edge lengths of 1 foot. What is the volume of the cube?

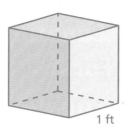

1 ft

A. 12 in.^{3} **C.** 144 in.^{3}

B. 36 in.^{3} **D.** 1728 in.^{3}

13. Which value of x makes the equation below true?

$$6(x - 3) = 4x - 7$$

F. -5.5 **H.** 1.1

G. -2 **I.** 5.5

14. The drawing below shows equal weights on two sides of a balance scale.

What can you conclude from the drawing?

A. A mug weighs one-third as much as a trophy.

B. A mug weighs one-half as much as a trophy.

C. A mug weighs twice as much as a trophy.

D. A mug weighs three times as much as a trophy.

2 Graphing and Writing Linear Equations

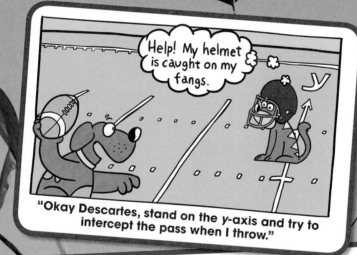

"Okay Descartes, stand on the y-axis and try to intercept the pass when I throw."

"Here's an easy example of a line with a slope of 1."

"You eat one mouse treat the first day. Two treats the second day. And so on. Get it?"

Strands Development

6th Grade

- Identify the coordinates of a point in the coordinate plane.
- Graph ordered pairs in the coordinate plane.
- Describe and compare data using ratios, and use appropriate notations, such as $\frac{a}{b}$, a to b, and $a : b$.
- Investigate and describe fractions, decimals, and percents as ratios.

7th Grade

- Represent relationships with tables, graphs, rules, and words.
- Solve single-step and multistep practical problems using proportional reasoning.

8th Grade

- Graph a linear equation in two variables.
- Solve practical problems involving rational numbers, percents, ratios, and proportions.

Math in History

There are two uses of the number 0 in mathematics.

★ Zero can be used as a place holder in a number system. For instance, the numbers 27 and 207 are different. The Mayans used zero in this way.

★ Zero can also be used to represent a number on the number line. The properties of 0, such as "the sum of zero and a number is that number" were described by Indian mathematicians over 3000 years ago.

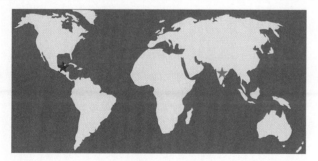

Pacing Guide for Chapter 2

Chapter Opener	1 Day
Section 1	
Activity	1 Day
Lesson	1 Day
Section 2	
Activity	1 Day
Lesson	1 Day
Section 3	
Activity	1 Day
Lesson	1 Day
Section 4	
Activity	1 Day
Lesson	1 Day
Study Help / Quiz	1 Day
Section 5	
Activity	1 Day
Lesson	1 Day
Section 6	
Activity	1 Day
Lesson	1 Day
Section 7	
Activity	1 Day
Lesson	1 Day
Section 8	
Activity	2 Days
Lesson	1 Day
Chapter Review / Tests	2 Days
Total Chapter 2	21 Days
Year-to-Date	42 Days

Check Your Resources

- Record and Practice Journal
- Resources by Chapter
- Skills Review Handbook
- Assessment Book
- Worked-Out Solutions

Technology For the Teacher

Dynamic Classroom

The Dynamic Planning Tool
Editable Teacher's Resources at
BigIdeasMath.com

Standards of Learning

6.11(a) The student will identify the coordinates of a point in a coordinate plane.

7.13(b) The student will evaluate algebraic expressions for given replacement values of the variables.

Additional Topics for Review

- Order of Operations
- Exponents
- Plotting points in Quadrant I

Try It Yourself

1. -12
2. -23

3. 15
4. $4\frac{3}{4}$

5. $(0, 4)$
6. $(4, 2)$

7. Point R
8. Point N

Record and Practice Journal

1. 5
2. 16

3. -5
4. $-38\frac{1}{2}$

5. 108
6. 65

7. $-3\frac{7}{19}$
8. 262

9. $\$50.00$

10. $(-5, 0)$
11. $(3, -5)$

12. Point F
13. Point G

14. Point B, Point H

15. Point C, Point E

16–20.

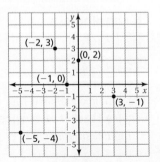

Math Background Notes

Vocabulary Review

- Evaluate
- Substitute
- Expression
- Coordinates
- Order of Operations

Evaluating Expressions Using Order of Operations

- Students should know how to substitute values into algebraic expressions and evaluate the results using order of operations.
- **Teaching Tip:** Sometimes color coding substitutions can help students to evaluate expressions. Each time you want to substitute a number in place of a variable, you must substitute your lead pencil for a colored pencil.
- Remind students that after they substitute values in for x and y, they must use the correct order of operations to continue simplifying the expression.
- **Common Error:** Encourage students to use a set of parentheses whenever they do a substitution. This will help students distinguish between subtracting 7 and multiplying by -7.

Plotting Points

- Students should know how to plot points in all four quadrants.
- **Common Error:** Students may write the coordinates backwards. Remind them that coordinates are written in alphabetical order with the x move (horizontal) written before the y move (vertical).
- **Common Error:** Students may also have difficulty with the negative numbers associated with plotting outside Quadrant I. Remind them that the negatives are directional. A negative x-value communicates a move to the left of the origin and a negative y-coordinate communicates a move downward from the origin.

Reteaching and Enrichment Strategies

If students need help. . .	If students got it. . .
Record and Practice Journal • Fair Game Review Skills Review Handbook Lesson Tutorials	Game Closet at *BigIdeasMath.com* Start the next section

What You Learned Before

"I estimate that we are on a slope of about −0.625. What do you think?"

Evaluating Expressions Using Order of Operations

Example 1 Evaluate $2xy + 3(x + y)$ when $x = 4$ and $y = 7$.

$$2xy + 3(x + y) = 2(4)(7) + 3(4 + 7)$$ Substitute 4 for x and 7 for y.
$$= 8(7) + 3(4 + 7)$$ Use order of operations.
$$= 56 + 3(11)$$ Simplify.
$$= 56 + 33$$ Multiply.
$$= 89$$ Add.

Try It Yourself

Evaluate the expression when $a = \dfrac{1}{4}$ and $b = 6$.

1. $-8ab$

2. $16a^2 - 4b$

3. $\dfrac{5b}{32a^2}$

4. $12a + (b - a - 4)$

Plotting Points

Example 2 Write the ordered pair that corresponds to Point U.

Point U is 3 units to the left of the origin and 4 units down. So, the x-coordinate is -3 and the y-coordinate is -4.

∴ The ordered pair $(-3, -4)$ corresponds to Point U.

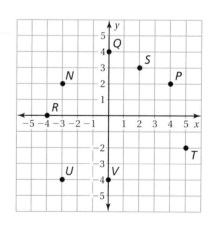

Example 3 Which point is located at $(5, -2)$?

Start at the origin. Move 5 units right and 2 units down.

∴ Point T is located at $(5, -2)$.

Try It Yourself

Use the graph to answer the question.

5. Write the ordered pair that corresponds to Point Q.

6. Write the ordered pair that corresponds to Point P.

7. Which point is located at $(-4, 0)$?

8. Which point is located in Quadrant II?

2.1 Graphing Linear Equations

STANDARDS OF LEARNING

8.16

Essential Question How can you recognize a linear equation? How can you draw its graph?

1 ACTIVITY: Graphing a Linear Equation

Work with a partner.

a. Use the equation $y = \frac{1}{2}x + 1$ to complete the table. (Choose any two x-values and find the y-values.)

	Solution Points		
x			
$y = \frac{1}{2}x + 1$			

b. Write the two ordered pairs given by the table. These are called **solution points** of the equation.

c. Plot the two solution points. Draw a line *exactly* through the two points.

d. Find a different point on the line. Check that this point is a solution point of the equation $y = \frac{1}{2}x + 1$.

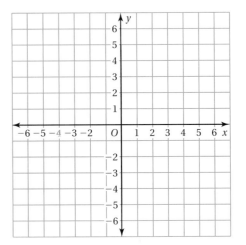

e. **GENERALIZE** Do you think it is true that *any* point on the line is a solution point of the equation $y = \frac{1}{2}x + 1$? Explain.

f. Choose five additional x-values for the table. (Choose positive and negative x-values.) Plot the five corresponding solution points. Does each point lie on the line?

	Solution Points				
x					
$y = \frac{1}{2}x + 1$					

g. **GENERALIZE** Do you think it is true that *any* solution point of the equation $y = \frac{1}{2}x + 1$ is a point on the line? Explain.

h. **THE MEANING OF A WORD** Why is $y = ax + b$ called a *linear equation*?

Laurie's Notes

Introduction

For the Teacher

- **Goal:** Students will use solution points to graph linear equations.
- In honor of René Descartes, the coordinate plane is often called the *Cartesian plane*.
- Throughout this chapter, you may encounter applications that show a graph of discrete data with a line through the points. At this point in the text, we do not think it is necessary for students to distinguish between discrete data (plotting points only) and continuous data (plotting points along with the line). Students can draw a line through discrete points to help them solve an exercise. They will learn more about discrete and continuous data at a later time.

Motivate

- Play a game of coordinate BINGO.
- Distribute small coordinate grids to students. They should plot ten ordered pairs, where the *x*- and *y*-coordinates are integers between −4 and 4.
- Generate a random ordered pair in the grid. Write the integers from −4 to 4 on slips of paper and place them in a bag. Draw and replace an integer twice to generate the ordered pair, then write it on the board.
- Each time you record a new ordered pair, the students check to see if it is one of their 10 ordered pairs. If it is, they put an X there. The goal is to be the first person with three X's. If a student thinks they have won, they read their ordered pairs for you to check against the master list.
- **?** "Are there ordered pairs that are not on lattice points, meaning the *x*- or *y*-coordinate is not an integer? Explain." yes; It's possible for the ordered pair to be $\left(3.5, \frac{1}{2}\right)$. Plot whatever example students give.
- Remind students that the ordered pairs are always (*x*, *y*), where *x* is the horizontal direction and *y* is the vertical direction.

Activity Notes

Activity 1

- Some students will recognize right away that if they substitute an even number for *x*, the *y*-coordinate will not be a fraction. It is likely that students will only try positive *x*-values. Encourage them to try negative values for *x*.
- In part (d), suggest that students consider only those ordered pairs that appear to be lattice points.
- Listen and discuss student responses to the generalizations in parts (e) and (g).
- **Big Idea:** The goal of this activity is for students to recognize and understand two related, but different, ideas. 1) *All* solution points of a linear equation lie on the same line. 2) *All* points on the line are solution points of the equation.

Standards of Learning

8.16 The student will graph a linear equation in two variables.

Previous Learning

Students should know about slope as a ratio. Students should know how to plot ordered pairs.

Activity Materials	
Introduction	**Textbook**
• small coordinate grid	• straightedge

Start Thinking! and Warm Up

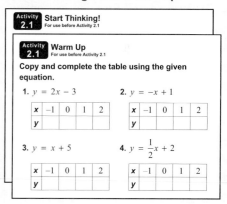

2.1 Record and Practice Journal

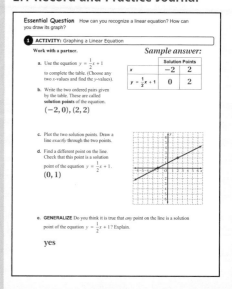

Differentiated Instruction

Kinesthetic

For students that are kinesthetic learners and have difficulty in plotting points in the coordinate plane, suggest they use a finger for tracing. Have the student place their finger at the origin and trace left or right along the *x*-axis to the first coordinate, then trace up or down to the second coordinate. Students should also practice writing the ordered pair of a plotted point. Guide students with questions such as, "Should you move left or right? How far? Should you move up or down? How far?"

2.1 Record and Practice Journal

f. Choose five additional *x*-values for the table. (Choose positive and negative *x*-values.) Plot the five corresponding solution points on the previous page. Does each point lie on the line? **Sample answer:**

Solution Points					
x	−6	−4	1	4	6
$y = \frac{1}{2}x + 1$	−2	−1	$1\frac{1}{2}$	3	4

g. **GENERALIZE** Do you think it is true that *any* solution point of the equation $y = \frac{1}{2}x + 1$ is a point on the line? Explain.

yes

h. **THE MEANING OF A WORD** Why is $y = ax + b$ called a *linear equation*?

The graph is a line.

2 HISTORY: Analytic Geometry

René Descartes was a French philosopher, scientist, and mathematician.

Up until the time of Descartes, *algebra* and *geometry* were separate fields of mathematics. Descartes's invention of the coordinate plane was of huge importance to mathematics. For the first time, people could "see" solutions of equations. No longer did people have to work with algebra from a purely symbolic point of view.

René Descartes (1596–1650)

Descartes's combination of geometry and algebra is called *analytic* (or algebraic) *geometry.* One of the main discoveries in analytic geometry is that all of the important types of graphs (lines, parabolas, circles, ellipses, and so on) can be represented by simple algebraic equations.

Within a few dozen years, other mathematicians were able to discover all of *calculus,* a field of mathematics that is of great value in business, science, and engineering.

In this book, you will study lines. In Algebra 1 and Algebra 2, you will study many other types of equations.

Line: $y = ax + b$ Parabola: $y = ax^2 + b$ Circle: $x^2 + y^2 = r^2$

What Is Your Answer?

3. **IN YOUR OWN WORDS** How can you recognize a linear equation? How can you draw its graph? Write an equation that is linear. Write an equation that is *not* linear.

The form $y = ax + b$ and its graph is a line; find solution points and draw a line through them.

4. Are you a visual learner? Most people can learn mathematics more easily when they see "pictures" of the mathematics. Why do you think Descartes's invention was important to mathematics?

Check students' work.

Laurie's Notes

History 2

- This activity gives students a broader perspective about graphing in the Cartesian plane. Ask volunteers to read this information aloud.
- **FYI:** Many articles have been written about Descartes and in most of them it is reported that Descartes was not healthy in his youth. Because of his delicate health, he was permitted to lie in bed until late morning. This was a custom which he followed until adulthood.

  It is reported that Descartes' invention of the coordinate plane, as a means of connecting algebra and geometry, came to him during a dream on November 10, 1619 while he was serving as a soldier in the army.
- **Extension:** Have students write a short report on a famous mathematician.

What Is Your Answer?

- Discuss students' responses to each question.

Closure

- Find three ordered pairs that are solutions of the equation $y = 2x - 3$. Draw the graph of the line. *Sample answer:* $(-1, -5)$, $(0, -3)$, and $(1, -1)$

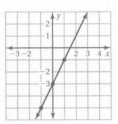

Technology For the Teacher

Dynamic Classroom

The Dynamic Planning Tool
Editable Teacher's Resources at *BigIdeasMath.com*

René Descartes was a French philosopher, scientist, and mathematician.

Up until the time of Descartes, *algebra* and *geometry* were separate fields of mathematics. Descartes's invention of the coordinate plane was of huge importance to mathematics. For the first time, people could "see" solutions of equations. No longer did people have to work with algebra from a purely symbolic point of view.

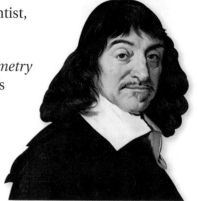

René Descartes (1596–1650)

That's my name too.

Descartes's combination of geometry and algebra is called *analytic* (or algebraic) *geometry*. One of the main discoveries in analytic geometry is that all of the important types of graphs (lines, parabolas, circles, ellipses, and so on) can be represented by simple algebraic equations.

Within a few dozen years, other mathematicians were able to discover all of *calculus*, a field of mathematics that is of great value in business, science, and engineering.

In this book, you will study lines. In Algebra 1 and Algebra 2, you will study many other types of equations.

Line: $y = ax + b$

Parabola: $y = ax^2 + b$

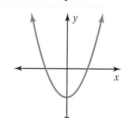

Circle: $x^2 + y^2 = r^2$

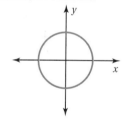

What Is Your Answer?

3. **IN YOUR OWN WORDS** How can you recognize a linear equation? How can you draw its graph? Write an equation that is linear. Write an equation that is *not* linear.

4. Are you a visual learner? Most people can learn mathematics more easily when they see "pictures" of the mathematics. Why do you think Descartes's invention was important to mathematics?

Use what you learned about graphing linear equations to complete Exercises 3 and 4 on page 66.

Check It Out
Lesson Tutorials
BigIdeasMath com

Key Vocabulary
linear equation, p. 64
solution of a linear
equation, p. 64

Remember

An ordered pair (x, y) is used to locate a point in a coordinate plane.

 **Key Idea**

Linear Equations

A **linear equation** is an equation whose graph is a line. The points on the line are **solutions** of the equation.

You can use a graph to show the solutions of a linear equation. The graph below is for the equation $y = x + 1$.

x	y	(x, y)
−1	0	(−1, 0)
0	1	(0, 1)
2	3	(2, 3)

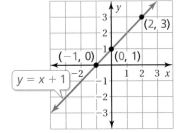

EXAMPLE 1 Graphing a Linear Equation

Graph $y = -2x + 1$.

Step 1: Make a table of values.

x	y = −2x + 1	y	(x, y)
−1	$y = -2(-1) + 1$	3	(−1, 3)
0	$y = -2(0) + 1$	1	(0, 1)
2	$y = -2(2) + 1$	−3	(2, −3)

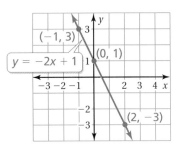

Step 2: Plot the ordered pairs.

Step 3: Draw a line through the points.

 Key Idea

Graphing a Horizontal Line

The graph of $y = a$ is a horizontal line passing through $(0, a)$.

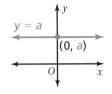

Multi-Language Glossary at BigIdeasMath com.

Laurie's Notes

Introduction

Connect

- **Yesterday:** Students explored the graphs of linear equations.
- **Today:** Students will graph linear equations using a table of values.

Motivate

- Discuss a fact about wind speeds related to Example 3. During a wild April storm in 1934, a wind gust of 231 miles per hour (372 kilometers per hour) pushed across the summit of Mt. Washington in New Hampshire. This wind speed still stands as the all-time surface wind speed record.

Lesson Notes

Key Idea

- Define *linear equation* and *solutions* of the equation.
- Note the use of color in the input-output table. The equation used is a simple equation that helps students focus on the representation of the solutions as ordered pairs. The *y*-coordinate is always 1 greater than the *x*-coordinate, just as the equation states.

Example 1

? As a quick review, ask a volunteer to review the rules for integer multiplication. If the factors have the same signs, the product is positive. If the factors have different signs, the product is negative.

- Write the 4-column table. Take the time to show how the *x*-coordinate is being substituted in the second column. The number in blue is the only quantity that varies (variable); the other quantities are always the same (constant). Values from the first and third columns form the ordered pair.

? "From the graph, can you estimate the solution when $x = \frac{1}{2}$? Verify your answer by evaluating the equation when $x = \frac{1}{2}$." yes; $\left(\frac{1}{2}, 0\right)$

Key Idea

- Students are sometimes confused by the equation $y = a$. Explain to students that a is a variable. It can equal any number.
- **Teaching Tip:** Another way to discuss the equation $y = a$ is to say that "y always equals a certain number, while x can equal anything." For example, if $y = -4$, the table of values will look like this:

x	-1	0	1	2
y	-4	-4	-4	-4

Start Thinking! and Warm Up

> **Lesson 2.1** Warm Up
> For use before Lesson 2.1
>
> **Lesson 2.1** Start Thinking!
> For use before Lesson 2.1
>
> Think about how much energy you have on an average day.
>
> Graph your energy level (on a scale of 0 to 10) throughout an average day.
>
> Are any sections of your graph linear?

Extra Example 1

Graph $y = \frac{1}{2}x - 3$.

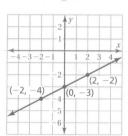

Extra Example 2

Graph $y = 4$.

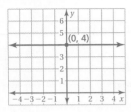

On Your Own

1–4. See Additional Answers.

Extra Example 3

The cost y (in dollars) for making friendship bracelets is $y = 0.5x + 2$, where x is the number of bracelets.

a. Graph the equation.

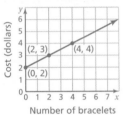

b. How many bracelets can be made for $10? 16

On Your Own

5. 8 hours after it enters the Gulf of Mexico

English Language Learners

Vocabulary

Make sure students understand that the graph of a *linear* equation is a *line*. Only two points are needed to graph a line, but if one of the points is incorrect the wrong line will be graphed. Plotting three points for a line in the coordinate plane and making sure that the points form a line provides students with a check when graphing.

Laurie's Notes

Example 2

? "What are other points on the line $y = -3$?" *Sample answer:* $(5, -3)$, or anything of the form $(x, -3)$

On Your Own

• Ask volunteers to share their graphs at the board.

Example 3

? "What does x represent in the problem? What does y represent?"
x = number of hours after the storm enters the Gulf of Mexico;
y = wind speed

• Work through the problem using the 4-column table to generate solutions of the equation.

• Note that the y-coordinate is much greater than the x-coordinate. For this reason, a broken vertical axis is used. Students should *not* scale the y-axis beginning at 0.

? "Why are only non-negative numbers substituted for x?" Because x equals the number of hours after the storm enters the Gulf of Mexico, you do not know if the equation makes sense for x-values before that.

• Note that the ordered pairs are all located in Quadrant I because x is a non-negative number. Even though this restriction was not stated explicitly, you know from reading the description of x that it needs to be non-negative.

• In part (b), help students read the graph. Starting with a y-value of 74 on the y-axis, trace horizontally until you reach the graph of the line, and then trace straight down (vertically) to the x-axis. The x-coordinate is 4.

On Your Own

• **Neighbor Check:** Have students work independently and then have their neighbor check their work. Have students discuss any discrepancies.

Closure

• Explain how you know if an equation is linear. *Sample answer:* The graph of the equation is a line.

Technology For the Teacher

Dynamic Classroom

The Dynamic Planning Tool
Editable Teacher's Resources at *BigIdeasMath.com*

EXAMPLE **2** **Graphing a Horizontal Line**

Graph $y = -3$.

The graph of $y = -3$ is a horizontal line passing through $(0, -3)$.

Plot $(0, -3)$. Draw a horizontal line through the point.

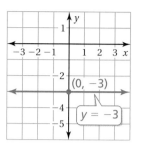

On Your Own

Now You're Ready
Exercises 5–13

Graph the linear equation.

1. $y = 3x$

2. $y = -\dfrac{1}{2}x + 2$

3. $y = \pi$

4. $y = -1.5$

EXAMPLE **3** **Real-Life Application**

The wind speed y (in miles per hour) of a tropical storm is $y = 2x + 66$, where x is the number of hours after the storm enters the Gulf of Mexico.

a. Graph the equation.

b. When does the storm become a hurricane?

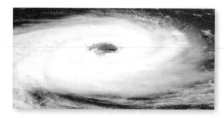

A tropical storm becomes a hurricane when wind speeds are at least 74 miles per hour.

a. Make a table of values.

x	$y = 2x + 66$	y	(x, y)
0	$y = 2(0) + 66$	66	$(0, 66)$
1	$y = 2(1) + 66$	68	$(1, 68)$
2	$y = 2(2) + 66$	70	$(2, 70)$
3	$y = 2(3) + 66$	72	$(3, 72)$

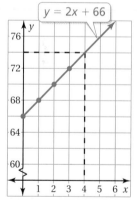

Plot the ordered pairs and draw a line through the points.

b. From the graph, you can see that $y = 74$ when $x = 4$.

∴ So, the storm becomes a hurricane 4 hours after it enters the Gulf of Mexico.

On Your Own

5. **WHAT IF?** In Example 3, the wind speed of the storm is $y = 1.5x + 62$. When does the storm become a hurricane?

 Vocabulary and Concept Check

1. **VOCABULARY** What type of graph represents the solutions of the equation $y = 2x + 3$?

2. **WHICH ONE DOESN'T BELONG?** Which equation does *not* belong with the other three? Explain your reasoning.

$$y = 0.5x - 0.2$$ $$4x + 3 = y$$ $$y = x^2 + 6$$ $$\frac{3}{4}x + \frac{1}{3} = y$$

 Practice and Problem Solving

Copy and complete the table. Plot the two solution points and draw a line *exactly* through the two points. Find a different solution point on the line.

3.

x		
$y = 3x - 1$		

4.

x		
$y = \frac{1}{3}x + 2$		

Graph the linear equation.

5. $y = -5x$

6. $y = \frac{1}{4}x$

7. $y = 5$

8. $y = x - 3$

9. $y = -7x - 1$

10. $y = -\frac{x}{3} + 4$

11. $y = \frac{3}{4}x - \frac{1}{2}$

12. $y = -\frac{2}{3}$

13. $y = 6.75$

14. **ERROR ANALYSIS** Describe and correct the error in graphing the equation.

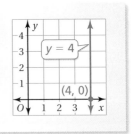

15. **MESSAGING** You sign up for an unlimited text messaging plan for your cell phone. The equation $y = 20$ represents the cost y (in dollars) for sending x text messages. Graph the equation.

16. **MAIL** The equation $y = 2x + 3$ represents the cost y (in dollars) of mailing a package that weighs x pounds.

   a. Graph the equation.

   b. Use the graph to estimate how much it costs to mail the package.

   c. Use the equation to find exactly how much it costs to mail the package.

Assignment Guide and Homework Check

Level	Day 1 Activity Assignment	Day 2 Lesson Assignment	Homework Check
Basic	3, 4, 25–29	1, 2, 5–19 odd, 14, 16	5, 7, 11, 16, 19
Average	3, 4, 25–29	1, 2, 9–14, 17, 19, 21, 22	11, 13, 19, 22
Advanced	3, 4, 25–29	1, 2, 10–24 even, 21, 23	10, 12, 18, 22

Common Errors

- **Exercises 5–13** Students may make a calculation error for one of the ordered pairs in a table of values. If they only find two ordered pairs for the graph, they may not recognize their mistake. Encourage them to find at least three ordered pairs when drawing a graph.
- **Exercises 7, 12, and 13** Students may draw a vertical line through a point on the x-axis instead of through the corresponding point on the y-axis. Remind them that the equation is a horizontal line. Ask them to identify the y-coordinate for several x-coordinates. For example, what is the y-coordinate for $x = 5$? $x = 6$? $x = -4$? Students should answer with the same y-coordinate each time.
- **Exercises 17–20** Students may make a mistake in solving for y, such as using the same operation instead of the opposite operation.

2.1 Record and Practice Journal

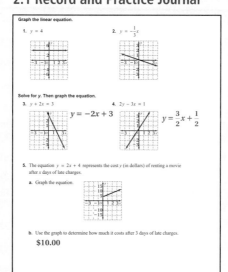

Vocabulary and Concept Check

1. a line
2. $y = x^2 + 6$ does not belong because it is not a linear equation.

Practice and Problem Solving

3. *Sample answer:*

x	0	1
$y = 3x - 1$	-1	2

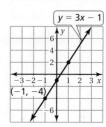

4. *Sample answer:*

x	0	3
$y = \dfrac{1}{3}x + 2$	2	3

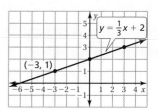

5.

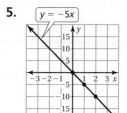

6–16. See Additional Answers.

Practice and Problem Solving

17. $y = 3x + 1$

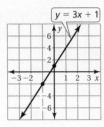

18–21. See Additional Answers.

22. See *Taking Math Deeper*.

23–24. See Additional Answers.

Fair Game Review

25. $(5, 3)$ **26.** $(-6, 6)$

27. $(2, -2)$ **28.** $(-4, -3)$

29. B

Mini-Assessment

Graph the linear equation.

1. Graph $y = -\dfrac{1}{2}x + 2$.

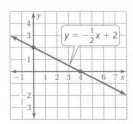

2. You have $100 in your savings account and plan to deposit $20 each month. Write and graph a linear equation that represents the balance in your account. $y = 20x + 100$

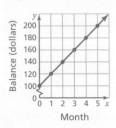

Taking Math Deeper

Exercise 22

Some of the information for this exercise is given in the photo and some is given in the text. It is a good idea to start by listing all of the given information.

 List the given information.
- The camera can store 250 pictures.
- 1 second of video = 2 pictures
- Video time used = 90 seconds
- Let y = number of pictures
- Let x = number of seconds of video

 a. Write and graph an equation for x and y.

$$y + 2x = 250$$
$$y = -2x + 250$$

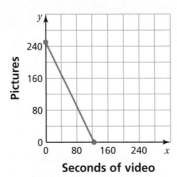

Graph it.

 b. Answer the question.

When $x = 90$, the value of y is as follows.

$$y = -2x + 250$$
$$= -2(90) + 250$$
$$= 70$$

Your camera can store 70 pictures.

Project

Research digital cameras. Find the number of pictures that can be stored on five different cameras. Compare the prices of the cameras. What do you consider to be the better buy? Why?

Reteaching and Enrichment Strategies

If students need help. . .	If students got it. . .
Resources by Chapter • Practice A and Practice B • Puzzle Time Record and Practice Journal Practice Differentiating the Lesson Lesson Tutorials Skills Review Handbook	Resources by Chapter • Enrichment and Extension Start the next section

Solve for y. Then graph the equation.

17. $y - 3x = 1$

18. $5x + 2y = 4$

19. $-\dfrac{1}{3}y + 4x = 3$

20. $x + 0.5y = 1.5$

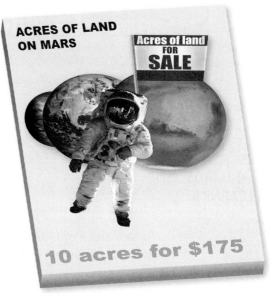

ACRES OF LAND ON MARS

Acres of land FOR SALE

10 acres for $175

21. SAVINGS You have $100 in your savings account and plan to deposit $12.50 each month.

   a. Write and graph a linear equation that represents the balance in your account.

   b. How many months will it take you to save enough money to buy 10 acres of land on Mars?

Video time: 1 min. 30 sec.

22. CAMERA One second of video on your digital camera uses the same amount of memory as two pictures. Your camera can store 250 pictures.

   a. Write and graph a linear equation that represents the number y of pictures your camera can store if you take x seconds of video.

   b. How many pictures can your camera store after you take the video shown?

23. SEA LEVEL Along the U.S. Atlantic Coast, the sea level is rising about 2 millimeters per year.

   a. Write and graph a linear equation that represents how much sea level rises over a period of time.

   b. How many millimeters has sea level risen since you were born?

24. **Geometry** The sum S of the measures of the angles of a polygon is $S = (n - 2) \cdot 180$, where n is the number of sides of the polygon. Plot four points (n, S) that satisfy the equation. Do the points lie on a line? Explain your reasoning.

 Fair Game Review What you learned in previous grades & lessons

Write the ordered pair corresponding to the point.
(Skills Review Handbook)

25. Point A

26. Point B

27. Point C

28. Point D

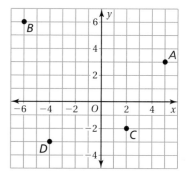

29. MULTIPLE CHOICE A debate team has 15 female members. The ratio of females to males is 3 : 2. How many males are on the debate team? *(Skills Review Handbook)*

   Ⓐ 6   **Ⓑ** 10   **Ⓒ** 22   **Ⓓ** 25

Essential Question How can the slope of a line be used to describe the line?

STANDARDS
OF LEARNING
8.3
8.16

Slope is the rate of change between any two points on a line. It is the measure of the *steepness* of the line.

To find the slope of a line, find the ratio of the change in *y* (vertical change) to the change in *x* (horizontal change).

$$\text{slope} = \frac{\text{change in } y}{\text{change in } x}$$

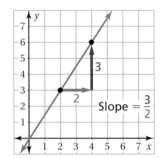

1 ACTIVITY: Finding the Slope of a Line

Work with a partner. Find the slope of each line using two methods.

> **Method 1:** Use the two black points. ●
>
> **Method 2:** Use the two pink points. ●

Do you get the same slope using each method?

a.

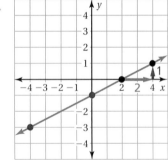

b.

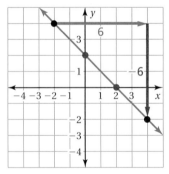

c.

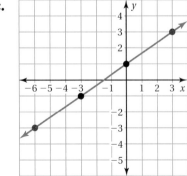

d.

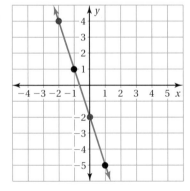

Laurie's Notes

Introduction

For the Teacher

- **Goal:** Students will learn that they can use any two points on a line to calculate the slope of that line.
- The formal definition of slope, when computed, uses subscripts $(y_2 - y_1)$. The subscript notation will be taught in a future course.

Motivate

- ❓ "How many of you have been on a roller coaster?"
- Discuss with students what makes one roller coaster more thrilling than another. Students will usually describe how quickly the coaster drops or the steepness of the hill. This is similar to the *change in y* of a line when finding the slope.

Activity Notes

Discuss

- ❓ "Does anyone remember what is meant by slope of a line?" At least one student should recall that it measures the steepness of a line.
- Write the definition for slope. Sketch the graph shown to demonstrate what is meant by change in *y* (red vertical arrow) and change in *x* (blue horizontal arrow).
- Remind students that slope is always the change in *y* in the numerator and the change in *x* in the denominator. This can be confusing for students because graphs are read from left to right, and we have a tendency to move in the *x*-direction first. For this reason, students want to write the change in *x* in the numerator.
- **Note:** In this book, the change in *x* will always be positive. However, you should show students that the change in *x* can be negative.
- ❓ "Can the change in *x* be negative? Explain." Yes; moving to the left horizontally is negative.
- ❓ "Can the change in *y* be negative? Explain." Yes; moving down vertically is negative.

Activity 1

- Encourage students to draw the change arrows for each pair of points. Label the change in *x* (or *y*) next to the arrow.
- **Big Idea:** The slope of a line is always the same regardless of what two ordered pairs are selected.
- **Common Error:** Students may forget to make the change negative when moving downward in the *y*-direction.

Standards of Learning

8.3(a) The student will solve practical problems involving rational numbers, percents, ratios, and proportions.
8.16 The student will graph a linear equation in two variables.

Previous Learning

Students should know that slope is the rate of change between two points on a line.

Start Thinking! and Warm Up

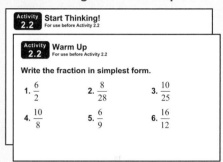

2.2 Record and Practice Journal

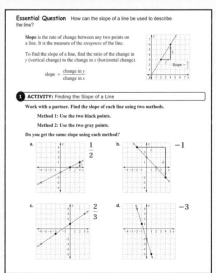

Differentiated Instruction

Kinesthetic

Help students develop number sense about slope. Have them draw lines in the coordinate plane through the following pairs of points.

(0, 0) and (3, 5)   (0, 0) and (3, 4)
(0, 0) and (3, 3)   (0, 0) and (3, 2)
(0, 0) and (3, 1)

Next have students find the slope of each line. Point out that the line passing through (3, 3) has a slope of 1. The lines with y-coordinates greater than 3 have a slope greater than 1. The lines with y-coordinates less than 3 have a slope less than 1. For positive slopes, the steeper lines will have a greater slope.

2.2 Record and Practice Journal

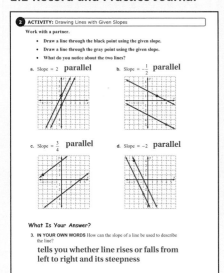

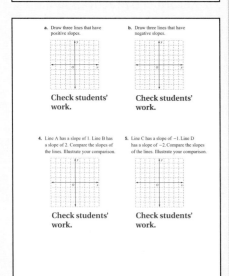

Laurie's Notes

Activity 2

- In addition to being able to determine the slope of a line that has been graphed, you want students to be able to draw a line that has a particular slope. This is the goal of Activity 2.

- **?** "What does it mean for a line to have a slope of $\frac{2}{3}$?" For every 2 units of change in the y-direction, there is a change of 3 units in the x-direction.

- **?** "What does it mean for a line to have a slope of -3?" For every -3 units of change in the y-direction, there is a change of 1 unit in the x-direction. This is the same as 3 units in the y-direction and -1 unit in the x-direction.

- Explain to students that $-3 = \frac{-3}{1} = \frac{3}{-1}$. Demonstrate what this means in a coordinate plane.

- **Teaching Tip:** If possible, give each pair of students two colored pencils. Have them draw the first line (through the black point) in one color and draw the second line (through the pink point) in the other color.

- **?** "What do you notice about the two lines you have drawn?" Students should observe that the lines are parallel. Students may also observe that the positive slopes rise (from left to right) and the negative slopes fall (from left to right).

- **Big Idea:** Slope is a measure of the steepness of a line. Two different lines with the same slope are parallel (they have the same steepness).

What Is Your Answer?

- Discuss student responses to each question. These are significant questions.

Closure

- Plot the point (0, 3). Draw the line through this point that has a slope of $\frac{1}{3}$. Name two points on the line. *Sample answer:* (3, 4), (−3, 2)

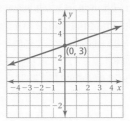

Technology
For
the **T**eacher

The Dynamic Planning Tool
Editable Teacher's Resources at *BigIdeasMath.com*

T-69

ACTIVITY: Drawing Lines with Given Slopes

Work with a partner.

- Draw a line through the black point using the given slope.

- Draw a line through the pink point using the given slope.

- What do you notice about the two lines?

a. Slope = 2

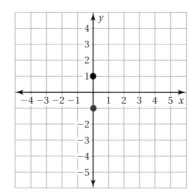

b. Slope = $-\dfrac{1}{2}$

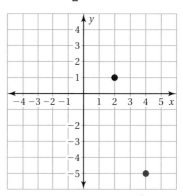

c. Slope = $\dfrac{3}{4}$

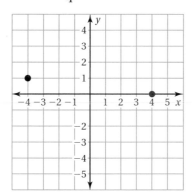

d. Slope = -2

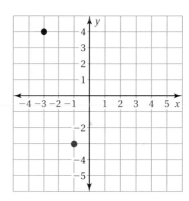

What Is Your Answer?

3. **IN YOUR OWN WORDS** How can the slope of a line be used to describe the line?

   a. Draw three lines that have positive slopes.

   b. Draw three lines that have negative slopes.

4. Line A has a slope of 1. Line B has a slope of 2. Compare the slopes of the lines. Illustrate your comparison.

5. Line C has a slope of −1. Line D has a slope of −2. Compare the slopes of the lines. Illustrate your comparison.

Practice

Use what you learned about the slope of a line to complete Exercises 4–6 on page 73.

Key Vocabulary 🔊
slope, p. 70
rise, p. 70
run, p. 70

🔑 Key Idea

Slope

The **slope** of a line is a ratio of the change in y (the **rise**) to the change in x (the **run**) between any two points on the line.

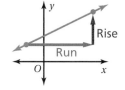

$$\text{slope} = \frac{\text{change in } y}{\text{change in } x} = \frac{\text{rise}}{\text{run}}$$

Positive slope   ***Negative slope***

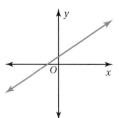   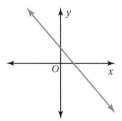

The line rises from left to right.   The line falls from left to right.

EXAMPLE ① **Finding the Slope of a Line**

Tell whether the slope of the line is *positive* or *negative.* Then find the slope.

a.

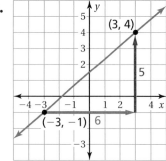

b.

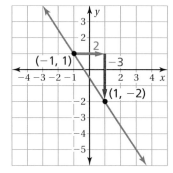

The line rises from left to right. So, the slope is positive.

$$\text{slope} = \frac{\text{rise}}{\text{run}}$$

$$= \frac{5}{6}$$

The line falls from left to right. So, the slope is negative.

$$\text{slope} = \frac{\text{rise}}{\text{run}}$$

$$= \frac{-3}{2}, \text{ or } -\frac{3}{2}$$

∴ The slope is $\frac{5}{6}$.   ∴ The slope is $-\frac{3}{2}$.

Laurie's Notes

Introduction

Connect

- **Yesterday:** Students explored slopes of lines.
- **Today:** Students will find the slopes of lines in a variety of contexts.

Motivate

- Have students plot four points: $A(5, 0)$, $B(0, 5)$, $C(-5, 0)$, and $D(0, -5)$. Connect the points to form the quadrilateral *ABCD*.
- ❓ "What type of quadrilateral is *ABCD*?" Without proof, students should say square.
- ❓ "What is the slope of each side, meaning the slopes of the lines through *AB*, *BC*, *CD*, and *DA*?" Slopes of *AB* and *CD* are both -1. Slopes of *BC* and *DA* are both 1.
- ❓ "If you drew another square inside *ABCD* that had one vertex at $(0, 3)$, could you predict what the slopes of the four sides would be?" Students should be able to visualize this and predict that two sides would have a slope of 1 and two sides would have a slope of -1.

Lesson Notes

Key Idea

- Write the Key Idea. Define slope of a line.
- Note the use of color in the definition and on the graph. The *change in y* and the *vertical change arrow* are both red. The *change in x* and the *horizontal change arrow* are both blue.
- Discuss the difference in positive and negative slopes, a concept students explored yesterday.
- Remind students that graphs are read from left to right.

Example 1

- Work through each part. The arrows, words, and numbers are color-coded.
- Students often ask if they can move in the *y*-direction first, followed by the *x*-direction. The answer is yes. Demonstrate this on either graph.
  - In part (a), start at $(-3, -1)$ and move up 5 units in the *y*-direction and then to the right 6 units in the *x*-direction. You will end at $(3, 4)$.
  - In part (b), start at $(-1, 1)$ and move down 3 units in the *y*-direction and then to the right 2 units in the *x*-direction. You will end at $(1, -2)$.

Start Thinking! and Warm Up

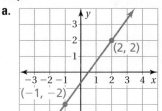

Lesson 2.2 Warm Up
For use before Lesson 2.2

Lesson 2.2 Start Thinking!
For use before Lesson 2.2

1. Each student must choose an ordered pair.

2. Choose a partner and work together to find the slope of the line joining your two points. Use a graph to help you.

3. Repeat the process several times with different partners.

Were any of the slopes positive? negative? zero?

Extra Example 1

Tell whether the slope of the line is *positive* or *negative*. Then find the slope.

a.

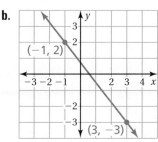

positive; $\dfrac{4}{3}$

b.

negative; $-\dfrac{5}{4}$

Extra Example 2

Find the slope of the line.

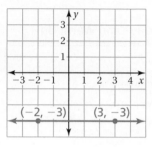

0

On Your Own

1. $-\dfrac{1}{5}$

2. 0

3. $\dfrac{5}{2}$

Extra Example 3

The points in the table lie on a line. Find the slope of the line. Then draw its graph.

x	−2	−1	0	1
y	−8	−5	−2	1

3

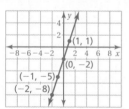

English Language Learners

Comprehension

The Key Idea box states "The slope of a line is a ratio of the change in y to the change in x between any two points on the line." Have students choose four points on a line. Use two points to find the slope. Then find the slope using the other two points. Students will find that the slopes are the same and should understand that the slope of the line is the same for the entire infinite length of the line.

Laurie's Notes

Example 2

? "How does a slope of $\dfrac{1}{2}$ compare to a slope of $\dfrac{1}{5}$? Describe the lines."
A slope of $\dfrac{1}{2}$ runs 2 units for every 1 unit it rises. A slope of $\dfrac{1}{5}$ runs 5 units for each 1 unit it rises. A slope of $\dfrac{1}{5}$ is not as steep.

? "What would a slope of $\dfrac{1}{10}$ look like?" A slope of $\dfrac{1}{10}$ is less steep than a slope of $\dfrac{1}{5}$, so it is almost flat.

? "How steep do you think a horizontal line is?" Listen for students to describe a horizontal line as having no rise. In this example, they will see it has a slope of 0.

- Work through the example.
- **Big Idea:** There is a difference between a slope of 0 and no slope. A line with no slope is vertical. A horizontal line has a slope of 0.

Example 3

? "What do you notice about the x-values and the y-values?" The x-values are increasing by 3 and the y-values are decreasing by 2.

- Compute the slope between any two points in the table.

- Using (1, 8) and (4, 6): slope $= \dfrac{\text{change in } y}{\text{change in } x} = \dfrac{6-8}{4-1} = -\dfrac{2}{3}$

- Using (1, 8) and (7, 4): slope $= \dfrac{\text{change in } y}{\text{change in } x} = \dfrac{4-8}{7-1} = -\dfrac{4}{6} = -\dfrac{2}{3}$

- **Connection:** The slope is the same regardless of which two points are selected. The slope triangles that are formed are similar. (Note: A slope triangle is the triangle formed by the line and the change in x and change in y arrows.)

? "The line has a negative slope. What do you notice about the line?" The line falls from left to right.

EXAMPLE **2** **Finding the Slope of a Horizontal Line**

Find the slope of the line.

The line is not rising or falling.
So, the rise is 0.

$$\text{slope} = \frac{\text{rise}}{\text{run}}$$

$$= \frac{0}{7}$$

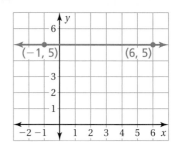

⋮• The slope is 0.

On Your Own

Now You're Ready
Exercises 7–12

Find the slope of the line.

1.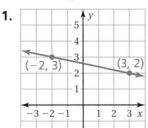

2.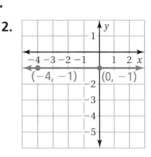

3.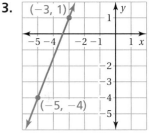

EXAMPLE **3** **Finding Slope from a Table**

The points in the table lie on a line. Find the slope of the line. Then draw its graph.

x	1	4	7	10
y	8	6	4	2

Choose any two points from the table. Then find the change in *y* and the change in *x*.

Use the points (1, 8) and (4, 6).

$$\text{slope} = \frac{\text{change in } y}{\text{change in } x}$$

$$= \frac{6 - 8}{4 - 1}$$

$$= \frac{-2}{3}$$

⋮• The slope is $-\frac{2}{3}$.

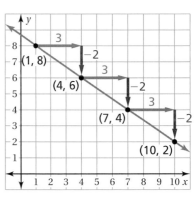

Now You're Ready
Exercises 15–18

The points in the table lie on a line. Find the slope of the line. Then draw its graph.

4.
x	1	3	5	7
y	2	5	8	11

5.
x	−3	−2	−1	0
y	6	4	2	0

Key Idea

Parallel Lines and Slopes

Two lines in the same plane that do not intersect are parallel lines. Two lines with the same slope are parallel.

EXAMPLE 4 Finding Parallel Lines

Which two lines are parallel? Explain.

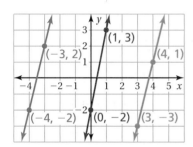

Find the slope of each line.

Blue Line	*Red Line*	*Green Line*
slope = $\dfrac{\text{rise}}{\text{run}}$	slope = $\dfrac{\text{rise}}{\text{run}}$	slope = $\dfrac{\text{rise}}{\text{run}}$
$= \dfrac{4}{1}$	$= \dfrac{5}{1}$	$= \dfrac{4}{1}$
$= 4$	$= 5$	$= 4$

The slope of the blue and green lines is 4. The slope of the red line is 5.

∴ The blue and green lines have the same slope, so they are parallel.

On Your Own

Now You're Ready
Exercises 21 and 22

6. Which two lines are parallel? Explain.

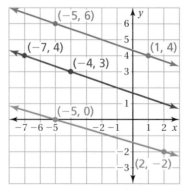

Laurie's Notes

On Your Own

- **Neighbor Check:** Have students work independently and then have their neighbor check their work. Have students discuss any discrepancies.
- **Connection:** In Question 4, students may recognize from the table that both *x* and *y* are increasing and the slope is positive. In Question 5, as *x* increases, the *y*-values are decreasing and the slope is negative.

Key Idea

- Students explored this idea yesterday. Students generally understand the fact that parallel lines have the same slope. They have the same steepness.

Example 4

- Work through the example. Students may look quickly and believe that all of the lines are parallel. They should compute the slope of each line to prove which lines are parallel.

On Your Own

- **Think-Pair-Share:** Students should read the question independently and then work with a partner to answer the question. When they have answered the question, the pair should compare their answer with another group and discuss any discrepancies.

Closure

- Plot the ordered pairs and find the slope of the line.

x	−1	0	1	2
y	−3	−1	1	3

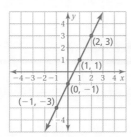

slope = 2

Technology For the Teacher

Dynamic Classroom

The Dynamic Planning Tool
Editable Teacher's Resources at *BigIdeasMath.com*

On Your Own

4. $\dfrac{3}{2}$

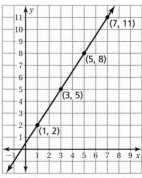

5. −2

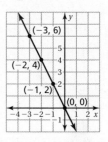

Extra Example 4

Which two lines are parallel? Explain.

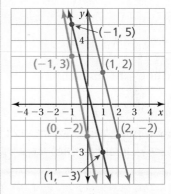

The blue and red lines both have a slope of −4, so they are parallel.

On Your Own

6. The blue and red lines both have a slope of $-\dfrac{1}{3}$, so they are parallel.

Vocabulary and Concept Check

1. **a.** B and C

   b. A

   c. no; All of the slopes are different.

2. *Sample answer:* When constructing a wheelchair ramp, you need to know the slope.

3. The line is horizontal.

Practice and Problem Solving

4.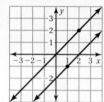

   The lines are parallel.

5.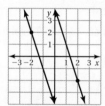

   The lines are parallel.

6.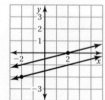

   The lines are parallel.

7. $\dfrac{3}{4}$ 8. $-\dfrac{5}{4}$

9. $-\dfrac{3}{5}$ 10. $\dfrac{1}{6}$

11. 0   12. $\dfrac{5}{2}$

Assignment Guide and Homework Check

Level	Day 1 Activity Assignment	Day 2 Lesson Assignment	Homework Check
Basic	4–6, 28–31	1–3, 7–14, 15–21 odd	7, 11, 14, 15, 21
Average	4–6, 28–31	1–3, 7–25 odd, 14, 22	7, 11, 14, 15, 22
Advanced	4–6, 28–31	1–3, 11–13, 16, 18, 21–27	12, 16, 22, 24, 26

Common Errors

- **Exercises 7–12** Students may find the reciprocal of the slope because they mix up rise and run. Remind them that the change in *y* is the numerator and the change in *x* is the denominator.
- **Exercises 7–12** Students may forget negatives, or include them when they are not needed. Remind them that if the line rises from left to right the slope is positive, and if the line falls from left to right the slope is negative.

2.2 Record and Practice Journal

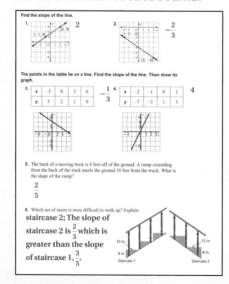

 Vocabulary and Concept Check

1. **CRITICAL THINKING** Refer to the graph.

   a. Which lines have positive slopes?

   b. Which line has the steepest slope?

   c. Are any two of the lines parallel? Explain.

2. **OPEN-ENDED** Describe a real-life situation that involves slope.

3. **REASONING** The slope of a line is 0. What do you know about the line?

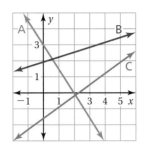

 Practice and Problem Solving

Draw a line through each point using the given slope. What do you notice about the two lines?

4. Slope = 1

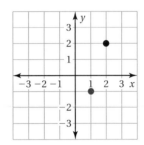

5. Slope = −3

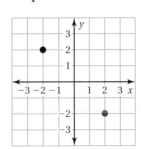

6. Slope = $\frac{1}{4}$

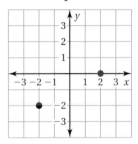

Find the slope of the line.

  7.

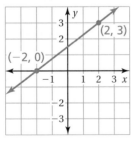

8.

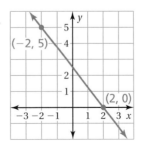

9.

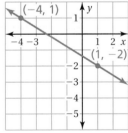

10.

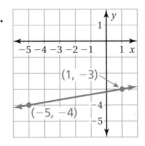

11.

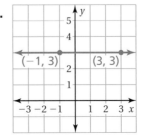

12.

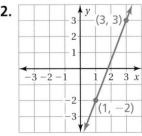

13. **ERROR ANALYSIS** Describe and correct the error in finding the slope of the line.

14. **CRITICAL THINKING** Is it more difficult to walk up the ramp or the hill? Explain.

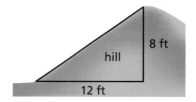

Slope $= \dfrac{2}{3}$

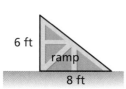

6 ft

ramp

8 ft

8 ft

hill

12 ft

The points in the table lie on a line. Find the slope of the line. Then draw its graph.

③ 15.

x	1	3	5	7
y	2	10	18	26

16.

x	−3	2	7	12
y	0	2	4	6

17.

x	−6	−2	2	6
y	8	5	2	−1

18.

x	−8	−2	4	10
y	8	1	−6	−13

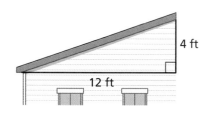

4 ft

12 ft

19. **PITCH** Carpenters refer to the slope of a roof as the *pitch* of the roof. Find the pitch of the roof.

20. **PROJECT** The guidelines for a wheelchair ramp suggest that the ratio of the rise to the run be no greater than 1 : 12.

a. Find a wheelchair ramp in your school or neighborhood. Measure its slope. Does the ramp follow the guidelines?

b. Design a wheelchair ramp that provides access to a building with a front door that is 2.5 feet higher than the sidewalk. Illustrate your design.

Which two lines are parallel? Explain.

④ 21.

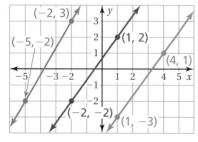

22.

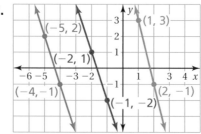

Common Errors

- **Exercise 14** Students may get confused because one of the slopes is negative and the other is positive. Tell them to think of the absolute values of the slopes when comparing. Encourage them to graph the slopes on a number line to check their answer.
- **Exercises 15–18** Students may reverse the *x*- and *y*-coordinates when plotting the ordered pairs given in the table. Remind them that the first row is the *x*-coordinate and the second row is the *y*-coordinate. Encourage students to write the ordered pairs before graphing.
- **Exercises 21 and 22** Students may use their eyes to guess which two lines are parallel without finding the actual slopes. Encourage them to find the slope of each line. The slopes of the lines are close enough that it is difficult to tell the difference visually.
- **Exercises 23 and 24** Students may not remember the definition of a parallelogram. Remind them that they have to compare the slopes of the opposite sides. Even if one pair of sides is parallel, the other pair may not be parallel. Remind students to compare both pairs of opposite sides.

Practice and Problem Solving

13. The 2 should be -2 because it goes down.

$$\text{Slope} = -\frac{2}{3}$$

14. The ramp because its slope is steeper.

15. 4

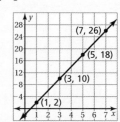

16. $\frac{2}{5}$

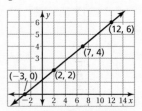

17. $-\frac{3}{4}$

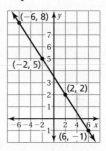

18–22. See Additional Answers.

Practice and Problem Solving

23–26. See Additional Answers.

27. See *Taking Math Deeper*.

Fair Game Review

28.

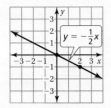

$y = -\frac{1}{2}x$

29.

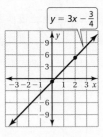

$y = 3x - \frac{3}{4}$

30.

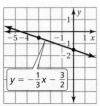

$y = -\frac{1}{3}x - \frac{3}{2}$

31. B

Mini-Assessment

Find the slope of the line.

1.

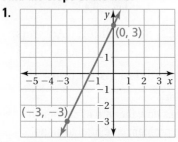

slope = 2

2.

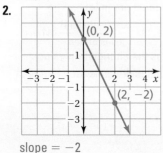

slope = −2

Taking Math Deeper

Exercise 27

This exercise is a nice example of the power of a diagram. Instead of using the drawing of the slide, encourage students to draw the slide in a coordinate plane. Once that is done, the question is easier to answer.

 Draw a diagram.

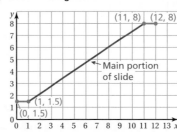

 Compare the slopes.

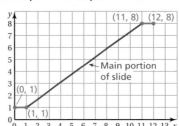

Because 0.7 > 0.65, the slide is steeper.

a. Find the slope of the slide.

$$\text{Slope} = \frac{\text{change in } y}{\text{change in } x}$$

$$= \frac{8 - 1.5}{11 - 1}$$

$$= \frac{6.5}{10}$$

$$= 0.65$$

b. $\text{Slope} = \dfrac{\text{change in } y}{\text{change in } x}$

$$= \frac{8 - 1}{11 - 1}$$

$$= \frac{7}{10}$$

$$= 0.7$$

Project

Many water parks and amusement parks have water slides. Find the height of a slide and calculate the slope of the main part of the slide.

Reteaching and Enrichment Strategies

If students need help. . .	If students got it. . .
Resources by Chapter • Practice A and Practice B • Puzzle Time Record and Practice Journal Practice Differentiating the Lesson Lesson Tutorials Skills Review Handbook	Resources by Chapter • Enrichment and Extension Start the next section

Tell whether the quadrilateral is a parallelogram. Explain.

23.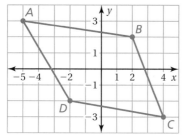

24.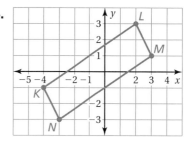

25. **TURNPIKE TRAVEL** The graph shows the cost of traveling by car on a turnpike.

    a. Find the slope of the line.

    b. Explain the meaning of the slope as a rate of change.

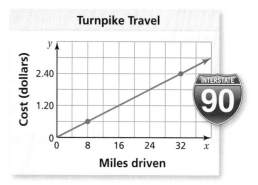

26. **BOAT RAMP** Which is steeper: the boat ramp or a road with a 12% grade? Explain. (*Note:* Road grade is the vertical increase divided by the horizontal distance.)

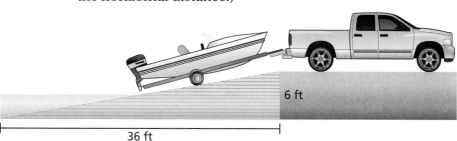

6 ft

36 ft

27. **Critical Thinking** The top and bottom of the slide are parallel to the ground.

    a. What is the slope of the main portion of the slide?

    b. How does the slope change if the bottom of the slide is only 12 inches above the ground? Is the slide steeper? Explain.

1 ft

8 ft

1 ft

18 in.

12 ft

 Fair Game Review What you learned in previous grades & lessons

Graph the linear equation. *(Section 2.1)*

28. $y = -\dfrac{1}{2}x$

29. $y = 3x - \dfrac{3}{4}$

30. $y = -\dfrac{x}{3} - \dfrac{3}{2}$

31. **MULTIPLE CHOICE** What is the prime factorization of 84? *(Skills Review Handbook)*

    Ⓐ $2 \times 3 \times 7$ Ⓑ $2^2 \times 3 \times 7$ Ⓒ $2 \times 3^2 \times 7$ Ⓓ $2^2 \times 21$

STANDARDS
OF LEARNING
8.16

Essential Question How can you describe the graph of the equation $y = mx + b$?

1 **ACTIVITY: Finding Slopes and y-Intercepts**

Work with a partner.

- **Graph the equation.**
- **Find the slope of the line.**
- **Find the point where the line crosses the y-axis.**

a. $y = -\dfrac{1}{2}x + 1$

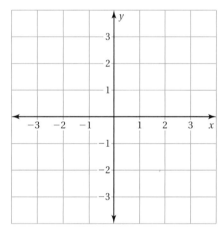

b. $y = -x + 2$

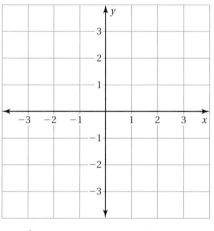

c. $y = -x - 2$

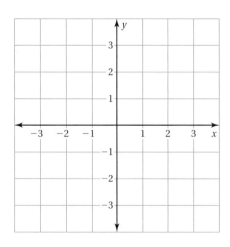

d. $y = \dfrac{1}{2}x + 1$

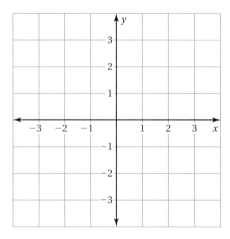

Laurie's Notes

Introduction

For the Teacher

- **Goal:** Students will explore the connection between the equation of a line and its graph.

Motivate

- **Preparation:** Make three demonstration cards on 8.5"x 11" paper. The x-axis is labeled "time" and the y-axis is labeled "distance from home."
- Sample cards A, B, and C are shown.

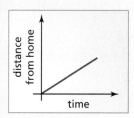 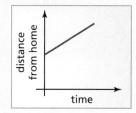 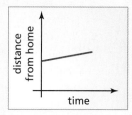

- Ask 3 students to hold the cards for the class to see.
- ? "Consider how the axes are labeled. What does the slope of the line represent?" $\dfrac{\text{distance}}{\text{time}} = \text{rate}$
- ? "What story does each card tell? How are the stories similar and different?" A: you begin at home; B: you travel at the same rate, but you start away from home; C: you start away from home, but you travel at a slower rate
- **Management Tip:** If you plan to use the demonstration cards again next year, laminate them.

Activity Notes

Activity 1

- ? "How do you graph an equation?" Plot several points, then connect the points with a line.
- ? "Is there a way to organize the points you need to plot?" Use an input-output table.
- Review with students how input-output tables are set up and what values of x they should substitute. When the coefficient of x is a fraction, it is wise to select x-values that are multiples of the denominator. This will eliminate fractional values.
- ? "How many points do you need in order to graph the equation?" Minimum is 2. Plot 3 to be safe.
- Remind students to evaluate the equation for $x = 0$. This will ensure that they find the point where the graph crosses the y-axis.
- The slope and the point where the line crosses the y-axis will be recorded in the table on the next page.
- Check students' work before going on to the Inductive Reasoning.

Standards of Learning

8.16 The student will graph a linear equation in two variables.

Previous Learning

Students should know how to find the slopes of lines.

Activity Materials	
Introduction	**Textbook**
• demonstration cards	• straightedge • grid paper
Closure	
• demonstration cards	

Start Thinking! and Warm Up

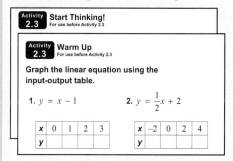

Activity 2.3 Start Thinking!
For use before Activity 2.3

Activity 2.3 Warm Up
For use before Activity 2.3

Graph the linear equation using the input-output table.

1. $y = x - 1$

x	0	1	2	3
y				

2. $y = \dfrac{1}{2}x + 2$

x	−2	0	2	4
y				

2.3 Record and Practice Journal

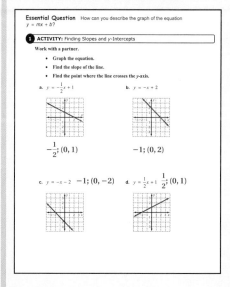

Essential Question How can you describe the graph of the equation $y = mx + b$?

1 ACTIVITY: Finding Slopes and y-Intercepts

Work with a partner.

- Graph the equation.
- Find the slope of the line.
- Find the point where the line crosses the y-axis.

a. $y = -\dfrac{1}{2}x + 1$ $-\dfrac{1}{2}; (0, 1)$

b. $y = -x + 2$ $-1; (0, 2)$

c. $y = -x - 2$ $-1; (0, -2)$

d. $y = \dfrac{1}{2}x + 1$ $\dfrac{1}{2}; (0, 1)$

English Language Learners

Build on Past Knowledge

Remind students from their study of rational numbers that the slope -2 can be written as the fraction $\frac{-2}{1}$. By writing the integer as a fraction, students can see that the slope has a run of 1 and a rise of -2. This will help in graphing the line of a linear function.

Inductive Reasoning

- Give students sufficient time to complete the table. Provide grid paper for Questions 6–12.
- Students should begin to observe patterns as they complete the table.
- Circulate to ensure that graphs are drawn correctly.
- Encourage students to draw the directed arrows in order to help them find the slope of the line.
- Have students put a few graphs on the board to help facilitate discussion.
- **?** When students have finished, ask a series of summary questions.
  - "Compare certain pairs of graphs such as 6 and 7; or 10 and 11. What do you observe?" They have the same steepness (slope) and the number at the end of the equation is the y-coordinate of where the graph crosses the y-axis.
  - "Where does the equation $y = x + 7$ cross the y-axis?" at $(0, 7)$
  - "Compare certain groups of graphs such as 3, 6, and 10; or 4, 7, and 11. What do you observe?" They cross the y-axis at the same point, but the slopes are different; the coefficient of x is the slope of the line.
  - "What is the slope of the equation $y = 7x + 2$?" slope $= 7$

Words of Wisdom

- Students may not use mathematical language to describe their observations. Listen for the concept, the vocabulary will come later.
- In equations such as $y = x - 2$, students do not always think of the subtraction operation as making the constant negative. You may need to remind students that this is the same as *adding the opposite*. So, $y = x - 2$ is equivalent to $y = x + (-2)$.

What Is Your Answer?

- These answers should follow immediately from discussing student observations.

Closure

- Refer back to the demonstration cards A, B, and C. Have students describe how the equations would be similar and how they would be different. *Sample answer:* A and B have the same slope, but different y-intercepts. B and C have different slopes, but the same y-intercept.

2.3 Record and Practice Journal

Inductive Reasoning

Work with a partner. Graph each equation. Then complete the table.

	Equation	Description of Graph	Slope of Graph	Point of Intersection with y-axis
1a	2. $y = -\frac{1}{2}x + 1$	Line	$-\frac{1}{2}$	$(0, 1)$
1b	3. $y = -x + 2$	Line	-1	$(0, 2)$
1c	4. $y = -x - 2$	Line	-1	$(0, -2)$
1d	5. $y = \frac{1}{2}x + 1$	Line	$\frac{1}{2}$	$(0, 1)$
	6. $y = x + 2$	Line	1	$(0, 2)$
	7. $y = x - 2$	Line	1	$(0, -2)$
	8. $y = \frac{1}{2}x - 1$	Line	$\frac{1}{2}$	$(0, -1)$
	9. $y = -\frac{1}{2}x - 1$	Line	$-\frac{1}{2}$	$(0, -1)$
	10. $y = 3x + 2$	Line	3	$(0, 2)$
	11. $y = 3x - 2$	Line	3	$(0, -2)$
	12. $y = -2x + 3$	Line	-2	$(0, 3)$

What Is Your Answer?

13. IN YOUR OWN WORDS How can you describe the graph of the equation $y = mx + b$?

a line with slope m and crosses the y-axis at $(0, b)$

a. How does the value of m affect the graph of the equation?

steepness of line

b. How does the value of b affect the graph of the equation?

Moves graph up and down.

c. Check your answers to parts (a) and (b) with three equations that are not in the table.

Check students' work.

14. Why is $y = mx + b$ called the "slope-intercept" form of the equation of a line?

m is the slope and b is the y-intercept.

Technology For the Teacher

Dynamic Classroom

The Dynamic Planning Tool
Editable Teacher's Resources at *BigIdeasMath.com*

Inductive Reasoning

Work with a partner. Graph each equation. Then copy and complete the table.

	Equation	Description of Graph	Slope of Graph	Point of Intersection with y-axis
1a	**2.** $y = -\dfrac{1}{2}x + 1$	Line	$-\dfrac{1}{2}$	(0, 1)
1b	**3.** $y = -x + 2$			
1c	**4.** $y = -x - 2$			
1d	**5.** $y = \dfrac{1}{2}x + 1$			
	6. $y = x + 2$			
	7. $y = x - 2$			
	8. $y = \dfrac{1}{2}x - 1$			
	9. $y = -\dfrac{1}{2}x - 1$			
	10. $y = 3x + 2$			
	11. $y = 3x - 2$			
	12. $y = -2x + 3$			

What Is Your Answer?

13. **IN YOUR OWN WORDS** How can you describe the graph of the equation $y = mx + b$?

    a. How does the value of m affect the graph of the equation?

    b. How does the value of b affect the graph of the equation?

    c. Check your answers to parts (a) and (b) with three equations that are not in the table.

14. Why is $y = mx + b$ called the "slope-intercept" form of the equation of a line?

Practice

Use what you learned about graphing linear equations in slope-intercept form to complete Exercises 4–6 on page 80.

Check It Out
Lesson Tutorials
BigIdeasMath ✓com

Key Vocabulary
x-intercept, p. 78
y-intercept, p. 78
slope-intercept form,
   p. 78

Key Ideas

Intercepts

The **x-intercept** of a line is the x-coordinate of the point where the line crosses the x-axis. It occurs when $y = 0$.

The **y-intercept** of a line is the y-coordinate of the point where the line crosses the y-axis. It occurs when $x = 0$.

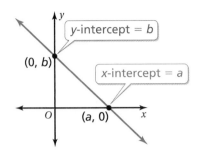

Slope-Intercept Form

Words An equation written in the form $y = mx + b$ is in **slope-intercept form**. The slope of the line is m and the y-intercept of the line is b.

Algebra

$$y = mx + b$$

slope   y-intercept

EXAMPLE 1 Identifying Slopes and y-Intercepts

Find the slope and y-intercept of the graph of each linear equation.

a. $y = -4x - 2$

$y = -4x + (-2)$ Write in slope-intercept form.

∴ The slope is -4 and the y-intercept is -2.

b. $y - 5 = \dfrac{3}{2}x$

$y = \dfrac{3}{2}x + 5$ Add 5 to each side.

∴ The slope is $\dfrac{3}{2}$ and the y-intercept is 5.

On Your Own

Now You're Ready
Exercises 7–15

Find the slope and y-intercept of the graph of the linear equation.

1. $y = 3x - 7$

2. $y - 1 = -\dfrac{2}{3}x$

◀ Multi-Language Glossary at BigIdeasMath ✓com.

Laurie's Notes

Introduction

Connect

- **Yesterday:** Students explored the connection between the equation of a line and its graph.
- **Today:** Students will use the slope-intercept form of a line to graph the line.

Motivate

- Share the following taxi information. All trips start at a convention center.

Destination	Distance	Taxi Fare
Football stadium	18.7 mi	$39 approx.
Airport	12 mi	$32 flat fee
Shopping district	9.5 mi	$20 approx.

- **?** "How do you think taxi fares are determined?" Answers will vary; listen for distance, number of passengers, tolls.
- Discuss why some locations, often involving airports, have flat fees associated with them.

Lesson Notes

Key Ideas

- Write the Key Ideas on the board. Draw the graph and discuss the vocabulary of this lesson: x-intercept, y-intercept, and slope-intercept form.
- Explain to students that the equation must be written with y as a function of x. This means that the equation must be solved for y.
- **FYI:** Students may ask why the letters m and b are used. Historically, there is no definitive answer. I tell my students that mathematicians, much older than myself, have used m for slope for centuries. Using b for the y-intercept appears to be an American phenomenon.

Example 1

- **?** "What is a linear equation?" an equation whose graph is a line
- Write part (a). This is written in the form $y = mx + b$, enabling students to quickly identify the slope and y-intercept.
- Write part (b).
- **?** "Is $y - 5 = \frac{3}{2}x$ in slope-intercept form?" no "Can you rewrite it so that it is?" yes; Add 5 to each side of the equation.

On Your Own

- **Think-Pair-Share:** Students should read each question independently and then work with a partner to answer the questions. When they have answered the questions, the pair should compare their answers with another group and discuss any discrepancies.

Lesson Materials
Textbook
• straightedge

Start Thinking! and Warm Up

Lesson 2.3 **Warm Up** For use before Lesson 2.3

Lesson 2.3 **Start Thinking!** For use before Lesson 2.3

Describe a situation involving online shopping that can be modeled with a linear equation.

What is the slope?

What is the y-intercept?

Extra Example 1

Find the slope and y-intercept of the graph of each linear equation.

a. $y = \frac{3}{4}x - 5$

slope: $\frac{3}{4}$; y-intercept: -5

b. $y + \frac{1}{2} = -6x$

slope: -6; y-intercept: $-\frac{1}{2}$

On Your Own

1. slope: 3; y-intercept: -7
2. slope: $-\frac{2}{3}$; y-intercept: 1

Extra Example 2

Graph $y = -\frac{2}{3}x - 2$. Identify the x-intercept.

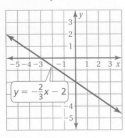

−3

Extra Example 3

The cost y (in dollars) for making friendship bracelets is $y = 0.5x + 2$, where x is the number of bracelets.

a. Graph the equation.

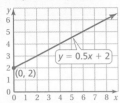

b. Interpret the slope and y-intercept.
The slope is 0.5. So, the cost per bracelet is $0.50. The y-intercept is 2. So, there is an initial cost of $2 to make the bracelets.

● On Your Own

3–5. See Additional Answers.

Differentiated Instruction

Kinesthetic

When graphing a linear function using the slope-intercept form, students must apply the slope correctly after plotting the point for the y-intercept. Have students plot (0, 3) in the coordinate plane. Then graph the lines $y = 4x + 3$, $y = \frac{1}{4}x + 3$, $y = -4x + 3$, and $y = -\frac{1}{4}x + 3$ in the same coordinate plane using (0, 3) as the starting point. Make sure students identify the correct rise and run for each line.

Laurie's Notes

● Example 2

? "How can knowing the slope and the y-intercept help you graph a line?" Listen for student understanding of what slope and y-intercept mean.

• Remind students that a slope of −3 can be interpreted as $\frac{-3}{1} = \frac{3}{-1}$.
Starting at the y-intercept, you can move to the right 1 unit and down 3 units, or to the left 1 unit and up 3 units. In both cases, you land on a point which satisfies the equation.

? **Extension:** "In this problem, you found the x-intercept by interpreting the slope and it coincidentally landed on the x-axis. If the line had missed the x-intercept, how would you find the x-intercept?" Set $y = 0$ and solve for x.

Example 3

? "Have any of you taken a taxi that had a meter on the front dashboard?"
• **FYI:** Not all taxis use meters. Where I live, which is rural, taxis charge a flat fee to travel from one region of town to another.
• Write the equation $y = 2.5x + 2$ on the board.
? "What is the slope and y-intercept for this equation?" Slope = 2.5 and y-intercept is 2.
• Suggest to students that because the slope is 2.5, any ratio equivalent to 2.5 can also be used, such as $\frac{2.5}{1} = \frac{5}{2}$. Using whole numbers instead of decimals improves the accuracy of graphing.
• Explain that the graph of this equation will only be in Quadrant I because it does not make sense to have a negative number of miles or a negative cost.
• Interpreting the slope and y-intercept is an important step, particularly for real-life applications.
? "What is the cost for a 2-mile taxi ride? a 10-mile taxi ride?" $7; $27

On Your Own

• Have students share results at the board after graphing the equations.

● Closure

• **Exit Ticket:** Graph $y - 4 = 2x$ and identify the slope and y-intercept.

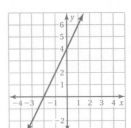

slope = 2
y-intercept = 4

Technology For the Teacher

Dynamic Classroom

The Dynamic Planning Tool
Editable Teacher's Resources at *BigIdeasMath.com*

EXAMPLE 2 **Graphing a Linear Equation in Slope-Intercept Form**

Graph $y = -3x + 3$. Identify the x-intercept.

Step 1: Find the slope and y-intercept.

$$y = -3x + 3$$

slope ⟶ ⟵ y-intercept

Step 2: The y-intercept is 3. So, plot $(0, 3)$.

Step 3: Use the slope to find another point and draw the line.

$$\text{slope} = \frac{\text{rise}}{\text{run}} = \frac{-3}{1}$$

Plot the point that is 1 unit right and 3 units down from $(0, 3)$. Draw a line through the two points.

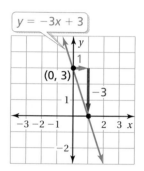

Study Tip

You can check the x-intercept by substituting $y = 0$ in the equation and solving for x.

$$y = -3x + 3$$
$$0 = -3x + 3$$
$$-3 = -3x$$
$$1 = x$$

⋮• The line crosses the x-axis at $(1, 0)$. So, the x-intercept is 1.

EXAMPLE 3 **Real-Life Application**

The cost y (in dollars) of taking a taxi x miles is $y = 2.5x + 2$.
(a) Graph the equation. (b) Interpret the y-intercept and slope.

a. The slope of the line is $2.5 = \dfrac{5}{2}$. Use the slope and y-intercept to graph the equation.

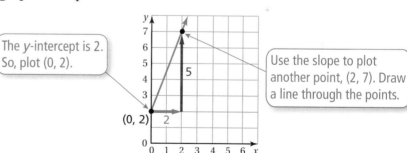

The y-intercept is 2. So, plot $(0, 2)$.

Use the slope to plot another point, $(2, 7)$. Draw a line through the points.

b. The slope is 2.5. So, the cost per mile is $2.50. The y-intercept is 2. So, there is an initial fee of $2 to take the taxi.

On Your Own

Now You're Ready
Exercises 18–23

Graph the linear equation. Identify the x-intercept.

3. $y = x - 4$

4. $y = -\dfrac{1}{2}x + 1$

5. In Example 3, the cost y (in dollars) of taking a different taxi x miles is $y = 2x + 1.5$. Interpret the y-intercept and slope.

Vocabulary and Concept Check

1. **VOCABULARY** How can you find the *x*-intercept of the graph of $2x + 3y = 6$?

2. **CRITICAL THINKING** Is the equation $y = 3x$ in slope-intercept form? Explain.

3. **OPEN-ENDED** Describe a real-life situation that can be modeled by a linear equation. Write the equation. Interpret the *y*-intercept and slope.

Practice and Problem Solving

Match the equation with its graph. Identify the slope and *y*-intercept.

4. $y = 2x + 1$

5. $y = \frac{1}{3}x - 2$

6. $y = -\frac{2}{3}x + 1$

A.
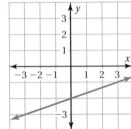

B.
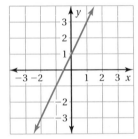

C.
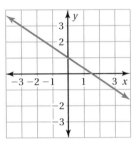

Find the slope and *y*-intercept of the graph of the linear equation.

 7. $y = 4x - 5$

8. $y = -7x + 12$

9. $y = -\frac{4}{5}x - 2$

10. $y = 2.25x + 3$

11. $y + 1 = \frac{4}{3}x$

12. $y - 6 = \frac{3}{8}x$

13. $y - 3.5 = -2x$

14. $y + 5 = -\frac{1}{2}x$

15. $y = 1.5x + 11$

16. **ERROR ANALYSIS** Describe and correct the error in finding the slope and *y*-intercept of the graph of the linear equation.

 $y = 4x - 3$

The slope is 4 and the y-intercept is 3.

17. **SKYDIVING** A skydiver parachutes to the ground. The height *y* (in feet) of the skydiver after *x* seconds is $y = -10x + 3000$.

    a. Graph the equation.

    b. Interpret the *x*-intercept and slope.

Assignment Guide and Homework Check

Level	Day 1 Activity Assignment	Day 2 Lesson Assignment	Homework Check
Basic	4–6, 29–33	1–3, 7–25 odd, 16	7, 15, 16, 19, 23
Average	4–6, 29–33	1–3, 13–16, 19–27 odd, 24, 26	14, 16, 19, 23, 24
Advanced	4–6, 29–33	1–3, 13–16, 18–28 even, 27	14, 16, 18, 22, 24

Common Errors

- **Exercises 7–15** Students may forget to include negatives with the slope and/or y-intercept. Remind them to look at the sign in front of the slope and the y-intercept. Also remind students that the equation is $y = mx + b$. This means that if the linear equation has "minus b," then the y-intercept is negative.

- **Exercises 11–14** Students may identify the opposite y-intercept because they forget to solve for y. Remind them that slope-intercept form has y by itself, so they must solve for y before identifying the slope and y-intercept.

- **Exercises 18–23** Students may use the reciprocal of the slope when graphing and may find an incorrect x-intercept. Remind them that slope is *rise* over *run*, so the numerator represents vertical change, not horizontal.

2.3 Record and Practice Journal

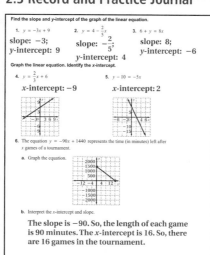

1. Find the x-coordinate of the point where the graph crosses the x-axis.

2. yes; The slope is 3 and the y-intercept is 0.

3. *Sample answer:* The amount of gasoline y (in gallons) left in your tank after you travel x miles is $y = -\frac{1}{20}x + 20$. The slope of $-\frac{1}{20}$ means the car uses 1 gallon of gas for every 20 miles driven. The y-intercept of 20 means there is originally 20 gallons of gas in the tank.

 Practice and Problem Solving

4. B; slope: 2; y-intercept: 1

5. A; slope: $\frac{1}{3}$; y-intercept: -2

6. C; slope: $-\frac{2}{3}$; y-intercept: 1

7. slope: 4; y-intercept: -5

8. slope: -7; y-intercept: 12

9. slope: $-\frac{4}{5}$; y-intercept: -2

10. slope: 2.25; y-intercept: 3

11. slope: $\frac{4}{3}$; y-intercept: -1

12. slope: $\frac{3}{8}$; y-intercept: 6

13. slope: -2; y-intercept: 3.5

14. slope: $-\frac{1}{2}$; y-intercept: -5

15. slope: 1.5; y-intercept: 11

16–17. See Additional Answers.

18.

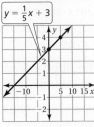

$y = \frac{1}{5}x + 3$

x-intercept: -15

19–27. See Additional Answers.

28. See *Taking Math Deeper*.

Fair Game Review

29. $y = 2x + 3$

30. $y = -\frac{4}{5}x + \frac{13}{5}$

31. $y = \frac{2}{3}x - 2$

32. $y = -\frac{7}{4}x + 2$

33. B

Mini-Assessment

Find the slope and *y*-intercept of the graph of the equation. Then graph the equation.

1. $y = -5x + 3$

slope $= -5$, y-intercept $= 3$

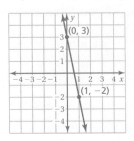

2. $y - 4 = \frac{1}{2}x$

slope $= \frac{1}{2}$, y-intercept $= 4$

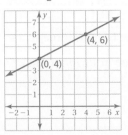

Taking Math Deeper

Exercise 28

This is a classic business problem. You have monthly costs for your business. The question is how much do you have to sell to cover your costs and start making a profit.

 Organize the given information.

- The site sells 5 banner ads.
- Monthly income is $0.005 per click.
- It costs $120 per month to run the site.
- Let *y* be the monthly income.
- Let *x* be the number of clicks per month.

 a. Write an equation for the income.

$y = 0.005x$

 b. Graph the equation.

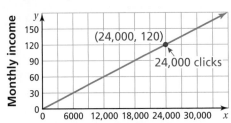

When the ads start to get 24,000 clicks a month, the income will be $120 per month. Each banner ad needs to average $\frac{24,000}{5} = 4800$ clicks. Any additional clicks per month will start earning a profit.

Project

Use the Internet or the school library to research methods for determining the number of clicks on a website.

Reteaching and Enrichment Strategies

If students need help...	If students got it...
Resources by Chapter • Practice A and Practice B • Puzzle Time Record and Practice Journal Practice Differentiating the Lesson Lesson Tutorials Skills Review Handbook	Resources by Chapter • Enrichment and Extension • School-to-Work Start the next section

Graph the linear equation. Identify the *x*-intercept.

② **18.** $y = \dfrac{1}{5}x + 3$

19. $y = 6x - 7$

20. $y = -\dfrac{8}{3}x + 9$

21. $y = -1.4x - 1$

22. $y + 9 = -3x$

23. $y - 4 = -\dfrac{3}{5}x$

24. PHONES The cost y (in dollars) of making a long distance phone call for x minutes is $y = 0.25x + 2$.

  a. Graph the equation.

  b. Interpret the slope and y-intercept.

25. APPLES Write a linear equation that models the cost y of picking x pounds of apples. Graph the equation.

Admission: $5.00
Apples: $0.75 per lb

26. ELEVATOR The basement of a building is 40 feet below ground level. The elevator rises at a rate of 5 feet per second. You enter the elevator in the basement. Write an equation that represents the height y (in feet) of the elevator after x seconds. Graph the equation.

27. BONUS You work in an electronics store. You earn a fixed amount of $35 per day, plus a 15% bonus on the merchandise you sell. Write an equation that models the amount y (in dollars) you earn for selling x dollars of merchandise in one day. Graph the equation.

28. *Critical Thinking* Six friends create a website. The website earns money by selling banner ads. The site has five banner ads. It costs $120 a month to operate the website.

  a. A banner ad earns $0.005 per click. Write a linear equation that represents the monthly income y (in dollars) for x clicks.

  b. Draw a graph of the equation in part (a). On the graph, label the number of clicks needed for the friends to start making a profit.

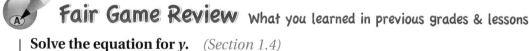

Fair Game Review What you learned in previous grades & lessons

Solve the equation for y. *(Section 1.4)*

29. $y - 2x = 3$

30. $4x + 5y = 13$

31. $2x - 3y = 6$

32. $7x + 4y = 8$

33. MULTIPLE CHOICE Which point is a solution of the equation $3x - 8y = 11$? *(Section 2.1)*

  Ⓐ $(1, 1)$ Ⓑ $(1, -1)$ Ⓒ $(-1, 1)$ Ⓓ $(-1, -1)$

STANDARDS OF LEARNING

8.16

Essential Question How can you describe the graph of the equation $ax + by = c$?

1 ACTIVITY: Using a Table to Plot Points

Work with a partner. You sold a total of $16 worth of tickets to a school concert. You lost track of how many of each type of ticket you sold.

$$\frac{\$4}{\text{Adult}} \cdot \frac{\text{Number of}}{\text{Adult Tickets}} + \frac{\$2}{\text{Child}} \cdot \frac{\text{Number of}}{\text{Child Tickets}} = \$16$$

a. Let x represent the number of adult tickets.

Let y represent the number of child tickets.

Write an equation that relates x and y.

b. Copy and complete the table showing the different combinations of tickets you might have sold.

Number of Adult Tickets, x					
Number of Child Tickets, y					

c. Plot the points from the table. Describe the pattern formed by the points.

d. If you remember how many adult tickets you sold, can you determine how many child tickets you sold? Explain your reasoning.

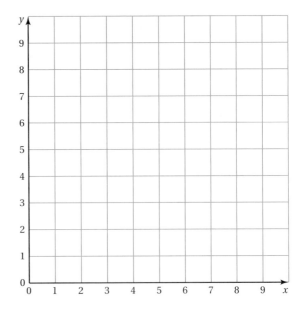

Laurie's Notes

Introduction

For the Teacher

- **Goal:** Students will explore the graph of a function in standard form.

Motivate

- **Preparation:** Make a set of equation cards on strips of paper. The equations are all the same when simplified and need to be written large enough to be read by students sitting at the back of the classroom.
- Here is a sample set of equations: $y = 2x + 1$, $-2x + y = 1$, $2x - y = -1$, $4x - 2y = -2$
- Ask 4 students to stand at the front of the room and hold the cards so only they can see the equations.
- As you state an ordered pair, the students holding the cards determine if it is a solution of the equation they are holding. If it is, they raise their hand. If not, they do nothing. State several ordered pairs, four that are solutions and two that are not. Plot all of the points that you state. Keep the ordered pairs simple.
- The four ordered pairs that are solutions will be in a line.
- ❓ "How many lines can pass through any two points?" one "How many lines pass through the four solutions points?" Students will say 4; now is the time to discuss the idea of one line written in different forms.
- Have each student reveal their equation to the class and read it aloud. Write each of the equations on the board.
- Explain to students that equations can be written in different forms. Today they will explore a new form of a linear equation.

Activity Notes

Activity 1

- Read the problem aloud. Discuss what the variables x and y represent.
- Note that a verbal model is shown for the equation $4x + 2y = 16$.
- ❓ "Could you have sold 5 adult tickets? Explain." No; 5 adult tickets would be $20, which is too much.
- Students may say that they do not know how to figure out x and y. Students may not realize that there is more than one solution. Remind students that *Guess, Check, and Revise* would be an appropriate strategy to use.
- Discuss part (c). The points lie on a line.
- Discuss part (d). Students may not recognize that in knowing x, they can substitute and solve for y. This is not an obvious step for students.
- ❓ "Could $x = 1.5$? Explain." No, you cannot sell 1.5 tickets.
- ❓ "What are the different numbers of adult tickets that are possible to sell?" 0, 1, 2, 3, 4
- **Note:** This is an example of a discrete domain; there are only 5 possible values for the variable x. This will be taught at a later time.

Standards of Learning

8.16 The student will graph a linear equation in two variables.

Previous Learning

Students should know how to graph lines in slope-intercept form.

Activity Materials	
Introduction	**Textbook**
• equation cards	• straightedge
Closure	
• equation cards	

Start Thinking! and Warm Up

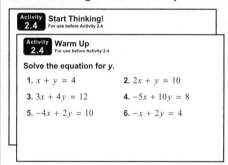

Activity 2.4 Start Thinking! For use before Activity 2.4

Activity 2.4 Warm Up For use before Activity 2.4

Solve the equation for y.

1. $x + y = 4$
2. $2x + y = 10$
3. $3x + 4y = 12$
4. $-5x + 10y = 8$
5. $-4x + 2y = 10$
6. $-x + 2y = 4$

2.4 Record and Practice Journal

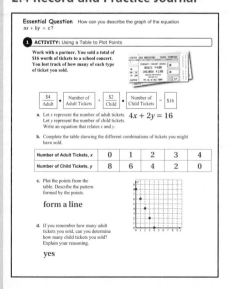

Essential Question How can you describe the graph of the equation $ax + by = c$?

① ACTIVITY: Using a Table to Plot Points

Work with a partner. You sold a total of $16 worth of tickets to a school concert. You lost track of how many of each type of ticket you sold.

$$\boxed{\frac{\$4}{\text{Adult}}} \cdot \boxed{\text{Number of Adult Tickets}} + \boxed{\frac{\$2}{\text{Child}}} \cdot \boxed{\text{Number of Child Tickets}} = \boxed{\$16}$$

a. Let x represent the number of adult tickets. Let y represent the number of child tickets. Write an equation that relates x and y. $4x + 2y = 16$

b. Complete the table showing the different combinations of tickets you might have sold.

Number of Adult Tickets, x	0	1	2	3	4
Number of Child Tickets, y	8	6	4	2	0

c. Plot the points from the table. Describe the pattern formed by the points.

form a line

d. If you remember how many adult tickets you sold, can you determine how many child tickets you sold? Explain your reasoning.

yes

Differentiated Instruction

Visual

Have students create a chart in their notebooks of the equation forms and how to graph them.

Slope-intercept form $y = mx + b$	• Plot $(0, b)$. • Use the slope m to plot a second point. • Draw a line through the two points.
Horizontal line $y = c$	• Draw a horizontal line through $(0, c)$.
Standard form $ax + by = c$	• Find the y-intercept. • Find the x-intercept. • Plot the associated points. Draw a line through the two points.

2.4 Record and Practice Journal

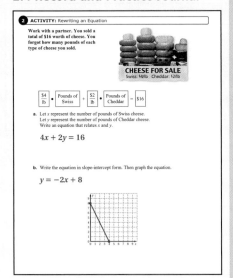

Laurie's Notes

Activity 2

• Read the problem aloud. Discuss what the variables x and y represent.
• Note that a verbal model is shown for the equation $4x + 2y = 16$.
? "Could you have sold 5 pounds of Swiss cheese? Explain." No; 5 pounds of Swiss cheese would be $20, which is too much.
• Give time for students to work with their partner. While this may be the same equation as Activity 1, the approach is different. Students are asked to write the equation in slope-intercept form. After the equation is in slope-intercept form, students can substitute a value for x, and find y. This is generally not the case for equations written in standard form.
? "Could $x = 1.5$? Explain." yes; You can buy a portion of a pound.
• **Note:** This is an example of a continuous domain; all numbers $0 \leq x \leq 4$ are possible. This will be taught at a later time.
• Students might observe that both examples have graphs in the first quadrant. This is common for real-life examples.

What Is Your Answer?

• **Question 3:** Students may guess that the graph is linear from Activity 1. However, some students may not be secure with this knowledge yet.

Closure

• Refer back to the equation cards. Rewrite the last three equations in slope-intercept form. $y = 2x + 1$

Technology For the Teacher

The Dynamic Planning Tool
Editable Teacher's Resources at *BigIdeasMath.com*

2   ACTIVITY: Rewriting an Equation

CHEESE FOR SALE
Swiss: $4/lb   Cheddar: $2/lb

Work with a partner. You sold a total of $16 worth of cheese. You forgot how many pounds of each type of cheese you sold.

$$\frac{\$4}{\text{lb}} \cdot \begin{matrix} \text{Pounds of} \\ \text{Swiss} \end{matrix} + \frac{\$2}{\text{lb}} \cdot \begin{matrix} \text{Pounds of} \\ \text{Cheddar} \end{matrix} = \$16$$

a. Let x represent the number of pounds of Swiss cheese.

Let y represent the number of pounds of Cheddar cheese.

Write an equation that relates x and y.

b. Write the equation in slope-intercept form. Then graph the equation.

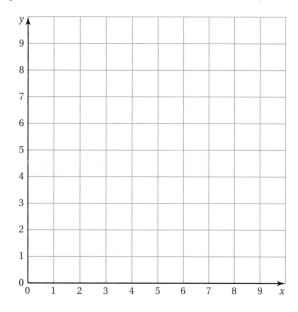

What Is Your Answer?

3. **IN YOUR OWN WORDS** How can you describe the graph of the equation $ax + by = c$?

4. Activities 1 and 2 show two different methods for graphing $ax + by = c$. Describe the two methods. Which method do you prefer? Explain.

5. Write a real-life problem that is similar to those shown in Activities 1 and 2.

Practice ▶ Use what you learned about graphing linear equations in standard form to complete Exercises 3 and 4 on page 86.

2.4 Lesson

Key Vocabulary 🔊
standard form, *p. 84*

 **Key Idea**

Standard Form of a Linear Equation

The **standard form** of a linear equation is

$$ax + by = c$$

where *a* and *b* are not both zero.

Study Tip

Any linear equation can be written in standard form.

EXAMPLE ① **Graphing a Linear Equation in Standard Form**

Graph $-2x + 3y = -6$.

Step 1: Write the equation in slope-intercept form.

$-2x + 3y = -6$	Write the equation.
$3y = 2x - 6$	Add 2x to each side.
$y = \dfrac{2}{3}x - 2$	Divide each side by 3.

Step 2: Use the slope and *y*-intercept to graph the equation.

$$y = \frac{2}{3}x + (-2)$$

slope

y-intercept

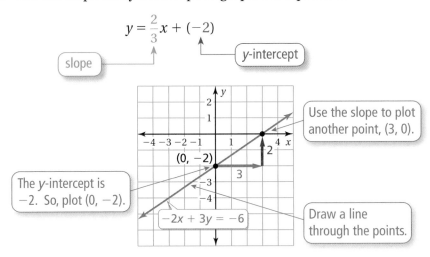

The *y*-intercept is -2. So, plot $(0, -2)$.

Use the slope to plot another point, $(3, 0)$.

$-2x + 3y = -6$

Draw a line through the points.

⬤ **On Your Own**

Now You're Ready
Exercises 5–10

Graph the linear equation.

1. $x + y = -2$

2. $-\dfrac{1}{2}x + 2y = 6$

3. $-\dfrac{2}{3}x + y = 0$

4. $2x + y = 5$

🔊 Multi-Language Glossary at BigIdeasMath✓com.

Laurie's Notes

Introduction

Connect
- **Yesterday:** Students explored the graph of an equation written in standard form.
- **Today:** Students will graph equations written in standard form.

Motivate
- ❓ "How many pairs of numbers can you think of that have a sum of 5?" Encourage students to write their numbers on paper as ordered pairs. Example, (2, 3)
- ❓ "Did any of you include numbers that are not whole numbers?" Check to see if anyone had negative numbers or rational numbers.
- Ask one student to name the x-coordinate in one of their ordered pairs and another student to provide the y-coordinate. Plot the ordered pairs in a coordinate plane.
- ❓ "What do you think the equation of this line would be?" $x + y = 5$

Lesson Notes

Key Idea
- Define the standard form of a linear equation.
- Students may ask why both a and b cannot be zero. Explain that if $a = 0$ and $b = 0$, you would not have the equation of a line.
- **Teaching Tip:** Students are often confused when the standard form is written with parameters a, b, and c. Students see 5 variables. Show examples of equations written in standard form and identify a, b, and c.

Example 1
- Have students identify a, b, and c. $a = -2$, $b = 3$, and $c = -6$
- ❓ "How do you solve for y?" Add $2x$ to each side, then divide both sides by 3.
- **Common Error:** Students only divide one of the two terms on the right side of the equation by 3. Relate this to fraction operations. You are separating the expression into two terms and then simplifying.
- ❓ "Now that the equation is in slope-intercept form, explain how to graph the equation." Plot the ordered pair for the y-intercept. To plot another point, start at $(0, -2)$ and move to the right 3 units and up 2 units. Note that you can also move 3 units to the left and down 2 units. Connect these points with a line.
- Substitute the additional ordered pairs into the original equation to verify that they are solutions of the equation.

On Your Own
- In Questions 2 and 3, the fractional coefficient of x may present a problem.

Goal
Today's lesson is graphing a line written in **standard form**.

Lesson Materials
Textbook
• straightedge

Start Thinking! and Warm Up

> **Lesson 2.4** Warm Up
> For use before Lesson 2.4

> **Lesson 2.4** Start Thinking!
> For use before Lesson 2.4
>
> You have $40 to spend on turkey and cheese for a party. At the deli, turkey is $10 per pound and cheese is $6 per pound.
>
> Is it easier to write an equation to represent the situation in *slope-intercept form* or *standard form*? Why?

Extra Example 1
Graph $3x - 2y = 2$.

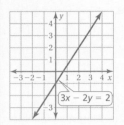

On Your Own

1.

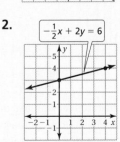

$x + y = -2$

2. $-\frac{1}{2}x + 2y = 6$

3–4. See Additional Answers.

Extra Example 2

Graph $5x - y = -5$ using intercepts.

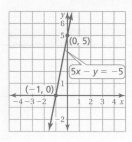

Extra Example 3

You have $2.40 to spend on grapes and bananas.

a. Graph the equation $1.2x + 0.6y = 2.4$, where x is the number of pounds of grapes and y is the number of pounds of bananas.

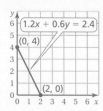

b. Interpret the intercepts. The x-intercept shows that you can buy 2 pounds of grapes, if you do not buy any bananas. The y-intercept shows that you can buy 4 pound of bananas, if you do not buy any grapes.

 On Your Own

5–7. See Additional Answers.

English Language Learners

Vocabulary

For English learners, relate the word *intercept* with the football term *interception*. A defensive player on a football team crosses the path of the football to catch it and make an interception. Similarly, the y-intercept is the point where the line crosses the y-axis and the x-intercept is where the line crosses the x-axis.

Laurie's Notes

Example 2

- Start with a simple equation in standard form, such as $x + y = 4$. In this example, $a = 1$, $b = 1$, and $c = 4$. Explain to students that this could be solved for y by subtracting x from each side of the equation. Instead, you want to leave the equation as it was written.
- **?** "Another way to think of this equation is *the sum of two numbers is 4*. Can you name some ordered pairs that would satisfy the equation?" Students should give many, including the two intercepts, (0, 4) and (4, 0).
- Explain to students that sometimes an equation in standard form is graphed by using the two intercepts, instead of rewriting the equation in slope-intercept form.
- Write the equation shown: $x + 3y = -3$.
- **?** "To find the x-intercept, what is the value of y? To find the y-intercept, what is the value of x?" 0; 0
- Finish the problem as shown.
- **Big Idea:** When the equation is in standard form, you can plot the points for the two intercepts and then draw the line through them.

Example 3

- Read the problem. Write the equation $1.5x + 0.6y = 6$ on the board.
- **?** "What are the intercepts for this equation?" The x-intercept is 4 and the y-intercept is 10.
- Interpreting the intercepts in part (b) is an important step, particularly for real-life applications.
- Explain to students that negative values of x and y are not included in the graph because it does not make sense to have negative pounds of apples and bananas.
- **?** "What is the cost of 2 pounds of apples and 5 pounds of bananas?" $6

On Your Own

- Students should work with a partner.

Closure

- **Writing Prompt:** To graph the equation $2x + y = 4$ … *Sample answer:* Find and plot the points for the x- and y-intercepts, then draw a line through these two points.

**Technology
For the Teacher**

The Dynamic Planning Tool
Editable Teacher's Resources at *BigIdeasMath.com*

EXAMPLE 2

Graphing a Linear Equation in Standard Form

Graph $x + 3y = -3$ using intercepts.

Step 1: To find the x-intercept, substitute 0 for y.

$$x + 3y = -3$$
$$x + 3(0) = -3$$
$$x = -3$$

To find the y-intercept, substitute 0 for x.

$$x + 3y = -3$$
$$0 + 3y = -3$$
$$y = -1$$

Step 2: Graph the equation.

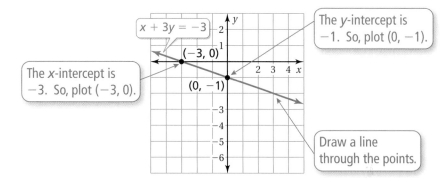

The y-intercept is -1. So, plot $(0, -1)$.

The x-intercept is -3. So, plot $(-3, 0)$.

Draw a line through the points.

EXAMPLE 3 Real-Life Application

Bananas $0.60/pound

Apples $1.50/pound

You have \$6 to spend on apples and bananas. **(a) Graph the equation $1.5x + 0.6y = 6$, where x is the number of pounds of apples and y is the number of pounds of bananas. (b) Interpret the intercepts.**

a. Find the intercepts and graph the equation.

x-intercept	y-intercept
$1.5x + 0.6y = 6$	$1.5x + 0.6y = 6$
$1.5x + 0.6(0) = 6$	$1.5(0) + 0.6y = 6$
$x = 4$	$y = 10$

$1.5x + 0.6y = 6$

b. The x-intercept shows that you can buy 4 pounds of apples if you don't buy any bananas. The y-intercept shows that you can buy 10 pounds of bananas if you don't buy any apples.

On Your Own

Now You're Ready
Exercises 16–18

Graph the linear equation using intercepts.

5. $2x - y = 8$

6. $x + 3y = 6$

7. WHAT IF? In Example 3, you buy y pounds of oranges instead of bananas. Oranges cost \$1.20 per pound. Graph the equation $1.5x + 1.2y = 6$. Interpret the intercepts.

 Vocabulary and Concept Check

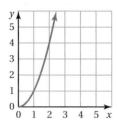

1. **VOCABULARY** Is the equation $y = -2x + 5$ in standard form? Explain.

2. **REASONING** Does the graph represent a linear equation? Explain.

 Practice and Problem Solving

Define two variables for the verbal model. Write an equation in slope-intercept form that relates the variables. Graph the equation.

3. $\dfrac{\$2.00}{\text{pound}} \cdot \begin{array}{c}\text{Pounds of}\\\text{peaches}\end{array} + \dfrac{\$1.50}{\text{pound}} \cdot \begin{array}{c}\text{Pounds of}\\\text{apples}\end{array} = \$15$

4. $\dfrac{16\text{ miles}}{\text{hour}} \cdot \begin{array}{c}\text{Hours}\\\text{biked}\end{array} + \dfrac{2\text{ miles}}{\text{hour}} \cdot \begin{array}{c}\text{Hours}\\\text{walked}\end{array} = \begin{array}{c}32\\\text{miles}\end{array}$

Write the linear equation in slope-intercept form.

 5. $2x + y = 17$

6. $5x - y = \dfrac{1}{4}$

7. $-\dfrac{1}{2}x + y = 10$

Graph the linear equation.

8. $-18x + 9y = 72$

9. $16x - 4y = 2$

10. $\dfrac{1}{4}x + \dfrac{3}{4}y = 1$

Use the graph to find the x- and y-intercepts.

11.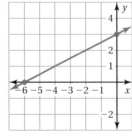

12.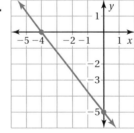

13.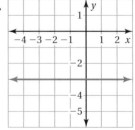

14. **ERROR ANALYSIS** Describe and correct the error in finding the x-intercept.

$$-2x + 3y = 12$$
$$-2(0) + 3y = 12$$
$$3y = 12$$
$$y = 4$$

15. **BRACELET** A charm bracelet costs $65, plus $25 for each charm.

   a. Write an equation in standard form that represents the total cost of the bracelet.

   b. How much does the bracelet shown cost?

Assignment Guide and Homework Check

Level	Day 1 Activity Assignment	Day 2 Lesson Assignment	Homework Check
Basic	3, 4, 24–26	1, 2, 5, 6, 8, 9, 11, 12, 14–19	6, 8, 12, 14, 16, 19
Average	3, 4, 24–26	1, 2, 5–13 odd, 14–21	7, 9, 13, 14, 16, 20
Advanced	3, 4, 24–26	1, 2, 8–14 even, 13, 16–23	10, 13, 14, 16, 20, 22

Common Errors

- **Exercises 5–10** Students may use the same operation instead of the opposite operation when rewriting the equation in slope-intercept form.
- **Exercises 11 and 12, 16–18** Students may mix up the x- and y-intercepts. Remind them that the x-intercept is the x-coordinate of where the line crosses the x-axis and the y-intercept is the y-coordinate of where the line crosses the y-axis.
- **Exercise 13** Because the line is horizontal and there is no x-intercept, students may say that the x-intercept is zero. Remind them that this would mean that the x-intercept is at the origin; however, there is no x-intercept.

2.4 Record and Practice Journal

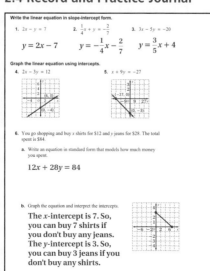

1. no; The equation is in slope-intercept form.

2. no; The graph is not a line.

 Practice and Problem Solving

3. $x =$ pounds of peaches
   $y =$ pounds of apples
   $y = -\frac{4}{3}x + 10$

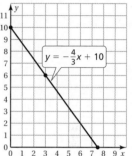

4. $x =$ hours biked
   $y =$ hours walked
   $y = -8x + 16$

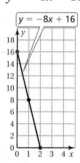

5. $y = -2x + 17$

6. $y = 5x - \frac{1}{4}$

7. $y = \frac{1}{2}x + 10$

8. $-18x + 9y = 72$

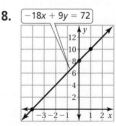

9–15. See Additional Answers.

Practice and Problem Solving

16–19. See Additional Answers.

20. See *Taking Math Deeper.*

21–23. See Additional Answers.

Fair Game Review

24. 1; 3; 5; 7; 9

25. 1; −2; −5; −8; −11

26. D

Mini-Assessment

1. Graph $-2x + 4y = 16$ using intercepts.

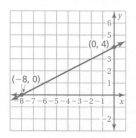

2. You have $12 to spend on pears and oranges.

a. Graph the equation $1.2x + 0.8y = 12$, where x is the number of pounds of pears and y is the number of pounds of oranges.

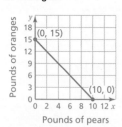

b. Interpret the intercepts.
The x-intercept shows that you can buy 10 pounds of pears if you do not buy any oranges. The y-intercept shows that you can buy 15 pounds of oranges if you do not buy any pears.

Taking Math Deeper

Exercise 20

As with many real-life problems, it helps to start by summarizing the given information.

 Summarize the given information.

- Let x = days for renting boat.
- Let y = days for renting scuba gear.
- Cost of boat = $250 per day.
- Cost of scuba gear = $50 per day.
- Total spent = $1000.

 a. Write an equation.

$$250x + 50y = 1000$$

 b. Graph the equation and interpret the intercepts.

$$y = -5x + 20$$

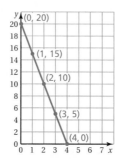

If $x = 0$, the group rented only the scuba gear for 20 days.
If $y = 0$, the group rented only the boat for 4 days.

Project

To go on a professional scuba diving tour, you need to be a certified diver. Use the school library or the Internet to research the requirements to become certified in scuba diving.

Reteaching and Enrichment Strategies

If students need help. . .	If students got it. . .
Resources by Chapter • Practice A and Practice B • Puzzle Time Record and Practice Journal Practice Differentiating the Lesson Lesson Tutorials Skills Review Handbook	Resources by Chapter • Enrichment and Extension • School-to-Work Start the next section

Graph the linear equation using intercepts.

2 **16.** $3x - 4y = -12$ **17.** $2x + y = 8$ **18.** $\frac{1}{3}x - \frac{1}{6}y = -\frac{2}{3}$

19. SHOPPING The amount of money you spend on x CDs and y DVDs is given by the equation $14x + 18y = 126$. Find the intercepts and graph the equation.

Boat: $250/day
Gear: $50/day

20. SCUBA Five friends go scuba diving. They rent a boat for x days and scuba gear for y days. The total spent is $1000.

   a. Write an equation in standard form that represents the situation.

   b. Graph the equation and interpret the intercepts.

21. WAGES You work at a restaurant as a host and a server. You earn $9.45 for each hour you work as a host and $7.65 for each hour you work as a server.

   a. Write an equation in standard form that models your earnings.

   b. Graph the equation.

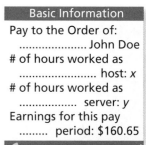

Basic Information
Pay to the Order of: .... John Doe
# of hours worked as .... host: x
# of hours worked as .... server: y
Earnings for this pay .... period: $160.65

22. REASONING Does the graph of every linear equation have an x-intercept? Explain your reasoning. Include an example.

23. **Critical Thinking** For a house call, a veterinarian charges $70, plus $40 an hour.

   a. Write an equation that represents the total fee y charged by the veterinarian for a visit lasting x hours.

   b. Find the x-intercept. Will this point appear on the graph of the equation? Explain your reasoning.

   c. Graph the equation.

 Fair Game Review *What you learned in previous grades & lessons*

Copy and complete the table of values. *(Skills Review Handbook)*

24.

x	-2	-1	0	1	2
$2x + 5$					

25.

x	-2	-1	0	1	2
$-5 - 3x$					

26. MULTIPLE CHOICE Which value of x makes the equation $4x - 12 = 3x - 9$ true? *(Section 1.3)*

   A -1 **B** 0   **C** 1   **D** 3

You can use a **process diagram** to show the steps involved in a procedure. Here is an example of a process diagram for graphing a linear equation.

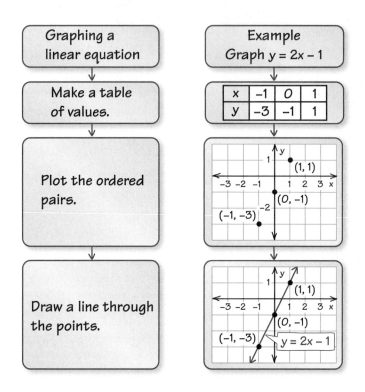

On Your Own

Make a process diagram with an example to help you study these topics.

1. finding the slope of a line

2. graphing a linear equation using
   a. slope and y-intercept
   b. x- and y-intercepts

After you complete this chapter, make process diagrams for the following topics.

3. writing equations in slope-intercept form

4. writing equations using a slope and a point

5. writing equations using two points

"Here is a process diagram with suggestions for what to do if a hyena knocks on your door."

Sample Answers

1.

Finding the Slope of a Line

↓

Determine whether the line rises or falls from left to right so you know whether the slope is positive or negative.

↓

Find the change in y or the rise. Find the change in x or the run.

↓

The slope is the ratio of the rise to run.

Example

(3, 2)

(−3,−2)

↓

The line rises from left to right. So, the slope is positive.

↓

(3, 2)

4

(−3,−2) 6

↓

$$\text{slope} = \frac{\text{rise}}{\text{run}} = \frac{4}{6} = \frac{2}{3}$$

2a.

Graphing a Linear Equation using Slope and y-Intercept

↓

Write the equation in slope-intercept form if necessary.

↓

Find the slope and y-intercept.

↓

Plot the point for the y-intercept.

↓

Use the slope to find another point and draw the line.

Example

Graph $3x + y = 2$.

↓

$y = -3x + 2$

↓

$y = -3x + 2$

slope   y-intercept

↓

(0,2)

↓

$\text{slope} = \frac{-3}{1}$
Plot the point that is 1 unit right and 3 units down from (0, 2).

(0, 2) 1

−3

$3x + y = 2$

2b. Available at *BigIdeasMath.com*.

List of Organizers
Available at *BigIdeasMath.com*

Comparison Chart
Concept Circle
Definition (Idea) and Example Chart
Example and Non-Example Chart
Formula Triangle
Four Square
Information Frame
Information Wheel
Notetaking Organizer
Process Diagram
Summary Triangle
Word Magnet
Y Chart

About this Organizer

A **Process Diagram** can be used to show the steps involved in a procedure. Process diagrams are particularly useful for illustrating procedures with two or more steps, and they can have one or more branches. As shown, students' process diagrams can have two parallel parts, in which the procedure is stepped out in one part and an example illustrating each step is shown in the other part. Or, the diagram can be made up of just one part, with example(s) included in the last "bubble" to illustrate the steps that precede it.

Technology
For the Teacher
Vocabulary Puzzle Builder

Answers

1–4. See Additional Answers.

5. $-\dfrac{1}{2}$

6. 2

7. slope: $\dfrac{1}{4}$
   y-intercept: -8

8. slope: -1
   y-intercept: 3

9. x-intercept: 4
   y-intercept: -6

10. x-intercept: 15
    y-intercept: 3

11.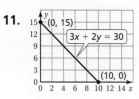

The x-intercept, 10, shows that your family can buy 10 pounds of beef if they do not buy any chicken. The y-intercept, 15, shows that your family can buy 15 pounds of chicken if they do not buy any beef.

12–14. See Additional Answers.

Alternative Quiz Ideas

100% Quiz	Math Log
Error Notebook	Notebook Quiz
Group Quiz	Partner Quiz
Homework Quiz	**Pass the Paper**

Pass the Paper

- Work in groups of four. The first student copies the problem and does a step, explaining his or her work.
- The paper is passed and the second student works through the next step, also explaining his or her work.
- This process continues until the problem is completed.
- The second member of the group starts the next problem. Students should be allowed to question and debate as they are working through the quiz.
- Student groups can be selected by the teacher, by students, through a random process, or any way that works for your class.
- The teacher walks around the classroom listening to the groups and asks questions to ensure understanding.

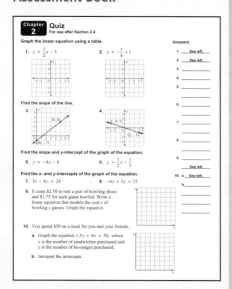
Reteaching and Enrichment Strategies

If students need help. . .	If students got it. . .
Resources by Chapter • Study Help • Practice A and Practice B • Puzzle Time Lesson Tutorials *BigIdeasMath.com* Practice Quiz Practice from the Test Generator	Resources by Chapter • Enrichment and Extension • School-to-Work Game Closet at *BigIdeasMath.com* Start the next section

Technology For the Teacher

Answer Presentation Tool
Big Ideas Test Generator

Check It Out
Progress Check
BigIdeasMath ✓com

Graph the linear equation using a table.   *(Section 2.1)*

1. $y = -12x$ **2.** $y = -x + 8$ **3.** $y = \dfrac{x}{3} - 4$ **4.** $y = 3.5$

Find the slope of the line.   *(Section 2.2)*

5. 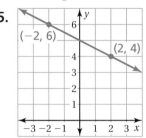   **6.**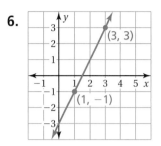

Find the slope and *y*-intercept of the graph of the equation.   *(Section 2.3)*

7. $y = \dfrac{1}{4}x - 8$ **8.** $y = -x + 3$

Find the *x*- and *y*-intercepts of the graph of the equation.   *(Section 2.4)*

9. $3x - 2y = 12$ **10.** $x + 5y = 15$

11. BARBEQUE The equation $3x + 2y = 30$ represents the amount of money your family spends on x pounds of beef and y pounds of chicken for a barbeque. Graph the equation and interpret the intercepts.   *(Section 2.4)*

12. BANKING A bank charges $3 each time you use an out-of-network ATM. At the beginning of the month, you have $1500 in your bank account. You withdraw $60 from your bank account each time you use an out-of-network ATM. Write and graph a linear equation that represents the balance in your account after you use an out-of-network ATM x times.   *(Section 2.1)*

13. STATE FAIR Write a linear equation that models the cost y of one person going on x rides at the fair. Graph the equation. *(Section 2.3)*

14. PAINTING You used $90 worth of paint for a school float.   *(Section 2.4)*

   a. Graph the equation $18x + 15y = 90$, where x is the number of gallons of blue paint and y is the number of gallons of white paint.

   b. Interpret the intercepts.

STANDARDS
OF LEARNING
8.16

Essential Question How can you write an equation of a line when you are given the slope and *y*-intercept of the line?

1 ACTIVITY: Writing Equations of Lines

Work with a partner.

- Find the slope of each line.
- Find the *y*-intercept of each line.
- Write an equation for each line.
- What do the three lines have in common?

a.

b.

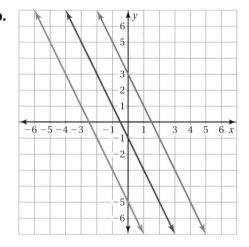

c.

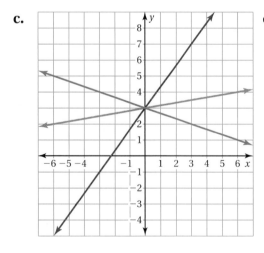

d.

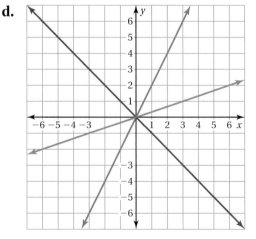

Laurie's Notes

Introduction

For the Teacher

- **Goal:** Students will determine the slope and y-intercept of a line by examining a graph. They will also write an equation in slope-intercept form.

Motivate

- If there is sufficient space in your classroom, hallway, or school foyer, make coordinate axes using masking tape. Use a marker to scale each axis with integers -5 through 5.
- Take turns having two students be the *rope anchors* who then will make a line on the coordinate axes while other students observe.
- Here are a series of directions you can give and some follow-up questions. Remind students that slope is rise over run and that the equation of a line in slope-intercept form is $y = mx + b$.
  - ❓ Make the line $y = x$. "What is the slope?" 1 "What is the y-intercept?" 0
  - ❓ Keep the same slope, but make the y-intercept 2. "What is the equation of this line?" $y = x + 2$
  - ❓ Use the y-intercept 2, but make the slope steeper. "What is the slope of this line?" Answers will vary.
  - ❓ Keep the same y-intercept, but make the slope $\frac{1}{2}$. "What is the equation?" $y = \frac{1}{2}x + 2$
- **Management Tip:** This activity can also be done by drawing the axes on the board and having the students hold the rope against the board.

Activity Notes

Activity 1

- ❓ "How do you determine the slope of a line drawn in a coordinate plane?" Use two points that you are sure are on the graph and find the rise and run between the points.
- ❓ "Does it matter whether you move left-to-right or right-to-left when you're finding the rise and run? Explain." No; Either way the slope will be the same.
- Students may have difficulty writing the equation in slope-intercept form. They think it should be harder to do!
- **FYI:** When the y-intercept is negative, students may leave their equation as $y = 3x + (-4)$ instead of $y = 3x - 4$. Remind students that it is more common to represent the equation as $y = 3x - 4$.
- **Teaching Tip:** If you have a student that is color blind, refer to the lines by a number or letter scheme (1, 2, 3 or A, B, C).
- Ask students to share what they found in common for each trio of lines.

Standards of Learning

8.16 The student will graph a linear equation in two variables.

Previous Learning

Students should know how to find the slope of a line. Students should know about parallel lines.

Activity Materials
Introduction
- masking tape - rope or yarn

Start Thinking! and Warm Up

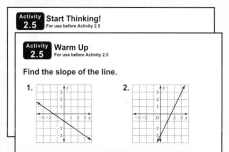

2.5 Record and Practice Journal

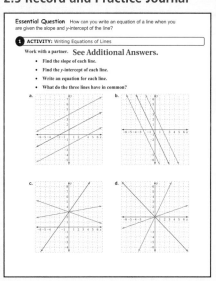

Differentiated Instruction

Visual

To avoid mistakes when substituting the variables, have students color code the slope and y-intercept of an equation.

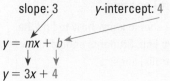

slope: 3 y-intercept: 4

$y = mx + b$

$y = 3x + 4$

2.5 Record and Practice Journal

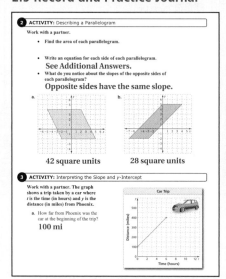

2 ACTIVITY: Describing a Parallelogram

Work with a partner.

- Find the area of each parallelogram.
- Write an equation for each side of each parallelogram.
  See Additional Answers.
- What do you notice about the slopes of the opposite sides of each parallelogram?
  Opposite sides have the same slope.

a.   b.

42 square units   28 square units

3 ACTIVITY: Interpreting the Slope and y-Intercept

Work with a partner. The graph shows a trip taken by a car where t is the time (in hours) and y is the distance (in miles) from Phoenix.

a. How far from Phoenix was the car at the beginning of the trip?
   100 mi

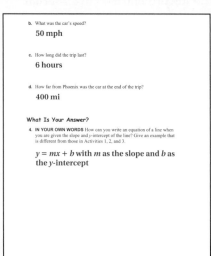

b. What was the car's speed?
   50 mph

c. How long did the trip last?
   6 hours

d. How far from Phoenix was the car at the end of the trip?
   400 mi

What Is Your Answer?

4. IN YOUR OWN WORDS How can you write an equation of a line when you are given the slope and y-intercept of the line? Give an example that is different from those in Activities 1, 2, and 3.

   $y = mx + b$ with m as the slope and b as the y-intercept

Laurie's Notes

Activity 2

? "How do you find the area of a parallelogram?" area = base × height

? "Are the base and height the sides of the parallelogram?" They could be if it's a rectangle. Otherwise, height is the perpendicular distance between the two bases.

- To find the base and height, students simply count the units on the diagram. Note that the height for the parallelogram in part (b) is outside the parallelogram.

- **Common Error:** The slope of the horizontal sides is zero. Students may say that you cannot find the slope *for a flat line.*

? "What is the equation of a horizontal line?" $y = b$

- The challenge in this activity is writing the equations for the diagonal sides of the figure in part (a). Suggest that by extending the sides using the slope, the students should be able to determine the y-intercept. For example: the slopes of the two diagonal sides are -2. This means a rise of -2 and a run of 1. Start at a vertex of one of the sides and use the slope to extend the side to the y-axis. Repeat the process for the other side.

- This activity reviews positive, negative, and zero slope.

Activity 3

- If students have difficulty getting started with this activity, remind them to read the labels on the axes. Another hint is to ask them how to interpret the y-intercept. The car was 100 miles from Phoenix at the beginning of the trip.

- Discuss answers to each part of the problem as a class.

? **Extension:** Draw the segment from (6, 400) to (12, 0) and explain that this represents the return trip. Ask the following questions.

  - "What is the slope of this line segment? What does the slope mean in the context of the problem?" slope ≈ -67; returning at a rate of about 67 mi/h

  - "What does the point (12, 0) mean in the context of the problem?" You have arrived in Phoenix.

  - "What would the graph look like if the car had stopped for 1 hour?" horizontal segment of length 1 unit

Closure

- **Exit Ticket:** What is the slope and y-intercept of the equation $y = 2x + 4$? slope = 2, y-intercept = 4 Write the equation of a line with a slope of 3 and a y-intercept of 1. $y = 3x + 1$

Technology For the Teacher

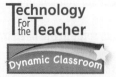

The Dynamic Planning Tool
Editable Teacher's Resources at *BigIdeasMath.com*

2 ACTIVITY: Describing a Parallelogram

Work with a partner.

- Find the area of each parallelogram.
- Write an equation for each side of each parallelogram.
- What do you notice about the slopes of the opposite sides of each parallelogram?

a.

b.

3 ACTIVITY: Interpreting the Slope and y-Intercept

Work with a partner. The graph shows a trip taken by a car where *t* is the time (in hours) and *y* is the distance (in miles) from Phoenix.

a. How far from Phoenix was the car at the beginning of the trip?

b. What was the car's speed?

c. How long did the trip last?

d. How far from Phoenix was the car at the end of the trip?

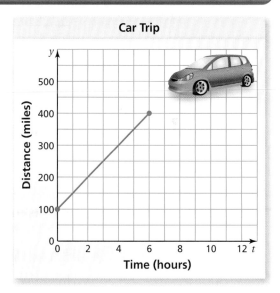

Car Trip

What Is Your Answer?

4. **IN YOUR OWN WORDS** How can you write an equation of a line when you are given the slope and *y*-intercept of the line? Give an example that is different from those in Activities 1, 2, and 3.

Practice

Use what you learned about writing equations in slope-intercept form to complete Exercises 3 and 4 on page 94.

Check It Out
Lesson Tutorials
BigIdeasMath ✔com

EXAMPLE 1   Writing Equations in Slope-Intercept Form

Write an equation of the line in slope-intercept form.

a.

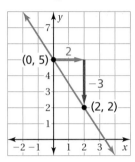

Find the slope and y-intercept.

$$\text{slope} = \frac{\text{rise}}{\text{run}} = \frac{-3}{2} = -\frac{3}{2}$$

Study Tip

After writing an equation, check that the given points are solutions of the equation.

Because the line crosses the y-axis at $(0, 5)$, the y-intercept is 5.

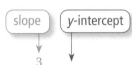

∴ So, the equation is $y = -\dfrac{3}{2}x + 5$.

b.

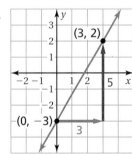

Find the slope and y-intercept.

$$\text{slope} = \frac{\text{rise}}{\text{run}} = \frac{5}{3}$$

Because the line crosses the y-axis at $(0, -3)$, the y-intercept is -3.

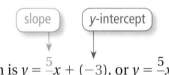

∴ So, the equation is $y = \dfrac{5}{3}x + (-3)$, or $y = \dfrac{5}{3}x - 3$.

● **On Your Own**

Now You're Ready
Exercises 5–10

Write an equation of the line in slope-intercept form.

1.

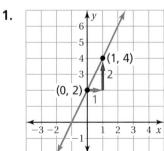

2.

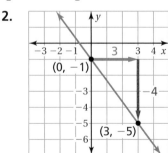

Laurie's Notes

Introduction

Connect

- **Yesterday:** Students developed an intuitive understanding about how to write the equation of a line when you know its slope and *y*-intercept.
- **Today:** Students will write the equation of a line given its slope and *y*-intercept.

Motivate

- **Story Time:** Tell students that as a child you loved to dig tunnels in the sand. Ask if any of them like to dig tunnels or if they have traveled through tunnels. Hold a paper towel tube or other similar model to pique student interest. Share some facts about tunnels.
  - The world's longest overland tunnel is a 21-mile-long rail link under the Alps in Switzerland and was built to ease highway traffic jams in the mountainous country. The tunnel took eight years to build and cost $3.5 billion. It reduces the time trains need to cross between Germany and Italy from 3.5 hours to just under 2 hours.
  - The world's longest underwater tunnel is Seikan Tunnel in Japan. It is 33.49 miles long and runs under the Tsugaru Strait. It opened in 1988 and took 17 years to construct.
  - The Channel Tunnel (Chunnel) connects England and France. It is 31 miles long and travels under the English Channel.

Lesson Notes

Example 1

- Write the slope-intercept form of an equation, $y = mx + b$. Review with students that the coefficient of *x* is the slope, and the constant *b* is the *y*-intercept.
- **?** "What do you know about the slope of the line just by inspection? Explain." Slope is negative because the graph falls left to right.
- **?** "What are the coordinates of the point where the line crosses the *y*-axis?" (0, 5)
- Use the slope and the *y*-intercept to write the equation.
- Work through part (b). Remind students that you want the more simplified equation $y = \frac{5}{3}x - 3$ instead of $y = \frac{5}{3}x + (-3)$. Stress that while both forms are correct, the simplified version is preferred.

On Your Own

- Before students begin these two problems, they should do a visual inspection. They should make a note of the sign of the slope and *y*-intercept. It is very easy to have the wrong sign(s) when the equation is written.

Goal Today's lesson is writing the equation of a line in slope-intercept form.

Lesson Materials
Introduction
• paper towel tube

Start Thinking! and Warm Up

 Warm Up For use before Lesson 2.5

 Start Thinking! For use before Lesson 2.5

A gym membership has a $20 enrollment fee and costs $40 per month.

Write an equation in slope-intercept form that represents the cost *y* after *x* months of joining the gym.

What does the slope represent?

What does the *y*-intercept represent?

Extra Example 1

Write an equation of the line in slope-intercept form.

a.

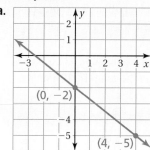

$$y = -\frac{3}{4}x - 2$$

b.

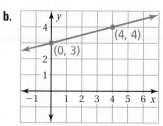

$$y = \frac{1}{4}x + 3$$

On Your Own

1. $y = 2x + 2$

2. $y = -\frac{4}{3}x - 1$

Extra Example 2

Write an equation of the line that passes through the points $(0, -1)$ and $(4, -1)$. $y = -1$

Extra Example 3

In Example 3, the points are (0, 3500) and (5, 1750).

a. Write an equation that represents the distance y (in feet) remaining after x months. $y = -350x + 3500$

b. How much time does it take to complete the tunnel? 10 months

On Your Own

3. $y = 5$

4. $8\frac{3}{4}$ mo

English Language Learners

Organization

Students will benefit by writing down the steps for writing an equation in slope-intercept form when given a graph. Have students write the steps in their notebooks. A poster with the steps could be posted in the classroom.

Step 1: Write the slope-intercept form of an equation.

Step 2: Determine the slope of the line.

Step 3: Determine the y-intercept of the line.

Step 4: Write the equation in slope-intercept form.

Example 2

- Make a quick sketch of the graph to reference as you work the problem.

- When finding the slope, students are unsure of how to simplify $\frac{0}{3}$. This is a good time to review the difference between $\frac{0}{3}$ and $\frac{3}{0}$.

- **Teaching Tip:** $\frac{3}{0}$ is undefined. The explanation I give students that seems to resonate with them is to write the problem $8 \div 4 = 2$ on the board. Then I rewrite it as $4\overline{)8}$. To check, multiply the quotient (2) times the divisor (4) and you get the dividend (8). In other words, 2 multiplied by 4 is 8. Do the same thing with $\frac{3}{0}$. Rewrite it using long division, $0\overline{)3}$. What do you multiply 0 by to get 3? There is no quotient, so you say $\frac{3}{0}$ is undefined. You cannot divide by 0.

- Students don't always recognize that $y = -4$ is a linear equation written in slope-intercept form. It helps to write the extra step of $y = (0)x + (-4)$ so students can see that the slope is 0.

Example 3

- Ask a volunteer to read the problem. Discuss information that can be *read* from the graph.

- ? "By visual inspection, what do you know about the sign of the slope and the y-intercept in this problem?" The slope is negative. The y-intercept is positive.

- Before moving on to part (b), ask students to interpret what a slope of -500 means in the context of this problem. A slope of -500 means that for each additional month of work, the distance left to complete is 500 feet less.

- The x-intercept for this graph is 7.

- Note that the graph is in Quadrant I. In the context of this problem, it doesn't make sense for time or distance to be negative.

On Your Own

- For Question 3, encourage students to sketch a graph of the line through the two points to give them a clue as to how to begin. This technique will help students start Question 4.

Closure

- **Writing Prompt:** For a line that has been graphed in a coordinate plane, you can write the equation by … finding the slope and y-intercept

Technology For the Teacher

The Dynamic Planning Tool
Editable Teacher's Resources at *BigIdeasMath.com*

EXAMPLE 2 **Standardized Test Practice**

Which equation is shown in the graph?

Ⓐ $y = -4$ Ⓑ $y = -3$

Ⓒ $y = 0$ Ⓓ $y = -3x$

Remember

The graph of $y = a$ is a horizontal line that passes through $(0, a)$.

Find the slope and y-intercept.

The line is horizontal, so the rise is 0.

$$\text{slope} = \frac{\text{rise}}{\text{run}} = \frac{0}{3} = 0$$

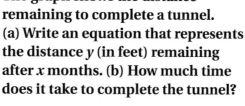

Because the line crosses the y-axis at $(0, -4)$, the y-intercept is -4.

∴ So, the equation is $y = 0x + (-4)$, or $y = -4$. The correct answer is Ⓐ.

EXAMPLE 3 **Real-Life Application**

The graph shows the distance remaining to complete a tunnel. **(a) Write an equation that represents the distance y (in feet) remaining after x months. (b) How much time does it take to complete the tunnel?**

a. Find the slope and y-intercept.

$$\text{slope} = \frac{\text{rise}}{\text{run}} = \frac{-2000}{4} = -500$$

Because the line crosses the y-axis at $(0, 3500)$, the y-intercept is 3500.

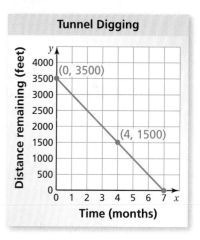

Tunnel Digging

∴ So, the equation is $y = -500x + 3500$.

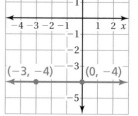

Engineers used tunnel boring machines like the ones shown above to dig an extension of the Metro Gold Line in Los Angeles. The new tunnels are 1.7 miles long and 21 feet wide.

b. The tunnel is complete when the distance remaining is 0 feet. So, find the value of x when $y = 0$.

$y = -500x + 3500$	Write the equation.
$0 = -500x + 3500$	Substitute 0 for y.
$-3500 = -500x$	Subtract 3500 from each side.
$7 = x$	Solve for x.

∴ It takes 7 months to complete the tunnel.

On Your Own

Now You're Ready
Exercises 13–15

3. Write an equation of the line that passes through $(0, 5)$ and $(4, 5)$.

4. WHAT IF? In Example 3, the points are $(0, 3500)$ and $(5, 1500)$. How long does it take to complete the tunnel?

 Vocabulary and Concept Check

1. **WRITING** Explain how to find the slope of a line given the intercepts of the line.

2. **WRITING** Explain how to write an equation of a line using its graph.

 Practice and Problem Solving

Write an equation for each side of the figure.

3.
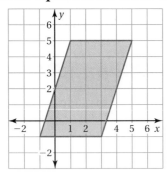

4.
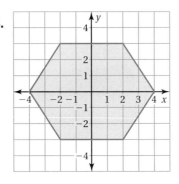

Write an equation of the line in slope-intercept form.

 5.
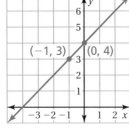

6.
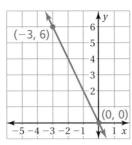

7.
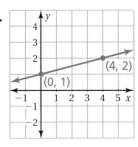

8.
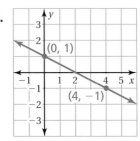

9.
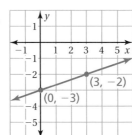

10.
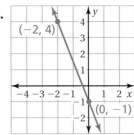

11. **ERROR ANALYSIS** Describe and correct the error in writing the equation of the line.

12. **BOA** A boa constrictor is 18 inches long at birth and grows 8 inches per year. Write an equation that represents the length y (in feet) of a boa constrictor that is x years old.

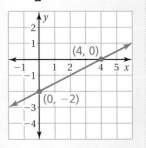
$y = \frac{1}{2}x + 4$

Assignment Guide and Homework Check

Level	Day 1 Activity Assignment	Day 2 Lesson Assignment	Homework Check
Basic	3, 4, 20–24	1, 2, 5–16	6, 9, 12, 13, 16
Average	3, 4, 20–24	1, 2, 6–17	6, 9, 12, 14, 16
Advanced	3, 4, 20–24	1, 2, 8–19	8, 14, 16, 18

Common Errors

- **Exercises 5–10** Students may write the reciprocal of the slope or forget a negative sign. Remind them of the definition of slope. Ask students to predict the sign of the slope based on the rise or fall of the line.
- **Exercises 13–15** Students may write the wrong equation when the slope is zero. For example, instead of $y = 5$, students may write $x = 5$. Ask them what is the rise of the graph (zero) and write this in slope-intercept form with the y-intercept as well, such as $y = 0x + 5$. Then ask students what happens when a variable (or any number) is multiplied by zero. Rewrite the equation as $y = 5$.

2.5 Record and Practice Journal

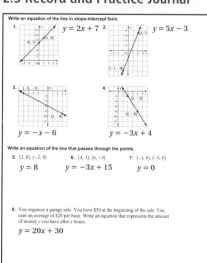

Write an equation of the line in slope-intercept form.

1. $y = 2x + 7$ 2. $y = 5x - 3$

3. $y = -x - 6$ 4. $y = -3x + 4$

Write an equation of the line that passes through the points.

5. $(3, 8), (-2, 8)$ 6. $(4, 3), (6, -3)$ 7. $(-1, 0), (-5, 0)$
   $y = 8$ $y = -3x + 15$ $y = 0$

8. You organize a garage sale. You have $30 at the beginning of the sale. You earn an average of $20 per hour. Write an equation that represents the amount of money y you have after x hours.
   $y = 20x + 30$

1. *Sample answer:* Find the ratio of the rise to the run between the intercepts.

2. *Sample answer:* Find the slope of the line between any two points. Then find the y-intercept. The equation of the line is $y = mx + b$, where m is the slope and b is the y-intercept.

 Practice and Problem Solving

3. $y = 3x + 2$;
   $y = 3x - 10$;
   $y = 5$;
   $y = -1$

4. $y = \frac{3}{2}x + 6$;
   $y = 3$;
   $y = -\frac{3}{2}x + 6$;
   $y = \frac{3}{2}x - 6$;
   $y = -3$;
   $y = -\frac{3}{2}x - 6$

5. $y = x + 4$

6. $y = -2x$

7. $y = \frac{1}{4}x + 1$

8. $y = -\frac{1}{2}x + 1$

9. $y = \frac{1}{3}x - 3$

10. $y = -\frac{5}{2}x - 1$

11. The x-intercept was used instead of the y-intercept.
    $y = \frac{1}{2}x - 2$

12. $y = \frac{2}{3}x + \frac{3}{2}$

13. $y = 5$ 14. $y = 0$

15. $y = -2$ 16. $y = 0.7x + 10$

17. See Additional Answers.

18. $y = -140x + 500$

19. See *Taking Math Deeper*.

 Fair Game Review

20–23.

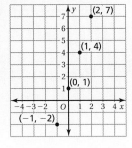

24. C

Mini-Assessment

Write an equation of the line in slope-intercept form.

1. $y = x + 2$

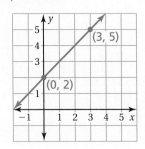

2. $y = -2x - 1$

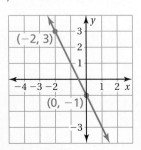

Taking Math Deeper

Exercise 19

This is a nice real-life problem using estimation. For this problem, remember that you are not looking for exact solutions. You want to know *about* how much the trees grow each year so that you can predict their approximate heights.

 Estimate the heights in the photograph.

   a. Height of 10-year-old tree: about 18 ft
     Height of 8-year-old tree: about 14 ft

 b. Plot the heights of the two trees.

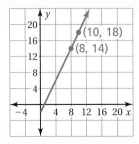 

 c. The trees are growing at a rate of about 2 feet per year. Because this would put the height of a 0-year-old tree at -2, it is better to adjust the rate of growth to be about 1.8 feet per year.

   d. A possible equation for the growth rate is $y = 1.8x$.

Project

Research information about the palm tree. Pick any kind of palm tree in which you are interested. How old is the longest living palm tree?

Reteaching and Enrichment Strategies

If students need help. . .	If students got it. . .

Resources by Chapter
  • Practice A and Practice B
  • Puzzle Time
Record and Practice Journal Practice
Differentiating the Lesson
Lesson Tutorials
Skills Review Handbook
	Resources by Chapter
	  • Enrichment and Extension
	  • School-to-Work
	  • Financial Literacy
	Start the next section

Write an equation of the line that passes through the points.

② 13. $(2, 5), (0, 5)$ **14.** $(-3, 0), (0, 0)$ **15.** $(0, -2), (4, -2)$

16. WALKATHON One of your friends gives you $10 for a charity walkathon. Another friend gives you an amount per mile. After 5 miles, you have raised $13.50 total. Write an equation that represents the amount y of money you have raised after x miles.

17. BRAKING TIME During each second of braking, an automobile slows by about 10 miles per hour.

   a. Plot the points $(0, 60)$ and $(6, 0)$. What do the points represent?

   b. Draw a line through the points. What does the line represent?

   c. Write an equation of the line.

18. PAPER You have 500 sheets of notebook paper. After 1 week, you have 72% of the sheets left. You use the same number of sheets each week. Write an equation that represents the number y of pages remaining after x weeks.

19. **Critical Thinking** The palm tree on the left is 10 years old. The palm tree on the right is 8 years old. The trees grow at the same rate.

   a. Estimate the height y (in feet) of each tree.

   b. Plot the two points (x, y), where x is the age of each tree and y is the height of each tree.

   c. What is the rate of growth of the trees?

   d. Write an equation that represents the height of a palm tree in terms of its age.

6 ft

Fair Game Review What you learned in previous grades & lessons

Plot the ordered pair in a coordinate plane. *(Skills Review Handbook)*

20. $(1, 4)$ **21.** $(-1, -2)$ **22.** $(0, 1)$ **23.** $(2, 7)$

24. MULTIPLE CHOICE Which of the following statements is true? *(Section 2.3)*

   Ⓐ The x-intercept is 5.

   Ⓑ The x-intercept is -2.

   Ⓒ The y-intercept is 5.

   Ⓓ The y-intercept is -2.

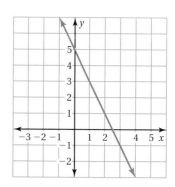

2.6 Writing Equations Using a Slope and a Point

STANDARDS OF LEARNING

8.16

Essential Question How can you write an equation of a line when you are given the slope and a point on the line?

1 ACTIVITY: Writing Equations of Lines

Work with a partner.

- Sketch the line that has the given slope and passes through the given point.
- Find the y-intercept of the line.
- Write an equation of the line.

a. $m = -2$

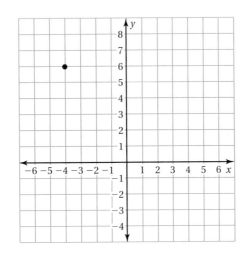

b. $m = \dfrac{1}{3}$

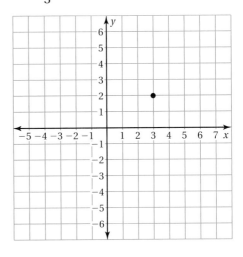

c. $m = -\dfrac{2}{3}$

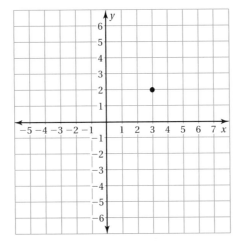

d. $m = \dfrac{5}{2}$

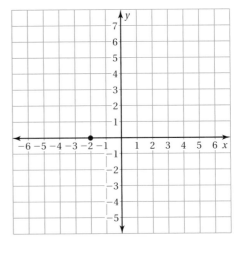

Laurie's Notes

Introduction

For the Teacher

- **Goal:** Students will explore writing an equation of a line given the slope and a point that is not on the *y*-axis.

Motivate

- Hold a piece of ribbon and a pair of scissors in your hands. Snip a one-foot piece of ribbon off. Repeat once or twice more.
- **?** "Do you know how long my ribbon was when I first started?" no
- Your question should prompt students to ask two obvious questions: "How much are you cutting off each time?" and "How many times have you made a cut?" How much you cut off is the slope (−1). How many times you cut the ribbon helps students work backwards to find the length before any cuts were made, which is the *y*-intercept.

Discuss

- Explain that today students will be writing the equation of a line. Some of the problems will be presented on the coordinate grid, while others will be presented as a story, like the ribbon. They need to figure out the slope and the *y*-intercept.

Activity Notes

Activity 1

- **?** "What does it mean for a line to have a slope of −2? A slope of $\frac{1}{3}$?"

  For every unit it runs, it falls 2 units. For every 3 units it runs, it rises 1.

- Students may also answer the last question by saying "over 1, down 2" and "over 3, up 1." These geometric answers are fine. Students will need this level of understanding to locate additional points on a line, in order to find the *y*-intercept.
- You cannot sketch the line immediately. You must first find additional points on the line.
- Students should start at the given point and use the slope to find additional points on the line. One of the points will give the *y*-intercept.
- For part (b), it might be helpful to think of the slope of $\frac{1}{3}$ as $\frac{-1}{-3}$. So, start at the point given and move left 3 units and then down 1 unit.
- **Common Error:** Students may interchange the rise and run. Have students look back at their graph to see if the slope looks correct to them.
- **Teaching Tip:** Encourage students to use a pencil and lightly trace the rise and run direction arrows as they locate additional points.
- To share student work, have transparency grids available for the overhead.
- **?** "What made it possible to write the equation of the line?" The slope was given and by using the slope, it was possible to find the *y*-intercept. Then substitute into the formula $y = mx + b$.

Standards of Learning

8.16 The student will graph a linear equation in two variables.

Previous Learning

Students should know how to plot ordered pairs and apply the definition of slope.

Activity Materials	
Introduction	**Textbook**
- scissors - yarn, rope, or ribbon	- straightedge - transparency grid

Start Thinking! and Warm Up

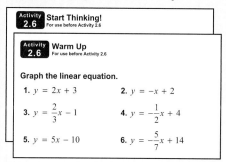

Activity 2.6 Start Thinking! For use before Activity 2.6

Activity 2.6 Warm Up For use before Activity 2.6

Graph the linear equation.

1. $y = 2x + 3$
2. $y = -x + 2$
3. $y = \frac{2}{3}x - 1$
4. $y = -\frac{1}{2}x + 4$
5. $y = 5x - 10$
6. $y = -\frac{5}{7}x + 14$

2.6 Record and Practice Journal

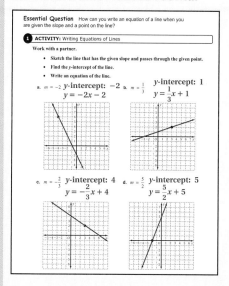

Essential Question How can you write an equation of a line when you are given the slope and a point on the line?

1 ACTIVITY: Writing Equations of Lines

Work with a partner.

- Sketch the line that has the given slope and passes through the given point.
- Find the *y*-intercept of the line.
- Write an equation of the line.

a. $m = -2$ *y*-intercept: −2 $y = -2x - 2$

b. $m = \frac{1}{3}$ *y*-intercept: 1 $y = \frac{1}{3}x + 1$

c. $m = -\frac{2}{3}$ *y*-intercept: 4 $y = -\frac{2}{3}x + 4$

d. $m = \frac{5}{2}$ *y*-intercept: 5 $y = \frac{5}{2}x + 5$

Differentiated Instruction

Kinesthetic

Write a list of linear equations on the board or overhead. Have students copy the equations onto index cards. On the back of each card students are to write the slope and y-intercept of the line. After the cards are completed, students can work in pairs to check each other's work. Finally students can quiz each other with the flash cards they made.

Activity 2

- The strategy is the same as for Activity 1. The slope may not be obvious.
- **Part (a):** If students do not understand what the slope is, suggest they work backwards and make a table of values. Students should use the variables t and A instead of x and y.

Month, t	0	1	2	3	4
Balance in Account, A	\$75	\$100	\$125	\$150	\$175

- ❓ Ask a few questions to guide students' understanding:
  - "What is the slope for this problem? What is the A-intercept?" slope = \$25; A-intercept = \$75
  - "Do you have enough information to write the equation?" yes; $A = 25t + 75$
  - "Explain why the slope is positive." You are putting money in the bank. Your account is growing.
- **Part (b):** Some students will need to make a table of values, while others will know the slope is -25.
- ❓ "What does the A-intercept mean in the context of this problem?" How much money you started with (in your account) 4 months ago.
- **Part (c):** Encourage students to plot points representing the population for prior years.
- **Big Idea:** For each of these real-life problems, the slope is given in words. A point on the line is given so that the P-intercept can be determined using the slope. Each problem is an example of writing an equation of a line, given the slope and a point on the line.

What Is Your Answer?

- **Neighbor Check:** Have students work independently and then have their neighbor check their work. Have students discuss any discrepancies.

2.6 Record and Practice Journal

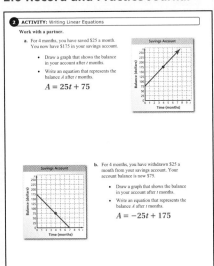

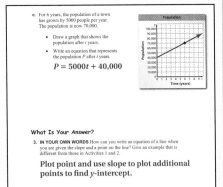

Closure

- Refer back to the ribbon and scissors. If the ribbon is now 7 feet and you made 4 equal cuts of 1-foot length, write the equation that gives the length of the ribbon R after n cuts. $R = 11 - n$ or $R = -n + 11$

Technology For the Teacher

Dynamic Classroom

The Dynamic Planning Tool
Editable Teacher's Resources at *BigIdeasMath.com*

Work with a partner.

a. For 4 months, you have saved $25 a month. You now have $175 in your savings account.

- Draw a graph that shows the balance in your account after t months.
- Write an equation that represents the balance A after t months.

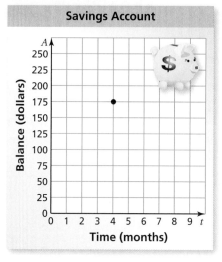

Savings Account

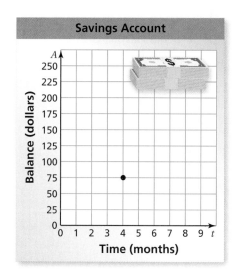

Savings Account

b. For 4 months, you have withdrawn $25 a month from your savings account. Your account balance is now $75.

- Draw a graph that shows the balance in your account after t months.
- Write an equation that represents the balance A after t months.

c. For 6 years, the population of a town has grown by 5000 people per year. The population is now 70,000.

- Draw a graph that shows the population after t years.
- Write an equation that represents the population P after t years.

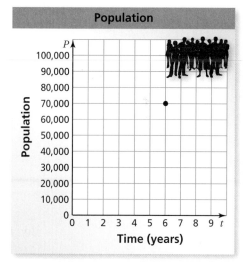

Population

What Is Your Answer?

3. IN YOUR OWN WORDS How can you write an equation of a line when you are given the slope and a point on the line? Give an example that is different from those in Activities 1 and 2.

Practice

Use what you learned about writing equations using a slope and a point to complete Exercises 3–5 on page 100.

EXAMPLE 1 **Writing Equations Using a Slope and a Point**

Write an equation of the line with the given slope that passes through the given point.

a. $m = \dfrac{2}{3};\ (-6, 1)$

Use a graph to find the y-intercept.

Check

Check that $(-6, 1)$ is a solution of the equation.

$y = \dfrac{2}{3}x + 5$

$1 \overset{?}{=} \dfrac{2}{3}(-6) + 5$

$1 = 1$ ✓

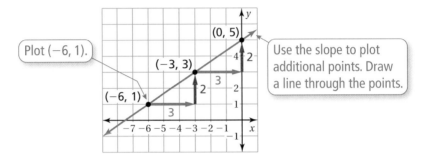

Plot $(-6, 1)$.

$(0, 5)$

Use the slope to plot additional points. Draw a line through the points.

$(-3, 3)$

$(-6, 1)$

Because the line crosses the y-axis at $(0, 5)$, the y-intercept is 5.

∴ So, the equation is $y = \dfrac{2}{3}x + 5$.

b. $m = -3;\ (1, -4)$

Use a graph to find the y-intercept.

Check

Check that $(1, -4)$ is a solution of the equation.

$y = -3x - 1$

$-4 \overset{?}{=} -3(1) - 1$

$-4 = -4$ ✓

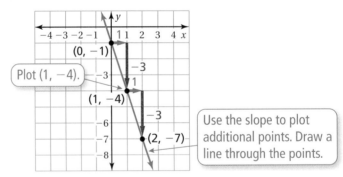

$(0, -1)$

Plot $(1, -4)$.

$(1, -4)$

$(2, -7)$

Use the slope to plot additional points. Draw a line through the points.

Because the line crosses the y-axis at $(0, -1)$, the y-intercept is -1.

∴ So, the equation is $y = -3x + (-1)$, or $y = -3x - 1$.

On Your Own

Now You're Ready
Exercises 6–11

Write an equation of the line with the given slope that passes through the given point.

1. $m = 1;\ (2, 0)$

2. $m = -\dfrac{1}{2};\ (2, 3)$

Laurie's Notes

Introduction

Connect

- **Yesterday:** Students developed an intuitive understanding of how to write the equation of a line given the slope and a point.
- **Today:** Students will write the equation of a line given the slope and a point.

Motivate

- ❓ "Have you seen an airplane come in for a landing either in real life, on the television, or in movies?" Most will answer yes.
- ❓ "Can you describe in words or with a picture what it looks like?" Listen for a smooth approach, meaning a constant rate of descent.
- ❓ "If the plane descends 200 feet per second, what is its height 5 seconds before it lands?" 1000 ft
- Make a sketch of this scenario and ask if it's possible to write an equation that models the height h of the airplane, t seconds before it lands.

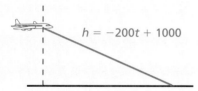

$$h = -200t + 1000$$

Lesson Notes

Example 1

- Write the slope-intercept form of a linear equation: $y = mx + b$.
- Discuss with students that it is possible to find the y-intercept using the slope and a point, and then plotting additional points on the graph.
- Write the given information: slope $m = \dfrac{2}{3}$ and the point is $(-6, 1)$.
- ❓ After plotting $(-6, 1)$ ask, "Is it possible to find additional points on the line? Explain." Yes; Use the slope of $\dfrac{2}{3}$ to plot additional points.
- Once additional points are plotted, use a straightedge to draw the line.
- Encourage students to check that the equation contains the given point.
- **Part (b):** The red and blue arrows make it look as though you started at the point $(0, -1)$. Starting at $(1, -4)$, you can also show the arrow going 1 unit to the left (run $= -1$) and up 3 units (rise $= 3$). The slope is -3.

On Your Own

- Students begin by plotting the known point. Ask students to lay their pencil on the ordered pair and angle their pencil so that the given slope is modeled. This gives students a visual image of the line and approximately what the y-intercept is. Model this process at the overhead using a piece of spaghetti and a transparency grid.

Goal Today's lesson is writing the equation of a line given a slope and a point.

Lesson Materials
Textbook
• straightedge

Start Thinking! and Warm Up

Lesson **2.6** Warm Up
For use before Lesson 2.6

Lesson **2.6** Start Thinking!
For use before Lesson 2.6

How is writing the equation of a line given the slope and a point on the line similar to writing the equation of a line given the slope and y-intercept? How is it different?

Extra Example 1

Write an equation of the line with the given slope that passes through the given point.

a. $m = \dfrac{5}{2}$; $(2, 2)$ $y = \dfrac{5}{2}x - 3$

b. $m = -\dfrac{4}{3}$; $(3, 6)$ $y = -\dfrac{4}{3}x + 10$

🔵 On Your Own

1. $y = x - 2$

2. $y = -\dfrac{1}{2}x + 4$

Extra Example 2

You are pulling down your kite at a rate of 2 feet per second. After 3 seconds, your kite is 54 feet above you.

a. Write an equation that represents the height y (in feet) of the kite above you after x seconds. $y = -2x + 60$

b. At what height was the kite flying? 60 ft

c. How long does it take to pull the kite down? 30 sec

 On Your Own

3. after 5.5 sec

English Language Learners

Visual

Encourage English learners to plot the given point in the coordinate plane and then use the slope. The graph will give them a visual reference they can use when writing the equation.

Example 2

- Ask a volunteer to read the problem. Discuss information that can be *read* from the illustration.
- ? "Have any of you parasailed?" Wait for students to respond. Explain that you want a smooth descent, like an airplane.
- ? "What is the slope for this problem? How did you know?" Slope is -10. The arrow pointing down means the slope is negative.
- Students may start at (2, 25) and want to plot additional points to the right of (2, 25). This approach is helpful in answering part (c); however, you still need to determine the y-intercept.
- **Extension:** Discuss the need to restrict this problem to the first quadrant.

Closure

- **Exit Ticket:** Write an equation of the line with a slope of 2 that passes through the point $(-1, 4)$. $y = 2x + 6$

Technology For the **Teacher**

Dynamic Classroom

The Dynamic Planning Tool
Editable Teacher's Resources at *BigIdeasMath.com*

EXAMPLE 2 Real-Life Application

You finish parasailing and are being pulled back to the boat. After 2 seconds, you are 25 feet above the boat. (a) Write an equation that represents the height y (in feet) above the boat after x seconds. (b) At what height were you parasailing? (c) When do you reach the boat?

10 feet per second

a. You are being pulled down at the rate of 10 feet per second. So, the slope is -10. You are 25 feet above the boat after 2 seconds. So, the line passes through $(2, 25)$.

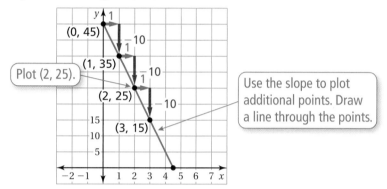

Plot (2, 25).

Use the slope to plot additional points. Draw a line through the points.

Because the line crosses the y-axis at $(0, 45)$, the y-intercept is 45.

So, the equation is $y = -10x + 45$.

Check

Check that $(2, 25)$ is a solution of the equation.

$$y = -10x + 45 \qquad \text{Write the equation.}$$

$$25 \stackrel{?}{=} -10(2) + 45 \qquad \text{Substitute.}$$

$$25 = 25 \checkmark \qquad \text{Simplify.}$$

b. You start descending when $x = 0$. The y-intercept is 45. So, you were parasailing at a height of 45 feet.

c. You reach the boat when $y = 0$.

$$y = -10x + 45 \qquad \text{Write the equation.}$$

$$0 = -10x + 45 \qquad \text{Substitute 0 for } y.$$

$$-45 = -10x \qquad \text{Subtract 45 from each side.}$$

$$4.5 = x \qquad \text{Solve for } x.$$

You reach the boat after 4.5 seconds.

On Your Own

3. **WHAT IF?** In Example 2, you are 35 feet above the boat after 2 seconds. When do you reach the boat?

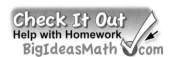
 Vocabulary and Concept Check

1. **WRITING** What information do you need to write an equation of a line?

2. **WRITING** Describe how to write an equation of a line using its slope and a point on the line.

 Practice and Problem Solving

Write an equation of the line with the given slope that passes through the given point.

3. $m = \dfrac{1}{2}$

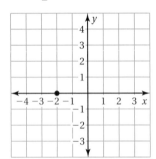

4. $m = -\dfrac{3}{4}$

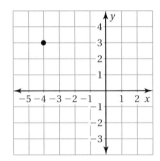

5. $m = -3$

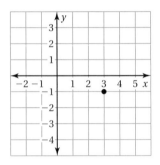

① 6. $m = -\dfrac{2}{3}$; $(3, 0)$

7. $m = \dfrac{3}{4}$; $(4, 8)$

8. $m = 4$; $(1, -3)$

9. $m = -\dfrac{1}{7}$; $(7, -5)$

10. $m = \dfrac{5}{3}$; $(3, 3)$

11. $m = -2$; $(-1, -4)$

12. **ERROR ANALYSIS** Describe and correct the error in writing an equation of the line with a slope of $\dfrac{1}{3}$ that passes through the point $(6, 4)$.

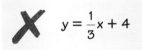
$$\text{✗}\quad y = \tfrac{1}{3}x + 4$$

13. **CHEMISTRY** At $0\,°C$, the volume of a gas is 22 liters. For each degree the temperature T (in degrees Celsius) increases, the volume V (in liters) of the gas increases by $\dfrac{2}{25}$. Write an equation that represents the volume of the gas in terms of the temperature.

Assignment Guide and Homework Check

Level	Day 1 Activity Assignment	Day 2 Lesson Assignment	Homework Check
Basic	3–5, 18, 19	1, 2, 7–13 odd, 12, 14	7, 9, 12, 14
Average	3–5, 18, 19	1, 2, 7, 9, 11, 12, 14, 15	7, 9, 12, 14
Advanced	3–5, 18, 19	1, 2, 10, 12, 14–17	10, 12, 14, 16

For Your Information
- **Exercise 1** There are many possible answers.
- **Exercise 17** Because of the lack of gravity in space, an astronaut's musculoskeletal system is not used as intensively, resulting in a reduction of bone and muscle strength and size.

Common Errors
- **Exercises 6–11** Students might use the reciprocal of the slope when plotting the second point. Remind students of the definition of slope.
- **Exercises 6–11** Students might say that the y-intercept is the y-coordinate of the given point. Remind them that the y-intercept is represented by b in the point $(0, b)$, and if the given point is not in this form, they need to use the slope to find where the line crosses the y-axis.
- **Exercise 13** Students might have trouble knowing which variable can be compared with x and y and may write the given point backwards. Review what the words "in terms of" mean when writing an equation. In this problem, V could be replaced by y and T could be replaced by x. Remind students to check their equation by substituting the given point and checking that it is a solution of the equation.

2.6 Record and Practice Journal

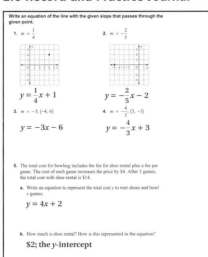

1. *Sample answer:* slope and a point

2. Plot the given point and use the slope to plot additional points to find the y-intercept. Then use the slope m and the y-intercept b to write the equation $y = mx + b$.

✎ Practice and Problem Solving

3. $y = \dfrac{1}{2}x + 1$

4. $y = -\dfrac{3}{4}x$

5. $y = -3x + 8$

6. $y = -\dfrac{2}{3}x + 2$

7. $y = \dfrac{3}{4}x + 5$

8. $y = 4x - 7$

9. $y = -\dfrac{1}{7}x - 4$

10. $y = \dfrac{5}{3}x - 2$

11. $y = -2x - 6$

12. The y-intercept is wrong.
$y = \dfrac{1}{3}x + 2$

13. $V = \dfrac{2}{25}T + 22$

14. a. $V = -4000x + 30,000$

b. \$30,000

15. See *Taking Math Deeper*.

16. a. $y = 30x + 20$

b. the flat fee for renting the airboat

17. a. $y = -0.03x + 2.9$

b. 2 g/cm^2

c. *Sample answer:* Eventually $y = 0$, which means the astronaut's bones will be very weak.

Fair Game Review

18.

19. B

Mini-Assessment

Write an equation of the line with the given slope that passes through the given point.

1. $m = 3$; $(1, 4)$ $y = 3x + 1$

2. $m = -2$; $(-2, 1)$ $y = -2x - 3$

3. $m = 1$; $(3, 5)$ $y = x + 2$

4. $m = \frac{1}{2}$; $(2, 1)$ $y = \frac{1}{2}x$

5. You rent a floor sander for \$24 per day. You pay \$82 for 3 days.

a. Write an equation that represents your total cost y (in dollars) after x days. $y = 24x + 10$

b. Interpret the y-intercept. The y-intercept is 10. This means you paid a deposit fee of \$10 to rent the sander.

Taking Math Deeper

Exercise 15

The challenge in this biology problem is to interpret the given information as a rate of change (or slope) and as an ordered pair.

 Translate the given information into math.

T = temperature (°F)
x = chirps per minute
Rate of change = 0.25 degree per chirp

 Write an equation.

Given point: $(x, T) = (40, 50)$

With a slope of 0.25, you can determine that the T-intercept of the line is 40. So, the equation is

a. $T = 0.25x + 40$.

 Use the equation.
If $x = 100$ chirps per minute, then

$T = 0.25(100) + 40$

b. $= 65°F$.

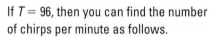

If $T = 96$, then you can find the number of chirps per minute as follows.

$$96 = 0.25x + 40$$
$$56 = 0.25x$$
$$224 = x$$

c. So, you would expect the cricket to make 224 chirps in one minute.

This relationship between temperature and cricket chirps was first published by Amos Dolbear in 1897 in an article called *The Cricket as a Thermometer*.

Project

Research other plants or animals that predict the temperature or weather.

Reteaching and Enrichment Strategies

If students need help...	If students got it...
Resources by Chapter • Practice A and Practice B • Puzzle Time Record and Practice Journal Practice Differentiating the Lesson Lesson Tutorials Skills Review Handbook	Resources by Chapter • Enrichment and Extension • School-to-Work • Financial Literacy • Technology Connection Start the next section

14. CARS After it is purchased, the value of a new car decreases $4000 each year. After 3 years, the car is worth $18,000.

   a. Write an equation that represents the value V (in dollars) of the car x years after it is purchased.

   b. What was the original value of the car?

15. CRICKETS According to Dolbear's Law, you can predict the temperature T (in degrees Fahrenheit) by counting the number x of chirps made by a snowy tree cricket in 1 minute. For a rise in temperature of 0.25 degree, the cricket makes an additional chirp each minute.

   a. A cricket chirps 40 times in 1 minute when the temperature is 50°F. Write an equation that represents the temperature in terms of the number of chirps in 1 minute.

   b. You count 100 chirps in 1 minute. What is the temperature?

   c. The temperature is 96°F. How many chirps would you expect the cricket to make?

Airboat
$30/hr

16. AIRBOATS You rent an airboat. The total cost includes a flat fee plus an hourly fee.

   a. After 4 hours the total cost is $140. Write an equation that represents the total cost y after x hours.

   b. Interpret the y-intercept.

17. **Critical Thinking** Bone mineral density is a measure of the strength of bones. The average bone mineral density of a female astronaut who has never been in space is 2.9 grams per square centimeter. For the first 3 years she spends in space, her bone density decreases by 0.03 gram per square centimeter per month.

   a. Write an equation that represents the bone mineral density y of a female astronaut in terms of the number x of months she spends in space.

   b. What is her bone mineral density after 2 years and 6 months in space?

   c. Explain why the amount of time an astronaut can spend in space is limited.

Fair Game Review *What you learned in previous grades & lessons*

18. Plot the ordered pairs in the same coordinate plane. *(Skills Review Handbook)*

$$(2, 5), (-3, -6), (0, 7), (-5, 0), (-8, 9)$$

19. MULTIPLE CHOICE What is the y-intercept of the equation $5x - 2y = 28$? *(Section 2.4)*

   Ⓐ $-\dfrac{5}{2}$ **Ⓑ** -14 **Ⓒ** $\dfrac{5}{2}$ **Ⓓ** 5.6

STANDARDS
OF LEARNING

8.16

Essential Question How can you write an equation of a line when you are given two points on the line?

1   ACTIVITY: Writing Equations of Lines

Work with a partner.

- Sketch the line that passes through the given points.
- Find the slope and *y*-intercept of the line.
- Write an equation of the line.

a.

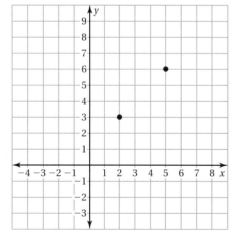

b.

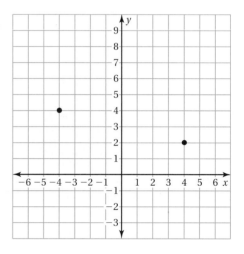

c.

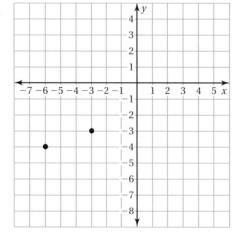

d.

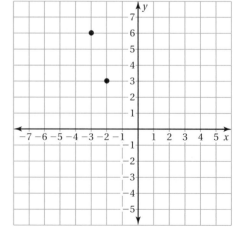

Laurie's Notes

Introduction

For the Teacher

- **Goal:** Students will explore how to write an equation for a line given two points on the line.
- **Big Idea:** The problems in this activity assume that the rate of change (slope) remains constant for a period of time, which in practice is unlikely. The goal is to practice some important mathematical skills in a context that is plausible.

Motivate

? "Have any of you ever taken a hot air balloon ride?"

- If you have taken a hot air balloon ride, share the experience with your students.
- Share a few "math tidbits" followed by posing a question that they will answer later.
  - Traditional balloons look like a sphere at the top and a truncated cone at the bottom.
  - The propane tanks are generally cylindrical.
  - One of the instruments on the balloon is the variometer which keeps track of the rate of climb (vertical speed).

Discuss

- Share a story about a friend who took a hot air balloon ride. Explain that your friend was holding a portable variometer and knew that at 2 minutes the height was 300 feet and at 3 minutes the height was 450 feet. At this rate, how many minutes did it take to reach 900 feet?

Activity Notes

Activity 1

? "How do you find the slope of the line between two points in the coordinate plane?" Draw the horizontal and vertical arrows that represent the run and the rise, and then find the ratio of rise to run.

- Given the similarity of this activity to the previous two, students should be able to get started right away. Once students have found the slope of the line, they will find the y-intercept as they did previously.
- All of the y-intercepts are integer values, so they will be easy for students to find.
- In a formal algebra class, the challenge of this lesson is the symbolism involved in the formulas. Having students draw the lines first, *see* the slope and y-intercept, and then write the equation, has eliminated this challenge.

? "What made it possible to be able to write the equation of the line?" Slope is found by using the definition of slope. Then by using the slope, you can find the y-intercept. Finally, substitute into the formula $y = mx + b$.

Standards of Learning

8.16 The student will graph a linear equation in two variables.

Previous Learning

Students should know how to plot points and find the slope between the two points. Students should know how to apply the definition of slope in order to find the y-intercept of a graph.

Start Thinking! and Warm Up

Activity 2.7 Start Thinking!
For use before Activity 2.7

Activity 2.7 Warm Up
For use before Activity 2.7

Write an equation of the line given slope m and y-intercept b.

1. $m = \frac{1}{2}, b = 3$ 2. $m = -2, b = 0$

3. $m = 1, b = -3$ 4. $m = \frac{1}{3}, b = -1$

5. $m = -\frac{3}{5}, b = \frac{1}{2}$ 6. $m = -\frac{7}{5}, b = -\frac{1}{5}$

2.7 Record and Practice Journal

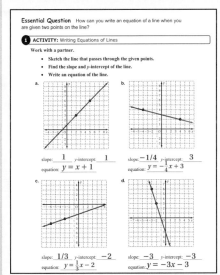

Essential Question How can you write an equation of a line when you are given two points on the line?

1 ACTIVITY: Writing Equations of Lines

Work with a partner.

- Sketch the line that passes through the given points.
- Find the slope and y-intercept of the line.
- Write an equation of the line.

a. slope: 1 y-intercept: 1
equation: $y = x + 1$

b. slope: $-1/4$ y-intercept: 3
equation: $y = -\frac{1}{4}x + 3$

c. slope: $1/3$ y-intercept: -2
equation: $y = \frac{1}{3}x - 2$

d. slope: -3 y-intercept: -3
equation: $y = -3x - 3$

English Language Learners

Group Activity

Form small groups of English learners and English speakers. Provide each group with enough information (slope and y-intercept, slope and a point, or two points) to write equations. After writing an equation, the equation should be graphed in the coordinate plane. Students can share their work at the board or overhead.

Activity 2

Part (a): Write the two ordered pairs that are described in words and are plotted on the graph, (1, 200) and (4, 800). Ask a few questions.

- "How did the height of the balloon change in the 3 minutes between these two points?" Height increased 600 feet.
- "What is the slope between these points?" $\text{slope} = \dfrac{\text{rise}}{\text{run}} = \dfrac{600}{3} = 200$
- "What units do you need to describe the slope?" ft per min
- Students should work backwards to find the h-intercept, which is 0.
- It is difficult for students to take the information they know and write the equation for the height h in terms of the time t. Students should be able to write $y = 200x + 0$, or $y = 200x$, but the direction sentence of "write an equation for the height h in terms of the time t" seems to overwhelm students. Have students look at the graph and how the axes are labeled. The time t is on the horizontal axis and the height h is on the vertical axis. In the equation $y = 200x$, replace x with t and replace y with h.
- "What does a slope of 200 mean in the context of this problem?" For every minute that passes, the height of the balloon increases 200 feet.
- "What does an h-intercept of 0 mean in the context of this problem?" The balloon starts at ground level.

- **Part (b):** Students use their answer (5, 1000) from part (a), along with the new ordered pair (6, 200), to find the slope. The balloon is descending (negative slope) at a rate of 800 feet per minute.
- Determining the h-intercept for this problem is challenging for two reasons: the h-intercept is off the graph and the balloon was never at that height. Suggest that students make a table of values.

Time (minutes), t	6	5	4	3	2	1	0
Height (feet), h	200	1000	1800	2600	3400	4200	5000

- "How do you use the equation to find out when the balloon will land on the ground?" Solve $0 = -800t + 5000$.

Closure

- Refer back to the balloon question posed at the beginning and ask students to write an equation for the height of the balloon in terms of the time in minutes. Find the time when the height is 900 feet. $y = 150x$; 6 min

2.7 Record and Practice Journal

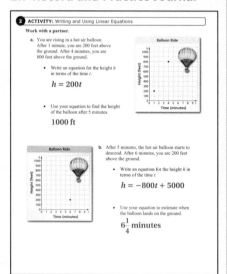

2 **ACTIVITY:** Writing and Using Linear Equations

Work with a partner.

a. You are rising in a hot air balloon. After 1 minute, you are 200 feet above the ground. After 4 minutes, you are 800 feet above the ground.

- Write an equation for the height h in terms of the time t.

$h = 200t$

- Use your equation to find the height of the balloon after 5 minutes.

1000 ft

b. After 5 minutes, the hot air balloon starts to descend. After 6 minutes, you are 200 feet above the ground.

- Write an equation for the height h in terms of the time t.

$h = -800t + 5000$

- Use your equation to estimate when the balloon lands on the ground.

$6\frac{1}{4}$ minutes

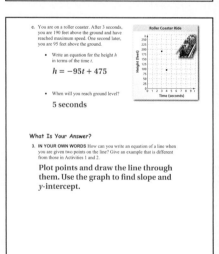

c. You are on a roller coaster. After 3 seconds, you are 190 feet above the ground and have reached maximum speed. One second later, you are 95 feet above the ground.

- Write an equation for the height h in terms of the time t.

$h = -95t + 475$

- When will you reach ground level?

5 seconds

What Is Your Answer?

3. IN YOUR OWN WORDS How can you write an equation of a line when you are given two points on the line? Give an example that is different from those in Activities 1 and 2.

Plot points and draw the line through them. Use the graph to find slope and y-intercept.

Technology For the Teacher

Dynamic Classroom

The Dynamic Planning Tool
Editable Teacher's Resources at *BigIdeasMath.com*

ACTIVITY: Writing and Using Linear Equations

Work with a partner.

a. You are rising in a hot air balloon. After 1 minute, you are 200 feet above the ground. After 4 minutes, you are 800 feet above the ground.

- Write an equation for the height h in terms of the time t.

- Use your equation to find the height of the balloon after 5 minutes.

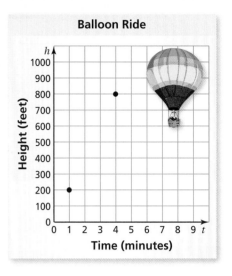

Balloon Ride

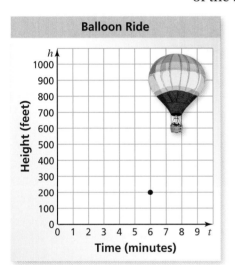

Balloon Ride

b. After 5 minutes, the hot air balloon starts to descend. After 6 minutes, you are 200 feet above the ground.

- Write an equation for the height h in terms of the time t.

- Use your equation to estimate when the balloon lands on the ground.

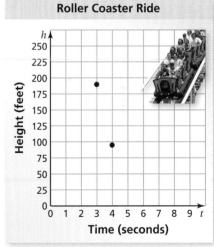

Roller Coaster Ride

c. You are on a roller coaster. After 3 seconds, you are 190 feet above the ground and have reached maximum speed. One second later, you are 95 feet above the ground.

- Write an equation for the height h in terms of the time t.

- When will you reach ground level?

What Is Your Answer?

3. IN YOUR OWN WORDS How can you write an equation of a line when you are given two points on the line? Give an example that is different from those in Activities 1 and 2.

Practice

Use what you learned about writing equations using two points to complete Exercises 3–5 on page 106.

2.7 Lesson

Check It Out
Lesson Tutorials
BigIdeasMathcom

EXAMPLE 1   Writing Equations Using Two Points

Write an equation of the line that passes through the points.

a. $(-6, 6), (-3, 4)$

Use a graph to find the slope and y-intercept.

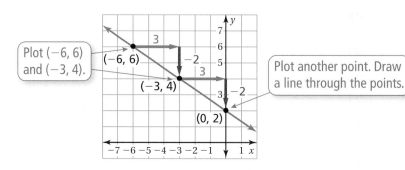

> **Study Tip**
>
> After writing an equation, check that the given points are solutions of the equation.

$$\text{slope} = \frac{\text{rise}}{\text{run}} = \frac{-2}{3} = -\frac{2}{3}$$

Because the line crosses the y-axis at $(0, 2)$, the y-intercept is 2.

∴ So, the equation is $y = -\dfrac{2}{3}x + 2$.

b. $(-2, -4), (1, -1)$

Use a graph to find the slope and y-intercept.

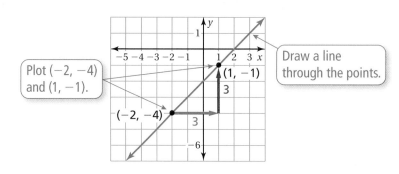

$$\text{slope} = \frac{\text{rise}}{\text{run}} = \frac{3}{3} = 1$$

Because the line crosses the y-axis at $(0, -2)$, the y-intercept is -2.

∴ So, the equation is $y = 1x + (-2)$, or $y = x - 2$.

On Your Own

> **Now You're Ready**
> Exercises 6–14

Write an equation of the line that passes through the points.

1. $(2, 3), (4, 4)$ **2.** $(-1, 2), (1, -4)$

Laurie's Notes

Introduction

Connect

- **Yesterday:** Students developed an intuitive understanding about writing the equation of a line given two points on the line.
- **Today:** Students will write an equation of a line given two points.

Motivate

- **Model:** Model what it looks like when you pour water out of a gallon jug into a bucket at a constant rate. Pour slowly! The bucket should have a uniform shape vertically.
- The variable x is the time in seconds. The variable y is the height of the water in the bucket.
- Write on the board: After 2 seconds, the height of the water in the bucket was 1 inch. Two seconds later, the height was 2 inches.
- ❓ "When will the height be 5 inches?" 10 sec

Discuss

- Discuss the water problem. You could work the problem now or wait until the end of the lesson for students to solve it on their own.
- Explain that when two data points are given and they describe a linear equation, it is possible to write the equation of the line.

Lesson Notes

Example 1

- **Part (a):** State and write the given information: points $(-6, 6)$ and $(-3, 4)$.
- Plot both points. Draw the line through the two points.
- ❓ "Is the slope positive or negative?" negative
- ❓ "What is the slope?" $-\dfrac{2}{3}$
- Use the slope to plot additional points and to find the point where the graph crosses the y-axis. Write the equation.
- Have students check to make sure that the equation contains the given points.
- **Part (b):** Students must be careful when plotting the points because the line through the given points already crosses the y-axis. If students do not have a sharp pencil, or if the straightedge is not lined up carefully, it may not be obvious to students that the y-intercept is -2.
- **Big Idea:** Before students attempt to write the equation of the line, they should know if the slope and y-intercept are positive or negative.

On Your Own

- Have students share their work at the overhead or at the board.
- Note that Question 2 is similar to part (b). The given ordered pairs are on opposite sides of the y-axis.

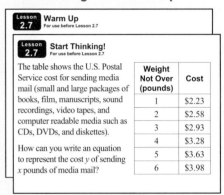

Goal Today's lesson is writing the equation of a line given two points.

Lesson Materials	
Introduction	**Textbook**
• bucket • gallon of water	• straightedge

Start Thinking! and Warm Up

Lesson 2.7 Warm Up For use before Lesson 2.7

Lesson 2.7 Start Thinking! For use before Lesson 2.7

The table shows the U.S. Postal Service cost for sending media mail (small and large packages of books, film, manuscripts, sound recordings, video tapes, and computer readable media such as CDs, DVDs, and diskettes).

How can you write an equation to represent the cost y of sending x pounds of media mail?

Weight Not Over (pounds)	Cost
1	$2.23
2	$2.58
3	$2.93
4	$3.28
5	$3.63
6	$3.98

Extra Example 1

Write an equation that passes through the points.

a. $(-2, 3), (-1, 1)$ $\quad y = -2x - 1$

b. $(-2, 2), (2, 4)$ $\quad y = \dfrac{1}{2}x + 3$

On Your Own

1. $y = \dfrac{1}{2}x + 2$

2. $y = -3x - 1$

Laurie's Notes

Extra Example 2

Write an equation that passes through
$(-4, -3)$ and $(4, 3)$. $y = \dfrac{3}{4}x$

Extra Example 3

A three-week old puppy weighs 24 ounces. Two weeks later, it weighs 36 ounces.

a. Write an equation to represent the weight y (in ounces) of the puppy x weeks after birth. $y = 6x + 6$

b. How old is the puppy when it weighs 60 ounces? 9 weeks

On Your Own

3. C

4. 8 weeks

Differentiated Instruction

Visual

Students can color code their notes to identify the different parts of the graphs and equations. As in the textbook, use red to show the rise of the graph and the numerator of the slope. Use blue to show the run of the graph and the denominator of the slope. Then green can be used to label the y-intercept on the graph and in the equation.

Example 2

- Plot the two points and draw the line through them.
- **?** "Is the slope positive or negative?" negative
- Only two choices have a negative slope, choice A and choice C.
- **Reasoning:** It appears that the y-intercept is 0, so choice A and choice C are still viable choices. It is necessary to actually find the slope.
- **?** "What is the slope for this problem? How did you know?" Slope is $-\dfrac{1}{2}$.

  The rise to run ratio is $-\dfrac{1}{2}$.
- **Common Error:** Students may find the reciprocal of the slope.
- **Alternate Approach:** Students can find the answer using a version of Guess, Check, and Revise. Students can substitute the ordered pairs into the equations and check to see which equation is true for *both* points.

Example 3

- Ask a student to read the problem and the information that is given in the photo.
- This example assumes that the kitten's weight is increasing at a constant rate, which may not be exactly true. For the contextual problems, it is assumed that the rate stays constant so that students can practice the algebraic skills for a problem that is plausible.
- **?** "In the graph, what do x and y represent?" x is the number of weeks and y is the weight of the kitten in ounces.
- Find the equation of the line. Use the equation to solve part (b).
- **?** "Interpret what the slope and y-intercept mean for this problem." Slope of 3 means the kitten's weight is increasing 3 ounces per week. The y-intercept of 3 means the kitten weighed 3 ounces at birth.

On Your Own

- These problems take time, but they provide a good assessment of students' understanding of the lesson.

Closure

- **Exit Ticket:** Write an equation of the line through the points $(0, 4)$ and $(2, 2)$. $y = -x + 4$

Technology
For
The **T**eacher

The Dynamic Planning Tool
Editable Teacher's Resources at *BigIdeasMath.com*

EXAMPLE 2 **Standardized Test Practice**

The graph of which equation passes through $(2, -1)$ and $(4, -2)$?

(A) $y = -\frac{1}{2}x$

(B) $y = \frac{1}{2}x$

(C) $y = -2x$

(D) $y = 2x$

Graph the line through the points. Find the slope and y-intercept.

$$\text{slope} = \frac{\text{rise}}{\text{run}} = \frac{-1}{2} = -\frac{1}{2}$$

Because the line crosses the y-axis at $(0, 0)$, the y-intercept is 0.

So, the equation is $y = -\frac{1}{2}x + 0$, or $y = -\frac{1}{2}x$.

The correct answer is (A).

EXAMPLE 3 **Real-Life Application**

22.5 oz

A 2-week old kitten weighs 9 ounces. Two weeks later, it weighs 15 ounces. (a) Write an equation to represent the weight y (in ounces) of the kitten x weeks after birth. (b) How old is the kitten in the photo?

a. The kitten weighs 9 ounces after 2 weeks and 15 ounces after 4 weeks. So, graph the line that passes through $(2, 9)$ and $(4, 15)$.

$$\text{slope} = \frac{\text{rise}}{\text{run}} = \frac{6}{2} = 3$$

Because the line crosses the y-axis at $(0, 3)$, the y-intercept is 3.

So, the equation is $y = 3x + 3$.

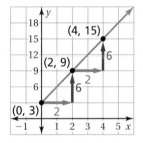

b. Find the value of x when $y = 22.5$.

$y = 3x + 3$	Write the equation.
$22.5 = 3x + 3$	Substitute 22.5 for y.
$19.5 = 3x$	Subtract 3 from each side.
$6.5 = x$	Solve for x.

The kitten in the photo is 6.5 weeks old.

● **On Your Own**

3. The graph of which equation in Example 2 passes through $(-2, 4)$ and $(-1, 2)$?

4. A 3-week old kitten weighs 12 ounces. Two weeks later, it weighs 18 ounces. How old is the kitten when it weighs 27 ounces?

 Vocabulary and Concept Check

1. **WRITING** Describe how to write an equation of a line using two points on the line.

2. **WHICH ONE DOESN'T BELONG?** Which pair of points does *not* belong with the other three? Explain your reasoning.

| (0, 1), (2, 3) | (1, 2), (4, 5) | (2, 3), (5, 6) | (1, 2), (4, 6) |

 Practice and Problem Solving

Find the slope and *y*-intercept of the line that passes through the points. Then write an equation of the line.

3. 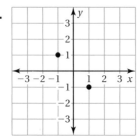   4. 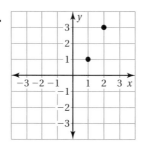   5.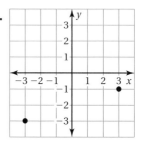

Write an equation of the line that passes through the points.

6. $(-1, -1)$, $(1, 5)$ 7. $(2, 4)$, $(3, 6)$ 8. $(-2, 3)$, $(2, 7)$

9. $(4, 1)$, $(8, 2)$ 10. $(-9, 5)$, $(-3, 3)$ 11. $(1, 2)$, $(-2, -1)$

12. $(-5, 2)$, $(5, -2)$ 13. $(2, -7)$, $(8, 2)$ 14. $(1, -2)$, $(3, -8)$

15. **ERROR ANALYSIS** Describe and correct the error in finding the equation of the line that passes through $(-1, -6)$ and $(3, 2)$.

16. **JET SKI** It costs $175 to rent a jet ski for 2 hours. It costs $300 to rent a jet ski for 4 hours. Write an equation that represents the cost *y* (in dollars) of renting a jet ski for *x* hours.

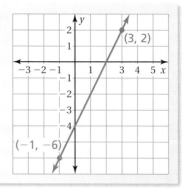

17. **CIRCUMFERENCE** Consider the circles shown.

    a. Plot the points $(2, 4\pi)$ and $(3, 6\pi)$.

    b. Write an equation of the line that passes through the two points. How does the equation relate to circles?

$C = 4\pi$ $C = 6\pi$

Assignment Guide and Homework Check

Level	Day 1 Activity Assignment	Day 2 Lesson Assignment	Homework Check
Basic	3–5, 22–25	1, 2, 7–17 odd, 16	2, 7, 16, 17
Average	3–5, 22–25	1, 2, 9–11, 15, 17–19	2, 10, 17, 18
Advanced	3–5, 22–25	1, 2, 12–15, 19–21	2, 12, 19, 20

Common Errors

- **Exercises 6–14** Students may plot the points, draw a line through the points, and then use the point where the line crosses the y-axis to find the y-intercept. Sometimes this is not the correct point because students may not be able to draw a straight line. Encourage them to use the slope to find the y-intercept.
- **Exercise 16** Students may write the first point one way and the second point another way. For example, a student may write (2, 175) and (300, 4). Encourage them to write a description of the ordered pair, for example, (hours, cost).
- **Exercise 17** Students may struggle when plotting the given points because π is used. Encourage them to scale the y-axis by increments of π.

2.7 Record and Practice Journal

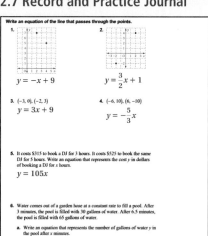

Write an equation of the line that passes through the points.

1. $y = -x + 9$
2. $y = \frac{3}{2}x + 1$
3. $(-3, 0), (-2, 3)$ $y = 3x + 9$
4. $(-6, 10), (6, -10)$ $y = -\frac{5}{3}x$
5. It costs $315 to book a DJ for 3 hours. It costs $525 to book the same DJ for 5 hours. Write an equation that represents the cost y in dollars of booking a DJ for x hours.
   $y = 105x$
6. Water comes out of a garden hose at a constant rate to fill a pool. After 3 minutes, the pool is filled with 30 gallons of water. After 6.5 minutes, the pool is filled with 65 gallons of water.
   a. Write an equation that represents the number of gallons of water y in the pool after x minutes.
   $y = 10x$
   b. How long will it take to fill a pool that needs 10,000 gallons of water?
   1000 minutes

Technology For the Teacher
Answer Presentation Tool
QuizShow

Vocabulary and Concept Check

1. Plot both points and draw the line that passes through them. Use the graph to find the slope and y-intercept. Then write the equation in slope-intercept form.

2. (1, 2), (4, 6); The slope of the line connecting these two points is $\frac{4}{3}$. The slope of the other pairs of points is 1.

Practice and Problem Solving

3. slope $= -1$; y-intercept: 0; $y = -x$

4. slope $= 2$; y-intercept: -1; $y = 2x - 1$

5. slope $= \frac{1}{3}$; y-intercept: -2; $y = \frac{1}{3}x - 2$

6. $y = 3x + 2$

7. $y = 2x$

8. $y = x + 5$

9. $y = \frac{1}{4}x$

10. $y = -\frac{1}{3}x + 2$

11. $y = x + 1$

12. $y = -\frac{2}{5}x$

13. $y = \frac{3}{2}x - 10$

14. $y = -3x + 1$

15. They switched the slope and y-intercept in the equation. $y = 2x - 4$

16. $y = 62.5x + 50$

17. See Additional Answers.

Practice and Problem Solving

18. a.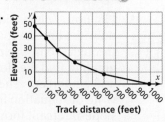

b. no; The graph is not a line.

c. $y = -\dfrac{1}{10}x + 48$

19. See Additional Answers.

20. See *Taking Math Deeper*.

21. a. $y = 14x - 108.5$

   b. 4 m

 ## Fair Game Review

22. 45   **23.** 175

24. −4.5   **25.** D

Mini-Assessment

Write an equation of the line that passes through the points.

1. $(-2, 1), (3, -4)$ $y = -x - 1$

2. $(-4, 0), (2, 3)$ $y = \dfrac{1}{2}x + 2$

3. $(-3, -8), (4, 6)$ $y = 2x - 2$

4. $(-2, 6), (3, -9)$ $y = -3x$

5. After 2 weeks, you have made $150 mowing lawns. After 4 weeks, you have made $300. Write an equation that represents your earnings y (in dollars) after x weeks. $y = 75x$

Taking Math Deeper

Exercise 20

As with many real-life problems, this one has a lot of information. Help students understand that they are not expected to look at this problem and see the solution immediately. Just take a deep breath, relax, and start to organize the given information.

 Translate the given information into math.

   Let $y =$ ounces of water and $x =$ time in seconds.
   First given point: (5, 58)
   Second given point: (20, 28)

   Note that "15 seconds later" means that the second time is $5 + 15 = 20$.

 Plot the two points.

 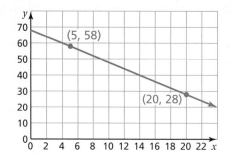

The slope is −2 ounces per second.
The y-intercept is 68. So, the equation is

   a. $y = -2x + 68$.

 Use the equation. When $x = 0$ seconds, the watering can has
   $y = -2(0) + 68$
   b. $= 68$ ounces.

The watering can will be empty when $y = 0$.
   $0 = -2x + 68$
   $2x = 68$
   c. $x = 34$ seconds

The watering can will be empty after 34 seconds.

Reteaching and Enrichment Strategies

If students need help. . .	If students got it. . .
Resources by Chapter • Practice A and Practice B • Puzzle Time Record and Practice Journal Practice Differentiating the Lesson Lesson Tutorials Skills Review Handbook	Resources by Chapter • Enrichment and Extension • School-to-Work • Financial Literacy • Technology Connection • Life Connections Start the next section

18. SOAP BOX DERBY The table shows the changes in elevation for a Soap Box Derby track.

Track Distance	Elevation
0 ft	48 ft
100 ft	38 ft
200 ft	28 ft
350 ft	18 ft
600 ft	8 ft
989 ft	0 ft

  a. Draw a Soap Box Derby track in a coordinate plane.

  b. Does each section of the track have the same slope? Explain.

  c. Write an equation that represents the elevation y (in feet) of the track between 100 feet and 200 feet.

19. CAR VALUE The value of a car decreases at a constant rate. After 3 years, the value of the car is $15,000. After 2 more years the value of the car is $11,000.

  a. Write an equation that represents the value y (in dollars) of the car after x years.

  b. Graph the equation.

  c. What is the y-intercept of the line? Interpret the y-intercept.

Leaning Tower of Pisa

(10.75, 42)

7.75 m

20. WATERING CAN You water the plants in your classroom at a constant rate. After 5 seconds, your watering can contains 58 ounces of water. Fifteen seconds later, the can contains 28 ounces of water.

  a. Write an equation that represents the amount y (in ounces) of water in the can after x seconds.

  b. How much water was in the can when you started watering the plants?

  c. When is the watering can empty?

21. **Critical Thinking** The Leaning Tower of Pisa in Italy was built between 1173 and 1350.

  a. Write an equation for the yellow line.

  b. The tower is 56 meters tall. How far off center is the top of the tower?

Fair Game Review What you learned in previous grades & lessons

Find the percent of the number. *(Skills Review Handbook)*

22. 15% of 300   **23.** 140% of 125   **24.** 6% of -75

25. MULTIPLE CHOICE What is the x-intercept of the equation $3x + 5y = 30$? *(Section 2.4)*

   Ⓐ -10 Ⓑ -6 Ⓒ 6   Ⓓ 10

STANDARDS OF LEARNING

8.16

Essential Question How can you use a linear equation in two variables to model and solve a real-life problem?

1 EXAMPLE: Writing a Story

Write a story that uses the graph at the right.

- In your story, interpret the slope of the line, the *y*-intercept, and the *x*-intercept.
- Make a table that shows data from the graph.
- Label the axes of the graph with units.
- Draw pictures for your story.

There are many possible stories. Here is one about a reef tank.

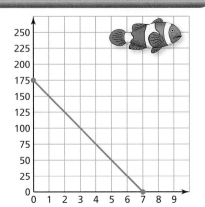

Tom works at an aquarium shop on Saturdays. One Saturday, when Tom gets to work, he is asked to clean a 175-gallon reef tank.

His first job is to drain the tank. He puts a hose into the tank and starts a siphon. Tom wonders if the tank will finish draining before he leaves work.

He measures the amount of water that is draining out and finds that 12.5 gallons drain out in 30 minutes. So, he figures that the rate is 25 gallons per hour. To see when the tank will be empty, Tom makes a table and draws a graph.

x-intercept: number of hours to empty the tank

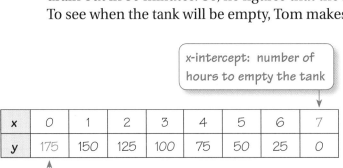

x	0	1	2	3	4	5	6	7
y	175	150	125	100	75	50	25	0

y-intercept: amount of water in full tank

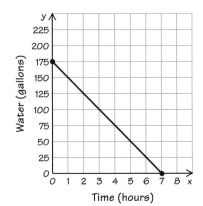

From the table and also from the graph, Tom sees that the tank will be empty after 7 hours. This will give him 1 hour to wash the tank before going home.

Laurie's Notes

Introduction

For the Teacher

- **Goal:** Students will develop an intuitive understanding of solving real-life problems.
- Students have already solved real-life problems involving linear equations. The skills in this lesson are not new. One skill that students have not had much practice with is interpreting the *x*-intercept.

Motivate

- **Time for a Story!** Tell students that you want to give your friend 10 pounds of chocolate for his birthday. The fancy bars of chocolate come in one-pound and half-pound bars. Hold up two rectangular blocks (or real bars).
- **?** "What are some different ways I could give my friend the 10 pounds of chocolate?" Answers will vary.
- Students should eventually give the two *simple* answers of 10 one-pound bars and no half-pound bars, or 20 half-pound bars and no one-pound bars. If you let *x* equal the number of one-pound bars and *y* equal the number of half-pound bars, these two solutions are (10, 0) and (0, 20). Plot the two points.

Discuss

- **?** Depending upon time, you may wish to ask a series of questions and have students answer them now or at the end of the lesson.
  - "Are there other combinations besides these two that will equal 10 pounds?" Make a table to show additional solutions.
  - "What is the slope of the line that goes through the two points?" -2
  - "Could you write an equation for the line through the two points?" $y = -2x + 20$
  - "If you bought 5 one-pound bars, how many half-pound bars would you need to purchase?" 10
  - "If a one-pound bar costs twice as much as a half-pound bar, what do you know about all of the possible gift combinations?" all cost the same

Activity Notes

Example 1

- Ask one or more students to read through the sample provided.
- The problem does not have to be about fish tanks, but it does need to use the ordered pairs (0, 175) and (7, 0). The table of values will be the same regardless of the context selected. Notice that the equation is not determined, although this could be an extension for some or all students.
- Here are some suggestions for ordered pairs:
  (# of weeks, $ in the bank); (# of hours biking, kilometers traveled); (# of hours reading, pages to read); (# of wheel barrows, pounds of dirt)

Standards of Learning

8.16 The student will graph a linear equation in two variables.

Previous Learning

Students should know how to write equations in slope-intercept form.

Activity Materials

Introduction	Textbook
• 2 rectangular blocks	• straightedge

Start Thinking! and Warm Up

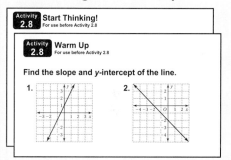

2.8 Record and Practice Journal

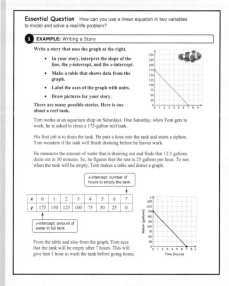

2.8 Record and Practice Journal

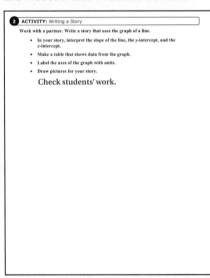

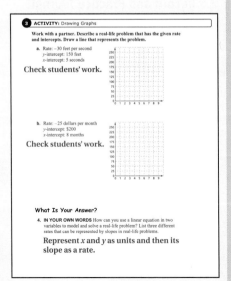

Laurie's Notes

Activity 2

- **Interdisciplinary:** This activity is open-ended. The goal is to integrate language arts skills while practicing mathematical skills.
- Depending upon time, you may choose not to do this activity.
- You modeled how this problem can be done with the chocolate bars at the beginning of the lesson.
- You may wish to return to this problem *after* students have brainstormed three different rates in Question 4.
- Students should share their stories with the whole class, drawing a sketch of the graph with the axes labeled.

Activity 3

? "What are the ordered pairs for the intercepts?" (0, 150) and (5, 0)

? "Explain how the rate is found." The change is 150 feet in 5 seconds, which simplifies to 30 feet per 1 second.

? "Why is the rate negative?" The amount of feet is decreasing as time increases.

- Students may need to see the graph to understand why the rate is negative.
- **Extension:** Ask students to sketch a graph that represents a rate of 30 feet per second.

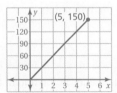

- **Connection:** For most contextual problems, the x- and y-intercepts will be positive numbers, and so the slope of the line between them is negative.

What Is Your Answer?

- **Whole Class Activity:** Have the class brainstorm 1 or 2 rates, and then ask students to think about two or three more on their own. This question will help students think about the variety of contexts in which linear equations can arise.
- **Possible Rates:** miles per hour, feet per second, miles per gallon, outs per inning, points per quarter, people per team, tiles per foot

Closure

- Refer back to the chocolate question given at the beginning of the lesson and ask students to write an equation for this problem. The rate of −2 means that for every 2 half-pound bars that are bought, there is one less one-pound bar. $y = -2x + 20$

Technology
For the Teacher

The Dynamic Planning Tool
Editable Teacher's Resources at *BigIdeasMath.com*

2 ACTIVITY: Writing a Story

Work with a partner. Write a story that uses the graph of a line.

- **In your story, interpret the slope of the line, the *y*-intercept, and the *x*-intercept.**
- **Make a table that shows data from the graph.**
- **Label the axes of the graph with units.**
- **Draw pictures for your story.**

3 ACTIVITY: Drawing Graphs

Work with a partner. Describe a real-life problem that has the given rate and intercepts. Draw a line that represents the problem.

a. Rate: −30 feet per second

   y-intercept: 150 feet

   x-intercept: 5 seconds

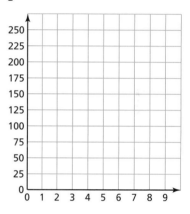

b. Rate: −25 dollars per month

   y-intercept: $200

   x-intercept: 8 months

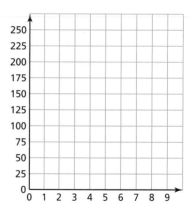

What Is Your Answer?

4. **IN YOUR OWN WORDS** How can you use a linear equation in two variables to model and solve a real-life problem? List three different rates that can be represented by slopes in real-life problems.

Practice

Use what you learned about solving real-life problems to complete Exercises 4 and 5 on page 112.

2.8 Lesson

Check It Out
Lesson Tutorials
BigIdeasMath√com

EXAMPLE **1** **Real-Life Application**

The percent *y* (in decimal form) of battery power remaining *x* hours after you turn on a laptop computer is $y = -0.2x + 1$. (a) Graph the equation. (b) Interpret the *x*- and *y*-intercepts. (c) After how many hours is the battery power at 75%?

a. Use the slope and the *y*-intercept to graph the equation.

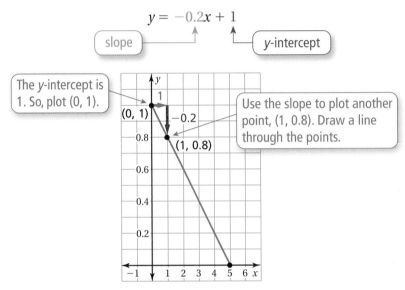

$$y = -0.2x + 1$$

slope ⟶ ⟶ *y*-intercept

The *y*-intercept is 1. So, plot (0, 1).

Use the slope to plot another point, (1, 0.8). Draw a line through the points.

b. To find the *x*-intercept, substitute 0 for *y* in the equation.

$y = -0.2x + 1$	Write the equation.
$0 = -0.2x + 1$	Substitute 0 for *y*.
$5 = x$	Solve for *x*.

⁖ The *x*-intercept is 5. So, the battery lasts 5 hours. The *y*-intercept is 1. So, the battery power is at 100% when you turn on the laptop.

c. Find the value of *x* when $y = 0.75$.

$y = -0.2x + 1$	Write the equation.
$0.75 = -0.2x + 1$	Substitute 0.75 for *y*.
$1.25 = x$	Solve for *x*.

⁖ The battery power is at 75% after 1.25 hours.

75% Remaining

On Your Own

Now You're Ready
Exercise 6

1. The amount *y* (in gallons) of gasoline remaining in a gas tank after driving *x* hours is $y = -2x + 12$. (a) Graph the equation. (b) Interpret the *x*- and *y*-intercepts. (c) After how many hours are there 5 gallons left?

Laurie's Notes

Introduction

Connect

- **Yesterday:** Students explored real-life problems involving rates, where the *x*- and *y*-intercepts were each positive.
- **Today:** Students will solve real-life problems using equations, graphs, and intercepts.
- **FYI:** The goal is to bring the concepts related to linear equations, graphing, and writing, together into one lesson with more focus on the interpretation of slope and intercepts.

Motivate

- Hold a digital camera and take some pictures of your students. You could also pretend to be taking pictures. Continue to take pictures until someone finally asks how many you're going to take.
- Say, "Until my memory card is full! But don't worry, it's only a 64 megabyte (64 MB) card." If someone asks, tell them that every picture uses about 4 MB.

Discuss

- Discuss how many pictures can be stored on the card. Every time a picture is taken, the megabytes remaining decrease.

Lesson Notes

Example 1

- Discuss the use of a laptop computer and what happens when the computer is running off the battery versus using the AC adapter.
- Read the problem. Write what an ordered pair represents in words: (# of hours computer runs on battery, % of battery remaining as a decimal)
- **?** "If you have just turned your fully charged computer on, how much battery power do you have?" 100%
- **?** "What is the ordered pair associated with turning your computer on?" (0, 1)
- **Common Error:** Students may say (0, 100), but remind them that the percent needs to be in decimal form.
- Refer to the equation and ask about the slope and *y*-intercept.
- Plot the point for the *y*-intercept and use the slope to plot additional points on the graph.
- **?** "The *y*-intercept means you just turned your computer on. What does the *x*-intercept mean?" The computer ran for 5 hours before the battery died.
- **?** **Big Idea:** Ask students why the graph is contained in Quadrant I only. It does not make sense for the battery power remaining to be greater than 1 (100%) or less than 0.

On Your Own

- This question is modeled after Example 1.

Goal Today's lesson is solving real-life problems.

Lesson Materials	
Introduction	**Textbook**
• SD or memory card of some type • digital camera	• straightedge

Start Thinking! and Warm Up

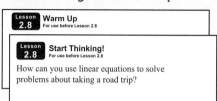

Lesson 2.8 Warm Up
For use before Lesson 2.8

Lesson 2.8 Start Thinking!
For use before Lesson 2.8

How can you use linear equations to solve problems about taking a road trip?

Extra Example 1

The percent *y* (in decimal form) of battery power remaining *x* hours after you turn on your handheld video game is $y = -0.3x + 1$.

a. Graph the equation.

b. Interpret the *x*- and *y*-intercepts.

The *x*-intercept is $3\frac{1}{3}$. So, the battery lasts $3\frac{1}{3}$ hours. The *y*-intercept is 1. So, the battery power is at 100% when you turn it on.

c. After how many hours is the battery power at 40%? after 2 hours

On Your Own

1. See Additional Answers.

Laurie's Notes

Extra Example 2

The graph shows the cost y (in dollars) of a BMX (Bicycle Motocross) track membership and entry fees for x races at the track.

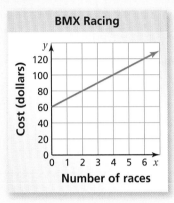

BMX Racing

a. Find the slope and y-intercept.
   slope: 10; y-intercept: 60

b. Write an equation of the line.
   $y = 10x + 60$

c. How much does it cost to be a member and enter 4 races? $100

On Your Own

2. a. The slope is $\frac{3}{2}$. So, the flag is raised at a rate of $\frac{3}{2}$ feet per second.

   b. $y = \frac{3}{2}x + 3$

   c. 16.5 or $16\frac{1}{2}$ ft

Differentiated Instruction

Visual

Encourage students to write down notes when solving word problems, or to underline relevant information and cross out irrelevant information. Allow students to do this on handouts and tests.

Example 2

- Ask a student to read the problem. Write in words what the ordered pairs represent: (°C, °F)
- ? "Explain in words what the two ordered pairs represent." 0°C is the same as 32°F. 30°C is the same as 86°F.
- Draw a sketch of the graph. In order to find the slope, it is helpful for students to see the arrows representing the change in x (30) and the change in y (54).
- ? "The slope is $\frac{9}{5}$. What other information is needed to write the equation of this line?" y-intercept
- The y-intercept is shown in the graph. Write the equation.
- When students evaluate the equation for $C = 15$, they may make an error multiplying the fraction and whole number. Remind students of how multiplication of fractions is performed, and to divide out the common factor of 5 before multiplying.
- **Note:** Students have seen the conversion formula $F = \frac{9}{5}C + 32$ before.

  Because you want to reference the y-intercept, the equation is written in terms of x and y.
- **FYI:** This is a real-life application where it makes sense for the graph to be found in Quadrants I, II and III.
- ? "What do you think *mean temperature of Earth* means?" Answers will vary.

On Your Own

- In interpreting the slope, the graph is read from left to right, so every 2 seconds the flag's height increases 3 feet.
- ? "Why does it make sense that the y-intercept is not 0?" Flag's height does not start on the ground.

Closure

- Draw a graph of the memory card problem. Find and interpret the slope. slope $= -4$; Megabytes of free space decrease by 4 for each picture taken. Write the equation of the line. $y = -4x + 64$ Find and interpret the x- and y-intercepts. 16 and 64; When 16 pictures have been taken, there is 0 MB remaining. When 0 pictures have been taken, there is 64 MB of storage.

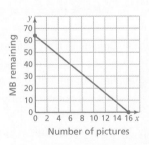

Number of pictures

Technology For the Teacher

Dynamic Classroom

The Dynamic Planning Tool
Editable Teacher's Resources at *BigIdeasMath.com*

EXAMPLE 2   Real-Life Application

The graph relates temperatures y (in degrees Fahrenheit) to temperatures x (in degrees Celsius). **(a)** Find the slope and y-intercept. **(b)** Write an equation of the line. **(c)** What is the mean temperature of Earth in degrees Fahrenheit?

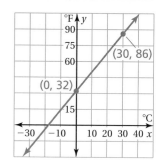

a.   slope $= \dfrac{\text{change in } y}{\text{change in } x} = \dfrac{54}{30} = \dfrac{9}{5}$

The line crosses the y-axis at $(0, 32)$. So, the y-intercept is 32.

∴ The slope is $\dfrac{9}{5}$ and the y-intercept is 32.

b.   Use the slope and y-intercept to write an equation.

slope y-intercept

∴ The equation is $y = \dfrac{9}{5}x + 32$.

c.   In degrees Celsius, the mean temperature of Earth is 15°. To find the mean temperature in degrees Fahrenheit, find the value of y when $x = 15$.

$y = \dfrac{9}{5}x + 32$ Write the equation.

$ = \dfrac{9}{5}(15) + 32$ Substitute 15 for x.

$ = 59$ Simplify.

∴ The mean temperature of Earth is 59°F.

Mean Temperature:
15°C

On Your Own

Now You're Ready
Exercise 7

2. The graph shows the height y (in feet) of a flag x seconds after you start raising it up a flagpole.

  a. Find and interpret the slope.

  b. Write an equation of the line.

  c. What is the height of the flag after 9 seconds?

Vocabulary and Concept Check

1. **REASONING** Explain how to find the slope, *y*-intercept, and *x*-intercept of the line shown.

2. **OPEN-ENDED** Describe a real-life situation that uses a negative slope.

3. **REASONING** In a real-life situation, what does the slope of a line represent?

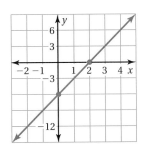

Practice and Problem Solving

Describe a real-life problem that has the given rate and intercepts. Draw a line that represents the problem.

4. Rate: −1.6 gallons per hour

   y-intercept: 16 gallons

   x-intercept: 10 hours

5. Rate: −45 pesos per week

   y-intercept: 180 pesos

   x-intercept: 4 weeks

6. **DOWNLOAD** You are downloading a song. The percent *y* (in decimal form) of megabytes remaining to download after *x* seconds is $y = -0.1x + 1$.

   a. Graph the equation.

   b. Interpret the *x*- and *y*-intercepts.

   c. After how many seconds is the download 50% complete?

7. **HIKING** The graph relates temperature *y* (in degrees Fahrenheit) to altitude *x* (in thousands of feet).

   a. Find the slope and *y*-intercept.

   b. Write an equation of the line.

   c. What is the temperature at sea level?

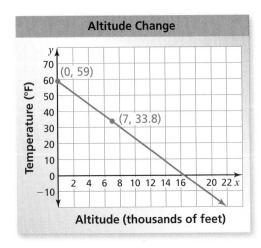

Assignment Guide and Homework Check

Level	Day 1 Activity Assignment	Day 2 Lesson Assignment	Homework Check
Basic	4, 5, 11–15	1–3, 6–8	2, 3, 6, 7, 8
Average	4, 5, 11–15	1–3, 6–9	2, 3, 6, 7, 8
Advanced	4, 5, 11–15	1–3, 7–10	2, 3, 7, 8

For Your Information

- **Exercise 8c** If you were to travel in a straight line, the speed would remain the same but the distance traveled would be less. So, it would take less time to make the trip.
- **Exercise 9** Ask students if their school lies on the line drawn between Denver and Beijing.

Common Errors

- **Exercise 6** Students may forget to convert the percent in part (c) to a decimal before substituting into the equation. Remind them that they need to convert percents to decimals before substituting.
- **Exercise 7** Students may struggle to find the change in y for the slope. Encourage them to focus on the y-coordinates and to write an expression that represents the change in temperature, $33.8 - 59$, to help find the change in y.

2.8 Record and Practice Journal

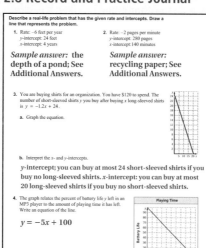

Vocabulary and Concept Check

1. The y-intercept is -6 because the line crosses the y-axis at the point $(0, -6)$. The x-intercept is 2 because the line crosses the x-axis at the point $(2, 0)$. You can use these two points to find the slope.

   $\text{Slope} = \dfrac{\text{change in } y}{\text{change in } x} = \dfrac{6}{2} = 3$

2. *Sample answer:* a balloon descending toward the ground

3. *Sample answer:* the rate at which something is happening

Practice and Problem Solving

4–5. See Additional Answers.

6. a.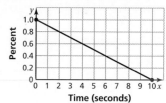

   b. The x-intercept is 10. So, it takes 10 seconds to download the song. The y-intercept is 1. So, 100% of the song needs to be downloaded.

   c. 5 sec

7. a. slope: -3.6
      y-intercept: 59

   b. $y = -3.6x + 59$

   c. 59°F

8. See Additional Answers.

9. **a.** Antananarivo: 19°S, 47°E
Denver: 39°N, 105°W
Brasilia: 16°S, 48°W
London: 51°N, 0°W
Beijing: 40°N, 116°E

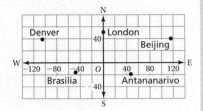

b. $y = \dfrac{1}{221}x + \dfrac{8724}{221}$

c. a place that is on the prime meridian

10. See *Taking Math Deeper*.

11–14. See Additional Answers.

15. B

Mini-Assessment

1. **You need $125 to buy an MP3 player. Your allowance per week is $5 and you earn $20 per lawn mowed.**

   a. Write an equation that represents your weekly income y (in dollars) for x lawns mowed. $y = 20x + 5$

   b. Interpret the y-intercept. The y-intercept is 5. This is your allowance, the amount you started with before mowing lawns.

   c. How many lawns do you need to mow to earn enough money in one week to buy the MP3 player? 6 lawns

Taking Math Deeper

Exercise 10

This is a classic "break-even" type of business problem. The band wants to invest $5000 in new equipment and is trying to project how many tickets need to be sold to pay for the equipment.

(1) Organize the given information.

R = band's revenue (income)
x = number of tickets sold
Income = $1500 + 30% of ticket sales
Price of each ticket = $20
Maximum capacity = 800

(2) Write an equation for the revenue.

R = 1500 + (30% of $20 times x)
= 1500 + 0.3(20)x
a. = 1500 + 6x

In other words, the band receives $6 per ticket. The organizers of the concert keep the remaining $14 to cover the expenses of auditorium rental, marketing, and salaries.

(3) Use the equation.
To find the number of tickets that need to be sold to earn a revenue of $5000, substitute 5000 for R and solve for x.

$5000 = 1500 + 6x$
$3500 = 6x$
$583.3 \approx x$

Round up.

b. So, if the band can sell 584 tickets to the concert, it will earn enough to pay for the new equipment. The capacity of this auditorium is 800, so this is possible.

Project

Draw a poster that could be used to advertise a concert by your favorite band.

Reteaching and Enrichment Strategies

If students need help. . .	If students got it. . .
Resources by Chapter • Practice A and Practice B • Puzzle Time Record and Practice Journal Practice Differentiating the Lesson Lesson Tutorials Skills Review Handbook	Resources by Chapter • Enrichment and Extension • School-to-Work • Financial Literacy • Technology Connection • Life Connections • Stories in History Start the next section

8. **TRAVEL** Your family is driving from Cincinnati to St. Louis. The graph relates your distance from St. Louis y (in miles) and travel time x (in hours).

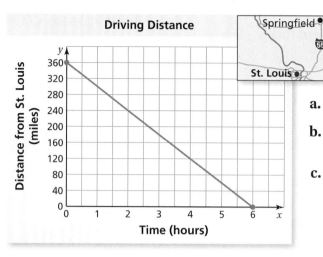

a. Interpret the x- and y-intercepts.

b. What is the slope? What does the slope represent in this situation?

c. Write an equation of the line. How would the graph and the equation change if you were able to travel in a straight line?

9. **PROJECT** Use a map or the Internet to find the latitude and longitude of your school to the nearest whole number. Then find the latitudes and longitudes of: Antananarivo, Madagascar; Denver, Colorado; Brasilia, Brazil; London, England; and Beijing, China.

a. Plot a point for each of the cities in the same coordinate plane. Let the positive y-axis represent north and the positive x-axis represent east.

b. Write an equation of the line that passes through Denver and Beijing.

c. In part (b), what geographic location does the y-intercept represent?

10. **Reasoning** A band is performing at an auditorium for a fee of $1500. In addition to this fee, the band receives 30% of each $20 ticket sold. The maximum capacity of the auditorium is 800 people.

a. Write an equation that represents the band's revenue R when x tickets are sold.

b. The band needs $5000 for new equipment. How many tickets must be sold for the band to earn enough money to buy the new equipment?

 Fair Game Review What you learned in previous grades & lessons

Solve the inequality. Graph the solution. *(Section 1.6)*

11. $1.5 \geq x + 2.8$

12. $k - \dfrac{1}{8} < -\dfrac{5}{8}$

13. $\dfrac{m}{1.8} \leq -4$

14. $25.6 > -3.2y$

15. **MULTIPLE CHOICE** Which equation is the slope-intercept form of $24x - 8y = 56$? *(Section 2.4)*

    (A) $y = -3x + 7$ (B) $y = 3x - 7$ (C) $y = -3x - 7$ (D) $y = 3x + 7$

Check It Out
Progress Check
BigIdeasMath.com

Write an equation of the line in slope-intercept form. *(Section 2.5)*

1.
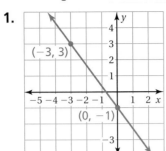

2.
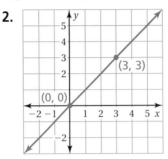

3.
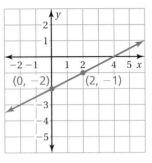

Write an equation of the line with the given slope that passes through the given point. *(Section 2.6)*

4. $m = 2$; $(1, 3)$

5. $m = -\dfrac{1}{8}$; $(8, -5)$

Write an equation of the line that passes through the points. *(Section 2.7)*

6. $\left(0, -\dfrac{2}{3}\right), \left(-3, -\dfrac{2}{3}\right)$

7. $(4, 0), (0, 4)$

8. **FISH POND** You are draining a fish pond. The amount y (in liters) of water remaining after x hours is $y = -60x + 480$. (a) Graph the equation. (b) Interpret the x- and y-intercepts. *(Section 2.8)*

9. **CONSTRUCTION** A construction crew is extending a highway sound barrier that is 13 miles long. The crew builds $\dfrac{1}{2}$ mile per week. Write an equation for the length y (in miles) of the barrier after x weeks. *(Section 2.5)*

10. **STORAGE** You pay $510 to rent a storage unit for 3 months. The total cost includes an initial deposit plus a monthly fee of $160. *(Section 2.6)*

   a. Write an equation that represents your total cost y (in dollars) after x months.

   b. Interpret the y-intercept.

11. **CORN** After 3 weeks, a corn plant is 2 feet tall. After 9 weeks, the plant is 8 feet tall. Write an equation that represents the height y (in feet) of the corn plant after x weeks. *(Section 2.7)*

12. **WATER** A recreation department bought bottled water to sell at a fair. The graph shows the number y of bottles remaining after each hour x. *(Section 2.8)*

   a. Find the slope and y-intercept.

   b. Write an equation of the line.

   c. The fair started at 10 A.M. When did the recreation department run out of bottled water?

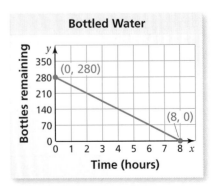

Alternative Assessment Options

Math Chat   Student Reflective Focus Question
Structured Interview   Writing Prompt

Structured Interview

Interviews can occur formally or informally. Ask a student to perform a task and to explain it as they work. Have them describe their thought process. Probe the student for more information. Do not ask leading questions. Keep a rubric or notes.

Teacher Prompts	Student Answers	Teacher Notes
Tell me a story about managing a checking account. Include Rate: -50 dollars/mo y-intercept: $300 x-intercept: 6 months	I opened a checking account and deposited $300. Each month, I withdrew $50. After 6 months, I had $0 in the checking account.	Student understands the meaning of slope, the y-intercept, and the x-intercept in a real-life problem.

Study Help Sample Answers

Remind students to complete Graphic Organizers for the rest of the chapter.

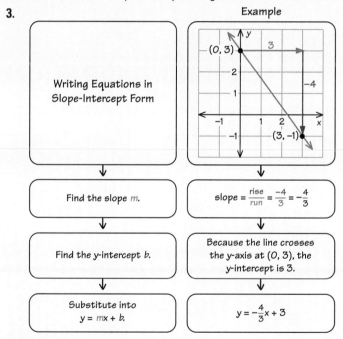

4–5. Available at *BigIdeasMath.com*

Reteaching and Enrichment Strategies

If students need help. . .	If students got it. . .
Resources by Chapter • Study Help • Practice A and Practice B • Puzzle Time Lesson Tutorials *BigIdeasMath.com* Practice Quiz Practice from the Test Generator	Resources by Chapter • Enrichment and Extension • School-to-Work Game Closet at *BigIdeasMath.com* Start the Chapter Review

Technology For the Teacher

Answer Presentation Tool

Assessment Book

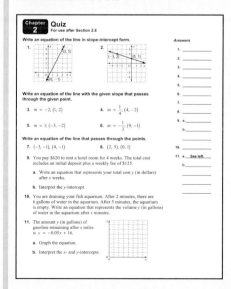

For the Teacher
Additional Review Options

- **Quiz***Show*
- Big Ideas Test Generator
- Game Closet at *BigIdeasMath.com*
- Vocabulary Puzzle Builder
- Resources by Chapter
  Puzzle Time
  Study Help

Answers

1.
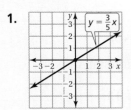

2.
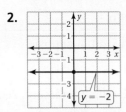

3.
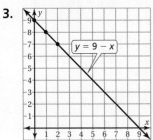

4.
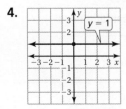

5.
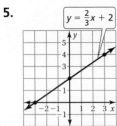

6.
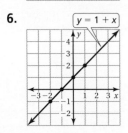

Review of Common Errors

Exercises 1–6

- Students may make a calculation error for one of the ordered pairs in a table of values. If they only find two ordered pairs for the graph, they may not recognize their mistake. Encourage them to find at least three ordered pairs when drawing a graph.

Exercises 2 and 4

- Students may draw a vertical line through a point on the *x*-axis instead of through the corresponding point on the *y*-axis. Remind them that the equation is a horizontal line. Ask them to identify the *y*-coordinate for several *x*-coordinates. For example, what is the *y*-coordinate for $x = 5$? $x = 6$? $x = -4$? Students should answer with the same *y*-coordinate each time.

Review Key Vocabulary

linear equation, *p. 64*
solution of a linear equation, *p. 64*
slope, *p. 70*
rise, *p. 70*
run, *p. 70*

x-intercept, *p. 78*
y-intercept, *p. 78*
slope-intercept form, *p. 78*
standard form, *p. 84*

Review Examples and Exercises

2.1 Graphing Linear Equations (pp. 62–67)

Graph $y = 3x - 1$.

Step 1: Make a table of values.

x	$y = 3x - 1$	y	(x, y)
-2	$y = 3(-2) - 1$	-7	$(-2, -7)$
-1	$y = 3(-1) - 1$	-4	$(-1, -4)$
0	$y = 3(0) - 1$	-1	$(0, -1)$
1	$y = 3(1) - 1$	2	$(1, 2)$

Step 2: Plot the ordered pairs.

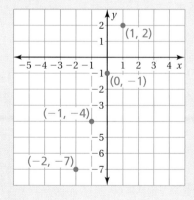

Step 3: Draw a line through the points.

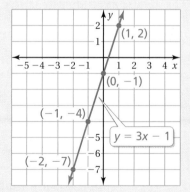

Exercises

Graph the linear equation.

1. $y = \dfrac{3}{5}x$

2. $y = -2$

3. $y = 9 - x$

4. $y = 1$

5. $y = \dfrac{2}{3}x + 2$

6. $y = 1 + x$

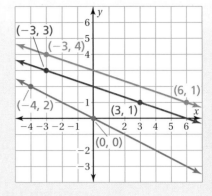

2.2 Slope of a Line (pp. 68–75)

Which two lines are parallel? Explain.

Find the slope of each line.

Red Line   **Blue Line**   **Green Line**

$\dfrac{-2}{6} = -\dfrac{1}{3}$ $\dfrac{-2}{4} = -\dfrac{1}{2}$ $\dfrac{-3}{9} = -\dfrac{1}{3}$

The red and green lines have the same slope, so they are parallel.

Exercises

The points in the table lie on a line. Find the slope of the line. Then draw its graph.

7.

x	0	1	2	3
y	−1	0	1	2

8.

x	−2	0	2	4
y	3	4	5	6

2.3 Graphing Linear Equations in Slope-Intercept Form (pp. 76–81)

Graph $y = 0.5x - 3$. Identify the x-intercept.

Step 1: Find the slope and y-intercept.

$$y = 0.5x + (-3)$$

slope y-intercept

Step 2: The y-intercept is -3. So, plot $(0, -3)$.

Step 3: Use the slope to find another point and draw the line.

$$\text{slope} = \frac{\text{rise}}{\text{run}} = \frac{1}{2}$$

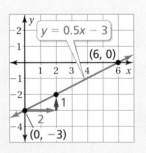

Plot the point that is 2 units right and 1 unit up from $(0, -3)$. Draw a line through the two points.

The line crosses the x-axis at $(6, 0)$. So, the x-intercept is 6.

Exercises

Graph the linear equation. Identify the x-intercept.

9. $y = 2x - 6$ 10. $y = -4x + 8$ 11. $y = -x - 8$

Review of Common Errors (continued)

Exercises 7 and 8

- Students may reverse the *x*- and *y*-coordinates when plotting the ordered pairs given in the table. Remind them that the first row is the *x*-coordinate and the second row is the *y*-coordinate. Encourage students to write the ordered pairs before graphing.

Exercises 9–11

- Students may forget to include negatives with the slope and/or *y*-intercept. Remind them to look at the sign in front of the slope and the *y*-intercept. Also remind students that the equation is $y = mx + b$. This means that if the linear equation has "minus *b*," then the *y*-intercept is negative.
- Students may use the reciprocal of the slope when graphing and may find an incorrect *x*-intercept. Remind them that slope is *rise* over *run*, so the numerator represents vertical change, not horizontal.

Answers

7. 1

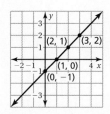

8. $\dfrac{1}{2}$

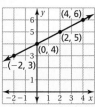

9.

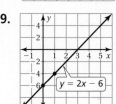

x-intercept: 3

10.

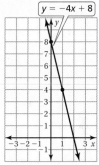

x-intercept: 2

11.

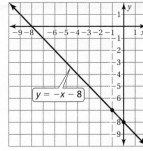

x-intercept: −8

Answers

12.

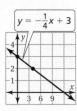

$y = -\frac{1}{4}x + 3$

13.

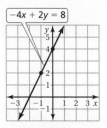

$-4x + 2y = 8$

14.

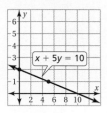

$x + 5y = 10$

15.

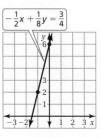

$-\frac{1}{2}x + \frac{1}{8}y = \frac{3}{4}$

Review of Common Errors (continued)

Exercises 12–15

- Students may use the same operation instead of the inverse operation when rewriting the equation in slope-intercept form. Remind them of the steps to rewrite an equation.
- Students may mix up the *x*- and *y*-intercepts. Remind them that the *x*-intercept is the *x*-coordinate of where the line crosses the *x*-axis and the *y*-intercept is the *y*-coordinate of where the line crosses the *y*-axis.

Exercises 16 and 17

- Students may write the reciprocal of the slope or forget a negative sign. Remind them of the definition of slope. Ask them to predict the sign of the slope based on the rise or fall of the line.

Exercises 18–20

- Students may use the reciprocal of the slope when finding the second point to plot. Remind them of the definition of slope.
- Students may say that the *y*-intercept is the *y*-coordinate of the given point. Remind them that the *y*-intercept is represented by *b* in the point (0, *b*), and if the given point is not in this form, they need to use the slope to find where the line crosses the *y*-axis.

Exercises 21 and 22

- Students may plot the points, draw a line through the points, and use the point where the line crosses the *y*-axis to find the *y*-intercept. Sometimes this is not the correct point because the line may not be perfectly drawn. Encourage students to use the slope to find the *y*-intercept.

Exercise 23

- Students may forget to include negatives with the slope and/or the *y*-intercept. Remind them to look at the sign in front of the slope and the *y*-intercept. Also remind them that the equation is $y = mx + b$. This means that if the linear equation has "minus *b*," then the *y*-intercept is negative.

Graphing Linear Equations in Standard Form *(pp. 82–87)*

Graph $8x + 4y = 16$.

Step 1: Write the equation in slope-intercept form.

$$8x + 4y = 16 \qquad \text{Write the equation.}$$

$$4y = -8x + 16 \qquad \text{Subtract } 8x \text{ from each side.}$$

$$y = -2x + 4 \qquad \text{Divide each side by 4.}$$

Step 2: Use the slope and y-intercept to plot two points.

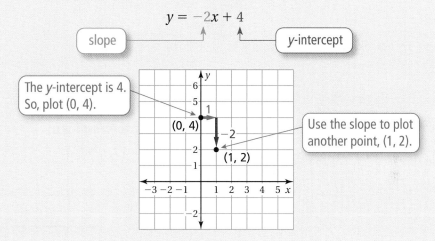

$$y = -2x + 4$$

slope y-intercept

The y-intercept is 4. So, plot (0, 4).

Use the slope to plot another point, (1, 2).

Step 3: Draw a line through the points.

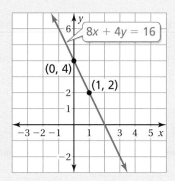

Exercises

Graph the linear equation.

12. $\dfrac{1}{4}x + y = 3$

13. $-4x + 2y = 8$

14. $x + 5y = 10$

15. $-\dfrac{1}{2}x + \dfrac{1}{8}y = \dfrac{3}{4}$

2.5 **Writing Equations in Slope-Intercept Form** *(pp. 90–95)*

Write an equation of the line in slope-intercept form.

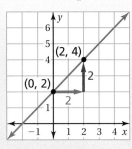

Find the slope and *y*-intercept.

$$\text{slope} = \frac{\text{rise}}{\text{run}} = \frac{2}{2} = 1$$

Because the line crosses the *y*-axis at (0, 2), the *y*-intercept is 2.

slope   *y*-intercept

∴ So, the equation is $y = 1x + 2$, or $y = x + 2$.

Exercises

Write an equation of the line in slope-intercept form.

16.
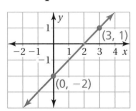

17.
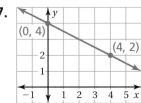

2.6 **Writing Equations Using a Slope and a Point** *(pp. 96–101)*

Write an equation of the line with a slope of $\frac{2}{3}$ that passes through the point (−3, −1).

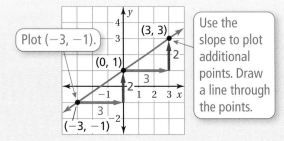

Plot (−3, −1).

Use the slope to plot additional points. Draw a line through the points.

Use a graph to find the *y*-intercept.

Because the line crosses the *y*-axis at (0, 1), the *y*-intercept is 1.

∴ So, the equation is $y = \frac{2}{3}x + 1$.

Exercises

Write an equation of the line with the given slope that passes through the given point.

18. $m = 3$; (4, 4)   **19.** $m = 2$; (2, 6)   **20.** $m = -0.5$; (−4, 2)

Review Game

Equations of Lines

Big Ideas
Game Closet

For the Student
Additional Practice
- Lesson Tutorials
- Study Help (textbook)
- Student Website
    Multi-Language Glossary
    Practice Assessments

Materials per Group:
- map of the city or town where students' homes and school are located
- pencil
- straight edge

Directions:

Students work in groups of four using a local map that includes their home and school locations. Maps can be downloaded from the Internet. The legend for distance on the map must be visible.

The teacher sets an origin, using a popular location like the zoo or library. Placing the origin away from the school will result in having *x*- and *y*-intercepts other than zero.

Each group will plot the points of the school and the point of one of their homes. They should draw a line through the points and write an equation for the line. They will repeat for each of their homes. Students should work with numbers representing actual miles.

Who Wins?

The first group to complete all school to home lines with the correct equations wins.

Answers

16. $y = x - 2$

17. $y = -\dfrac{1}{2}x + 4$

18. $y = 3x - 8$

19. $y = 2x + 2$

20. $y = -0.5x$

21. $y = -x - 2$

22. $y = \dfrac{1}{2}x - 1$

23. a.

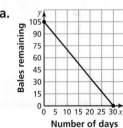

b. The *x*-intercept is the number of days it takes to feed all the hay to the cows. The *y*-intercept represents how many bales of hay there were originally.

c. 70 bales

My Thoughts on the Chapter

Teacher Tip
Not allowed to write in your teaching edition? Use sticky notes to record your thoughts.

What worked. . .

What did not work. . .

What I would do differently. . .

2.7 Writing Equations Using Two Points (pp. 102–107)

Write an equation of the line that passes through the points (2, 3) and (−2, −3).

Use a graph to find the slope and y-intercept.

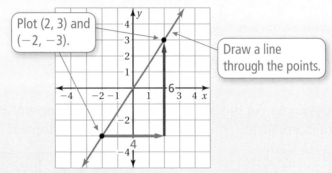

Plot (2, 3) and (−2, −3).

Draw a line through the points.

$$\text{slope} = \frac{\text{rise}}{\text{run}} = \frac{6}{4} = \frac{3}{2}$$

Because the line crosses the y-axis at (0, 0), the y-intercept is 0.

So, the equation is $y = \frac{3}{2}x + 0$, or $y = \frac{3}{2}x$.

Exercises

Write an equation of the line that passes through the points.

21. (−2, 0), (2, −4)

22. (−2, −2), (4, 1)

2.8 Solving Real-Life Problems (pp. 108–113)

The amount y (in dollars) of money you have left after playing x games at a carnival is y = −0.75x + 10. How much money do you have after playing eight games?

$y = -0.75x + 10$	Write the equation.
$= -0.75(8) + 10$	Substitute 8 for x.
$= 4$	Simplify.

You have $4 left after playing 8 games.

Exercises

23. HAY The amount y (in bales) of hay remaining after feeding cows for x days is y = −3.5x + 105. (a) Graph the equation. (b) Interpret the x- and y-intercepts. (c) How many bales are left after 10 days?

Check It Out
Test Practice
BigIdeasMath.com

Find the slope and *y*-intercept of the graph of the linear equation.

1. $y = 6x - 5$

2. $y + 4.3 = 0.1x$

3. $-\dfrac{1}{2}x + 2y = 7$

Graph the linear equation.

4. $y = 2x + 4$

5. $y = -\dfrac{1}{2}x - 5$

6. $-3x + 6y = 12$

7. Write an equation of the line in slope-intercept form.

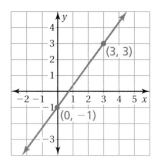

8. The points in the table lie on a line. Find the slope of the line. Then draw its graph.

x	y
−1	−4
0	−1
1	2
2	5

Write an equation of the line with the given slope that passes through the given point.

9. $m = -3$; $(-2, -2)$

10. $m = \dfrac{2}{3}$; $(3, 3)$

Write an equation of the line that passes through the points.

11. $(-1, 5), (3, -3)$

12. $(-4, 1), (4, 3)$

13. $(-2, 5), (-1, 1)$

14. BRAILLE Because of its size and detail, Braille takes longer to read than text. A person reading Braille reads at 25% the rate of a person reading text. Write an equation that represents the average rate *y* of a Braille reader in terms of the average rate *x* of a text reader.

15. CABLE CAR The graph shows the distance *y* (in meters) that a cable car travels up a mountain in *x* minutes.

   a. Find and interpret the slope.

   b. Write an equation of the line.

   c. How far does the cable car travel in 15 minutes?

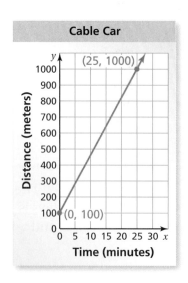

Cable Car

Test Item References

Chapter Test Questions	Section to Review
4, 5	2.1
8	2.2
1–3	2.3
6	2.4
7	2.5
9, 10	2.6
11–13	2.7
14, 15	2.8

Test-Taking Strategies

Remind students to quickly look over the entire test before they start so that they can budget their time. Students should jot down the formula for the slope-intercept form of a linear equation on the back of their test before they begin. Encourage students to use the **Stop** and **Think** strategy before answering.

Common Assessment Errors

- **Exercises 1–3** Students may use the reciprocal of the slope when graphing and may find an incorrect y-intercept.
- **Exercises 4–6** Students may make a calculation error for one of the ordered pairs in a table of values. If they only find two ordered pairs for the graph, they may not recognize their mistake.
- **Exercise 7** Students may write the reciprocal of the slope or forget a negative sign.
- **Exercises 9 and 10** Students may use the reciprocal of the slope when finding the second point to plot and/or may think that the y-intercept is the y-coordinate of the given point.
- **Exercises 11–13** Students may plot the points, draw a line through the points, and use the point where the line crosses the y-axis to find the y-intercept. This may not be the correct point because the line may not be perfectly drawn.
- **Exercise 14** Students may have difficulty using the given information to come up with an equation. Point out that the two rates are proportional.

Reteaching and Enrichment Strategies

If students need help. . .	If students got it. . .
Resources by Chapter • Practice A and Practice B • Puzzle Time Record and Practice Journal Practice Differentiating the Lesson Lesson Tutorials Practice from the Test Generator Skills Review Handbook	Resources by Chapter • Enrichment and Extension • School-to-Work • Financial Literacy • Life Connections • Stories in History Game Closet at *BigIdeasMath.com* Start Standardized Test Practice

Answers

1. slope: 6; y-intercept: -5

2. slope: 0.1; y-intercept: -4.3

3. slope: $\dfrac{1}{4}$; y-intercept: $\dfrac{7}{2}$

4–6. See Additional Answers.

7. $y = \dfrac{4}{3}x - 1$

8. See Additional Answers.

9. $y = -3x - 8$

10. $y = \dfrac{2}{3}x + 1$

11. $y = -2x + 3$

12. $y = \dfrac{1}{4}x + 2$

13. $y = -4x - 3$

14. $y = 0.25x$

15. **a.** slope: 36; The slope is the speed at which the cable car is traveling, 36 meters per minute.

b. $y = 36x + 100$

c. 540 m

Assessment Book

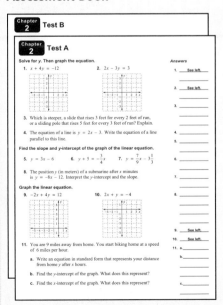

T-120

After Answering Easy Questions, Relax
Answer Easy Questions First
Estimate the Answer
Read All Choices before Answering
Read Question before Answering
Solve Directly or Eliminate Choices
Solve Problem before Looking at
   Choices
Use Intelligent Guessing
Work Backwards

About this Strategy

When taking a multiple choice test, be sure to read each question carefully and thoroughly. After reading the question, estimate the answer before trying to solve.

Answers

1. C
2. F
3. B
4. H

Item Analysis

1. **A.** The student misreads the graph, either going across from 60 or going down from the corresponding point on the graph.

   B. The student misreads the graph, either going across from 60 or going down from the corresponding point on the graph.

   C. Correct answer

   D. The student misreads the graph, either going across from 60 or going down from the corresponding point on the graph.

2. **F.** Correct answer

   G. The student reads the slope correctly, but uses the wrong point to identify the *y*-intercept.

   H. The student reads the *y*-intercept correctly, but miscalculates the slope.

   I. The student finds the slope and *y*-intercept incorrectly.

3. **A.** The student multiplies correctly by 60, but then divides by 8 instead of 4.

   B. Correct answer

   C. The student multiplies correctly by 60, but then fails to convert to gallons.

   D. The student multiplies correctly by 60, but then multiplies by 4 instead of dividing.

4. **F.** The student interchanges correct values for *x* and *y*.

   G. The student makes two errors: interchanging *x* and *y*, and assigning a negative sign incorrectly.

   H. Correct answer

   I. The student makes a mistake with a correct solution (4, 2) and assigns a negative value to 2, forgetting that there is already a minus sign in the equation.

5. **A.** Correct answer

   B. The student accounts for the variable term correctly, but fails to realize that the starting point is three years prior to the point at which the value is 21,000.

   C. The student accounts for the variable term correctly, but is confused by the roles of 21,000 and three years time. The student decides that subtracting them makes sense because the car is depreciating.

   D. The student is badly confused, subtracting numbers out of desperation and fails to account for the proper role of 2,500.

Technology
For the Teacher

Big Ideas Test Generator

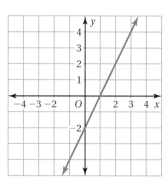

1. The graph below shows the value of United States dollars compared to Guatemalan quetzals.

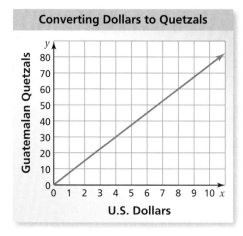

Converting Dollars to Quetzals

What is the value of 60 quetzals?

- **A.** $6
- **B.** $7
- **C.** $8
- **D.** $9

2. Which equation matches the line shown in the graph?

- **F.** $y = 2x - 2$
- **G.** $y = 2x + 1$
- **H.** $y = x - 2$
- **I.** $y = x + 1$

3. A faucet releases 6 quarts of water per minute. How many gallons of water will the faucet release in one hour?

- **A.** 45 gal
- **B.** 90 gal
- **C.** 360 gal
- **D.** 1440 gal

4. The equation $6x - 5y = 14$ is written in standard form. Which point lies on the graph of this equation?

- **F.** $(-4, -1)$
- **G.** $(-2, 4)$
- **H.** $(-1, -4)$
- **I.** $(4, -2)$

5. A car's value depreciates at a rate of $2,500 per year. Three years after a car is purchased, its value is $21,000. Which equation can be used to find v, its value in dollars, n years after it is purchased?

A. $v = 28,500 - 2,500n$

C. $v = 18,500 - 2,500n$

B. $v = 21,000 - 2,500n$

D. $v = 18,500 - n$

6. A cell phone plan costs $10 per month plus $0.10 for each minute used. Last month, you spent $18.50 using this plan. This can be modeled by the equation below, where m represents the number of minutes used.

$$0.1m + 10 = 18.5$$

How many minutes did you use last month?

F. 8.4 min

H. 185 min

G. 85 min

I. 285 min

7. What is the slope of the line that passes through the points $(2, -2)$ and $(8, 1)$?

8. It costs $40 to rent a car for one day. In addition, the rental agency charges you for each mile driven, as shown in the graph.

Think
Solve
Explain

Part A Determine the slope of the line joining the points on the graph.

Part B Explain what the slope represents.

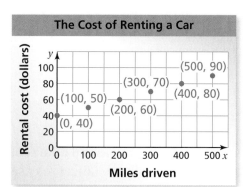

9. You bought a lead pencil for $5 and three identical markers. You spent $12.47 in all. Which equation could be used to find the price p of one marker?

A. $5 + p = 12.47$

C. $3(5 + p) = 12.47$

B. $5 + 3p = 12.47$

D. $3p = 12.47 + 5$

Item Analysis (continued)

6. **F.** The student correctly subtracts 10 from both sides, but then subtracts 0.1 instead of dividing.

   G. Correct answer

   H. The student ignores 10 and simply divides by 0.1.

   I. The student adds 10 to both sides, and then divides by 0.1.

7. **Gridded Response:** Correct answer: 0.5, or $\frac{1}{2}$

   Common Error: The student performs subtraction incorrectly for the y-terms, yielding an answer of $\frac{1}{6}$ or $-\frac{1}{6}$.

8. **2 points** The student demonstrates a thorough understanding of the slope of a line and what it represents, explains the work fully, and calculates the slope accurately. The slope of the line is $\frac{50 - 40}{100 - 0} = \frac{10}{100} = \frac{1}{10} = 0.10$. The slope represents the rental cost per mile driven, $0.10 per mile.

   1 point The student's work and explanations demonstrate a lack of essential understanding. The formula for the slope of a line is misstated, or the student incorrectly states what the slope of the line represents.

   0 points The student provides no response, a completely incorrect or incomprehensible response, or a response that demonstates insufficient understanding of the slope of a line and what it represents.

9. **A.** The student adds together the lead pencil and one marker instead of three markers.

   B. Correct answer

   C. The student overthinks the problem and decides that the factor of 3 applies to the sum.

   D. The student accounts for the three markers, but gets muddled on how things add together.

Answers

5. A

6. G

7. $\frac{1}{2}$

8. *Part A* 0.10

   Part B $0.10 per mile

9. B

Answers

10. I

11. B

12. H

13. 180 kg

14. C

Item Analysis (continued)

10. **F.** The student mistakes slope for meaning that a line passes through (0, 0).

    G. The student mistakes a vertical line for zero slope.

    H. The student mistakes slope for meaning that a line passes through (0, 0).

    I. Correct answer

11. **A.** The student divides M by 3, but fails to divide $(K + 7)$ by 3.

    B. Correct answer

    C. The student divides K by 3, but fails to divide 7 by 3.

    D. The student subtracts 7 instead of adding it to both sides.

12. **F.** The student picks the coefficient of x from the equation, failing to convert to slope-intercept form.

    G. The student divides properly by 2, but attaches an incorrect sign since x initially has a positive coefficient.

    H. Correct answer

    I. The student correctly moves $5x$ to the opposite side of the equation, but fails to divide by 2.

13. **Gridded Response:** Correct answer: 180 kg

    Common Error: The student does not know the correct conversion rate from grams to kilograms, yielding an answer of 1800 or 18,000.

14. **A.** The student incorrectly assumes that adding 4 to the y-value of a point is the same as saying the slope is 4. Correct point would have 1 added to a as well.

    B. The student incorrectly assumes that because the ratio $8 : 2 = 4$, the point must lie on the line of slope 4.

    C. Correct answer

    D. The student calculates the slope correctly and gets $4 \cdot \frac{b}{a}$, but then assumes this fits the initial problem because its point was (a, b) and its slope was 4.

Extra Example for Standardized Test Practice

1. What value of x makes the equation shown below true?

$$11x - 7 = 3(x + 1)$$

Answer for Extra Example

1. **Gridded Response:**

   Correct answer: 1.25

   Common Error: The student does not properly distribute the factor 3 in the right hand side of the equation, yielding an incorrect answer of $x = 1$.

10. Which line has a slope of 0?

F.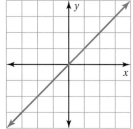

H.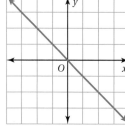

G.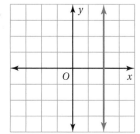

I.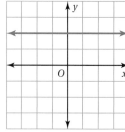

11. Solve the formula $K = 3M - 7$ for M.

A. $M = K + 7$

C. $M = \dfrac{K}{3} + 7$

B. $M = \dfrac{K + 7}{3}$

D. $M = \dfrac{K - 7}{3}$

12. The linear equation $5x + 2y = 10$ is written in standard form. What is the slope of the graph of this equation?

F. 5

H. -2.5

G. 2.5

I. -5

13. A package of breakfast cereal is labeled "750 g." This cereal is shipped in cartons that hold 24 packages. What is the total mass, in kilograms, of the breakfast cereal in 10 cartons?

14. A line has a slope of 4 and passes through the point (a, b). Which point must also lie on this line?

A. $(a, b + 4)$

C. $(a + 1, b + 4)$

B. $(2a, 8b)$

D. $(2a, 5b)$

3 Functions

"Here's how I remember that the range is the *y*-values."

"Where the deer and the antelope play, huh?"

"I draw a cabin on the *y*-axis. Then, I hum 'Home, Home on the range'."

"I wondered where my cat treats were going."

"It is my treat-converter function machine. However many cat treats I input, the machine outputs TWICE that many dog biscuits. Isn't that cool?"

Strands Development

5th Grade
• Describe and express the relationship found in a number pattern.

7th Grade
• Represent relationships with tables, graphs, rules, and words.

8th Grade
• Make connections between any two representations (tables, graphs, words, and rules) of a given relationship. • Identify the domain, range, independent variable, or dependent variable in a given situation. • Make comparisons, predictions, and inferences using information displayed in graphs.

Math in History

Formulas for the volumes of solids have been known and used in many cultures.

★ There are records of Japanese mathematicians using a Chinese text that was written around 200 B.C. The third section of the text contains methods for finding the volumes of prisms, cylinders, pyramids, and cones.

★ Around 628 A.D., a book called Brahmasphutasiddhanta was written by the Indian mathematician Brahmagupta. The book has 25 chapters. In one of them, he describes methods for calculating the volume of a prism and a cone.

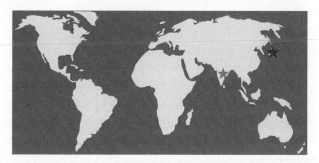

Pacing Guide for Chapter 3

Chapter Opener	1 Day
Section 1 Activity Lesson	 1 Day 1 Day
Section 2 Activity Lesson	 1 Day 1 Day
Study Help / Quiz	1 Day
Section 3 Activity Lesson	 1 Day 1 Day
Section 4 Activity Lesson	 1 Day 1 Day
Chapter Review / Tests	2 Days
Total Chapter 3	12 Days
Year-to-Date	54 Days

Check Your Resources

- Record and Practice Journal
- Resources by Chapter
- Skills Review Handbook
- Assessment Book
- Worked-Out Solutions

Technology For the Teacher

The Dynamic Planning Tool
Editable Teacher's Resources at
BigIdeasMath.com

Standards of Learning

7.12 The student will represent relationships with tables, graphs, rules, and words.

Additional Topics for Review

- Adding and subtracting decimals and fractions
- Multiplying fractions and decimals
- Plotting points and identifying coordinates in Quadrant I

Try It Yourself

1. As the input decreases by 2, the output increases by 3.

2. As the input increases by 2, the output increases by 1.

3. As the input decreases by 1, the output decreases by 3.5.

Record and Practice Journal

1. As the input increases by 1, the output increases by 2.

2. As the input increases by 2, the output increases by 5.

3. As the input increases by 4, the output increases by 3.

4. As the input increases by 1, the output decreases by 7.

5. As the hours increase by 1, the customers increase by 15.

6. Input   Output

As the input increases by 2, the output increases by 2.

7–10. See Additional Answers.

Math Background Notes

Vocabulary Review

- Input
- Output
- Mapping Diagram

Recognizing Patterns

- Students have been working with patterns since elementary school. They should know how to use mapping diagrams and In and Out tables. They should know how to use graphs to represent and identify patterns.
- Remind students that mapping diagrams, In and Out tables, graphs, and words are four different ways that can be used to express or describe a pattern.
- **Common Error:** Some students may try to find a pattern between the input and output values. Remind them that they are not searching for how the input values relate to output values but rather, how the input values relate to one another and how the output values relate to one another.
- **Teaching Tip:** Some students may have difficulty identifying the pattern. Encourage these students to search for context clues first. For example, are the input values getting progressively greater? If so, the pattern will most likely involve addition or multiplication. If the numbers are all even, try adding or multiplying by even numbers first to try to find the pattern.
- **Teaching Tip:** Rather than trying to identify the pattern using the points on a graph, encourage students to transfer the information contained in the ordered pairs into a mapping diagram as in Example 3. Then use the mapping diagram to find the pattern.

Reteaching and Enrichment Strategies

If students need help. . .	If students got it. . .
Record and Practice Journal • Fair Game Review Skills Review Handbook Lesson Tutorials	Game Closet at *BigIdeasMath.com* Start the next section

What You Learned Before

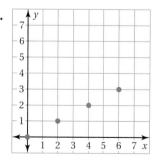

"Do you think the stripes in this shirt make me look too linear?"

● Recognizing Patterns

Describe the pattern of inputs and outputs.

Example 1

Input	Output
2	→ 0
4	→ 3
6	→ 6
8	→ 9

∴ As the input increases by 2, the output increases by 3.

Example 2

Input, x	6	1	−4	−9	−14
Output, y	7	8	9	10	11

∴ As the input x decreases by 5, the output y increases by 1.

Example 3 Draw a mapping diagram for the graph. Then describe the pattern of inputs and outputs.

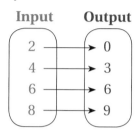

Input	Output
1	→ 1
2	→ 3
3	→ 5
4	→ 7

∴ As the input increases by 1, the output increases by 2.

Try It Yourself

Describe the pattern of inputs x and outputs y.

1. Input, x   Output, y

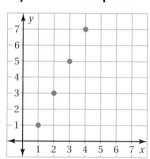

Input	Output
0	→ −2
−2	→ 1
−4	→ 4
−6	→ 7

2.

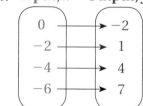

3.

Input, x	0	−1	−2	−3	−4
Output, y	7	3.5	0	−3.5	−7

3.1 Domain and Range of a Function

Essential Question How can you find the domain and range of a function?

STANDARDS
OF LEARNING
8.17

1 ACTIVITY: The Domain and Range of a Function

Work with a partner. In Activity 1 in Section 2.4, you completed the table shown below. The table shows the number of adult and child tickets sold for a school concert.

input →
output →

Number of Adult Tickets, x	0	1	2	3	4
Number of Child Tickets, y	8	6	4	2	0

The variables x and y are related by the linear equation $4x + 2y = 16$

a. Write the equation in *function form* by solving for y.

b. The **domain** of a function is the set of all input values. Find the domain of the function.

　　Domain =

　Why is $x = 5$ not in the domain of the function?

　Why is $x = \dfrac{1}{2}$ not in the domain of the function?

c. The **range** of a function is the set of all output values. Find the range of the function.

　　Range =

d. Functions can be described in many ways.
   - by an equation
   - by an input-output table
   - in words
   - by a graph
   - as a set of ordered pairs

Use the graph to write the function as a set of ordered pairs.

$\left(\rule{0.6cm}{0pt},\rule{0.6cm}{0pt}\right), \left(\rule{0.6cm}{0pt},\rule{0.6cm}{0pt}\right), \left(\rule{0.6cm}{0pt},\rule{0.6cm}{0pt}\right),$

$\left(\rule{0.6cm}{0pt},\rule{0.6cm}{0pt}\right), \left(\rule{0.6cm}{0pt},\rule{0.6cm}{0pt}\right)$

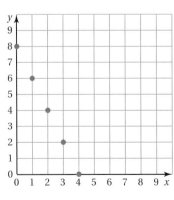

Laurie's Notes

Introduction

For the Teacher

- **Goal:** Students will develop an understanding of domain and range by exploring familiar problems.
- The language of functions can be challenging for students, more so than the actual concepts.

Motivate

- Ask for a volunteer who will not mind you measuring his or her head for a hat. See the chart for sizes.

Hat Size	$6\frac{1}{2}$	$6\frac{5}{8}$	$6\frac{3}{4}$	$6\frac{7}{8}$	7	$7\frac{1}{8}$	$7\frac{1}{4}$	$7\frac{3}{8}$	$7\frac{1}{2}$	$7\frac{5}{8}$	$7\frac{3}{4}$	$7\frac{7}{8}$	8
Inches	$20\frac{1}{2}$	$20\frac{7}{8}$	$21\frac{1}{4}$	$21\frac{5}{8}$	22	$22\frac{1}{2}$	$22\frac{7}{8}$	$23\frac{1}{4}$	$23\frac{5}{8}$	24	$24\frac{3}{8}$	$24\frac{3}{4}$	$25\frac{1}{4}$
Centimeters	52	53	54	55	56	57	58	59	60	61	62	63	64
	X-SMALL		SMALL		MEDIUM		LARGE		X-LARGE		XX-LARGE		

- **?** "What is the input for determining your hat size?" size of your head in inches or centimeters
- **?** "What are the outputs?" hat size as a number $\left(6\frac{1}{2}, 6\frac{5}{8}, \ldots\right)$ or a category (X-small, small, …)
- **Discuss:** Relate the input and output for determining the hat size to the new vocabulary, domain and range.

Activity Notes

Activity 1

- This problem involves reading the language of functions. Students should pay attention to the vocabulary.
- **?** "Recall that the linear equation $4x + 2y = 16$ is written in standard form. What other common form have you used to write linear equations?" slope-intercept form
- Writing the equation in slope-intercept form results in an equation in function form. Students may write $y = 8 - 2x$, which is equivalent to $y = -2x + 8$.
- This problem focuses attention on the domain, the set of all input values. We also describe domain as the *permissible values* for x, meaning what numbers can be substituted for x. In the context of this problem, it makes sense that x can only be a whole number between 0 and 4, inclusive.
- Once the domain values are determined, a set of output values, the range, result.
- **?** "Why are the ordered pairs of the graph not connected?" The function has whole number solutions. You cannot have fractional or negative numbers of tickets sold.
- **?** "How many solutions are there for this function?" five

Standards of Learning

8.17 The student will identify the domain, range, independent variable, or dependent variable in a given situation.

Previous Learning

Students should know how to determine solutions of a linear equation.

Activity Materials
Introduction

- tape measure

Start Thinking! and Warm Up

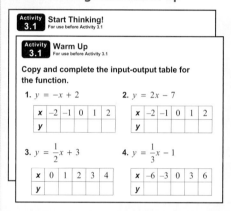

3.1 Record and Practice Journal

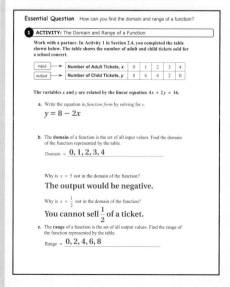

English Language Learners

Vocabulary

Students will find it helpful to relate the words *input* and *output* with the prepositions *in* and *out*.

Activity 2

- **Connection:** Students have graphed linear equations whose domain and range were the set of real numbers. In fact, students plotted 3 to 4 points that satisfied the equation and then connected the points to graph the linear equation. If the domain is restricted to only a finite set of values, the range becomes restricted to a finite set of values, and the number of solutions is finite.

- Students may ask why they are only using five values for *x* in parts (a) and (b), and why they are not connecting the ordered pairs in the graph in parts (c) and (d). Again, the focus is on domain and range. Remind students that if you only use certain domain values (inputs for *x*), the range values (outputs for *y*) are determined by using the function rule (equation).

- **?** "What is the resulting range for the function $y = -3x + 4$ with a domain of $-2, -1, 0, 1, 2$?" $10, 7, 4, 1, -2$

- Students often make these problems more difficult than they are. Remind them to use substitution to evaluate the functions (equations) for parts (a) and (b), then use their eyesight to read the ordered pair solutions for parts (c) and (d). Then students record their answers in the input-output table.

- **?** To focus attention on the language of functions, ask students to describe the function rule for each problem. For instance, the function rule for part (a) is *multiply the input by* -3 *and then add 4*. Students will need to find the function rule for parts (c) and (d). $y = 10 - x; y = x - 2$

What Is Your Answer?

- **Question 4 Extension:** Gather data from students who are willing to share their shoe size and to have their foot measured. How well does the rule fit the data?

Closure

- **Writing Prompt:** Describe what is meant by the domain and range of a function.

3.1 Record and Practice Journal

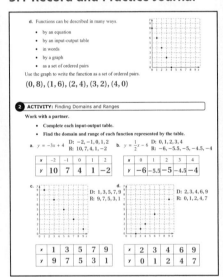

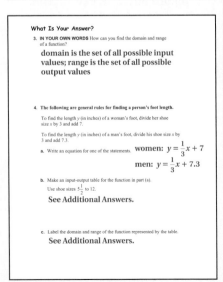

Technology **F**or the **T**eacher

Dynamic Classroom

The Dynamic Planning Tool
Editable Teacher's Resources at *BigIdeasMath.com*

Work with a partner.

- Copy and complete each input-output table.

- Find the domain and range of the function represented by the table.

a. $y = -3x + 4$

x	−2	−1	0	1	2
y					

b. $y = \dfrac{1}{2}x - 6$

x	0	1	2	3	4
y					

c.

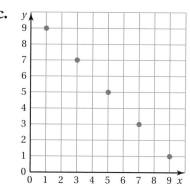

x					
y					

d.

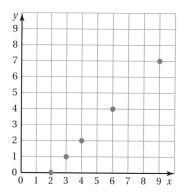

x					
y					

What Is Your Answer?

3. IN YOUR OWN WORDS How can you find the domain and range of a function?

4. The following are general rules for finding a person's foot length.

To find the length y (in inches) of a woman's foot, divide her shoe size x by 3 and add 7.

To find the length y (in inches) of a man's foot, divide his shoe size x by 3 and add 7.3.

© 2010 Zappos.com, Inc.

a. Write an equation for one of the statements.

b. Make an input-output table for the function in part (a). Use shoe sizes $5\dfrac{1}{2}$ to 12.

c. Label the domain and range of the function on the table.

Practice

Use what you learned about the domain and range of a function to complete Exercise 3 on page 130.

Check It Out
Lesson Tutorials
BigIdeasMath ✓com

Key Vocabulary 🔊
function, *p. 128*
domain, *p. 128*
range, *p. 128*
independent variable,
  p. 128
dependent variable,
  p. 128

 **Key Idea**

Functions

A **function** is a relationship that pairs each *input* with exactly one *output*. The **domain** is the set of all possible input values. The **range** is the set of all possible output values.

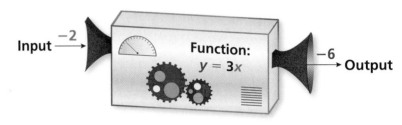

EXAMPLE **1**   **Finding Domain and Range from a Graph**

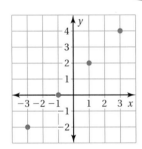

Find the domain and range of the function represented by the graph.

Write the ordered pairs. Identify the inputs and outputs.

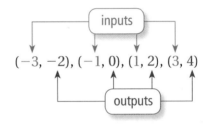

∴ The domain is −3, −1, 1, and 3. The range is −2, 0, 2, and 4.

On Your Own

Now You're Ready
Exercises 4–6

Find the domain and range of the function represented by the graph.

1.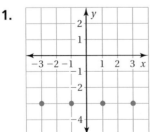

2.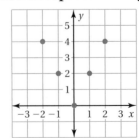

When an equation represents a function, the variable that represents input values is the **independent variable**. The variable that represents output values is the **dependent variable**. This variable *depends* on the value of the independent variable.

🔊 Multi-Language Glossary at BigIdeasMath ✓com.

Laurie's Notes

Introduction

Connect

- **Yesterday:** Students explored the domain and range of functions by revisiting familiar problems.
- **Today:** Students will identify the domain and range of a function from a graph and table of values.

Motivate

- **?** "Could someone describe how a vending machine works?" Listen for: put in money, make a selection, and item comes out.
- Explain that a vending machine is like a function. You make a selection (the input) and a specific item comes out (the output).
- Sometimes there are several inputs that give the same output (3 different buttons for the same bottled water), but there are never several different outputs of the same input (if the vending machine is working properly).

Lesson Notes

Key Idea

- Write the Key Idea. The graphic of a *function machine* should help students conceptualize the idea of entering an input value, applying a rule, and obtaining the output value.
- In discussing the definition of a function, describe what is meant by *each input is paired with exactly one output*. This means:
  - one unique input yields one unique output, or
  - two or more inputs yields the same output.
  - The equation is *not* a function if one unique input yields more than one output.

Example 1

- Point out to students that the inputs, or *x*-coordinates, are the domain, and the outputs, or *y*-coordinates, are the range.
- **?** "Is each input paired with exactly one output?" yes

On Your Own

- **Question 1:** Students may say this is not a function because there is only one number in the range (students should not list it 4 times). Every domain value is paired with the same range value, and that is okay. Remind students it is only the repeat of *x*-values they need to consider.

Write

- Write the definitions of independent variable and dependent variable.
- Use an example to help make the point about the dependent variable *depending* on the value of the independent variable.
- **Example:** In the equation $y = 0.99x$, cost *y* in dollars of buying songs *depends* on the number *x* of songs. So, *x* is the independent variable and *y* is the dependent variable.

 Goal Today's lesson is identifying the **domain** and **range** of a **function**.

Start Thinking! and Warm Up

Lesson 3.1	Warm Up
	For use before Lesson 3.1

Lesson 3.1 **Start Thinking!**
For use before Lesson 3.1

The installation and set-up fees for cable internet come to $150. The monthly cost for internet access is $40 per month.

Write a function for the cost *y* of *x* months of internet service.

What are the domain and range of the function if you only have internet service for 6 months?

Extra Example 1

Find the domain and range of the function represented by the graph.

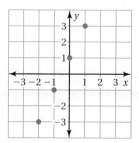

domain: $-2, -1, 0, 1$; range: $-3, -1, 1, 3$

On Your Own

1. domain: $-3, -1, 1, 3$
   range: -3

2. domain: $-2, -1, 0, 1, 2$
   range: $0, 2, 4$

Extra Example 2

The domain of the function represented by $x + y = 5$ is $-3, -2, -1, 0,$ and 1. What is the range of the function?
8, 7, 6, 5, 4

Extra Example 3

x	0	1	2	3	4
y	0.11	0.18	0.27	0.37	0.47

a. The table shows the percent y (in decimal form) of the moon that was visible at midnight x days after August 10, 2013. Interpret the domain and range. The domain is 0, 1, 2, 3, and 4. So, the table shows the data for August 10, 11, 12, 13, and 14. The range is 0.11, 0.18, 0.27, 0.37, and 0.47. So, the table shows that the moon was more visible each day.

b. What percent of the moon was visible on August 12, 2013? 27%

⬤ On Your Own

3–4. See Additional Answers.

5. a. The domain is 0, 1, 2, 3, and 4. It represents December 17, 18, 19, 20, and 21.

The range is 0.2, 0.3, 0.4, 0.5, and 0.6. These amounts are increasing, so the moon was more visible each day.

b. 60%

Differentiated Instruction

Kinesthetic

Have students build their own function machine using a shoe box, index cards, and sticky notes. Write the function on the sticky note and put it on the box. Write numbers on the index cards to use as the input and output values of the function.

Laurie's Notes

Example 2

- Write the equation. Note that the equation is in function form.
- Discuss with students that equations written in function form have all computations on one side of the equation. In addition, the dependent variable is on one side of the equal sign and the independent variable is on the other side. When the value of the independent variable changes, and the arithmetic is performed, the dependent variable changes.
- **Extension:** Ask students to describe the patterns in the input-output table. The x-values increase by 2 and the y-values decrease by 4.

Example 3

- **FYI:** During the full moon, the moon's illuminated side is facing Earth and appears to be completely illuminated by direct sunlight. During a new moon, the moon's unilluminated side is facing Earth and the moon is not visible.
- **?** Ask a few questions to help students understand the problem.
  - "What is the independent variable in this problem?" number of days after January 24, 2011 "What is the dependent variable?" percent of the moon visible at midnight, written as a decimal
  - "What day does $x = 3$ represent?" January 27, 2011
  - Ask a volunteer to make a statement relating the independent and dependent variables. Listen for: the percent of the moon visible at midnight depends on how many days past January 24, 2011 it is.
  - "Is the moon becoming more or less visible in the week following January 24, 2011? Explain." less; The percents are decreasing.
  - "If this problem were continued, what values would make sense for the domain? What values make sense for the range?" domain: whole numbers; range: decimals between 0 and 1 inclusive

On Your Own

- **Question 4:** Students may rewrite this equation in function form, or they may reason that the question is asking, "What numbers sum to -3?"
- **Question 5:** Ask students if the data suggests that they are moving towards a full moon or away from a full moon.

⬤ Closure

- **Exit Ticket:** Make an input-output table for the function $2x + y = 3$ using the inputs $-2, 0, 2, 4$.

x	−2	0	2	4
y	7	3	−1	−5

Technology
For the Teacher

The Dynamic Planning Tool
Editable Teacher's Resources at *BigIdeasMath.com*

EXAMPLE **2** **Finding the Range of a Function**

The domain of the function represented by $y = -2x + 8$ is $-2, 0, 2,$ and $4.$ What is the range of the function?

Make an input-output table.

Because x represents the input values, x is the independent variable.

Because y represents the output values, y is the dependent variable.

Input, x	$-2x + 8$	Output, y
-2	$-2(-2) + 8$	12
0	$-2(0) + 8$	8
2	$-2(2) + 8$	4
4	$-2(4) + 8$	0

∴ So, the range is 12, 8, 4, and 0.

EXAMPLE **3** **Real-Life Application**

The table shows the percent y (in decimal form) of the moon that was visible at midnight x days after January 24, 2011. (a) Interpret the domain and range. (b) What percent of the moon was visible on January 26, 2011?

x	y
0	0.76
1	0.65
2	0.54
3	0.43
4	0.32

a. Zero days after January 24 is January 24. One day after January 24 is January 25. So, the domain of 0, 1, 2, 3, and 4 represents January 24, 25, 26, 27, and 28.

The range is 0.76, 0.65, 0.54, 0.43, and 0.32. These amounts are decreasing, so the moon was less visible each day.

b. January 26, 2011 corresponds to the input $x = 2$. When $x = 2$, $y = 0.54$. So, 0.54, or 54% of the moon was visible on January 26, 2011.

● **On Your Own**

Now You're Ready
Exercises 9–11

Copy and complete the input-output table for the function. Then find the domain and range of the function represented by the table.

3. $y = 2x - 3$

x	-1	0	1	2
y				

4. $x + y = -3$

x	0	1	2	3
y				

5. The table shows the percent y (in decimal form) of the moon that was visible at midnight x days after December 17, 2012.
(a) Interpret the domain and range.
(b) What percent of the moon was visible on December 21, 2012?

x	0	1	2	3	4
y	0.2	0.3	0.4	0.5	0.6

 ## Vocabulary and Concept Check

1. **VOCABULARY** How are independent variables and dependent variables different?

2. **DIFFERENT WORDS, SAME QUESTION** Which is different? Find "both" answers.

Find the range of the function represented by the table.

Find the inputs of the function represented by the table.

Find the x-values of the function represented by $(2, 7)$, $(4, 5)$, and $(6, -1)$.

Find the domain of the function represented by $(2, 7)$, $(4, 5)$, and $(6, -1)$.

x	2	4	6
y	7	5	-1

 ## Practice and Problem Solving

3. The number of earrings and headbands you can buy with \$24 is represented by the equation $8x + 4y = 24$. The table shows the number of earrings and headbands.

   a. Write the equation in function form.
   b. Find the domain and range.
   c. Why is $x = 6$ not in the domain of the function?

Earrings, x	0	1	2	3
Headbands, y	6	4	2	0

Find the domain and range of the function represented by the graph.

 4.
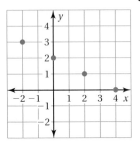

5.
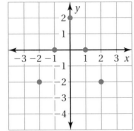

6.
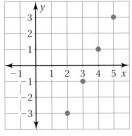

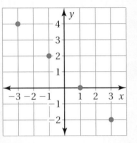

The domain is −2, 0, 2, and 4.

The range is −3, −1, 1, 3.

7. **ERROR ANALYSIS** Describe and correct the error in finding the domain and range of the function represented by the graph.

8. **REASONING** Find the domain and range of the function represented by the table.

Tickets, x	2	3	5	8
Cost, y	\$14	\$21	\$35	\$56

Assignment Guide and Homework Check

Level	Day 1 Activity Assignment	Day 2 Lesson Assignment	Homework Check
Basic	3, 15–19	1, 2, 4–11	2, 4, 8, 10
Average	3, 15–19	1, 2, 4–7, 9–12	2, 4, 10, 12
Advanced	3, 15–19	1, 2, 6, 7, 9–14	2, 6, 10, 12

For Your Information

- **Exercise 14** This problem is an example of a continuous domain. Discrete and continuous domains will be discussed in the next section.

Common Errors

- **Exercises 4–6** Students may mix up the domain and range. For example, a student may give all the *y*-values of the coordinates as the domain. This can happen with all the ordered pairs, or only one or two. Remind students that the *x*-coordinates are the domain and the *y*-coordinates are the range, as shown in Example 1.
- **Exercises 9–11** Students may make mistakes when substituting the values of *x* and solving for *y*. For example, a student may write $y = 6(2) + 2 = 6(4) = 24$ instead of $y = 6(2) + 2 = 12 + 2 = 14$. Remind them of the order of operations.

3.1 Record and Practice Journal

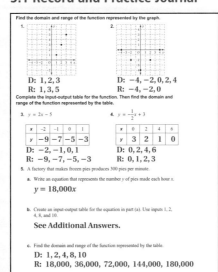

Vocabulary and Concept Check

1. *Sample answer:* An independent variable represents an input value, and a dependent variable represents an output value.

2. Find the range of the function represented by the table.; 7, 5, −1; 2, 4, 6

Practice and Problem Solving

3. **a.** $y = 6 - 2x$

   b. domain: 0, 1, 2, 3
   range: 6, 4, 2, 0

   c. $x = 6$ is not in the domain because it would make *y* negative, and it is not possible to buy a negative number of headbands.

4. domain: −2, 0, 2, 4
   range: 3, 2, 1, 0

5. domain: −2, −1, 0, 1, 2
   range: −2, 0, 2

6. domain: 2, 3, 4, 5
   range: −3, −1, 1, 3

7. The domain and range are switched. The domain is −3, −1, 1, and 3. The range is −2, 0, 2, and 4.

8. domain: 2, 3, 5, 8
   range: 14, 21, 35, 56

9.

x	−1	0	1	2
y	−4	2	8	14

   domain: −1, 0, 1, 2
   range: −4, 2, 8, 14

10.

x	0	4	8	12
y	−2	−3	−4	−5

   domain: 0, 4, 8, 12
   range: −2, −3, −4, −5

Practice and Problem Solving

11.

x	−1	0	1	2
y	1.5	3	4.5	6

domain: −1, 0, 1, 2
range: 1.5, 3, 4.5, 6

12. a. domain: 1, 2, 3
range: 6.856, 7.923, 8.135

b. The domain represents the round of competition. The range represents the scores received by the vaulter.

c. 7.638

13. See *Taking Math Deeper*.

14. See Additional Answers.

Fair Game Review

15–18. See Additional Answers.

19. D

Mini-Assessment

Find the domain and range of the function represented by the graph.

1.

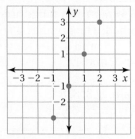

domain: −1, 0, 1, 2;
range: −3, −1, 1, 3

2.

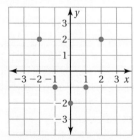

domain: −2, −1, 0, 1, 2;
range: −2, −1, 2

Taking Math Deeper

Exercise 13

The manatee is a gray, waterplant-eating mammal that reaches up to 15 feet in length and can weigh more than 2000 pounds. Humans (especially motor boats) are the cause of about half of all manatee deaths.

 Find a function.

   Let x = manatee's weight in pounds.
   Let y = weight of food per day.

a. y = 12% of x
   $= 0.12x$

x is the input, so it is the independent variable. y is the output, so it is the dependent variable.

 Describe the function.

Create an input-output table for the function. Then, identify the domain and range.

b.

Input, x	150	300	450	600	750	900
Output, y	18	36	54	72	90	108

For the function, the domain is the set of positive numbers that are possible weights of manatees. An approximation would be the positive numbers up to 2000.
The range would be the positive numbers up to about 240.

c. *For the input-output table shown*, the domain is the x-values and the range is the y-values.

 Use the function.

The manatees weigh a total of $300 + 750 + 1050 = 2100$ pounds.

d. In a day, these manatees would eat
   $y = 0.12(2100) = 252$ pounds of food.
   In a week, they would eat
   $y = 7(252) = 1764$ pounds of food.

That's a lot.

Reteaching and Enrichment Strategies

If students need help...	If students got it...
Resources by Chapter • Practice A and Practice B • Puzzle Time Record and Practice Journal Practice Differentiating the Lesson Lesson Tutorials Skills Review Handbook	Resources by Chapter • Enrichment and Extension Start the next section

Copy and complete the input-output table for the function. Then find the domain and range of the function represented by the table.

9. $y = 6x + 2$

x	−1	0	1	2
y				

10. $y = -\dfrac{1}{4}x - 2$

x	0	4	8	12
y				

11. $y = 1.5x + 3$

x	−1	0	1	2
y				

12. VAULTING In the sport of vaulting, a vaulter performs a routine while on a moving horse. For each round x of competition, the vaulter receives a score y from 1 to 10.

   a. Find the domain and range of the function represented by the table.

   b. Interpret the domain and range.

   c. What is the mean score of the vaulter?

x	y
1	6.856
2	7.923
3	8.135

13. MANATEE A manatee eats about 12% of its body weight each day.

   a. Write an equation that represents the amount y (in pounds) of food a manatee eats each day for its weight x. Identify the independent variable and the dependent variable.

   b. Create an input-output table for the equation in part (a). Use the inputs 150, 300, 450, 600, 750, and 900.

   c. Find the domain and range of the function represented by the table.

   d. The weights of three manatees are 300 pounds, 750 pounds, and 1050 pounds. What is the total amount of food that these three manatees eat in a day? in a week?

14. **Critical Thinking** Describe the domain and range of the function.

   a. $y = |x|$ **b.** $y = -|x|$ **c.** $y = |x| - 6$ **d.** $y = -|x| + 4$

Fair Game Review What you learned in previous grades & lessons

Graph the linear equation. *(Section 2.1)*

15. $y = 2x + 8$ **16.** $5x + 6y = 12$ **17.** $-x - 3y = 2$ **18.** $y = 7x - 5$

19. MULTIPLE CHOICE The minimum number of people needed for a group rate at an amusement park is 8. Which inequality represents the number of people needed to get the group rate? *(Section 1.5)*

   Ⓐ $x \leq 8$ Ⓑ $x > 8$ Ⓒ $x < 8$ Ⓓ $x \geq 8$

STANDARDS OF LEARNING
8.17

Essential Question How can you decide whether the domain of a function is discrete or continuous?

1 EXAMPLE: Discrete and Continuous Domains

In Activities 1 and 2 in Section 2.4, you studied two real-life problems represented by the same equation.

$$4x + 2y = 16 \quad \text{or} \quad y = -2x + 8$$

a.

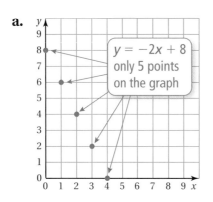

$y = -2x + 8$
only 5 points on the graph

Domain (*x*-values): 0, 1, 2, 3, 4

Range (*y*-values): 8, 6, 4, 2, 0

The domain is **discrete** because it consists of only the numbers 0, 1, 2, 3, and 4.

b.

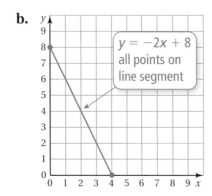

$y = -2x + 8$
all points on line segment

Domain (*x*-values): $x \geq 0$ and $x \leq 4$
(All numbers from 0 to 4)

Range (*y*-values): $y \geq 0$ and $y \leq 8$
(All numbers from 0 to 8)

The domain is **continuous** because it consists of all numbers from 0 to 4 on the number line.

Laurie's Notes

Introduction

For the Teacher

- **Goal:** Students will develop an understanding of discrete and continuous domains by exploring familiar problems.

Motivate

- Pass out strips of paper, perhaps 2 inches by 8 inches. Have students fold the paper in half.
- On one half of the paper, have students describe a variable that must be an integer (i.e., 4, −5, 20). On the other half, have them describe a variable that could be a fraction or decimal (i.e., $2\frac{1}{2}$, 4.8, −3.1). Students should write a description of the variable instead of giving a numerical example. Samples:

People at a movie (130)	Hours you work (2.2)
Problems assigned (18)	Length of fingernails (1.6 cm)
Buses on the road (15)	Yards lost on the play $\left(8\frac{1}{2}\right)$

- Have students tear the paper in half and place in two piles.
- Read and discuss examples in each pile.

Activity Notes

Example 1

- Discuss the two problems on this page. Make note of the vocabulary, discrete and continuous, used to describe the domain of each problem.
- **?** "Why are the ordered pairs of the graph not connected in part (a)?" The function has whole number solutions. You cannot have fractional or negative numbers of tickets sold.
- **?** "What do the intercepts of each graph represent?" Part (a): (0, 8) represents 8 child tickets sold and no adult tickets sold; (4, 0) represents 4 adult tickets sold and no child tickets sold; Part (b): (0, 8) represents 8 pounds of Cheddar sold and no pounds of Swiss sold; (4, 0) represents 4 pounds of Swiss sold and no pounds of Cheddar sold.
- Review the inequality notation used to describe the domain and range for part (b). These two inequalities describe all of the numbers between 0 and 4, including 0 and 4.
- Ask students to describe the range in words.
- Refer to the variables described by students on the strips of paper. The integer variables described are examples of discrete domains. The fraction or decimal variables described are examples of continuous domains.
- **Common Error:** It is incorrect to say that discrete domains are finite and continuous domains are infinite. A domain can be discrete and infinite, such as the set of counting numbers.

Standards of Learning

8.17 The student will identify the domain, range, independent variable, or dependent variable in a given situation.

Previous Learning

Students should know how to find solutions of a linear equation.

Activity Materials
Introduction
• paper strips

Start Thinking! and Warm Up

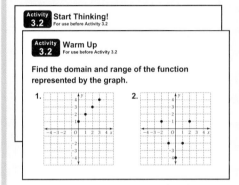

3.2 Record and Practice Journal

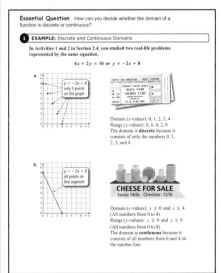

Differentiated Instruction

Auditory

Help students understand the concept of a function by showing them how it is used in everyday life. For example, the number of plates to set on the dinner table is a function of the number of people expected to eat. A person earning an hourly wage has an income that is a function of the number of hours worked. Discuss with students other instances of functions in life.

Words of Wisdom

- Students may ask you to explain each of the two problems, meaning, show them how to do the problems! Resist the tendency to jump in and solve the problems for them. Students should work with their partner and work through the problem. They need to read and think!

Activity 2

- **Part (a):** Rooms are $75 a night ($69 + $6). If 10 rooms are rented for 2 nights, the cost is $75 × 10 × 2 = $1500. Write a verbal model to help you find an equation: Cost = cost per night × number of rooms × 2 nights; if x = the number of rooms rented, the equation is $y = (75)2x = 150x$.
- **Part (b):** There are 36 pieces of luggage that will vary in weight between 25 and 45 pounds. The approximate total weight equals the number of pieces of luggage times the average weight of each piece. If x = average weight of each piece of luggage, the equation is $y = 36x$.
- "Is the domain of part (a) discrete or continuous? Explain." discrete; The number of rooms must be a whole number.
- "Is the domain of part (b) discrete or continuous? Explain." continuous; The weight of each piece of luggage is between 25 and 45 pounds, but could be a fraction of a pound.

What Is Your Answer?

- **Think-Pair-Share:** Students should read the question independently and then work with a partner to answer the question. When they have answered the question, the pair should compare their answer with another group and discuss any discrepancies.

Closure

- **Exit Ticket:** Sketch a graph of the two examples suggested in Question 3. Students should scale the axes with reasonable numbers.

3.2 Record and Practice Journal

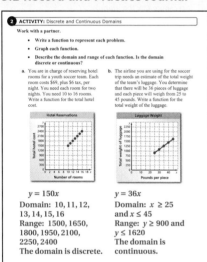

2 ACTIVITY: Discrete and Continuous Domains

Work with a partner.

- Write a function to represent each problem.
- Graph each function.
- Describe the domain and range of each function. Is the domain discrete or continuous?

a. You are in charge of reserving hotel rooms for a youth soccer team. Each room costs $69, plus $6 tax, per night. You need each room for two nights. You need 10 to 16 rooms. Write a function for the total hotel cost.

b. The airline you are using for the soccer trip needs an estimate of the total weight of the team's luggage. You determine that there will be 36 pieces of luggage and each piece will weigh from 25 to 45 pounds. Write a function for the total weight of the luggage.

$y = 150x$

Domain: 10, 11, 12, 13, 14, 15, 16
Range: 1500, 1650, 1800, 1950, 2100, 2250, 2400
The domain is discrete.

$y = 36x$

Domain: $x \geq 25$ and $x \leq 45$
Range: $y \geq 900$ and $y \leq 1620$
The domain is continuous.

What Is Your Answer?

3. IN YOUR OWN WORDS How can you decide whether the domain of a function is discrete or continuous? Describe two real-life examples of functions: one with a discrete domain and one with a continuous domain.

discrete consists of only certain numbers in an interval; continuous consists of all numbers in an interval

The Dynamic Planning Tool
Editable Teacher's Resources at *BigIdeasMath.com*

ACTIVITY: Discrete and Continuous Domains

Work with a partner.

- Write a function to represent each problem.
- Graph each function.
- Describe the domain and range of each function. Is the domain discrete or continuous?

a. You are in charge of reserving hotel rooms for a youth soccer team. Each room costs $69, plus $6 tax, per night. You need each room for two nights. You need 10 to 16 rooms. Write a function for the total hotel cost.

b. The airline you are using for the soccer trip needs an estimate of the total weight of the team's luggage. You determine that there will be 36 pieces of luggage and each piece will weigh from 25 to 45 pounds. Write a function for the total weight of the luggage.

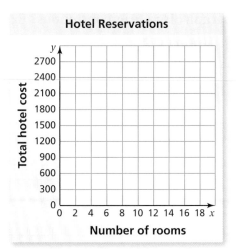

Hotel Reservations

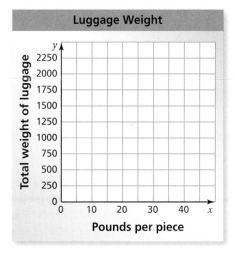

Luggage Weight

What Is Your Answer?

3. IN YOUR OWN WORDS How can you decide whether the domain of a function is discrete or continuous? Describe two real-life examples of functions: one with a discrete domain and one with a continuous domain.

Practice

Use what you learned about discrete and continuous domains to complete Exercises 3 and 4 on page 136.

Key Vocabulary 🔊
discrete domain,
  p. 134
continuous domain,
  p. 134

🔑 Key Idea

Discrete and Continuous Domains

A **discrete domain** is a set of input values that consists of only certain numbers in an interval.

Example: Integers from 1 to 5

A **continuous domain** is a set of input values that consists of all numbers in an interval.

Example: All numbers from 1 to 5

EXAMPLE 1   Graphing Discrete Data

The function $y = 15.95x$ represents the cost y (in dollars) of x tickets for a museum. Graph the function using a domain of 0, 1, 2, 3, and 4. Is the domain of the graph discrete or continuous? Explain.

Make an input-output table.

Museum Tickets

Input, x	$15.95x$	Output, y	Ordered Pair, (x, y)
0	15.95(0)	0	(0, 0)
1	15.95(1)	15.95	(1, 15.95)
2	15.95(2)	31.9	(2, 31.9)
3	15.95(3)	47.85	(3, 47.85)
4	15.95(4)	63.8	(4, 63.8)

Plot the ordered pairs. Because you cannot buy part of a ticket, the graph consists of individual points.

∴ So, the domain is discrete.

⚫ On Your Own

1. The function $m = 50 - 9d$ represents the amount of money m (in dollars) you have after buying d DVDs. Graph the function. Is the domain discrete or continuous? Explain.

Laurie's Notes

Introduction

Connect

- **Yesterday:** Students explored problems with discrete and continuous domains.
- **Today:** Students will graph functions and determine if the domain is discrete or continuous.

Motivate

- **FYI:** Share some trivia about the words *continuous* and *discrete*.
- The word *continuous* derives from a Latin root meaning *to hang together* or *to cohere*. This same root gives us the noun *continent* (an expanse of land unbroken by sea).
- The word *discrete* derives from a Latin root meaning *to separate*. This same root yields the verb *discern* (to recognize as distinct or separate) and the cognate *discreet* (to show discernment).

Lesson Notes

Key Idea

- The number line graphs of each example should help students visualize the difference between these two types of domains.
- **Common Error:** Discrete functions do not need to exclude fractions or decimals. A discrete domain might be shoe sizes from 6 to 9, including the half sizes such as $6\frac{1}{2}$.

Example 1

- The table displayed is a good reminder of how equations are evaluated and how solutions can be recorded as ordered pairs.
- **?** "Is this data set a function? Explain." yes; Each input is paired with exactly one output.
- Students may ask why the outputs are not written with the $ symbol and a digit in the hundredths position. If describing the answer to a contextual problem, such as "what is the cost for 2 people to visit the museum?", the answer would be stated with the units ($31.90). Otherwise, the *y*-coordinate is stated as a real number.
- **?** "What do you notice about the range of this discrete function?" The range is discrete also.

On Your Own

- **?** "Could you buy 0 DVDs? 1 DVD? 2 DVDs? What is the greatest number of DVDs you have money to purchase?" yes; yes; yes; 5
- **?** "Is it possible to spend all of your money on DVDs? Explain." no; if you buy 5 DVDs, you have $5 remaining which is not enough to buy a sixth DVD.

Start Thinking! and Warm Up

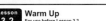

Lesson 3.2 | Warm Up
For use before Lesson 3.2

Lesson 3.2 | Start Thinking!
For use before Lesson 3.2

Discuss whether the following functions have discrete or continuous domains.

A. The air temperature over the course of a day

B. The cost of hot dogs

C. The distance traveled on a road trip

D. The weight of a baby over his first month

E. The cost of parking for a certain number of hours at a parking garage

Extra Example 1

The function $y = 12.90x$ represents the cost y (in dollars) of x admission tickets for a museum. Graph the function using the domain of 0, 1, 2, 3, and 4. Is the domain discrete or continuous? Explain.

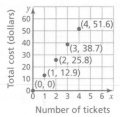

The domain is discrete because you cannot buy part of a ticket.

On Your Own

1.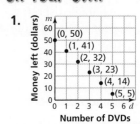

The domain is discrete because you cannot buy part of a DVD.

Extra Example 2

A cereal bar contains 155 calories. The number c of calories consumed is a function of the number b of bars eaten. Graph the function. Is the domain discrete or continuous?

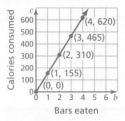

The domain is continuous because you can eat part of a cereal bar.

Extra Example 3

You conduct an experiment on the distance traveled at 55 miles per hour. (a) What is the domain of the function? $t \geq 1$ and $t \leq 4$ (b) Is the domain discrete or continuous? The domain is continuous because the time can be any value between 1 and 4, inclusive.

Input Time, t (hours)	Output Distance, d (miles)
1	55
2	110
3	165
4	220

● On Your Own

2. See Additional Answers.

3. The data is discrete because you cannot have part of a story.

English Language Learners

Vocabulary

Have students add the key vocabulary words *function, domain, range, independent variable, dependent variable, discrete domain,* and *continuous domain* to their notebooks. Definitions, examples, and pictures should accompany the words.

Laurie's Notes

Example 2

- Read the problem. This context will be familiar to students. Students will recognize that it is possible to eat some portion of a cereal bar, meaning this is a continuous domain.
- Discuss the graph of this function. Although the table of values stops at the ordered pair (4, 520), it is possible to consume more than 4 cereal bars.
- The domain is *restricted* in the sense that the number of cereal bars must be non-negative.

? **Extension:** "What is the slope and c-intercept of this function?" 130; 0

Example 3

- Read the problem and discuss the table.

? "What are the values of the domain?" Listen for: time (in seconds) between 2 and 10, inclusive.

? "What are the values of the range?" Listen for: distance (in miles) between 0.434 and 2.17, inclusive.

- **Note:** The two inequalities $t \geq 2$ and $t \leq 10$ can also be written as a compound inequality, $2 \leq t \leq 10$. This is true for each of the multiple choice answers. Students have not learned how to read or write compound inequalities, but they will often recognize that the variable is between two numbers.

On Your Own

- These are nice questions that provide another context for understanding the difference between continuous and discrete domains.

● Closure

- **Exit Ticket:** Explain how to determine if a graph has a continuous or discrete domain. Listen for: if the points on the graph are connected then it is continuous, but if the points are separated then it is discrete.

The Dynamic Planning Tool
Editable Teacher's Resources at *BigIdeasMath.com*

EXAMPLE 2   Graphing Continuous Data

A cereal bar contains 130 calories. The number c of calories consumed is a function of the number b of bars eaten. Graph the function. Is the domain of the graph discrete or continuous?

Make an input-output table.

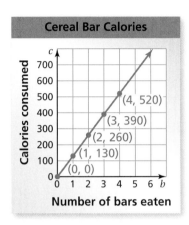

Cereal Bar Calories

Input, b	Output, c	Ordered Pair, (b, c)
0	0	$(0, 0)$
1	130	$(1, 130)$
2	260	$(2, 260)$
3	390	$(3, 390)$
4	520	$(4, 520)$

Plot the ordered pairs. Because you can eat part of a cereal bar, b can be any value greater than or equal to 0. Draw a line through the points.

∴ So, the domain is continuous.

EXAMPLE 3   Standardized Test Practice

You conduct an experiment on the speed of sound waves in dry air at 86°F. You record your data in a table. Which of the following is true?

Input Time, t (seconds)	Output Distance, d (miles)
2	0.434
4	0.868
6	1.302
8	1.736
10	2.170

Ⓐ The domain is $t \geq 2$ and $t \leq 10$ and it is discrete.

Ⓑ The domain is $t \geq 2$ and $t \leq 10$ and it is continuous.

Ⓒ The domain is $d \geq 0.434$ and $d \leq 2.17$ and it is discrete.

Ⓓ The domain is $d \geq 0.434$ and $d \leq 2.17$ and it is continuous.

The domain is the set of possible input values, or the time t. The time t can be any value from 2 to 10. So, the domain is continuous.

∴ The correct answer is Ⓑ.

On Your Own

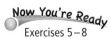
Now You're Ready
Exercises 5–8

2. A 20-gallon bathtub is draining at a rate of 2.5 gallons per minute. The number g of gallons remaining is a function of the number m of minutes. Graph the function. Is the domain discrete or continuous?

3. Are the data shown in the table discrete or continuous? Explain.

Number of Stories	1	2	3	4	5
Height of Building (feet)	12	24	36	48	60

 Vocabulary and Concept Check

1. **VOCABULARY** Explain how continuous domains and discrete domains are different.

2. **WRITING** Describe how you can use a graph to determine whether a domain is discrete or continuous.

 Practice and Problem Solving

Describe the domain and range of the function. Is the domain discrete or continuous?

3.
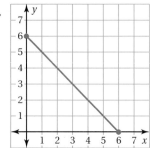

4.
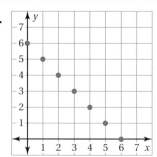

Graph the function. Is the domain of the graph discrete or continuous?

 5.

Input Bags, x	Output Marbles, y
2	20
4	40
6	60

6.

Input Years, x	Output Height of a Tree, y (feet)
0	3
1	6
2	9

7.

Input Width, x (inches)	Output Volume, y (cubic inches)
5	50
10	100
15	150

8.

Input Hats, x	Output Cost, y (dollars)
0	0
1	8.45
2	16.9

9. **ERROR ANALYSIS** Describe and correct the error in classifying the domain.

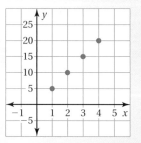
2.5 is in the domain.

10. **YARN** The function $m = 40 - 8.5b$ represents the amount m of money (in dollars) that you have after buying b balls of yarn. Graph the function using a domain of 0, 1, 2, and 3. Is the domain discrete or continuous?

Assignment Guide and Homework Check

Level	Day 1 Activity Assignment	Day 2 Lesson Assignment	Homework Check
Basic	3, 4, 16–19	1, 2, 5–11	2, 6, 8, 10
Average	3, 4, 16–19	1, 2, 7–13	2, 8, 10, 12
Advanced	3, 4, 16–19	1, 2, 8–15	2, 8, 12, 14

Common Errors

- **Exercises 5–8** Students may mistake the output for the domain and say that the domain is continuous when it is actually discrete. Encourage them to think about the context of the problem. For example, you cannot buy part of a hat, so the domain is discrete.
- **Exercises 5–8** When graphing the function, students may connect the points without considering if the data are discrete or continuous. Remind them that the graph displays discrete and continuous data differently, so the graphs should be different.
- **Exercise 11** Students may say that both functions will have a discrete domain because length is often given as a whole number. Encourage them to think about a context for the two functions, for example, the length of a snake and the cost for several shirts.

3.2 Record and Practice Journal

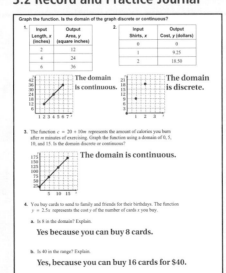

1. A discrete domain consists of only certain numbers in an interval, whereas a continuous domain consists of all numbers in an interval.

2. If the graph is a line covering all inputs on an interval, then it is a continuous domain. If a graph consists of just points, then it is a discrete domain.

Practice and Problem Solving

3. domain: $x \geq 0$ and $x \leq 6$
   range: $y \geq 0$ and $y \leq 6$;
   continuous

4. domain: 0, 1, 2, 3, 4, 5, 6
   range: 0, 1, 2, 3, 4, 5, 6;
   discrete

5.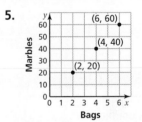

   discrete

6–8. See Additional Answers.

9. 2.5 is not in the domain because the domain is discrete, consisting only of 1, 2, 3, and 4.

10.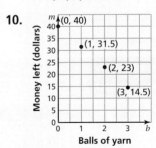

    discrete

11. The function with an input of length has a continuous domain because you can use any length, but you cannot have half a shirt.

12–13. See Additional Answers.

14. a. yes; The weight of 10 books is 52 pounds.

   b. no; The box can hold at most 10 books.

   c. See Additional Answers.

   d. discrete

15. See *Taking Math Deeper.*

 Fair Game Review

16. 1   **17.** $-\dfrac{5}{2}$

18. $\dfrac{1}{3}$ **19.** C

Mini-Assessment

Graph the function. Is the domain discrete or continuous?

1.

Cups, x	0	3	6	9
Cost, y ($)	0	6	12	18

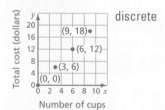

discrete

2.

Time, x (h)	0	1	2	3
Distance, y (mi)	0	55	110	165

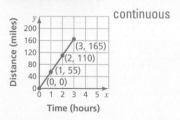

continuous

T-137

Taking Math Deeper

Exercise 15

A nice way to start this problem is to draw one possible arrangement. This confirms that everyone understands the question.

① Draw one possible arrangement.

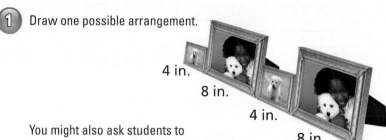

4 in.
8 in.
4 in.
8 in.

You might also ask students to cut out six lengths of grid paper that are 4 units long and three lengths that are 8 units long. With these, they can form and record each possible arrangement.

② Write a function.

   Let x = number of pictures in 4-inch frames.
   Let y = number of pictures in 8-inch frames.

$4x + 8y = 24$	Sum is 24 inches.
$8y = 24 - 4x$	Subtract $4x$ from each side.
a. $\quad y = 3 - 0.5x$	Divide each side by 8.

③ Graph the function.

Input, x	0	1	2	3	4	5	6
Output, y	3	2.5	2	1.5	1	0.5	0

Note that 1, 3, and 5 are not in the domain because they create "half" pictures.

b.

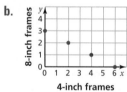

Discrete

c. The domain is discrete.

Reteaching and Enrichment Strategies

If students need help. . .	If students got it. . .
Resources by Chapter • Practice A and Practice B • Puzzle Time Record and Practice Journal Practice Differentiating the Lesson Lesson Tutorials Skills Review Handbook	Resources by Chapter • Enrichment and Extension Start the next section

11. **REASONING** The input of one function is *length*. The input of another function is *number of shirts*. Which function has a continuous domain? Explain.

12. **DISTANCE** The function $y = 3.28x$ converts length from x meters to y feet. Graph the function. Is the domain discrete or continuous?

13. **AREA** The area A of the triangle is a function of the height h. Graph the function. Is the domain discrete or continuous?

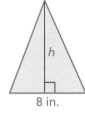

8 in.

14. **PACKING** You are packing books into boxes. The box can hold at most 10 books. The function $y = 5.2x$ represents the weight y (in pounds) of x books.

    a. Is 52 in the range? Explain.

    b. Is 15 in the domain? Explain.

    c. Graph the function.

    d. Is the domain discrete or continuous?

15. **Reasoning** You want to fill a 2-foot shelf with framed pictures. There are x pictures in 4-inch frames and y pictures in 8-inch frames.

    a. Write a function for this situation.

    b. Graph the function.

    c. Is the domain discrete or continuous?

4 in.

8 in.

 Fair Game Review What you learned in previous grades & lessons

Find the slope of the line. *(Section 2.2)*

16.
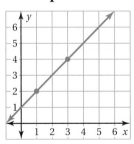

17.
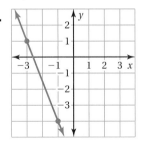

18.
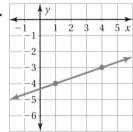

19. **MULTIPLE CHOICE** What is the y-intercept of the graph of the linear equation? *(Section 2.3)*

    Ⓐ −4   Ⓑ −2

    Ⓒ 2   Ⓓ 4

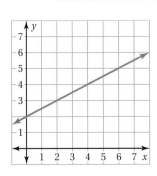

You can use a **comparison chart** to compare two topics. Here is an example of a comparison chart for domain and range.

	Domain	Range
Definition	the set of all possible input values	the set of all possible output values
Algebra Example: $y = mx + b$	x-values	corresponding y-values
Ordered pairs Example: (–4, 0), (–3, 1), (–2, 2), (–1, 3)	–4, –3, –2, –1	0, 1, 2, 3
Table Example: x: –1, 0, 2, 3 y: 1, 0, 4, 9	–1, 0, 2, 3	0, 1, 4, 9
Graph Example:	–3, –1, 2, 3	–1, 1, 2

On Your Own

Make a comparison chart to help you study and compare these topics.

1. discrete data and continuous data

After you complete this chapter, make comparison charts for the following topics.

2. linear functions with positive slopes and linear functions with negative slopes

3. linear functions and nonlinear functions

"Creating a comparison chart causes canines to crystalize concepts."

Sample Answers

1.

	Discrete Data	Continuous Data
Definition	Data that consist of only certain numbers in an interval	Data that consist of all numbers in an interval
Words	• integers from 0 through 4 • the number of books in a library	• all numbers from 0 through 4 • gallons of water in a puddle
Table		

Discrete Data Table:

Input Number in group, x	Output Total cost of tickets, y (dollars)
2	15
3	22.5
4	30
5	37.5

Continuous Data Table:

Input Years, x	Output Height of a tree, y (feet)
0	1
1	3
2	5
3	7

Graphs
Number line

Coordinate axes

List of Organizers
Available at *BigIdeasMath.com*

Comparison Chart
Concept Circle
Definition (Idea) and Example Chart
Example and Non-Example Chart
Formula Triangle
Four Square
Information Frame
Information Wheel
Notetaking Organizer
Process Diagram
Summary Triangle
Word Magnet
Y Chart

About this Organizer

A **Comparison Chart** can be used to compare two topics. Students list different aspects of the two topics in the left column. These can include *algebra, definition, description, equation(s), graph(s), table(s),* and *words*. Students write about or give examples illustrating these aspects in the other two columns for the topics being compared. Comparison charts are particularly useful with topics that are related but that have distinct differences. Students can place their comparison charts on note cards to use as a quick study reference.

Technology For the Teacher
Vocabulary Puzzle Builder

Answers

1. domain: $-4, -1, 2, 5$
   range: $2, 1, 0, -1$

2. domain: $-2, -1, 0, 1, 2$
   range: $-1, 1, 3$

3. domain: $-1, 1, 3, 5$
   range: -1

4.

x	0	1	2	3
y	-6	-1	4	9

   domain: $0, 1, 2, 3$
   range: $-6, -1, 4, 9$

5.

x	-1	0	1	2
y	4	2	0	-2

   domain: $-1, 0, 1, 2$
   range: $4, 2, 0, -2$

6.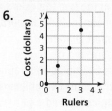

   discrete

7–11. See Additional Answers.

Alternative Quiz Ideas

100% Quiz	Math Log
Error Notebook	Notebook Quiz
Group Quiz	**Partner Quiz**
Homework Quiz	Pass the Paper

Partner Quiz

- Students should work in pairs. Each pair should have a small white board.
- The teacher selects certain problems from the quiz and writes one on the board.
- The pairs work together to solve the problem and write their answer on the white board.
- Students show their answers and, as a class, discuss any differences.
- Repeat for as many problems as the teacher chooses.
- For the word problems, teachers may choose to have students read them out of the book.

Reteaching and Enrichment Strategies

If students need help. . .	If students got it. . .
Resources by Chapter • Study Help • Practice A and Practice B • Puzzle Time Lesson Tutorials *BigIdeasMath.com* Practice Quiz Practice from the Test Generator	Resources by Chapter • Enrichment and Extension • School-to-Work Game Closet at *BigIdeasMath.com* Start the next section

Technology for the Teacher

Answer Presentation Tool
Big Ideas Test Generator

Assessment Book

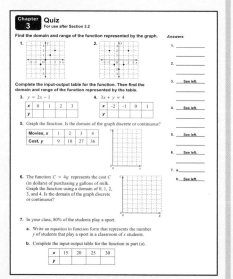

Find the domain and range of the function represented by the graph. *(Section 3.1)*

1.
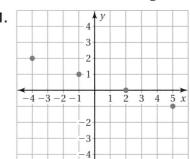

2.
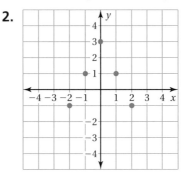

3.
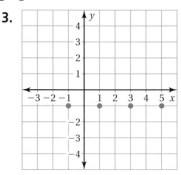

Copy and complete the input-output table for the function. Then find the domain and range of the function represented by the table. *(Section 3.1)*

4. $y = 5x - 6$

x	0	1	2	3
y				

5. $2x + y = 2$

x	−1	0	1	2
y				

Graph the function. Is the domain of the graph discrete or continuous? *(Section 3.2)*

6.

Rulers, x	Cost, y
0	0
1	1.5
2	3
3	4.5

7.

Gallons, x	Miles Remaining, y
0	300
1	265
2	230
3	195

8.

Minutes, x	0	10	20	30
Height, y	40	35	30	25

9.

Relay Teams, x	2	4	6	8
Athletes, y	8	16	24	32

10. VIDEO GAME The function $m = 30 - 3r$ represents the amount m (in dollars) of money you have after renting r video games. Graph the function using a domain of 0, 1, 2, 3, and 4. Is the domain of the graph discrete or continuous? *(Section 3.2)*

11. WATER Water accounts for about 60% of a person's body weight. *(Section 3.1)*

a. Write an equation that represents the water weight y of a person who weighs x pounds. Identify the independent variable and the dependent variable.

b. Make an input-output table for the function in part (a). Use the inputs 100, 120, 140, and 160.

STANDARDS
OF LEARNING
8.14

Essential Question How can you use a linear function to describe a linear pattern?

1 ACTIVITY: Finding Linear Patterns

Work with a partner.

- Plot the points from the table in a coordinate plane.
- Write a linear equation for the function represented by the graph.

a.

x	0	2	4	6	8
y	150	125	100	75	50

b.

x	4	6	8	10	12
y	15	20	25	30	35

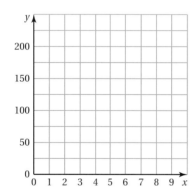

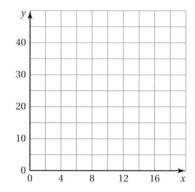

c.

x	−4	−2	0	2	4
y	4	6	8	10	12

d.

x	−4	−2	0	2	4
y	1	0	−1	−2	−3

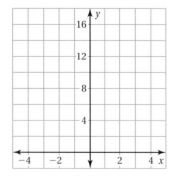

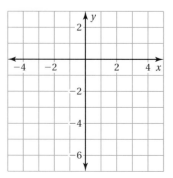

Laurie's Notes

Standards of Learning

8.14 The student will make connections between any two representations (tables, graphs, words, and rules) of a given relationship.

Introduction

For the Teacher

- **Goal:** Students will explore linear patterns in tables and graphs to write linear equations.

Motivate

- Do a quick matching game with students. Have 4–5 graphs on the board with slopes and y-intercepts that are different enough so that students can distinguish between them. Write the equations in a list. Have students work with a partner to match the correct equation with each graph.
- Make sure that students are still focusing on key information from the graph. Is it increasing or decreasing from left to right? Is the slope steeper than 1 or close to 0? Is the y-intercept positive or negative?

Previous Learning

Students should know how to write a linear equation in slope-intercept form. Students should know common geometric formulas, such as area and perimeter.

Start Thinking! and Warm Up

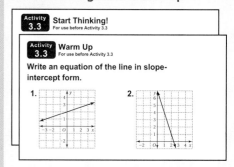

Activity Notes

Activity 1

- ❓ "What do you notice about the scaling on the axes for each problem?" Answers will vary. Students should recognize the difference of how the x- and y-axes are scaled in each problem.
- ❓ "For each problem, you are asked to write a linear equation for the function. How will you do this?" Find the slope and y-intercept.
- Give sufficient time for students to work through the four problems.
- From the graphs, students should be able to determine the slope. It is important that students pay attention to how the axes are scaled when they record values for rise and run.
- **Another Way:** From the table of values, the y-intercept is given for 3 of the 4 problems. In part (a), the ordered pair (0, 150) gives the y-intercept, $b = 150$. To find the slope from the table, notice that every time x increases by 2, y decreases by 25. This means that the run is 2 and the rise is -25. So, $m = \dfrac{\text{rise}}{\text{run}} = \dfrac{-25}{2} = -12.5$. Now write the equation in slope-intercept form, $y = -12.5x + 150$.
- When students have finished, check their equations.
- ❓ "What numeric patterns do you see in the table?" Listen for how the x- and y-values are changing.
- Make sure students recognize the connection between the numeric patterns in the table and the slope of the line.
- **FYI:** For students, recognizing a pattern in the table is the easy part. Helping students translate the pattern into a slope, and then into an equation, is the challenging part. This takes practice.

3.3 Record and Practice Journal

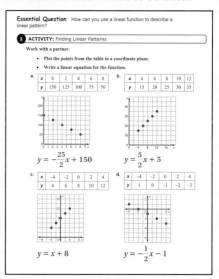

Differentiated Instruction

Visual

Explain to students that representing a function table as a list of ordered pairs is for convenience. Once the function is represented by ordered pairs, it can be graphed in a coordinate plane. This is a visual representation of the function and is an excellent way to show students the connection between algebra and geometry.

3.3 Record and Practice Journal

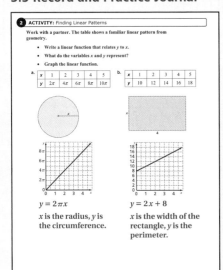

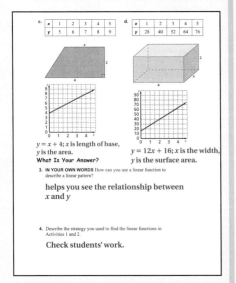

Laurie's Notes

Activity 2

- The challenge in these problems is that the equation relates to a geometric formula. The figure shown for each problem should provide a hint as to what the variables x and y represent in the problem.

- **Part (a):** Two formulas involving π and circles are circumference ($C = 2\pi r$) and area ($A = \pi r^2$). Substitute the value of x for the radius in each formula. The value of the circumference will match the y-values in the table.

- **Part (b):** Two formulas involving rectangles are perimeter ($P = 2\ell + 2w$) and area ($A = \ell w$). Substitute 4 for the length and the value of x for the width in each formula. The value of the perimeter will match the y-values in the table.

- ❓ "Could y represent the perimeter for part (c)? Explain." no; You only know 3 of the 4 side lengths.

- **Part (c):** The formula for the area of a trapezoid is $A = \frac{1}{2}(b + B)h$. Substitute 4 for B, 2 for h, and the value of x for the length of the shorter base. The value of the area will match the y-values in the table.

- **Part (d):** Two formulas involving a rectangular prism are surface area ($S = 2\ell w + 2wh + 2\ell h$) and volume ($V = \ell wh$). Substitute 4 for the length, 2 for the height, and the value of x for the width in each formula. The value of the surface area will match the y-values in the table.

- ❓ **Extension:** "In part (c), how does the diagram of the trapezoid change as the value of x increases?" When $x = 4$, the trapezoid has the shape of a rectangle. When $x > 4$, the upper base becomes the longer of the two bases.

- Note that in each of these problems, there is a numeric pattern in the table. Have students describe the numeric pattern.

What Is Your Answer?

- **Think-Pair-Share:** Students should read each question independently and then work with a partner to answer the questions. When they have answered the questions, the pair should compare their answers with another group and discuss any discrepancies.

Closure

- **Exit Ticket:** Plot the points given in the table and write a linear equation for the function.

x	−2	0	2	4	6
y	2	3	4	5	6

$y = \frac{1}{2}x + 3$

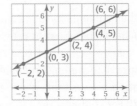

Technology For the Teacher

The Dynamic Planning Tool
Editable Teacher's Resources at *BigIdeasMath.com*

ACTIVITY: Finding Linear Patterns

Work with a partner. The table shows a familiar linear pattern from geometry.

- Write a linear function that relates y to x.
- What do the variables x and y represent?
- Graph the linear function.

a.

x	1	2	3	4	5
y	2π	4π	6π	8π	10π

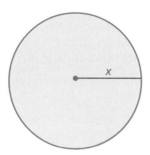

b.

x	1	2	3	4	5
y	10	12	14	16	18

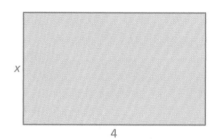

c.

x	1	2	3	4	5
y	5	6	7	8	9

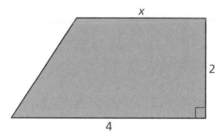

d.

x	1	2	3	4	5
y	28	40	52	64	76

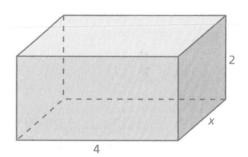

What Is Your Answer?

3. **IN YOUR OWN WORDS** How can you use a linear function to describe a linear pattern?

4. Describe the strategy you used to find the linear functions in Activities 1 and 2.

Practice

Use what you learned about linear function patterns to complete Exercises 3 and 4 on page 144.

A **linear function** is a function whose graph is a line.

Key Vocabulary
linear function,
  p. 142

EXAMPLE 1 **Finding a Linear Function Using a Graph**

Use the graph to write a linear function that relates *y* to *x*.

The points lie on a line. Find the slope and *y*-intercept of the line.

$$\text{slope} = \frac{\text{rise}}{\text{run}} = \frac{3}{2}$$

Because the line crosses the *y*-axis at $(0, -3)$, the *y*-intercept is -3.

∴ So, the linear function is $y = \dfrac{3}{2}x - 3$.

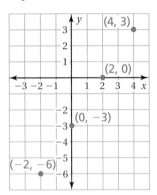

EXAMPLE 2 **Finding a Linear Function Using a Table**

Use the table to write a linear function that relates *y* to *x*.

x	−3	−2	−1	0
y	9	7	5	3

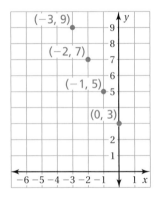

Plot the points in the table.

The points lie on a line. Find the slope and *y*-intercept of the line.

$$\text{slope} = \frac{\text{rise}}{\text{run}} = \frac{-2}{1} = -2$$

Because the line crosses the *y*-axis at $(0, 3)$, the *y*-intercept is 3.

∴ So, the linear function is $y = -2x + 3$.

● **On Your Own**

Now You're Ready
Exercises 5–10

Use the graph or table to write a linear function that relates *y* to *x*.

1.

2.

x	−2	−1	0	1
y	2	2	2	2

◀)) Multi-Language Glossary at BigIdeasMath✔com.

Laurie's Notes

Introduction

Connect

- **Yesterday:** Students gained additional practice in writing linear equations.
- **Today:** Students will write linear functions by recognizing patterns in graphical and tabular information.

Motivate

- Tell the story of Amos Dolbear, who in 1898 noticed that warmer crickets seemed to chirp faster. Dolbear made a detailed study of cricket chirp rates based on the temperature of the crickets' environment and came up with the cricket chirping temperature formula known as Dolbear's Law. Remember that the formula is actually a linear function with a slope and y-intercept!

Lesson Notes

Example 1

- Review the definition of a function and the vocabulary associated with functions: domain and range.
- Plot the ordered pairs of the function.
- **Teaching Tip:** To find the slope, draw a right triangle with the hypotenuse between two of the points. Label the legs of the triangle to represent the rise and run. Then compute the slope.
- ❓ "Does it matter what two points you select to find the slope? Explain." no; The ratio of rise to run will be the same because the slope triangles are actually similar. It is unlikely students will say this; however, it is the case.
- **Big Idea:** Demonstrate that it does not matter what two points are selected to compute the slope. The slope between $(0, -3)$ and $(2, 0)$ is $\frac{3}{2}$. The slope between $(0, -3)$ and $(4, 3)$ is $\frac{6}{4} = \frac{3}{2}$.

Example 2

- Plot the ordered pairs and repeat the steps from Example 1.
- ❓ "Can you tell anything about the slope without plotting the points? Explain." yes; As x increases by 1 (run), y decreases by 2 (rise).

On Your Own

- **Common Error:** Students may say the slope for Question 1 is -2 instead of $-\frac{1}{2}$. It is very easy to state the reciprocal of the slope.
- **Question 2:** Students may need to graph this function. Once graphed, they will recognize this as a horizontal line whose equation is $y = 2$.

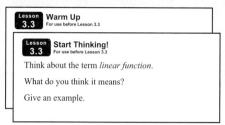
Extra Example 1

Use the graph to write a linear function that relates y to x.

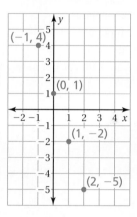

$y = -3x + 1$

Extra Example 2

Use the table to write a linear function that relates y to x.

x	-2	0	2	4
y	-2	-1	0	1

$y = \frac{1}{2}x - 1$

On Your Own

1. $y = -\frac{1}{2}x - 1$

2. $y = 2$

Graph the data.

Hours Jogging, x	Calories Burned, y
2	800
4	1600
6	2400
8	3200

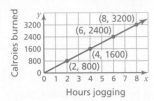

a. Is the domain discrete or continuous? continuous

b. Write a linear function that relates y to x. $y = 400x$

c. How many calories do you burn in 2.5 hours? 1000 calories

⬤ On Your Own

3.
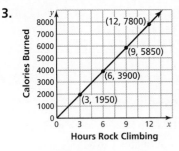

a. continuous

b. $y = 650x$

c. 3575 calories

English Language Learners

Classroom

This chapter gives English learners a chance to share with the rest of the class and the opportunity to build their confidence. Many examples and exercises use tables and graphs giving English learners a rest from interpreting sentences.

Laurie's Notes

⬤ Example 3

- Read the problem and discuss the ordered pairs in the table.
- **?** Ask questions to check understanding.
  - "Is the slope positive or negative? How do you know?" Listen for positive slope and for recognition that the x- and y-values in the table are both increasing.
  - "What is the domain? Is it continuous?" hours kayaking ≥ 0; yes
  - "What is the range?" calories burned ≥ 0
  - "Explain what a slope of 300 means in the context of this problem." The person is burning 300 calories per hour kayaking.
  - "Explain why a y-intercept of 0 makes sense." If you haven't kayaked yet, you haven't burned any calories.
- **Extension:** Ask students to determine how long the person would have to kayak in order to burn 1000 calories (i.e., given y, solve for x).

On Your Own

- Compare the slope of this line to the slope of the line in Example 3. Which slope is greater? Which line is steeper? Question 3 has the greater slope and the line is steeper.

Summary

- Discuss the Summary. Students should be able to describe how a table of values and a graph can represent a function, and how information is *read* from the graph and table in order to write the linear function.

⬤ Closure

- **Exit Ticket:** Write the table of values on the board and ask students to write the equation that relates the temperature to the number of chirps. Acknowledge that this is an approximation and not every Snowy Tree cricket will chirp exactly the same.

Chirps per minute	0	16	32	48	64
Temperature (°F)	40	44	48	52	56

$T = 0.25N + 40$ (Have students check this equation with the one they wrote for Exercise 15 in Section 3.2. It is the same equation.)

EXAMPLE 3 Real-Life Application

Hours Kayaking, x	Calories Burned, y
2	600
4	1200
6	1800
8	2400

Graph the data in the table. (a) Is the domain discrete or continuous? (b) Write a linear function that relates y to x. (c) How many calories do you burn in 4.5 hours?

a. Plot the points. Time can represent any value greater than or equal to 0, so the domain is continuous. Draw a line through the points.

b. The slope is $\dfrac{600}{2} = 300$ and the y-intercept is 0.

∴ So, the linear function is $y = 300x$.

c. Find the value of y when $x = 4.5$.

$y = 300x$ Write the equation.

$= 300(4.5)$ Substitute 4.5 for x.

$= 1350$ Multiply.

∴ You burn 1350 calories in 4.5 hours of kayaking.

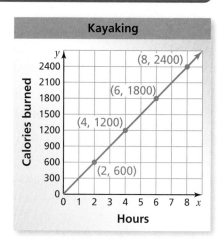

Kayaking graph with points (2, 600), (4, 1200), (6, 1800), (8, 2400). Axes: Calories burned vs Hours.

 **On Your Own**

Hours Rock Climbing, x	Calories Burned, y
3	1950
6	3900
9	5850
12	7800

3. Graph the data in the table.

    a. Is the domain discrete or continuous?

    b. Write a linear function that relates y to x.

    c. How many calories do you burn in 5.5 hours?

Summary

Representing a Function

Words An output is 2 more than the input.

Equation $y = x + 2$

Input-Output Table

Input, x	−1	0	1	2
Output, y	1	2	3	4

Graph

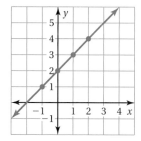

Vocabulary and Concept Check

1. **VOCABULARY** Describe four ways to represent a function.

2. **VOCABULARY** Is the function represented by the graph a linear function? Explain.

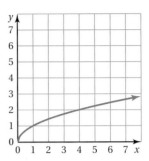

Practice and Problem Solving

The table shows a familiar linear pattern from geometry. Write a linear function that relates y to x. What do the variables x and y represent? Graph the linear function.

3.

x	1	2	3	4	5
y	π	2π	3π	4π	5π

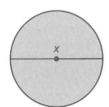

4.

x	1	2	3	4	5
y	2	4	6	8	10

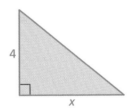

Use the graph or table to write a linear function that relates y to x.

 5.

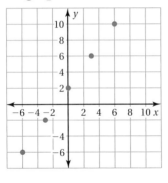

6.

7.

8.

x	−2	−1	0	1
y	−4	−2	0	2

9.

x	−8	−4	0	4
y	2	1	0	−1

10.

x	−3	0	3	6
y	3	5	7	9

11. **MOVIES** The table shows the cost y (in dollars) of renting x movies.

   a. Graph the data. Is the domain of the graph discrete or continuous?

   b. Write a linear function that relates y to x.

   c. How much does it cost to rent three movies?

Number of Movies, x	0	1	2	4
Cost, y	0	3	6	12

Assignment Guide and Homework Check

Level	Day 1 Activity Assignment	Day 2 Lesson Assignment	Homework Check
Basic	3, 4, 15–18	1, 2, 5–11	2, 6, 8, 11
Average	3, 4, 15–18	1, 2, 5–10, 12	2, 6, 8, 12
Advanced	3, 4, 15–18	1, 2, 6–14 even, 13	2, 6, 8, 12

Common Errors

- **Exercises 5 and 6** Students may find the wrong slope because they may misread the scale on an axis. Encourage them to label the points and to use the points they know to write the slope.
- **Exercise 7** Students may not remember how to write the equation for a horizontal line. They may write $x = 3$ instead of $y = 3$. Encourage them to think about the slope-intercept form of an equation.
- **Exercises 8–10** Students may write the reciprocal of the slope when writing the equation from the table. Encourage them to substitute a point into the equation and check to make sure that the equation is true for that point.

3.3 Record and Practice Journal

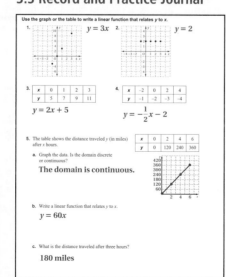

1. words, equation, table, graph

2. no; The graph is not a line.

Practice and Problem Solving

3. $y = \pi x$; x is the diameter; y is the circumference.

4. $y = 2x$; x is the base of the triangle; y is the area of the triangle.

5. $y = \dfrac{4}{3}x + 2$

6. $y = -4x - 2$

7. $y = 3$

8. $y = 2x$

9. $y = -\dfrac{1}{4}x$

10. $y = \dfrac{2}{3}x + 5$

11. a.

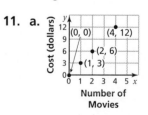

discrete

b. $y = 3x$ c. $9

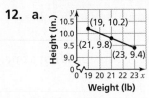
12. a.

Height (in.) vs Weight (lb) graph with points (19, 10.2), (21, 9.8), (23, 9.4)

linear

b. $y = -0.2x + 14$

c. 9.7 in.

13. See *Taking Math Deeper.*

14. See *Additional Answers.*

15. $y = x$

16. $y = -2x + 1$

17. $y = 1$

18. B

Mini-Assessment

Use the graph or table to write a linear function that relates *y* to *x*.

1.

Coordinate grid graph

$y = \frac{1}{2}x + 2$

2.

x	−2	−1	0	1
y	9	4	−1	−6

$y = -5x - 1$

Taking Math Deeper

Exercise 13

Students might find it interesting to discover that there is a correlation between years of education and salary. Of course, the correlation only relates annual salaries. There are many examples of people with no years of education beyond high school who have big salaries.

① Graph the data. Describe the pattern.

a.

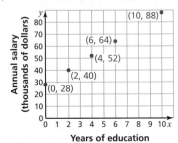

Annual salary (thousands of dollars) vs Years of education graph with points (0, 28), (2, 40), (4, 52), (6, 64), (10, 88)

The pattern is that for every 2 years of additional education, the annual salary increases by $12,000.

② Write a function.

Let x = years of education beyond high school.
Let y = annual salary.

y-intercept = 28
slope = 6

b. $y = 6x + 28$

③ Use the function.

For 8 years of education beyond high school, the annual salary is

c. $y = 6(8) + 28 = 76$, or $76,000.

Check this on the graph to see that it fits the pattern.

Project

Select four careers in which you might be interested. List the annual salary for each. Also list the amount of education required for each career.

Reteaching and Enrichment Strategies

If students need help...	If students got it...
Resources by Chapter • Practice A and Practice B • Puzzle Time Record and Practice Journal Practice Differentiating the Lesson Lesson Tutorials Skills Review Handbook	Resources by Chapter • Enrichment and Extension • School-to-Work Start the next section

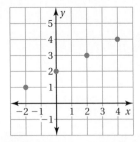

12. **BIKE JUMPS** A bunny hop is a bike trick in which the rider brings both tires off the ground without using a ramp. The table shows the height y (in inches) of a bunny hop on a bike that weighs x pounds.

Weight, x	19	21	23
Height, y	10.2	9.8	9.4

   a. Graph the data. Then describe the pattern.

   b. Write a linear function that relates the height of a bunny hop to the weight of the bike.

   c. What is the height of a bunny hop on a bike that weighs 21.5 pounds?

Years of Education, x	Annual Salary, y
0	28
2	40
4	52
6	64
10	88

13. **SALARY** The table shows a person's annual salary y (in thousands of dollars) after x years of education beyond high school.

   a. Graph the data.

   b. Write a linear function that relates the person's annual salary to the number of years of education beyond high school.

   c. What is the annual salary of the person after 8 years of education beyond high school?

14. **Critical Thinking** The Heat Index is calculated using the relative humidity and the temperature. For every 1 degree increase in the temperature from 94°F to 98°F at 75% relative humidity, the Heat Index rises 4°F.

   a. On a summer day, the relative humidity is 75%, the temperature is 94°F, and the Heat Index is 122°F. Construct a table that relates the temperature t to the Heat Index H. Start the table at 94°F and end it at 98°F.

   b. Write a linear function that represents this situation.

   c. Estimate the Heat Index when the temperature is 100°F.

Fair Game Review What you learned in previous grades & lessons

Write an equation of the line that passes through the points. *(Section 2.7)*

15. $(0, 0), (4, 4)$ 16. $(-4, 9), (1, -1)$ 17. $(-2, 1), (3, 1)$

18. **MULTIPLE CHOICE** You buy a pair of gardening gloves for $2.25 and x packets of seeds for $0.88 each. Which equation represents the total cost y? *(Skills Review Handbook)*

   Ⓐ $y = 0.88x - 2.25$ Ⓑ $y = 0.88x + 2.25$

   Ⓒ $y = 2.25x - 0.88$ Ⓓ $y = 2.25x + 0.88$

STANDARDS
OF LEARNING
8.13

Essential Question How can you recognize when a pattern in real life is linear or nonlinear?

1 ACTIVITY: Finding Patterns for Similar Figures

Work with a partner. Copy and complete each table for the sequence of similar rectangles. Graph the data in each table. Decide whether each pattern is linear or nonlinear.

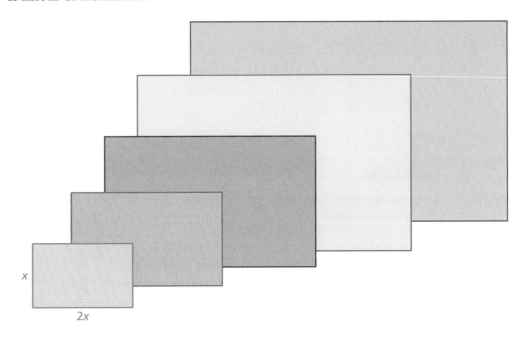

a. Perimeters of Similar Rectangles

x	1	2	3	4	5
P					

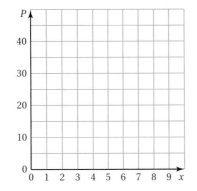

b. Areas of Similar Rectangles

x	1	2	3	4	5
A					

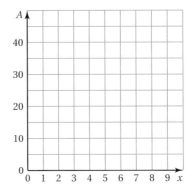

Laurie's Notes

Introduction

For the Teacher

- **Goal:** Students will compare tables and graphs of linear and nonlinear functions.
- Many students get to this point and believe that all equations are linear because that is all they have seen. It is important for students to recognize that not all equations are linear, and therefore not all graphs are linear.
- In future math courses, students will study specific nonlinear functions such as quadratics, exponentials, and rational, just to name a few. For now it is fine to simply refer to them collectively as nonlinear.

Motivate

- ❓ "How many of you would like to try skydiving? Why?"
- Share with students that the first successful parachute jump made from a moving airplane was made by Captain Albert Berry in St. Louis, in 1912.
- The first parachute jump from a balloon was completed by André-Jacques Garnerin in 1797 over Monceau Park in Paris.

Activity Notes

Activity 1

- ❓ "What does it mean for two rectangles to be similar?" Corresponding sides are proportional and corresponding angles have the same measure.
- ❓ "What is the relationship between the length and the width of the green rectangle?" The length is twice the width.
- ❓ "What is the relationship between the length and the width of the yellow rectangle? How do you know?" The length is twice the width. Because the rectangles are similar, the lengths of all the rectangles will be twice the widths.
- Explain to students that they will find the perimeter and area of each rectangle for the side lengths given, and then plot the results.
- **Teaching Tip:** It may be helpful to set up a table that includes a row for the second dimension as shown.

Width	x	1	2	3	4	5
Length	$2x$	2	4	6	8	10
Perimeter	P					

- Encourage students to be accurate with their graphing. Because only 5 points are being plotted for each graph, it is possible that students will not see the curvature of the area graph. Students should recognize, however, that the numeric data for area does not have a constant difference between y-values.

Standards of Learning

8.13(a) The student will make comparisons, predictions, and inferences, using information displayed in graphs.

Previous Learning

Students should know common geometric formulas, such as area and perimeter.

Activity Materials
Textbook
• handkerchief
• floss
• tape
• small figure

Start Thinking! and Warm Up

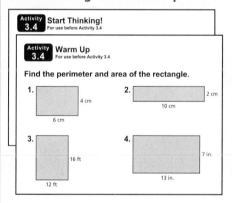

Activity 3.4 Start Thinking! For use before Activity 3.4

Activity 3.4 Warm Up For use before Activity 3.4

Find the perimeter and area of the rectangle.

1. 4 cm, 6 cm
2. 10 cm, 2 cm
3. 16 ft, 12 ft
4. 7 in., 13 in.

3.4 Record and Practice Journal

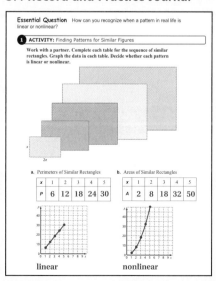

Essential Question How can you recognize when a pattern in real life is linear or nonlinear?

1 ACTIVITY: Finding Patterns for Similar Figures

Work with a partner. Complete each table for the sequence of similar rectangles. Graph the data in each table. Decide whether each pattern is linear or nonlinear.

a. Perimeters of Similar Rectangles

x	1	2	3	4	5
P	6	12	18	24	30

linear

b. Areas of Similar Rectangles

x	1	2	3	4	5
A	2	8	18	32	50

nonlinear

Visual

Students may be able to describe how the sequence of output numbers is changing, for example, *start with 2 and add 3*, but they may find it difficult to write a function rule for changing an input value to an output value. If students determine that the output increases or decreases by a constant value as the input increases, the function will have an *ax* term. Have students create function tables for equations such as $y = x + 3$, $y = 4x - 1$, and $y = 0.5x$ to see this pattern.

3.4 Record and Practice Journal

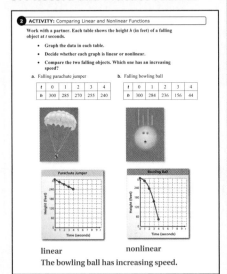

linear   nonlinear

The bowling ball has increasing speed.

What Is Your Answer?

3. **IN YOUR OWN WORDS** How can you recognize when a pattern in real life is linear or nonlinear? Describe two real-life patterns: one that is linear and one that is nonlinear. Use patterns that are different from those described in Activities 1 and 2.

If the rate of change is constant, the pattern is linear.

Laurie's Notes

Activity 2

- This activity is similar to Activity 1, except the ordered pairs are already given. Discuss the two falling objects—one with a parachute and one that is free falling.
- **?** "Do you think there is a difference in the rate at which two objects fall when one is attached to a parachute and the other is left to free fall? Explain." Listen for discussion of rate. It is unlikely students will bring up acceleration.
- If you have the means to make a small parachute (handkerchief, tape, dental floss, small figurine), you could model the difference in a parachute-controlled fall versus a free fall.
- Again, it is necessary for students to be accurate when plotting the ordered pairs given the scale on the *y*-axis.
- **?** After students have plotted the points, ask about the two graphs. First note that the two graphs begin at the same height (*y*-intercept), 300 feet.
  - "How far has the jumper fallen after 4 seconds?" 60 ft "How far has the bowling ball fallen after 4 seconds?" 256 ft
  - "Describe the flight of the jumper." falling at a constant rate of 15 ft/sec
  - "Describe the flight of the bowling ball." Listen for students to describe that the bowling ball is picking up speed as it falls.
- **Extension:** Students could write a linear equation for the jumper, but not the bowling ball.

What Is Your Answer?

- Students may need help thinking of real-life patterns that are nonlinear. You might suggest area or volume relationships, or even simple story graphs about time and distance.

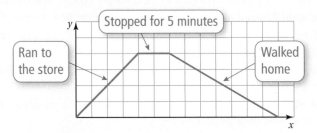

Closure

- Draw two functions with a domain of $x \geq 0$. Have one that is linear and one that is nonlinear. Describe how the graphs are alike and how they are different. Answers will vary.

The Dynamic Planning Tool

Editable Teacher's Resources at *BigIdeasMath.com*

ACTIVITY: Comparing Linear and Nonlinear Functions

Work with a partner. Each table shows the height _h_ (in feet) of a falling object at _t_ seconds.

- **Graph the data in each table.**
- **Decide whether each graph is linear or nonlinear.**
- **Compare the two falling objects. Which one has an increasing speed?**

a. Falling parachute jumper

_t_	0	1	2	3	4
_h_	300	285	270	255	240

b. Falling bowling ball

_t_	0	1	2	3	4
_h_	300	284	236	156	44

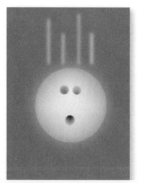

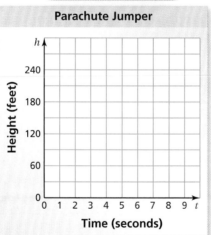

Parachute Jumper

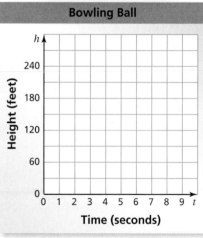

Bowling Ball

What Is Your Answer?

3. IN YOUR OWN WORDS How can you recognize when a pattern in real life is linear or nonlinear? Describe two real-life patterns: one that is linear and one that is nonlinear. Use patterns that are different from those described in Activities 1 and 2.

Practice

Use what you learned about comparing linear and nonlinear functions to complete Exercises 3–6 on page 150.

Check It Out
Lesson Tutorials
BigIdeasMath⬚com

Key Vocabulary ◀))
nonlinear function,
p. 148

The graph of a linear function shows a constant rate of change. A **nonlinear function** does not have a constant rate of change. So, its graph is *not* a line.

EXAMPLE **1** **Identifying Functions from Tables**

Does the table represent a *linear* or *nonlinear* function? Explain.

a.

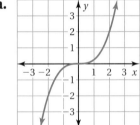

x	3	6	9	12
y	40	32	24	16

As *x* increases by 3, *y* decreases by 8. The rate of change is constant. So, the function is linear.

b.

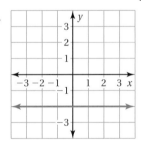

x	1	3	5	7
y	2	11	33	88

As *x* increases by 2, *y* increases by different amounts. The rate of change is *not* constant. So, the function is nonlinear.

EXAMPLE **2** **Identifying Functions from Graphs**

Does the graph represent a *linear* or *nonlinear* function? Explain.

a.

The graph is *not* a line.
So, the function is nonlinear.

b.

The graph is a line.
So, the function is linear.

 On Your Own

Now You're Ready
Exercises 3–11

Does the table or graph represent a *linear* or *nonlinear* function? Explain.

1.

x	*y*
0	25
7	20
14	15
21	10

2.

x	*y*
2	8
4	4
6	0
8	−4

3.

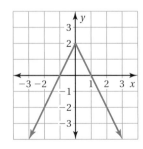

◀)) Multi-Language Glossary at BigIdeasMath⬚com.

Laurie's Notes

Introduction

Connect

- **Yesterday:** Students explored the graphs of functions that were linear and nonlinear.
- **Today:** Students will compare linear and nonlinear functions.

Motivate

- Ask 5 students to complete a table of values, where the domain is the same for 5 functions.

	−3	−2	−1	0	1	2	3
$y = x + 2$	−1	0	1	2	3	4	5
$y = x − 2$	−5	−4	−3	−2	−1	0	1
$y = 2x$	−6	−4	−2	0	2	4	6
$y = \dfrac{x}{2}$	$-\dfrac{3}{2}$	−1	$-\dfrac{1}{2}$	0	$\dfrac{1}{2}$	1	$\dfrac{3}{2}$
$y = x^2$	9	4	1	0	1	4	9

- Spend time discussing the many patterns in the table. Discuss one function at a time. Ask students for their observations about patterns, changes in y-values, slope, and y-intercept.
- For $y = x^2$, students want it to have a constant slope. Draw a quick plot of the points and show it is not a linear function.

Lesson Notes

Example 1

- Copy the first table of values. Draw attention to the change in x (increasing by 3 each time) and the change in y (decreasing by 8 each time). Because the rate of change is constant, the function is linear.
- Copy the second table of values. Draw attention to the change in x (increasing by 2 each time) and the change in y (increasing by different amounts each time). This is a nonlinear function.

Example 2

- Part (b) may seem obvious, but the horizontal line seems like a special case to students. They may not be sure it is a linear function.
- ❓ "What is the slope of this line?" 0 "What is the constant rate of change?" Each time x increases by 1, y stays the same.

On Your Own

- ❓ "What are the constant rates of change for Questions 1 and 2?" $-\dfrac{5}{7}$; −2
- ❓ "Why is Question 3 not a linear function?" There are two parts of this function. The rate of change is positive, then negative.

Goal
Today's lesson is comparing linear and **nonlinear functions**.

Start Thinking! and Warm Up

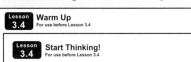

Lesson 3.4 Warm Up For use before Lesson 3.4

Lesson 3.4 Start Thinking! For use before Lesson 3.4

Describe two real-life situations at an amusement park: one that can be represented by a linear function and one that cannot.

Extra Example 1

Does the table represent a *linear* or *nonlinear* function? Explain.

x	3	4	5	6
y	1	2	3	4

linear; As x increases by 1, y increases by 1.

Extra Example 2

Does the graph represent a *linear* or *nonlinear* function? Explain.

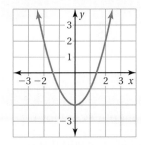

nonlinear; The graph is not a line.

On Your Own

1. linear; As x increases by 7, y decreases by 5.

2. linear; As x increases by 2, y decreases by 4.

3. nonlinear; The graph is not a line.

Extra Example 3

Does $y = 6x - 3$ represent a *linear* function? Yes, the equation is written in slope-intercept form.

Extra Example 4

Account A earns simple interest. Account B earns compound interest. The table shows the balances for 5 years. Graph the data and compare the graphs.

Year, t	Account A Balance	Account B Balance
0	$50	$50
1	$55	$55
2	$60	$60.50
3	$65	$66.55
4	$70	$73.21
5	$75	$80.53

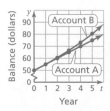

The function representing the balance of Account A is linear. The function representing the balance of Account B is nonlinear.

⬤ On Your Own

4. linear; The equation is in slope-intercept form.

5. linear; The equation can be written in slope-intercept form.

6. nonlinear; The equation cannot be written in slope-intercept form.

English Language Learners

Vocabulary

Begin the lesson by reviewing the terms *function* and *linear function*. Define *nonlinear function* and compare it to linear function.

Laurie's Notes

Example 3

- Discuss each equation. Remind students that all linear functions can be written in slope-intercept form.
- Students often see $y = \dfrac{4}{x}$ and $y = \dfrac{x}{4}$ as *the same kind of function*. So, many students think this will be a linear function. Remind students of how fractions are multiplied, and use the examples $\dfrac{4}{x}$ and $\dfrac{x}{4}$.

$$\frac{4}{x} = \frac{4}{1} \cdot \frac{1}{x} = 4 \cdot \frac{1}{x} \qquad \frac{x}{4} = \frac{x}{1} \cdot \frac{1}{4} = x \cdot \frac{1}{4} = \frac{1}{4} \cdot x$$

So, $y = \dfrac{x}{4}$ is linear with a slope of $\dfrac{1}{4}$. The equation $y = \dfrac{4}{x}$ cannot be written as a linear equation.

Example 4

- **Financial Literacy:** Ask a volunteer to read the problem. In addition to looking at linear and nonlinear functions, you also want to integrate financial literacy skills when appropriate.
- ❓ "Each time the year increases by 1, what happens to the balance of Account A?" It increases by $10.
- ❓ "Each time the year increases by 1, what happens to the balance of Account B?" It increases by a greater amount each year.
- The graph of Account B's balance is starting to curve a bit, while the graph of Account A's balance is a line.
- **Note:** Simple interest will be covered in the next chapter. Students do not need to know how to calculate the interest to do the problem.

On Your Own

- Students should see the exponent of 2 in Question 6 and quickly decide that the function is nonlinear.
- ❓ "What are the slopes of the equations in Questions 4 and 5?" 1; $\dfrac{4}{3}$

Closure

- **Exit Ticket:** Describe how to determine if a function is linear or nonlinear from (a) the equation, (b) a table of values, and (c) a graph.

EXAMPLE 3 **Standardized Test Practice**

Which equation represents a *nonlinear* function?

Ⓐ $y = 4.7$ Ⓑ $y = \pi x$

Ⓒ $y = \dfrac{4}{x}$ Ⓓ $y = 4(x - 1)$

The equations $y = 4.7$, $y = \pi x$, and $y = 4(x - 1)$ can be rewritten in slope-intercept form. So, they are linear functions.

The equation $y = \dfrac{4}{x}$ cannot be rewritten in slope-intercept form. So, it is a nonlinear function.

∴ The correct answer is Ⓒ.

EXAMPLE 4 **Real-Life Application**

Account A earns simple interest. Account B earns compound interest. The table shows the balances for 5 years. Graph the data and compare the graphs.

Year, t	Account A Balance	Account B Balance
0	$100	$100
1	$110	$110
2	$120	$121
3	$130	$133.10
4	$140	$146.41
5	$150	$161.05

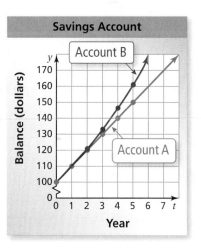

The balance of Account A has a constant rate of change of $10. So, the function representing the balance of Account A is linear.

The balance of Account B increases by different amounts each year. Because the rate of change is not constant, the function representing the balance of Account B is nonlinear.

● **On Your Own**

Now You're Ready
Exercises 12–14

Does the equation represent a *linear* or *nonlinear* function? Explain.

4. $y = x + 5$ **5.** $y = \dfrac{4x}{3}$ **6.** $y = 1 - x^2$

3.4 Exercises

 Vocabulary and Concept Check

1. **VOCABULARY** Describe how linear functions and nonlinear functions are different.

2. **WHICH ONE DOESN'T BELONG?** Which equation does *not* belong with the other three? Explain your reasoning.

$$5y = 2x \qquad y = \frac{2}{5}x \qquad 10y = 4x \qquad 5xy = 2$$

 Practice and Problem Solving

Graph the data in the table. Decide whether the function is *linear* or *nonlinear*.

① 3.

x	0	1	2	3
y	4	8	12	16

4.

x	1	2	3	4
y	1	2	6	24

5.

x	6	5	4	3
y	21	15	10	6

6.

x	−1	0	1	2
y	−7	−3	1	5

Does the table or graph represent a *linear* or *nonlinear* function? Explain.

② 7.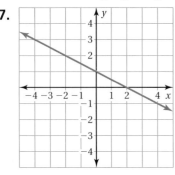

8.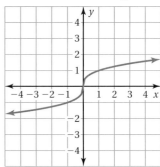

9.

x	5	11	17	23
y	7	11	15	19

10.

x	−3	−1	1	3
y	9	1	1	9

11. **VOLUME** The table shows the volume V (in cubic feet) of a cube with a side length of x feet. Does the table represent a linear or nonlinear function? Explain.

Side Length, x	1	2	3	4	5	6	7	8
Volume, V	1	8	27	64	125	216	343	512

Assignment Guide and Homework Check

Level	Day 1 Activity Assignment	Day 2 Lesson Assignment	Homework Check
Basic	3–6, 20–24	1, 2, 7–15	2, 8, 9, 14
Average	3–6, 20–24	1, 2, 7–10, 13–17	8, 9, 14, 16
Advanced	3–6, 20–24	1, 2, 8–14 even, 15–19	8, 14, 16, 17

Common Errors

- **Exercises 3–6, 9, and 10** Students may say that the function is linear because the *x*-values are increasing or decreasing by the same amount each time. Encourage them to examine the *y*-values to see if the graph represents a line.
- **Exercises 12–14** Students may not rewrite the equation in slope-intercept form and will guess if the equation is linear. Remind them to attempt to write the equation in slope-intercept form as a check.
- **Exercise 16** Students may try to graph the function to determine if it is linear and make an incorrect assumption depending upon how they scale their axes. Encourage them to examine the change in *y* for each *x*-value.

Technology **F**or the **T**eacher

Answer Presentation Tool
QuizShow

3.4 Record and Practice Journal

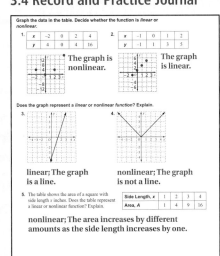

Vocabulary and Concept Check

1. A linear function has a constant rate of change. A nonlinear function does not have a constant rate of change.

2. $5xy = 2$; It cannot be written in slope-intercept form.

Practice and Problem Solving

3.

   linear

4.

   nonlinear

5.

   nonlinear

6.

   linear

7. linear; The graph is a line.

8. nonlinear; The graph is not a line.

9. linear; As *x* increases by 6, *y* increases by 4.

10. nonlinear; As *x* increases by 2, *y* changes by different amounts.

11. nonlinear; As *x* increases by 1, *V* increases by different amounts.

Practice and Problem Solving

12. linear; The equation can be written in slope-intercept form.

13. linear; The equation can be written in slope-intercept form.

14. nonlinear; The equation cannot be written in slope-intercept form.

15. See *Taking Math Deeper.*

16. nonlinear; As x decreases by 65, y increases by different amounts.

17. nonlinear; x decreases by different amounts and y decreases by different amounts.

18. nonlinear

19. linear; As the height increases by 1, the volume increases by 9π.

Fair Game Review

20. obtuse   **21.** straight

22. acute   **23.** right

24. C

Mini-Assessment

Does the table or graph represent a *linear* or *nonlinear* function? Explain.

1.
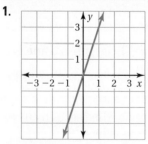

linear; The graph is a line.

2.

x	−2	0	2	4
y	8	0	8	64

nonlinear; The rate of change is not constant.

Taking Math Deeper

Exercise 15

Students can learn a valuable lesson about mathematics from this problem. Even though the problem does not specifically ask them to draw a graph, it is still a good idea. *Seeing* the relationship between pounds and cost is easier than simply finding the relationship using algebra.

 Plot the two given points.

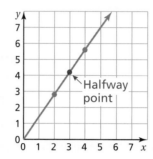 

 Find the halfway point.

Because you want the table to represent a linear function and 3 is halfway between 2 and 4, you need to find the number that is halfway between $2.80 and $5.60. This number is the mean of $2.80 and $5.60.

a. Mean $= \dfrac{2.80 + 5.60}{2} = 4.20$

 Write a function.

Let $x =$ pounds of seeds.

Let $y =$ cost.

y-intercept $= 0$

slope $= \dfrac{5.60 - 2.80}{4 - 2} = 1.4$

b. $y = 1.4x$

Project

Plant some sunflower seeds. Keep track of the progress of the plants until they bloom.

Reteaching and Enrichment Strategies

If students need help...	If students got it...
Resources by Chapter • Practice A and Practice B • Puzzle Time Record and Practice Journal Practice Differentiating the Lesson Lesson Tutorials Skills Review Handbook	Resources by Chapter • Enrichment and Extension • School-to-Work Start the next section

Does the equation represent a *linear* or *nonlinear* function? Explain.

③ 12. $2x + 3y = 7$

13. $y + x = 4x + 5$

14. $y = \dfrac{8}{x^2}$

15. SUNFLOWER SEEDS The table shows the cost y (in dollars) of x pounds of sunflower seeds.

Pounds, x	Cost, y
2	2.80
3	?
4	5.60

  a. What is the missing y-value that makes the table represent a linear function?

  b. Write a linear function that represents the cost y of x pounds of seeds.

16. LIGHT The frequency y (in terahertz) of a light wave is a function of its wavelength x (in nanometers). Does the table represent a linear or nonlinear function? Explain.

Color	Red	Yellow	Green	Blue	Violet
Wavelength, x	660	595	530	465	400
Frequency, y	454	504	566	645	749

17. LIGHTHOUSES The table shows the heights x (in feet) of four Florida lighthouses and the number y of steps in each. Does the table represent a linear or nonlinear function? Explain.

Lighthouse	Height, x	Steps, y
Ponce de Leon Inlet	175	213
St. Augustine	167	219
Cape Canaveral	145	179
Key West	86	98

18. PROJECT The wooden bars of a xylophone produce different musical notes when struck. The pitch of a note is determined by the length of the bar. Use the Internet or some other reference to decide whether the pitch of a note is a linear function of the length of the bar.

19. Geometry The radius of the base of a cylinder is 3 feet. Is the volume of the cylinder a linear or nonlinear function of the height of the cylinder? Explain.

 **Fair Game Review** *What you learned in previous grades & lessons*

Classify the angle as *acute, obtuse, right*, or *straight*. *(Skills Review Handbook)*

20.

21.

22.

23.

24. MULTIPLE CHOICE What is the value of x? *(Skills Review Handbook)*

    Ⓐ 25   Ⓑ 35   Ⓒ 55   Ⓓ 125

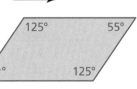

Use the graph or table to write a linear function that relates _y_ to _x_. *(Section 3.3)*

1.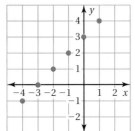

2.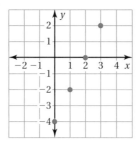

3.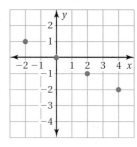

4.

x	0	1	2	3
y	2	1	0	−1

5.

x	−3	0	3	6
y	−3	−1	1	3

Does the table or graph represent a *linear* or *nonlinear* function? Explain. *(Section 3.4)*

6.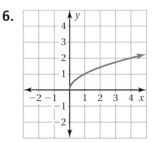

7.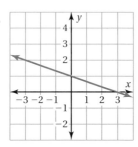

8.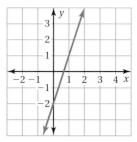

9.

x	y
0	0
2	−2
4	−4
6	−6

10.

x	y
1	−2
3	7
5	23
7	47

11.

x	y
0	3
3	0
6	3
9	6

12. ADVERTISING The table shows the revenue _R_ (in millions of dollars) of a company when it spends _A_ (in millions of dollars) on advertising. *(Section 3.3)*

Advertising, A	Revenue, R
0	2
2	6
4	10
6	14
8	18

   a. Write a linear function that relates the revenue to the advertising cost.

   b. What is the revenue of the company when it spends $10 million on advertising?

13. CHICKEN SALAD The equation $y = 7.9x$ represents the cost _y_ (in dollars) of buying _x_ pounds of chicken salad. Does this equation represent a linear or nonlinear function? Explain. *(Section 3.4)*

Alternative Assessment Options

Math Chat   Student Reflective Focus Question

Structured Interview   **Writing Prompt**

Writing Prompt

Ask students to write two different stories. One story should involve data whose domain is continuous and the other story should involve data whose domain is discrete. Both sets of data should be linear. Students should graph their data and write linear functions that relate y to x. They should include a summary in each story describing how they know whether the domains are discrete or continuous. Students can share their stories and summaries with the class.

Study Help Sample Answers

Remind students to complete Graphic Organizers for the rest of the chapter.

2.

	Linear Functions with Positive Slopes	Linear Functions with Negative Slopes
Algebra slope-intercept form: $y = mx + b$	m is positive	m is negative
Description	Graph is a line that rises from left to right (as x increases, y increases).	Graph is a line that falls from left to right (as x increases, y decreases).
Equations In slope-intercept form	$y = \frac{1}{2}x - 3$ $y = 3x$	$y = -\frac{1}{2}x - 3$ $y = -x + 1$
Not in slope-intercept form	$x - 3y = 0$ $x + 3 = y - 3$	$3x + 2y = 10$ $2x = 8 - \frac{2}{3}y$
Table	x | 0 | 1 | 2 | 3 y | 0 | 3 | 6 | 9	x | 0 | 1 | 2 | 3 y | 0 | -2 | -4 | -6
Graph		

3. Available at *BigIdeasMath.com*.

Reteaching and Enrichment Strategies

If students need help. . .	If students got it. . .
Resources by Chapter • Study Help • Practice A and Practice B • Puzzle Time Lesson Tutorials *BigIdeasMath.com* Practice Quiz Practice from the Test Generator	**Resources by Chapter** • Enrichment and Extension • School-to-Work Game Closet at *BigIdeasMath.com* Start the Chapter Review

Answers

1. $y = x + 3$

2. $y = 2x - 4$

3. $y = -\frac{1}{2}x$

4. $y = -x + 2$

5. $y = \frac{2}{3}x - 1$

6. nonlinear; The graph is not a line.

7. linear; The graph is a line.

8. linear; The graph is a line.

9. linear; As x increases by 2, y decreases by 2.

10. nonlinear; As x increases by 2, y increases by different amounts.

11. nonlinear; As x increases by 3, y changes by different amounts.

12. **a.** $R = 2A + 2$

     b. $22 million

13. linear; The equation is in slope-intercept form.

Technology For the Teacher

Answer Presentation Tool

Assessment Book

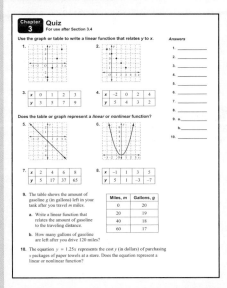

Additional Review Options

- **Quiz**Show
- Big Ideas Test Generator
- Game Closet at *BigIdeasMath.com*
- Vocabulary Puzzle Builder
- Resources by Chapter
  Puzzle Time
  Study Help

Answers

1. domain: $-5, -4, -3, -2$
   range: $3, 1, -1, -3$

2. domain: $-2, -1, 0, 1, 2$
   range: $-4, -2, 0$

3.

x	y
−1	−4
0	−1
1	2
2	5

   domain: $-1, 0, 1, 2$
   range: $-4, -1, 2, 5$

4.

x	y
0	2
1	−2
2	−6
3	−10

   domain: $0, 1, 2, 3$
   range: $2, -2, -6, -10$

Review of Common Errors

Exercises 1 and 2

- Students may confuse the domain and range. Remind them that the domain is the set of all possible input values (the *x*-coordinates) and the range is the set of all possible output values (the *y*-coordinates).

Exercises 3 and 4

- Students may make errors when finding or solving for *y*. Remind them how to use the order of operations, and (in Exercise 4) how to solve for *y*.

Exercises 5 and 6

- Students may see decimal numbers in a table and think that the function is continuous, or see whole numbers in a table and think that the function is discrete. Encourage them to think about the context of the problem. Point out that you can drive for part of an hour or part of a mile, but you cannot buy part of a stamp.
- Students may graph the function incorrectly. Remind them that discrete data points are not connected, but continuous data points are.

Exercises 7–9

- Students may try to write the linear function without first finding the slope and *y*-intercept, or they may use the reciprocal of the slope in their function. Encourage them to check their work by making sure that all of the given points are solutions.

Exercise 10

- Students may notice that all of the values of *y* are the same and not be able to write the linear function. Encourage them to plot the points, and if necessary, remind them how to write the equation of a horizontal line.

Exercises 11 and 12

- Students may guess their answer, or they may think that because the *x*-values are increasing by the same amount, the function is linear. Encourage them to examine the *y*-values or to plot the given points so that they can tell if the table represents a linear or nonlinear function.

Exercise 13

- Students may think that a graph represents a linear function if part(s) of the graph appear to be straight. Point out that the graph of a linear function is not curved and does not change direction.

Check It Out
Vocabulary Help
BigIdeasMath √com

Review Key Vocabulary

function, *p. 128*	independent variable, *p. 128*	continuous domain, *p. 134*
domain, *p. 128*	dependent variable, *p. 128*	linear function, *p. 142*
range, *p. 128*	discrete domain, *p. 134*	nonlinear function, *p. 148*

Review Examples and Exercises

3.1 **Domain and Range of a Function** *(pp. 126–131)*

Find the domain and range of the function represented by the graph.

Write the ordered pairs. Identify the inputs and outputs.

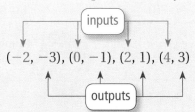

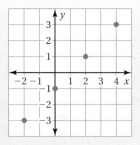

∴ The domain is $-2, 0, 2,$ and $4.$ The range is $-3, -1, 1,$ and $3.$

Exercises

Find the domain and range of the function represented by the graph.

1.

2.

Copy and complete the input-output table for the function. Then find the domain and range of the function represented by the table.

3. $y = 3x - 1$

x	y
−1	
0	
1	
2	

4. $4x + y = 2$

x	y
0	
1	
2	
3	

3.2 Discrete and Continuous Domains (pp. 132–137)

The function $y = 19.5x$ represents the cost y (in dollars) of x yearbooks. Graph the function. Is the domain of the graph discrete or continuous?

Make an input-output table.

Input, x	$19.5x$	Output, y	Ordered Pair, (x, y)
0	19.5(0)	0	(0, 0)
1	19.5(1)	19.5	(1, 19.5)
2	19.5(2)	39	(2, 39)
3	19.5(3)	58.5	(3, 58.5)
4	19.5(4)	78	(4, 78)

Plot the ordered pairs.

Yearbooks

Cost (dollars) vs Number of yearbooks, with points (0, 0), (1, 19.5), (2, 39), (3, 58.5), (4, 78).

Because you cannot buy part of a yearbook, the graph consists of individual points.

⋮ So, the domain is discrete.

Exercises

Graph the function. Is the domain of the graph discrete or continuous?

5.

Hours, x	Miles, y
0	0
1	4
2	8
3	12
4	16

6.

Stamps, x	Cost, y
20	8.4
40	16.8
60	25.2
80	33.6
100	42

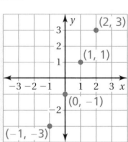

3.3 Linear Function Patterns (pp. 140–145)

Use the graph to write a linear function that relates y to x.

The points lie on a line. Find the slope and y-intercept of the line.

$$\text{slope} = \frac{\text{rise}}{\text{run}} = \frac{2}{1} = 2$$

Because the line crosses the y-axis at $(0, -1)$, the y-intercept is -1.

Graph showing points (2, 3), (1, 1), (0, −1), (−1, −3).

⋮ So, the linear function is $y = 2x - 1$.

Review Game

Writing Linear Functions

For the Student
Additional Practice
- Lesson Tutorials
- Study Help (textbook)
- Student Website
   Multi-Language Glossary
   Practice Assessments

Materials per Group:
- paper
- two yard sticks
- pencils

Directions:
- Divide the class into an even number of groups.
- Groups pair up to compete against each other.
- Each pair of groups makes a paper football.
- Students in each pair of groups take turns flicking the football with their fingers as high and as far as they can. Students from the other group measure and record the length and height that the football travels. Both groups have to agree on the measurements. Length can be measured after the football has come to rest, but height must be measured while it is moving.
- Each student writes the domain and range of both the ascent and descent of the football when they took their turn. The domain is the length traveled and the range is the height traveled. (See figure below.) Students write one linear function to approximate the ascent and another linear function to approximate the descent.

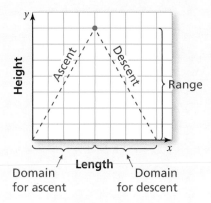

Who Wins?

Each student earns their group a point for each inch achieved in length and height. Points only count if the linear functions correctly model the motion of the football and the domains and ranges are clearly identified. The group with the most points wins.

Answers

5.
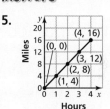

continuous

6.
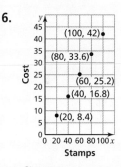

discrete

7. $y = -x - 2$

8. $y = \dfrac{1}{3}x + 3$

9. $y = 3x + 1$

10. $y = -7$

11. linear, As x increases by 3, y increases by 9.

12. nonlinear; As x increases by 2, y changes by different amounts.

13. nonlinear; The graph is not a line.

My Thoughts on the Chapter

Teacher Tip

Not allowed to write in your teaching edition? Use sticky notes to record your thoughts.

What worked. . .

What did not work. . .

What I would do differently. . .

Exercises

Use the graph or table to write a linear function that relates _y_ to _x_.

7.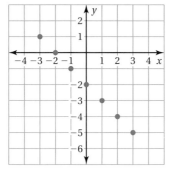

8.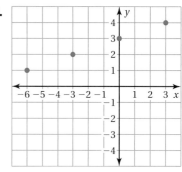

9.

x	−2	−1	0	1
y	−5	−2	1	4

10.

x	−2	0	2	4
y	−7	−7	−7	−7

3.4 **Comparing Linear and Nonlinear Functions** *(pp. 146–151)*

Does the table represent a *linear* or *nonlinear* function? Explain.

a.

$$+2 \quad +2 \quad +2$$

x	0	2	4	6
y	0	1	4	9

$$+1 \quad +3 \quad +5$$

As *x* increases by 2, *y* increases by different amounts. The rate of change is *not* constant. So, the function is nonlinear.

b.

x	y
0	50
5	40
10	30
15	20

+5 / −10

As *x* increases by 5, *y* decreases by 10. The rate of change is constant. So, the function is linear.

Exercises

Does the table or graph represent a *linear* or *nonlinear* function? Explain.

11.

x	y
3	1
6	10
9	19
12	28

12.

x	y
1	3
3	1
5	1
7	3

13.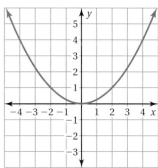

Check It Out
Test Practice
BigIdeasMath✓com

1. Find the domain and range of the function represented by the graph.

2. Copy and complete the input-output table for the function $y = 7x - 3$. Then find the domain and range of the function represented by the table.

x	-1	0	1	2
y				

Graph the function. Is the domain of the graph discrete or continuous?

3.

Hair Clips, x	Cost, y
0	0
1	1.5
2	3
3	4.5

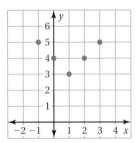

4.

Minutes, x	Gallons, y
0	60
5	45
10	30
15	15

5. Write a linear function that relates y to x.

6. Does the table represent a *linear* or *nonlinear* function? Explain.

x	0	2	4	6
y	8	0	-8	-16

7. **SAVINGS** You save 15% of your monthly earnings x (in dollars).

   a. Write an equation that represents the amount y (in dollars) you save each month. Identify the independent variable and the dependent variable.

   b. Create an input-output table for the equation in part (a). Use the inputs 25, 30, 35, and 40.

   c. What is the total amount saved during those 4 months?

8. **FOOD DRIVE** You are putting cans of food into boxes for a food drive. One box holds 30 cans of food. Write a linear function that represents the number y of cans of food that will fit in x boxes.

9. **SURFACE AREA** The table shows the surface area S (in square inches) of a cube with a side length of x inches. Does the table represent a linear or nonlinear function? Explain.

Side Length, x	1	2	3	4
Surface Area, S	6	24	54	96

Test Item References

Chapter Test Questions	Section to Review
1, 2, 7	3.1
3, 4	3.2
5, 8	3.3
6, 9	3.4

Test-Taking Strategies

Remind students to quickly look over the entire test before they start so that they can budget their time. This test involves analyzing pairs of concepts that students can easily confuse, such as domain and range, input and output, rise and run, discrete and continuous, and linear and nonlinear. So, it is important that students use the **Stop** and **Think** strategy before they answer a question.

Common Assessment Errors

- **Exercise 1** Students may confuse the domain and range. Remind them that the domain is the set of all possible input values (the x-coordinates) and the range is the set of all possible output values (the y-coordinates).
- **Exercise 2** Students may make order of operations errors when finding y. Remind them how to use the order of operations.
- **Exercises 3 and 4** Students may see decimal numbers in a table and think that the function is continuous, or see whole numbers in a table and think that the function is discrete. Encourage them to think about the context of the problem. For example, you cannot buy part of a hair clip, so the domain of the function in Exercise 3 is discrete.
- **Exercises 3 and 4** Students may graph the function incorrectly. Remind them that discrete data points are not connected, but continuous data points are.
- **Exercise 5** Students may try to write the linear function without first finding the slope and y-intercept, or they may use the reciprocal of the slope in their function. Encourage them to check their work by making sure that all of the given points are solutions.
- **Exercise 6** Students may guess their answer without providing an explanation. Encourage them to examine the y-values or to plot the given points so that they can tell if the table represents a linear or nonlinear function.

Reteaching and Enrichment Strategies

If students need help. . .	If students got it. . .

Resources by Chapter
  • Practice A and Practice B
  • Puzzle Time
Record and Practice Journal Practice
Differentiating the Lesson
Lesson Tutorials
Practice from the Test Generator
Skills Review Handbook
	Resources by Chapter
	  • Enrichment and Extension
	  • School-to-Work
	Game Closet at *BigIdeasMath.com*
	Start Standardized Test Practice

Answers

1. domain: $-1, 0, 1, 2, 3$
   range: $5, 4, 3$

2.

x	-1	0	1	2
y	-10	-3	4	11

   domain: $-1, 0, 1, 2$
   range: $-10, -3, 4, 11$

3–4. See Additional Answers.

5. $y = \dfrac{1}{2}x - 1$

6. linear; As x increases by 2, y decreases by 8.

7. **a.** $y = 0.15x$; The independent variable is your monthly earnings x and the dependent variable is the amount y you save each month.

   b.

x	25	30	35	40
y	3.75	4.5	5.25	6

   c. $19.50

8. $y = 30x$

9. nonlinear; As x increases by 1, S increases by different amounts.

Assessment Book

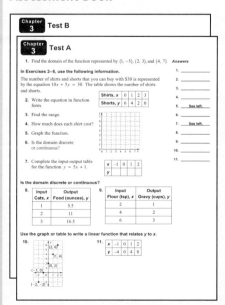

T-156

After Answering Easy Questions, Relax
Answer Easy Questions First
Estimate the Answer
Read All Choices before Answering
Read Question before Answering
Solve Directly or Eliminate Choices
Solve Problem before Looking at
   Choices
Use Intelligent Guessing
Work Backwards

About this Strategy

When taking a multiple choice test, be sure to read each question carefully and thoroughly. One way to answer the question is to work backwards. Try putting the responses into the question, one at a time, and see if you get a correct solution.

Answers

1. D
2. F
3. $200
4. B

Item Analysis

1. **A.** The student thinks that reversing the domain gets you the range.

   B. The student takes 5 away from each domain element, ignoring the coefficient 0.2.

   C. The student performs an arithmetic error subtracting integers.

   D. Correct answer

2. **F.** Correct answer

   G. The student picks the number 1 from the formula.

   H. The student uses the numbers in the formula: $1 - 0.25 = 0.75$.

   I. The student picks the number 0.25 from the formula.

3. **Gridded Response:** Correct answer: $200

   Common Error: The student divides $500 by 5, or $800 by 10.

4. **A.** The student thinks that a line with a negative slope is nonlinear.

   B. Correct answer

   C. The student thinks that a horizontal line is nonlinear.

   D. The student thinks that a steep line with a positive slope is nonlinear.

5. **F.** The student uses the incorrect inequality symbol.

   G. The student uses the incorrect inequality symbol.

   H. Correct answer

   I. The student uses the incorrect inequality symbol.

6. **Gridded Response:** Correct answer: 3°F

   Common Error: The student subtracts 36 from 54, but fails to divide the result by 6.

7. **A.** The student only includes the domain values greater than or equal to 0.

   B. The student finds the range.

   C. Correct answer

   D. The student puts the domain and range together.

Technology
For the Teacher

Big Ideas Test Generator

1. The domain of the function $y = 0.2x - 5$ is 5, 10, 15, 20. What is the range of this function?

   A. 20, 15, 10, 5

   B. 0, 5, 10, 15

   C. 4, 3, 2, 1

   D. $-4, -3, -2, -1$

Test-Taking Strategy
Work Backwards

For x cats, a litter box is changed $y = 3x$ times per month. How many cats are there when $y = 12$?

Ⓐ 1   Ⓑ 2   Ⓒ 3   Ⓓ 4

Share a litter box? Please!

KEEP OFF!

"Work backwards by trying 1, 2, 3, and 4. You will see that 3(4) = 12. So, D is correct."

2. A toy runs on a rechargeable battery. During use, the battery loses power at a constant rate. The percent P of total power left in the battery x hours after being fully charged can be found using the equation shown below. When will the battery be fully discharged?

$$P = -0.25x + 1$$

   F. After 4 hours of use

   G. After 1 hour of use

   H. After 0.75 hour of use

   I. After 0.25 hour of use

3. A limousine company charges a fixed cost for a limousine and an hourly rate for its driver. It costs $500 to rent the limousine for 5 hours and $800 to rent the limousine for 10 hours. What is the fixed cost, in dollars, to rent the limousine?

4. Which graph shows a nonlinear function?

   A.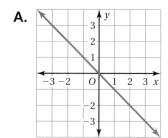

   B.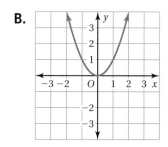

   C.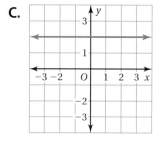

   D.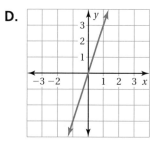

5. In many states, you must be at least 14 years old to operate a personal watercraft. Which inequality represents this situation?

F. $y > 14$ **H.** $y \geq 14$

G. $y < 14$ **I.** $y \leq 14$

6. The temperature fell by the same number of degrees each hour over a six-hour period. How many degrees Fahrenheit did the temperature fall each hour?

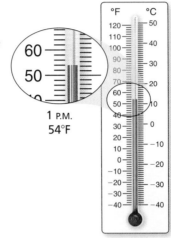

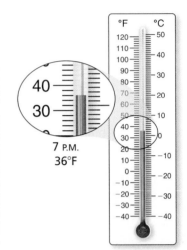

7. What is the domain of the function graphed in the coordinate plane below?

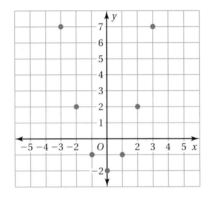

A. $0, 1, 2, 3$ **C.** $-3, -2, -1, 0, 1, 2, 3$

B. $-2, -1, 2, 7$ **D.** $-2, -1, 0, 1, 2, 3, 7$

8. What value of w makes the equation below true?

$$\frac{w}{3} = 3(w - 1) - 1$$

F. $\dfrac{3}{2}$ **H.** $\dfrac{3}{4}$

G. $\dfrac{5}{4}$ **I.** $\dfrac{1}{2}$

Item Analysis

8. **F.** Correct answer

G. The student multiplies both sides by 3, but fails to distribute the 3 correctly on the right side.

H. The student starts by distributing the 3 on the right side incorrectly.

I. The student multiplies both sides by 3, distributes the 3 correctly, but does not distribute the 9 correctly. Alternatively, the student starts by distributing the 3 on the right side correctly. But when multiplying both sides by 3, the student does not distribute it across the expression $3w - 4$ correctly.

9. **A.** The student subtracts 5 and -3 incorrectly.

B. The student subtracts 5 and -3 incorrectly, and subtracts -4 and 1 incorrectly.

C. Correct answer

D. The student subtracts -4 and 1 incorrectly.

10. **F.** The student picks the slope of the problem and ignores the need to find a y-intercept.

G. The student picks the slope of the problem and the y-value from the point (6, 1) for the y-intercept.

H. Correct answer

I. The student approaches the problem properly, but misplaces a negative sign for y.

11. **2 points** The student demonstrates a thorough understanding of how to determine whether data show a linear function or a nonlinear function, explains the work fully, and relates perimeter to a linear function and area to a nonlinear function. The first table shows a linear function. The second table shows a nonlinear function.

1 point The student's work and explanations demonstrate a lack of essential understanding. The slope formula is used incorrectly or a graph of the data is incomplete.

0 points The student provides no response, a completely incorrect or incomprehensible response, or a response that demonstates insufficient understanding of linear functions and nonlinear functions.

9. C

10. H

11. *Part A* yes

   Part B no

12. B

Answers for Extra Examples

1. **A.** The student ignores the starting amount of $300.

    B. The student combines the starting and weekly amounts incorrectly.

    C. The student reverses the roles of the starting and weekly amounts.

    D. Correct answer

2. **F.** The student identifies the domain incorrectly.

    G. The student identifies the domain incorrectly.

    H. Correct answer

    I. The student identifies the domain correctly but thinks it is discrete.

Item Analysis (continued)

12. **A.** The student multiplies by 1000 because there are 1000 mL in 1 L.

    B. Correct answer

    C. The student has the right idea, but uses the wrong relationship of 1 L = 100 mL.

    D. The student divides by 1000 because there are 1000 mL in 1 L.

Extra Examples for Standardized Test Practice

1. Deanna started a savings account with $300 and added $20 per month to the account. Let n be the number of weeks that Deanna added money to the account and let a be the total amount in her account. Which equation describes the relationship between a and n?

    A. $a = 20n$ **C.** $a = 300n + 20$

    B. $a = 320n$ **D.** $a = 20n + 300$

2. Julia is studying how attendance at an amusement park is related to temperature. To build her study, Julia uses the temperature each day as an input value and amusement park attendance as a daily output value. Which statement best describes this situation?

    F. The domain is daily attendance and it is continuous.

    G. The domain is daily attendance and it is discrete.

    H. The domain is temperature and it is continuous.

    I. The domain is temperature and it is discrete.

9. What is the slope of the line shown in the graph below?

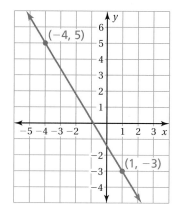

A. $-\dfrac{2}{5}$

B. $-\dfrac{2}{3}$

C. $-\dfrac{8}{5}$

D. $-\dfrac{8}{3}$

10. A line with slope of $\dfrac{1}{3}$ contains the point (6, 1). What is the equation of the line?

F. $y = \dfrac{1}{3}x$

G. $y = \dfrac{1}{3}x + 1$

H. $x - 3y = 3$

I. $x + 3y = 3$

11. The tables show how the perimeter and area of a square are related to its side length. Examine the data in the table.

Think
Solve
Explain

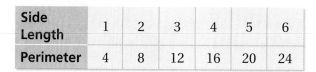

Side Length	1	2	3	4	5	6
Perimeter	4	8	12	16	20	24

Side Length	1	2	3	4	5	6
Area	1	4	9	16	25	36

Part A Does the first table show a linear function? Explain your reasoning.

Part B Does the second table show a linear function? Explain your reasoning.

12. A bottle of orange extract marked 25 mL costs $2.49. What is the cost per liter?

A. $2490.00 per L

B. $99.60 per L

C. $9.96 per L

D. $0.00249 per L

4 Percents

"Here's my sales strategy. I buy each dog bone for $0.05."

"Then I mark each one up to $1. Then, I have a 75% off sale. Cool, huh?"

"Dear Vet: I have this strange feeling that I am wagging my tail 15% fewer times than I used to wag it."

"Oh look. He already answered me."

"Dear Newton, I only practice general vet work. I need to refer you to a dog tail specialist."

Strands Development

6th Grade
• Investigate and describe percents as ratios.
• Identify a percent from a representation.
• Demonstrate equivalent relationships between fractions, decimals, and percents.
• Compare and order fractions, decimals, and percents.

7th Grade
• Compare and order fractions, decimals, percents, and numbers written in scientific notation.

8th Grade
• Solve problems involving percents.
• Find the percent increase of decrease.

Math in History

The concept of percent goes back to Roman times. However, the percent symbol is more recent.

★ Percent has been used since the end of the fifteenth century in business problems such as computing interest, profit, and taxes. However, the idea had its origin much earlier. When the Roman emperor Augustus levied a tax on all goods sold at auction, the rate was $\frac{1}{100}$.

★ In the Middle Ages, as large denominations of money came to be used, 100 became a common base for computation. Italian manuscripts of the fifteenth century contained such expressions as "20 p 100" to indicate 20%. The percent sign, %, evolved from a symbol introduced in an anonymous Italian manuscript from 1425. Instead of "per 100" or "P cento," which were common at that time, this author used the symbol $\frac{\circ}{\circ}$. The current symbol, using a slanted line, is relatively modern.

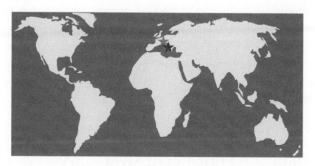

Pacing Guide for Chapter 4

Chapter Opener	1 Day

Section 1
  Activity
  Lesson
	
	1 Day
	1 Day

Section 2
  Activity
  Lesson
	
	1 Day
	1 Day

Study Help / Quiz	1 Day

Section 3
  Activity
  Lesson
	
	1 Day
	1 Day

Section 4
  Activity
  Lesson
	
	1 Day
	1 Day

Chapter Review / Tests	2 Days
Total Chapter 4	12 Days
Year-to-Date	66 Days

Check Your Resources

- Record and Practice Journal
- Resources by Chapter
- Skills Review Handbook
- Assessment Book
- Worked-Out Solutions

Technology
For the **Teacher**

The Dynamic Planning Tool
Editable Teacher's Resources at
BigIdeasMath.com

6.2(b) The student will identify a given fraction, decimal, or percent from a representation.

6.2(c) The student will demonstrate equivalent relationships among fractions, decimals, and percents.

Additional Topics for Review

- The division algorithm
- Greatest common factor
- Simplifying fractions
- Place value

Try It Yourself

1. 6%   **2.** 100%

3. 80%   **4.** $0.35, \frac{7}{20}$

5. $60\%, \frac{3}{5}$ **6.** 52%, 0.52

7. $0.1, \frac{1}{10}$ **8.** $85\%, \frac{17}{20}$

9. 20%, 0.2

Record and Practice Journal

1. 18%   **2.** 10%

3. 58%   **4.** 93%

5. 0.625   **6.** 0.525

7. $\frac{13}{50}$ **8.** $\frac{79}{100}$

9. $\frac{13}{20}$ **10.** 65%

11. 94%   **12.** $\frac{13}{25}$

13. $\frac{31}{100}$ **14.** 6%

15. 84%   **16.** 0.22

17. 1.91

18–20.

Percent	Decimal	Fraction
45%	0.45	$\frac{9}{20}$
73%	0.73	$\frac{73}{100}$
30%	0.3	$\frac{3}{10}$

Math Background Notes

Vocabulary Review

- Numerator
- Denominator
- Equivalent fraction
- Percent

Writing Percents Using Models

- Students should know how to work with models and percents.
- Remind students that the word percent comes from per cent, or per one hundred.
- To express what percent of the model is shaded, students should count the number of blocks per hundred that are shaded.
- If time permits, you may want to provide examples of percents greater than 100%.

Writing Percents, Decimals, and Fractions

- Students know how to convert between percents, decimals, and fractions. Students may require additional practice to achieve mastery.
- **Multiple Representations:** To convert from fractions to decimals, suggest that students convert the given fraction to an equivalent fraction with a denominator that is a power of ten. In Example 3, students can rewrite $\frac{3}{5}$ as $\frac{6}{10}$. Students that have mastered place value will realize that six-tenths can be expressed as the decimal 0.6 without having to employ the division algorithm. Alternatively, students could simply use the division algorithm to complete Example 3.

Reteaching and Enrichment Strategies

If students need help. . .	If students got it. . .
Record and Practice Journal 　• Fair Game Review Skills Review Handbook Lesson Tutorials	Game Closet at *BigIdeasMath.com* Start the next section

What You Learned Before

"The fact that these two percents do not total 100 is a sad commentary on humans."

Writing Percents Using Models

What percent of the model is shaded?

Example 1

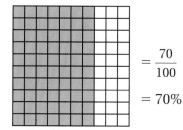

$$= \frac{70}{100}$$

$$= 70\%$$

Example 2

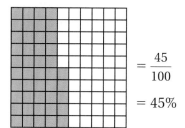

$$= \frac{45}{100}$$

$$= 45\%$$

Try It Yourself
What percent of the model is shaded?

1.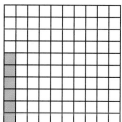

2.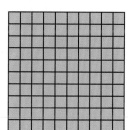

3.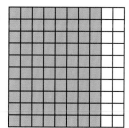

Writing Decimals, Percents, and Fractions

Example 3 Write $\frac{3}{5}$ as a decimal.

$$\frac{3}{5} = \frac{3 \cdot 2}{5 \cdot 2} = \frac{6}{10} = 0.6$$

Example 4 Write $\frac{3}{5}$ as a percent.

$$\frac{3}{5} = \frac{3 \cdot 20}{5 \cdot 20} = \frac{60}{100} = 60\%$$

Multiply to make the denominator 100.

Try It Yourself

Copy and complete the table.

	Percent	Decimal	Fraction
4.	35%		
5.		0.6	
6.			$\frac{13}{25}$

	Percent	Decimal	Fraction
7.	10%		
8.		0.85	
9.			$\frac{1}{5}$

**STANDARDS
OF LEARNING**
8.3

Essential Question How can you use models to estimate percent questions?

1 **ACTIVITY: Estimating a Percent**

Work with a partner. Estimate the locations of 50%, 75%, 40%, 6%, and 65% on the model. 50% is done for you.

0% .... 50% 100%

2 **ACTIVITY: Estimating a Part of a Number**

The statement "25% of 12 is 3" has three numbers. In real-life problems, any one of these numbers can be unknown.

Part → $\dfrac{3}{12}$ = 0.25 = 25% ← Percent

Whole →

Which number is missing?	Question	Type of Question
3	What is 25% of 12?	Find a part of a number.
25%	3 is what percent of 12?	Find a percent.
12	3 is 25% of what?	Find the whole.

Work with a partner. Estimate the answer to each question using a model.

a. **Sample:** What number is 50% of 30?

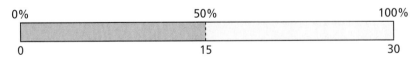

0%   50%   100%
0   15   30

∴ So, from the model, 15 is 50% of 30.

b. What number is 75% of 30?   **c.** What number is 40% of 30?

d. What number is 6% of 30?   **e.** What number is 65% of 30?

Laurie's Notes

Introduction

For the Teacher

- **Goal:** Students will use the percent bar model to help solve three types of percent problems.

Motivate

- Share with students that sometimes their thinking can get *scrambled up* while solving percent problems, so an egg model would be a good way to introduce the chapter!
- **?** Use an egg carton to ask and to help visualize a few simple percent problems.
    - "What is 75% of 12?" 9
    - "3 is what percent of 12?" 25%
    - "12 is 50% of what number?" 24

Activity Notes

Activity 1

- **FYI:** You may want to begin with a quick review of fractional equivalents of the following common percents:
  $10\%, 20\%, 30\%, 40\%, 60\%, 70\%, 80\%, 90\%, 25\%, 50\%, 75\%, 33\frac{1}{3}\%, 66\frac{2}{3}\%$

- **Representation:** The percent bar model is an effective tool for estimating an answer, or judging the reasonableness of an answer if students have an understanding of fractional parts of a whole.
- The length of the bar is 100%, the whole. Percents near 50% are about $\frac{1}{2}$ of the whole.
- Students should be able to judge percents near 25% $\left(\frac{1}{4}\right)$ and 75% $\left(\frac{3}{4}\right)$.
- Students should locate the percents on the same model.
- When students have finished, draw a percent bar model on the board. Have volunteers share their answers.
- Remind students that these are approximations. Check for reasonableness in their approximations. For example, 40% is closer to 50% than 25%.

Activity 2

- Use an egg carton as a visual model when discussing the three numbers in the statement "25% of 12 is 3."
- Students work with a partner to answer the questions.
- **FYI:** Some students may find it helpful to use a long strip of paper that they can fold or write on when answering questions.
- **Summarize:** In each of the questions, the whole (30) was known and a part (percent) of it was found. Because all of the percents are less than 100%, all of the parts are less than 30 (the whole).
- **?** **Extension:** "What number is 150% of 30?" 45

Standards of Learning

8.3(a) The student will solve practical problems involving rational numbers, percents, ratios, and proportions.

Previous Learning

Students should know how to solve simple percent problems.

Activity Materials
Introduction
• egg carton (one dozen)

Start Thinking! and Warm Up

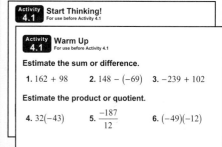

4.1 Record and Practice Journal

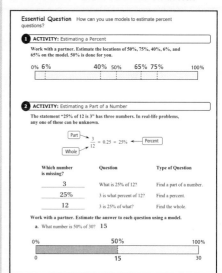

Differentiated Instruction

Visual

Some students will benefit from seeing how fractions and percents relate. Draw a circle on the board. Write 100% on top of the circle and 1 underneath. Explain that both of these values describe the area of the circle. Draw one-half of a circle and one-fourth of a circle and ask students to give you two representations.

$\frac{1}{2}$ and 50%, $\frac{1}{4}$ and 25%

4.1 Record and Practice Journal

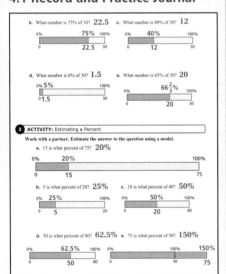

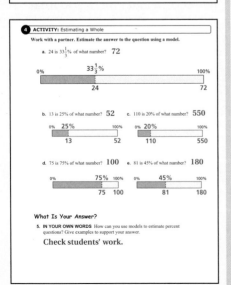

Activity 3

- Encourage students to draw a percent bar model for each problem. You could also provide strips of paper that students can fold or write on.
- It is important that students be able to approximate the part in the whole model. Ask questions such as, "Is it greater than or less than one-half? Is it greater than or less than one-quarter?"
- **Common Error:** In part (e), students may misread 50 as the part of 75. Help students with this by drawing a bar model to represent the whole (50).
- ❓ "How much more is needed to make 75?" 25
- ❓ "How much do I need to extend the bar to show 25?"

  a length $\frac{1}{2}$ as long as 50
- ❓ "So, 75 is what percent of 50?" 150%

Activity 4

- For most students, this is the most challenging of the 3 types of percent problems.
- Talk about the model shown for the sample. The 24 is drawn first and you know it is $\frac{1}{3}$ of the whole $\left(33\frac{1}{3}\%\right)$. Next, draw two more thirds. Each one represents 24.
- **Strategy:** You are given the part of the whole. Add enough additional parts until you have a whole. For part (d), you know 3 equal parts would make 75, so each part must be 25.
- You may need to offer a hint for part (e). Ask what 81 and 45 have as a common factor. 9 From that information, you can conclude that 5% must be 9.

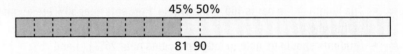

- When students have finished, have them describe their strategy to their classmates. Hearing others' thinking is helpful.

Closure

- Use the model shown. What 3 questions could be asked? "24 is what percent of 60?"; "What is 40% of 60?"; "24 is 40% of what number?"

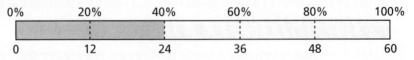

Technology For the Teacher

The Dynamic Planning Tool
Editable Teacher's Resources at *BigIdeasMath.com*

③ ACTIVITY: Estimating a Percent

Work with a partner. Estimate the answer to the question using a model.

a. **Sample:** 15 is what percent of 75?

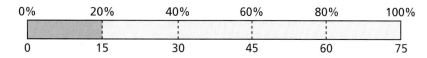

∴ So, 15 is 20% of 75.

b. 5 is what percent of 20?   c. 18 is what percent of 40?

d. 50 is what percent of 80?   e. 75 is what percent of 50?

④ ACTIVITY: Estimating a Whole

Work with a partner. Estimate the answer to the question using a model.

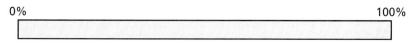

a. **Sample:** 24 is $33\frac{1}{3}$% of what number?

∴ So, 24 is $33\frac{1}{3}$% of 72.

b. 13 is 25% of what number?   c. 110 is 20% of what number?

d. 75 is 75% of what number?   e. 81 is 45% of what number?

What Is Your Answer?

5. **IN YOUR OWN WORDS** How can you use models to estimate percent questions? Give examples to support your answer.

Practice

Use what you learned about estimating percent questions to complete Exercises 4–9 on page 166.

Key Vocabulary
percent, *p. 164*

A **percent** is a ratio whose denominator is 100. Here are two examples.

$$4\% = \frac{4}{100} = 0.04 \qquad 25\% = \frac{25}{100} = 0.25$$

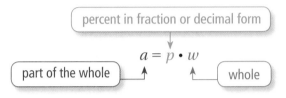 **Key Idea**

The Percent Equation

Words To represent "*a* is *p* percent of *w*," use an equation.

percent in fraction or decimal form

$$a = p \cdot w$$

part of the whole   whole

Numbers $15 = 0.5 \cdot 30$

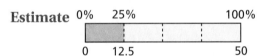 **EXAMPLE 1 Finding a Part of a Number**

What number is 24% of 50?

Estimate 0%   25%   100%

0   12.5   50

Common Error

Remember to convert a percent to a fraction or decimal before using the percent equation. For Example 1, write 24% as $\frac{24}{100}$.

$a = p \cdot w$ Write percent equation.

$= \frac{24}{100} \cdot 50$ Substitute $\frac{24}{100}$ for *p* and 50 for *w*.

$= 12$ Multiply.

∴ So, 12 is 24% of 50.   **Reasonable?** $12 \approx 12.5$ ✓

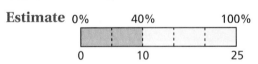 **EXAMPLE 2 Finding a Percent**

9.5 is what percent of 25?

Estimate 0%   40%   100%

0   10   25

$a = p \cdot w$ Write percent equation.

$9.5 = p \cdot 25$ Substitute 9.5 for *a* and 25 for *w*.

$0.38 = p$ Divide each side by 25.

∴ Because 0.38 equals 38%, 9.5 is 38% of 25.   **Reasonable?** $38\% \approx 40\%$ ✓

Laurie's Notes

Introduction

Connect

- **Yesterday:** Students used the percent bar model to explore three types of percent problems.
- **Today:** Students will use the percent equation to solve three types of percent problems.

Motivate

- The 2007 population of the United States was approximately 300 million (*Source:* U.S. Census Bureau) with about 25% being under 18 years old. About how many people in the U.S. are under the age of 18?
  about 75,000,000

Lesson Notes

Key Idea

- Write the Key Idea.
- **Connection:** Students should know how to find a percent of a number by multiplying. The percent equation builds upon this idea to find the missing percent or the unknown whole. When you know two of the three quantities in this equation, you can solve for the third.
- ❓ To help students think through how the equation will be used, use a numeric example ($2 \times 4 = 8$) or a variable example ($a \cdot b = c$).
  - "If you know a and b, how do you solve for c?" Multiply a and b.
  - "If you know a and c, how do you solve for b?" Divide c by a.
  - "If you know b and c, how do you solve for a?" Divide c by b.
- **FYI:** Students often get lost in the language of these problems. It is important to help students translate the problems and make sense of the information that is given.

Example 1

- Another way to phrase this question is "24% of 50 is what number?"
- **Estimate:** 24% is close to 25%, and 25% is $\frac{1}{4}$.
- ❓ "What is $\frac{1}{4}$ of 50?" 12.5
- If time permits, write 24% as a decimal and work the problem again.

Example 2

- Read the example as "9.5 is a part of 25."
- ❓ "Is 9.5 more or less than half of 25?" less
- ❓ Draw the percent bar model explaining that it represents 25. Draw the half mark (50%) and ask how much that would represent. 12.5
- ❓ Now draw the quarter mark (25%) and ask how much that would represent. 6.25 Through this process, students should recognize that 9.5 is between 25% and 50% of 25.
- **Common Error:** Students may forget that the decimal answer to the division problem needs to be rewritten as a percent.
- Note that the percent bar model is divided into 5 equal parts instead of 4.

Goal Today's lesson is finding **percents** using the percent equation.

Start Thinking! and Warm Up

Lesson 4.1 **Warm Up** For use before Lesson 4.1

Lesson 4.1 **Start Thinking!** For use before Lesson 4.1

At a soccer game, your team scored 6 goals during regular play and 4 goals on penalty kicks. Use a model to show the percent of goals that were not scored by penalty kicks.

Extra Example 1

What number is 73% of 200? 146

Extra Example 2

36.4 is what percent of 40? 91%

Laurie's Notes

Extra Example 3

18 is 15% of what number? 120

On Your Own

1. $a = 0.1 \cdot 20$; 2
2. $a = 1.5 \cdot 40$; 60
3. $3 = p \cdot 600$; 0.5%
4. $18 = p \cdot 20$; 90%
5. $8 = 0.8 \cdot w$; 10
6. $90 = 0.18 \cdot w$; 500

Extra Example 4

Your total cost for lunch is $18.50 for food and $1.48 for tax.

a. Find the percent of sales tax on the food total. 8%

b. Find the amount of an 18% tip on the food total. $3.33

On Your Own

7. $5.50

English Language Learners

Vocabulary

English learners may have trouble identifying which is the *whole* and which is the *part of the whole* in a percent equation. Have students write percent equations for the statements "20% of 300 is 60" and "125% of 50 is 62.5." Suggest that they start by substituting the percent *p* into the equation. Next, substitute the whole *w*. In most cases, this is the number after the word *of*. The remaining number is the part of the whole *a*.

Example 3

- This type of problem, finding a whole, is a bit harder. Knowing fractional equivalents is extremely helpful in developing a sense about the size of the answer.
- **?** "What is the part?" 39 "So, 39 is a part of something."
- **?** "How big of a part is it, approximately?" 52%, about half
- Help students reason that if 39 is half of something, the whole must be about 80. Only at this point does it make sense to translate what is known into an equation. 39 is 52% of some number.
- **Common Error:** Students may divide 39 by 52 and ignore the decimals completely.

On Your Own

- Have students work with a partner on these problems. Encourage students to sketch the percent bar model and record the information they know. Then write the percent equation.
- Have students put their work on the board.

Example 4

- **?** "In addition to paying for what you ordered (food and drink), what other costs are there when you eat at a restaurant?" sales tax and tip
- Review decimal operations as you work through each part.

On Your Own

- Model finding 10%, and then double for 20%.

Closure

- **Exit Ticket:** Use the percent equation to answer the question, 12 is what percent of 48? 25%

Technology For the Teacher

The Dynamic Planning Tool
Editable Teacher's Resources at *BigIdeasMath.com*

EXAMPLE **3** **Finding a Whole**

39 is 52% of what number?

Estimate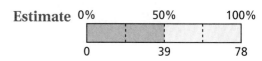

$a = p \cdot w$ Write percent equation.

$39 = 0.52 \cdot w$ Substitute 39 for a and 0.52 for p.

$75 = w$ Divide each side by 0.52.

⋮• So, 39 is 52% of 75.   **Reasonable?** $75 \approx 78$

● **On Your Own**

Now You're Ready
Exercises 10–17

Write and solve an equation to answer the question.

1. What number is 10% of 20?
2. What number is 150% of 40?
3. 3 is what percent of 600?
4. 18 is what percent of 20?
5. 8 is 80% of what number?
6. 90 is 18% of what number?

EXAMPLE **4** **Real-Life Application**

8th Street Cafe

DATE: May04'10 05:45PM
TABLE: 29
SERVER: CHARITY

Food Total	**27.50**
Tax	**1.65**
Subtotal	**29.15**

TIP: _____

TOTAL: _____

Thank You

a. **Find the percent of sales tax on the food total.**
b. **Find the amount of a 16% tip on the food total.**

a. Answer the question: $1.65 is what percent of $27.50?

$a = p \cdot w$ Write percent equation.

$1.65 = p \cdot 27.50$ Substitute 1.65 for a and 27.50 for w.

$0.06 = p$ Divide each side by 27.50.

⋮• Because 0.06 equals 6%, the percent of sales tax is 6%.

b. Answer the question: What tip amount is 16% of $27.50?

$a = p \cdot w$ Write percent equation.

$= 0.16 \cdot 27.50$ Substitute 0.16 for p and 27.50 for w.

$= 4.40$ Multiply.

⋮• So, the amount of the tip is $4.40.

● **On Your Own**

7. **WHAT IF?** In Example 4, find the amount of a 20% tip on the food total.

 Vocabulary and Concept Check

1. **VOCABULARY** Write the percent equation in words.

2. **REASONING** A number n is 150% of number m. Is n *greater than*, *less than*, or *equal to m*? Explain your reasoning.

3. **DIFFERENT WORDS, SAME QUESTION** Which is different? Find "both" answers.

What number is 20% of 55?	55 is 20% of what number?
20% of 55 is what number?	0.2 • 55 is what number?

 Practice and Problem Solving

Estimate the answer to the question using a model.

4. What number is 24% of 80?

5. 15 is what percent of 40?

6. 15 is 30% of what number?

7. What number is 120% of 70?

8. 20 is what percent of 52?

9. 48 is 75% of what number?

Write and solve an equation to answer the question.

① **10.** 20% of 150 is what number?

11. 45 is what percent of 60?

② **12.** 35% of what number is 35?

13. 32% of 25 is what number?

③ **14.** 29 is what percent of 20?

15. 0.5% of what number is 12?

16. What percent of 300 is 51?

17. 120% of what number is 102?

ERROR ANALYSIS Describe and correct the error in using the percent equation.

18. What number is 35% of 20?

19. 30 is 60% of what number?

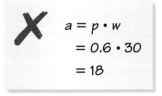

$$a = p \cdot w$$
$$= 35 \cdot 20$$
$$= 700$$

$$a = p \cdot w$$
$$= 0.6 \cdot 30$$
$$= 18$$

20. BASEBALL A pitcher throws 75 pitches. Of these, 72% were strikes. How many strikes did the pitcher throw?

21. FUNDRAISING Your school raised 125% of its fundraising goal. The school raised $6750. What was the goal?

22. SURFBOARD The sales tax on a surfboard is $12. What is the percent of sales tax?

Assignment Guide and Homework Check

Level	Day 1 Activity Assignment	Day 2 Lesson Assignment	Homework Check
Basic	4–9, 32–36	1–3, 11–17 odd, 18–22, 28	11, 15, 20, 28
Average	4–9, 32–36	1–3, 11–19 odd, 22–26, 28, 29	11, 15, 23, 28
Advanced	4–9, 32–36	1–3, 18, 19, 22–27, 29–31	24, 26, 27, 30

Common Errors

- **Exercises 4–17** Students may not know what number to substitute for each variable. Walk through each type of question with the students. Emphasize that the word *is* means *equals*, and *of* means *to multiply*. Tell students to write the question and then write the meaning of each word or group of words underneath.
- **Exercises 20–22** Students will mix up the whole and the part when trying to write the percent equation for the word problems. Ask them to identify each part of the equation before writing it in the equation format. For example, in Exercise 20, ask "How many total pitches did the pitcher throw?" 75 "Which variable in the percent equation does this number represent?" The whole Continue to ask questions for each of the variables.
- **Exercise 28** Students may not realize that the sum of the parts of a circle graph equals 100%.

4.1 Record and Practice Journal

Write and solve an equation to answer the question.

1. 40% of 60 is what number?
$$a = 0.4 \cdot 60; \ 24$$

2. 17 is what percent of 50?
$$17 = p \cdot 50; \ 34\%$$

3. 38% of what number is 57?
$$57 = 0.38 \cdot w; \ 150$$

4. 44% of 25 is what number?
$$a = 0.44 \cdot 25; \ 11$$

5. 52 is what percent of 50?
$$52 = p \cdot 50; \ 104\%$$

6. 150% of what number is 18?
$$18 = 1.5 \cdot w; \ 12$$

7. You put 60% of your paycheck into your savings account. Your paycheck is $235. How much money do you put in your savings account?
$141

8. You made lemonade and iced tea for a school fair. You made 15 gallons of lemonade and 60% is gone. About 52% of the iced tea is gone. The ratio of gallons of lemonade to gallons of iced tea was 3 : 2.

a. How many gallons of lemonade are left?
6 gallons

b. How many gallons of iced tea did you make?
10 gallons

c. About how many gallons of iced tea are left?
4.8 gallons

Technology For the Teacher
Answer Presentation Tool
QuizShow

Vocabulary and Concept Check

1. A part of the whole is equal to a percent times the whole.

2. greater than; Because $150\% = 1.5$, $n = 1.5 \cdot m$.

3. 55 is 20% of what number?; 275; 11

Practice and Problem Solving

4. about 20

5. 37.5%

6. 50

7. 84

8. about 37.5%

9. 64

10. $a = 0.2 \cdot 150; \ 30$

11. $45 = p \cdot 60; \ 75\%$

12. $35 = 0.35 \cdot w; \ 100$

13. $a = 0.32 \cdot 25; \ 8$

14. $29 = p \cdot 20; \ 145\%$

15. $12 = 0.005 \cdot w; \ 2400$

16. $51 = p \cdot 300; \ 17\%$

17. $102 = 1.2 \cdot w; \ 85$

18. The percent was not converted to a decimal or fraction.
$$a = p \cdot w$$
$$= 0.35 \cdot 20$$
$$= 7$$

19. 30 represents the part of the whole.
$$30 = 0.6 \cdot w$$
$$50 = w$$

20. 54 strikes

21. $5400

22. 5%

23. 26 years old

24. 70 years old

25. 56 signers

26. 70%

27. If the percent is less than 100%, the percent of a number is less than the number. If the percent is equal to 100%, the percent of a number will equal the number. If the percent is greater than 100%, the percent of a number is greater than the number.

28. a. 80 students

  b. 30 students

29. See *Taking Math Deeper.*

30. false; If W is 25% of Z, then Z : W is 100 : 25, because Z represents the whole.

31. 92%

Fair Game Review

32. 0.6   **33.** 0.88

34. 0.25   **35.** 0.36

36. A

Mini-Assessment

Write and solve an equation to answer the question.

1. 52 is what percent of 80? 65%

2. 28 is 35% of what number? 80

3. What number is 25% of 92? 23

4. What percent of 250 is 60? 24%

5. A new laptop computer costs $800. The sales tax on the computer is $48. What is the percent of sales tax? 6%

Taking Math Deeper

Exercise 29

Any problem that has this much given information is difficult for students. Encourage students to begin by organizing the information with a table or a diagram. When organizing the information, it is a good idea to add as much other information as you can find... *before looking at the questions.*

1. Organize the given information.

2. Add other information.

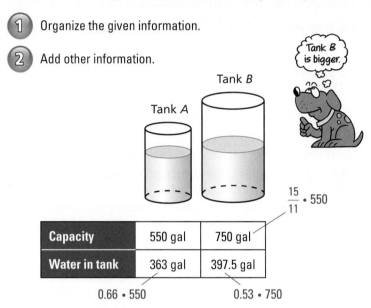

	Tank A	Tank B
Capacity	550 gal	750 gal
Water in tank	363 gal	397.5 gal

$\frac{15}{11} \cdot 550$

0.66 • 550   0.53 • 750

3. Now the questions are easy.
   a. Tank A has 363 gallons of water.
   b. The capacity of tank B is 750 gallons.
   c. Tank B has 397.5 gallons of water.

Project

Use your school library or the Internet to research how a water tower works. How does the water get into the tower? How long does it take for the water to drain out? How often is the water completely exchanged; in other words, if a gallon goes in today when will that gallon be draining out? What other interesting things did you discover?

Reteaching and Enrichment Strategies

If students need help. . .	If students got it. . .
Resources by Chapter • Practice A and Practice B • Puzzle Time Record and Practice Journal Practice Differentiating the Lesson Lesson Tutorials Skills Review Handbook	Resources by Chapter • Enrichment and Extension Start the next section

PUZZLE There were *w* signers of the Declaration of Independence. The youngest was Edward Rutledge, who was *x* years old. The oldest was Benjamin Franklin, who was *y* years old.

23. *x* is 25% of 104. What was Rutledge's age?

24. 7 is 10% of *y*. What was Franklin's age?

25. *w* is 80% of *y*. How many signers were there?

26. *y* is what percent of $(w + y - x)$?

Favorite Sport

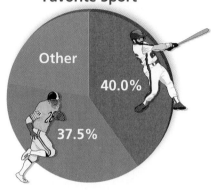

27. REASONING How can you tell whether the percent of a number will be *greater than*, *less than*, or *equal to* the number?

28. SURVEY In a survey, a group of students were asked their favorite sport. "Other" sports were chosen by 18 people.

    a. How many students participated?

    b. How many chose football?

29. WATER TANK Water tank *A* has a capacity of 550 gallons and is 66% full. Water tank *B* is 53% full. The ratio of the capacity of tank *A* to tank *B* is 11 : 15.

    a. How much water is in tank *A*?

    b. What is the capacity of tank *B*?

    c. How much water is in tank *B*?

30. TRUE OR FALSE? Tell whether the statement is *true* or *false*. Explain your reasoning.

    If *W* is 25% of *Z*, then *Z* : *W* is 75 : 25.

31. Reasoning The table shows your test results for math class. What test score is needed on the last exam to earn 90% of the total points?

Test Score	Point Value
83%	100
91.6%	250
88%	150
?	300

 Fair Game Review *What you learned in previous grades & lessons*

Simplify. Write as a decimal. *(Skills Review Handbook)*

32. $\dfrac{10 - 4}{10}$ **33.** $\dfrac{25 - 3}{25}$ **34.** $\dfrac{105 - 84}{84}$ **35.** $\dfrac{170 - 125}{125}$

36. MULTIPLE CHOICE There are 160 people in a grade. The ratio of boys to girls is 3 to 5. Which proportion can you use to find the number *x* of boys? *(Skills Review Handbook)*

    Ⓐ $\dfrac{3}{8} = \dfrac{x}{160}$ **Ⓑ** $\dfrac{3}{5} = \dfrac{x}{160}$ **Ⓒ** $\dfrac{5}{8} = \dfrac{x}{160}$ **Ⓓ** $\dfrac{3}{5} = \dfrac{160}{x}$

4.2 Percents of Increase and Decrease

STANDARDS OF LEARNING

8.3

Essential Question What is a percent of decrease? What is a percent of increase?

① ACTIVITY: Percent of Decrease

Each year in the Columbia River Basin, adult salmon swim up river to streams to lay eggs and hatch their young.

To go up the river, the adult salmon use fish ladders. But, to go down the river, the young salmon must pass through several dams.

There are electric turbines at each of the eight dams on the main stem of the Columbia and Snake Rivers. About 88% of the young salmon pass through these turbines unharmed.

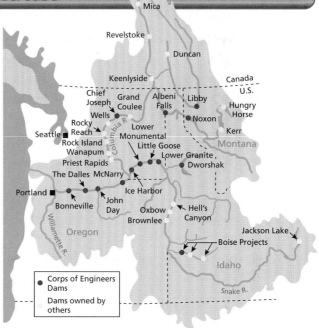

Copy and complete the table and the bar graph to show the number of young salmon that make it through the dams.

Dam	0	1	2	3	4	5	6	7	8
Salmon	1000	880	774						

88% of 1000 = 0.88 • 1000   88% of 880 = 0.88 • 880

= 880   = 774.4 ≈ 774

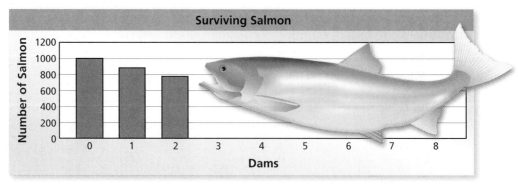

Laurie's Notes

Introduction

For the Teacher

- **Goal:** Students will explore percent decrease and increase by working through real-life problems.
- Use of a calculator will help facilitate the computation so that students can focus on how the numbers are changing.

Motivate

- Talk about the new compact fluorescent light bulbs. Fluorescent light bulbs use 75% less energy than incandescent light bulbs (percent decrease) and last up to 900% longer (percent increase).
- If your school has replaced incandescent light bulbs with fluorescent light bulbs, discuss the potential savings.

Activity Notes

Activity 1

- **Representation:** Although the difference between the decimal point and the multiplication dot are clear in the textbook, it may not be as clear when you write it on the board. You may consider using parentheses to show the multiplication: (0.88)(1000).
- Have a student read the story information.
- ❓ "What percent of salmon makes it through each dam?" 88%
- ❓ "What percent of salmon does not make it through each dam?" 12%
- Discuss the general concept of fewer salmon at dam 2 than dam 1.
- **FYI:** Electric turbines in the dams generate electricity. These turbines are what affect the survival rate of the young salmon.
- Students should follow the two calculations shown. Remind students to round their answers to a whole number of salmon at each dam.
- Check students' results before completing the graph.
- **Big Idea:** Each entry is 12% less than the previous entry. The *amount* of decrease is changing, but the *percent* is not.
- Have students describe patterns they observe in the numbers and the bar graph.

Standards of Learning

8.3(a) The student will solve practical problems involving rational numbers, percents, ratios, and proportions.
8.3(b) The student will determine the percent increase or decrease for a given situation.

Previous Learning

Students should be able to find a percent of a number, round decimal values, and convert between fractions, decimals, and percents.

Activity Materials
Textbook
• calculators

Start Thinking! and Warm Up

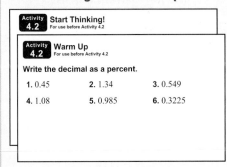

Activity 4.2	Start Thinking! For use before Activity 4.2

Activity 4.2 Warm Up For use before Activity 4.2

Write the decimal as a percent.

1. 0.45   2. 1.34   3. 0.549
4. 1.08   5. 0.985   6. 0.3225

4.2 Record and Practice Journal

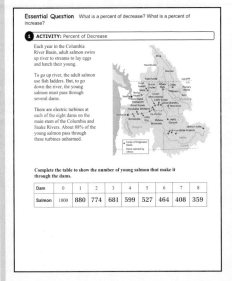

Essential Question What is a percent of decrease? What is a percent of increase?

1 ACTIVITY: Percent of Decrease

Each year in the Columbia River Basin, adult salmon swim up river to streams to lay eggs and hatch their young.

To go up river, the adult salmon use fish ladders. But, to go down the river, the young salmon must pass through several dams.

There are electric turbines at each of the eight dams on the main stem of the Columbia and Snake Rivers. About 88% of the young salmon pass through these turbines unharmed.

Complete the table to show the number of young salmon that make it through the dams.

Dam	0	1	2	3	4	5	6	7	8
Salmon	1000	880	774	681	599	527	464	408	359

English Language Learners

Visual Aid

Demonstrate writing a percent as a decimal. Locate the decimal point in the 7%.

7.%

Draw two arrows to show that the decimal point moves two places *left*.

.7.%

Write zeros to the left of the number if needed.

007.%

Rewrite as a decimal with the decimal point two places to the left and without the percent sign.

0.07

4.2 Record and Practice Journal

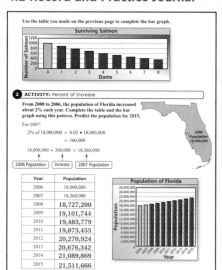

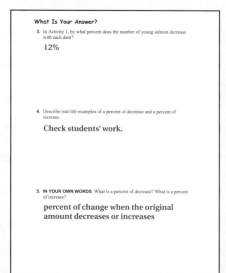

Activity 2

- Read the information. Look at the map and the information on current population.
- Work through the first year with the students. There are two steps involved: 1) find the amount the population has increased, and 2) add this amount to the current population.
- ? "How much did the population increase in 2007?" 360,000
- ? "What percent did the population increase in 2007?" 2%
- Remind students to round their answers to a whole number and add this number to the current population.
- Check students' results before completing the graph.
- **Big Idea:** Each entry is 2% more than the previous entry. The *amount* of increase is changing, but the *percent* is not.
- **Extension:** Discuss how projections are made based upon current trends.

What Is Your Answer?

- For Question 4, students could discuss this at home and bring ideas to class.

Closure

- "You scored 80 points on your first test. If your score increased 10% on the next test, what is your score?" 88 points

Technology **F**or the **T**eacher

Dynamic Classroom

The Dynamic Planning Tool
Editable Teacher's Resources at *BigIdeasMath.com*

ACTIVITY: Percent of Increase

From 2000 to 2006, the population of Florida increased about 2% each year. Copy and complete the table and the bar graph using this pattern. Predict the population in 2015.

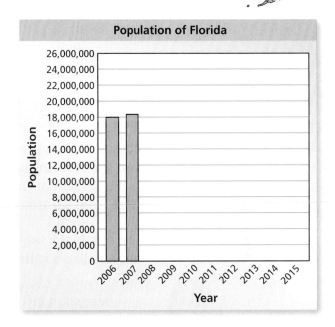

2006 Population 18,000,000

For 2007:

$$2\% \text{ of } 18{,}000{,}000 = 0.02 \cdot 18{,}000{,}000$$

$$= 360{,}000$$

$$18{,}000{,}000 + 360{,}000 = 18{,}360{,}000$$

2006 Population · Increase · 2007 Population

Year	Population
2006	18,000,000
2007	18,360,000
2008	
2009	
2010	
2011	
2012	
2013	
2014	
2015	

Population of Florida

What Is Your Answer?

3. In Activity 1, by what percent does the number of young salmon decrease with each dam?

4. Describe real-life examples of a percent of decrease and a percent of increase.

5. **IN YOUR OWN WORDS** What is a percent of decrease? What is a percent of increase?

 **Practice** Use what you learned about percent of increase and percent of decrease to complete Exercises 13–18 on page 172.

Section 4.2   Percents of Increase and Decrease   **169**

Check It Out
Lesson Tutorials
BigIdeasMath com

Key Vocabulary 🔊
percent of change,
  p. 170
percent of increase,
  p. 170
percent of decrease,
  p. 170

A **percent of change** is the percent that a quantity changes from the original amount.

$$\text{percent of change} = \frac{\text{amount of change}}{\text{original amount}}$$

🔑 Key Idea

Percents of Increase and Decrease

When the original amount increases, the percent of change is called a **percent of increase**.

$$\text{percent of increase} = \frac{\text{new amount} - \text{original amount}}{\text{original amount}}$$

When the original amount decreases, the percent of change is called a **percent of decrease**.

$$\text{percent of decrease} = \frac{\text{original amount} - \text{new amount}}{\text{original amount}}$$

EXAMPLE 1 Finding a Percent of Increase

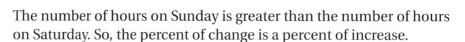

The table shows the number of hours you spent online last weekend. What is the percent of change in your online time from Saturday to Sunday?

Day	Hours Online
Saturday	2
Sunday	4.5

The number of hours on Sunday is greater than the number of hours on Saturday. So, the percent of change is a percent of increase.

$$\text{percent of increase} = \frac{\text{new amount} - \text{original amount}}{\text{original amount}}$$

$$= \frac{4.5 - 2}{2} \qquad \text{Substitute.}$$

$$= \frac{2.5}{2} \qquad \text{Subtract.}$$

$$= 1.25, \text{ or } 125\% \qquad \text{Write as a percent.}$$

⋮ Your online time increased 125% from Saturday to Sunday.

⬤ On Your Own

Find the percent of change. Round to the nearest tenth of a percent, if necessary.

1. 10 inches to 25 inches

2. 57 people to 65 people

🔊 Multi-Language Glossary at BigIdeasMath ✓com.

Laurie's Notes

Introduction

Connect

- **Yesterday:** Students explored two real-life problems with quantities that decreased or increased by a percent.
- **Today:** Students will use a percent change formula to solve problems.

Motivate

- Cell phone ownership is increasing each year. Pose a question such as: "If 400 people in your neighborhood had a cell phone last year and one year later 500 people had a cell phone, what percent has cell phone ownership increased?"

Lesson Notes

Key Idea

- Explain the difference between *amount* of change and *percent* of change. Refer to the salmon and population activities.
- Use the cell phone example to help identify vocabulary:

  original amount $= 400$,

  amount of change $= 100$,

  percent of change $= \dfrac{100}{400} = 25\%$.

Example 1

- Read the information in the table to your students.
- ❓ "Did the online use increase or decrease from Saturday to Sunday?"
  increase
- ❓ "How much did the online use increase from Saturday to Sunday?" 2.5 h
- Have students write the equation, substitute the values, and then simplify. The original amount is 2. The new amount is 4.5. Because the number of hours increased, you are finding a **percent of increase**. Percent of

  increase $= \dfrac{4.5 - 2}{2} = 1.25 = 125\%$.

- **Common Error:** Students think the answer is 1.25. This decimal must still be converted to a percent. This often happens when the percent answer is greater than 100%.
- **Connection:** Draw a percent bar model of this problem.

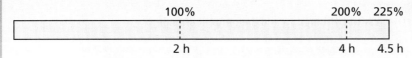

| 100% | | 200% 225% |

2 h   4 h   4.5 h

The percent of increase is 125% beyond the 100%.

On Your Own

- In Question 1, the length has more than doubled, so the percent of increase is greater than 100%.
- In Question 2, the number of people has not doubled, so the percent of increase is less than 100%.

Goal Today's lesson is using a **percent change** formula to solve problems.

Start Thinking! and Warm Up

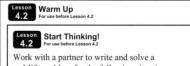

Lesson **4.2** Warm Up
For use before Lesson 4.2

Lesson **4.2** Start Thinking!
For use before Lesson 4.2

Work with a partner to write and solve a real-life problem for the following situation: $250 decreased by 35%.

Extra Example 1

Find the percent of change from 40 hours to 50 hours. increase of 25%

On Your Own

1. 150% increase

2. about 14.0% increase

Extra Example 2

Find the percent of change from 20 days to 12 days. decrease of 40%

 On Your Own

3. about 44.44% decrease

Extra Example 3

Your email account contains 135 messages. You delete 60% of the messages. How many messages are left? 54 messages

 On Your Own

4. 220 songs

Differentiated Instruction

Vocabulary

Make sure students understand the difference between *increased by 150%* and *increased to 150%*. The percent of increase in the first case is 150%. The percent of increase in the second case is 50%, because the increase does not include the original amount. By the same token, there is a difference between *decreased by 25%* and *decreased to 25%*. In the first case, it means taking 25% and leaving 75%. In the second case, it means to leave 25% and take away 75%.

Laurie's Notes

Example 2

- "How much did the number of home runs change each year?" decrease of 8, increase of 18, decrease of 8
- ? "What is the original amount?" 28
- ? "What is the new amount?" 20
- Students should now use the **percent of decrease** formula.
- This problem involves a number of skills: reading a bar graph, using the percent of decrease formula, converting a fraction to a decimal, and converting a decimal to a percent.
- The answer is rounded to the nearest tenth of a percent.
- ? "Is the percent change from 2006 to 2007 more or less than 100%? How do you know?" The number of home runs more than doubled, so the increase is greater than 100%.

On Your Own

- If you have small white boards available, have each student solve Question 3 on their white board. Have students hold up their white boards and then have students determine their mistakes.

Example 3

- Have students identify what information is given in the problem.
- ? "What is the amount of increase or decrease?" not given
- "What percent are you given?" 20% decrease
- Because you are given the percent of decrease (percent) and the original amount (whole), you can use the percent equation to find the amount of decrease (part).
- **Review:** The *amount* of change is 50 songs. The *percent* of change is 20%.
- **Common Error:** If students do not read carefully, they may answer 50 songs. 50 is how many songs were deleted. The question is asking how many songs are left.
- **Connection:** Find 10% using mental math and double to find 20%.
- **Alternative Method:** If you delete 20%, then you have 80% left on your MP3 player.

$$80\% \text{ of } 250 = 0.8 \cdot 250$$
$$= 200$$

Closure

- **Writing Prompt:** To find the percent change...

 Technology For the Teacher

The Dynamic Planning Tool
Editable Teacher's Resources at *BigIdeasMath.com*

EXAMPLE (2) **Finding a Percent of Decrease**

The bar graph shows a softball player's home run totals. What was the percent of change from 2007 to 2008?

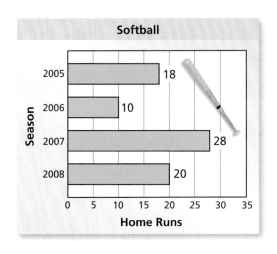

Softball

The number of home runs decreased from 2007 to 2008. So, the percent of change is a percent of decrease.

$$\text{percent of decrease} = \frac{\text{original amount} - \text{new amount}}{\text{original amount}}$$

$$= \frac{28 - 20}{28} \qquad \text{Substitute.}$$

$$= \frac{8}{28} \qquad \text{Subtract.}$$

$$\approx 0.286, \text{ or } 28.6\% \qquad \text{Write as a percent.}$$

⋮ The number of home runs decreased about 28.6%.

On Your Own

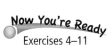
Now You're Ready
Exercises 4–11

3. What was the percent of change from 2005 to 2006?

EXAMPLE (3) **Standardized Test Practice**

You have 250 songs on your MP3 player. You delete 20% of the songs. How many songs are left?

Ⓐ 50   Ⓑ 150   Ⓒ 200   Ⓓ 300

Find the amount of decrease.

$$20\% \text{ of } 250 = 0.2 \cdot 250 \qquad \text{Write as multiplication.}$$

$$= 50 \qquad \text{Multiply.}$$

The decrease is 50 songs. So, there are $250 - 50 = 200$ songs left.

⋮ The correct answer is Ⓒ.

On Your Own

Now You're Ready
Exercises 13–22

4. WHAT IF? After deleting the 50 songs in Example 3, you add 10% more songs. How many songs are on the MP3 player?

 Vocabulary and Concept Check

1. **VOCABULARY** How do you know whether a percent of change is a *percent of increase* or a *percent of decrease*?

2. **NUMBER SENSE** Without calculating, which has a greater percent of increase?
   - 5 bonus points on a 50-point exam
   - 5 bonus points on a 100-point exam

3. **WRITING** What does it mean to have a 100% decrease?

 Practice and Problem Solving

Identify the percent of change as an *increase* or *decrease*. Then find the percent of change. Round to the nearest tenth of a percent, if necessary.

① ② 4. 12 inches to 36 inches

5. 75 people to 25 people

6. 50 pounds to 35 pounds

7. 24 songs to 78 songs

8. 10 gallons to 24 gallons

9. 72 paper clips to 63 paper clips

10. 16 centimeters to 44.2 centimeters

11. 68 miles to 42.5 miles

12. ERROR ANALYSIS Describe and correct the error in finding the percent increase from 18 to 26.

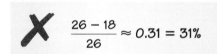

$$\frac{26 - 18}{26} \approx 0.31 = 31\%$$

Find the new amount.

③ 13. 8 meters increased by 25%

14. 15 liters increased by 60%

15. 50 points decreased by 26%

16. 25 penalties decreased by 32%

17. 68 students increased by 125%

18. 1000 grams decreased by 94%

19. 62 kilograms decreased by 32%

20. 124 ounces decreased by 67%

21. ERROR ANALYSIS Describe and correct the error in using the percent of change to find a new amount.

25 is decreased by 40%.
40% of 25 = 0.4 • 25
         = 10
So, 25 + 10 = 35.

22. VIDEO GAME Last week, you finished Level 2 of a video game in 32 minutes. Today, you finish Level 2 in 28 minutes. What is your percent of change?

Assignment Guide and Homework Check

Level	Day 1 Activity Assignment	Day 2 Lesson Assignment	Homework Check
Basic	13–18, 34–38	1–3, 5–11 odd, 12, 19–22, 28	9, 12, 20, 22
Average	13–18, 34–38	1–3, 8–12, 19–21, 23, 25, 28, 29	9, 12, 20, 23, 28
Advanced	13–18, 34–38	1–3, 12, 21, 23–27, 30–33	12, 24, 27, 30

Common Errors

- **Exercises 4–11** Students may mix up where to place the numbers in the equation to find percent of change. When they do not put the numbers in the right place, they might find a negative number in the numerator. First, emphasize that students must know if it is increasing or decreasing before they start the problem. Next, tell students that the number in the denominator is going to be the original or starting number given for both increasing and decreasing percents of change. Finally, the numerator should never have a negative answer. If students get a negative number, it is because they found the wrong difference. The numerator is always the greater number minus the lesser number.

- **Exercises 13–20** Students may find the percent of the number and forget to add or subtract from the original amount. Remind them that these are two-step problems. Before evaluating, tell students to write down what needs to be done for each step.

4.2 Record and Practice Journal

Identify the percent of change as an increase or decrease. Then find the percent of change. Round to the nearest tenth of a percent, if necessary.

1. 25 points to 50 points

   increase; 100%

2. 125 invitations to 75 invitations

   decrease; 40%

3. 32 pages to 28 pages

   decrease; 12.5%

4. 7 players to 10 players

   increase; 42.9%

Find the new amount.

5. 120 books increased by 55%

   186 books

6. 80 members decreased by 65%

   28 members

7. One week, 72 people got a speeding ticket. The next week, only 36 people got a speeding ticket. What is the percent of change in speeding tickets?

   50% decrease

8. The number of athletes participating in the Paralympics rose from 130 athletes in 1952 to 3806 athletes in 2004. What is the percent of change? Round your answer to the nearest tenth of a percent.

   2827.7% increase

Vocabulary and Concept Check

1. If the original amount decreases, the percent of change is a percent of decrease. If the original amount increases, the percent of change is a percent of increase.

2. 5 bonus points on a 50-point exam

3. The new amount is now 0.

Practice and Problem Solving

4. increase; 200%

5. decrease; 66.7%

6. decrease; 30%

7. increase; 225%

8. increase; 140%

9. decrease; 12.5%

10. increase; 176.3%

11. decrease; 37.5%

12. The denominator should be 18, which is the original amount.
$$\frac{26 - 18}{18} \approx 0.44 = 44\%$$

13. 10 m   **14.** 24 L

15. 37 points   **16.** 17 penalties

17. 153 students

18. 60 g

19. 42.16 kg   **20.** 40.92 oz

21. They should have subtracted 10 in the last step because 25 is decreased by 40%.
$$40\% \text{ of } 25 = 0.4 \cdot 25$$
$$= 10$$
So, $25 - 10 = 15$.

22. 12.5% decrease

23. increase; 100%

24. decrease; 25%

25. increase; 133.3%

26. decrease; 70%

27. Increasing 20 to 40 is the same as increasing 20 by 20. So, it is a 100% increase. Decreasing 40 to 20 is the same as decreasing 40 by one-half of 40. So, it is a 50% decrease.

28. **a.** about 16.95% increase

    b. 161,391 people

29. **a.** 100% increase

    b. 300% increase

30. about 24.52% decrease

31. See Additional Answers.

32. See *Taking Math Deeper*.

33. 10 girls

Fair Game Review

34. $a = 0.25 \cdot 64;\ 16$

35. $39.2 = p \cdot 112;\ 35\%$

36. $5 = 0.05 \cdot w;\ 100$

37. $18 = 0.32 \cdot w;\ 56.25$

38. A

Mini-Assessment

Identify the percent of change as an *increase* or *decrease*. Then find the percent of change.

1. 15 meters to 36 meters increase; 140%

2. 20 songs to 70 songs increase; 250%

3. 90 people to 45 people decrease; 50%

4. 65 pounds to 40 pounds decrease; 38.5%

5. Yesterday, it took 40 minutes to drive to school. Today, it took 32 minutes to drive to school. What is your percent of change? The number of minutes it took to get to school decreased by 20%.

Taking Math Deeper

Exercise 32

This exercise is difficult because the percent of increase is given backwards. A good way to start is to use a table to organize the given information.

 Organize given information.

	Donation	Increase over previous year
This year	$10,120	15%
1 year ago	x	10%
2 years ago	y	

② Find last year's donation.

$x + 0.15x = 10{,}120$	Write the equation.
$1.15x = 10{,}120$	Combine like terms.
$x = \$8800$	Divide each side by 1.15.

③ Find donation from 2 years ago.

$y + 0.1y = 8800$	Write the equation.
$1.1y = 8800$	Combine like terms.
$y = \$8000$	Divide each side by 1.1.

Project

Plan a fundraiser for your school. Write a proposal that includes the purpose of the fundraiser, the type of activity, the length of time, and the amount of money you would like to raise. Be prepared to present your proposal to the class.

Reteaching and Enrichment Strategies

If students need help. . .	If students got it. . .
Resources by Chapter • Practice A and Practice B • Puzzle Time Record and Practice Journal Practice Differentiating the Lesson Lesson Tutorials Skills Review Handbook	Resources by Chapter • Enrichment and Extension Start the next section

Identify the percent of change as an *increase* or *decrease*. Then find the percent of change. Round to the nearest tenth of a percent, if necessary.

23. $\frac{1}{4}$ to $\frac{1}{2}$ **24.** $\frac{4}{5}$ to $\frac{3}{5}$ **25.** $\frac{3}{8}$ to $\frac{7}{8}$ **26.** $\frac{5}{4}$ to $\frac{3}{8}$

27. CRITICAL THINKING Explain why a change from 20 to 40 is a 100% increase, but a change from 40 to 20 is a 50% decrease.

28. POPULATION The table shows population data for a community.

Year	Population
2000	118,000
2006	138,000

    a. What is the percent of change from 2000 to 2006?

    b. Use this percent of change to predict the population in 2012.

29. GEOMETRY Suppose the length and width of the sandbox are doubled.

    a. Find the percent of change in the perimeter.

    b. Find the percent of change in the area.

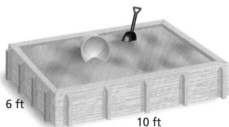

6 ft

10 ft

June   September

30. RUNNING Find the percent of change in the time to run a mile from June to September.

31. CRITICAL THINKING A number increases by 10% and then decreases by 10%. Will the result be *greater than*, *less than*, or *equal to* the original number? Explain.

32. DONATIONS Donations to an annual fundraiser are 15% greater this year than last year. Last year, donations were 10% greater than the year before. The amount raised this year is $10,120. How much was raised 2 years ago?

33. **Reasoning** Forty students are in the science club. Of those, 45% are girls. This percent increases to 56% after new girls join the club. How many new girls join?

Fair Game Review What you learned in previous grades & lessons

Write and solve an equation to answer the question. *(Section 4.1)*

34. What number is 25% of 64?

35. 39.2 is what percent of 112?

36. 5 is 5% of what number?

37. 18 is 32% of what number?

38. MULTIPLE CHOICE The graph of which equation passes through $(-2, 3)$ and $(1, -3)$? *(Section 2.7)*

    (**A**) $y = -2x - 1$ (**B**) $y = -\frac{1}{2}x - 1$ (**C**) $y = \frac{1}{2}x - 1$ (**D**) $y = 2x + 1$

You can use a **summary triangle** to explain a concept. Here is an example of a summary triangle for finding a percent of a number.

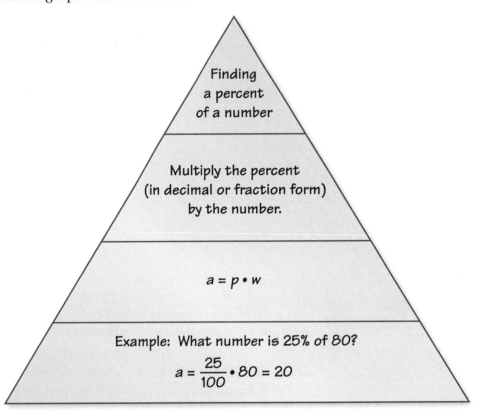

Finding a percent of a number

Multiply the percent (in decimal or fraction form) by the number.

$a = p \cdot w$

Example: What number is 25% of 80?

$a = \dfrac{25}{100} \cdot 80 = 20$

On Your Own

Make a summary triangle to help you study these topics.

1. finding the percent given a number and a part of the number

2. finding the number given a part of the number and a percent

3. percent of increase

4. percent of decrease

After you complete this chapter, make summary triangles for the following topics.

5. discount

6. markup

7. simple interest

"I'm posting my new summary triangle on my daily blog. Do you think it will get me more hits?"

Sample Answers

1.

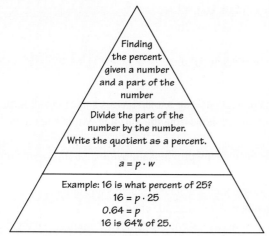

Finding the percent given a number and a part of the number

Divide the part of the number by the number. Write the quotient as a percent.

$a = p \cdot w$

Example: 16 is what percent of 25?
$16 = p \cdot 25$
$0.64 = p$
16 is 64% of 25.

2.

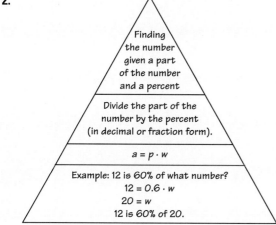

Finding the number given a part of the number and a percent

Divide the part of the number by the percent (in decimal or fraction form).

$a = p \cdot w$

Example: 12 is 60% of what number?
$12 = 0.6 \cdot w$
$20 = w$
12 is 60% of 20.

3.

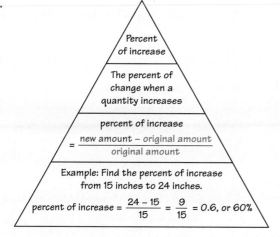

Percent of increase

The percent of change when a quantity increases

$\text{percent of increase} = \dfrac{\text{new amount} - \text{original amount}}{\text{original amount}}$

Example: Find the percent of increase from 15 inches to 24 inches.

$\text{percent of increase} = \dfrac{24 - 15}{15} = \dfrac{9}{15} = 0.6, \text{ or } 60\%$

4. Available at *BigIdeasMath.com*.

List of Organizers
Available at *BigIdeasMath.com*

Comparison Chart
Concept Circle
Definition (Idea) and Example Chart
Example and Non-Example Chart
Formula Triangle
Four Square
Information Frame
Information Wheel
Notetaking Organizer
Process Diagram
Summary Triangle
Word Magnet
Y Chart

About this Organizer

A **Summary Triangle** can be used to explain a concept. Typically, the summary triangle is divided into 3 or 4 parts. In the top part, students write the concept being explained. In the middle part(s), students write any procedure, explanation, description, definition, theorem, and/or formula(s). In the bottom part, students write an example to illustrate the concept. A summary triangle can be used as an assessment tool, in which blanks are left for students to complete. Also, students can place their summary triangles on note cards to use as a quick study reference.

Technology For the Teacher
Vocabulary Puzzle Builder

Answers

1. $a = 0.28 \cdot 75$; 21

2. $42 = 0.21 \cdot w$; 200

3. $36 = p \cdot 45$; 80%

4. $a = 0.68 \cdot 12$; 8.16

5. $66 = p \cdot 55$; 120%

6. increase; 200%

7. decrease; 30%

8. decrease; 61.9%

9. increase; 43.8%

10. decrease; 17.3%

11. increase; 100%

12. 50 text messages

13. 17 passes

14. 93.33%

15. **a.** 2.5% increase

    b. 7.5% increase

16. $16,000

Assessment Book

Write and solve an equation to answer the question.

1. What number is 80% of 65?
2. 45 is 90% of what number?
3. 125 is what percent of 200?
4. 32 is what percent of 640?

Identify the percent of change as an *increase* or *decrease*. Then find the percent of change. Round to the nearest tenth of a percent, if necessary.

5. 120 pounds to 180 pounds
6. 10 feet to 8 feet
7. 400 meters to 350 meters
8. 12 gallons to 36 gallons

Find the new amount.

9. 25 points increased by 20%
10. 620 miles decreased by 15%
11. 21 ounces decreased by 35%
12. 340 grams increased by 120%
13. You earned a 90% on a science test. You answered 18 questions correctly. How many questions were on the test?
14. The table shows the percentage of total athletes at a school that play certain sports. Twenty athletes play baseball. How many athletes are there at the school?

Sport	Baseball	Football	Other
Percentage	7%	30%	45%

15. The number of customers that a small restaurant serves increases by 25% each week. The restaurant served 400 customers the first week it was open. How many customers did the restaurant serve during the third week?
16. You have $100 in your bank account. The first year, your account increases by 7%. The second year, your account decreases by 7%. How much money do you have in your bank account after two years?

Alternative Quiz Ideas

100% Quiz	Math Log
Error Notebook	Notebook Quiz
Group Quiz	**Partner Quiz**
Homework Quiz	Pass the Paper

Partner Quiz

- Students should work in pairs. Each pair should have a small white board.
- The teacher selects certain problems from the quiz and writes one on the board.
- The pairs work together to solve the problem and write their answer on the white board.
- Students show their answers and, as a class, discuss any differences.
- Repeat for as many problems as the teacher chooses.
- For the word problems, teachers may choose to have students read them out of the book.

Reteaching and Enrichment Strategies

If students need help...	If students got it...
Resources by Chapter	Resources by Chapter
• Study Help	• Enrichment and Extension
• Practice A and Practice B	• School-to-Work
• Puzzle Time	Game Closet at *BigIdeasMath.com*
Lesson Tutorials	Start the next lesson
BigIdeasMath.com Practice Quiz	
Practice from the Test Generator	

Technology For the Teacher

Answer Presentation Tool
Big Ideas Test Generator

4.1–4.2   Quiz

Write and solve an equation to answer the question. *(Section 4.1)*

1. What number is 28% of 75?

2. 42 is 21% of what number?

3. 36 is what percent of 45?

4. What number is 68% of 12?

5. 66 is what percent of 55?

Identify the percent of change as an *increase* or *decrease*. Then find the percent of change. Round to the nearest tenth of a percent, if necessary. *(Section 4.2)*

6. 8 inches to 24 inches

7. 300 miles to 210 miles

8. $42.00 to $16.00

9. 32 points to 46 points

10. 185 pounds to 153 pounds

11. 35 people to 70 people

12. **TEXT MESSAGES** You have 44 text messages in your inbox. How many messages can your cell phone hold? *(Section 4.1)*

13. **COMPLETIONS** A quarterback completed 68% of his passes in a game. He threw 25 passes. How many passes did the quarterback complete? *(Section 4.1)*

14. **QUIZ** You answered 14 questions correctly on a 15-question quiz. What percent did you receive on the quiz? Round to the nearest hundredth. *(Section 4.1)*

15. **FRUIT JUICE** The graph shows the amount of fruit juice available per person in the United States during a six-year period. *(Section 4.2)*

    a. What is the percent of change from 2002 to 2005?

    b. What is the percent of change from 2002 to 2003?

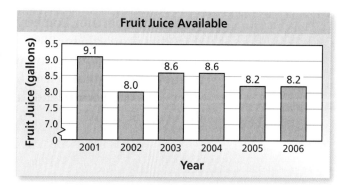

16. **CAR** A car loses 15% of its original value each year. After one year, a car has a value of $13,600. What is the original value of the car? *(Section 4.2)*

4.3 Discounts and Markups

STANDARDS
OF LEARNING
8.3

Essential Question How can you find discounts and markups efficiently?

1 ACTIVITY: Comparing Discounts

Work with a partner. The same pair of sneakers is on sale at three stores. Which one is the best buy?

a. Regular Price: $45 **b.** Regular Price: $49 **c.** Regular Price: $39

a.
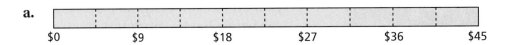

b.
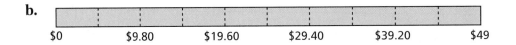

c.
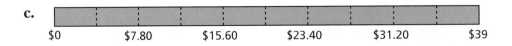

2 ACTIVITY: Finding the Original Price

Work with a partner. You buy a shirt that is on sale for 30% off. You pay $22.40. Your friend wants to know the original price of the shirt. How can your friend find the original price?

Laurie's Notes

Introduction

For the Teacher

- **Goal:** Students will use a percent bar model to visualize discounts and markups.

Motivate

- Show a newspaper circular that advertises a discount (sale).

Activity Notes

Activity 1

- Explain that sale items involve a *percent* discount and the *amount* of discount. If possible, use the newspaper circular to make this distinction.
- The percent bar models are divided into 10 equal parts. Dollar amounts for items are shown on the bars.
- Discuss how the dollar amounts can be computed. Students can use mental math to find 10% and multiply by the correct amount.
- **Big Idea:** When you *save* 40% ($18), you *pay* 60% ($27). Starting at $45, move to the left 40%, that is the savings.
- **Extension:** Determine the amount you save *and* the price paid. This will not be possible for the last example because the amount of discount varies.
- **?** "How do you decide the best buy?" Listen for the lowest final price instead of the greatest savings because the original prices may vary.
- **?** "What does the phrase, "up to 70% off" mean?" Percent off will vary from 0% up to 70%.

Activity 2

- **Connection:** Finding the original price is the same as finding the whole. $22.40 is the part.
- **?** "What percent does $22.40 represent of the original price?" 70%
- **?** "How does the percent bar model help you think about the original price?"

    Students might describe the $22.40 as 70% or about $\frac{2}{3}$ of the original price.

    So, another $\frac{1}{3}$ has to be added on to find the original price.

- Use the percent equation: $22.40 is 70% of what number?
- **?** "Why is 70% used instead of 30%?" Because $22.40 is the part and it is 70% of the whole, or original price.
- **Struggling Students:** Students sometimes struggle with this concept. Reinforce by constantly telling students "30% off the original price is the same as paying 70% of the original price."

Standards of Learning

8.3(a) The student will solve practical problems involving rational numbers, percents, ratios, and proportions.
8.3(b) The student will determine the percent increase or decrease for a given situation.

Previous Learning

Students should be able to find a percent of a number, round decimal values, and convert between fractions, decimals, and percents.

Activity Materials	
Introduction	**Textbook**
• newspaper circular	• calculator

Start Thinking! and Warm Up

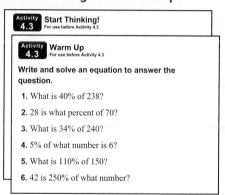

Activity 4.3 Start Thinking!
For use before Activity 4.3

Activity 4.3 Warm Up
For use before Activity 4.3

Write and solve an equation to answer the question.

1. What is 40% of 238?
2. 28 is what percent of 70?
3. What is 34% of 240?
4. 5% of what number is 6?
5. What is 110% of 150?
6. 42 is 250% of what number?

4.3 Record and Practice Journal

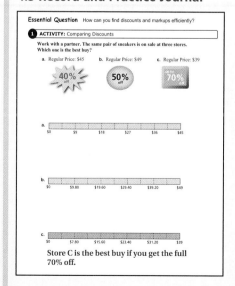

Essential Question How can you find discounts and markups efficiently?

1 ACTIVITY: Comparing Discounts

Work with a partner. The same pair of sneakers is on sale at three stores. Which one is the best buy?

a. Regular Price: $45   b. Regular Price: $49   c. Regular Price: $39

Store C is the best buy if you get the full 70% off.

Vocabulary

English learners may not be familiar with terms used in business, such as *discount, markup, purchase price,* and *selling price.* Take time to explain these terms.

Laurie's Notes

Activity 3

- **Discuss:** A store purchases an item for *x* dollars. The store needs to sell this item for more than *x* dollars (markup) to cover operating costs and to make a profit.
- **Explain:** A store purchases an item for $2 and sells it for $4. This represents a 100% markup ($2 + 100% of $2).
- **Tip:** Have students put 100% above the $250 store cost in part (a).
- **?** "How does the selling price compare to the price the store paid for the item?" 125% greater, or 225% of the store's cost
- **Reasoning:** If a $10 item sells for $25, the $10 item was *marked up 150%* and the selling price is *250% of $10*. One way to show this to students is to write: (100% of $10) + (150% of $10) = (250% of $10) = $25.

Words of Wisdom

- Be careful with language. This is not an obvious concept for students. Try to use consistent language with every example; store purchase price, store selling price, original price, markup amount, discount amount, and sale price.

What Is Your Answer?

- You want students to discover that they can find the selling price after a 25% discount by multiplying by 0.75 (one step) *or* by multiplying by 0.25 and then subtracting the result from the original price (two steps).
- Similarily, for markups, you can multiply the cost by 1.75 (one step) for a 75% markup *or* multiply by 0.75 and then add to the cost (two steps).

Closure

- You purchased an item marked 25% off. What percent of the original price did you pay? 75%

4.3 Record and Practice Journal

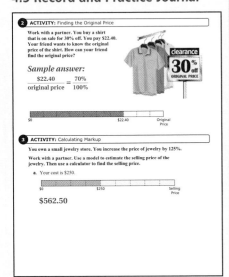

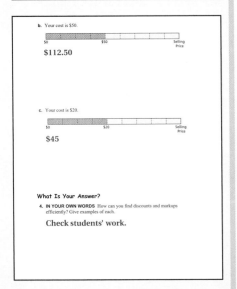

You own a small jewelry store. You increase the price of the jewelry by 125%.

Work with a partner. Use a model to estimate the selling price of the jewelry. Then use a calculator to find the selling price.

a. Your cost is $250.

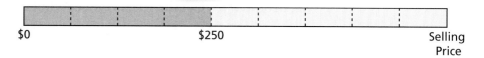

b. Your cost is $50.

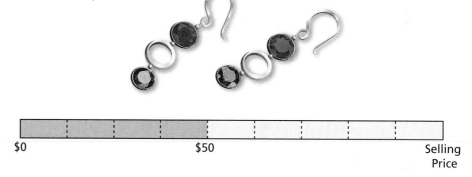

c. Your cost is $20.

What Is Your Answer?

4. IN YOUR OWN WORDS How can you find discounts and markups efficiently? Give examples of each.

Practice

Use what you learned about discounts and markups to complete Exercises 4, 9, 14, and 18–20 on pages 180 and 181.

Key Vocabulary ◀))
discount, *p. 178*
markup, *p. 178*

 **Key Ideas**

Discounts

A **discount** is a decrease in the original price of an item.

Markups

To make a profit, stores charge more than what they pay. The increase from what the store pays to the selling price is called a **markup**.

EXAMPLE ① **Finding a Sale Price**

The original price of the shorts is $35. What is the sale price?

Method 1:   First, find the discount. The discount is 25% of $35.

$a = p \cdot w$		Write percent equation.
$= 0.25 \cdot 35$		Substitute 0.25 for p and 35 for w.
$= 8.75$		Multiply.

Next, find the sale price.

sale price	=	original price	−	discount
	=	35	−	8.75
	=	26.25		

∴ The sale price is $26.25.

Method 2:   First, find the percent of the original price.

$$100\% - 25\% = 75\%$$

Next, find the sale price.

$$\text{sale price} = 75\% \text{ of } \$35$$
$$= 0.75 \cdot 35$$
$$= 26.25$$

Study Tip

A 25% discount is the same as paying 75% of the original price.

∴ The sale price is $26.25.   **Check**

On Your Own

Now You're Ready
Exercises 4–8

1. The original price of a skateboard is $50. The sale price includes a 20% discount. What is the sale price?

◀) Multi-Language Glossary at BigIdeasMath✓com.

Laurie's Notes

Introduction

Connect

- **Yesterday:** Students explored discounts and markups using a percent bar model.
- **Today:** Students will use the percent equation to find discounts and markups of items.

Motivate

? **Story Time:** "A store buys an MP3 player for $100 and marks it up 50%. The store has a 50% off sale. You purchase the MP3 player. What do you pay?" $75 "Did the store lose money?" yes

Lesson Notes

Key Ideas

- Discuss each concept using examples from the previous day's activity.
- Use the following to help students understand the vocabulary.

$$\text{wholesale price} + \text{markup} = \text{retail price}$$
$$\text{(or selling price)}$$

what a store pays   increase in price   price you pay

Example 1

- Two methods are shown. Both methods require two steps. In the first method, you multiply to find the amount of discount, then you subtract to find the sale price. In the second method, you subtract first to find the percent of the original price you will pay, then you use the percent equation to find the sale price.
- Work through each method.
- **Connection:** The amount of discount is a *part* of the *whole* original price. The percent equation is used to find the amount of the discount.
- **Common Error:** Students find the discount or the amount saved ($8.75) instead of the sale price ($26.25).
- Discuss the *Study Tip.* Try other discounts (i.e., 30%) and ask what percent you are paying (70%).

? "Why is the percent bar model divided into 4 parts?"

Because the discount is 25% or $\frac{1}{4}$.

On Your Own

? "How should the percent bar model be divided and why?" 5 parts

because $20\% = \frac{1}{5}$

Goal Today's lesson is using the percent equation to find **discounts** and **markups**.

Start Thinking! and Warm Up

| Lesson 4.3 | Warm Up |
For use before Lesson 4.3

| Lesson 4.3 | Start Thinking! |
For use before Lesson 4.3

You go to a store to buy a new pair of jeans. You find 2 pairs of jeans each on sale for a different price. Explain which is a better bargain.

Regular Price: $35; Discount: 30%

Regular Price: $40; Discount: 35%

Extra Example 1

The original price of a T-shirt is $15. The sale price includes a 35% discount. What is the sale price? $9.75

On Your Own

1. $40

Laurie's Notes

Extra Example 2

The discount on a package of athletic socks is 15%. It is on sale for $17. What is the original price of the package of athletic socks? $20

Extra Example 3

A store pays $15 for a baseball cap. The percent markup is 60%. What is the selling price? $24

 On Your Own

2. $20

3. $90

4. The selling price is 120% of $70. So, the selling price is 1.2(70) = $84.

Differentiated Instruction

Visual

Some students may have a hard time remembering the relationships between *sale price*, *selling price*, *discount*, and *markup*. Have them copy the verbal models into their notebooks.

Discount

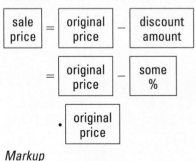

Markup

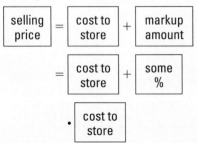

Example 2

- "What is the percent equation?" $a = p \cdot w$
- "What do you know in this problem?" 33 is the part and 60% is the percent.
- **Common Error:** Students multiply 33 by 60% (or 40%). Students need to remember that 33 is a *part* of the original price, it's not the *whole*.

Example 3

- Work through the problem as shown. Encourage students to use mental math to find 20% of $70. 10% of 70 is 7. So, 20% of 70 is 2(7), or 14.
- Two steps were used to answer the question: 1) Find 20% of $70 and 2) add this amount to the original amount of $70.
- "Could this problem be done in one step? Explain." yes; 120% of $70 = $84
- "Explain why the 120% makes sense." You pay 100% of the store's cost plus an additional 20% markup for a total of 120%.
- **Common Error:** Students find the markup ($14) instead of the selling price ($84).
- **Extension:** Have students draw a percent bar model for this problem. The model will be divided into fifths.

Closure

- **Writing Prompt:** Explain two ways to find the sale price for an item marked 30% off. 1) Find the amount of discount and subtract from the original price. 2) Find the percent of the original price and multiply the percent by the original price.
- **Extension:** "If an item is marked up and then discounted the same percent, will the store make a profit? Explain." no; the *amount of markup* will be less than the *amount of discount,* so the store will sell the item for less than what it paid.
- **Extension:** "Is a 25% discount followed by a 10% discount the same as a 35% discount? Explain." no; The sale price for an item discounted 25% followed by a 10% discount would be 0.75(0.9) = 0.675, or 67.5% of the original price. The sale price for an item discounted 35% would be 65% of the original price.

Technology
For the Teacher

The Dynamic Planning Tool
Editable Teacher's Resources at *BigIdeasMath.com*

EXAMPLE **2** **Finding an Original Price**

What is the original price of the shoes?

The sale price is
$100\% - 40\% = 60\%$
of the original price.

Answer the question: 33 is 60% of what number?

$a = p \cdot w$	Write percent equation.
$33 = 0.6 \cdot w$	Substitute 33 for a and 0.6 for p.
$55 = w$	Divide each side by 0.6.

∴ The original price of the shoes is $55.

Check 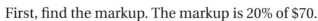 ✓

EXAMPLE **3** **Finding a Selling Price**

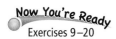

A store pays $70 for a bicycle. The percent of markup is 20%. What is the selling price?

First, find the markup. The markup is 20% of $70.

$a = p \cdot w$	Write percent equation.
$= 0.20 \cdot 70$	Substitute 0.20 for p and 70 for w.
$= 14$	Multiply.

Next, find the selling price.

selling price = cost to store + markup

$= \quad\quad 70 \quad\quad + \quad 14$

$= 84$

∴ The selling price is $84.

On Your Own

Now You're Ready
Exercises 9–20

2. The discount on a DVD is 50%. It is on sale for $10. What is the original price of the DVD?

3. A store pays $75 for an aquarium. The markup is 20%. What is the selling price?

4. Solve Example 3 using a different method.

 Vocabulary and Concept Check

1. **WRITING** Describe how to find the sale price of an item that has been discounted 25%.

2. **WRITING** Describe how to find the selling price of an item that has been marked up 110%.

3. **REASONING** Which would you rather pay? Explain your reasoning.

   a. | 6% tax on a discounted price | or | 6% tax on the original price |

   b. | 30% markup on a $30 shirt | or | $30 markup on a $30 shirt |

 Practice and Problem Solving

Copy and complete the table.

		Original Price	Percent of Discount	Sale Price
①	4.	$80	20%	
	5.	$42	15%	
	6.	$120	80%	
	7.	$112	32%	
	8.	$69.80	60%	
②	9.		25%	$40
	10.		5%	$57
	11.		80%	$90
	12.		64%	$72
	13.		15%	$146.54
	14.	$60		$45
	15.	$82		$65.60
	16.	$95		$61.75

17. **YOU BE THE TEACHER** The cost to a store for an MP3 player is $60. The selling price is $105. A classmate says that the markup is 175% because $\frac{\$105}{\$60} = 1.75$. Is your classmate correct? If not, explain how to find the correct percent of markup.

Assignment Guide and Homework Check

Level	Day 1 Activity Assignment	Day 2 Lesson Assignment	Homework Check
Basic	4, 9, 14, 18–20, 26–29	1–3, 5, 7, 11–17 odd, 21	5, 11, 15, 17
Average	4, 9, 14, 18–20, 26–29	1–3, 5, 7, 11–17 odd, 21, 22	5, 11, 15, 17
Advanced	4, 9, 14, 18–20, 26–29	1–3, 8, 12, 16, 17, 21–25	8, 12, 16, 17, 24

Common Errors

- **Exercises 4–8** Students may write the discount amount as the sale price instead of subtracting it from the original amount. When students copy the table, ask them to add another column titled "Discount Amount." Remind them to subtract the discount amount from the original price.
- **Exercises 9–16** Remind students that there is an extra step in the problem. They should subtract the percent of discount from 100% to find the percent of the original price of the item.
- **Exercises 18–20** Students may find the markup and not the selling price. Remind them that they must add the markup to the cost to obtain the selling price.

Vocabulary and Concept Check

1. *Sample answer:* Multiply the original price by 100% − 25% = 75% to find the sale price.

2. Find the markup by taking 110% of the amount. Then add the amount and the markup to find the selling price.

3. **a.** 6% tax on a discounted price; The discounted price is less, so the tax is less.

   b. 30% markup on a $30 shirt; 30% of $30 is less than $30.

Practice and Problem Solving

4. $64
5. $35.70
6. $24
7. $76.16
8. $27.92
9. $53.33
10. $60
11. $450
12. $200
13. $172.40
14. 25%
15. 20%
16. 35%
17. no; Only the amount of markup should be in the numerator, $\frac{105 - 60}{60} = 0.75$. So, the percent of markup is 75%.

4.3 Record and Practice Journal

Complete the table.

	Original Price	Percent of Discount	Sale Price
1.	$20	20%	**$16**
2.	$95	35%	**$61.75**
3.	**$222**	75%	$55.50
4.	**$130**	40%	$78

Find the cost to store, percent of markup, or selling price.

5. Cost to store: $20
   Markup: 15%
   Selling price: ?
   $23

6. Cost to store: ?
   Markup: 80%
   Selling Price: $100.80
   $56

7. Cost to store: $110
   Markup: ?
   Selling price: $264
   140%

8. A store buys an item for $10. To earn a profit of $25, what percent does the store need to markup the item?
   250%

9. Your dinner at a restaurant costs $13.65 after you use a coupon for a 25% discount. You leave a tip for $3.00.

   a. How much was your dinner before the discount?
   $18.20

   b. You tip your server based on the price before the discount. What percent tip did you leave? Round your answer to the nearest tenth of a percent.
   16.5%

Technology For the Teacher

Answer Presentation Tool
QuizShow

Practice and Problem Solving

18. $77   **19.** $36

20. 140%

21. "Multiply $45.85 by 0.1" and "Multiply $45.85 by 0.9, then subtract from $45.85." Both will give the sale price of $4.59. The first method is easier because it is only one step.

22. a. store C

   b. The markup percent of store A may decrease so it may be cheaper there.

23. no; $31.08

24. See *Taking Math Deeper*.

25. $30

Fair Game Review

26. 170   **27.** 180

28. 1152   **29.** C

Mini-Assessment

Find the price, discount, markup, or cost to store.

1. Original price: $50
   Discount: 15%
   Sale price: ? $42.50

2. Original price: $35
   Discount: ?
   Sale price: $31.50 10%

3. Cost to store: $75
   Markup: ?
   Selling price: $112.50 50%

4. Cost to store: ?
   Markup: 15%
   Selling price: $85.10 $74

5. The sale price for a bicycle is $89.90. The sale price includes a discount of 20%. What is the original price of the bicycle? $112.38

Taking Math Deeper

Exercise 24

A good way to approach this problem is to take things one step at a time. Also, in problems like this, it is much easier to round up to $40 and $30 for easier calculations.

 Find the percent of discount.
   a. 10 is 25% of 40.

   It is easier to round $39.99 to $40 before doing the calculations.

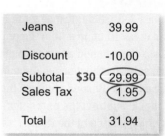

Jeans	$40	39.99
Discount		-10.00
Subtotal		29.99
Sales Tax		1.95
Total		31.94

 Find the percent of sales tax.

   1.95 is what % of 30?

   $$1.95 = p \cdot 30$$
   $$0.065 = p$$

   b. Sales tax = 6.5%.

Jeans		39.99
Discount		-10.00
Subtotal	$30	29.99
Sales Tax		1.95
Total		31.94

 Find the actual markup.

   $$x + 0.6x = 40$$
   $$1.6x = 40$$
   $$x = \$25 \quad \text{Wholesale}$$

The $40 jeans cost the store $25. After the discount of $10, the markup is $5. Find the percent of markup by answering "5 is what % of 25?"

   c. $5 is a 20% markup on $25.

$5 markup

Project

Check the newspaper or local advertisements for a store near you. Select five items that are on sale. Prepare a chart that shows the original price, the percent of discount, and the sale price. How much would you save if you purchased all five items at the sale price?

Reteaching and Enrichment Strategies

If students need help. . .	If students got it. . .
Resources by Chapter • Practice A and Practice B • Puzzle Time Record and Practice Journal Practice Differentiating the Lesson Lesson Tutorials Skills Review Handbook	Resources by Chapter • Enrichment and Extension • School-to-Work Start the next section

Find the cost to store, percent of markup, or selling price.

③ **18.** Cost to store: $70
Markup: 10%
Selling price: [ ]

19. Cost to store: [ ]
Markup: 75%
Selling price: $63

20. Cost to store: $75
Markup: [ ]
Selling price: $180

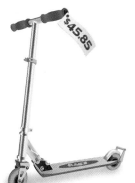

21. SCOOTER The scooter is on sale for 90% off the original price. Which of the methods can you use to find the sale price? Which method do you prefer? Explain.

> Multiply $45.85 by 0.9.

> Multiply $45.85 by 0.1.

> Multiply $45.85 by 0.9, then add to $45.85.

> Multiply $45.85 by 0.9, then subtract from $45.85.

22. GAMING You are shopping for a video game system.

a. At which store should you buy the system?

b. Store A has a weekend sale. How can this change your decision in part (a)?

Store	Cost to Store	Markup
A	$162	40%
B	$155	30%
C	$160	25%

23. STEREO A $129.50 stereo is discounted 40%. The next month, the sale price is discounted 60%. Is the stereo now "free"? If not, what is the sale price?

24. CLOTHING You buy a pair of jeans at a department store.

a. What is the percent of discount to the nearest percent?

b. What is the percent of sales tax to the nearest tenth of a percent?

c. The price of the jeans includes a 60% markup. After the discount, what is the percent of markup to the nearest percent?

Department Store

Jeans	39.99
Discount	-10.00
Subtotal	29.99
Sales Tax	1.95
Total	31.94

Thank You

25. **Critical Thinking** You buy a bicycle helmet for $22.26, which includes 6% sales tax. The helmet is discounted 30% off the selling price. What is the original price?

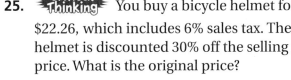

 Fair Game Review *What you learned in previous grades & lessons*

Evaluate. *(Skills Review Handbook)*

26. 2000(0.085)

27. 1500(0.04)(3)

28. 3200(0.045)(8)

29. MULTIPLE CHOICE Which measurement is greater than 1 meter? *(Skills Review Handbook)*

Ⓐ 38 inches   Ⓑ 1 yard   Ⓒ 3.4 feet   Ⓓ 98 centimeters

4.4 Simple Interest

STANDARDS
OF LEARNING

8.3

Essential Question How can you find the amount of simple interest earned on a savings account? How can you find the amount of interest owed on a loan?

Simple interest is money earned on a savings account or an investment. It can also be money you pay for borrowing money.

Write the annual interest rate in decimal form.

Simple Interest	=	Principal	×	Annual Interest Rate	×	Time
($)		($)		(% per yr)		(Years)

$$I = Prt$$

1 ACTIVITY: Finding Simple Interest

Work with a partner. You put $100 in a savings account. The account earns 6% simple interest per year. (a) Find the interest earned and the balance at the end of 6 months. (b) Copy and complete the table. Then make a bar graph that shows how the balance grows in 6 months.

a. $I = Prt$ Write simple interest formula.

$ = 100(0.06)\left(\dfrac{6}{12}\right)$ Substitute values.

$ = 3$ Multiply.

⸭ At the end of 6 months, you earn $3 in interest. So, your balance is $100 + $3 = $103.

b.

Time	Interest	Balance
0 month	$0	$100
1 month		
2 months		
3 months		
4 months		
5 months		
6 months	$3	$103

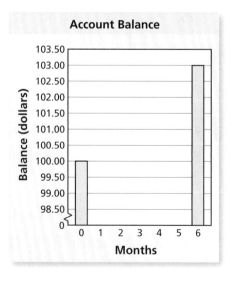

Laurie's Notes

Introduction

For the Teacher

- **Goal:** Students will use the simple interest formula to determine the amount of interest earned in a savings account.
- Students should assume that deposits are made at the beginning of the interest period in all banking problems, unless otherwise stated.

Motivate

- **Tell the Story:** Baseball legend Ken Griffey Jr. played a prank on (former) teammate Josh Fogg one season. He owed Fogg some money and paid him back in pennies. Griffey stacked 60 cartons, each holding $25 worth of pennies, in Fogg's locker. Not only did Fogg not get paid interest, he had to haul all the pennies to the bank!

Activity Notes

Discuss

- Today's investigation involves three activities. Given time constraints and your own students, you may not complete all three.
- **Financial Literacy:** You want students to have some understanding of the cost of borrowing money or the ability to earn money when it is deposited in a bank, not to become trained loan officers.
- **Discuss:** When you *deposit* money, you should *earn* money. When you *borrow* money, you should *pay* money.
- Define *simple interest formula.*
- **Discuss:** Interest earned/owed is influenced by how much money is involved (principal), the rate you pay/earn, and the amount of time.
- Make clear that it is an *annual* interest rate and the time is in *years*.

Activity 1

- This activity uses the simple interest formula. The principal stays the same for each month's calculation.
- **Demonstrate:** After one month, you earn $100(0.06)\left(\dfrac{1}{12}\right) = \$0.50$. This $0.50 is added to the principal.
- Get students started on month 2. Students should use $100 for the principal and $\dfrac{2}{12}$ for the time. Interest earned $= \$100(0.06)\left(\dfrac{2}{12}\right) = \$1.00$.
- Students should work with a partner to complete the table and the graph.

Standards of Learning

8.3(a) The student will solve practical problems involving rational numbers, percents, ratios, and proportions.

Previous Learning

Students should be familiar with finding a percent of a number, rounding decimal values, and converting between fractions, decimals, and percents.

Activity Materials
Textbook
• calculator

Start Thinking! and Warm Up

4.4 Record and Practice Journal

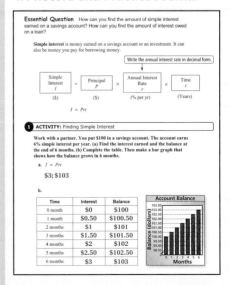

Differentiated Instruction

Auditory
Discuss the meaning of the word *interest*. An interest rate is often expressed as an annual percentage of the principal.

Laurie's Notes

Activity 2

- You may wish to use the information to demonstrate the impact of carrying a large credit card debt.
- **Discuss:** How a credit card operates, how you can get one, and how it works (consumer, store, bank).
- **Community:** If your local bank has an education or outreach coordinator, consider having them come in as a guest speaker.
- Read through the information given. Calculate the interest owed for one month, $\$5000(0.18)\left(\dfrac{1}{12}\right) = \$75$, or at the higher interest rate, $\$5000(0.20)\left(\dfrac{1}{12}\right) \approx \$83.33$.
- **Discuss:** Why should you shop around for the lowest interest rates? Why should you keep your principal as small as possible?
- Remind the students that the consumer needs to pay the interest ($75 to $83.34) *plus* they need to be paying off the principal.

Activity 3

- The national debt is a complicated concept. The intent of this activity is to raise awareness, and to use the simple interest formula with a really large number.
- **Caution:** If you use a calculator for this problem, the debt and simple interest will appear in scientific notation.
- **Representation:** It will be helpful to write out the simple interest formula using the decimal numbers so that students can see all of the zeros: $I = (12,000,000,000,000)(0.03)(1)$. This has a greater impact than scientific notation.
- **Extension:** Many local newspapers print the national debt and the approximate per person debt each day. Record this information once a week for about 2 months to get a sense for how the numbers are changing. You can even do this for the entire school year.

4.4 Record and Practice Journal

2 ACTIVITY: Financial Literacy

Work with a partner. Use the following information to write a report about credit cards. In the report, describe how a credit card works. Include examples that show the amount of interest paid each month on a credit card.

U.S. Credit Card Data

- A typical family in the United States owes about $5000 in credit card debt.
- A typical credit card interest rate is 18% to 20% per year. This is called the annual percentage rate.

Check student's work.

3 ACTIVITY: The National Debt

Work with a partner. In 2010, the United States owed about $12 trillion in debt. The interest rate on the national debt is about 3% per year.

a. Write $12 trillion in decimal form. How many zeros does this number have?

$12,000,000,000,000; 12

b. How much interest does the United States pay each year on its national debt?

$360 billion

c. How much interest does the United States pay each day on its national debt?

$986,301,369.90

d. The United States has a population of about 310 million people. Estimate the amount of interest that each person pays per year toward interest on the national debt.

about $1161

What Is Your Answer?

4. **IN YOUR OWN WORDS** How can you find the amount of simple interest earned on a savings account? How can you find the amount of interest owed on a loan? Give examples with your answer.

Use $I = Prt.$

Closure

- **Exit Ticket:** What do you need to know in order to compute simple interest? Principal, annual interest rate, and time

Technology
For
the Teacher

Dynamic Classroom

The Dynamic Planning Tool
Editable Teacher's Resources at *BigIdeasMath.com*

2 ACTIVITY: Financial Literacy

Work with a partner. Use the following information to write a report about credit cards. In the report, describe how a credit card works. Include examples that show the amount of interest paid each month on a credit card.

U.S. Credit Card Data

- A typical family in the United States owes about $5000 in credit card debt.

- A typical credit card interest rate is 18% to 20% per year. This is called the annual percentage rate.

3 ACTIVITY: The National Debt

Work with a partner. In 2010, the United States owed about $12 trillion in debt. The interest rate on the national debt is about 3% per year.

a. Write $12 trillion in decimal form. How many zeros does this number have?

b. How much interest does the United States pay each year on its national debt?

c. How much interest does the United States pay each day on its national debt?

d. The United States has a population of about 310 million people. Estimate the amount of interest that each person pays per year toward interest on the national debt.

What Is Your Answer?

4. **IN YOUR OWN WORDS** How can you find the amount of simple interest earned on a savings account? How can you find the amount of interest owed on a loan? Give examples with your answer.

Use what you learned about simple interest to complete Exercises 4–7 on page 186.

4.4 Lesson

Check It Out
Lesson Tutorials
BigIdeasMath.com

Key Vocabulary ◀))
interest, *p. 184*
principal, *p. 184*
simple interest,
   p. 184

Interest is money paid or earned for the use of money. The **principal** is the amount of money borrowed or deposited.

 Key Idea

Simple Interest

Words **Simple interest** is money paid or earned only on the principal.

Algebra

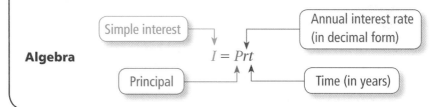

EXAMPLE **1** **Finding Interest Earned**

You put $500 in a savings account. The account earns 3% simple interest per year. (a) What is the interest earned after 3 years? (b) What is the balance after 3 years?

a. $I = Prt$ Write simple interest formula.

    $= 500(0.03)(3)$ Substitute 500 for P, 0.03 for r, and 3 for t.

    $= 45$ Multiply.

  ⋮•   The interest earned is $45 after 3 years.

b. To find the balance, add the interest to the principal.

  ⋮•   So, the balance is $500 + $45 = $545 after 3 years.

EXAMPLE **2** **Finding an Annual Interest Rate**

You put $1000 in an account. The account earns $100 simple interest in 4 years. What is the annual interest rate?

       $I = Prt$ Write simple interest formula.

       $100 = 1000(r)(4)$ Substitute 100 for I, 1000 for P, and 4 for t.

       $100 = 4000r$ Simplify.

       $0.025 = r$ Divide each side by 4000.

⋮•   The annual interest rate of the account is 0.025, or 2.5%.

      ◀)) Multi-Language Glossary at BigIdeasMath✓com.

Laurie's Notes

Introduction

Connect
- **Yesterday:** Students explored the simple interest formula, applying it to several consumer applications.
- **Today:** Students will use the simple interest formula and knowledge of equation solving to solve for different variables in the formula.

Motivate
- Just imagine that when you are older, you win a $5 million lottery. If you deposit that money for 10 years at 6% simple interest, how much will you have at the end of 10 years? $8,000,000

Lesson Notes

Key Idea
- **Vocabulary:** interest, money paid or earned, principal, amount of money borrowed or deposited, balance
- **Representation:** Write the formula in words first.
  Simple Interest = (Principal)(Annual interest rate)(Time)
- **Explain:** Simple interest is only one type of interest. There are also compound and exponential interest calculations. The interest rate is written as a decimal. Time is written in terms of years. When time is given in months, remember to express it as a fraction of a year or as a decimal. For example, 9 months = $\frac{9}{12}$ or 0.75 year.
- **Connection:** This formula is similar to the volume formula for a rectangular prism; three variables are multiplied together. Knowing 3 of the 4 variables, you can solve for the fourth.

Example 1
- Read the information given.
- There are two parts to the problem: Calculate the interest earned and then determine the amount (balance) in the account.
- ❓ "What operation is performed in writing *Prt*?" multiplication
- ❓ "In calculating 500(0.03)(3), what order is the multiplication performed?" Order doesn't matter, multiplication is commutative.
- **Explain:** Your balance is the original principal *plus* the interest earned.
- **Extension:** If time permits, "What would your balance be if the interest rate had been 6% instead of 3%?" $590

Example 2
- This example uses the Division Property of Equality to solve for the interest rate.
- ❓ "Why does 1000(*r*)(4) = 4000*r*?" Commutative Property of Multiplication
- **Common Error:** Students divide 4000 by 100 instead of 100 by 4000.
- ❓ "How do you write a decimal as a percent?" Move the decimal point two places to the right. (Multiply by 100.) Then add a percent symbol.

Goal Today's lesson is using the **simple interest** formula.

Start Thinking! and Warm Up

Lesson 4.4	Warm Up
For use before Lesson 4.4	

Lesson 4.4 Start Thinking!
For use before Lesson 4.4

You earned $150 babysitting. You want to open a savings account. What factors must you consider before opening an account?

Extra Example 1

You put $200 in a savings account. The account earns 2% simple interest per year.
- **a.** What is the interest earned after 5 years? $20
- **b.** What is the balance after 5 years? $220

Extra Example 2

You put $700 in an account. The account earns $224 simple interest in 8 years. What is the annual interest rate? 4%

On Your Own

1. $511.25

2. 2%

Extra Example 3

Using the pictograph in Example 3, how long does it take an account with a principal of $400 to earn $36 interest? 6 years

Extra Example 4

You borrow $300 to buy a guitar. The simple interest rate is 12%. You pay off the loan after 4 years. How much do you pay for the loan? $444

 On Your Own

3. 2.5 yr

4. $270

English Language Learners

Vocabulary

Review with English learners the mathematical meanings of principal, interest, and balance because these words have multiple meanings in the English language. They should understand that interest is paid to customers when they deposit money into an account. When a person borrows money, the person pays interest to the bank.

Laurie's Notes

On Your Own

- **Neighbor Check**: Have students work independently and then have their neighbor check their work. Have students discuss any discrepancies.
- Check accuracy of decimals in these problems.

Example 3

- Discuss the diagram.
- **?** "Why would a bank offer different interest rates for different principals?" Students may not understand that banks are using deposited money to loan to other people.
- Work through the problem.
- **?** "What is 6.25 as a mixed number?" $6\frac{1}{4}$
- **Connection:** Students may wonder why anyone would want to know how long it takes to earn $100 in interest. Use an example of depositing money for a future purchase (car, house, college education).

Example 4

- Remind students that the simple interest formula is used to calculate interest *earned* when you *deposit* money and to calculate interest *owed* when you *borrow* money.
- **Discuss:** There are two parts to the problem: 1) Calculate the interest owed and 2) determine the total cost you must pay back for the loan.
- **Extension:** Have students find the monthly payment. $1050 ÷ 60 = $17.50

On Your Own

- **Neighbor Check:** Have students work independently and then have their neighbor check their work. Have students discuss any discrepancies.

Closure

- **Exit Ticket:** Assume $1000 was deposited at 5% simple interest when you were born. Approximately how much is the account worth today? age 11: $1550, age 12: $1600, age 13: $1650, age 14: $1700

Technology **F**or the **T**eacher

The Dynamic Planning Tool
Editable Teacher's Resources at *BigIdeasMath.com*

On Your Own

Now You're Ready
Exercises 4–16

1. In Example 1, what is the balance of the account after 9 months?

2. You put $350 in an account. The account earns $17.50 simple interest in 2.5 years. What is the annual interest rate?

EXAMPLE ③ **Finding an Amount of Time**

A bank offers three savings accounts. The simple interest rate is determined by the principal. How long does it take an account with a principal of $800 to earn $100 interest?

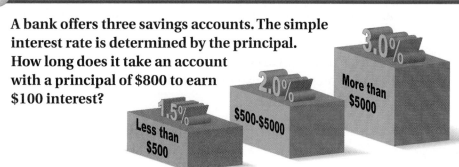

The pictogram shows that the interest rate for a principal of $800 is 2%.

$I = Prt$	Write simple interest formula.
$100 = 800(0.02)(t)$	Substitute 100 for I, 800 for P, and 0.02 for r.
$100 = 16t$	Simplify.
$6.25 = t$	Divide each side by 16.

∴ The account earns $100 in interest in 6.25 years.

EXAMPLE ④ **Finding Amount Paid on a Loan**

You borrow $600 to buy a violin. The simple interest rate is 15%. You pay off the loan after 5 years. How much do you pay for the loan?

$I = Prt$	Write simple interest formula.
$= 600(0.15)(5)$	Substitute 600 for P, 0.15 for r, and 5 for t.
$= 450$	Multiply.

To find the amount you pay, add the interest to the loan amount.

∴ So, you pay $600 + $450 = $1050 for the loan.

On Your Own

Now You're Ready
Exercises 17–27

3. In Example 3, how long does it take an account with a principal of $10,000 to earn $750 interest?

4. **WHAT IF?** In Example 4, you pay off the loan after 2 years. How much money do you save?

 Vocabulary and Concept Check

1. **VOCABULARY** Define each variable in $I = Prt$.

2. **WRITING** In each situation, tell whether you would want a *higher* or *lower* interest rate. Explain your reasoning.

   a. You borrow money   b. You open a savings account

3. **REASONING** An account earns 6% simple interest. You want to find the interest earned on $200 after 8 months. What conversions do you need to make before you can use the formula $I = Prt$?

 Practice and Problem Solving

An account earns simple interest. (a) Find the interest earned. (b) Find the balance of the account.

1   4. $600 at 5% for 2 years   5. $1500 at 4% for 5 years

    6. $350 at 3% for 10 years   7. $1800 at 6.5% for 30 months

    8. $700 at 8% for 6 years   9. $1675 at 4.6% for 4 years

   10. $925 at 2% for 2.4 years   11. $5200 at 7.36% for 54 months

12. **ERROR ANALYSIS** Describe and correct the error in finding the simple interest earned on $500 at 6% for 18 months.

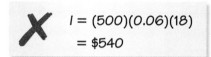
$$I = (500)(0.06)(18)$$
$$= \$540$$

Find the annual simple interest rate.

2   13. $I = \$24$, $P = \$400$, $t = 2$ years   14. $I = \$562.50$, $P = \$1500$, $t = 5$ years

   15. $I = \$54$, $P = \$900$, $t = 18$ months   16. $I = \$160.67$, $P = \$2000$, $t = 8$ months

Find the amount of time.

3   17. $I = \$30$, $P = \$500$, $r = 3\%$ 18. $I = \$720$, $P = \$1000$, $r = 9\%$

   19. $I = \$54$, $P = \$800$, $r = 4.5\%$ 20. $I = \$450$, $P = \$2400$, $r = 7.5\%$

21. **BANKING** A savings account earns 5% annual simple interest. The principal is $1200. What is the balance after 4 years?

22. **SAVINGS** You put $400 in an account. The account earns $18 simple interest in 9 months. What is the annual interest rate?

23. **CD** You put $3000 in a CD (certificate of deposit) at the promotional rate. How long will it take to earn $336 in interest?

Certificate of Deposit

This certificate is the original Specimen and valid document from the treasury and Security department of this here trust financial group & associates. The agreement herein construed are thorough, correct and binding on the parties. Alterations made to this after it has been legally signed.

Promotional Rate 5.6%
Simple Interest

DIRECTOR'S SIGNATURE

Assignment Guide and Homework Check

Level	Day 1 Activity Assignment	Day 2 Lesson Assignment	Homework Check
Basic	4–7, 38–40	1–3, 9–27 odd, 12, 22	9, 13, 17, 22, 25
Average	4–7, 38–40	1–3, 8–12 even, 13–19 odd, 23, 25, 27, 32–34	8, 13, 17, 25, 32
Advanced	4–7, 38–40	1–3, 12, 23, 24, 26, 28–32, 34–37	24, 30, 34, 36

Common Errors

- **Exercises 4–11** Students may forget to change the percent to a decimal. Remind them that before they can put the percent into the equation, they must change the percent to a fraction or a decimal.
- **Exercises 7 and 11** Students may not change months into years and calculate a much greater interest amount. Remind them that the simple interest formula is for *years* and that the time must be changed to years.
- **Exercises 15 and 16** Students may not change the time from months to years. Remind them that the time is in years.
- **Exercises 24–27** Students may only find the amount of interest paid for the loan. Remind them that the total amount paid on a loan is the original principal plus the interest.

4.4 Record and Practice Journal

An account earns simple interest. (a) Find the interest earned. (b) Find the balance of the account.

1. $400 at 7% for 3 years
   a. $84
   b. $484

2. $1200 at 5.6% for 4 years
   a. $268.80
   b. $1468.80

Find the annual simple interest rate.

3. $I = \$18$, $P = \$200$, $t = 18$ months
   6%

4. $I = \$310$, $P = \$1000$, $t = 5$ years
   6.2%

Find the amount of time.

5. $I = \$60$, $P = \$750$, $r = 4\%$
   2 years

6. $I = \$825$, $P = \$2500$, $r = 5.5\%$
   6 years

7. You put $500 in a savings account. The account earns $15.75 simple interest in 6 months. What is the annual interest rate?
   6.3%

8. You put $1000 in an account. The simple interest rate is 4.5%. After a year, you put in another $550. What is your total interest after 2 years from the time you opened the account?
   $114.75

Vocabulary and Concept Check

1. I = simple interest,
   P = principal,
   r = annual interest rate (in decimal form),
   t = time (in years)

2. **a.** lower interest rate because you would pay less

   b. higher interest rate because you would receive more

3. You have to change 6% to a decimal and 8 months to a fraction of a year.

Practice and Problem Solving

4. **a.** $60 **b.** $660

5. **a.** $300 **b.** $1800

6. **a.** $105 **b.** $455

7. **a.** $292.50 **b.** $2092.50

8. **a.** $336 **b.** $1036

9. **a.** $308.20 **b.** $1983.20

10. **a.** $44.40 **b.** $969.40

11. **a.** $1722.24 **b.** $6922.24

12. They didn't convert 18 months to years.
    $$I = 500(0.06)\left(\frac{18}{12}\right)$$
    $$= \$45$$

13. 3%   14. 7.5%

15. 4%   16. 12.05%

17. 2 yr   18. 8 yr

19. 1.5 yr   20. 2.5 yr

21. $1440

22. 6%

23. 2 yr

24. $1770   **25.** $2720

26. $3660   **27.** $6700.80

28. $2550   **29.** $8500

30. 4 yr   **31.** 5.25%

32. See *Taking Math Deeper*.

33. 4 yr

34. $77.25

35. 12.5 yr; Substitute $2000 for *P* and *I*, 0.08 for *r*, and solve for *t*.

36. $300

37. Year 1 = $520
Year 2 = $540.80
Year 3 = $562.43

Fair Game Review

38. 27, 35, 43

39. 40, 25, 10

40. A

Mini-Assessment

Find the annual simple interest rate.

1. $I = \$60$, $P = \$500$, $t = 3$ years   4%

2. $I = \$45$, $P = \$600$, $t = 2$ years   3.75%

Find the amount of time.

3. $I = \$117$, $P = \$1300$, $r = 3\%$ 3 yr

4. $I = \$71.50$, $P = \$1100$, $r = 3.25\%$ 2 yr

5. A savings account earns 4.5% annual simple interest. The principal is $1300. What is the balance after 3 years? $1475.50

Taking Math Deeper

Exercise 32

This problem isn't particularly difficult. However, it is a good opportunity for students to pick up some **financial literacy**. That is, when you pay for items with a credit card, you almost always have to pay interest. In other words, you are taking out a loan.

 Find the amount spent.

Total = $175.54

Zoo Trip	
Tickets	67.70
Food	62.34
Gas	45.50
Total Cost	175.54

 Find the interest paid.

$$I = Prt$$ Write the formula.

$$= 175.54 \cdot 0.12 \cdot \frac{3}{12}$$ Substitute amounts.

$$\approx \$5.27$$ Simplify.

③ Find the total cost of the trip.

Total = 175.54 + 5.27
= $180.81

How much interest would I pay if I didn't pay the charge for 1 year? for 2 years?

Project

Many credit cards charge different rates of interest. Use the school library or the internet to research the amount of interest charged by three different credit card companies. Compare the cost of the trip to the zoo based on the different interest rates. Why should you be careful when selecting a credit card and charging items to the card?

Reteaching and Enrichment Strategies

If students need help...	If students got it...
Resources by Chapter • Practice A and Practice B • Puzzle Time Record and Practice Journal Practice Differentiating the Lesson Lesson Tutorials Skills Review Handbook	Resources by Chapter • Enrichment and Extension • School-to-Work Start the next section

Find the amount paid for the loan.

④ **24.** $1500 at 9% for 2 years

25. $2000 at 12% for 3 years

26. $2400 at 10.5% for 5 years

27. $4800 at 9.9% for 4 years

Copy and complete the table.

	Principal	Interest Rate	Time	Simple Interest
28.	$12,000	4.25%	5 years	
29.		6.5%	18 months	$828.75
30.	$15,500	8.75%		$5425.00
31.	$18,000		54 months	$4252.50

32. ZOO A family charges a trip to the zoo on a credit card. The simple interest rate is 12%. The charges are paid after 3 months. What is the total amount paid for the trip?

Zoo Trip

Tickets	67.70
Food	62.34
Gas	45.50
Total Cost	?

33. MONEY MARKET You deposit $5000 in an account earning 7.5% simple interest. How long will it take for the balance of the account to be $6500?

11.8% Simple Interest
Equal monthly
payments for 2 years.

34. LOANS A music company offers a loan to buy a drum set for $1500. What is the monthly payment?

35. REASONING How many years will it take for $2000 to double at a simple interest rate of 8%? Explain how you found your answer.

36. LOANS You have two loans, for 2 years each. The total interest for the two loans is $138. On the first loan, you pay 7.5% simple interest on a principal of $800. On the second loan, you pay 3% simple interest. What is the principal for the second loan?

37. *Critical Thinking* You put $500 in an account that earns 4% annual interest. The interest earned each year is added to the principal to create a new principal. Find the total amount in your account after each year for 3 years.

Fair Game Review *What you learned in previous grades & lessons*

Write the next three terms of the arithmetic sequence. *(Skills Review Handbook)*

38. −5, 3, 11, 19, . . .

39. 100, 85, 70, 55, . . .

40. MULTIPLE CHOICE What is the solution of $4x + 5 = -11$? *(Section 1.2)*

Ⓐ −4 Ⓑ −1.5 Ⓒ 1.5 Ⓓ 4

Check It Out
Progress Check
BigIdeasMath.com

Find the price, discount, markup, or cost to store. *(Section 4.3)*

1. Original price: $30
   Discount: 10%
   Sale price: ?

2. Original price: $55
   Discount: ?
   Sale price: $46.75

3. Original price: ?
   Discount: 75%
   Sale price: $74.75

4. Cost to store: $152
   Markup: 50%
   Selling price: ?

5. Cost to store: $20
   Markup: ?
   Selling price: $32

6. Cost to store: ?
   Markup: 80%
   Selling price: $21.60

An account earns simple interest. Find the interest earned, principal, interest rate, or time. *(Section 4.4)*

7. Interest earned: ?
   Principal: $1200
   Interest rate: 2%
   Time: 5 years

8. Interest earned: $25
   Principal: $500
   Interest rate: 5%
   Time: ?

9. Interest earned: $76
   Principal: $800
   Interest rate: ?
   Time: 2 years

10. Interest earned: $119.88
    Principal: ?
    Interest rate: 3.6%
    Time: 3 years

11. **DIGITAL CAMERA** A digital camera costs $229. The camera is on sale for 30% off and you have a coupon for an additional 15% off the original price. What is the final price? *(Section 4.3)*

12. **WATER SKIS** The original price of the water skis was $200. What is the percent of discount? *(Section 4.3)*

SALE
$150

2 Ways to Own:
1. $75 cash back with 3.5% simple interest
2. No interest for 2 years

13. **SAXOPHONE** A saxophone costs $1200. A store offers two loan options. Which option saves more money if you pay the loan in 2 years? *(Section 4.4)*

14. **LOAN** You borrow $200. The simple interest rate is 12%. You pay off the loan after 2 years. How much do you pay for the loan? *(Section 4.4)*

Alternative Assessment Options

Math Chat — Student Reflective Focus Question
Structured Interview — **Writing Prompt**

Writing Prompt
Ask students to write a story about making purchases and saving money. The students should include discounts and markups in the story. If they have money left over from their purchases, they should place it in a savings account. The students should include simple interest in the story. Then have students share their stories with the class.

Study Help Sample Answers
Remind students to complete Graphic Organizers for the rest of the chapter.

5.

6.

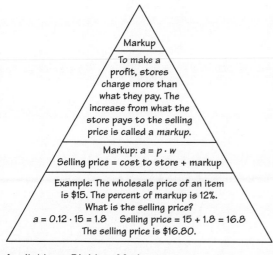

7. Available at *BigIdeasMath.com*

Reteaching and Enrichment Strategies

If students need help...	If students got it...
Resources by Chapter • Study Help • Practice A and Practice B • Puzzle Time Lesson Tutorials *BigIdeasMath.com* Practice Quiz Practice from the Test Generator	Resources by Chapter • Enrichment and Extension • School-to-Work Game Closet at *BigIdeasMath.com* Start the Chapter Review

Technology For the Teacher
Answer Presentation Tool

Assessment Book

Chapter 4 Quiz
For use after Section 4.4

Find the price, discount, markup, or cost to store.

1. Original price: $130
Discount: 60%
Sale price: ?

2. Original price: $32
Discount: ?
Sale price: $8

3. Original price: ?
Discount: 20%
Sale price: $14.40

4. Cost to store: $45
Markup: 35%
Selling price: ?

5. Cost to store: $50
Markup: ?
Selling price: $60

6. Cost to store: ?
Markup: 110%
Selling price: $105

An account earns simple interest. Find the interest earned, principal, interest rate, or time.

7. Interest earned: ?
Principal: $1450
Interest rate: 9%
Time: 5 years

8. Interest earned: $10
Principal: $250
Interest rate: 4%
Time: ?

9. Interest earned: $40
Principal: $400
Interest rate: ?
Time: 2 years

10. Interest earned: $45
Principal: ?
Interest rate: 3%
Time: 2 years

11. Interest earned: $750
Principal: ?
Interest rate: 12.5%
Time: 4 years

12. Interest earned: $120
Principal: $640
Interest rate: 6.25%
Time: ?

13. Store A sells a watch for $50 and offers a 5% discount. Store B sells the same watch for $60 and offers a 20% discount. From which store should you buy?

14. A store sells a television for $1000. Customers can choose to receive a 10% discount and pay it off with a loan at a simple interest rate of 4%, or they can choose to pay the full price and pay it off in 3 years with no interest. If the customer plans to pay it off in 3 years, which option is best?

15. A store offers a loan for $900 to buy a computer. The terms of the loan are for 9% simple interest and equal monthly payments for three years. What is the monthly payment?

Answers
1. _____
2. _____
3. _____
4. _____
5. _____
6. _____
7. _____
8. _____
9. _____
10. _____
11. _____
12. _____
13. _____
14. _____
15. _____

For the Teacher
Additional Review Options
- **Quiz**Show
- Big Ideas Test Generator
- Game Closet at *BigIdeasMath.com*
- Vocabulary Puzzle Builder
- Resources by Chapter
  Puzzle Time
  Study Help

Answers

1. $a = 0.24 \cdot 25$; 6

2. $9 = p \cdot 20$; 45%

3. $10.2 = 0.85 \cdot w$; 12

4. $a = 0.83 \cdot 20$; 16.6

5. 120 parking spaces

Review of Common Errors

Exercises 1–5
- Students may not know what number to substitute for each variable. Walk through each type of question with the students. Emphasize that the word "is" means "equals," and "of" means "multiplied by."
- Students may mix up the whole and the part when trying to write the percent equation for the word problems. Ask students to identify each part of the equation before writing it in the equation format.

Exercises 6–9
- Students may mix up where to place the numbers in the equation to find percent of change. When students do not put the numbers in the right place, they might find a negative number in the numerator. Emphasize that students must know if it is increasing or decreasing before they can do anything else. The numerator should never have a negative answer. If students get a negative number, then they need to switch the order of the numbers in the problem and then subtract.

Exercises 10 and 11
- Students may just find the markup and not the selling price. Remind them that they must add the markup to the cost to store.
- Remind students that the sale price is not the percent of discount multiplied by the original price.

Exercises 12–18
- Students may forget to change the percent to a decimal. Remind them that before they can put the percent into the equation, they must change the percent to a fraction or a decimal.

4 Chapter Review

Review Key Vocabulary

percent, *p. 164*
percent of change, *p. 170*
percent of increase, *p. 170*

percent of decrease, *p. 170*
discount, *p. 178*
markup, *p. 178*

interest, *p. 184*
principal, *p. 184*
simple interest, *p. 184*

Review Examples and Exercises

4.1 The Percent Equation *(pp. 162–167)*

What number is 72% of 25?

$$a = p \cdot w \qquad \text{Write percent equation.}$$
$$= 0.72 \cdot 25 \qquad \text{Substitute 0.72 for } p \text{ and 25 for } w.$$
$$= 18 \qquad \text{Multiply.}$$

∴ So, 72% of 25 is 18.

28 is what percent of 70?

$$a = p \cdot w \qquad \text{Write percent equation.}$$
$$28 = p \cdot 70 \qquad \text{Substitute 28 for } a \text{ and 70 for } w.$$
$$0.4 = p \qquad \text{Divide each side by 70.}$$

∴ Because 0.4 = 40%, 28 is 40% of 70.

22.1 is 26% of what number?

$$a = p \cdot w \qquad \text{Write percent equation.}$$
$$22.1 = 0.26 \cdot w \qquad \text{Substitute 22.1 for } a \text{ and 0.26 for } p.$$
$$85 = w \qquad \text{Divide each side by 0.26.}$$

∴ So, 22.1 is 26% of 85.

Exercises

Write and solve an equation to answer the question.

1. What number is 24% of 25?
2. 9 is what percent of 20?
3. 85% of what number is 10.2?
4. 83% of 20 is what number?

5. **PARKING** 15% of the school parking spaces are handicap spaces. The school has 18 handicap spaces. How many parking spaces are there?

4.2 **Percents of Increase and Decrease** (pp. 168–173)

The table shows the number of skim boarders at a beach on Saturday and Sunday. What was the percent of change in boarders from Saturday to Sunday?

The number of skim boarders on Sunday is less than the number of skim boarders on Saturday. So, the percent of change is a percent of decrease.

Day	Number of Skim Boarders
Saturday	12
Sunday	9

$$\text{percent of decrease} = \frac{\text{original amount} - \text{new amount}}{\text{original amount}}$$

$$= \frac{12 - 9}{12} \qquad \text{Substitute.}$$

$$= \frac{3}{12} \qquad \text{Subtract.}$$

$$= 0.25 = 25\% \qquad \text{Write as a percent.}$$

⁖ The number of skim boarders decreased by 25% from Saturday to Sunday.

Exercises

Identify the percent of change as an *increase* or *decrease*. Then find the percent of change. Round to the nearest tenth of a percent, if necessary.

6. 6 yards to 36 yards

7. 6 hits to 3 hits

8. 120 meals to 52 meals

9. 35 words to 115 words

4.3 **Discounts and Markups** (pp. 176–181)

What is the original price of the tennis racquet?

The sale price is 100% − 30% = 70% of the original price.

Answer the question: 21 is 70% of what number?

$$a = p \cdot w \qquad \text{Write percent equation.}$$

$$21 = 0.7 \cdot w \qquad \text{Substitute 21 for } a \text{ and 0.7 for } p.$$

$$30 = w \qquad \text{Divide each side by 0.7.}$$

⁖ The original price of the tennis racquet is $30.

SALE 30% off
Now $21

Exercises

Find the price.

10. Original price: $50
Discount: 15%
Sale price: ?

11. Original price: ?
Discount: 20%
Sale price: $75

Review Game

Percents of Increase and Decrease

Big Ideas
Game Closet

Materials per Group
- 1 deck of cards with the jacks, queens, kings, and aces removed
- paper
- pencil
- calculator

Directions
Each group starts with 108 points. The cards are placed face down in the middle of the group. One member of the group turns a card over. If the card is red, the face value of the card is subtracted from the number of points. If the card is black, the face value of the card is added to the number of points. Group members take turns calculating the percent increase or decrease and turning cards over. The starting number of points at each player's turn is the same as the ending number of points at the previous player's turn. The group should be back to 108 points after going through all of the cards.

Who Wins?
The group with the highest mean percent increase wins. To find the mean percent increase, add the percent increases and divide the sum by 18.

For the Student
Additional Practice
- Lesson Tutorials
- Study Help (textbook)
- Student Website
    Multi-Language Glossary
    Practice Assessments

Answers
6. increase; 500%
7. decrease; 50%
8. decrease; 56.7%
9. increase; 228.6%
10. $42.50
11. $93.75
12. **a.** $36
   b. $336
13. **a.** $280
   b. $2280
14. 1.7%
15. 7.1%
16. 3 years
17. 6 years
18. 4%

My Thoughts on the Chapter

What worked. . .

What did not work. . .

What I would do differently. . .

4.4 Simple Interest (pp. 182–187)

You put $200 in a savings account. The account earns 2% simple interest per year.

a. What is the interest after 4 years?

b. What is the balance after 4 years?

a. $I = Prt$ 　　　　Write simple interest formula.

　　　$= 200(0.02)(4)$ 　　Substitute 200 for P, 0.02 for r, and 4 for t.

　　　$= 16$ 　　　　Multiply.

　　⋰ The interest earned is $16 after 4 years.

b. The balance is the principal plus the interest.

　　⋰ So, the balance is $200 + $16 = $216 after 4 years.

You put $500 in an account. The account earns $55 simple interest in 5 years. What is the annual interest rate?

　　　　$I = Prt$ 　　　　Write simple interest formula.

　　　$55 = 500(r)(5)$ 　　Substitute 55 for I, 500 for P, and 5 for t.

　　　$55 = 2500r$ 　　　Simplify.

　　$0.022 = r$ 　　　　Divide each side by 2500.

⋰ The annual interest rate of the account is 0.022, or 2.2%.

Exercises

An account earns simple interest.

a. Find the interest earned.

b. Find the balance of the account.

12. $300 at 4% for 3 years

13. $2000 at 3.5% for 4 years

Find the annual simple interest rate.

14. $I = $17, P = $500, t = 2$ years

15. $I = $426, P = $1200, t = 5$ years

Find the amount of time.

16. $I = $60, P = $400, r = 5\%$

17. $I = $237.90, P = $1525, r = 2.6\%$

18. SAVINGS You put $100 in an account. The account earns $2 simple interest in 6 months. What is the annual interest rate?

Check It Out
Test Practice
BigIdeasMath ✓com

Write and solve an equation to answer the question.

1. 16% of 150 is what number?

2. 10 is 40% of what number?

3. 27 is what percent of 75?

4. What number is 35% of 56?

Identify the percent of change as an *increase* or *decrease*. Then find the percent of change. Round to the nearest tenth of a percent, if necessary.

5. 4 strikeouts to 10 strikeouts

6. $24.00 to $18.00

Find the price, discount, or markup.

7. Original price: $15
   Discount: 5%
   Sale price: ?

8. Original price: $189
   Discount: ?
   Sale price: $75.60

9. Cost to store: $15
   Markup: ?
   Selling price: $24.75

10. Cost to store: $5.50
    Markup: 75%
    Selling price: ?

An account earns simple interest. Find the interest earned, principal, interest rate, or time.

11. Interest earned: ?
    Principal: $450
    Interest rate: 6%
    Time: 8 years

12. Interest earned: $27
    Principal: ?
    Interest rate: 1.5%
    Time: 2 years

13. Interest earned: $116.25
    Principal: $1550
    Interest rate: ?
    Time: 9 months

14. Interest earned: $45.60
    Principal: $2400
    Interest rate: 3.8%
    Time: ?

15. **MOVIE PREVIEWS** There are eight previews before a movie. Seventy-five percent of the previews are for comedies. How many previews are for comedies?

16. **BOOK** What was the original price of the book?

17. **TEXT MESSAGES** The cost of a text message increases from $0.10 per message to $0.25 per message. What is the percent increase in the cost of sending a text message?

The WORLD around us
20% off
A pictu

Only
$7.00

18. **INVESTMENT** You put $800 in an account that earns 4% simple interest. Find the total amount in your account after each year for 3 years.

Test Item References

Chapter Test Questions	Section to Review
1–4, 15	4.1
5, 6, 16	4.2
7–10, 16, 17	4.3
11–14, 18	4.4

Test-Taking Strategies

Remind students to quickly look over the entire test before they start so that they can budget their time. Students should estimate and check for reasonableness as they work through the test. Some students will benefit from putting essential information on the back of their test before they begin.

Common Assessment Errors

- **Exercises 1–4** Students may not know what numbers to substitute for the variables. Review each type of question with students. Emphasize that the word "is" means "equals" and "of" means "multiplied by." Ask students to identify the whole, the part of the whole, and the percent.
- **Exercises 5 and 6** Students might place the numbers in the percent of change formulas incorrectly. Remind them that they should have the difference between the greater amount and the lesser amount in the numerator, so the numerator should never be negative. Also point out that the original amount should always be in the denominator.
- **Exercises 7 and 10** Students may write the discount or markup amount as the new price instead of subtracting it from or adding it to the original price. Remind them to subtract or add as appropriate to find the sale or selling price.
- **Exercises 8 and 9** Students may treat the difference in the prices as the percent of discount or markup. Remind students that the discount or markup should be a *percent*, and that this percent is found by using the original price and the difference in prices in the percent equation.
- **Exercises 11–14** Students may forget to write the percent as a decimal, forget to convert time to years (if necessary), or use the wrong inverse operation to solve for the unknown value. Review the simple interest formula and the Division Property of Equality.

Reteaching and Enrichment Strategies

If students need help. . .	If students got it. . .
Resources by Chapter • Practice A and Practice B • Puzzle Time Record and Practice Journal Practice Differentiating the Lesson Lesson Tutorials Practice from the Test Generator Skills Review Handbook	Resources by Chapter • Enrichment and Extension • School-to-Work Game Closet at *BigIdeasMath.com* Start Standardized Test Practice

Answers

1. $a = 0.16 \cdot 150$; 24
2. $10 = 0.4 \cdot w$; 25
3. $27 = p \cdot 75$; 36%
4. $a = 0.35 \cdot 56$; 19.6
5. increase; 150%
6. decrease; 25%
7. $14.25
8. 60%
9. 65%
10. $9.63
11. $216
12. $900
13. 10%
14. 6 months
15. 6 previews
16. $8.75
17. 150%
18. Year 1: $832
    Year 2: $864
    Year 3: $896

Assessment Book

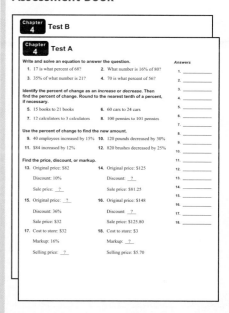

Available at *BigIdeasMath.com*

After Answering Easy Questions, Relax
Answer Easy Questions First
Estimate the Answer
Read All Choices before Answering
Read Question before Answering
Solve Directly or Eliminate Choices
Solve Problem before Looking at
  Choices
Use Intelligent Guessing
Work Backwards

About this Strategy

When taking a multiple choice test, be sure to read each question carefully and thoroughly. It is also very important to read each answer choice carefully. Do not pick the first answer you think is correct. If two answer choices are the same, eliminate them both. There can only be one correct answer.

Answers

1. C
2. G
3. 152 lb
4. D

Technology
For
the Teacher

Big Ideas Test Generator

Item Analysis

1. **A.** The student finds 30% of $8.50 but does not subtract this amount from $8.50.

   B. The student thinks that 30% is equivalent to $3.00 and subtracts this amount from $8.50.

   C. Correct answer

   D. The student thinks that 30% is equivalent to $0.30 and subtracts this amount from $8.50.

2. **F.** The student divides incorrectly or converts measures incorrectly to choose an incorrect box.

   G. Correct answer

   H. The student divides incorrectly or converts measures incorrectly to choose an incorrect box.

   I. The student divides incorrectly or converts measures incorrectly to choose an incorrect box.

3. **Gridded Response:** Correct answer: 152 lb

   Common Error: The student finds only the loss, getting an answer of 8.

4. **A.** The student chooses a proportion that will find what percent 17 is of 43.

   B. The student chooses a proportion that will find 43% of 17.

   C. The student chooses a proportion that will find 17% of 43.

   D. Correct answer

5. **F.** The student misreads the graph.

   G. The student finds the value of 20 minutes and adds 5 to that value because 25 minutes is 5 minutes later.

   H. Correct answer

   I. The student misreads the graph.

6. **A.** Correct answer

   B. The student makes a arithmetic error relating c and m.

   C. The student picks an equation that fits (10, 90).

   D. The student interchanges the roles of c and m.

7. **F.** The student uses the slope of 3 instead of -3.

   G. The student interchanges the coordinates when finding the equation.

   H. Correct answer

   I. The student works correctly, but uses the wrong sign on the term 14.

1. A movie theater offers 30% off the price of a movie ticket to students from your school. The regular price of a movie ticket is $8.50. What is the discounted price that you would pay for a ticket?

   A. $2.55

   B. $5.50

   C. $5.95

   D. $8.20

2. You are comparing the prices of four boxes of cereal. Two of the boxes contain free extra cereal.

   - Box F costs $3.59 and contains 16 ounces.

   - Box G costs $3.79 and contains 16 ounces, plus an additional 10% for free.

   - Box H costs $4.00 and contains 500 grams.

   - Box I costs $4.69 and contains 500 grams, plus an additional 20% for free.

   Which box has the least unit cost? (1 ounce = 28.35 grams)

   F. Box F

   G. Box G

   H. Box H

   I. Box I

3. James is getting ready for wrestling season. As part of his preparation, he plans to lose 5% of his body weight. James currently weighs 160 pounds. How much will he weigh, in pounds, after he loses 5% of his weight?

4. Which proportion represents the problem below?

   > "17% of a number is 43. What is the number?"

   A. $\dfrac{17}{43} = \dfrac{n}{100}$

   B. $\dfrac{n}{17} = \dfrac{43}{100}$

   C. $\dfrac{n}{43} = \dfrac{17}{100}$

   D. $\dfrac{43}{n} = \dfrac{17}{100}$

Test-Taking Strategy

Read Question Before Answering

About 0.4 of cats are polydactyl. Of 80 cats, how many have 5 toes per paw?

Ⓐ 32 Ⓑ 30% Ⓒ 48 Ⓓ 58

Not fair. I'm a cartoon character and I have only 4 toes per paw.

"Keep on your toes and read the questions before choosing your answer."

The graph below shows how many calories c are burned during m minutes of playing basketball. Use the graph for Exercises 5 and 6.

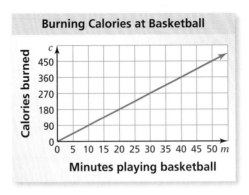

Burning Calories at Basketball

5. How many calories are burned in 25 minutes?

   F. 180 cal

   G. 185 cal

   H. 225 cal

   I. 270 cal

6. Which equation fits the data given in the graph?

   A. $c = 9m$

   B. $c = 90m$

   C. $c = m + 80$

   D. $m = 9c$

7. The line shown in the graph below has a slope of -3. What is the equation of the line?

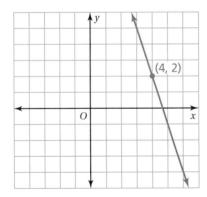

(4, 2)

   F. $y = 3x - 10$

   G. $y = -3x + 10$

   H. $y = -3x + 14$

   I. $y = -3x - 14$

8. A lighting store is holding a clearance sale. The store is offering discounts on all the lamps it sells. As the sale progresses, the store will increase the percent of discount it is offering.

   You want to buy a lamp that has an original price of $40. You will buy the lamp when its price is marked down to $10. What percent discount will you have received?

Item Analysis (continued)

8. **Gridded Response:** Correct answer: 75%

   Common Error: The student finds what percent 10 is of 40, and gets an answer of 25%.

9. **A.** The student finds what percent 60 is of 660.

   B. Correct answer

   C. The student finds 60% of 660 and misplaces the decimal point.

   D. The student thinks that the difference of the scores is equivalent to the percent.

10. **F.** The student performs the first step correctly, but then subtracts P rather than dividing.

   G. The student performs the first step correctly, but then divides A by P instead of dividing the entire expression by P.

   H. The student performs the first step correctly, but then divides P by P instead of dividing the entire expression by P.

   I. Correct answer

11. **4 points** The student demonstrates a thorough understanding of interpreting a problem involving simple interest. In Part A, the student correctly determines that it would take 2.5 years. In Part B, the student correctly determines that an initial deposit of $4000 is not large enough. The student provides clear and complete work and explanations.

   3 points The student demonstrates an understanding of interpreting a problem involving simple interest, but the student's work and explanations demonstrate an essential but less than thorough understanding.

   2 points The student demonstrates a partial understanding of interpreting a problem involving simple interest. The student's work and explanations demonstrate a lack of essential understanding.

   1 point The student demonstrates a limited understanding of interpreting a problem involving simple interest. The student's response is incomplete and exhibits many flaws.

   0 points The student provides no response, a completely incorrect or incomprehensible response, or a response that demonstrates insufficient understanding of interpreting a problem involving simple interest.

Answers

5. H

6. A

7. H

8. 75%

Answers

9. B

10. I

11. *Part A* 2.5 years
    Part B no

12. D

13. H

Answers for Extra Examples

1. **A.** Correct answer
   B. The student aligns the decimal point of the estimated product with the first estimated factor.
   C. The student thinks that the product is positive because the greater factor is positive.
   D. The student aligns the decimal point of the estimated product with the first estimated factor. The student also thinks that the product is positive because the greater factor is positive.

2. **F.** The student finds the value of $2 - 6 - 9$.
   G. The student finds the value of $-2 + 6 - 9$.
   H. Correct answer
   I. The student finds the value of $-2 + 6 - (-9)$.

Item Analysis (continued)

12. **A.** The student does not recognize that -3 was already distributed correctly.
    B. The student does not recognize that -3 was already distributed correctly.
    C. The student makes the right correction but finds the incorrect sum of -45 and 6.
    D. Correct answer

13. **F.** The student simply moves $3x$ to the right side of the equation and picks up its coefficient.
    G. The student makes a mistake with a negative sign, either when moving terms or when dividing by the coefficient of y.
    H. Correct answer
    I. The student adds $3x$ to the right side of the equation and picks up its coefficient.

Extra Examples for Standardized Test Practice

1. Which of the following is closest to the value of the expression below?
$$0.041 \cdot (-0.0038)$$
   A. -0.00016 **C.** 0.00016
   B. -0.016 **D.** 0.016

2. What is the value of the expression below?
$$2 - 6 - (-9)$$
   F. -13 **H.** 5
   G. -5 **I.** 13

9. A student scored 600 the first time she took the mathematics portion of her college entrance exam. The next time she took the exam, she scored 660. Her second score represents what percent increase over her first score?

A. 9.1%

B. 10%

C. 39.6%

D. 60%

10. Solve the formula below for I.

$$A = P + PI$$

F. $I = A - 2P$

G. $I = \dfrac{A}{P} - P$

H. $I = A - \dfrac{P}{P}$

I. $I = \dfrac{A - P}{P}$

11. You are planning to deposit $4000 in an account that earns 5% simple interest per year. You will not make any other deposits or withdrawals.

Think
Solve
Explain

Part A How long would it take for your account to contain $4500? Show your work and explain your reasoning.

Part B You would like the account to contain $5100 after 4 years. Would your initial $4000 deposit be large enough? Show your work and explain your reasoning.

12. Brad was solving the equation in the box shown.

What should Brad do to correct the error that he made?

$$-3(2 - 5w) = -45$$
$$-6 + 15w = -45$$
$$9w = -45$$
$$\frac{9w}{9} = \frac{-45}{9}$$
$$w = -5$$

A. Distribute -3 to get $6 - 15w$.

B. Distribute -3 to get $-6 - 15w$.

C. Add 6 to both sides to get $15w = -51$.

D. Add 6 to both sides to get $15w = -39$.

13. What is the slope of the line given by $3x - 6y = 33$?

F. -3

G. $-\dfrac{1}{2}$

H. $\dfrac{1}{2}$

I. 3

5 Angles and Polygons

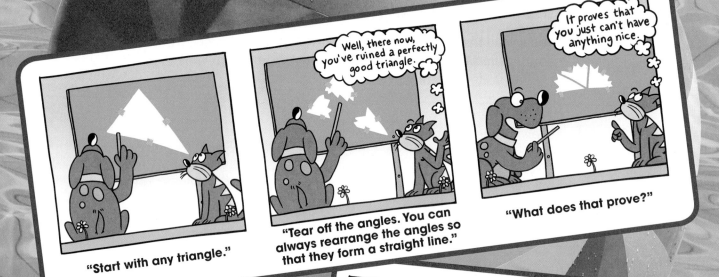

"Start with any triangle."

"Tear off the angles. You can always rearrange the angles so that they form a straight line."

"Well, there now, you've ruined a perfectly good triangle."

"What does that prove?"

"It proves that you just can't have anything nice."

"Let's use shadows and similar triangles to indirectly measure the height of the giant hyena standing right behind you."

Maybe if I sit perfectly still he won't see me.

Strands Development

6th Grade

- Determine congruence of segments, angles, and polygons.
- Solve problems involving perimeter and area.

7th Grade

- Determine whether quadrilaterals and triangles are similar, and write proportions to express relationships between corresponding sides.
- Represent transformations (reflections, dilations, rotations, and translations) by graphing in the coordinate plane.

8th Grade

- Measure and describe relationships among vertical, adjacent, supplementary, and complementary angles.
- Solve problems involving proportions.
- Apply transformations to plane figures.
- Solve area and perimeter problems involving composite plane figures.

Math in History

Geometry and special ratios have been used in the building industry for thousands of years.

★ The geometry used in the Indus Valley Civilization of North India and Pakistan from around 3000 B.C. was developed mostly as a result of building cities. The geometry originated from practical things, such as designing bricks. Brick sizes were in a perfect ratio of 4 : 2 : 1. Even today, the ratio for brick dimensions 4 : 2 : 1 is considered optimal for effective bonding.

★ Omar Khayyám (born 1048 A.D.) was a Persian mathematician, philosopher, and poet who described his philosophy through poems known as quatrains in the Rubaiyat of Omar Khayyám. Omar Khayyám is known for using geometry to solve algebraic equations.

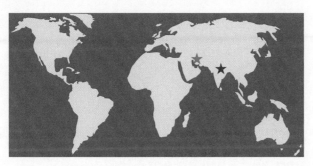

Pacing Guide for Chapter 5

Chapter Opener	1 Day
Section 1 Activity Lesson	 1 Day 1 Day
Section 2 Activity Lesson	 1 Day 1 Day
Section 3 Activity Lesson	 1 Day 1 Day
Study Help / Quiz	1 Day
Section 4 Activity Lesson	 1 Day 1 Day
Section 5 Activity Lesson	 1 Day 1 Day
Section 6 Activity Lesson	 1 Day 1 Day
Section 7 Activity Lesson	 1 Day 1 Day
Chapter Review / Tests	2 Days
Total Chapter 5	18 Days
Year-to-Date	84 Days

Check Your Resources

- Record and Practice Journal
- Resources by Chapter
- Skills Review Handbook
- Assessment Book
- Worked-Out Solutions

Technology For the Teacher

Dynamic Classroom

The Dynamic Planning Tool
Editable Teacher's Resources at
BigIdeasMath.com

Standards of Learning

7.6 The student will determine whether plane figures—quadrilaterals and triangles—are similar and write proportions to express the relationships between corresponding sides of similar figures.

Additional Topics for Review

- Identifying similar figures
- Cross Products Property
- Solving simple equations
- Obtuse, acute, and right angles
- Naming polygons

Try It Yourself

1. 10 in.
2. 12.5 mm

Record and Practice Journal

1. $x = 3$
2. $x = 24$
3. $x = 4.5$
4. $x = 18$
5. $x = 8$
6. $x = 8$
7. $x = 30$
8. $x = 4$
9. $x = 9$
10. $x = 9$
11. 60 feet

Math Background Notes

Vocabulary Review

- Similar Figures
- Proportion
- Ratio
- Cross Products Property
- Corresponding Parts
- Polygon

Finding Unknown Measures in Similar Polygons

- Students should be able to write proportions and use them to solve problems.
- Remind students that a complete answer includes a measure and the appropriate units for that measurement.
- **Common Student Question:** "Is that the only proportion that works?" The answer to this question is *no*. In Example 1, 16 and 12 appear in the numerators of the ratios because they both describe the red triangle. Similarly, 18 and *x* are in the denominators of the ratios because they describe the blue triangle. The position of the measurements in the ratios is irrelevant as long as students are consistent. For example, writing the proportion $\frac{18}{16} = \frac{x}{12}$ is also correct. In this proportion, the measurements describing the blue triangle appear in the numerators.
- **Common Student Question:** "Does the order in which I cross multiply matter?" The answer to this question is *no*. It makes no difference whether you multiply downward to the right or downward to the left first. Encourage students to develop a method and use that method every time for consistency.
- **Common Error:** Some students struggle when given the ratio of the perimeters. Some will be unsure of how to incorporate this ratio with the given side lengths of the polygons. Remind students that the smaller polygon will have the smaller perimeter.

Reteaching and Enrichment Strategies

If students need help. . .	If students got it. . .
Record and Practice Journal • Fair Game Review Skills Review Handbook Lesson Tutorials	Game Closet at *BigIdeasMath.com* Start the next section

What You Learned Before

● **Finding Unknown Measures in Similar Polygons**

Example 1 The two triangles are similar. Find the value of *x*.

$$\frac{16}{18} = \frac{12}{x}$$ Write a proportion.

$16x = 216$ Use Cross Products Property.

$x = 13.5$ Divide each side by 16.

∴ So, *x* is 13.5 yards.

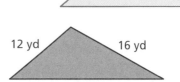

Example 2 The two quadrilaterals are similar. The ratio of their perimeters is 4 : 5. Find the value of *x*.

$$\frac{4}{5} = \frac{x}{25}$$ Write a proportion.

$100 = 5x$ Use Cross Products Property.

$20 = x$ Divide each side by 5.

∴ So, *x* is 20 centimeters.

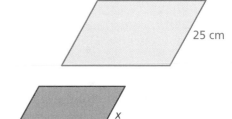

Try It Yourself

The polygons are similar. Find the value of *x*.

1.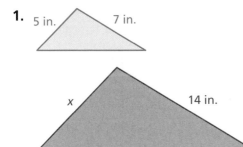

2. The ratio of the perimeters is 2 : 1.

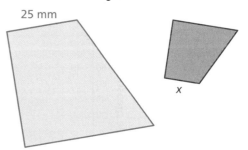

5.1 Classifying Angles

STANDARDS OF LEARNING

8.6

Essential Question How can you classify two angles as complementary or supplementary?

Classification of Angles

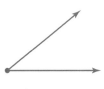

Acute:
Less than 90°

Right:
Equal to 90°

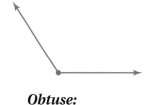

Obtuse:
Greater than 90° and less than 180°

Straight:
Equal to 180°

1 ACTIVITY: Complementary and Supplementary Angles

Work with a partner.

- **Copy and complete each table.**
- **Graph each function. Is the function linear?**
- **Write an equation for y as a function of x.**
- **Describe the domain of each function.**

a. Two angles are **complementary** if the sum of their measures is 90°. In the table, x and y are complementary.

x	15°	30°	45°	60°	75°
y					

b. Two angles are **supplementary** if the sum of their measures is 180°. In the table, x and y are supplementary.

x	30°	60°	90°	120°	150°
y					

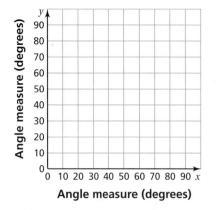

Angle measure (degrees)

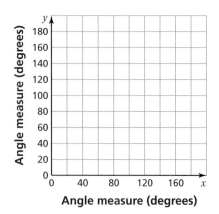

Angle measure (degrees)

Laurie's Notes

Introduction

For the Teacher

- **Goal:** Students will explore the properties of complementary and supplementary angles.
- Do not assume that all students will recall the vocabulary of angles, know how to use a protractor, or know what an angle measure means.

Motivate

- **Preparation:** Make a model to practice estimation skills with angle measures. Cut two circles (6-inch diameter) out of file folders. Cut a slit in each. On one circle, label every 10°. The second circle is shaded. Insert one circle into the other so the angle measure faces you and the shaded angle faces the students.
- Ask students to estimate the measure of the shaded angle. You can read the answer from your side of the model. Repeat several times.

| Labeled | Shaded | Your view | Students' view |

Activity Notes

Discuss

- ❓ "What names do you use to classify angles, and what does each mean?"
  acute: less than 90°, right: 90°, obtuse: greater than 90°, straight: 180°
- **Caution:** Do not draw every angle in this chapter with the initial ray horizontal and extending rightward. Use varied orientation to gauge students' understanding of reading angle measures.

Activity 1

- Students should read the definition of complementary and supplementary angles, complete the table, and then plot the ordered pairs.
- ❓ "What is the slope and y-intercept for part (a)?" slope = −1; y-intercept = 90
- ❓ "What makes sense for the domain of this function?" angle measures between 0 and 90, but not including 0° and 90° (Note: In higher-level math courses, zero degree angles are allowed.)
- This may be the first time students have seen a domain where the endpoints of the interval are not included. The endpoints are not included because a 90° angle does not have a complement.
- **Big Idea:** As an angle increases, its complement decreases. This should make sense because the sum of the two angle measures must always be 90°. A similar pattern occurs with supplementary angles.
- ❓ "What is the range of each function?" part (a): $0° < y < 90°$ and part (b): $0° < y < 180°$

Standards of Learning

8.6(a) The student will verify by measuring and describe the relationships among vertical angles, adjacent angles, supplementary angles, and complementary angles.

Previous Learning

Students should know basic vocabulary associated with angles.

Activity Materials
Introduction
• two circles cut out of file folders

Start Thinking! and Warm Up

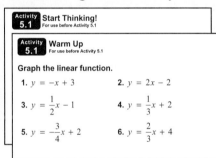

Activity 5.1 Start Thinking!
For use before Activity 5.1

Activity 5.1 Warm Up
For use before Activity 5.1

Graph the linear function.

1. $y = -x + 3$

2. $y = 2x - 2$

3. $y = \frac{1}{2}x - 1$

4. $y = \frac{1}{3}x + 2$

5. $y = -\frac{3}{4}x + 2$

6. $y = \frac{2}{3}x + 4$

5.1 Record and Practice Journal

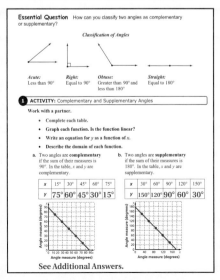

Essential Question How can you classify two angles as complementary or supplementary?

Classification of Angles

Acute: Less than 90° *Right:* Equal to 90° *Obtuse:* Greater than 90° and less than 180° *Straight:* Equal to 180°

① ACTIVITY: Complementary and Supplementary Angles

Work with a partner.

- Complete each table. Is the function linear?
- Graph each function.
- Write an equation for y as a function of x.
- Describe the domain of each function.

a. Two angles are **complementary** if the sum of their measures is 90°. In the table, x and y are complementary.

x	15°	30°	45°	60°	75°
y	75°	60°	45°	30°	15°

b. Two angles are **supplementary** if the sum of their measures is 180°. In the table, x and y are supplementary.

x	30°	60°	90°	120°	150°
y	150°	120°	90°	60°	30°

See Additional Answers.

Illustrate

Explain to English learners that the name *right angle* does not come from the orientation of the angle opening to the right, as shown in the activity. Students might think that if the angle opens to the left, it is called a *left angle*. Point out that any angle that measures 90° is a *right angle*.

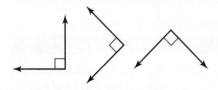

5.1 Record and Practice Journal

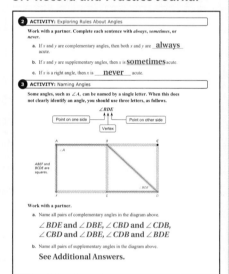

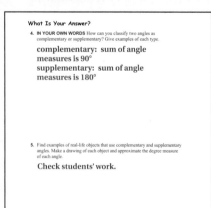

Laurie's Notes

Activity 2

- Give time for partners to discuss the problems. The graphs and tables of values from Activity 1 should help students think through their answers.
- **Teaching Tip:** When answers are *sometimes* true, it is important to give students a sample of when the statement is true and when the statement is false. For example, in part (b), $x = 75°$ and $y = 105°$ which makes x acute, or $x = 105°$ and $y = 75°$ which makes x obtuse.

Activity 3

- This activity reviews how angles are named. Discuss when there is a need for three letters instead of one. Also discuss that $\angle EBD$ and $\angle DBE$ name the same angle (because the vertex position is the same).
- **?** "What other angles could be named using just one letter?" $\angle C$, $\angle F$
- Although the right angles are not labeled in this diagram, it is assumed that those which appear to be right angles are right angles.

What Is Your Answer?

- **Think-Pair-Share:** Students should read each question independently and then work with a partner to answer the questions. When they have answered the questions, the pair should compare their answers with another group and discuss any discrepancies.

Closure

- Look around the room. Name angles that appear to be acute, right, obtuse, or straight. Name angles that appear to be complementary or supplementary.

Technology For the Teacher

Dynamic Classroom

The Dynamic Planning Tool
Editable Teacher's Resources at *BigIdeasMath.com*

2 ACTIVITY: Exploring Rules About Angles

Work with a partner. Copy and complete each sentence with *always*, *sometimes*, or *never*.

a. If *x* and *y* are complementary angles, then both *x* and *y* are _____ acute.

b. If *x* and *y* are supplementary angles, then *x* is _____ acute.

c. If *x* is a right angle, then *x* is _____ acute.

3 ACTIVITY: Naming Angles

Some angles, such as ∠A, can be named by a single letter. When this does not clearly identify an angle, you should use three letters, as follows.

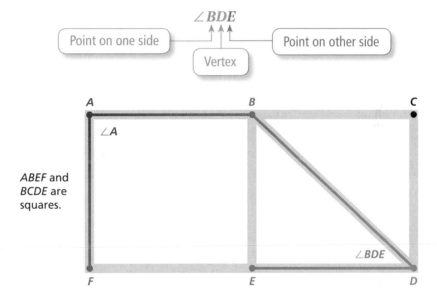

ABEF and *BCDE* are squares.

Work with a partner.

a. Name all pairs of complementary angles in the diagram above.

b. Name all pairs of supplementary angles in the diagram above.

What Is Your Answer?

4. IN YOUR OWN WORDS How can you classify two angles as complementary or supplementary? Give examples of each type.

5. Find examples of real-life objects that use complementary and supplementary angles. Make a drawing of each object and approximate the degree measure of each angle.

Practice Use what you learned about classifying angles to complete Exercises 3–5 on page 202.

Key Vocabulary
complementary angles, *p. 200*
supplementary angles, *p. 200*
adjacent angles, *p. 201*
vertical angles, *p. 201*

 Key Ideas

Complementary Angles

Words   Two angles are **complementary angles** if the sum of their measures is 90°.

Examples

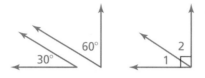

∠1 and ∠2 are complementary angles.

Supplementary Angles

Words   Two angles are **supplementary angles** if the sum of their measures is 180°.

Examples

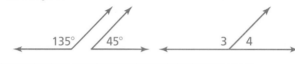

∠3 and ∠4 are supplementary angles.

EXAMPLE **1**   **Classifying Pairs of Angles**

Tell whether the angles are *complementary*, *supplementary*, or *neither*.

a.   70° + 110° = 180°

∴ So, the angles are supplementary.

b.   41° + 49° = 90°

∴ So, the angles are complementary.

c.   128° + 62° = 190°

∴ So, the angles are *neither* complementary nor supplementary.

 **On Your Own**

Now You're Ready
Exercises 6–11

Tell whether the angles are *complementary*, *supplementary*, or *neither*.

1.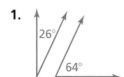

2.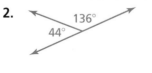

3.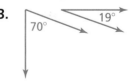

Multi-Language Glossary at BigIdeasMath.com.

Laurie's Notes

Introduction

Connect

- **Yesterday:** Students explored two pairs of angles, complementary and supplementary.
- **Today:** Students will classify several pairs of angles.

Motivate

- Because this chapter will be focusing on geometry, students should know we credit Euclid for the study of geometry. He is often called the Father of Geometry. Euclid was a Greek mathematician best known for his 13 books on geometry known as *The Elements*. This work influenced the development of Western mathematics for more than 2000 years.
- We do not know a lot about Euclid, though one quote is often attributed to him. When a colleague was lamenting about the length of his 13 books, it is reported that Euclid replied, "There is no royal road to Geometry."

Lesson Notes

Key Ideas

- Write the *Key Ideas*. Define and sketch complementary angles and supplementary angles.
- **Common Misconception:** Students sometimes believe that complementary or supplementary angles must be adjacent to (touching) each other because this is the way they are often drawn. In this diagram, they are drawn with an orientation to suggest that the sum is 90° (complementary) or 180° (supplementary), but they do not need to have this orientation. For example, ∠A and ∠B are complementary, however, it is not immediately obvious because of their orientation.

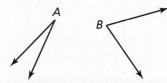

Example 1

- In this example, students sum the angle measures and determine if they add to 90°, 180°, or neither. Make sure students do not rely on their eyesight. They should actually add the angle measures.

On Your Own

- **Think-Pair-Share:** Students should read each question independently and then work with a partner to answer the questions. When they have answered the questions, the pair should compare their answers with another group and discuss any discrepancies.

Goal Today's lesson is classifying angles.

Lesson Materials
Textbook
• scissors

Start Thinking! and Warm Up

Lesson **5.1** Warm Up
For use before Lesson 5.1

Lesson **5.1** Start Thinking!
For use before Lesson 5.1

Complete the statement.

Two angles are ___?___ if the sum of their measures is 90°.

Two angles are ___?___ if the sum of their measures is 180°.

People often have trouble remembering which is 90° and which is 180°. Make up your own way to help you remember the definitions.

Extra Example 1

Tell whether the angles are *complementary, supplementary,* or *neither.*

a.

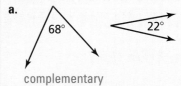

complementary

b.

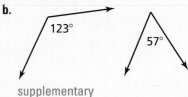

supplementary

c.

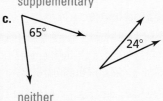

neither

On Your Own

1. complementary
2. supplementary
3. neither

Laurie's Notes

Extra Example 2

Tell whether the angles are _adjacent_ or _vertical_. Then find the value of _x_.

a.

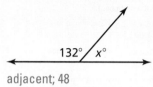

adjacent; 48

b.

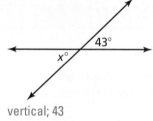

vertical; 43

On Your Own

4. adjacent; 95

5. vertical; 90

6. adjacent; 21

Differentiated Instruction

Visual

Help students visualize vertical angles. Draw vertical angles on the board or overhead.

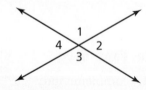

Point out that the lines creating vertical angles form an "X" and that vertical angles do _not_ share sides.

Key Ideas

- **?** "Does anyone remember what the term _congruent angles_ mean?" two angles that have the same measure
- Draw two pairs of congruent angles and remind students of the marks used to show that the angles are congruent.
- **?** "What does the word _adjacent_ mean?" side-by-side Point out two students in the class that are seated adjacent to one another and two students that are not adjacent to one another.
- Write the Key Ideas. Define and sketch adjacent angles and vertical angles.
- **Model:** When two lines intersect, two pairs of vertical angles are formed. Vertical angles are congruent. Demonstrate this with a pair of scissors that have straight blades. To make a small cut, you do not open your hands very wide because you want the vertical angle to be small. If you want to make a larger cut, you open your hands wide so that the vertical angle will be greater.

Example 2

- Work through each part as shown.
- **Extension:** In part (a), "What is the measure of the two remaining angles? How do you know?" 110°; The two remaining angles are supplementary with 70°.
- Remind students of the meaning of the symbol used to mark right angles.

Closure

- True or False?
  1. Vertical angles are always acute. false
  2. Supplementary angles could be congruent. true
  3. Complementary angles sum to 180°. false
  4. Vertical angles are congruent. true
  5. Adjacent angles could be congruent. true

Technology For the Teacher

Dynamic Classroom

The Dynamic Planning Tool
Editable Teacher's Resources at _BigIdeasMath.com_

 Key Ideas

Adjacent Angles

Words Two angles are **adjacent angles** if they share a common side and have the same vertex.

Examples

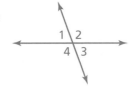

∠1 and ∠2 are adjacent.

∠2 and ∠4 are not adjacent.

Vertical Angles

Words Two angles are **vertical angles** if they are opposite angles formed by the intersection of two lines. Vertical angles are congruent.

Examples

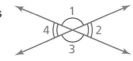

∠1 and ∠3 are vertical angles.

∠2 and ∠4 are vertical angles.

EXAMPLE 2 Finding Angle Measures

Tell whether the angles are *adjacent* or *vertical*. Then find the value of *x*.

a.

The angles are vertical angles. Because vertical angles are congruent, the angles have the same measure.

∴ So, *x* is 70.

b.

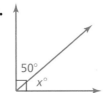

The angles are adjacent angles. Because the angles are complementary, the sum of their measures is 90°.

$$x + 50 = 90$$
$$x = 40$$

∴ So, *x* is 40.

On Your Own

Now You're Ready
Exercises 12–14

Tell whether the angles are *adjacent* or *vertical*. Then find the value of *x*.

4.

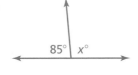

5.

6.

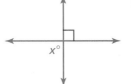

 Vocabulary and Concept Check

1. **VOCABULARY** Explain how complementary angles and supplementary angles are different.

2. **WRITING** When two lines intersect, how many pairs of vertical angles are formed? How many pairs of adjacent angles are formed? Explain.

 Practice and Problem Solving

Tell whether the statement is *always*, *sometimes*, or *never* true. Explain.

3. If x and y are supplementary angles, then x is obtuse.

4. If x and y are right angles, then x and y are supplementary angles.

5. If x and y are complementary angles, then y is a right angle.

Tell whether the angles are *complementary*, *supplementary*, or *neither*.

① 6.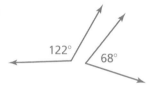
122° 68°

7.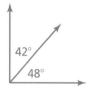
42° 48°

8.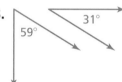
59° 31°

9.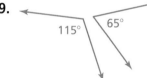
115° 65°

10.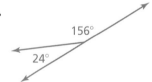
156° 24°

11.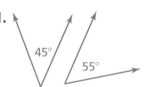
45° 55°

Tell whether the angles are *adjacent* or *vertical*. Then find the value of x.

② 12.
$x°$ 35°

13.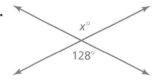
$x°$ 128°

14.
117° $x°$

15. **ERROR ANALYSIS** Describe and correct the error in finding the value of x.

16. **TRIBUTARY** A tributary joins a river at an angle. Find the value of x.

✗ The value of x is 55 because vertical angles are complementary.

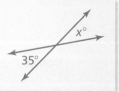

$x°$ $x°$
35°

$x°$ 127°

Assignment Guide and Homework Check

Level	Day 1 Activity Assignment	Day 2 Lesson Assignment	Homework Check
Basic	3–5, 27–30	1, 2, 6–16	2, 6, 8, 10, 12, 16
Average	3–5, 27–30	1, 2, 7, 9, 11–15, 17, 19–23	7, 9, 11, 12, 17, 20
Advanced	3–5, 27–30	1, 2, 15, 17–26	18, 20, 24, 25

For Your Information

- **Exercise 21** Students may not understand what a *vanishing point* is. A vanishing point is a point in a perspective drawing to which parallel lines appear to converge.

Common Errors

- **Exercises 6–11** Students may mix up the terms *supplementary* and *complementary*. Remind them of the definitions and use the alliteration that complementary angles are corners and supplementary angles are straight.
- **Exercises 12–14** Students may think that there is not enough information to determine the value of *x*. Remind them of the definitions they have learned in the lesson and ask if any of those could apply to the angles. For example, Exercise 12 is a right angle and there are two angles within. These two angle measures must add to 90°, so a student can use the definition of complementary angles to find *x*.

5.1 Record and Practice Journal

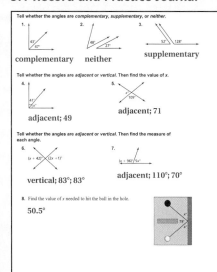

Vocabulary and Concept Check

1. The sum of the measures of two complementary angles is 90°. The sum of the measures of two supplementary angles is 180°.

2. two pairs; four pairs; There are two pairs of opposite angles when two lines intersect, and 4 pairs of adjacent angles.

Practice and Problem Solving

3. sometimes; Either *x* or *y* may be obtuse.

4. always; 90° + 90° = 180°

5. never; Because *x* and *y* must both be less than 90° and greater than 0°.

6. neither

7. complementary

8. complementary

9. supplementary

10. supplementary

11. neither

12. adjacent; 55

13. vertical; 128

14. adjacent; 63

15. Vertical angles are congruent. The value of *x* is 35.

16. 53

17. vertical; 75°; 75°

18. adjacent; 60°; 30°

19. adjacent; 140°; 40°

20. *Sample answer:* 120°; It is supplementary with a 60° angle, but it is greater than 90°, so it cannot be complementary with another angle.

Practice and Problem Solving

21. **a.** $\angle CBD$ and $\angle DBE$;
   $\angle ABF$ and $\angle FBE$

   b. $\angle ABE$ and $\angle CBE$;
   $\angle ABD$ and $\angle CBD$;
   $\angle CBF$ and $\angle ABF$

22. $\angle 1 = 130°$, $\angle 2 = 50°$,
   $\angle 3 = 130°$

23. Adjacent angles are not
   defined by their measure, so
   they can be complementary,
   supplementary, or neither.

24. $54°$

25. See *Taking Math Deeper*.

26. $x = 10$; $y = 20$

Fair Game Review

27. 75   **28.** 29.3

29. 35   **30.** B

Mini-Assessment

**Tell whether the angles are
complementary, supplementary,
or *neither.*

1.

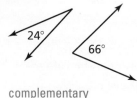

complementary

2.

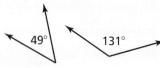

supplementary

3.

neither

Taking Math Deeper

Exercise 25

This exercise is a good lesson for students. The definition of vertical angles is related to the *position* of the angles. However, the definitions of complementary angles and supplementary angles are only based on the *measures* of the angles and not on the position of the angles.

 Draw the angles.

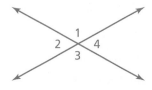

 $\angle 2$ and $\angle 4$ are complementary.

$$\angle 2 = \angle 4 \qquad \text{Vertical angles}$$
$$\angle 2 + \angle 4 = 90 \qquad \text{Complementary angles}$$

Solving this implies that $\angle 2 = 45°$ and $\angle 4 = 45°$.

③ $\angle 2$ and $\angle 4$ are supplementary.

$$\angle 2 = \angle 4 \qquad \text{Vertical angles}$$
$$\angle 2 + \angle 4 = 180 \qquad \text{Supplementary angles}$$

Solving this implies that $\angle 2 = 90°$ and $\angle 4 = 90°$.

Project

Look around your classroom, school, home, or anywhere you go. Find examples of complementary and supplementary angles. How do you know they are complementary or supplementary? What is the most common angle you find?

Reteaching and Enrichment Strategies

If students need help. . .	If students got it. . .
Resources by Chapter • Practice A and Practice B • Puzzle Time Record and Practice Journal Practice Differentiating the Lesson Lesson Tutorials Skills Review Handbook	Resources by Chapter • Enrichment and Extension Start the next section

T-203

Tell whether the angles are *adjacent* or *vertical*. Then find the measure of each angle.

17.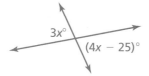
$3x°$
$(4x - 25)°$

18.
$4x°$
$2x°$

19.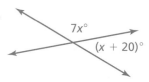
$7x°$
$(x + 20)°$

20. **OPEN-ENDED** Give an example of an angle that can be a supplementary angle but cannot be a complementary angle. Explain.

21. **VANISHING POINT** The vanishing point of the picture is represented by point *B*.

    a. Name two pairs of complementary angles.

    b. Name three pairs of supplementary angles.

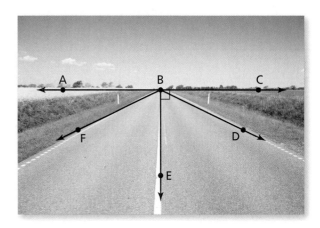

22. **INTERSECTION** What are the measures of the other three angles formed by the intersection?

23. **REASONING** Can adjacent angles be supplementary? complementary? neither? Explain.

24. **RATIO** The measures of two complementary angles have a ratio of 3 : 2. What is the measure of the larger angle?

25. **REASONING** Two angles are vertical angles. What are their measures if they are also complementary angles? supplementary angles?

26. Find the values of *x* and *y*.

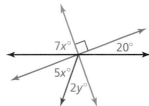
$7x°$ $20°$
$5x°$
$2y°$

 Fair Game Review *What you learned in previous grades & lessons*

Solve the equation. Check your solution. *(Section 1.1 and Section 1.2)*

27. $x + 60 + 45 = 180$

28. $x + 58.5 + 92.2 = 180$

29. $x + x + 110 = 180$

30. **MULTIPLE CHOICE** The graph of which equation has a slope of $-\dfrac{1}{2}$ and passes through the point (6, 4)? *(Section 2.6)*

    Ⓐ $y = x + 3$ Ⓑ $y = -\dfrac{1}{2}x + 7$ Ⓒ $y = -\dfrac{1}{2}x + 1$ Ⓓ $y = \dfrac{1}{2}x - 3$

5.2 Angles and Sides of Triangles

STANDARDS OF LEARNING

8.6
8.15

Essential Question How can you classify triangles by their angles?

1 ACTIVITY: Exploring the Angles of a Triangle

Work with a partner.

a. Draw a triangle that has an obtuse angle. Label the angles *A*, *B*, and *C*.

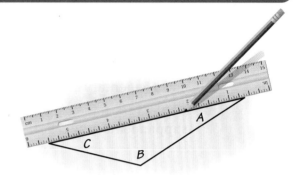

b. Carefully cut out the triangle. Tear off the three corners of the triangle.

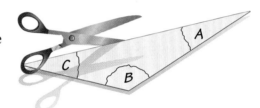

c. Draw a straight line on a piece of paper. Arrange angles *A* and *B* as shown.

d. Place the third angle as shown. What does this tell you about the sum of the measures of the angles?

e. Draw three other triangles that have different shapes. Repeat parts (b)–(d) for each one. Do you get the same result as in part (d)? Explain.

f. Write a rule about the sum of the measures of the angles of a triangle. Compare your rule with the rule you wrote in Activity 2 in Section 1.1. Did you get the same result? Explain.

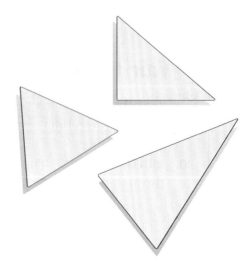

Laurie's Notes

Introduction

For the Teacher

- **Goal:** Students will explore the sum of the angle measures of a triangle.
- Many students will have heard of the property they are investigating today. Having heard the property and internalizing it for all triangles are two different levels of knowledge.
- **Management Tip:** There will be torn pieces of scrap paper resulting from this investigation. To help keep the room clean, cluster 4–6 desks together in a circle and tape a recycled paper or plastic bag to the front edge of one of the desks. Students are expected to put scraps of paper in the bag when they are finished with the investigation.

Motivate

- Make teams of three students. Give them 3 minutes to make a list of as many words as they can that begin with the prefix *tri-*.
- Some examples are: triangle, triathlon, tricycle, tri-fold, triangulate, triad, triaxial, trilogy, trimester, trinary, trinity, trio, trilingual, trillium.
- Provide dictionaries if necessary.
- The goal of this activity is to demonstrate that *tri-* is a common prefix.

Activity Notes

Activity 1

- The directions for this activity are direct and easy to follow.
- The sides of the triangle must be straight; otherwise the three angles will not lie adjacent to one another when placed about a point on the line.
- **Teaching Tip:** If you cannot gain access to enough pairs of scissors, you can cut out several triangles in advance using a paper cutter. It is okay to have multiple copies of the same triangle because different pairs of students will get one copy of the triangle.
- The conclusion, or rule, that students should discover is that the angle measures of any triangle will sum to 180°.

Standards of Learning

8.6(a) The student will verify by measuring and describe the relationships among vertical angles, adjacent angles, supplementary angles, and complementary angles.
8.6(b) The student will measure angles of less than 360°.
8.15 The student will **(a)** solve multistep linear equations in one variable on one and two sides of the equation; **(b)** solve two-step linear inequalities and graph the results on a number line; and **(c)** identify properties of operations used to solve an equation.

Activity Materials
Textbook
- scissors
- straightedge
- scrap paper

Start Thinking! and Warm Up

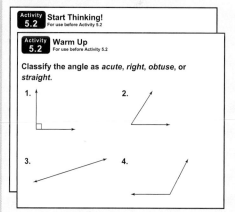

5.2 Record and Practice Journal

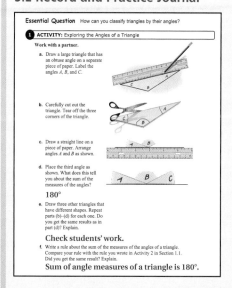

Differentiated Instruction

Kinesthetic

When talking about right, acute, and obtuse angles of a triangle, ask students if it is possible to draw a triangle with 2 right angles. Students should see by drawing the two right angles with a common side that the remaining two sides of the right angles will never meet. So, no triangle can be formed with 2 right angles. Ask students if it is possible for a triangle to have 2 obtuse angles. Students should reach the same conclusion. No triangle can be formed with 2 obtuse angles.

5.2 Record and Practice Journal

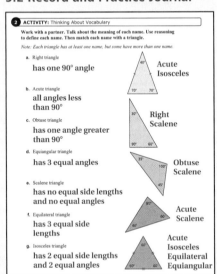

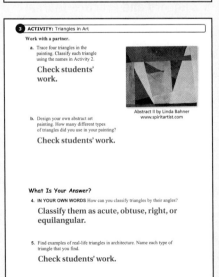

Laurie's Notes

Activity 2

- Note that the directions ask students to think about the meaning of each name. Share some historical information about the names.
  - Acute comes from the Latin *acus* which means *needle*. An acute angle is sharp, or pointed.
  - Obtuse comes from the Latin *ob* and *tudere* which means to *beat against*. An object gets blunt or rounded when it is beaten, just like an obtuse angle is blunt compared to an acute angle.
  - The term scalene derives from the Greek *skalenos* which means *unequal*.
  - The term isosceles derives from the Greek *isos* (same) and *skelos* (leg).
  - The prefix *equi-* means *equal* or *equally*. *Lateral* means *side*.
- **?** "What do the marks on the sides of the blue and orange triangles mean?" The sides have the same length (congruent).
- Remind students that each triangle has at least one name, but some have more than one name. All of the names will be used at least once.
- **?** "Which triangle has the most names? Explain." The orange triangle is acute, equiangular, equilateral, and isosceles. (Students may not call it isosceles. By definition, an isosceles triangle has at least two congruent sides. You can discuss this in the lesson when isosceles is formally defined.)

Activity 3

- Begin with a discussion of abstract art. It appears that artists use random colors and shapes. However, the paintings are often meticulously planned, such as the one shown by Linda Bahner.
- Students should be able to place paper on top of the image and trace four triangles. Because there are more than four triangles, students should reference color and relative position (red, lower left) to remember which triangle they traced.

What Is Your Answer?

- Have students work in pairs.

Closure

- Use a straightedge to draw an example of the following types of triangles.
  1. acute triangle
  2. obtuse triangle
  3. right triangle (Students should use the corner of their paper to make sure it is a right triangle.)

Technology For the Teacher

Dynamic Classroom

The Dynamic Planning Tool
Editable Teacher's Resources at *BigIdeasMath.com*

2 ACTIVITY: Thinking About Vocabulary

Work with a partner. Talk about the meaning of each name. Use reasoning to define each name. Then match each name with a triangle.

Note: Each triangle has at least one name, but some have more than one name.

a. Right triangle

b. Acute triangle

c. Obtuse triangle

d. Equiangular triangle

e. Scalene triangle

f. Equilateral triangle

g. Isosceles triangle

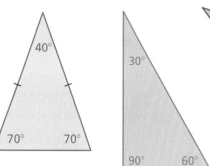

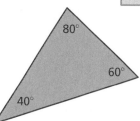

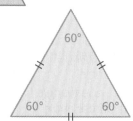

3 ACTIVITY: Triangles in Art

Work with a partner.

a. Trace four triangles in the painting. Classify each triangle using the names in Activity 2.

b. Design your own abstract art painting. How many different types of triangles did you use in your painting?

Abstract II by Linda Bahner
www.spiritartist.com

What Is Your Answer?

4. **IN YOUR OWN WORDS** How can you classify triangles by their angles?

5. Find examples of real-life triangles in architecture. Name each type of triangle that you find.

Practice Use what you learned about angles of triangles to complete Exercises 3–5 on page 208.

Key Vocabulary 🔊))
isosceles triangle,
   p. 206
congruent sides,
   p. 206
equilateral triangle,
   p. 206
equiangular triangle,
   p. 206

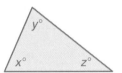 **Key Idea**

Angle Measures of a Triangle

Words   The sum of the angle measures
of a triangle is 180°.

Algebra $x + y + z = 180$

EXAMPLE (1)   **Finding Angle Measures**

Find each value of x. Then classify each triangle.

Remember

An *acute triangle* has all
acute angles.
A *right triangle* has one
right angle.
An *obtuse triangle* has
one obtuse angle.

a.

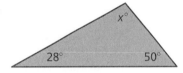

$x + 28 + 50 = 180$
$x + 78 = 180$
$x = 102$

⋮ The value of x is 102. The
triangle has an obtuse angle.
So, it is an obtuse triangle.

b.

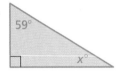

$x + 59 + 90 = 180$
$x + 149 = 180$
$x = 31$

⋮ The value of x is 31. The
triangle has a right angle.
So, it is a right triangle.

⬤ **On Your Own**

Now You're Ready
Exercises 6–8

Find the value of x. Then classify the triangle.

1.

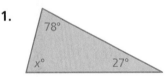

2.

 **Key Ideas**

Remember

A *scalene triangle* has
no congruent sides.

Isosceles Triangle

An **isosceles triangle** has at least two sides
that are **congruent** (have the same length).

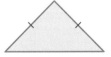

Equilateral Triangle

An **equilateral triangle** has three
congruent sides.

An equilateral triangle is also **equiangular**
(three congruent angles).

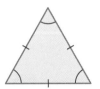

🔊 Multi-Language Glossary at BigIdeasMath✓com.

Laurie's Notes

Introduction

Connect

- **Yesterday:** Students explored the sum of the angle measures of a triangle and the vocabulary associated with triangles.
- **Today:** Students will find the missing angle measure of a triangle and classify the triangle.

Motivate

? Discuss the Ohio State flag.

The blue triangle represents hills and valleys. The red and white stripes represent roads and waterways. The 13 leftmost stars represent the 13 original colonies. The 4 stars on the right bring the total to 17, representing that Ohio was the 17th state admitted to the Union.

Lesson Notes

Key Idea

- The property is written with variables to suggest that you can solve an equation to find the third angle when you know the other two angles. This is also called the *Triangle Sum Theorem*.
- **?** "What type of angles are the remaining angles of a right triangle? a triangle with an obtuse angle?" Both are acute.
- **?** "Do you think an obtuse triangle could have a right angle? Explain." no; The sum of the angle measures would be greater than 180°.

Example 1

- Some students may argue that all they need to do is add the angle measures and subtract from 180. Remind them that they are practicing a *process*, one that works when the three angle measures are given as algebraic expressions, such as $(x + 10)°$, $(x + 20)°$, and $(x + 30)°$.

Key Ideas

- Define and sketch isosceles and equilateral triangles. Discuss how the sides and angles are marked to show that they are congruent (same length and same measure).
- **Common Misconception:** Draw a series of isosceles and equilateral triangles in different orientations so that students do not think that the triangles must be sitting on a base.
- Make note of the words *at least two sides* in the definition of isosceles. This means that it would be okay for all three sides to be congruent and still call it isosceles. So, all equilateral triangles are isosceles.
- **?** "Are all isosceles triangles equilateral? Explain." No; if the triangle only has two congruent sides, then it only satisfies the definition of isosceles.

Start Thinking! and Warm Up

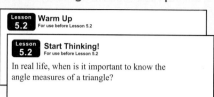

Lesson 5.2 **Warm Up** For use before Lesson 5.2

Lesson 5.2 **Start Thinking!** For use before Lesson 5.2

In real life, when is it important to know the angle measures of a triangle?

Extra Example 1

Find each value of x. Then classify each triangle.

a.

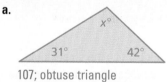

107; obtuse triangle

b.

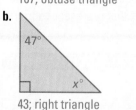

43; right triangle

On Your Own

1. 75; acute triangle
2. 91; obtuse triangle

Extra Example 2

Find the value of *x*. Then classify the triangle.

25; obtuse triangle

Extra Example 3

A car travels around the park shown below. What is the value of *x*?

62

On Your Own

3. 30; obtuse isosceles triangle

4. 60; equilateral, equiangular, acute, and isosceles triangle

5. 54.3

English Language Learners

Illustrate

Have students copy the empty table into their notebooks and then complete it with triangles that represent both attributes.

	Acute	Right	Obtuse
Scalene	△	△	△
Isosceles	△	△	△
Equilateral	△	not possible	not possible

Example 2

- Share the symbolism of each flag.
  - **Jamaica:** The yellow divides the flag into four triangles and represents sunshine and natural resources. Black represents the burdens overcome by the people and the hardships in the future. Green represents the land and hope for the future.
  - **Cuba:** The blue stripes refer to the three old divisions of the island and the two white stripes represent the strength of the independent ideal. The red triangle symbolizes equality, fraternity and freedom, and the blood shed in the struggle for independence. The white star symbolizes the absolute freedom among the Cuban people.
- Set up and solve the equations as shown.
- **?** "How would you classify the green triangle on the Jamaican flag?" obtuse isosceles
- Students may ask if an isosceles triangle also has two congruent angles as in this example. Students will explore this property in Exercise 18.

Example 3

- Add a little interest by sharing information from the Department of the Navy website, *history.navy.mil*. The *Bermuda Triangle* is an imaginary area located off the southeastern Atlantic coast of the U.S. where a supposedly high incidence of unexplained disappearances of ships and aircraft occurs. The vertices of the triangle are Bermuda; Miami, Florida; and San Juan, Puerto Rico.
- Set up the equation and work through the problem as shown.

On Your Own

- **Question 4:** Students may look at the problem and state all of the angles are 60°. Ask what equation they can use to check their answer.

Closure

- **Exit Ticket:** Find the value of *x*. Then classify the triangle.

a.
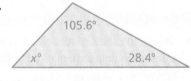
75; acute triangle

b.

46; obtuse triangle

Technology For the Teacher

The Dynamic Planning Tool
Editable Teacher's Resources at *BigIdeasMath.com*

EXAMPLE (2) **Finding Angle Measures**

Find the value of x. Then classify each triangle.

a. Flag of Jamaica

$$x + x + 128 = 180$$
$$2x + 128 = 180$$
$$2x = 52$$
$$x = 26$$

⁝ The value of x is 26. Two of
the sides are congruent. So,
it is an isosceles triangle.

b. Flag of Cuba

$$x + x + 60 = 180$$
$$2x + 60 = 180$$
$$2x = 120$$
$$x = 60$$

⁝ The value of x is 60. All
three angles are congruent.
So, it is an equilateral and
equiangular triangle.

EXAMPLE (3) **Standardized Test Practice**

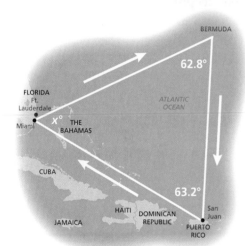

An airplane leaves from Miami and travels around the
Bermuda Triangle. What is the value of x?

(A) 26.8   (B) 27.2   (C) 54   (D) 64

Use what you know about the angle measures of a
triangle to write an equation.

$$x + 62.8 + 63.2 = 180 \qquad \text{Write equation.}$$
$$x + 126 = 180 \qquad \text{Add.}$$
$$x = 54 \qquad \text{Subtract 126 from each side.}$$

⁝ The value of x is 54. The correct answer is (C).

On Your Own

Now You're Ready
Exercises 9–11

Find the value of x. Then classify the triangle in as many ways
as possible.

3.

4.

5. In Example 3, the airplane leaves from Fort Lauderdale.
The angle measure at Bermuda is 63.9° and the angle
measure at San Juan is 61.8°. Find the value of x.

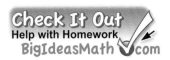
Check It Out
Help with Homework
BigIdeasMath ✓ com

 ## Vocabulary and Concept Check

1. **VOCABULARY** Compare equilateral and isosceles triangles.

2. **REASONING** Describe how to find the missing angle of the triangle.

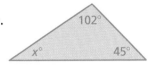
102°
x° 45°

 ## Practice and Problem Solving

Classify the triangle in as many ways as possible.

3.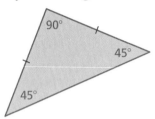
90°
45°
45°

4.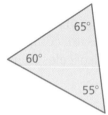
65°
60°
55°

5.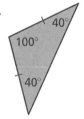
40°
100°
40°

Find the value of x. Then classify the triangle in as many ways as possible.

① 6.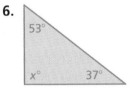
53°
x° 37°

7.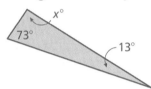
x°
73°
13°

8.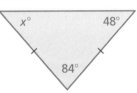
x° 48°
84°

② 9.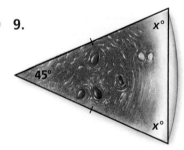
x°
45°
x°

10.
60°
x° x°

11.
132°
x° x°

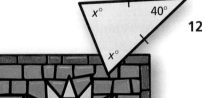
x° 40°
x°

12. **ERROR ANALYSIS** Describe
and correct the error
in classifying the triangle.

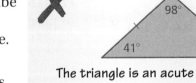
✗
98°
41° 41°

The triangle is an acute triangle,
because it has acute angles.

13. **MOSAIC TILE** A mosaic is
a pattern or picture made
of small pieces of
colored material.

a. Find the value of x.

b. Classify the triangle used in the mosaic in two ways.

Assignment Guide and Homework Check

Level	Day 1 Activity Assignment	Day 2 Lesson Assignment	Homework Check
Basic	3–5, 21–24	1, 2, 6–13	2, 6, 10, 12
Average	3–5, 21–24	1, 2, 7–17 odd, 12, 18	7, 9, 12, 15, 18
Advanced	3–5, 21–24	1, 2, 12, 14–20	12, 14, 16, 18

Common Errors

- **Exercises 3–11** Students may not classify the triangle using all the possible words. Encourage them to think about the vocabulary.
- **Exercises 6–11** Students may solve for *x*, but forget to classify the triangle. Remind them to read the directions carefully and to answer the question.
- **Exercises 14–17** Students may recognize that the angles do not form a triangle, but may not know how to change the first angle so that all three angles will make a triangle. If the sum of the measure is greater than 180°, encourage them to decrease the first angle measure. If the sum of the measure is less than 180°, encourage them to increase the first angle measure.

5.2 Record and Practice Journal

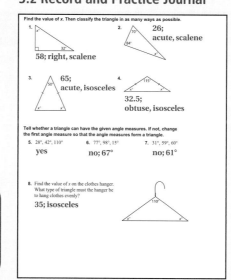

Find the value of x. Then classify the triangle in as many ways as possible.

1. 58; right, scalene

2. 26; acute, scalene

3. 65; acute, isosceles

4. 32.5; obtuse, isosceles

Tell whether a triangle can have the given angle measures. If not, change the first angle measure so that the angle measures form a triangle.

5. 28°, 42°, 110° yes

6. 77°, 98°, 15° no; 67°

7. 31°, 59°, 60° no; 61°

8. Find the value of x on the clothes hanger. What type of triangle must the hanger be to hang clothes evenly? 35; isosceles

 Vocabulary and Concept Check

1. An equilateral triangle has three congruent sides. An isosceles triangle has at least two congruent sides. So, an equilateral triangle is a specific type of isosceles triangle.

2. Subtract 102 and 45 from 180.

 Practice and Problem Solving

3. right isosceles triangle

4. acute scalene triangle

5. obtuse isosceles triangle

6. 90; right scalene triangle

7. 94; obtuse scalene triangle

8. 48; acute isosceles triangle

9. 67.5; acute isosceles triangle

10. 60; equilateral, equiangular, acute, and isosceles triangle

11. 24; obtuse isosceles triangle

12. The triangle is not an acute triangle because acute triangles have 3 angles less than 90°. The triangle is an obtuse triangle because it has one angle that is greater than 90°.

13. **a.** 70

    b. acute isosceles triangle

14. yes

15. no; 39.5°

16. no; $28\frac{2}{3}°$

17. yes

18. a. green: 65; purple: 25; red: 45

   b. The angles opposite the congruent sides are congruent.

   c. An isosceles triangle has at least two angles that are congruent.

19. See Additional Answers.

20. See *Taking Math Deeper*.

 Fair Game Review

21. $x + 9 + 12 = 28$; 7

22. $4x + 10 = 22$; 3

23. $6x = 30$; 5

24. A

Mini-Assessment

Find the value of x. Then classify each triangle.

1.

63; acute isosceles triangle

2.

60; equiangular, equilateral, acute, and isosceles triangle

3.

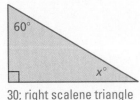

30; right scalene triangle

Taking Math Deeper

Exercise 20

This problem gives students an opportunity to experiment with angle measures. To perform the experiment, students need a flat surface and 15 playing cards. The experiment is easier if the surface is non-slippery, such as a computer mouse pad. Have your students experiment with stacking cards using different angles before describing the limitations for *x*.

 a. Solve for *x*.

$$x + x + 36 = 180$$
$$2x = 144$$
$$x = 72$$

 Describe the limitations for *x*.

   b. If $x = 60$, then the three cards form an equilateral triangle. This is not possible because the two upright cards would have to be exactly on the edges of the base card. So, $x > 60$.

   If $x = 90$, then the two upright cards would be vertical, which is not possible. The card structure would not be stable. So, $x < 90$.

 Test your conclusions.

Use a deck of cards to test your conclusions. In practice, the limits on *x* are probably closer to $70 < x < 80$.

Project

Use a deck of cards to research different ways of building card towers.

Reteaching and Enrichment Strategies

If students need help. . .	If students got it. . .
Resources by Chapter • Practice A and Practice B • Puzzle Time Record and Practice Journal Practice Differentiating the Lesson Lesson Tutorials Skills Review Handbook	Resources by Chapter • Enrichment and Extension Start the next section

Tell whether a triangle can have the given angle measures. If not, change the first angle measure so that the angle measures form a triangle.

14. 76.2°, 81.7°, 22.1°

15. 115.1°, 47.5°, 93°

16. $5\frac{2}{3}°$, $64\frac{1}{3}°$, 87°

17. $31\frac{3}{4}°$, $53\frac{1}{2}°$, $94\frac{3}{4}°$

18. CRITICAL THINKING Consider the three isosceles triangles.

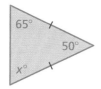
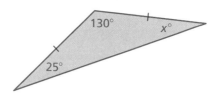

   a. Find the value of x for each triangle.

   b. What do you notice about the angle measures of each triangle?

   c. Write a rule about the angle measures of an isosceles triangle.

19. REASONING Explain why all triangles have at least two acute angles.

20. CARDS One method of stacking cards is shown.

   a. Find the value of x.

   b. **Critical Thinking** Describe how to stack the cards with different angles. Is the value of x limited? If so, what are the limitations? Explain your reasoning.

 Fair Game Review What you learned in previous grades & lessons

Write and solve an equation to find x. *(Skills Review Handbook)*

21. $P = 28$ cm

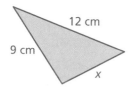

22. $P = 22$ in.

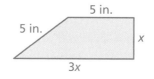

23. $P = 30$ m

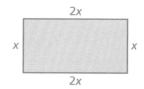

24. MULTIPLE CHOICE You have $10 for text messages. Each message costs $0.25. Which equation represents the amount of money you have after x messages? *(Section 2.1)*

   Ⓐ $y = -0.25x + 10$

   Ⓑ $y = 0.25x - 10$

   Ⓒ $y = -0.25x - 10$

   Ⓓ $y = 0.25x + 10$

5.3 Angles of Polygons

Essential Question How can you find a formula for the sum of the angle measures of any polygon?

1 ACTIVITY: The Sum of the Angle Measures of a Polygon

Work with a partner. Find the sum of the angle measures of each polygon with n sides.

a. **Sample:** Quadrilateral: $n = 4$

Draw a line that divides the quadrilateral into two triangles.

Because the sum of the angle measures of each triangle is 180°, the sum of the angle measures of the quadrilateral is 360°.

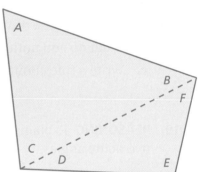

$$(A + B + C) + (D + E + F) = 180° + 180°$$
$$= 360°$$

b. Pentagon: $n = 5$

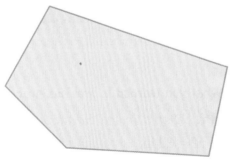

c. Hexagon: $n = 6$

d. Heptagon: $n = 7$

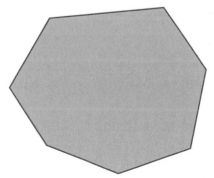

e. Octagon: $n = 8$

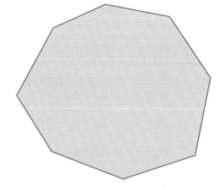

Laurie's Notes

Introduction

For the Teacher

- **Goal:** Students will investigate the sum of the angle measures of several polygons.
- You may need to review the definition of a polygon: A polygon is a closed plane figure made up of 3 or more line segments that intersect only at their endpoints.

Motivate

- ❓ "How many of you are looking forward to getting your driver's license?"
- Tell them that they will likely be tested on road signs.
- Draw several shapes and ask students if they know the names of the shapes and what they are used for on highway signs.

Activity Notes

Activity 1

- Work through part (a) with students.
- Draw the quadrilateral on the board.
- ❓ Use your non-writing hand to cover up the lower portion of the quadrilateral and ask, "What do you know about the angles of this triangle?" Angle measures sum to 180°.
- Label the angles *A*, *B*, and *C* as shown and write: $A + B + C = 180$.
- ❓ Now cover up the top portion of the quadrilateral and ask, "What do you know about the angles of this triangle?" Angle measures sum to 180°.
- Label the angles *D*, *E*, and *F* as shown and write: $D + E + F = 180$.
- Write the two equations together: $(A + B + C) + (D + E + F) = 360$.
- Note that when you combine *C* and *D*, it forms one of the angles of the original quadrilateral. The same is true for *B* and *F*.
- ❓ "Would this same technique work for any quadrilateral?" yes
- ❓ "What can you conclude about the sum of the angle measures of any quadrilateral?" Sum to 360°.
- Explain that they will use a similar technique to find the sum of the angle measures of polygons with more than 4 sides. It is important that the diagonals drawn divide the polygon into triangles whose angles are part of the original polygon. The simplest method is to draw the diagonals from one vertex.
- Ask volunteers to share their results with the class.
- **Another Way:** Cut polygons out of waxed paper. Tear the angles off, one at each vertex, similar to Activity 1 of Section 5.2. If you place the four angles about a point, they will *fill the space*, meaning 360°. Do this on the overhead. Now do the same thing for the pentagon. Place the 5 angles next to one another, about a point. The 5th angle, and perhaps a portion of the 4th, will overlap the angles below them. The waxed paper should show that you have gone 1.5 revolutions about the point, or 540°.

Standards of Learning

8.6(b) The student will measure angles of less than 360°.

Previous Learning

Students should know how to solve multi-step equations.

Activity Materials
Textbook
• waxed paper • straightedge

Start Thinking! and Warm Up

| Activity 5.3 | **Start Thinking!** For use before Activity 5.3 |

Activity 5.3 Warm Up For use before Activity 5.3

Find the value of *y* for the given value of *x*.

1. $y = \dfrac{1}{2}x - 3;\ x = -2$

2. $y = -x + 2;\ x = 15$

3. $y = 10(x - 2);\ x = 10$

4. $y = 13(x - 3);\ x = 1$

5. $y = \dfrac{3}{2}x + \dfrac{5}{2};\ x = -2$

6. $y = 3(x + 4);\ x = -5$

5.3 Record and Practice Journal

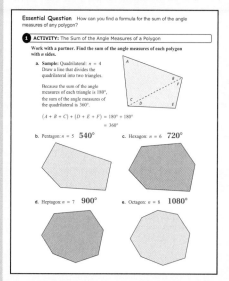

Essential Question How can you find a formula for the sum of the angle measures of any polygon?

1 ACTIVITY: The Sum of the Angle Measures of a Polygon

Work with a partner. Find the sum of the angle measures of each polygon with *n* sides.

a. **Sample:** Quadrilateral: *n* = 4
Draw a line that divides the quadrilateral into two triangles.

Because the sum of the angle measures of each triangle is 180°, the sum of the angle measures of the quadrilateral is 360°.

$(A + B + C) + (D + E + F) = 180° + 180°$
$= 360°$

b. Pentagon: *n* = 5 **540°**   c. Hexagon: *n* = 6 **720°**

d. Heptagon: *n* = 7 **900°**   e. Octagon: *n* = 8 **1080°**

Kinesthetic

Another way to discover the sum of the angle measures of a polygon is to have the students cut the polygon into triangles. This can be done for convex and concave polygons.

5.3 Record and Practice Journal

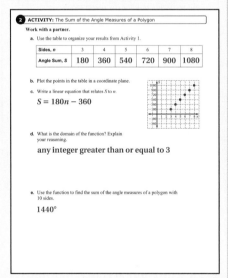

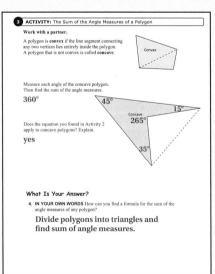

Laurie's Notes

Activity 2

- Students should know that the first value is 180°. They should recognize that the remaining values are multiples of 180. Note that the vertical axis has been scaled by increments of 180 to make plotting easier and more accurate.

- **?** "What is the slope of the line? Explain." slope = 180; When n increases by 1 (run), S increases by 180 (rise).

- Students may have difficulty with part (d). First, the domain must be only whole numbers because you cannot have 3.5 sides. Second, n must be greater than or equal to 3 because a triangle has the least number of sides of any polygon.

- **?** "What do you call a domain that is not continuous?" discrete

- **Connection:** Another way to write the formula $S = 180n - 360$ is $S = 180(n - 2)$. The quantity $(n - 2)$ is the number of triangles that can be made when you draw all the diagonals from one vertex in an n-gon. This number is multiplied by 180 because there are 180° in every one of the triangles.

$n = 3$	$n = 4$	$n = 5$	$n = 6$
1 triangle	2 triangles	3 triangles	4 triangles

Activity 3

- Students may have heard the words **convex** and **concave** before. These words are often used to describe a lens or mirror. Students will say that a concave polygon *caves in* or is *dented in*.

- **Note:** The rule for the sum of the angle measures of a polygon *does* apply to concave polygons. Students can use the triangle approach in Activity 1 to see this. All you need to do is include angle measures that are greater than 180°.

What Is Your Answer?

- **Neighbor Check** Have students work independently and then have their neighbor check their work. Have students discuss any discrepancies.

Closure

- **Exit Ticket:** Use your equation to find the sum of the angle measures of a polygon with 12 sides. 1800°

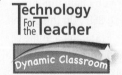

Technology For the Teacher

The Dynamic Planning Tool
Editable Teacher's Resources at *BigIdeasMath.com*

2 ACTIVITY: The Sum of the Angle Measures of a Polygon

Work with a partner.

a. Use the table to organize your results from Activity 1.

Sides, n	3	4	5	6	7	8
Angle Sum, S						

b. Plot the points in the table in a coordinate plane.

c. Write a linear equation that relates S to n.

d. What is the domain of the function? Explain your reasoning.

e. Use the function to find the sum of the angle measures of a polygon with 10 sides.

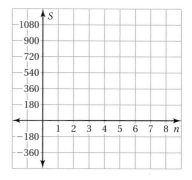

3 ACTIVITY: The Sum of the Angle Measures of a Polygon

Work with a partner.

A polygon is convex if the line segment connecting any two vertices lies entirely inside the polygon. A polygon that is not convex is called concave.

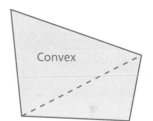

Measure each angle of the concave polygon. Then find the sum of the angle measures.

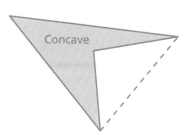

Does the equation you found in Activity 2 apply to concave polygons? Explain.

What Is Your Answer?

4. IN YOUR OWN WORDS How can you find a formula for the sum of the angle measures of any polygon?

Practice

Use what you learned about angles of polygons to complete Exercises 4–6 on page 215.

Check It Out
Lesson Tutorials
BigIdeasMath.com

A **polygon** is a closed plane figure made up of three or more line segments that intersect only at their endpoints.

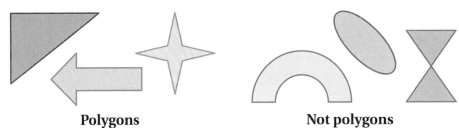

Polygons   **Not polygons**

Key Idea

Angle Measures of a Polygon

The sum S of the angle measures of a polygon with n sides is

$$S = (n - 2) \cdot 180°.$$

EXAMPLE ① **Finding the Sum of the Angle Measures of a Polygon**

Reading

For polygons whose names you have not learned, you can use the phrase "*n*-gon," where *n* is the number of sides. For example, a 15-gon is a polygon with 15 sides.

Find the sum of the angle measures of the school crossing sign.

The sign is in the shape of a pentagon. It has 5 sides.

$S = (n - 2) \cdot 180°$ Write the formula.

$ = (5 - 2) \cdot 180°$ Substitute 5 for *n*.

$ = 3 \cdot 180°$ Subtract.

$ = 540°$ Multiply.

⋮• The sum of the angle measures is 540°.

On Your Own

Now You're Ready
Exercises 7–9

Find the sum of the angle measures of the green polygon.

1.
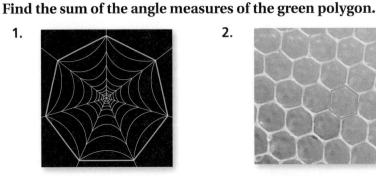

2.
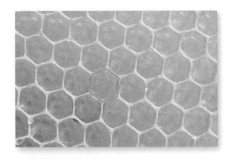

◀) Multi-Language Glossary at BigIdeasMath.com.

Laurie's Notes

Introduction

Connect
- **Yesterday:** Students explored finding the sum of the angle measures of a polygon.
- **Today:** Students will use a formula to find the missing angle measure of a polygon.

Motivate
- **?** "Did you ever wonder why bees use a hexagonal structure for their honeycomb? Why not squares? or circles? or octagons?"
- Draw a few cells of the honeycomb.

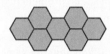

- Mathematicians have concluded that a hexagon is the most appropriate geometric form for the maximum use of a given area. This means that a hexagonal cell requires the minimum amount of wax for construction while it stores the maximum amount of honey.

Lesson Notes

Key Idea
- Write the definition of a polygon. Draw examples of shapes which are and are not polygons. Students should be able to explain why some are not polygons.
- In all of the samples shown, the interior is shaded. The polygon is the figure formed by the line segments. The polygonal region contains the interior of the polygon.
- Write the Key Idea. This is the same equation that students wrote yesterday, but in the more common form. This form highlights the fact that the sum is a multiple of 180°.

Example 1
- Review the names of common polygons: Triangle (3), Quadrilateral (4), Pentagon (5), Hexagon (6), Octagon (8), and Decagon (10). It is also common to say n-gon and replace n with 9 to talk about a 9-sided polygon.
- Read the problem. The polygon is a pentagon.
- Write the equation, substitute 5 for n, and solve.

On Your Own
- **Think-Pair-Share:** Students should read each question independently and then work with a partner to answer the questions. When they have answered the questions, the pair should compare their answers with another group and discuss any discrepancies.
- **?** "What are the names of the polygons in Questions 1 and 2?"
  7-gon or heptagon; hexagon

Goal
Today's lesson is finding angle measures of a **polygon**.

Start Thinking! and Warm Up

Lesson 5.3 **Warm Up** For use before Lesson 5.3

Lesson 5.3 **Start Thinking!** For use before Lesson 5.3

Explain how you can draw an octagon on graph paper to make it easy to find the angle measures. Use this method to find each angle measure.

What is the sum of the angle measures? Does this agree with the equation you wrote in Activity 2?

Extra Example 1
Find the sum of the angle measures of the polygon.

720°

On Your Own

1. 900°
2. 720°

Extra Example 2

Find the value of *x*.

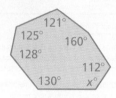

124

On Your Own

3. 105

4. 75

5. 35

Example 2

- **Connection:** This example integrates equation solving with finding a missing angle.
- **?** "How many sides does the polygon have?" 7
- **?** "How do you find the sum of the measures of all of the angles of a 7-gon?" Solve $(7 - 2)180 = 900$.
- Once the sum is known, write and solve the equation as shown. Caution students to be careful with their arithmetic.

On Your Own

- Students should check with their neighbor to make sure they are setting up the equation correctly. Each problem has two parts: Determining the sum of all of the angle measures, and then writing the equation to solve for the missing angle.
- In Question 4, remind students that the symbol for a right angle means the angle measures 90°.
- In Question 5, two angles are missing, each with a measure of $2x°$. The sum of the angle measures of this pentagon is 540°, so $2x + 145 + 145 + 2x + 110 = 540$. The steps are to combine like terms, isolate the variable, and solve.
- **Common Error:** Students will solve for the variable correctly, but then forget to substitute this value back into the variable expression to solve for the angle measure. In Question 5, students were only asked to solve for *x*. If they had been asked to find the measure of the angle, there would be one last step. In this case, $x = 35$ and the two missing angles are each 70°.

Example 3

- Review the definition of a regular polygon. Point out to students that squares and equilateral triangles are examples of regular polygons.
- A regular hexagon has 6 congruent angles. If the angle measures of a hexagon sum to 720° and the 6 angles are congruent, it should make sense to students why they divide 720 by 6.
- Look back to the honeycomb you drew at the beginning of the lesson. There are three 120° angles about one point.
- You can show a video of the cloud system from the website *jpl.nasa.gov*.

Extra Example 3

Find the measure of each angle of a regular 12-gon.

150°

English Language Learners

Vocabulary

Preview the *Key Vocabulary* in this chapter. Understanding geometry depends on understanding the terminology used. Have students write key vocabulary words in their notebooks. Include definitions and examples to help distinguish between words (e.g., convex polygon and concave polygon).

EXAMPLE 2 **Finding an Angle Measure of a Polygon**

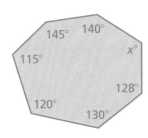

Find the value of x.

Step 1: The polygon has 7 sides. Find the sum of the angle measures.

$$S = (n - 2) \cdot 180°$$ Write the formula.

$$= (7 - 2) \cdot 180°$$ Substitute 7 for n.

$$= 900°$$ Simplify. The sum of the angle measures is 900°.

Step 2: Write and solve an equation.

$$140 + 145 + 115 + 120 + 130 + 128 + x = 900$$

$$778 + x = 900$$

$$x = 122$$

∴ The value of x is 122.

On Your Own

Find the value of x.

Now You're Ready
Exercises 12–14

3.

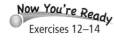

135°
110°   125°
125°   120°
$x°$

4.

$x°$
115°
80°

5.

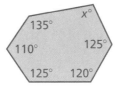

145° 145°
$2x°$ $2x°$
110°

In a **regular polygon**, all of the sides are congruent and all of the angles are congruent.

EXAMPLE 3 **Real-Life Application**

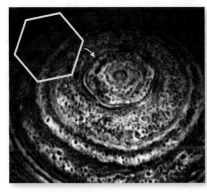

The hexagon is about 15,000 miles across. Approximately four Earths could fit inside it.

A cloud system discovered on Saturn is in the approximate shape of a regular hexagon. Find the measure of each angle of the hexagon.

Step 1: A hexagon has 6 sides. Find the sum of the angle measures.

$$S = (n - 2) \cdot 180°$$ Write the formula.

$$= (6 - 2) \cdot 180°$$ Substitute 6 for n.

$$= 720°$$ Simplify. The sum of the angle measures is 720°.

Step 2: Divide the sum by the number of angles, 6.

$$720° \div 6 = 120°$$

∴ The measure of each angle is 120°.

On Your Own

Now You're Ready
Exercises 16–18

Find the measure of each angle of the regular polygon.

6. octagon   **7.** decagon   **8.** 18-gon

 Key Idea

Convex and Concave Polygons

A polygon is **convex** if every line segment connecting any two vertices lies entirely inside the polygon.

A polygon is **concave** if at least one line segment connecting any two vertices lies outside the polygon.

EXAMPLE ④ Identifying Convex and Concave Polygons

Tell whether the polygon is *convex* or *concave*. Explain.

The Meaning of a Word

Concave

To remember the term con**cave**, think of a polygon that is "**cave**d in."

"Caved in"

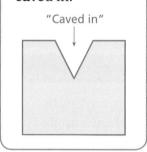

a.

b.

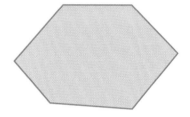

∴ A line segment connecting two vertices lies outside the polygon. So, the polygon is concave.

∴ No line segment connecting two vertices lies outside the polygon. So, the polygon is convex.

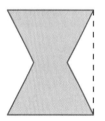

On Your Own

Now You're Ready
Exercises 22–24

Tell whether the polygon is *convex* or *concave*. Explain.

9.   **10.**   **11.**

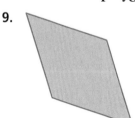      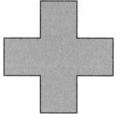

Laurie's Notes

On Your Own

- **Think-Pair-Share:** Students should read each question independently and then work with a partner to answer the questions. When they have answered the questions, the pair should compare their answers with another group and discuss any discrepancies.

Key Idea

- Write the definitions of convex and concave polygons. Draw samples of each. Note the *Meaning of a Word* box.

Example 4

- Students usually do not have trouble making sense of convex and concave polygons.

Closure

- A pentagon has two right angles and the other three angles are all congruent. What is the measure of one of the missing angles? 120°

On Your Own

6. 135°

7. 144°

8. 160°

Extra Example 4

Tell whether the polygon is *convex* or *concave*. Explain.

a.

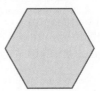

convex; No line segment connecting two vertices lies outside the polygon.

b.

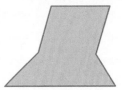

concave; A line segment connecting two vertices lies outside the polygon.

On Your Own

9. convex; No line segment connecting two vertices lies outside the polygon.

10. concave; A line segment connecting two vertices lies outside the polygon.

11. concave; A line segment connecting two vertices lies outside the polygon.

1. *Sample answer:*

2. The second figure doesn't belong because it is not made up entirely of line segments.

3. What is the measure of an angle of a regular pentagon?; 108°; 540°

 Practice and Problem Solving

4. 360°

5. 1260°

6. 900°

7. 1080°

8. 720°

9. 1800°

10. The right side of the formula is $(n - 2) \cdot 180°$, not $n \cdot 180°$.
$$S = (n - 2) \cdot 180°$$
$$= (13 - 2) \cdot 180°$$
$$= 11 \cdot 180°$$
$$= 1980°$$

11. no; The angle measures given add up to 535°, but the sum of the angle measures of a pentagon is 540°.

12. 43

13. 135

14. 90

15. 140°

16. 60°

17. 140°

18. 150°

Assignment Guide and Homework Check

Level	Day 1 Activity Assignment	Day 2 Lesson Assignment	Homework Check
Basic	4–6, 33–37	1–3, 7, 9–13, 16, 17, 19–23, 27	7, 12, 16, 20, 22
Average	4–6, 33–37	1–3, 7–25 odd, 22, 27–30	7, 13, 17, 22, 30
Advanced	4–6, 33–37	1–3, 11, 14, 15, 18–21, 23–26, 29–32	14, 18, 24, 26, 30

Common Errors

- **Exercises 4–6** Students may struggle dividing the polygon into triangles. Encourage them to trace the polygon in pen in their notebooks, and then draw triangles with a pencil so that they can erase lines if necessary.
- **Exercises 7–9** Students may forget to subtract 2 from the number of sides when using the formula to find the sum of the angle measures. Remind them of the formula and encourage them to write the formula before substituting the number of sides.
- **Exercise 11** Students may say that because the sum of the angle measures is close to the value found when using the formula, a pentagon can have these angle measures. Remind them that the sum of the angle measures must be *exactly* the same as the sum found with the formula for the polygon to be drawn with the given angles.

5.3 Record and Practice Journal

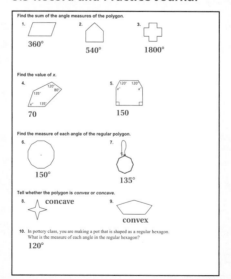

 Vocabulary and Concept Check

1. **VOCABULARY** Draw a regular polygon that has three sides.

2. **WHICH ONE DOESN'T BELONG?** Which figure does *not* belong with the other three? Explain your reasoning.

3. **DIFFERENT WORDS, SAME QUESTION** Which is different? Find "both" answers.

What is the measure of an angle of a regular pentagon?	What is the sum of the angle measures of a convex pentagon?
What is the sum of the angle measures of a regular pentagon?	What is the sum of the angle measures of a concave pentagon?

 Practice and Problem Solving

Use triangles to find the sum of the angle measures of the polygon.

4.

5.

6.

Find the sum of the angle measures of the polygon.

① 7.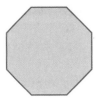

8.

9.

10. **ERROR ANALYSIS** Describe and correct the error in finding the sum of the angle measures of a 13-gon.

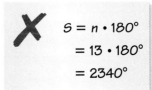
$S = n \cdot 180°$
$= 13 \cdot 180°$
$= 2340°$

11. **NUMBER SENSE** Can a pentagon have angles that measure 120°, 105°, 65°, 150°, and 95°? Explain.

Find the value of *x*.

② 12.

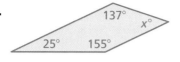

13.

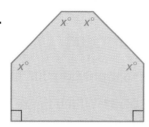

14.

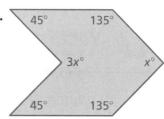

15. **REASONING** The sum of the angle measures in a regular polygon is 1260°. What is the measure of one of the angles of the polygon?

Find the measure of each angle of the regular polygon.

③ 16.

17.

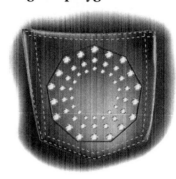

18.

19. **ERROR ANALYSIS** Describe and correct the error in finding the measure of each angle of a regular 20-gon.

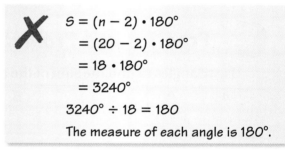

$S = (n - 2) \cdot 180°$
$= (20 - 2) \cdot 180°$
$= 18 \cdot 180°$
$= 3240°$
$3240° \div 18 = 180$
The measure of each angle is 180°.

20. **FIRE HYDRANT** A fire hydrant bolt is in the shape of a regular pentagon.

   a. What is the measure of each angle?

   b. Why are fire hydrants made this way?

21. **PUZZLE** The angles of a regular polygon each measure 165°. How many sides does the polygon have?

Tell whether the polygon is *convex* or *concave*. Explain.

④ 22.

23.

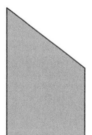

24.

25. **CRITICAL THINKING** Can a concave polygon be regular? Explain.

26. **OPEN-ENDED** Draw a polygon that has congruent sides but is not regular.

Common Errors

- **Exercises 12–14** Students may forget to include one or more of the given angles when writing an equation for the missing angles. For example, in Exercise 13, students may write $4x = 720$. Remind them to include all of the angles. Encourage them to write the equation and then count the number of terms to make sure that there are the same number of terms as angles before simplifying.

- **Exercises 16–18** Students may find the sum of the angle measures of the regular polygon, but forget to divide by the number of angles to answer the question. Remind them that they are finding the measure of *one* angle. Because all the angles are congruent (by the definition of a regular polygon), they can divide the sum of the angle measures by the number of angles.

- **Exercises 22–24** Students may not try to connect all the vertices of the polygon and state that the polygon is convex. Remind them to connect all the vertices with all the others. One strategy is to start with one vertex and connect it to all the other vertices, and then rotate clockwise to the next vertex and repeat the process.

English Language Learners
Vocabulary

Many English mathematical names are influenced by Latin and Greek names for numbers.

English	Latin	Greek
one	unus	heis
two	duo	duo
three	tres	tria
four	quattuor	tettara
five	quinque	pente
six	sex	hex
seven	septe	hepta
eight	octo	okto
nine	nove	ennea
ten	dece	deka

Spanish speakers will recognize the similarity of numbers in Spanish to the numbers in Latin.

 Practice and Problem Solving

19. The sum of the angle measures should have been divided by the number of angles, 20. $3240° \div 20 = 162°$; The measure of each angle is $162°$.

20. **a.** $108°$

    b. *Sample answer:* So the same wrench can unscrew any fire hydrant bolt.

21. 24 sides

22. concave; A line segment connecting two vertices lies outside the polygon.

23. convex; No line segment connecting two vertices lies outside the polygon.

24. concave; A line segment connecting two vertices lies outside the polygon.

25. no; All of the angles would not be congruent.

26. See Additional Answers.

Practice and Problem Solving

27. $135°$

28.

29. $120°$

30. a. 11 sides

b. $147°$

31. See *Taking Math Deeper*.

32. See *Additional Answers*.

Fair Game Review

33. 9

34. 2

35. 3

36. 6

37. D

Mini-Assessment

Find the sum of the angle measures of the polygon.

1.

$1080°$

2.

$1440°$

3. Tell whether the polygon is *convex* or *concave*. Explain.

convex; No line segment connecting two vertices lies outside the polygon.

Taking Math Deeper

Exercise 31

This problem is an interesting comparison of linear and nonlinear functions. In Activity 2 on page 211, students discovered that the sum S of the angle measures of a polygon is a linear function of the number n of sides of the polygon.

$$S = (n - 2) \cdot 180$$
$$= 180n - 360$$

However, when you change the formula to represent the angle measure a of each angle in a regular polygon, the function is no longer linear.

$$a = \frac{S}{n} = 180 - \frac{360}{n}$$

 Complete the table.

Sides of a Regular Polygon, n	3	4	5	6	7	8	9	10
Measure of One Angle (degrees), a	60	90	108	120	128.6	135	140	144

 Algebraic Reasoning: The pattern is not linear because the function

$$a = 180 - \frac{360}{n}$$

cannot be written in slope-intercept form, $a = mn + b$.

 Graphical Reasoning: The function is not linear because the points in the graph do not lie on a line.

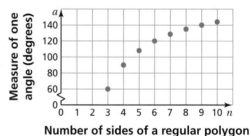

Number of sides of a regular polygon

Reteaching and Enrichment Strategies

If students need help. . .	If students got it. . .
Resources by Chapter • Practice A and Practice B • Puzzle Time Record and Practice Journal Practice Differentiating the Lesson Lesson Tutorials Skills Review Handbook	Resources by Chapter • Enrichment and Extension • School-to-Work Start the next section

27. STAINED GLASS The center of the stained glass window is in the shape of a regular polygon. What is the measure of each angle of the polygon?

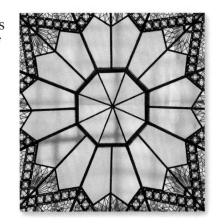

28. PENTAGON Draw a pentagon that has two right angles, two 45° angles, and one 270° angle.

29. GAZEBO The floor of a gazebo is in the shape of a heptagon. Four of the angles measure 135°. The other angles have equal measures. Find the measure of each of the remaining angles.

30. MONEY The border of a Susan B. Anthony dollar is in the shape of a regular polygon.

   a. How many sides does the polygon have?

   b. What is the measure of each angle of the border? Round your answer to the nearest degree.

31. REASONING Copy and complete the table. Does the table represent a linear function? Explain.

Sides of a Regular Polygon, *n*	3	4	5	6	7	8	9	10
Measure of One Angle, *a*								

32. ≡Geometry≡ When tiles can be used to cover a floor with no empty spaces, the collection of tiles is called a *tessellation*.

   a. Create a tessellation using equilateral triangles.

   b. Find two more regular polygons that form tessellations.

   c. Create a tessellation that uses two different regular polygons.

 Fair Game Review *What you learned in previous grades & lessons*

Solve the proportion. *(Skills Review Handbook)*

33. $\dfrac{x}{12} = \dfrac{3}{4}$ **34.** $\dfrac{14}{21} = \dfrac{x}{3}$ **35.** $\dfrac{x}{9} = \dfrac{2}{6}$ **36.** $\dfrac{4}{10} = \dfrac{x}{15}$

37. MULTIPLE CHOICE The ratio of tulips to daisies is 3 : 5. Which of the following could be the total number of tulips and daisies? *(Skills Review Handbook)*

   Ⓐ 6   **Ⓑ** 10   **Ⓒ** 15   **Ⓓ** 16

You can use an **example and non-example chart** to list examples and non-examples of a vocabulary word or item. Here is an example and non-example chart for complementary angles.

Complementary Angles

Examples	Non-Examples
30° 60°	30° 150°
45° 45°	
16°	119°
89°, 1°	63°, 26°

On Your Own

Make an example and non-example chart to help you study these topics.

1. isosceles triangles

2. equilateral triangles

3. regular polygons

4. convex polygons

5. concave polygons

After you complete this chapter, make example and non-example charts for the following topics.

6. similar triangles

7. transformations

8. composite figures

"What do you think of my example & non-example chart for popular cat toys?"

Sample Answers

1. Isosceles Triangles

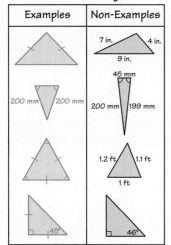

Examples	Non-Examples

2. Equilateral Triangles

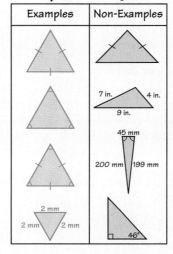

Examples	Non-Examples

3. Regular Polygons

Examples	Non-Examples

4. Convex Polygons

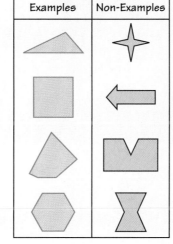

Examples	Non-Examples

5. Concave Polygons

Examples	Non-Examples

Technology
For the Teacher

Vocabulary Puzzle Builder

Answers

1. neither

2. complementary

3. supplementary

4. adjacent; $x = 146$

5. adjacent; $x = 16$

6. vertical; $x = 59$

7. $x = 60$; isosceles, equilateral, equiangular, acute

8. $x = 115$; obtuse, scalene

9. $x = 45$; right, isosceles

10. $1080°$

11. concave

12. $x = 58$

13. $x = 126$

14. $x = 70$

15. $\angle 1 = 65°$, $\angle 2 = 115°$, $\angle 3 = 65°$

16. 25 sides

17. isosceles, acute

Assessment Book

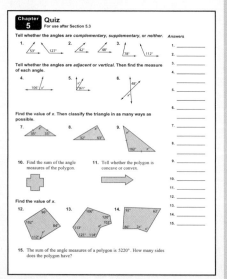

Alternative Quiz Ideas

100% Quiz	Math Log
Error Notebook	**Notebook Quiz**
Group Quiz	Partner Quiz
Homework Quiz	Pass the Paper

Notebook Quiz

A notebook quiz is used to check students' notebooks. Students should be told at the beginning of the course what the expectations are for their notebooks: notes, class work, homework, date, problem number, goals, definitions, or anything else that you feel is important for your class. They also need to know that it is their responsibility to obtain the notes when they miss class.

1. On a certain day, what was the answer to the warm up question?

2. On a certain day, how was this vocabulary term defined?

3. For Section 5.2, what is the answer to On Your Own Question 1?

4. For Section 5.3, what is the answer to the Essential Question?

5. On a certain day, what was the homework assignment?

Give the students 5 minutes to answer these questions.

Reteaching and Enrichment Strategies

If students need help. . .	If students got it. . .
Resources by Chapter • Study Help • Practice A and Practice B • Puzzle Time Lesson Tutorials *BigIdeasMath.com* Practice Quiz Practice from the Test Generator	Resources by Chapter • Enrichment and Extension • School-to-Work Game Closet at *BigIdeasMath.com* Start the next section

Technology For the Teacher

Answer Presentation Tool
Big Ideas Test Generator

Tell whether the angles are *complementary*, *supplementary*, or *neither*.   *(Section 5.1)*

1.
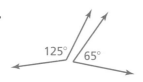

2.

3.
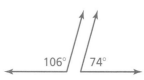

Tell whether the angles are *adjacent* or *vertical*. Then find the value of *x*.   *(Section 5.1)*

4.
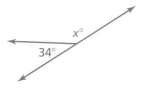

5.

6.
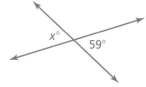

Find the value of *x*. Then classify the triangle in as many ways as possible.   *(Section 5.2)*

7.

8.
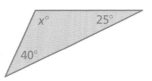

9.

10. Find the sum of the angle measures of the polygon.   *(Section 5.3)*

11. Tell whether the polygon is concave or convex.   *(Section 5.3)*

Find the value of *x*.   *(Section 5.3)*

12.
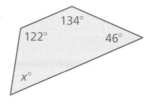

13.
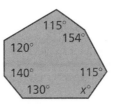

14.
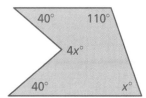

15. **RAILROAD CROSSING** What are the measures of the other three angles formed by the intersection of the road and the railroad tracks?   *(Section 5.1)*

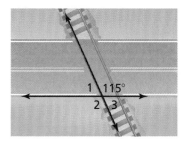

16. **REASONING** The sum of the angle measures of a polygon is 4140°. How many sides does the polygon have?   *(Section 5.3)*

17. **FLAG** Classify the triangle on the flag of the Czech Republic in as many ways as possible.   *(Section 5.2)*

STANDARDS
OF LEARNING
8.3

Essential Question Which properties of triangles make them special among all other types of polygons?

You already know that two triangles are **similar** if and only if the ratios of their corresponding side lengths are equal.

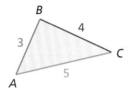

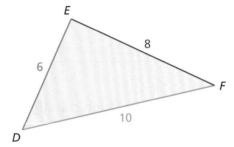

For example, $\triangle ABC$ is similar to $\triangle DEF$ because the ratios of their corresponding side lengths are equal.

$$\frac{6}{3} = \frac{10}{5} = \frac{8}{4}$$

1 ACTIVITY: Angles of Similar Triangles

Work with a partner.

- Discuss how to make a triangle that is larger than $\triangle XYZ$ and has the *same* angle measures as $\triangle XYZ$.

- Measure the lengths of the sides of the two triangles.

- Find the ratios of the corresponding side lengths. Are they all the same? What can you conclude?

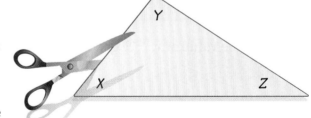

Laurie's Notes

Introduction

For the Teacher

- **Goal:** Students will explore properties of similar triangles.
- **Big Idea:** Triangles are special in several ways because these properties are not true for quadrilaterals.
  - First, when the corresponding sides are proportional, the corresponding angles are congruent. For quadrilaterals, this can be contradicted by a square and a rhombus.

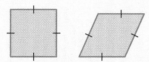

  - Second, when the corresponding angles are congruent, the corresponding sides are proportional. For quadrilaterals, this can be contradicted by a square and a rectangle.

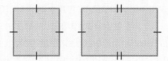

Motivate

- The word *similar* and *simile* sound alike! A simile is a figure of speech in which two essentially unlike things are compared. For example, "He eats like a horse" or "She is as slow as molasses."
- Ask students to give other examples.

Activity Notes

Activity 1

- Explain the definition of similar triangles by drawing the triangles shown. Label the side lengths and write the ratios of corresponding sides.
- The goal of this activity is to make two triangles with the same angle measures whose side lengths are not congruent. To check if the angles are congruent, measure the angles of the second triangle with a protractor.
- **Big Idea:** If two triangles have the same angle measures, then the triangles are similar. This is a property that is only true for triangles.
- **Another Way:** Ask students to make a triangle with angles of 40°, 60°, and 80° using a protractor. Do not specify the side length. Use a metric ruler to measure the 3 sides to the nearest centimeter. Each pair of students will find the ratio of corresponding sides for their two triangles. Using a calculator, compare the three ratios; they should be the same.

Standards of Learning

8.3(a) The student will solve practical problems involving rational numbers, percents, ratios, and proportions.

Previous Learning

Students should know the definition of similar triangles.

Activity Materials
Textbook
- scissors - ruler - protractor - calculator

Start Thinking! and Warm Up

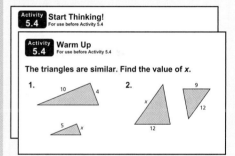

5.4 Record and Practice Journal

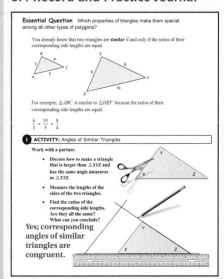

Visual

Make pairs of similar polygons out of cardboard. Hand out the polygons to your students. Have students find another student in the room with a polygon similar to their own.

5.4 Record and Practice Journal

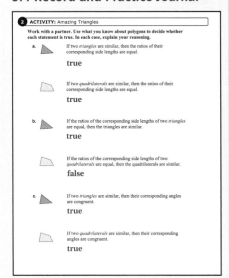

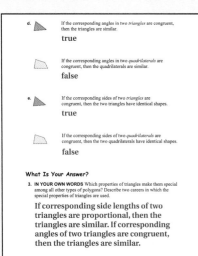

Laurie's Notes

Activity 2

• In this activity, students must read carefully and critically. The questions presented are related to the Big Ideas discussed on the previous page.

• To help students visualize the statements, make simple models out of bendable straws. By making a slit in the straws, one straw can be inserted into another to make polygons. Make samples of different sized equilateral triangles, squares, and rectangles. Because the straws are bendable, the square can become a rhombus, and the rectangle can become a parallelogram.

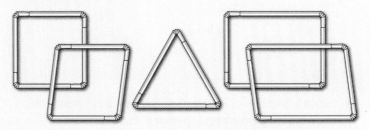

• When students have finished, discuss each statement. Have models available to help with the explanation. Each statement is true for triangles! Only parts (a) and (c) are true for quadrilaterals.
  • Part (a): This is the definition of similar polygons.
  • Part (b): Use the square and rhombus to show it is false.
  • Part (c): This is the definition of similar polygons.
  • Part (d): Use the square and rectangle to show it is false.
  • Part (e): Use the square and rhombus to show it is false.

What Is Your Answer?

• **Think-Pair-Share:** Students should read each question independently and then work with a partner to answer the questions. When they have answered the questions, the pair should compare their answers with another group and discuss any discrepancies.

Closure

• True or False?
  1. All equilateral triangles are similar. *true*
  2. All squares are similar. *true*
  3. All rhombuses are similar. *false*
  4. All rectangles are similar. *false*

Technology
For the **Teacher**

Dynamic Classroom

The Dynamic Planning Tool
Editable Teacher's Resources at *BigIdeasMath.com*

Work with a partner. Use what you know about polygons to decide whether each statement is true. In each case, explain your reasoning.

a.   If two triangles are similar, then the ratios of their corresponding side lengths are equal.

  If two quadrilaterals are similar, then the ratios of their corresponding side lengths are equal.

b.   If the ratios of the corresponding sides of two triangles are equal, then the triangles are similar.

  If the ratios of the corresponding sides of two quadrilaterals are equal, then the quadrilaterals are similar.

c.   If two triangles are similar, then their corresponding angles are congruent.

  If two quadrilaterals are similar, then their corresponding angles are congruent.

d.   If the corresponding angles in two triangles are congruent, then the triangles are similar.

  If the corresponding angles in two quadrilaterals are congruent, then the quadrilaterals are similar.

e.   If the corresponding sides of two triangles are congruent, then the two triangles have identical shapes.

  If the corresponding sides of two quadrilaterals are congruent, then the two quadrilaterals have identical shapes.

What Is Your Answer?

3. IN YOUR OWN WORDS Which properties of triangles make them special among all other types of polygons? Describe two careers in which the special properties of triangles are used.

 Use what you learned about similar triangles to complete Exercises 3 and 4 on page 224.

5.4 Lesson

Check It Out
Lesson Tutorials
BigIdeasMath✓com

Key Vocabulary 🔊
similar triangles,
  p. 222
indirect measurement,
  p. 223

Triangles that have the same shape but not necessarily the same size are **similar triangles**.

🔑 Key Idea

Angles of Similar Triangles

Words Two triangles have the same angle measures if and only if they are similar.

Example

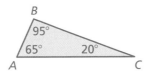
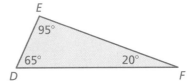

Triangle *ABC* is similar to triangle *DEF*: △*ABC* ~ △*DEF*.

Study Tip

If two angles in one triangle are congruent to two angles in another triangle, then the third angles are also congruent.

EXAMPLE ① **Identifying Similar Triangles**

Tell whether the triangles are similar. Explain.

a.

$$75 + 50 + x = 180$$
$$125 + x = 180$$
$$x = 55$$

$$y + 50 + 55 = 180$$
$$y + 105 = 180$$
$$y = 75$$

∴ The triangles have the same angle measures, 75°, 50°, and 55°. So, they are similar.

b.

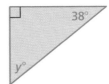

$$x + 90 + 42 = 180$$
$$x + 132 = 180$$
$$x = 48$$

$$90 + 38 + y = 180$$
$$128 + y = 180$$
$$y = 52$$

∴ The triangles do not have the same angle measures. So, they are not similar.

🔊 Multi-Language Glossary at BigIdeasMath✓com.

Laurie's Notes

Introduction

Connect

- **Yesterday:** Students explored special properties of similar triangles.
- **Today:** Students will use similar triangles to solve real-life problems.

Motivate

- Have pairs of students put a visual barrier (i.e., a notebook) between them. One student draws a triangle using a straightedge. This student now gives directions to the second student who will draw a triangle based on the information given. The only information the first student may give is angle measure! In fact, after the second angle measure is given, the second student should know the measure of the third angle.
- The triangles should be similar.
- ❓ "What do you notice about the triangles?" similar
- ❓ "How do you know they are similar?" Listen for same shape, different size; students may also mention yesterday's activities.

Lesson Notes

Key Idea

- Write the informal definition and draw examples of similar triangles.
- Write the Key Idea. This is the first time students have probably seen the phrase *if and only if*. It means two statements have been combined into one statement. The two statements are:
  - If two triangles have the same angle measures, then they are similar.
  - If two triangles are similar, then they have the same angle measures.
- The *if and only if* phrase is an example of a bi-conditional statement.
- Note the Study Tip. Refer to a sample pair of triangles that you drew earlier. Label two of the three angles in each triangle.
- **Another Way:** Work through a few examples to help students see why, when two angles in two triangles are congruent, the third angles are congruent.
- ❓ "What do you know about the measure of the third angle in each triangle?" Listen for the numeric answer and a statement that the third angles are congruent.

Example 1

- Draw the two triangles and label the given information. Ask students to solve for the missing angle measure of each triangle.
- ❓ "Are the triangles similar? Explain." For the first pair, yes, because the triangles have the same angle measures. For the second pair, no, because the triangles do not have the same angle measures.
- Students are influenced by the orientation of the triangles and how they appear. Students will say that they look similar. Always make students verify or explain their thinking.

Goal Today's lesson is using **similar triangles** to solve problems.

Lesson Materials
Introduction
• protractor
• ruler

Start Thinking! and Warm Up

Thales was a Greek philosopher and mathematician who lived around 600 B.C. There are several accounts of how he used indirect measurement to find the height of the Great Pyramid in Giza.

According to one account, when his shadow was the same length as his height, he measured the length of the Great Pyramid's shadow.

What does this have to do with similar triangles?

Extra Example 1

Tell whether the triangles are similar. Explain.

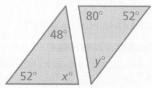

yes; The triangles have the same angle measures, 52°, 48°, and 80°.

T-222

Laurie's Notes

On Your Own

1. no; The triangles do not have the same angle measures.

2. yes; The triangles have the same angle measures, 90°, 66°, and 24°.

Extra Example 2

You plan to cross a river and want to know how far it is to the other side. You take measurements on your side of the river and make the drawing shown.

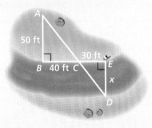

a. Explain why $\triangle ABC$ and $\triangle DEC$ are similar. Because two angles in $\triangle ABC$ are congruent to two angles in $\triangle DEC$, the third angles are also congruent. The triangles have the same angle measures, so they are similar.

b. What is the distance x across the river? 37.5 ft

On Your Own

3. 44 ft

English Language Learners

Build on Past Knowledge

Ask students to give examples of items that are similar. Ask students if similar items are exactly alike. Explain to students that *similar figures* are figures that have the same shape, but not necessarily the same size.

On Your Own

- **Think-Pair-Share:** Students should read each question independently and then work with a partner to answer the questions. When they have answered the questions, the pair should compare their answers with another group and discuss any discrepancies.

Example 2

- Indirect measurement is used when you want to know the measurement of some length (or angle) and you cannot measure the object directly.
- Ask a volunteer to read the problem. Make a rough sketch of the diagram.
- **?** "What do you know about the angles in either triangle?" $\angle B$ and $\angle E$ are right angles. The vertical angles are congruent (mark the diagram to show the congruent angles).
- **?** "What do you know about the third angle in each triangle?" They are congruent.
- Because the triangles are similar, the corresponding sides will have the same ratio. Setting up the ratios is challenging for students. Talk about the sides in terms of being the shorter leg of the right triangle and the longer leg of the right triangle.
- Use the Multiplication Property of Equality or the Cross Products Property to solve. Check the reasonableness of the answer.

On Your Own

- **Think-Pair-Share:** Students should read the question independently and then work with a partner to answer the question. When they have answered the question, the pair should compare their answer with another group and discuss any discrepancies.

Closure

- **Exit Ticket:** Are the two triangles similar? Explain.

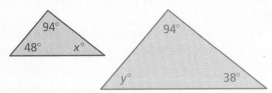

The triangles have the same angle measures, 94°, 48°, and 38°. So, the triangles are similar.

Now You're Ready
Exercises 5–8

Tell whether the triangles are similar. Explain.

1.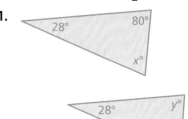

2.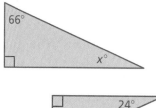

Indirect measurement uses similar figures to find a missing measure when it is difficult to find directly.

EXAMPLE ② **Using Indirect Measurement**

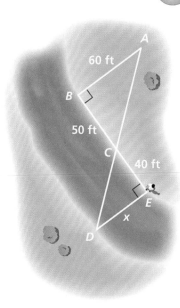

You plan to cross a river and want to know how far it is to the other side. You take measurements on your side of the river and make the drawing shown. (a) Explain why △ABC and △DEC are similar. (b) What is the distance x across the river?

a. ∠B and ∠E are right angles, so they are congruent. ∠ACB and ∠DCE are vertical angles, so they are congruent.

Because two angles in △ABC are congruent to two angles in △DEC, the third angles are also congruent. The triangles have the same angle measures, so they are similar.

b. The ratios of the corresponding side lengths in similar triangles are equal. Write and solve a proportion to find x.

$$\frac{x}{60} = \frac{40}{50}$$ Write a proportion.

$$60 \cdot \frac{x}{60} = 60 \cdot \frac{40}{50}$$ Multiply each side by 60.

$$x = 48$$ Simplify.

∴ The distance across the river is 48 feet.

● On Your Own

Now You're Ready
Exercise 12

3. **WHAT IF?** The distance from vertex A to vertex B is 55 feet. What is the distance across the river?

 Vocabulary and Concept Check

1. **REASONING** How can you use similar triangles to find a missing measurement?

2. **WHICH ONE DOESN'T BELONG?** Which triangle does *not* belong with the other three? Explain your reasoning.

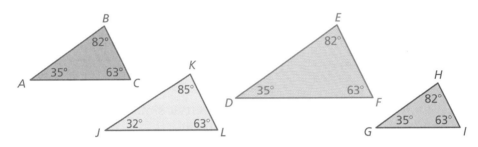

 Practice and Problem Solving

Make a triangle that is larger than the one given and has the same angle measures. Find the ratios of the corresponding side lengths.

3.

4.

Tell whether the triangles are similar. Explain.

5.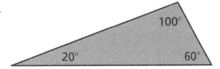

6.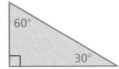

7.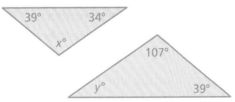

8.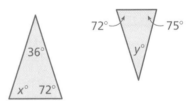

9. **ERROR ANALYSIS** Describe and correct the error in using indirect measurement.

$$\frac{16}{18} = \frac{x}{8}$$

$$18x = 128$$

$$x \approx 7$$

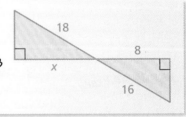

Assignment Guide and Homework Check

Level	Day 1 Activity Assignment	Day 2 Lesson Assignment	Homework Check
Basic	3, 4, 16–20	1, 2, 5–12	2, 6, 10, 12
Average	3, 4, 16–20	1, 2, 5–12, 14	2, 6, 10, 12
Advanced	3, 4, 16–20	1, 2, 8–15	2, 8, 10, 12

Common Errors

- **Exercises 5–8** Students may find the missing angle measure for one of the triangles and then make a decision about the similarity of the triangles. While it is possible to use this method, encourage them to find the missing angles of both triangles to verify that they are correct.
- **Exercises 10 and 11** Students may incorrectly identify congruent angles and find the wrong value for x. Encourage them to label the angles of the triangles with A, B, C, and D, E, F, and then write which angles are congruent before solving for x.

5.4 Record and Practice Journal

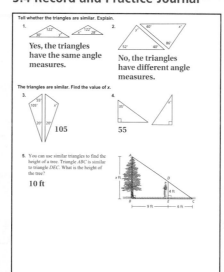

Vocabulary and Concept Check

1. Write a proportion that uses the missing measurement because the ratios of corresponding side lengths are equal.

2. $\triangle JKL$ because the other three triangles are similar.

Practice and Problem Solving

3–4. Student should draw a triangle with the same angle measures as the textbook. The ratio of the corresponding side lengths, $\dfrac{\text{student's triangle length}}{\text{book's triangle length}}$, should be greater than 1.

5. yes; The triangles have the same angle measures, 107°, 39°, and 34°.

6. no; The triangles do not have the same angle measures.

7. no; The triangles do not have the same angle measures.

8. yes; The triangles have the same angle measures, 81°, 51°, and 48°.

9. The numerators of the fractions should be from the same triangle.

$$\frac{18}{16} = \frac{x}{8}$$
$$16x = 144$$
$$x = 9$$

10. 50

11. 65

12. 100 steps

13. no; Each side increases by 50%, so each side is multiplied by a factor of $\frac{3}{2}$. The area is $\frac{3}{2}\left(\frac{3}{2}\right) = \frac{9}{4}$ or 225% of the original area, which is a 125% increase.

14. See Additional Answers.

15. See *Taking Math Deeper*.

Fair Game Review

16. nonlinear; The equation cannot be rewritten in slope-intercept form.

17. linear; The equation can be rewritten in slope-intercept form.

18. linear; The equation can be rewritten in slope-intercept form.

19. nonlinear; The equation cannot be rewritten in slope-intercept form.

20. C

Mini-Assessment

Tell whether the triangles are similar. Explain.

1.

yes; The triangles have the same angle measures, 51°, 55°, and 74°.

2.

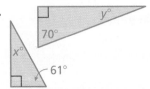

no; The triangles do not have the same angle measures.

Taking Math Deeper

Exercise 15

This problem can be solved using the fact that when two triangles are similar, the ratios of corresponding sides are equal.

 a. Solve for x.

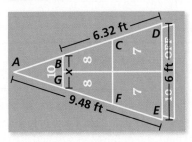

$$\frac{x}{6} = \frac{9.48 - 6.32}{9.48}$$

$$6 \cdot \frac{x}{6} = 6 \cdot \frac{3.16}{9.48}$$

$$x = 2 \text{ ft}$$

Similar triangles

 b. Solve for CF. Let $y = CF$.

$$\frac{y}{6} = \frac{2(9.48 \div 3)}{9.48}$$

$$6 \cdot \frac{y}{6} = 6 \cdot \frac{6.32}{9.48}$$

$$y = 4 \text{ ft}$$

 Notice that the bases of the three similar triangles form a linear pattern: 2, 4, and 6.

Project

Research the game of shuffleboard. What are the rules? Are there tournaments? Compare shuffleboard to the Olympic sport of curling.

Reteaching and Enrichment Strategies

If students need help...	If students got it...
Resources by Chapter • Practice A and Practice B • Puzzle Time Record and Practice Journal Practice Differentiating the Lesson Lesson Tutorials Skills Review Handbook	Resources by Chapter • Enrichment and Extension • School-to-Work Start the next section

The triangles are similar. Find the value of *x*.

10.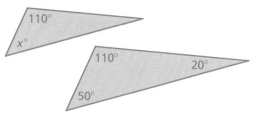

11.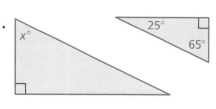

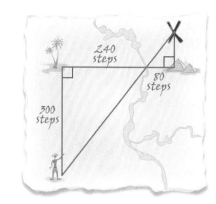

② 12. **TREASURE** The map shows the number of steps you must take to get to the treasure. However, the map is old and the last dimension is unreadable. How many steps do you take from the pyramids to the treasure?

13. **CRITICAL THINKING** The side lengths of a triangle are increased by 50% to make a similar triangle. Does the area increase by 50% as well? Explain.

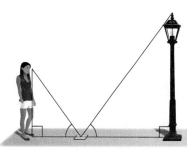

14. **PROJECT** Using a mirror, a tape measure, and indirect measurement, you can find the height of a lamppost. Place the mirror flat on the ground 6 feet from the lamppost. Move away from the mirror and the lamppost until you can see the top of the lamppost in the mirror. Measure the distance between yourself and the mirror. Then use similar triangles to find the height of the lamppost.

15. **Geometry** The drawing shows the scoring zone of a standard shuffleboard court. $\triangle DAE \sim \triangle BAG \sim \triangle CAF$. The lengths of segments *AG*, *GF*, and *FE* are equal.

   a. Find *x*.   **b.** Find *CF*.

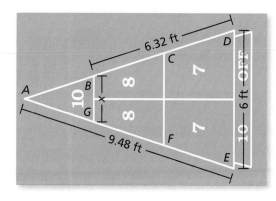

Fair Game Review *What you learned in previous grades & lessons*

Does the equation represent a *linear* or *nonlinear* function? Explain. *(Section 3.4)*

16. $y = \dfrac{5}{x}$ 17. $y = -5.4x + \pi$ 18. $y = 2x - 8$ 19. $y = 6x^2 + x - 1$

20. **MULTIPLE CHOICE** Which two lines are parallel? *(Section 2.2)*

   Ⓐ blue and red   Ⓑ red and green

   Ⓒ green and blue   Ⓓ all three are parallel

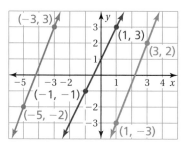

5.5 Polygons and Transformations

STANDARDS OF LEARNING

8.8

Essential Question How can transformations be used in calligraphy?

There are three basic ways to move objects on a flat surface.

1. Translate the object.

2. Reflect the object.

3. Rotate the object.

---

1 **ACTIVITY: Making Ambigrams for Names**

Work with a partner. An *ambigram* is a word that is the same when it is rotated 180°.

a. Some names can be made into ambigrams. Identify each person's name.

b. Make an ambigram of your own name or the name of someone you know. Use a name that is different from the 6 names shown above.

Laurie's Notes

Standards of Learning

8.8(a) The student will apply transformations to plane figures.
8.8(b) The student will identify applications of transformations.

Previous Learning

Students learned about transformations in a previous grade.

Introduction

For the Teacher

- **Goal:** Review transformations using a fun, visual approach.
- Scott Kim is an artist and puzzle designer. His graphic designs of *transformed* words will excite your students. You will find many terrific resources for this lesson at his website *www.scottkim.com*.

Motivate

- Share some history of calligraphy with students. The word calligraphy (*kallos* "beauty" + *graphein* "to write") means beautiful writing.
- The Japanese and Chinese developed many forms of calligraphy. Although today a computer can display our typed words in many different fonts, the handwork of a calligraphist is considered an art.
- As a warm up for today's investigation, show students the following and ask what they notice.

Start Thinking! and Warm Up

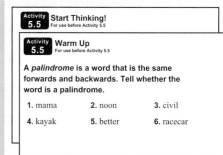

Activity Notes

Discuss

? "Do you remember the four types of transformations?" Listen for students to say translations, reflections, rotations, and dilations. Informally you may hear slide, flip, and turn.

- Discuss each transformation informally.
- A *translation* moves every point of the figure the same distance and in the same direction.
- A *reflection* creates a mirror image of the original figure.
- In a *rotation*, the figure rotates about a point.
- In a *dilation*, the figure is made larger or smaller with respect to a fixed point.
- For translations, reflections, and rotations, the original figure and its image are congruent.

Activity 1

- To assist students in creating their own ambigrams, you can provide ambigram alphabets found on the Internet.
- When students have finished, check their names.

5.5 Record and Practice Journal

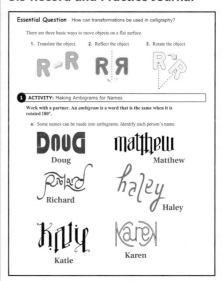

Differentiated Instruction

Kinesthetic

Give students examples of translations, reflections, rotations, and dilations in the classroom. You can move a chair to show a translation, use a mirror to show a reflection, spin the chair around to show a rotation, and place a transparency on the overhead to show a dilation.

5.5 Record and Practice Journal

b. Make an ambigram of your own name or the name of someone you know. Use a name that is different from the 6 names shown on the previous page.

Check students' work.

2 ACTIVITY: Making Palindrome Names

Work with a partner. A *palindrome* is a word that is the same forwards and backwards. Some palindrome names are also *reflective* because they can be reflected horizontally or vertically to produce the same name.

a. Decide whether each palindrome name is reflective. Explain.

HANNAH **EVE**
no   no
OTTO **ANNA** **BOB**
yes   no   yes

b. Find other names that are palindromes. Are they reflective horizontally? vertically?

Check students' work.

3 ACTIVITY: Making Anagram Name Pairs

Work with a partner. Two names are *anagrams* if the letters in one name can be translated to make the other name.

a. Find the common names that are anagrams of the following names.

MYRA HAMLET ARNOLD
Mary   Thelma   Ronald
EDNA AILEEN
Dean   Elaine
MAY GALEN BRYAN
Amy   Angel   Barny

b. Find other pairs of anagram names. Can you make another name from the letters in your name?

Check students' work.

What Is Your Answer?

4. **IN YOUR OWN WORDS** How can transformations be used in calligraphy?
Sample answer: Calligraphy translates and dilates basic pen strokes to create words.

5. Use the Internet or some other resource to find ways that mathematics (including geometry) is used in calligraphy.

Check students' work.

Laurie's Notes

Activity 2

- Write the ancient Latin palindrome on the board: "sator arepo tenet opera rotas." It loosely translates to "The farmer uses his plough as his form of work." A stone tablet like the one shown below was found in the ruins of Pompeii, which Mt. Vesuvius buried in ash in 79 A.D.

- Students may be familiar with the "Madam I'm Adam" palindrome.
- Before students begin this activity, review the symmetry of each block letter of the alphabet. Ask partners to sort the letters into one of four categories: no symmetry, vertical symmetry, horizontal symmetry, or both vertical and horizontal symmetry. The list will help students think about names that are palindromes.
- Students will have fun with this activity. Give them sufficient time to investigate before sharing findings as a class.

Activity 3

- Some students are very quick with anagrams.
- Explore part (b) at the board by having a student write only one of the anagram names and having the rest of the class try to figure out the second name.

What Is Your Answer?

- If the Internet is available in your classroom, there are many resources for students to explore.

Closure

- Describe an interesting feature of the following words or phrases.
  - never odd or even palindrome
  - DECKED horizontal symmetry
  - MATH Every letter has vertical symmetry.

Technology
For
the **T**eacher

The Dynamic Planning Tool
Editable Teacher's Resources at *BigIdeasMath.com*

2 ACTIVITY: Making Palindrome Names

Work with a partner. A *palindrome* is a word that is the same forwards and backwards. Some palindrome names are also *reflective* because they can be reflected horizontally or vertically to produce the same name.

a. Decide whether each palindrome name is reflective. Explain.

HANNAH EVE

OTTO ANNA BOB

b. Find other names that are palindromes. Are they reflective horizontally? vertically?

3 ACTIVITY: Making Anagram Name Pairs

Work with a partner. Two names are *anagrams* if the letters in one name can be translated to make the other name.

a. Find common names that are anagrams of the following names.

MYRA HAMLET ARNOLD

EDNA AILEEN

MAY GALEN BRYAN

b. Find other pairs of anagram names. Can you make another name from the letters in your name?

What Is Your Answer?

4. IN YOUR OWN WORDS How can transformations be used in calligraphy?

5. Use the Internet or some other resource to find ways that mathematics (including geometry) is used in calligraphy.

Practice Use what you learned about ambigrams to complete Exercises 3 and 4 on page 231.

Check It Out
Lesson Tutorials
BigIdeasMath ✓com

Key Vocabulary ◀))
translation, *p. 228*
reflection, *p. 228*
rotation, *p. 228*
dilation, *p. 230*

 **Key Ideas**

Translations

A **translation**, or *slide*, is a transformation in which a figure moves but does not turn. Every point of the figure moves the same distance and in the same direction.

Reflections

A **reflection**, or *flip*, is a transformation in which a figure is reflected in a line called the *line of reflection*. A reflection creates a mirror image of the original figure.

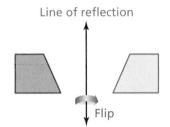

Rotations

A **rotation**, or *turn*, is a transformation in which a figure is rotated about a point called the *center of rotation*. The number of degrees a figure rotates is the *angle of rotation*.

For these transformations, the original figure and its image are congruent.

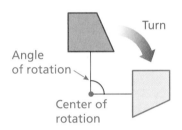

Remember

A *transformation* changes a figure into another figure. The new figure is called the *image*.

EXAMPLE ① **Translating a Figure**

The vertices of a parallelogram are $A(-4, -3)$, $B(-2, -2)$, $C(3, -4)$, and $D(1, -5)$. Translate the parallelogram 2 units left and 4 units up. What are the coordinates of the image?

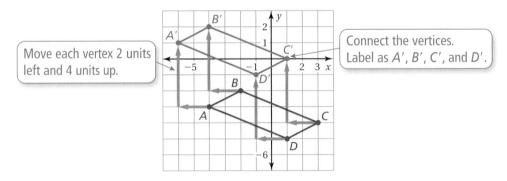

Move each vertex 2 units left and 4 units up.

Connect the vertices. Label as A', B', C', and D'.

∴ The coordinates of the image are $A'(-6, 1)$, $B'(-4, 2)$, $C'(1, 0)$, and $D'(-1, -1)$.

◀) Multi-Language Glossary at BigIdeasMath ✓com.

Laurie's Notes

Introduction

Connect

- **Yesterday:** Students reviewed transformations.
- **Today:** Students will apply transformations to polygons in the coordinate plane.

Motivate

- Make a large open area in the classroom for this activity. You could also move to a different location, such as the gym.
- Use masking tape to form two axes, each about 16 feet long. Use a marker to increment the axes from −5 to 5 (at a minimum).
- You need eight volunteers—four will form the vertices of a quadrilateral and hold the yarn, and the other four will be the scribes who keep track of the coordinates of the vertices.
- Have four students stand at coordinates that form a rectangle (parallelogram, trapezoid); holding the yarn to form the quadrilateral. Scribes record the coordinates at the board.
- Give directions for a transformation such as: move 2 units right and 3 units down (a translation), or keep the same *x*-coordinate but use the opposite of your *y*-coordinate (a reflection in the *x*-axis). Each time you give a new transformation, the scribe writes the new coordinates below the previous coordinates. You want students to be observing patterns.
- Try several transformations with different quadrilaterals. Choose new volunteers when you change to a new quadrilateral.

Lesson Notes

Key Ideas

- Write the Key Ideas. Write the definitions of translation, reflection, and rotation on the board. Transformations should be familiar to students, however it would be helpful to model each transformation on an overhead using a polygon.
- Remind students of the vocabulary. In the diagram, the original figure is red and the image (the new figure) is blue.

Example 1

- The opening activity will help remind students how ordered pairs are plotted. They should be ready to plot parallelogram *ABCD*.
- ❓ "In which quadrants are the vertices before the translation?" *A* and *B* are in Quadrant III. *C* and *D* are in Quadrant IV.
- Work through the example as shown.
- ❓ "How are the vertices of the image related to the corresponding vertices of the original figure?" *x*-coordinates are 2 units less. *y*-coordinates are 4 units more.
- ❓ "Are the two parallelograms congruent? Explain." Yes, the parallelograms are the same size and shape.

Goal Today's lesson is transforming figures in the coordinate plane.

Lesson Materials
Introduction
• masking tape
• marker
• yarn

Start Thinking! and Warm Up

Choose a partner. Imagine that you and your partner are creating a new company. Discuss what the company will sell and come up with a company name.

Create a company logo that uses one of the following transformations: translation, reflection, or rotation. Tell which transformation your logo contains.

Extra Example 1

The vertices of a triangle are *J*(−2, 1), *K*(−1, 3), and *L*(0, 0). Translate the triangle 4 units right and 2 units down. What are the coordinates of the image? *J*′(2, −1), *K*′(3, 1), *L*′(4, −2)

Laurie's Notes

On Your Own

1. $J'(-1, -1)$, $K'(2, -4)$, $L'(-1, -4)$

2. $J'(-4, -4)$, $K'(-1, -1)$, $L'(-4, -1)$

3. $J'(4, -4)$, $K'(1, -1)$, $L'(4, -1)$

Example 2

- Help students think about reflections by talking about folding (creasing) a piece of graph paper on the y-axis. Where would the red pentagon land when the paper is creased?
- **Common Error:** Students often think about reflecting vertically so that vertex Y doesn't move and actually reflect in the line $x = -1$. Another common error is for students to reflect correctly but label the image incorrectly, often alphabetically in a clockwise orientation.
- Work through the example as shown.
- ❓ "Does every vertex move the same distance as they do in a translation? Explain." no; In a reflection, the point farthest from the line of reflection moves the farthest.
- ❓ "How are the vertices of the image related to the corresponding vertices of the original figure?" The x-coordinates are opposites. The y-coordinates are the same.
- ❓ "Are the two pentagons congruent? Explain." Yes, the pentagons are the same size and shape.

Example 3

- **Representation:** The rotation is the most difficult of the transformations for students. Give them tracing paper. Have them draw the original figure, rotate the tracing paper 90° clockwise, and then locate the vertices of the image. Model the process at the overhead with a clear transparency on top of the coordinate grid. To know that you have rotated 90°, mark an upward arrow (north) on the clear transparency. Rotate the trapezoid until the arrow is sideways (east).
- Work through the example as shown.
- **Extension:** Ask students "If (a, b) is a vertex of the original figure, what are the coordinates of the vertex after the rotation in this example?" $(b, -a)$
- ❓ "Are the two trapezoids congruent? Explain." Yes, the trapezoids are the same size and shape.

On Your Own

- Rotations will be the most challenging. Tracing paper will help. Be sure the rotation is done about the origin and not about the vertex K.
- Ask volunteers to share their results at the board.

EXAMPLE 2 **Reflecting a Figure**

The vertices of a pentagon are $V(-4, -5)$, $W(-4, -1)$, $X(-2, -1)$, $Y(-1, -3)$, and $Z(-2, -5)$. Reflect the pentagon in the y-axis. What are the coordinates of the image?

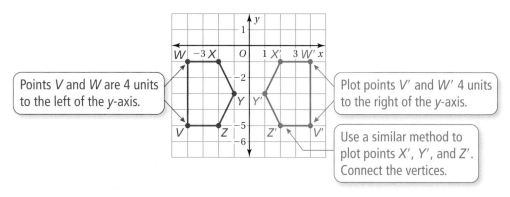

Points V and W are 4 units to the left of the y-axis.

Plot points V' and W' 4 units to the right of the y-axis.

Use a similar method to plot points X', Y', and Z'. Connect the vertices.

∴ The coordinates of the image are $V'(4, -5)$, $W'(4, -1)$, $X'(2, -1)$, $Y'(1, -3)$, and $Z'(2, -5)$.

EXAMPLE 3 **Rotating a Figure**

The vertices of a trapezoid are $P(2, -2)$, $Q(4, -2)$, $R(5, -5)$, and $S(4, -5)$. Rotate the trapezoid 90° clockwise about the origin. What are the coordinates of the image?

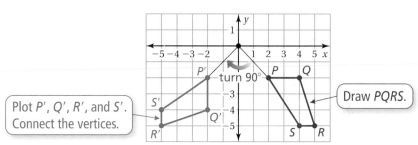

turn 90°

Plot P', Q', R', and S'. Connect the vertices.

Draw $PQRS$.

∴ The coordinates of the image are $P'(-2, -2)$, $Q'(-2, -4)$, $R'(-5, -5)$, and $S'(-5, -4)$.

● **On Your Own**

Now You're Ready
Exercises 5–10

Find the coordinates of the image after the transformation.

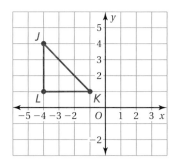

1. a translation of 3 units right and 5 units down

2. a reflection in the x-axis

3. a rotation of 180° about the origin

 **Key Idea**

Dilations

A **dilation** is a transformation in which a figure is made larger or smaller with respect to a fixed point called the *center of dilation*.

The original figure and its image are similar.

Center of dilation

The ratio of the side lengths of the image to the corresponding side lengths of the original figure is the *scale factor* of the dilation. To dilate a figure in the coordinate plane with respect to the origin, multiply the coordinates of each vertex by the scale factor k.

- When $k > 1$, the dilation is called an *enlargement*.
- When $k > 0$ and $k < 1$, the dilation is called a *reduction*.

EXAMPLE ④ **Dilating a Figure**

Draw the image of kite *FGHJ* after a dilation with a scale factor of 2. Identify the type of dilation.

Multiply each x- and y-coordinate by the scale factor 2.

Vertices of *FGHJ*	$(x \cdot 2, y \cdot 2)$	Vertices of *F′G′H′J′*
$F(1, 3)$	$(1 \cdot 2, 3 \cdot 2)$	$F'(2, 6)$
$G(2, 4)$	$(2 \cdot 2, 4 \cdot 2)$	$G'(4, 8)$
$H(3, 3)$	$(3 \cdot 2, 3 \cdot 2)$	$H'(6, 6)$
$J(2, 1)$	$(2 \cdot 2, 1 \cdot 2)$	$J'(4, 2)$

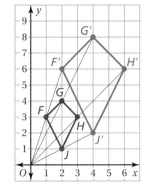

Study Tip

You can check your answer by drawing a line from the origin through each vertex of the original figure. The vertices of the image should lie on these lines.

⠿ The dilation is an *enlargement* because the scale factor is greater than 1.

On Your Own

Now You're Ready
Exercises 11–13

4. Draw the image of rhombus *JKLM* after a dilation with a scale factor of $\frac{1}{2}$. Identify the type of dilation.

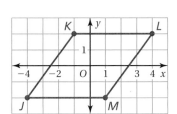

Laurie's Notes

Key Idea

- Students studied dilations in a previous grade.
- Write the Key Idea.
- Students can visualize dilations using a flashlight. Objects placed in the beam of light appear larger when projected on a wall.
- Review the vocabulary *scale factor* with students. Connect this to their understanding of similar triangles.
- Ask students to think about when enlargements and reductions of actual objects are made. For instance, scale models of cars and blue prints for houses are reductions of the actual object. The screen at a movie theater displays an enlargement of the original images.

Example 4

- Draw kite *FGHJ*.
- Ask students to identify attributes of the kite such as the type of symmetry (vertical), congruent sides (*FG* and *HG*; *JF* and *JH*), congruent angles (∠*F* and ∠*H*), and classification of angles (∠*F* and ∠*H* are obtuse; ∠*J* is acute; ∠*G* is right).
- Make a table of the vertices as shown and record the new vertices after each coordinate is multiplied by 2.
- Note that the questions asked above about kite *FGHJ* are also true for kite *F′G′H′J′*.
- **?** "How do the lengths of the sides of the two kites compare?" The lengths of the sides of the image are twice as long as the lengths of the sides of the original kite.
- **?** "Do the kites appear similar? Explain." Yes, the kites are the same shape, but not the same size, and the corresponding angles are congruent.

On Your Own

- Have students use the Study Tip shown to check their answers.

Closure

- Draw a trapezoid in Quadrant II. Translate the trapezoid so that it is entirely in Quadrant IV. Describe the translation.

The Dynamic Planning Tool
Editable Teacher's Resources at *BigIdeasMath.com*

Technology For the Teacher

Dynamic Classroom

English Language Learners

Vocabulary

Discuss the meanings of the words *translation, reflection, rotation,* and *dilation.* Give real-life examples of each. Use the words *slide* for translation, *flip* for reflection, and *turn* for rotation.

Extra Example 4

The vertices of a triangle are $D(0, 5)$, $E(5, 5)$, and $F(5, 0)$. Draw the image of triangle *DEF* after a dilation with a scale factor of $\frac{2}{5}$. Identify the type of dilation.

reduction

On Your Own

4.
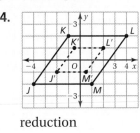

reduction

1. **a.** rotation

   b. translation

   c. reflection

   d. dilation

2. dilation; The original figure and the image are not congruent.

Practice and Problem Solving

3. Anthony; yes; It is the same when rotated 180°.

4. Michelle; yes; It is the same when rotated 180°.

5. $A'(-2, 9)$, $B'(2, 9)$, $C'(2, 2)$, $D'(-1, 2)$

6. $A'(5, 5)$, $B'(9, 5)$, $C'(9, -2)$, $D'(6, -2)$

7. $A'(0, 8)$, $B'(-4, 8)$, $C'(-4, 1)$, $D'(-1, 1)$

8. $A'(0, -8)$, $B'(4, -8)$, $C'(4, -1)$, $D'(1, -1)$

9. $A'(8, 0)$, $B'(8, -4)$, $C'(1, -4)$, $D'(1, -1)$

10. $A'(-8, 0)$, $B'(-8, 4)$, $C'(-1, 4)$, $D'(-1, 1)$

11. $A'(0, 24)$, $B'(12, 24)$, $C'(12, 3)$, $D'(3, 3)$

12. $A'(0, 2)$, $B'(1, 2)$,

    $C'\left(1, \dfrac{1}{4}\right)$, $D'\left(\dfrac{1}{4}, \dfrac{1}{4}\right)$

13. enlargement; reduction

14. The blue triangle was reflected in the x-axis instead of the y-axis.

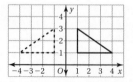

Assignment Guide and Homework Check

Level	Day 1 Activity Assignment	Day 2 Lesson Assignment	Homework Check
Basic	3, 4, 33–36	1, 2, 5–13 odd, 14–16, 17–23 odd, 29	5, 11, 17, 19, 23, 29
Average	3, 4, 33–36	1, 2, 6–14 even, 15, 17–21, 26, 27–31 odd	8, 15, 17, 21, 26, 31
Advanced	3, 4, 33–36	1, 2, 6–14 even, 17, 22–32	10, 17, 24, 28, 32

Common Errors

- **Exercises 7 and 8** Students may reflect in the incorrect axis. Ask them to make a chart that describes which direction to move when reflecting in each axis.
- **Exercises 9 and 10** Students may rotate the trapezoid in the wrong direction. Remind them what clockwise and counterclockwise mean. Before rotating the figure, it may be helpful for students to draw an arrow to indicate the direction that the trapezoid will rotate.

5.5 Record and Practice Journal

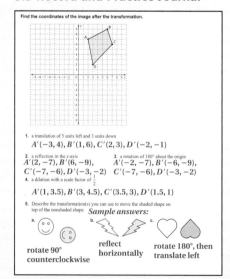

Find the coordinates of the image after the transformation.

1. a translation of 5 units left and 3 units down
   $A'(-3, 4)$, $B'(1, 6)$, $C'(2, 3)$, $D'(-2, -1)$

2. a reflection in the x-axis,
   $A'(2, -7)$, $B'(6, -9)$, $C'(-7, -6)$, $D'(-3, -2)$

3. a rotation of 180° about the origin
   $A'(-2, -7)$, $B'(-6, -9)$, $C'(-7, -6)$, $D'(-3, -2)$

4. a dilation with a scale factor of $\frac{1}{2}$
   $A'(1, 3.5)$, $B'(3, 4.5)$, $C'(3.5, 3)$, $D'(1.5, 1)$

5. Describe the transformation(s) you can use to move the shaded shape on top of the nonshaded shape. **Sample answers:**

   a. rotate 90° counterclockwise
   b. reflect horizontally
   c. rotate 180°, then translate left

Technology for the **T**eacher

Answer Presentation Tool

Quiz*Show*

 Vocabulary and Concept Check

1. **VOCABULARY** Identify the transformation shown.

   a.   b.    c.    d.

2. **WHICH ONE DOESN'T BELONG?** Which transformation does *not* belong with the other three? Explain your reasoning.

   | translation | reflection | rotation | dilation |

 Practice and Problem Solving

Identify the name. Is the name an ambigram? Explain.

3. ANTHONY

4. MICHELLE

Find the coordinates of the image after the transformation.

① 5. a translation of 2 units left and 1 unit up

6. a translation of 5 units right and 3 units down

② 7. a reflection in the *y*-axis

8. a reflection in the *x*-axis

③ 9. a rotation of 90° clockwise about the origin

10. a rotation of 90° counterclockwise about the origin

④ 11. a dilation with a scale factor of 3

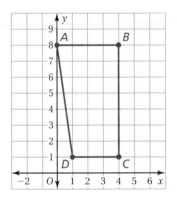

12. a dilation with a scale factor of $\frac{1}{4}$

13. Identify each type of dilation in Exercises 11 and 12.

14. **ERROR ANALYSIS** Describe and correct the error in reflecting the blue triangle in the *y*-axis.

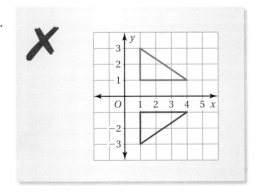

15. **OPEN-ENDED** Draw a polygon in a coordinate plane. Translate the polygon 4 units left and 5 units down.

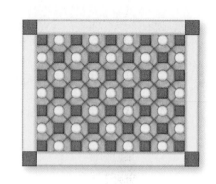

16. **AREA RUG** Describe how translations are used in the design of the area rug.

17. **ERROR ANALYSIS** Describe and correct the error in describing the transformation.

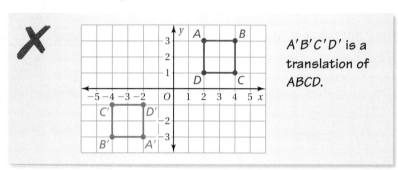

A′B′C′D′ is a translation of ABCD.

Tell whether a polygon and its image are congruent after the transformation. Explain.

18. translation

19. reflection

20. rotation

21. dilation

REASONING A polygon lies entirely in Quadrant I. In which quadrant will the image lie after the given transformation?

22. a reflection in the *x*-axis

23. a reflection in the *y*-axis

24. a rotation of 180° about the origin

25. a dilation with a scale factor of 2

26. **CRITICAL THINKING** The blue square is the image of the red square after a transformation. How can the vertices of each figure be labeled so that the transformation is a translation? a reflection? a rotation? Explain.

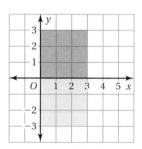

27. **CARTOON** A cartoonist enlarges Newton as shown. What is the scale factor?

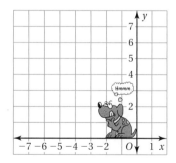

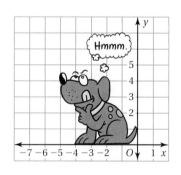

Common Errors

- **Exercises 22–25** Students with minimal spatial skills may not be able to determine the quadrant in which the image will lie. Give them graph paper and have them form a conclusion after trying a few examples.

15. *Sample answer:*

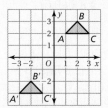

16. *Sample answer:* Translate the pattern below repeatedly to form the rug.

17. The vertices do not correspond for a translation. $A'B'C'D'$ is a 180° rotation of $ABCD$.

18. yes; The polygon and its image have the same size and shape.

19. yes; The polygon and its image have the same size and shape.

20. yes; The polygon and its image have the same size and shape.

21. no; The polygon and its image have the same shape but not the same size.

22. Quadrant IV

23. Quadrant II

24. Quadrant III

25. Quadrant I

26. See Additional Answers.

27. 2

Practice and Problem Solving

28. dilation (reduction with a scale factor of 0.5)

29. See *Taking Math Deeper*.

30. *Sample answer:* Reflect D and N in a vertical line, reflect A in a horizontal line, rotate C 90° clockwise, rotate E 90° counterclockwise, and then translate the letters to appear in the correct order.

31. 270° counterclockwise; 270° clockwise

32. a. $(x - 3, y + 2)$

   b. $(-x, y)$

   c. $(-x, -y)$

   d. $(5x, 5y)$

Fair Game Review

33. domain: $-1, 1, 3, 5$
range: $0, 1, 2, 3$

34. domain: $-2, -1, 0, 1, 2$
range: $2, 0, -2$

35. domain: $-5, -4, -3, -2$
range: $-5, -3, -1, 1$

36. C

Mini-Assessment

Find the coordinates of the image after the transformation.

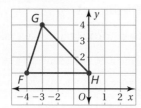

1. a translation of 3 units right and 4 units up $F'(-1, 5), G'(0, 8), H'(3, 5)$

2. a reflection in the *x*-axis $F'(-4, -1), G'(-3, -4), H'(0, -1)$

3. a rotation 90° clockwise $F'(1, 4), G'(4, 3), H'(1, 0)$

4. a dilation with a scale factor of 2 $F'(-8, 2), G'(-6, 8), H'(0, 2)$

Taking Math Deeper

Exercise 29

Some students have a difficult time picturing this type of question. Others can do it easily. For students who have a difficult time, you might make an enlarged copy of each pattern and ask students to fold the patterns over and hold them up to a light to check that the pattern aligns with itself.

 a. This pattern has 3 lines of symmetry.

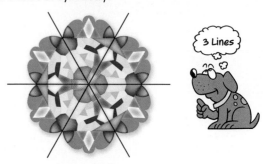

 b. This pattern has 4 lines of symmetry.

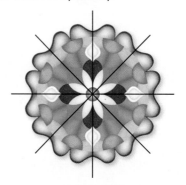

 A kaleidoscope is made using an isosceles triangle of mirrors. The number of lines of symmetry depends on the angle between the two congruent sides.

Reteaching and Enrichment Strategies

If students need help...	If students got it...
Resources by Chapter • Practice A and Practice B • Puzzle Time Record and Practice Journal Practice Differentiating the Lesson Lesson Tutorials Skills Review Handbook	Resources by Chapter • Enrichment and Extension • School-to-Work • Financial Literacy Start the next section

28. REASONING The vertices of a polygon are $A(-8, 4)$, $B(6, 4)$, $C(10, -12)$, and $D(-8, -12)$. The coordinates of the image are $A'(-4, 2)$, $B'(3, 2)$, $C'(5, -6)$, and $D'(-4, -6)$. Identify the type of transformation.

29. KALEIDOSCOPE A pattern has a line of symmetry if the pattern can be mapped onto itself by a reflection in the line. Find the number of lines of symmetry in each kaleidoscope pattern.

a.

b.

30. OPEN-ENDED Describe the transformation(s) you can use to rearrange the letters to spell DANCE.

31. REASONING What rotation is the same as 90° clockwise? 90° counterclockwise?

32. *Critical Thinking* A vertex of a figure is (x, y). Find the coordinates of the vertex after the given transformation.

a. a translation of 3 units left and 2 units up   b. a reflection in the y-axis

c. a rotation of 180° about the origin   d. a dilation with a scale factor of 5

 Fair Game Review *What you learned in previous grades & lessons*

Find the domain and range of the function represented by the graph. *(Section 3.1)*

33.

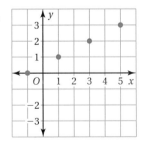

34.

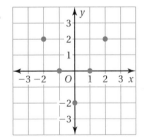

35.

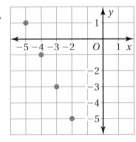

36. MULTIPLE CHOICE A store pays $25 for a video game. The percent of markup is 80%. What is the selling price? *(Section 4.3)*

  Ⓐ $20   Ⓑ $30   Ⓒ $45   Ⓓ $70

STANDARDS OF LEARNING
8.11

Essential Question How can you find the perimeter of a composite figure?

1 ACTIVITY: Finding a Pattern

Work with a partner. Describe the pattern of the perimeters. Use your pattern to find the perimeter of the tenth figure in the sequence. (Each small square has a perimeter of 4.)

a.

b.

c.

2 ACTIVITY: Finding a Distance

Work with a partner.

a. Estimate the distance to the gold.

b. Estimate the distance to the silver.

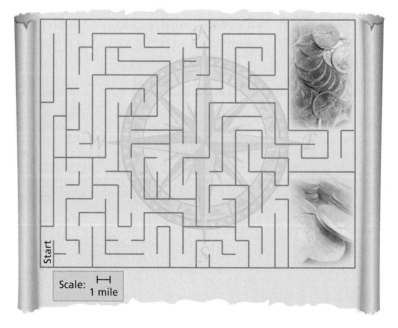

Scale: ⊢—⊣
1 mile

Start

Laurie's Notes

Introduction

For the Teacher

- **Goal:** Students will develop an intuitive understanding of finding perimeters of composite figures by focusing on their component parts.
- Today's activities take a problem-solving approach to the topic of finding perimeters of composite figures.
- Explain to students that composite figures are composed of more than one geometric shape.

Motivate

- Draw the following "equations." Ask students how they would find the perimeter of the last figure knowing the dimensions of the figures on the left side of the equation.

- These puzzles should help focus students' thinking on how they will find the perimeter of a composite figure, without defining composite figures!

Activity Notes

Activity 1

- Students should describe the pattern of the perimeter in words. For instance, the figures in part (a) have perimeters which are *increasing by 2* each time.
- **Common Error:** Remind students that perimeter is the distance *around* the figure and that interior segments are not included.
- **Representation:** For part (c), if students leave their answer in terms of π, they are more likely to see the pattern.
- ❓ "How is the perimeter changing in part (a)? Can you explain why?"
  increasing by 2; Explanations will vary.
- ❓ "How is the perimeter changing in part (b)? Can you explain why?"
  increasing by 4; Explanations will vary.
- ❓ "How is the perimeter changing in part (c)? Can you explain why?"
  increasing by π; Explanations will vary.

Activity 2

- This is an adaptation of a perimeter problem. Students are finding the total distance traveled instead of the distance around a figure.
- Explain the scale for the maze. Have students use the edge of their paper to measure and approximate the perimeter of the maze. This will help students understand how to use the scale in this problem.
- ❓ "Is the distance to the gold or silver greater than the perimeter of the maze?" yes for both the gold and silver

Standards of Learning

8.11 The student will solve practical area and perimeter problems involving composite plane figures.

Previous Learning

Students should know how to find the perimeter and circumference for common shapes.

Activity Materials
Textbook
• square tiles

Start Thinking! and Warm Up

> **Activity 5.6** Start Thinking!
> For use before Activity 5.6
>
> **Activity 5.6** Warm Up
> For use before Activity 5.6
>
> **Find the perimeter or circumference of the figure described.**
>
> 1. square with side length 4 cm
> 2. rectangle with length 5 ft and width 3.5 ft
> 3. rectangle with length 19 in. and width 7 in.
> 4. triangle with side lengths 7 m, 8 m, and 10 m
> 5. circle with radius 9 in.
> 6. circle with diameter 20 ft

5.6 Record and Practice Journal

> **Essential Question** How can you find the perimeter of a composite figure?
>
> **1 ACTIVITY: Finding a Pattern**
>
> Work with a partner. Describe the pattern of the perimeters. Use your pattern to find the perimeter of the tenth figure in the sequence. (Each small square has a perimeter of 4.)
>
> a.
>
> The perimeter of each figure is 2 greater than the last; 22.
>
> b.
>
> The perimeter of each figure is 4 greater than the last; 40.
>
> c.
>
> The perimeter of each figure is π greater than the last; about 33.4.

English Language Learners

Visual

Have students find rectangular, trapezoidal, triangular, and circular regions in the school and on the school grounds. Then ask students to calculate the perimeter of these regions.

5.6 Record and Practice Journal

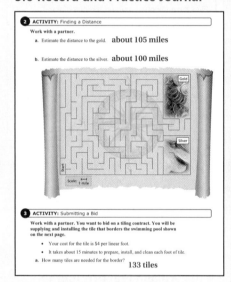

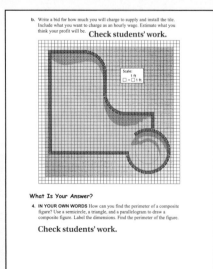

Laurie's Notes

Activity 3

- **Real World:** Share with your students that builders and contractors submit bids for work that they want to do. If more than one bid is received, the consumer selects the builder or contractor based upon a number of factors, one of which is the cost that is quoted.
- In this problem, assume that each pair of students is bidding on the job. They could even have a name for their two-person company. Their bid sheet (work done) should be neat and organized and easily understood by the pool's owner—you!
- Explain the term *$4 per linear foot* so that all students understand. In construction, when the width of material (in this case, the tile) is predetermined, the cost is given in terms of the length, not in terms of area (square foot).
- Students should count the number of tiles surrounding the pool and use the scale given on the diagram to determine how much tile is needed.
- Make sure students include a labor charge based on the information given. Students will set their own hourly wage. Is it realistic?
- Discuss general results with the whole class. Compare the quotes, separating out the material and labor.
- **Extension:** List the hourly wages and the number of hours of labor that each company charges. Use this data and find the mean, median, and range of the hourly wages and the total labor charge.

What Is Your Answer?

- **Neighbor Check:** Have students work independently and then have their neighbor check their work. Have students discuss any discrepancies.

Closure

- Find the perimeter of the arrow. 60 cm

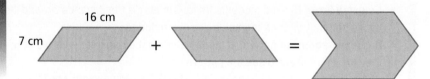

16 cm

7 cm

Technology For the Teacher

Dynamic Classroom

The Dynamic Planning Tool
Editable Teacher's Resources at *BigIdeasMath.com*

Work with a partner. You want to bid on a tiling contract. You will be supplying and installing the brown tile that borders the swimming pool.

- **Your cost for the tile is $4 per linear foot.**
- **It takes about 15 minutes to prepare, install, and clean each foot of tile.**

a. How many brown tiles are needed for the border?

b. Write a bid for how much you will charge to supply and install the tile. Include what you want to charge as an hourly wage. Estimate what you think your profit will be.

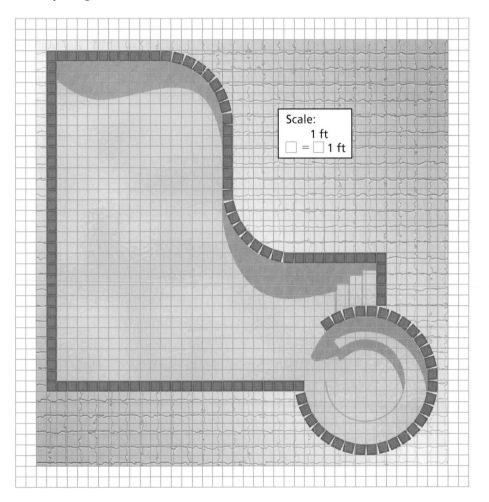

Scale:
1 ft
□ = □ 1 ft

What Is Your Answer?

4. **IN YOUR OWN WORDS** How can you find the perimeter of a composite figure? Use a semicircle, a triangle, and a parallelogram to draw a composite figure. Label the dimensions. Find the perimeter of the figure.

Practice ▷ Use what you learned about perimeters of composite figures to complete Exercises 3–5 on page 238.

Check It Out
Lesson Tutorials
BigIdeasMath.com

Key Vocabulary
composite figure,
p. 236

A **composite figure** is made up of triangles, squares, rectangles, semicircles, and other two-dimensional figures. Here are two examples.

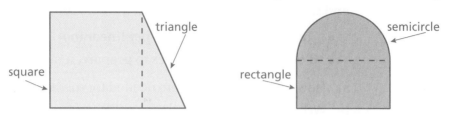

To find the perimeter of a composite figure, find the distance around the figure.

EXAMPLE ① **Finding a Perimeter Using Grid Paper**

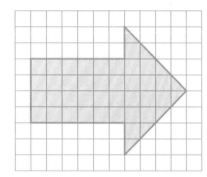

Each square on the grid paper is 1 square inch. Estimate the perimeter of the arrow.

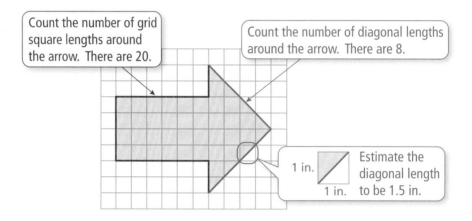

Count the number of grid square lengths around the arrow. There are 20.

Count the number of diagonal lengths around the arrow. There are 8.

1 in.
1 in.
Estimate the diagonal length to be 1.5 in.

Length of 20 grid square lengths: $20 \times 1 = 20$ inches

Length of 8 diagonal lengths: $8 \times 1.5 = 12$ inches

∴ The perimeter is about $20 + 12 = 32$ inches.

On Your Own

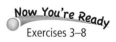
Now You're Ready
Exercises 3–8

1. Each square on the grid paper is 1 square foot. Estimate the perimeter of the red figure.

2. Measure the diagonal of a square whose area is exactly one square foot. Is the diagonal length closer to 1.5 feet or 1.4 feet? Explain.

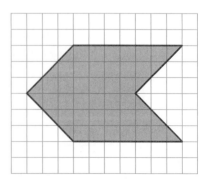

◀) Multi-Language Glossary at BigIdeasMath✓com.

Laurie's Notes

Introduction

Connect

- **Yesterday:** Students used a variety of problem-solving skills to find the perimeter of several composite figures.
- **Today:** Students will use formulas to find the perimeter of composite figures.

Motivate

- If you have a set of tangrams, use them to share a puzzle with students. Place the 7 pieces on the overhead and ask a volunteer to rearrange the pieces into a square. The solution is shown. Then rearrange the pieces to form the bird shown. Ask how the perimeter changes from the square to the bird.

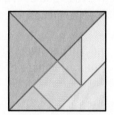 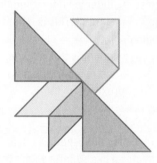

- The goal is not to find the perimeter of the bird, only to recognize that as more segments are exposed (on the perimeter), the perimeter will increase.
- The figures that students work with today are composed of common geometric shapes. Students should be familiar with how to find the perimeter of each.
- Introduce the vocabulary word *composite figure.*

Lesson Notes

Example 1

- The arrow is a shape that students discussed at the beginning of yesterday's lesson.
- Students are asked to estimate the perimeter, because the slanted lengths are irrational numbers.
- **Common Error:** Students may think the diagonal of the square is 1 inch because the side lengths are 1 inch. Have them think about the *short-cut* of walking across the diagonal of a square versus walking the two side lengths.

On Your Own

- Question 1 is very similar to the first example.
- Ask a volunteer to share their thinking and solution to the problem.

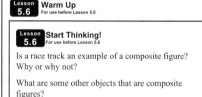

Lesson Materials
Introduction
• tangrams

Start Thinking! and Warm Up

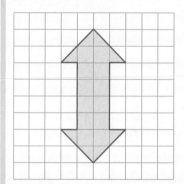

Extra Example 1

Each square on the grid paper is 1 square centimeter. Estimate the perimeter of the arrow.

about 24 cm

On Your Own

1. about 32 ft

2. It is closer to 1.4 ft; The diagonal measures about 17 inches. By multiplying 17 inches by $\frac{1 \text{ ft}}{12 \text{ in.}}$, you find that 17 inches is about 1.4 feet.

Extra Example 2

The figure is made of a semicircle and a square. Find the perimeter.

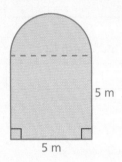

5 m

5 m

about 22.85 m

Extra Example 3

Find the perimeter of the running track in Example 3 when the radius of the semicircle is 20 yards and the length of the rectangle is 50 yards. about 225.6 yd

 On Your Own

    3. about 41.12 m

    4. about 291.3 seconds

Differentiated Instruction

Auditory

Review the two formulas for circumference, $C = \pi d$ and $C = 2\pi r$. On the board or overhead, derive the formulas for diameter, $d = \dfrac{C}{\pi}$, and radius, $r = \dfrac{C}{2\pi}$. Have students copy the four formulas in their notebooks to use as a quick reference when doing word problems. Remind students that the circumference of a semicircle is half of a full circle.

Laurie's Notes

Example 2

- Draw the diagram for the problem.
- **?** "What is the diameter of the semicircle?" 10 ft
- Explain to students that although the third side of the triangle is shown (which is also the diameter of the circle), it is not part of the perimeter.
- **?** "Could $\dfrac{22}{7}$ be used for π?" yes "Why do you think 3.14 was used?"

  The diameter is 10, which is not a multiple of 7.

Example 3

- Draw the diagram for the problem.
- **?** "What are the dimensions of the rectangle?" 100 m by 64 m
- **?** "What is the diameter of the semicircles?" 64 m
- Make sure students understand that they have to add both straight-aways of the running track. This is where the $100 + 100$ comes from in the answer statement.
- Point out to students that in Examples 2 and 3 the answers are stated to be *about* a certain number. The answers are approximations because 3.14 is only an approximation for π.

On Your Own

- Students may think there is not enough information to solve Question 3. The quadrilateral is a square, so the diameter of the semicircles is 8 meters.
- Question 4 is challenging. The perimeter of the outfield is part of the circumference of a circle with a radius of 225 feet, not 300 feet.
- **Neighbor Check:** Have students work independently and then have their neighbor check their work. Have students discuss any discrepancies.
- When students have finished, ask volunteers to show their work at the board.

Closure

- Find the perimeter of the room shown. 64 ft

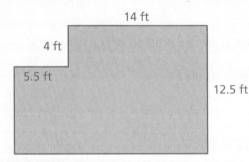

14 ft

4 ft

5.5 ft

12.5 ft

Technology For the Teacher

Dynamic Classroom

The Dynamic Planning Tool
Editable Teacher's Resources at *BigIdeasMath.com*

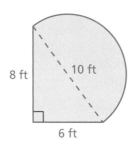

The figure is made up of a semicircle and a triangle. Find the perimeter.

The distance around the triangular part of the figure is 6 + 8 = 14 feet.

The distance around the semicircle is one-half the circumference of a circle with a diameter of 10 feet.

$$\frac{C}{2} = \frac{\pi d}{2}$$ Divide the circumference by 2.

$$\approx \frac{3.14 \cdot 10}{2}$$ Substitute 3.14 for π and 10 for d.

$$= 15.7$$ Simplify.

∴ The perimeter is about 14 + 15.7 = 29.7 feet.

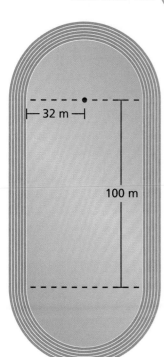

The running track is made up of a rectangle and two semicircles. Find the perimeter.

The semicircular ends of the track form a circle with a radius of 32 meters. Find its circumference.

$$C = 2\pi r$$ Write formula for circumference.

$$\approx 2 \cdot 3.14 \cdot 32$$ Substitute 3.14 for π and 32 for r.

$$= 200.96$$ Multiply.

∴ The perimeter is about 100 + 100 + 200.96 = 400.96 meters.

● **On Your Own**

3. The figure is made up of a square and two semicircles. Find the perimeter.

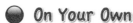
8 m

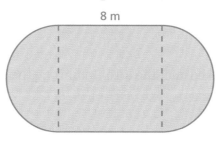

4. Running at 4 ft/sec, how long would it take a person to run around the baseball field?

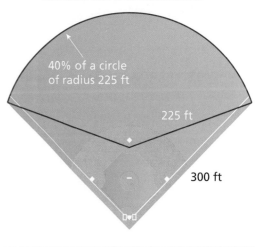

40% of a circle of radius 225 ft

225 ft

300 ft

 Vocabulary and Concept Check

1. **NUMBER SENSE** Is the perimeter of a composite figure *greater than*, *less than*, or *equal to* the sum of the perimeters of each figure separately? Explain.

2. **OPEN-ENDED** Draw a composite figure formed by a parallelogram and a trapezoid.

 Practice and Problem Solving

Each square on the grid paper is 1 square inch. Estimate the perimeter of the figure.

① 3. 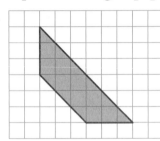   4. 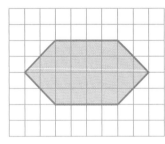   5.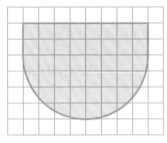

6. 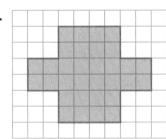   7. 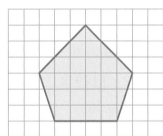   8.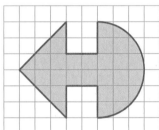

Find the perimeter of the figure.

② 9. 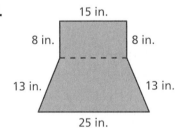   10. (see figure)   11. (see figure)

12. **ERROR ANALYSIS** Describe and correct the error in finding the perimeter of the figure.

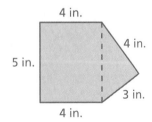

> Perimeter = 4 + 3 + 4 + 5 + 4 + 5
> = 25 in.

Assignment Guide and Homework Check

For Your Information

- **Exercise 1** Some students may include the choice *equal to*. This is true when composite figures do *not* share a common side, but do share a common vertex.

Common Errors

- **Exercises 3–8** Students may count the sides of the squares inside the figure. Remind them that they are finding the perimeter, so they only need to count the outside lengths.
- **Exercises 5 and 8** Students may have difficulty estimating the curved portions of the figure. Give students tracing paper and tell them to trace the line as straight instead of curved and compare it with the length of the side of a square to help them estimate the length.
- **Exercises 9–11, 13–15** Students may include the dotted lines in their calculation of the perimeter. Remind them that the dotted lines are for reference and sometimes give information to find another length. Only the outside lengths are counted.

5.6 Record and Practice Journal

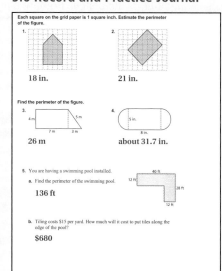

Vocabulary and Concept Check

1. less than and equal to; The perimeter is *less than* when figures making up a composite figure share a common side (dashed line).

The perimeter is *equal to* when the figures making up a composite figure share a common vertex.

2. *Sample answer:*

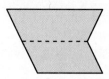

Practice and Problem Solving

3. 19.5 in.   4. 20 in.

5. 25.5 in.   6. 28 in.

7. 19 in.   8. 30 in.

9. 56 m   10. 82 in.

11. 30 cm

12. The length of the rectangle was counted twice.
Perimeter = 4 + 3 + 4 + 5 + 4 = 20 in.

Practice and Problem Solving

13. about 26.85 in.

14. about 50.26 in.

15. about 36.84 ft

16. **a.** 1875 ft   **b.** $16,875

17. See *Taking Math Deeper.*

18. See Additional Answers.

19. Yes; *Sample answer:* By adding the triangle shown by the dashed line to the L-shaped figure, you *reduce* the perimeter.

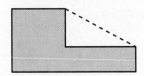

Fair Game Review

20. 19.35	**21.** 279.68
22. 153.86	**23.** 205
24. D	

Mini-Assessment

Find the perimeter of the figure.

1.

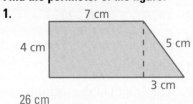

2.

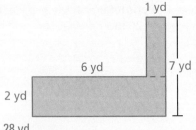

3. Find the perimeter of the garden.

about 58 ft

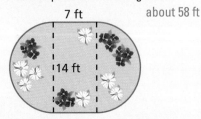

Taking Math Deeper

Exercise 17

This problem asks students to add 15 feet to the perimeter of a flower garden. There are infinitely many ways to do this. This is a good problem to assign to pairs of students and then have students share the way they increased the perimeter.

① Draw a diagram. Label the lengths.

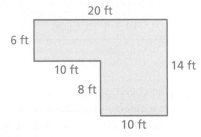

② **a.** Find the perimeter.

$$P = 6 + 20 + 14 + 10 + 8 + 10 = 68 \text{ ft}$$

③ **b.** Add 15 feet to the perimeter.

Notice that the additional 10 feet is a "wash." It is both added and subtracted from the perimeter.

Project

Design a garden for your school. Prepare a poster that you can use to present your idea to the principal.

Reteaching and Enrichment Strategies

If students need help. . .	If students got it. . .
Resources by Chapter • Practice A and Practice B • Puzzle Time Record and Practice Journal Practice Differentiating the Lesson Lesson Tutorials Skills Review Handbook	Resources by Chapter • Enrichment and Extension • School-to-Work • Financial Literacy • Technology Connection Start the next section

Find the perimeter of the figure.

13.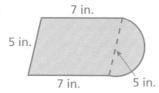
7 in.
5 in.
7 in.
5 in.

14.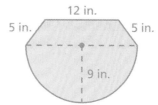
12 in.
5 in.   5 in.
9 in.

15.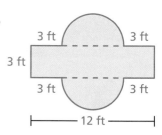
3 ft   3 ft
3 ft
3 ft   3 ft
12 ft

240 ft   285 ft
450 ft   450 ft

450 ft

16. PASTURE A section of land is to be fenced in for a horse pasture.

   a. Find the perimeter of the pasture.

   b. Fencing costs $27 per yard. How much will it cost to fence in the pasture?

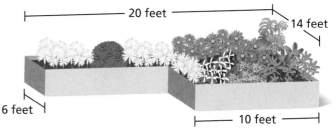
20 feet
14 feet
6 feet
10 feet

17. GARDEN A garden is built on a rooftop.

   a. Find the perimeter of the garden.

   b. You want to increase the perimeter by 15 feet. Draw a diagram of how you would do this. Is there more than one way? Explain.

18. In Example 3 on page 237, the track has six lanes. Explain why the starting points for the six runners are staggered. Draw a diagram as part of your explanation.

19. **Critical Thinking** Is it possible to add a figure to a composite figure without increasing its perimeter? Explain and draw a diagram to support your answer.

Fair Game Review What you learned in previous grades & lessons

Evaluate the expression. (Skills Review Handbook)

20. $2.15(3)^2$ **21.** $4.37(8)^2$ **22.** $3.14(7)^2$ **23.** $8.2(5)^2$

24. MULTIPLE CHOICE Which expression represents "6 less than 5 times a number x?" (Skills Review Handbook)

   A $(6-5)x$ **B** $6-5x$ **C** $\dfrac{6}{5x}$ **D** $5x-6$

5.7 Areas of Composite Figures

STANDARDS OF LEARNING
8.11

Essential Question How can you find the area of a composite figure?

1 ACTIVITY: Estimating Area

Work with a partner.

a. Choose a state. On grid paper, draw a larger outline of the state.

b. Use your drawing to estimate the area (in square miles) of the state.

c. Which state areas are easy to find? Which are difficult? Why?

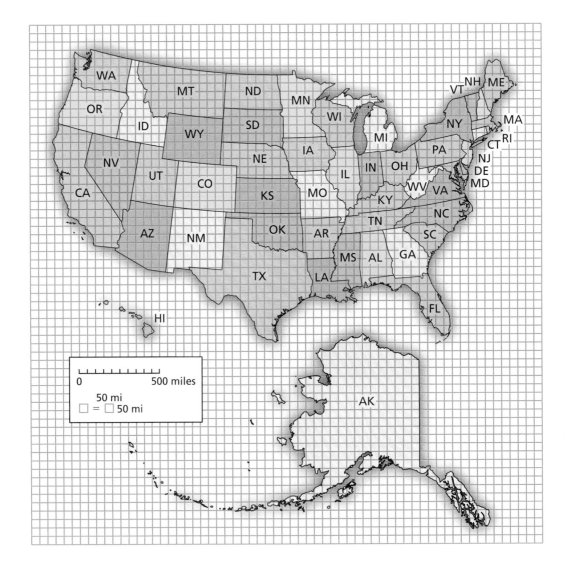

Laurie's Notes

Introduction

For the Teacher
- **Goal:** Students will develop an intuitive understanding of the area of composite figures by focusing on their component parts.
- Select one or more of the activities based upon time available and student interest. You may also wish to spend two days on this lesson.

Motivate
- Share U.S. state trivia in question/answer format.
- Largest states: Alaska, Texas, California
- Smallest states: Rhode Island, Delaware, Connecticut
- Most densely populated states: New Jersey, Rhode Island, Massachusetts

Activity Notes

Activity 1
- ❓ Ask a variety of questions about the attributes of the states: state with most coastline; states with no coastline; state furthest north, south, east, and west.
- Questions are answered by using eyesight only. The goal is to get students thinking about the states and how each might be described.
- Distribute rulers, if requested.
- **Big Idea:** Each square in the grid is 2500 square miles. Each state is composed of whole squares and parts of whole squares. Students will find the area of the state by finding the area of composite figures.
- Your class size may dictate how you implement this activity. Here are a few strategies.
  - Students are assigned states within one particular region.
  - Students use $\frac{1}{2}$-inch or 1-inch grid paper to draw the larger outline.

    This is *not* a lesson on scale drawings. A larger copy of the state allows students to record their areas for each part on the drawing.
  - Students are given an enlarged photocopy of the state to use.
  - Assign the same state to two students. Have each student make a drawing and then compare their estimates for the non-square parts of the state.
- Discuss part (c). States with straighter borders are easier to draw and to estimate their areas.
- **Extension:** Drawings of adjacent states can be cut out and taped together on a bulletin board. Students can do outside research to gather information about their state: population, population density; or to rank the states by area and find the mean and median of the state areas.

Standards of Learning
8.11 The student will solve practical area and perimeter problems involving composite plane figures.

Previous Learning
Students should know area formulas.

Activity Materials
Textbook
• rulers • scissors

Start Thinking! and Warm Up

Activity 5.7 Start Thinking!
For use before Activity 5.7

Activity 5.7 Warm Up
For use before Activity 5.7

Find the area of the figure described.
1. square with side length 10 ft
2. square with side length 16 in.
3. rectangle with length 15 m and width 10 m
4. triangle with base 5 cm and height 12 cm
5. circle with radius 10 ft
6. circle with diameter 100 yd

5.7 Record and Practice Journal

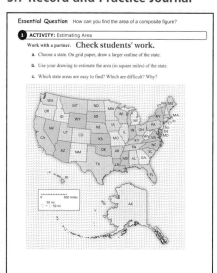

Essential Question How can you find the area of a composite figure?

1 ACTIVITY: Estimating Area

Work with a partner. **Check students' work.**
  a. Choose a state. On grid paper, draw a larger outline of the state.
  b. Use your drawing to estimate the area (in square miles) of the state.
  c. Which state areas are easy to find? Which are difficult? Why?

Differentiated Instruction

Kinesthetic

Using grid paper, have students draw and cut out a square 4 units on each side. Next, have students draw and cut out a rectangle that is 3 units by 2 units. Have students place the two figures so that they are touching, but not overlapping. Ask them to find the combined area by finding the area of each piece. Have them draw other shapes that are touching on the grid paper, for example a square with a semicircle on top. Find the total area. Discuss how they could use this idea to find the area of other figures.

5.7 Record and Practice Journal

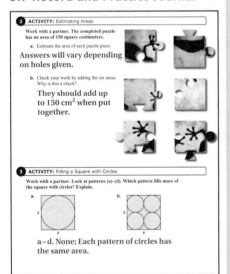

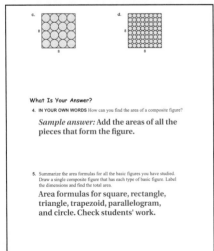

Laurie's Notes

Activity 2

- Students will work with actual-size pieces. The interlocking cuts are geometric shapes of which students should know how to find the area.
- Students will need to make accurate measurements to the nearest tenth of a centimeter.
- Scaled pieces are shown in the textbook.
- This activity reviews measurement, computation with decimals, and area formulas.
- Watch for computation errors.
- The completed puzzle is shown at the right.

Activity 3

- **Big Idea:** Each square has the same amount of green. Students can determine the radius of the circles. Then they can find the sum of the areas of circles in each diagram.
- You may need to suggest a table format to help guide student thinking.

Number of Circles	Radius of One Circle	Total Area
1	4	$1 \times \pi(4)^2 = 16\pi$ square units
4	2	$4 \times \pi(2)^2 = 16\pi$ square units
16	1	$16 \times \pi(1)^2 = 16\pi$ square units
64	$\frac{1}{2}$	$64 \times \pi\left(\frac{1}{2}\right)^2 = 16\pi$ square units

- Students find the results of this activity surprising.

What Is Your Answer?

- Question 5 is a nice summary problem that could become a small project.

Closure

- Does the area of a figure change when it is divided into smaller regions? Explain. No. As each region becomes smaller the number of regions increase, but the total area remains the same.

Technology For the Teacher

Dynamic Classroom

The Dynamic Planning Tool
Editable Teacher's Resources at *BigIdeasMath.com*

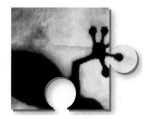

2 ACTIVITY: Estimating Areas

Work with a partner. The completed puzzle has an area of 150 square centimeters.

a. Estimate the area of each puzzle piece.

b. Check your work by adding the six areas. Why is this a check?

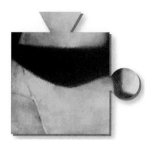

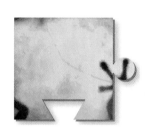

3 ACTIVITY: Filling a Square with Circles

Work with a partner. Which pattern fills more of the square with circles? Explain.

a.

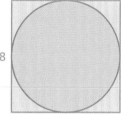

b.

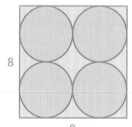

c.

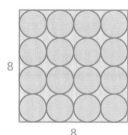

d.

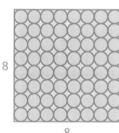

What Is Your Answer?

4. **IN YOUR OWN WORDS** How can you find the area of a composite figure?

5. Summarize the area formulas for all the basic figures you have studied. Draw a single composite figure that has each type of basic figure. Label the dimensions and find the total area.

Practice Use what you learned about areas of composite figures to complete Exercises 3–5 on page 244.

Check It Out
Lesson Tutorials
BigIdeasMath ✓com

To find the area of a composite figure, split it up into figures with areas you know how to find. Then add the areas of those figures.

EXAMPLE 1   Finding an Area Using Grid Paper

Each square on the grid paper is 1 square meter. Find the area of the yellow figure.

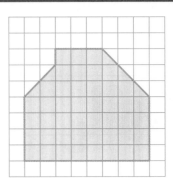

Count the number of squares that lie entirely in the figure. There are 45.

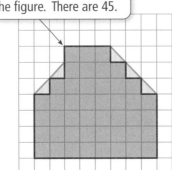

Count the number of half-squares in the figure. There are 5.

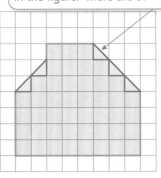

The area of a half-square is $1 \div 2 = 0.5$ square meter.

Area of 45 squares: $45 \times 1 = 45$ square meters

Area of 5 half-squares: $5 \times 0.5 = 2.5$ square meters

∴ So, the area is $45 + 2.5 = 47.5$ square meters.

On Your Own

Now You're Ready
Exercises 3–8

Find the area of the shaded figure.

1.
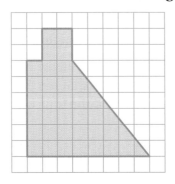

2.
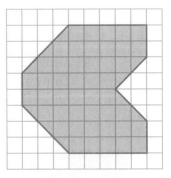

Laurie's Notes

Introduction

Connect

- **Yesterday:** Students gained an intuitive understanding about how to find the area of composite figures.
- **Today:** Students will divide composite figures into familiar geometric shapes and use known area formulas to find the total area.

Motivate

- Draw the following "equations." Ask students how they would find the area of the last figure knowing the areas of the figures on the left side of the equation.

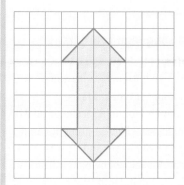

- These quick puzzles should help focus students' thinking on how they will find the area of a composite figure.
- Discuss the strategy of dividing a composite figure into smaller regions that are geometric figures with known area formulas.

Lesson Notes

Example 1

- Work through the example as shown and then try an alternate approach.
- **?** "What is the name of the yellow polygon?" heptagon
- **?** "Can you think of another way to find the area of the heptagon? Explain." Yes. Listen for a suggestion that divides the heptagon into a rectangle, a triangle, and a trapezoid.
- Note: The rectangle has dimensions 4×8, the triangle has a base of 2 and height of 2, and the trapezoid has bases of 3 and 6 and a height of 3. The total area is 47.5 square meters.
- **?** "Are there other strategies for finding the area of the yellow heptagon?" Yes, it could be divided into a rectangle and two trapezoids using two parallel horizontal lines (or two parallel vertical lines).
- Point out the solution is in square meters, because it was stated at the beginning that each square on the grid paper is 1 square meter.
- **Extension:** Ask students if the area of their classroom is more or less than 48 square meters. Hold two meter sticks perpendicular to each other as a visual clue.

On Your Own

- Encourage students to find more than one method to find the area of each.
- Have students share different strategies at the board.

Start Thinking! and Warm Up

> **Lesson 5.7** Warm Up
> For use before Lesson 5.7
>
> **Lesson 5.7** Start Thinking!
> For use before Lesson 5.7
>
> Draw a picture of a house with a roof and a chimney.
>
> How can you use a ruler and some calculations to find the area covered by your drawing?
>
> Use a ruler and the method you described to estimate the area of the house.

Extra Example 1

Each square on the grid paper is 1 square yard. Find the area of the figure.

16 yd^2

On Your Own

1. 37 square units
2. 51 square units

Extra Example 2

Find the area of the pool and the deck. The figure is made up of a right triangle, a square and a semicircle.

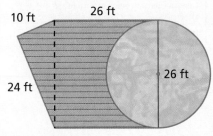

about 1061.33 ft^2

Extra Example 3

Find the area of the figure made up of a triangle, a rectangle, and a trapezoid.

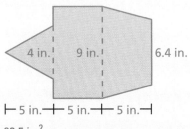

93.5 in.^{2}

⬤ On Your Own

3. 90 m^2

4. about 10.28 ft^2

English Language Learners

Vocabulary

Formulas use letters to represent specific items or measures. For instance, in the formula for the area of a rectangle, $A = bh$, A represents area, b represents the base, and h represents the height. Review with your English learners the capital and lowercase letters used in formulas.

area *(A)*   base *(b)*
circumference *(C)*   diameter *(d)*
distance *(d)*   height *(h)*
length *(ℓ)*   perimeter *(P)*
radius *(r)*   rate *(r)*
time *(t)*   volume *(V)*
width *(w)*

Laurie's Notes

Example 2

- After Example 1, it should be clear to students that this composite figure will be divided into a semicircle and a rectangle.
- **?** "What are the dimensions of the rectangle?" 19 ft by 12 ft
- **?** "What is the radius of the circle?" 6 ft
- In calculating the area of the semicircle, watch for student errors in multiplying and dividing decimals.
- **Extension:** Ask students if the area of a semicircle of radius 6 is the same as area of a circle of radius 3. The answer is no! 18π compared to 9π

Example 3

- Draw the composite figure without the interior dotted lines. Ask students to think about how the figure could be divided into regions with known area formulas. They may come up with more than three regions.
- Label the diagram with the dimensions given. I find it helpful to draw small arrows from the measurement to the segment it is associated with, especially for interior dimensions.
- Work through the problem, questioning students along the way about the process.
- **?** "How do you find the area of a triangle? How do you multiply $\frac{1}{2}$ by 11.2? What units are used to label area?"
- **Common Misconception:** In a right triangle, the height is a side length. It is not an interior measurement.

On Your Own

- Have students share their strategies for these two problems. Question 4 might be done as 4 semicircles or 2 circles.

⬤ Closure

- **Exit Ticket:** Find the area. 100 units^2

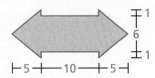

Technology
For the **T**eacher

The Dynamic Planning Tool
Editable Teacher's Resources at *BigIdeasMath.com*

EXAMPLE 2 Finding an Area

Find the area of the portion of the basketball court shown.

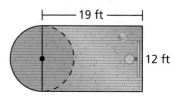
19 ft

12 ft

The figure is made up of a rectangle and a semicircle. Find the area of each figure.

Area of rectangle

$$A = \ell w$$

$$= (19)(12)$$

$$= 228$$

Area of semicircle

$$A = \frac{\pi r^2}{2}$$

$$\approx \frac{3.14 \cdot (6)^2}{2}$$

The semicircle has a radius of $\frac{12}{2} = 6$ feet.

$$= 56.52$$

⋮• So, the area is about $228 + 56.52 = 284.52$ square feet.

EXAMPLE 3 Finding an Area

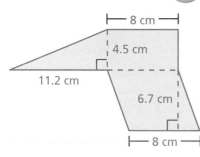
8 cm
4.5 cm
11.2 cm
6.7 cm
8 cm

Find the area of the figure.

The figure is made up of a triangle, a rectangle, and a parallelogram. Find the area of each figure.

Area of triangle

$$A = \frac{1}{2}bh$$

$$= \frac{1}{2}(11.2)(4.5)$$

$$= 25.2$$

Area of rectangle

$$A = \ell w$$

$$= (8)(4.5)$$

$$= 36$$

Area of parallelogram

$$A = bh$$

$$= (8)(6.7)$$

$$= 53.6$$

⋮• So, the area is $25.2 + 36 + 53.6 = 114.8$ square centimeters.

On Your Own

Now You're Ready
Exercises 9 and 10

Find the area of the figure.

3.

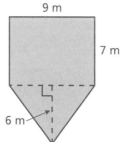
9 m
7 m
6 m

4.

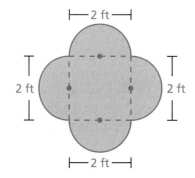
├─ 2 ft ─┤
2 ft   2 ft
├─ 2 ft ─┤

 Vocabulary and Concept Check

1. **REASONING** Describe two different ways to find the area of the figure. Name the types of figures you used and the dimensions of each.

2. **REASONING** Draw a trapezoid. Suppose you can't remember the formula for the area of a trapezoid. Explain how you can think of the trapezoid as a composite figure to find its area.

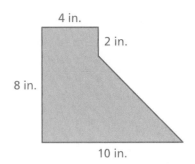

 Practice and Problem Solving

Each square on the grid paper is 1 square inch. Find the area of the figure.

① 3.
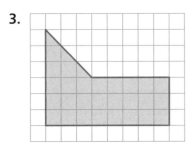

4.
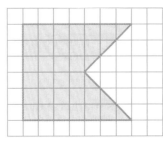

5.
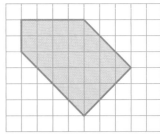

6.
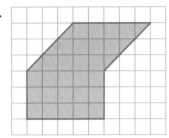

7.
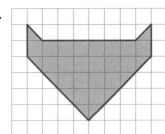

8.
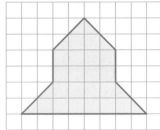

Find the area of the figure.

② ③ 9.
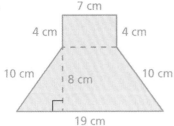

10.
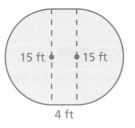

11. **OPEN-ENDED** Trace your hand and your foot on grid paper. Then estimate the area of each. Which one has the greater area?

Assignment Guide and Homework Check

Level	Day 1 Activity Assignment	Day 2 Lesson Assignment	Homework Check
Basic	3–5, 18–22	1, 2, 6–13	2, 6, 9, 12
Average	3–5, 18–22	1, 2, 8–13, 15, 16	8, 9, 12, 15
Advanced	3–5, 18–22	1, 2, 7, 8, 12–17	8, 12, 15, 16

Common Errors

- **Exercises 3–8** Students may forget to count all the squares inside the figure and just count the ones along the border because this is what they did for perimeter. Remind them that the area includes everything inside the figure.
- **Exercises 9 and 10** Students may forget to include one of the areas of the composite figures or may count one area more than once. Tell them to break apart the figure into several figures. Draw and label each figure and then find the area of each part. Finally add the areas of each part together for the area of the whole figure.
- **Exercises 12–14** Students may forget to subtract the unshaded area from the figure. Remind them that in this situation instead of adding on the area of a figure they must subtract a portion out. Give a real-life example to help students understand, like tiling a bathroom floor but taking out the part where the sink or toilet is.

5.7 Record and Practice Journal

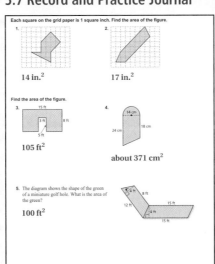

 ## Vocabulary and Concept Check

1. *Sample answer:* You could add the areas of an 8-inch × 4-inch rectangle and a triangle with a base of 6 inches and a height of 6 inches. Also you could add the area of a 2-inch × 4-inch rectangle to the area of a trapezoid with a height of 6 inches, and base lengths of 4 inches and 10 inches.

2. *Sample answer:* You can think of the trapezoid as a rectangle and two triangles.

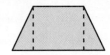 ## Practice and Problem Solving

3. 28.5 in.^2 4. 33 in.^2

5. 25 in.^2 6. 30 in.^2

7. 25 in.^2 8. 24 in.^2

9. 132 cm^2

10. about 236.625 ft^2

11. *Answer will include but is not limited to:* Tracings of a hand and foot on grid paper, estimates of the areas, and a statement of which is greater.

Practice and Problem Solving

12. 89 m^2 **13.** 23.5 in.^2

14. about 21.87 ft^2

15. 24 m^2

16. $P = $ about 94.2 ft
     $A = $ about 628 ft^2

17. See *Taking Math Deeper*.

Fair Game Review

18. $x - 12$ **19.** $y \div 6$

20. $b + 3$ **21.** $7w$

22. A

Mini-Assessment

Find the area of the figure.

1.

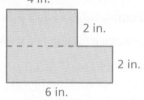

4 in.

2 in.

2 in.

6 in.

20 in.^2

2.

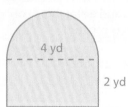

4 yd

2 yd

about 14.28 yd^2

3. Find the area of the red region.
about 3.44 in.^2

2 in.

Taking Math Deeper

Exercise 17

This problem is not conceptually difficult. However, it does have a lot of calculations and it is difficult to do without a calculator. Before starting the calculations, suggest that students think about which design is more efficient. Each design will fit on an 11×17 sheet of paper. By cutting and folding each pattern, a student can see how much overlap each design has. The design with the greatest overlap is the least efficient.

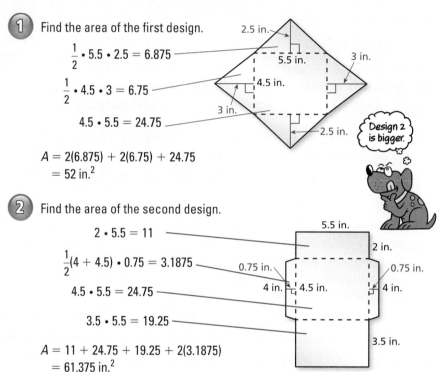

① Find the area of the first design.

$\frac{1}{2} \cdot 5.5 \cdot 2.5 = 6.875$

$\frac{1}{2} \cdot 4.5 \cdot 3 = 6.75$

$4.5 \cdot 5.5 = 24.75$

$A = 2(6.875) + 2(6.75) + 24.75$
$\quad = 52 \text{ in.}^2$

2.5 in.   5.5 in.   3 in.   4.5 in.   3 in.   2.5 in.

Design 2 is bigger.

② Find the area of the second design.

$2 \cdot 5.5 = 11$

$\frac{1}{2}(4 + 4.5) \cdot 0.75 = 3.1875$

$4.5 \cdot 5.5 = 24.75$

$3.5 \cdot 5.5 = 19.25$

$A = 11 + 24.75 + 19.25 + 2(3.1875)$
$\quad = 61.375 \text{ in.}^2$

5.5 in.   2 in.   0.75 in.   0.75 in.   4 in.   4.5 in.   4 in.   3.5 in.

③ **a.** So, the second design has the greater area. Answer the question.

$500 \cdot 61.375 = 30{,}687.5 \text{ in.}^2$ (500 envelopes using Design 2)

$\dfrac{30{,}687.5}{52} \approx 590.1$ (number of envelopes using Design 1)

b. You could make 90 more envelopes using Design 1.

Reteaching and Enrichment Strategies

If students need help. . .	If students got it. . .
Resources by Chapter • Practice A and Practice B • Puzzle Time Record and Practice Journal Practice Differentiating the Lesson Lesson Tutorials Skills Review Handbook	Resources by Chapter • Enrichment and Extension • School-to-Work • Financial Literacy • Technology Connection • Life Connections Start the next section

Find the area of the figure.

12.
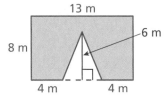
13 m
6 m
8 m
4 m   4 m

13.
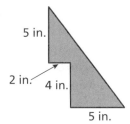
5 in.
2 in.   4 in.
5 in.

14.
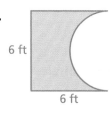
6 ft
6 ft

15. AREA The figure is made up of a square and a rectangle. Find the area of the shaded region.

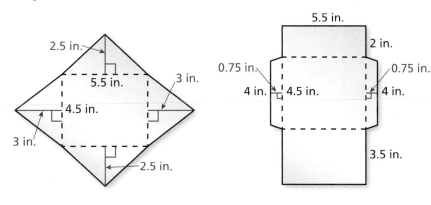
7 m
3 m
16 m

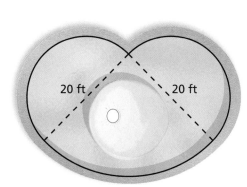
20 ft   20 ft

16. FOUNTAIN The fountain is made up of two semicircles and a quarter circle. Find the perimeter and area of the fountain.

17. **Critical Thinking** You are deciding on two different designs for envelopes.

2.5 in.
5.5 in.
4.5 in.
3 in.
3 in.
2.5 in.

5.5 in.
2 in.
0.75 in.   0.75 in.
4 in.   4.5 in.   4 in.
3.5 in.

a. Which design has the greater area?

b. You make 500 envelopes using the design with the greater area. Using the same amount of paper, how many more envelopes can you make with the other design?

Fair Game Review What you learned in previous grades & lessons

Write the phrase as an expression. *(Skills Review Handbook)*

18. 12 less than a number x

19. a number y divided by 6

20. a number b increased by 3

21. the product of 7 and a number w

22. MULTIPLE CHOICE What number is 0.02% of 50? *(Section 4.1)*

Ⓐ 0.01   Ⓑ 0.1   Ⓒ 1   Ⓓ 100

The triangles are similar. Find the value of x. *(Section 5.4)*

1.
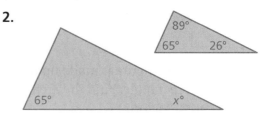

45°
$x°$
95°
45°   40°

2.

89°
65°   26°

65° $x°$

The vertices of a triangle are $L(1, -1)$, $M(3, -1)$, **and** $N(3, -4)$. **Find the coordinates of the image after the transformation.** *(Section 5.5)*

3. a translation of 2 units right and 7 units up

4. a reflection in the *y*-axis

5. a rotation of 180° about the origin

6. a dilation with a scale factor of 2

Find the perimeter and area of the figure. *(Section 5.6 and Section 5.7)*

7.
8 in.
12 in.
20 in.
24 in.

8.
8 ft   6 ft
8 ft
10 ft

9.
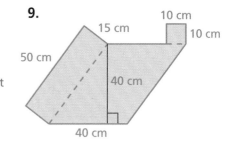
10 cm
15 cm   10 cm
50 cm   40 cm
40 cm

12 ft
14 ft   8 ft
10 ft
18 ft

10. **GARDEN** Part of a yard is being fenced in to make a vegetable garden. How many feet of fencing are needed to surround the garden? *(Section 5.6)*

11. **PERIMETER** The side lengths of a right triangle are doubled to make a similar triangle. Does the perimeter double as well? Explain. *(Section 5.4)*

12. **CARD** The heart-shaped card is made by placing a square and two semicircles together. What is the area of the card? *(Section 5.7)*

8 cm   8 cm

Alternative Assessment Options

Math Chat	Student Reflective Focus Question
Structured Interview	Writing Prompt

Math Chat

- Put students in pairs to complete and discuss the exercises from the quiz. The discussion should include discussing terms such as similar triangles, transformations, and perimeters and areas of composite figures.
- The teacher should walk around the classroom listening to the pairs and ask questions to ensure understanding.

Study Help Sample Answers

Remind students to complete Graphic Organizers for the rest of the chapter.

6.

Similar Triangles

Examples	Non-Examples

95°
65° 20°

95°
65° 20°

95°
65° 20°

96°
64° 20°

75° $x°$ $y°$ 55°
50°
50°

38°
$x°$ 42° $y°$

B
50 ft 60 ft
D C A
x 40 ft
E
△ABC and △DEC

B
80°
50 ft 60 ft
D C A
x 40 ft
E
△ABC and △DEC

7–8. Available at *BigIdeasMath.com*

Reteaching and Enrichment Strategies

If students need help. . .	If students got it. . .
Resources by Chapter • Study Help • Practice A and Practice B • Puzzle Time Lesson Tutorials *BigIdeasMath.com* Practice Quiz Practice from the Test Generator	Resources by Chapter • Enrichment and Extension • School-to-Work Game Closet at *BigIdeasMath.com* Start the Chapter Review

Answers

1. $x = 95$

2. $x = 26$

3. $L'(3, 6), M'(5, 6), N'(5, 3)$

4. $L'(-1, -1), M'(-3, -1),$ $N'(-3, -4)$

5. $L'(-1, 1), M'(-3, 1), N'(-3, 4)$

6. $L'(2, -2), M'(6, -2), N'(6, -8)$

7. 88 in.; 352 in.^{2}

8. about 49.12 ft; about 154.24 ft^2

9. 230 cm; 2450 cm^2

10. 60 ft

11. See Additional Answers.

12. about 114.24 cm^2

Technology
For the Teacher
Answer Presentation Tool

Assessment Book

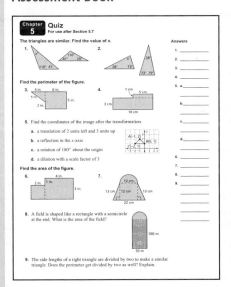

T-246

For the Teacher
Additional Review Options
- **Quiz**Show
- Big Ideas Test Generator
- Game Closet at *BigIdeasMath.com*
- Vocabulary Puzzle Builder
- Resources by Chapter
    Puzzle Time
    Study Help

Answers

1. adjacent; $x = 21$

2. vertical; $x = 84$

Review of Common Errors

Exercise 1
- Students may not be able to set up the correct equation. Point out that the two angles make up a right (90°) angle.

Exercise 2
- Students may not realize that the labeled angles are vertical angles and that they are congruent. Review vertical angles with students.

Check It Out
Vocabulary Help
BigIdeasMath [check]com

Review Key Vocabulary

complementary angles, p. 200
supplementary angles, p. 200
adjacent angles, p. 201
vertical angles, p. 201
isosceles triangle, p. 206

congruent sides, p. 206
equilateral triangle, p. 206
equiangular triangle, p. 206
polygon, p. 212
regular polygon, p. 213
convex polygon, p. 214
concave polygon, p. 214

similar triangles, p. 222
indirect measurement, p. 223
translation, p. 228
reflection, p. 228
rotation, p. 228
dilation, p. 230
composite figure, p. 236

Review Examples and Exercises

5.1 Classifying Angles (pp. 198–203)

Tell whether the angles are *adjacent* or *vertical*. Then find the value of x.

The angles are adjacent angles. Because the angles are supplementary, the sum of their measures is 180°.

$$x + 123 = 180$$
$$x = 57$$

So, x is 57.

Exercises

Tell whether the angles are *adjacent* or *vertical*. Then find the value of x.

1.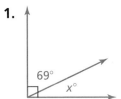

2.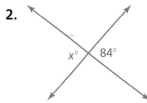

5.2 Angles and Sides of Triangles (pp. 204–209)

Find the value of x. Then classify the triangle.

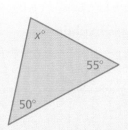

$$x + 50 + 55 = 180$$
$$x + 105 = 180$$
$$x = 75$$

The value of x is 75. The triangle has three acute angle measures, 50°, 55°, and 75°. So, it is an acute triangle.

Exercises

Find the value of x. Then classify the triangle in as many ways as possible.

3.

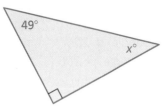

4.

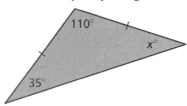

5.3 **Angles of Polygons** *(pp. 210–217)*

Find the value of x.

Step 1: The polygon has 6 sides. Find the sum of the angle measures.

$S = (n - 2) \cdot 180°$ Write the formula.

$= (6 - 2) \cdot 180°$ Substitute 6 for *n*.

$= 720$ Simplify. The sum of the angle measures is 720°.

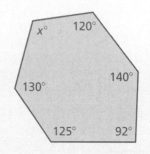

Step 2: Write and solve an equation.

$$130 + 125 + 92 + 140 + 120 + x = 720$$

$$607 + x = 720$$

$$x = 113$$

∴ The value of *x* is 113.

Exercises

Find the value of x.

5.

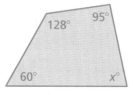

6.

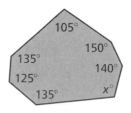

7.

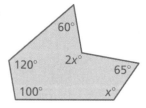

Tell whether the polygon is *convex* or *concave*. Explain.

8.

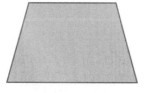

9.

10.

Review of Common Errors (continued)

Exercises 3 and 4

- Students may solve for *x*, but forget to classify the triangle. Remind them to read the directions carefully and to answer the question.

Exercises 5–7

- Students may forget to include one or more of the angles when writing an equation to find the value of *x*. Remind students to include all of the angles. Encourage them to write the equation and then count the number of terms to make sure that there is the same number of terms as there are angles before solving.

Exercises 8–10

- Students may not adequately explain why the polygon is convex or concave. Remind students to connect all the vertices with all the others. One strategy is to start with one vertex and connect it to all the other vertices, and then rotate clockwise to the next vertex and repeat the process.

Answers

3. $x = 41$; right, scalene

4. $x = 35$; isosceles, obtuse

5. $x = 77$

6. $x = 110$

7. $x = 125$

8. convex; No line segment connecting two vertices lies outside the polygon.

9. concave; A line segment connecting two vertices lies outside the polygon.

10. concave; A line segment connecting two vertices lies outside the polygon.

11. yes; The triangles have the same angle measures, 90°, 68°, and 22°.

12. $x = 50$

Review of Common Errors (continued)

Exercise 11

- Students may find the missing angle measure for only one of the triangles and then make a decision about the similarity of the triangles. While it is possible to use this method, encourage them to find the missing angles of *both* triangles to verify that they are correct.

Exercise 12

- Students may incorrectly identify congruent angles and find the wrong value for *x*. Encourage them to mark which angles are congruent before finding *x*.

Exercises 13–16

- Students may try to find the coordinates of the images without drawing the image and make a mistake. Encourage them to draw the original triangle and each image on their own axes so that there is no confusion.

Exercises 17–22

- Students may include the dashed lines in their calculation of the perimeter. Remind them that the dashed lines are for reference and sometimes give information to find another length. Only the outside lengths are counted.

Exercises 23–26

- Students may forget to include the area of one or more parts of a composite figure or count a part more than once. Tell them to draw and label each part, find the area of each part, and add the areas of the parts to find the area of the composite figure.

5.4 Using Similar Triangles (pp. 220–225)

Tell whether the triangles are similar. Explain.

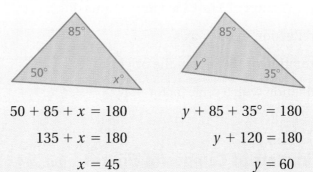

$$50 + 85 + x = 180 \qquad\qquad y + 85 + 35° = 180$$
$$135 + x = 180 \qquad\qquad\quad y + 120 = 180$$
$$x = 45 \qquad\qquad\qquad\qquad y = 60$$

⋮• The triangles do not have the same angle measures. So, they are not similar.

Exercises

11. Tell whether the triangles are similar. Explain.

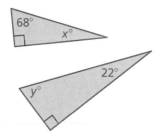

12. The triangles are similar. Find the value of x.

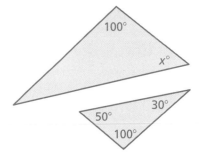

5.5 Polygons and Transformations (pp. 226–233)

The vertices of a trapezoid are $A(0, -1)$, $B(4, 1)$, $C(3, -2)$, and $D(1, -3)$. Translate the trapezoid 5 units right and 5 units up. What are the coordinates of the image?

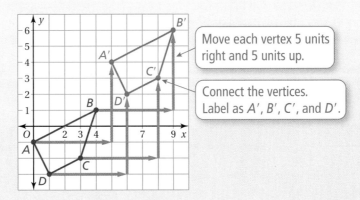

Move each vertex 5 units right and 5 units up.

Connect the vertices. Label as A', B', C', and D'.

⋮• The coordinates of the image are $A'(5, 4)$, $B'(9, 6)$, $C'(8, 3)$, and $D'(6, 2)$.

Exercises

Find the coordinates of the image after the transformation.

13. a translation of 3 units left and 4 units down

14. a reflection in the *y*-axis

15. a rotation of 180° about the origin

16. a dilation with a scale factor of 3

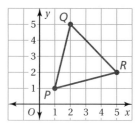

5.6 **Perimeters of Composite Figures** *(pp. 234–239)*

The figure is made up of a semicircle and a square. Find the perimeter. Use 3.14 for π.

The distance around the square part is 6 + 6 + 6 = 18 meters. The distance around the curved part is one-half the circumference of a circle with *d* = 6 meters.

$$\frac{C}{2} = \frac{\pi d}{2}$$ Divide the circumference by 2.

$$\approx \frac{3.14 \cdot 6}{2}$$ Substitute 3.14 for π and 6 for *d*.

$$= 9.42$$ Simplify.

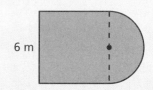

6 m

∴ The perimeter of the figure is about 18 + 9.42 = 27.42 meters.

Exercises

Find the perimeter of the figure.

17.

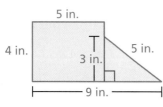

5 in.
4 in.
3 in.
5 in.
9 in.

18.

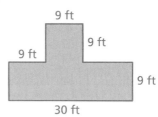

9 ft
9 ft
9 ft
9 ft
30 ft

19.

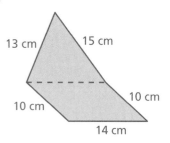

13 cm
15 cm
10 cm
10 cm
14 cm

20.

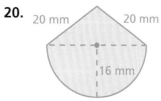

20 mm
20 mm
16 mm

21.

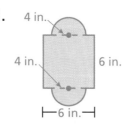

4 in.
4 in.
6 in.
6 in.

22.

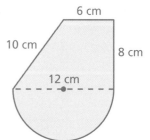

6 cm
10 cm
8 cm
12 cm

Review Game

Finding Angle Measures

Big Ideas
Game Closet

For the Student
Additional Practice
- Lesson Tutorials
- Study Help (textbook)
- Student Website
  Multi-Language Glossary
  Practice Assessments

Materials per Group
- deck of playing cards
- paper
- pencil
- stopwatch

Directions
Divide the class into equally sized groups. A group member lays down two cards next to each other, and below this pair lays down another two cards next to each other. Then they multiply the values of the cards in each pair. (Count kings, queens, jacks, and aces as 10.) These are used to represent the measures of two angles of a triangle. The group member then finds the angle measure of the third angle. Other members time the one working and make sure the computed angle is correct. Each group member takes a turn going through the deck as fast as he or she can. If there is a combination that is impossible to use, they must identify this and move on.

Who wins?
The fastest member in a group after 2 rounds competes against the fastest members in the other groups. The winner is the fastest student.

Answers

13. $P'(-2, -3)$, $Q'(-1, 1)$, $R'(2, -2)$

14. $P'(-1, 1)$, $Q'(-2, 5)$, $R'(-5, 2)$

15. $P'(-1, -1)$, $Q'(-2, -5)$, $R'(-5, -2)$

16. $P'(3, 3)$, $Q'(6, 15)$, $R'(15, 6)$

17. 24 in.

18. 96 ft

19. 62 cm

20. about 90.24 mm

21. about 28.56 in.

22. about 42.84 cm

23. about 79.25 in.^{2}

24. 29 in.^{2}

25. about 31.625 ft^2

26. about $1200

My Thoughts on the Chapter

What worked. . .

Teacher Tip

Not allowed to write in your teaching edition? Use sticky notes to record your thoughts.

What did not work. . .

What I would do differently. . .

5.7 Areas of Composite Figures *(pp. 240–245)*

Find the area of the figure.

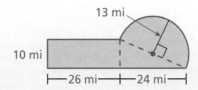

The figure is made up of a rectangle, a triangle, and a semicircle.
Find the area of each figure.

Area of rectangle	*Area of triangle*	*Area of semicircle*
$A = \ell w$	$A = \dfrac{1}{2}bh$	$A = \dfrac{\pi r^2}{2}$
$= (26)(10)$	$= \dfrac{1}{2}(10)(24)$	$\approx \dfrac{3.14 \cdot (13)^2}{2}$
$= 260$	$= 120$	$= 265.33$

So, the area of the figure is about $260 + 120 + 265.33 = 645.33$ square miles.

Exercises

Find the area of the figure.

23.

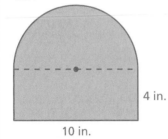

24.

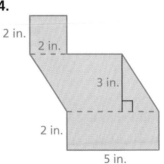

25.

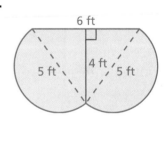

26. FLOORING Oak flooring costs $4 per square foot. Estimate how much it costs to buy oak flooring for the room shown?

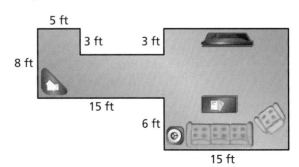

Check It Out
Test Practice
BigIdeasMath✓com

Tell whether the angles are *adjacent* or *vertical*. Then find the value of *x*.

1.
113°
$x°$

2.
$x°$
56°

3.
$x°$ 74°

Find the value of *x*. Then classify the triangle in as many ways as possible.

4.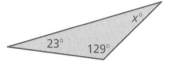
$x°$
23° 129°

5.
$x°$
68° 44°

6.
$x°$
$x°$ $x°$

7. Tell whether the polygon is *convex* or *concave*. Explain.

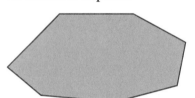

8. Find the value of *x*.

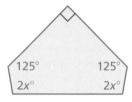
125° 125°
$2x°$ $2x°$

Find the perimeter and area of the figure.

9.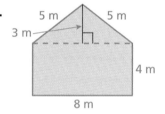
5 m 5 m
3 m
4 m
8 m

10.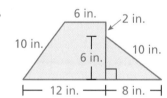
6 in. 2 in.
10 in. 10 in.
6 in.
12 in. 8 in.

11.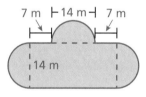
7 m 14 m 7 m
14 m

The vertices of a parallelogram are *W*(4, 4), *X*(8, 4), *Y*(10, 1), and *Z*(6, 1). Find the coordinates of the image after the transformation.

12. a translation of 4 units left and 5 units down

13. a reflection in the *x*-axis

14. a rotation of 90° counterclockwise about the origin

15. a dilation with a scale factor of $\frac{1}{2}$

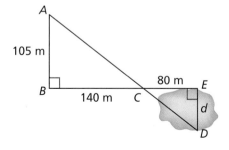
A
105 m
80 m
E
B
140 m C
d
D

16. POND Use the given measurements to find the distance *d* across the pond.

Test Item References

Chapter Test Questions	Section to Review
1–3	5.1
4–6	5.2
7, 8	5.3
16	5.4
12–15	5.5
9–11	5.6
9–11	5.7

Test-Taking Strategies

Remind students to quickly look over the entire test before they start so that they can budget their time. Students should jot down the formula for the sum of interior angles of a polygon on the back of their test before they begin. Students need to use the **Stop** and **Think** strategy before answering questions.

Common Assessment Errors

- **Exercises 2 and 3** Students may not be able to set up the correct equation. Point out that the two angles in Exercise 2 make up a right (90°) angle and that the two angles in Exercise 3 make up a straight (180°) angle.
- **Exercises 4–6** Students may solve for x, but forget to classify the triangle. Remind them to read the directions carefully and to answer the question.
- **Exercise 8** Students may forget to include one or more of the angles when writing an equation to find the value of x. Remind them to include all the angles. Encourage students to write the equation and then count the number of terms to make sure that there is the same number of terms as there are angles before solving.
- **Exercises 9–11** When calculating the perimeter of the figure, students may count the dashed lines. Remind them that the dashed lines are for reference and that only the outside lengths are counted. When calculating the area of the figure, students may forget to include the area of one or more parts or count part(s) more than once. Tell them to draw and label each part, find the area of each part, and add the areas of the parts.

Reteaching and Enrichment Strategies

If students need help. . .	If students got it. . .
Resources by Chapter • Practice A and Practice B • Puzzle Time Record and Practice Journal Practice Differentiating the Lesson Lesson Tutorials Practice from the Test Generator Skills Review Handbook	Resources by Chapter • Enrichment and Extension • School-to-Work • Financial Literacy • Life Connections Game Closet at *BigIdeasMath.com* Start Standardized Test Practice

Answers

1. vertical; $x = 113$

2. adjacent; $x = 34$

3. adjacent; $x = 106$

4. $x = 28$; obtuse, scalene

5. $x = 68$; acute, isosceles

6. $x = 60$; acute, isosceles, equilateral, equiangular

7. convex; No line segment connecting two vertices lies outside the polygon.

8. $x = 50$

9. $P = 26$ m, $A = 44$ m^2

10. $P = 48$ in., $A = 96$ in.^{2}

11. $P \approx 108$ m, $A \approx 623$ m^2

12. $W'(0, -1), X'(4, -1),$ $Y'(6, -4), Z'(2, -4)$

13. $W'(4, -4), X'(8, -4),$ $Y'(10, -1), Z'(6, -1)$

14. $W'(-4, 4), X'(-4, 8),$ $Y'(-1, 10), Z'(-1, 6)$

15. $W'(2, 2), X'(4, 2),$ $Y'\left(5, \dfrac{1}{2}\right), Z'\left(3, \dfrac{1}{2}\right)$

16. 60 m

Assessment Book

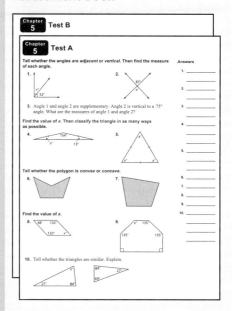

After Answering Easy Questions, Relax
Answer Easy Questions First
Estimate the Answer
Read All Choices before Answering
Read Question before Answering
Solve Directly or Eliminate Choices
Solve Problem before Looking at Choices
Use Intelligent Guessing
Work Backwards

About this Strategy

When taking a multiple choice test, be sure to read each question carefully and thoroughly. Sometimes it is easier to solve the problem and then look for the answer among the choices.

Answers

1. 147°
2. B
3. F
4. 152°
5. D

Item Analysis

1. **Gridded Response:** Correct answer: 147°

   Common Error: The student might divide 180 by 11.

2. **A.** The student adds 11 and 1.6 together before dividing.
   B. Correct answer
   C. The student divides first and then subtracts.
   D. The student subtracts 1.6 instead of dividing.

3. **F.** Correct answer
   G. The student has the correct slope but the wrong *y*-intercept, perhaps confusing the *x*- and *y*-intercepts.
   H. The student has the correct *y*-intercept but the wrong slope.
   I. The student has the wrong slope and the wrong *y*-intercept, perhaps confusing the *x*- and *y*-intercepts.

4. **Gridded Response:** Correct answer: 152°

   Common Error: The student subtracts 28 from 100, yielding an answer of 72.

5. **A.** The student overlooks the exponent, not realizing that it makes the function nonlinear.
   B. The student overlooks the fact that *x* is in the denominator, not realizing that it makes the function nonlinear.
   C. The student overlooks the fact that *x* and *y* are being multiplied, not realizing that it makes the function nonlinear.
   D. Correct answer

6. **F.** The student finds the point where the line crosses the *y*-axis.
   G. The student finds the correct point, but writes its coordinates in reverse.
   H. The student finds the point where the line crosses the *y*-axis and then writes its coordinates in reverse.
   I. Correct answer

7. **A.** Correct answer
   B. The student finds the range.
   C. The student includes both the domain and the range.
   D. The student picks the first ordered pair.

1. The border of a Canadian one-dollar coin is shaped like an 11-sided regular polygon. The shape was chosen to help visually-impaired people identify the coin. How many degrees are in each angle along the border? Round your answer to the nearest degree.

Test-Taking Strategy

Solve Problem Before Looking at Choices

Could someone scratch my base angles?

Your ears are isosceles triangles with base angles of 70°. Find the top angle.

Ⓐ 30° Ⓑ 35° Ⓒ 40° Ⓓ 45°

"Solve the problem before looking at the choices. You know $180 - 2(70) = 40$. So the answer is C."

2. A public utility charges its residential customers for natural gas based on the number of therms used each month. The formula below shows how the monthly cost C in dollars is related to the number t of therms used.

$$C = 11 + 1.6t$$

Solve this formula for t.

A. $t = \dfrac{C}{12.6}$

B. $t = \dfrac{C - 11}{1.6}$

C. $t = \dfrac{C}{1.6} - 11$

D. $t = C - 12.6$

3. Which equation matches the line shown in the graph?

F. $y = x - 5$

G. $y = x + 5$

H. $y = -x - 5$

I. $y = -x + 5$

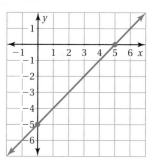

4. $\angle 1$ and $\angle 2$ form a straight angle. $\angle 1$ has a measure of 28°. Find the measure of $\angle 2$, in degrees.

5. Which equation represents a linear function?

A. $y = x^2$

B. $y = \dfrac{2}{x}$

C. $xy = 1$

D. $x + y = 1$

6. At which point does the graph of the equation $4x + 5y = 12$ cross the x-axis?

    F. $(0, 2.4)$ **H.** $(2.4, 0)$

    G. $(0, 3)$ **I.** $(3, 0)$

7. What is the domain of the function graphed in the coordinate plane?

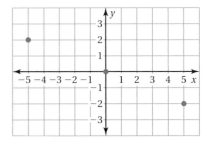

    A. $-5, 0, 5$ **C.** $-5, -2, 0, 2, 5$

    B. $-2, 0, 2$ **D.** $-5, 2$

8. The sum S of the angle measures of a polygon with n sides can be found using a formula.

Part A Write the formula.

Part B A quadrilateral has angles measuring 100, 90, and 90 degrees. Find the measure of its fourth angle. Show your work and explain your reasoning.

Part C The sum of the measures of the angles of the pentagon shown is 540 degrees. Divide the pentagon into triangles to show why this must be true. Show your work and explain your reasoning.

9. The line shown in the graph has a slope of $\frac{2}{5}$.

    What is the equation of the line?

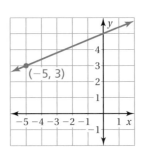

    F. $x = \frac{2}{5}y + 5$ **H.** $x = \frac{2}{5}y + 1$

    G. $y = \frac{2}{5}x + 5$ **I.** $y = \frac{2}{5}x + 1$

Item Analysis (continued)

8. **4 points** The student demonstrates a thorough understanding of writing and applying the angle sum formula for polygons, as well as how it relates to the fact that there are 180 degrees in a triangle. The student's work in Part B shows step-by-step how the fourth angle measures 80 degrees. The student's explanation in part C makes the algebraic-geometric connection clear.

   3 points The student demonstrates an essential but less than thorough understanding. In particular, Parts A and B should be completed fully and clearly, but Part C may lack full explanation of the algebraic-geometric connection.

   2 points The student's work and explanations demonstrate a lack of essential understanding. The formula in Part A should be properly stated, but Part B may show an error in application. Part C lacks any explanation.

   1 point The student demonstrates limited understanding. The student's response is incomplete and exhibits many flaws, including, but not limited to, the inability to state the proper formula in Part A.

   0 points The student provides no response, a completely incorrect or incomprehensible response, or a response that demonstrates insufficient understanding of writing, applying, and understanding the angle sum formula for polygons.

9. **F.** The student interchanges x and y.

   G. Correct answer

   H. The student interchanges x and y, and then mishandles slopes, going down 2 and right 5.

   I. The student mishandles slope, going down 2 and right 5.

10. **A.** The student adds 4 degrees to the original temperature.

    B. The student adds 12 degrees to the original temperature.

    C. The student adds 4 degrees to the Heat Index.

    D. Correct answer

11. **F.** The student subtracts 3 instead of adding 3.

    G. Correct answer

    H. The student subtracts 3 instead of adding and then multiplies instead of dividing.

    I. The student multiplies instead of dividing.

12. **A.** The student subtracts 4 from 5 because that is the relationship between sides BC and AB in triangle ABC.

    B. Correct answer

    C. The student finds the length of $\overline{DF}$.

    D. The student assumes that $\overline{DE}$ is congruent to $\overline{AB}$.

Answers

6. I

7. A

8. *Part A* $S = (n - 2) \cdot 180$

   Part B 80°

   Part C The sum of the angle measures of a triangle is 180 degrees. Because the pentagon can be divided into three triangles, the sum of the angle measures of a pentagon is

   $180 + 180 + 180 = 540$ or
   $(n - 2) \cdot 180 =$
   $(5 - 2) \cdot 180 =$
   $3 \cdot 180 = 540.$

   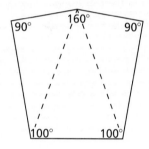

9. G

Answers

10. D

11. G

12. B

13. G

Answer for Extra Example

1. **A.** The student finds what percent $15.00 is of $6.00.

   B. Correct answer

   C. The student subtracts $6.00 from $15.00 to get $9.00 and thinks that this means 90%.

   D. The student finds what percent $6.00 is of $15.00.

Item Analysis (continued)

13. **F.** The student mistakes the roles of slope and intercept, thinking same intercept means what same slope means.

    G. Correct answer

    H. The student chooses a conclusion for lines that have the same intercept and the same slope, overlooking that these lines have different slopes.

    I. The student is confused by the problem and is grasping at straws.

Extra Example for Standardized Test Practice

1. The value of one of Kevin's baseball cards was $6.00 when he first got it. The value of this card is now $15.00. What was the percent increase in the value of the card?

   A. 250%   **C.** 90%

   B. 150%   **D.** 40%

10. On a hot summer day, the temperature was 95°F, the relative humidity was 75%, and the Heat Index was 122°F. For every degree that the temperature rises, the Heat Index increases by 4 degrees. The temperature rises to 98°F. What is the Heat Index?

A. 99°F

C. 126°F

B. 107°F

D. 134°F

11. Which value of x makes the equation below true?

$$5x - 3 = 11$$

F. 1.6

H. 40

G. 2.8

I. 70

12. In the diagram below, $\triangle ABC \sim \triangle DEF$. What is the value of x?

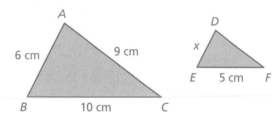

A. 1 cm

C. 4.5 cm

B. 3 cm

D. 6 cm

13. Two lines have the same y-intercept. The slope of one line is 1 and the slope of the other line is −1. What can you conclude?

F. The lines are parallel.

G. The lines meet at exactly one point.

H. The lines meet at more than one point.

I. The situation described is impossible.

6 Surface Areas of Solids

"I want to paint my dog house. To make sure I buy the correct amount of paint, I want to calculate the lateral surface area."

"Then, because I want to paint the inside and the outside, I will multiply by 2. Does this seem right to you?"

"Dear Sir: Why do you sell dog food in tall cans and sell cat food in short cans?"

"Neither of these shapes is the optimal use of surface area when compared to volume."

Strands Development

6th Grade

- Define pi as the ratio of circumference to diameter.
- Solve problems involving circumference and area of a circle given the diameter or radius.

7th Grade

- Describe volume and surface area of cylinders.
- Solve problems involving volume and surface area of rectangular prisms and cylinders.
- Describe how changing one dimension of a rectangular prism affects the surface area and volume.

8th Grade

- Construct three-dimensional models, given the top or bottom, side, and front views.
- Investigate and solve problems involving volume and surface area of prisms, cylinders, cones, and pyramids.
- Describe how changing one dimension of a figure affects the surface area and volume.

Math in History

There are infinitely many regular polygons. However, there are only five possible regular polyhedrons (a convex polyhedron whose vertices are all congruent and whose sides are congruent regular polygons).

★ Although named after the Greek mathematician Plato, the Platonic solids have been known since antiquity. Models of them can be found among the carved stone balls created by the late Neolithic people of Scotland at least 1000 years before Plato.

★ The ancient Greeks studied the Platonic solids extensively. Some sources credit Pythagoras with their discovery. Other evidence suggests he may have only been familiar with the tetrahedron, cube, and dodecahedron, and that the discovery of the octahedron and icosahedron belong to Theaetetus, a contemporary of Plato.

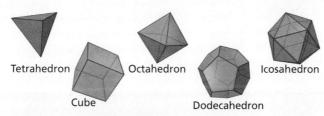

Tetrahedron   Octahedron   Icosahedron
Cube   Dodecahedron

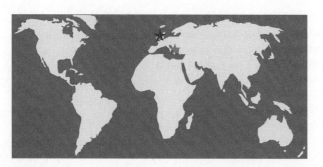

Pacing Guide for Chapter 6

Chapter Opener	1 Day
Section 1 Activity Lesson	 1 Day 1 Day
Section 2 Activity Lesson	 1 Day 1 Day
Section 3 Activity Lesson	 1 Day 1 Day
Study Help / Quiz	1 Day
Section 4 Activity Lesson	 1 Day 1 Day
Section 5 Activity Lesson	 1 Day 1 Day
Section 6 Activity Lesson	 1 Day 2 Days
Chapter Review / Tests	2 Days
Total Chapter 6	17 Days
Year-to-Date	101 Days

Check Your Resources

- Record and Practice Journal
- Resources by Chapter
- Skills Review Handbook
- Assessment Book
- Worked-Out Solutions

The Dynamic Planning Tool
Editable Teacher's Resources at
BigIdeasMath.com

Standards of Learning

6.10(b) The student will solve practical problems involving circumference and area of a circle, given the diameter or radius.

8.11 The student will solve practical area and perimeter problems involving composite plane figures.

Additional Topics for Review

- Identifying polygons
- Basic area formulas (square, rectangle, triangle, parallelogram, trapezoid, etc.)
- Exponents
- Finding surface area of prisms without formulas
- Faces, edges, and vertices

Try It Yourself

1. about 145.12 m^2

2. 86 cm^2

3. $25\pi \approx 78.5$ ft^2

4. $169\pi \approx 530.7$ in.^{2}

5. $12.25\pi \approx 38.5$ cm^2

Record and Practice Journal

1. 51 m^2

2. about 146.93 m^2

3. 74 in.^{2} 4. 171 in.^{2}

5. 81 ft^2 6. 88 in.^{2}

7. $444

8. about 314 in.^{2}

9. about 113.04 m^2

10. about 452.16 cm^2

11. about 153.86 ft^2

12. about 490.625 yd^2

13. about 706.5 mm^2

14. about 502.4 cm^2

Math Background Notes

Vocabulary Review

- Area
- Composite figures
- Pi

Finding Areas of Composite Figures

- Students should be able to compute areas of composite figures.
- Remind students to identify the basic figures contained in the composite figure before they consider the area.
- Remind students that to find the area of a composite figure, all they need do is sum the areas of the basic figures together.
- **Teaching Tip:** Sometimes students find it helpful to "break up" the composite figure. For instance, rather than working with the composite figure in Example 1, have students draw the triangle separately from the square and mark the dimensions on each figure. Ask students to find the area of each figure and then sum these quantities to determine the area of the composite figure.
- **Common Error:** Students will often think that the problem does not provide enough information to be solved. In Example 1, some students may think they have not been given the base of the triangle. Try to help students see that the basic shapes contained in the figure are just as important as how the shapes fit together. Because the base of the triangle stretches the same length as the top of the square, the base must measure 10 inches.

Finding Areas of Circles

- Students should be able to compute areas of circles.
- You may wish to review the concept of pi with students. Pi is the ratio of a circle's circumference (perimeter) to its diameter. This ratio is constant regardless of the size of the circle. As a result of its frequent appearance in mathematics, the symbol π is used to represent the ratio. Students should be familiar with using 3.14 as an approximate value of pi.
- **Common Error:** You may want to review the relationship between a circle's diameter and radius before completing Example 3. Students will often substitute a circle's diameter rather than its radius into the formula.

Reteaching and Enrichment Strategies

If students need help...	If students got it...
Record and Practice Journal • Fair Game Review Skills Review Handbook Lesson Tutorials	Game Closet at *BigIdeasMath.com* Start the next section

What You Learned Before

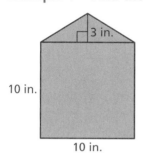

"Name these shapes."

(speech bubble: Polly Prism, Prissy Pyramid, Cici Cylinder, and Connie Cone)

● Finding Areas of Composite Figures

Example 1 Find the area.

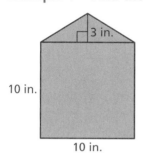

Area = Area of square + Area of triangle

$$A = s^2 + \frac{1}{2}bh$$

$$= 10^2 + \left(\frac{1}{2} \cdot 10 \cdot 3\right)$$

$$= 100 + 15$$

$$= 115 \text{ in.}^2$$

Try It Yourself

Find the area.

1.

2.

● Finding Areas of Circles

Example 2 Find the area.

$$A = \pi r^2$$

$$= \pi \cdot (7)^2$$

$$= 49\pi$$

$$\approx 153.9 \text{ mm}^2$$

Example 3 Find the area.

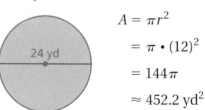

$$A = \pi r^2$$

$$= \pi \cdot (12)^2$$

$$= 144\pi$$

$$\approx 452.2 \text{ yd}^2$$

Try It Yourself

Find the area.

3.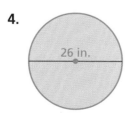

4.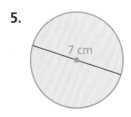

5.

STANDARDS OF LEARNING

8.9

Essential Question How can you draw three-dimensional figures?

Dot paper can help you draw three-dimensional figures, or solids. Shading parallel sides the same color helps create a three-dimensional illusion.

Square Dot Paper

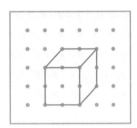

Face-On View

Isometric Dot Paper

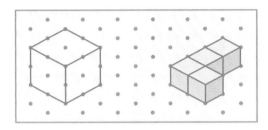

Corner View

1 ACTIVITY: Finding Surface Areas and Volumes

Work with a partner.

Draw the front, side, and top views of each stack of cubes. Then find the surface area and volume. Each small cube has side lengths of 1 unit.

a. **Sample:**

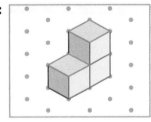

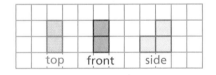

Volume: 3 cubic units

Surface Area: 14 square units

b.

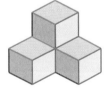

c.

d.

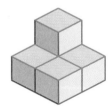

e.

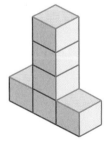

f.

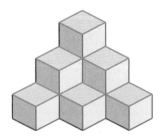

g.

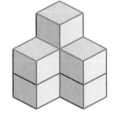

Laurie's Notes

Introduction

For the Teacher

- **Goal:** Students will use cubes and isometric dot paper to investigate the surface area and volume of solids.

Motivate

- Place a cube-shaped tissue box on a desk. Ask students to describe what they see when standing directly in front of the cube (front view), to the side of the cube (side view), and looking down on the cube (top view).
- Now place a rectangular prism (a shoe box) on the same surface. Describe all three views.
- Place a cube on top of a rectangular prism creating a solid that might be similar to the one shown in part (a) of Activity 1.
- Describe all three views. Students are challenged to ignore the difference in depth when describing a solid from one of the view points. They should focus on the surface that they see, not the depth of the solid. This can often be confusing to students.

Activity Notes

Activity 1

- If enough cubes are available, give each pair of students 10 cubes to create the models on their desk or table. To see each view, the students need to be at "eye level" with the solid.
- **Teaching Tip:** Another way to help students think about the top view is to ask them, "If you want to paint the top, what shapes would you paint?" Two squares would be painted. Repeat this strategy for each view.
- Discuss surface area. The surface area is the painting concept. How many square faces would be painted if the entire figure was painted?
- **Connection:** Although only 3 views are drawn, a solid has 6 views. Students may discover through this activity that the surface area can be found by sketching the 3 views, counting the total square units of the 3 views, and then doubling this number to find the surface area of the solid.
- Discuss volume. How many cubes are necessary to build the figure? Students are often confused by the cubes that are not visible in the picture. Explain that parts (b), (d), (f), and (g) would fit into the corner of a room. There are cubes behind cubes that are supporting the top cubes.
- **Scaffolding:** You may want half the class to work on parts (b), (d), and (f), while the other half works on parts (c), (e), and (g).
- Generally, it is the side view that is often challenging to draw.
- Check to see if students notice a connection between the squares drawn in the three views and the surface area.
- Check to see if students understand that the volume is the same number as the number of cubes used to build the figure.

Standards of Learning

8.9 The student will construct a three-dimensional model, given the top or bottom, side, and front views.

Previous Learning

Students should be able to identify the edges, faces, and vertices of three-dimensional solids.

Activity Materials	
Introduction	**Textbook**
• cube-shaped tissue box • shoe box	• wooden or plastic cubes

Start Thinking! and Warm Up

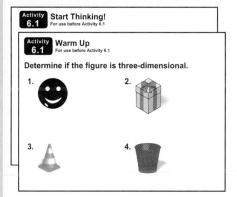

6.1 Record and Practice Journal

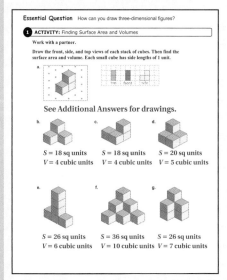

See Additional Answers for drawings.

b. $S = 18$ sq units, $V = 4$ cubic units
c. $S = 18$ sq units, $V = 4$ cubic units
d. $S = 20$ sq units, $V = 5$ cubic units
e. $S = 26$ sq units, $V = 6$ cubic units
f. $S = 36$ sq units, $V = 10$ cubic units
g. $S = 26$ sq units, $V = 7$ cubic units

Differentiated Instruction

Kinesthetic

Provide building blocks or cubes for students to use. Students may work in pairs. Each student builds a solid out of sight of his/her partner and draws front, top, and side views. Students meet at a neutral site and trade drawings. At the building site, the student builds the solid shown in the drawing. Students get together to compare their drawings and models.

6.1 Record and Practice Journal

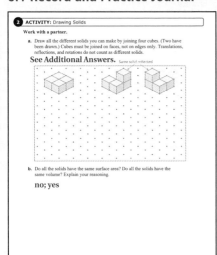

2 ACTIVITY: Drawing Solids

Work with a partner.

a. Draw all the different solids you can make by joining four cubes. (Two have been drawn.) Cubes must be joined on faces, not on edges only. Translations, reflections, and rotations do not count as different solids.

See Additional Answers. Same solid reflected

b. Do all the solids have the same surface area? Do all the solids have the same volume? Explain your reasoning.

no; yes

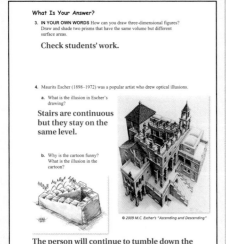

What Is Your Answer?

3. **IN YOUR OWN WORDS** How can you draw three-dimensional figures? Draw and shade two prisms that have the same volume but different surface areas.

Check students' work.

4. Maurits Escher (1898–1972) was a popular artist who drew optical illusions.

a. What is the illusion in Escher's drawing?

Stairs are continuous but they stay on the same level.

b. Why is the cartoon funny? What is the illusion in the cartoon?

© 2009 M.C. Escher's "Ascending and Descending"

The person will continue to tumble down the stairs forever.

Laurie's Notes

Activity 2

- If enough cubes are available, give each pair of students 4 cubes.
- If needed, suggest to students that they draw all of the possibilities where the cubes are in one layer (no stacking). There are 5 arrangements possible. Then try to stack just one cube, resulting in a solid different from the previous 5 solids.
- **Common Error:** Students forget that a solid can be turned and rotated, giving a new appearance, but it is still congruent to the original view.
- Each time a new solid is made, have students record the surface area and volume next to the sketch in order to answer part (b).
- Check to see if students recognized that all solids had a volume of 4.
- Check to see if students found a smaller surface area for the *compact* view of the $2 \times 2 \times 1$ prism shown.
- **Connection:** Students are often surprised that two figures can have the same volume, but different surface areas. This is similar to the concept of two rectangles having the same area but different perimeters.

What Is Your Answer?

- For Question 3, students should refer back to their sketches from the first activity.
- Ask if any students have heard of M.C. Escher. Even if they don't think they have heard of him, they have probably seen his work. Discuss the picture and give some background information on Escher and his artwork.

Closure

- How did the three views of a solid help you determine the surface area of the figure? Answers will vary.

Technology For the Teacher

Dynamic Classroom

The Dynamic Planning Tool
Editable Teacher's Resources at *BigIdeasMath.com*

ACTIVITY: Drawing Solids

Work with a partner.

a. Draw all the different solids you can make by joining four cubes. (Two have been drawn.) Cubes must be joined on faces, not on edges only. Translations, reflections, and rotations do not count as different solids.

Same solid reflected

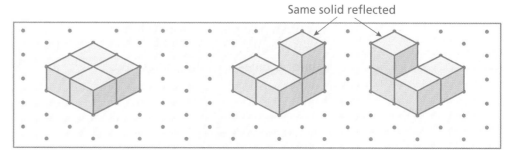

b. Do all the solids have the same surface area? Do all the solids have the same volume? Explain your reasoning.

What Is Your Answer?

3. **IN YOUR OWN WORDS** How can you draw three-dimensional figures? Draw and shade two prisms that have the same volume but different surface areas.

4. Maurits Escher (1898–1972) was a popular artist who drew optical illusions.

   a. What is the illusion in Escher's drawing?

   b. Why is the cartoon funny? What is the illusion in the cartoon?

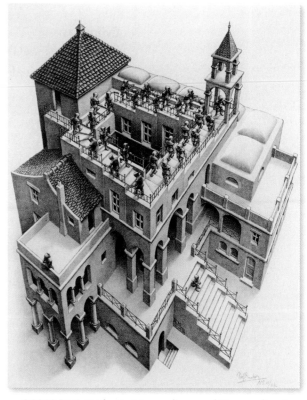

©2009 M.C. Escher's "Ascending and Descending"

Practice

Use what you learned about three-dimensional figures to complete Exercises 7–9 on page 262.

Key Vocabulary 🔊
solid, *p. 260*
polyhedron, *p. 260*
lateral face, *p. 260*

A **solid** is a three-dimensional figure that encloses a space. A **polyhedron** is a solid whose faces are all polygons.

 **Key Ideas**

Prisms

A prism is a polyhedron that has two parallel, identical bases. The **lateral faces** are parallelograms.

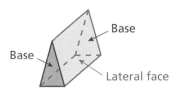

Triangular Prism

Pyramids

A pyramid is a polyhedron that has one base. The lateral faces are triangles.

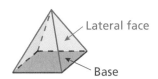

Rectangular Pyramid

The shape of the base tells the name of the prism or the pyramid.

Cylinders

A cylinder is a solid that has two parallel, identical circular bases.

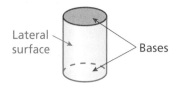

Cones

A cone is a solid that has one circular base and one vertex.

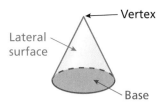

EXAMPLE ① **Drawing a Prism**

Draw a rectangular prism.

Step 1	**Step 2**	**Step 3**
Draw identical rectangular bases.	Connect corresponding vertices.	Change any *hidden* lines to dashed lines.

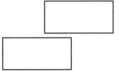 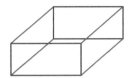 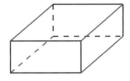

🔊 Multi-Language Glossary at BigIdeasMath ⩗ com.

Laurie's Notes

Introduction

Connect

- **Yesterday:** Students explored surface area and volume by using cubes and isometric dot paper.
- **Today:** Students will be introduced to the vocabulary of common solids and asked to sketch several solids.

Motivate

- Collect and display solids from school or home that are examples of the four solids introduced in today's lesson: prisms, pyramids, cylinders, and cones.
- Ask a volunteer to select one solid and describe it using mathematical vocabulary. You want students to say "cylinder" instead of "can of peas." Besides naming the object, they should identify its features or attributes. They may say that the cylinder has two circles, top and bottom (circular bases), and then a round side (lateral portion).
- **?** "Are there any other solids in the collection that share the same features or attributes?" Students may pick up another cylinder, *or* they may pick up a cone because it has one circular face, *or* a prism because it has two congruent bases and a lateral portion. There is no one correct answer. Listen to students' reasoning as to what attribute(s) the second solid shares with the first.
- Repeat this process for several solids.

Lesson Notes

Key Ideas

- The point of the vocabulary is not to memorize definitions, but to have a sense as to the attributes of the solid. This will help in generalizing surface area and volume formulas later.
- Mention to students that prisms and pyramids have a qualifying name, given the type of base. A triangular prism has two bases that are triangles.
- **Common Error:** Students often think that the face that is "on the bottom" is the base. The solid does not need to be oriented so that it is resting on a base. Demonstrate this with several solids.
- It may be helpful to use vocabulary, such as vertex (vertices) and edge.

Example 1

- Explain that hidden edges are those that are not visible when looking at the solid. You can demonstrate this by holding a prism and facing it toward the students.
- **?** "What is the maximum number of faces that any student can see?" 3
- **?** "What edges are not visible?" Listen for students' descriptions. Generally speaking, it is the edges in the back of the prism.

Goal Today's lesson is sketching three-dimensional **solids** accurately.

Lesson Materials
Introduction
• real-life prisms, pyramids, cylinders, and cones

Start Thinking! and Warm Up

Explain how to find the surface area of a three-dimensional figure that is made up of cubes.

English Language Learners

Vocabulary

By this time, students should be able to tell the difference between a prism and a pyramid. Discuss the terms *base* and *face*. Explain that all the surfaces of prisms and pyramids are *faces*. Prisms have two bases that are congruent polygons and parallel to each other. Pyramids have only one face that is called the base.

Extra Example 1

Draw a pentagonal prism.

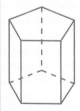

T-260

Extra Example 2

Draw a rectangular pyramid.

 **On Your Own**

1.
2.

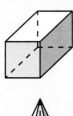

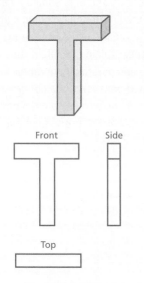

Extra Example 3

Draw the front, side, and top views of the solid.

Front   Side

Top

 **On Your Own**

> **3–5.** See Additional Answers.

Laurie's Notes

Example 2

- Demonstrate how to sketch a triangular pyramid.
- Drawings of objects may differ based on perspective. For instance, the point in step 1 could be placed below the triangle, or different lines in step 3 could be dashed. Each would offer a different perspective of the same object.

On Your Own

- Ask volunteers to draw their sketches at the board.

Example 3

- This example connects to yesterday's activity.
- Remind students that they need to take a *bird's eye view* in each of the three directions. It is hard for students to see that the depth is not what is being drawn when the cone and pyramid slope away from the base. Students may try to draw a triangle that is sloping backward.

On Your Own

- **Think-Pair-Share:** Students should view each solid independently and then work with a partner to draw the views of the solids. When they have drawn the views, the pair should compare their drawings with another group and discuss any discrepancies.
- Have volunteers share their drawings.

Closure

- Sketch a rectangular prism. Draw the front, side, and top views.

EXAMPLE **2**   **Drawing a Pyramid**

Draw a triangular pyramid.

Step 1

Draw a triangular base and a point.

Step 2

Connect the vertices of the triangle to the point.

Step 3

Change any *hidden* lines to dashed lines.

⬤ **On Your Own**

Now You're Ready
Exercises 10–15

Draw the solid.

1. Square prism

2. Pentagonal pyramid

EXAMPLE **3**   **Drawing Views of a Solid**

Draw the front, side, and top views of the paper cup.

The front view is a triangle.

The side view is a triangle.

The top view is a circle.

⬤ **On Your Own**

Now You're Ready
Exercises 16–21

Draw the front, side, and top views of the solid.

3.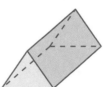

4.

5.

Check It Out
Help with Homework
BigIdeasMath √com

 Vocabulary and Concept Check

1. **VOCABULARY** Compare and contrast prisms and cylinders.

2. **VOCABULARY** Compare and contrast pyramids and cones.

3. **WRITING** Give examples of prisms, pyramids, cylinders, and cones in real life.

Identify the shape of the base. Then name the solid.

4.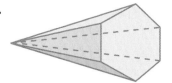

5.

6.

 Practice and Problem Solving

Draw the front, side, and top views of the stack of cubes. Then find the surface area and volume.

7.

8.

9.

Draw the solid.

① ② 10. Triangular prism

11. Pentagonal prism

12. Rectangular pyramid

13. Hexagonal pyramid

14. Cone

15. Cylinder

Draw the front, side, and top views of the solid.

③ 16.

17.

18.

19.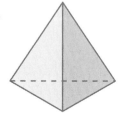

20.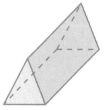

21.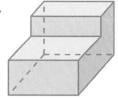

Assignment Guide and Homework Check

Level	Day 1 Activity Assignment	Day 2 Lesson Assignment	Homework Check
Basic	7–9, 29–32	1–6, 11–25 odd, 22, 24	4, 11, 19, 24
Average	7–9, 29–32	1–6, 11–25 odd, 24, 26	4, 11, 19, 24
Advanced	7–9, 29–32	1–6, 11–13, 20, 21, 24–28	4, 11, 21, 24

For Your Information
- **Exercise 22** The pyramid was built 18 B.C.–12 B.C. as a tomb for a Roman magistrate. It measures 100 Roman feet (22 meters) square at the base and is 125 Roman feet (27 meters) high.

Common Errors
- **Exercises 10–15** Students may mix up the different types of solids. Remind them of the definition of each solid and give a few real-life examples of each solid.
- **Exercises 16–21** Students may have difficulty visualizing the front, side, and top views of the solid. Create paper objects for those who are struggling to draw the different sides of the solid.
- **Exercises 24 and 25** Students may not be able to see how the shapes go together. Have them cut out pieces of paper or use blocks to model the solid.

6.1 Record and Practice Journal

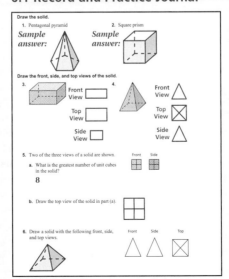

Vocabulary and Concept Check

1. Prisms and cylinders both have two parallel, identical bases. The bases of a cylinder are circles. The bases of a prism are polygons. A prism has lateral faces that are parallelograms or rectangles. A cylinder has one smooth, round lateral surface.

2. Pyramids and cones both have one base and one vertex not at the base. The base of a cone is a circle. The base of a pyramid is a polygon. A pyramid has lateral faces that are triangles. A cone has one smooth lateral surface.

3–6. See Additional Answers.

Practice and Problem Solving

7. front:

   side:

   top:

   surface area: 34 units^2
   volume: 10 units^3

8. front:

   side:

   top:

   surface area: 34 units^2
   volume: 9 units^3

9–21. See Additional Answers.

22–25. See Additional Answers.

26. *Answer should include, but is not limited to:* an original drawing of a house; a description of any solids that make up any part of the house

27. See *Taking Math Deeper.*

28. See Additional Answers.

Fair Game Review

29. 28 m^2 **30.** 12 cm^2

31. 15 ft^2 **32.** B

Mini-Assessment

You and a friend attend a birthday party. Draw the front, side, and top views of the solid.

1.

Front Side Top

2.

Front Side Top

3.

Front Side Top
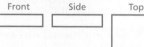

Taking Math Deeper

Exercise 27

This type of problem begs to be touched, felt, and seen. Give students 9 cubes and ask them to construct different solids that have the given top and side views.

① Help me see it.
Build different solids out of 9 cubes.

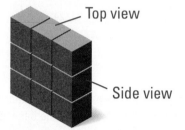
 Top view
 Side view

c. Front view

a. The greatest number of cubes is 9.

② Here is a different one.

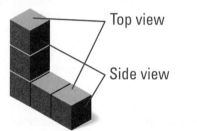
 Top view
 Side view

c. Front view

b. The least number of cubes is 5.

③ Here are the other possibilities (does not include reflections).

Lots of solids

Reteaching and Enrichment Strategies

If students need help. . .	If students got it. . .
Resources by Chapter • Practice A and Practice B • Puzzle Time Record and Practice Journal Practice Differentiating the Lesson Lesson Tutorials Skills Review Handbook	Resources by Chapter • Enrichment and Extension Start the next section

22. PYRAMID ARENA The Pyramid of Caius Cestius in Rome is in the shape of a square pyramid. Draw a sketch of the pyramid.

23. RESEARCH Use the Internet to find a picture of the Washington Monument. Describe its shape.

Draw a solid with the following front, side, and top views.

24.

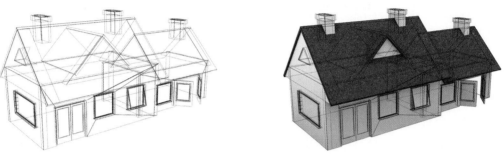

25.

26. PROJECT Design and draw a house. Name the different solids that can be used to make a model of the house.

27. REASONING Two of the three views of a solid are shown.

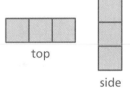

   a. What is the greatest number of unit cubes in the solid?

   b. What is the least number of unit cubes in the solid?

   c. Draw the front views of both solids in parts (a) and (b).

28. **Reasoning** Draw two different solids with five faces.

   a. Write the number of vertices and edges for each solid.

   b. Explain how knowing the numbers of edges and vertices helps you draw a three-dimensional figure.

Fair Game Review What you learned in previous grades & lessons

Find the area. *(Skills Review Handbook)*

29.

4 m

7 m

30.

3 cm

8 cm

31.

6 ft

3 ft

4 ft

32. MULTIPLE CHOICE You borrow $200 and agree to repay $240 at the end of 2 years. What is the simple interest rate per year? *(Section 4.4)*

   (A) 5%   (B) 10%   (C) 15%   (D) 20%

Essential Question How can you use a formula to find the surface area of a prism?

STANDARDS
OF LEARNING
8.7

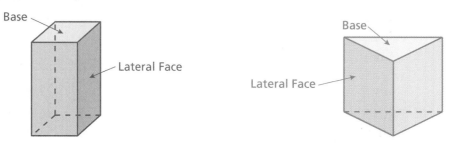

Rectangular Prism   **Triangular Prism**

The **surface area** of a prism is the sum of the areas of all its faces. A two-dimensional representation of a solid is called a **net**.

---

1   ACTIVITY: Surface Area of a Triangular Prism

Work with a partner.

a. Use the net for the triangular prism to find its surface area.

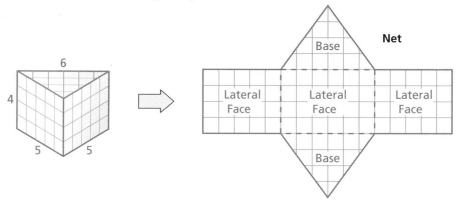

b. Copy the net for a triangular prism. Label each side. Then use your drawing to write a formula for the surface area of a triangular prism.

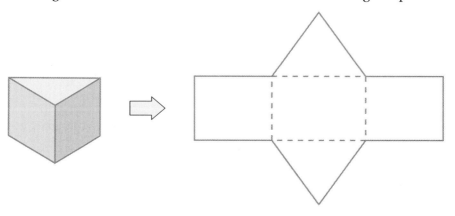

Laurie's Notes

Introduction

For the Teacher

- **Goal:** Students will develop an intuition about how to find the surface area of a prism.
- **Big Idea:** In this section and the next, you want students to see the connection between the prism and the cylinder—*structurally they are the same*! The prism and cylinder each have two congruent bases and a lateral portion.
- **Teaching Tip:** It is very helpful to use snap together polygon frames to make the polyhedra. The solids can be folded and unfolded into the nets very quickly and easily.

Motivate

- Have available 2 cardboard boxes that have been folded. These are commonly used for donuts, pizza, and similar items.
- Holding the assembled boxes, ask students to visualize and then describe the cardboard net that would result if the boxes were "unfolded."
- Unfold the box and cut one of the sides so that students can see the net of the box.
- Explain the connection between the cardboard net and the surface area of the prism.

Discuss

- Review the vocabulary of prisms (base, lateral face).
- Point out that prisms are named by the shapes of their bases. For instance, a triangular prism has triangular bases.

Activity Notes

Activity 1

- ❓ "How many faces does a triangular prism have and what shapes are they?" 5 faces; 2 triangles and 3 rectangles; Students may note that the triangles are congruent faces.
- ❓ "What are the bases of a triangular prism?" the triangles "How do you find the area of a triangle?" one-half the product of its base and its height
- ❓ "How many faces make up the lateral portion of the prism?" 3 "When the pieces of the lateral faces are unfolded, what shape does it form?" rectangle "What are the dimensions?" 4 units by 16 units
- ❓ "How do you find the area of a rectangle?" the product of its length and its width
- Students may recognize that the dimensions of the lateral portion of the prism are the height of the prism and the perimeter of the base of the prism. If they do observe this, they may find an efficient way to find the area of the lateral faces and add this to twice the area of a base.
- Remember, there is no best way for finding surface area. If the approach a student takes yields the correct answer and it makes sense to the student, it is the best method for that student.

Standards of Learning

8.7(a) The student will investigate and solve practical problems involving volume and surface area of prisms, cylinders, cones, and pyramids.
8.7(b) The student will describe how changing one measured attribute of the figure affects the volume and surface area.

Previous Learning

Students have found surface areas of rectangular prisms.

Activity Materials	
Introduction	**Textbook**
• cardboard boxes	• polygon frames • scissors • scrap paper • prism-shaped objects • tape measures • rulers

Start Thinking! and Warm Up

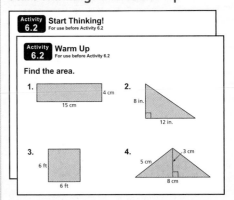

6.2 Record and Practice Journal

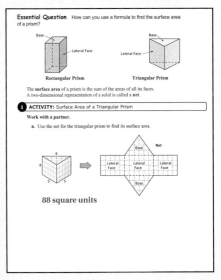

English Language Learners

Vocabulary

English learners may be familiar with the word *net* in everyday context. In finance, the net profit describes the bottom line of a financial transaction. In fishing, a net is a collection of knotted strings used to catch fish. In mathematical context, *net* or *geometric net* is used to mean the two-dimensional representation of a solid object.

Activity 2

- Students should be able to determine the unlabeled dimensions to find the area of each face and the surface area.
- **Common Misconception:** The base of a solid is not always the horizontal face.
- ❓ "How do you know which edge represents the height?" The height is the distance between the two bases. (3 units in this activity)
- When the height is doubled, the surface area does not double. This generally surprises students. While the lateral surface area doubles, the entire surface area does not double because the area of each base does not change.
- **Extension:** Have students create the net described in part (c), cut it out, and fold it to form a solid.

What Is Your Answer?

- For Question 4, make sure you have prism-shaped objects already in the classroom that students can measure. Be sure to have measuring devices readily available.

Closure

- **Exit Ticket:** What is the surface area of a pizza box that has a 13-inch square base and a 1-inch height? 390 in.^{2}

6.2 Record and Practice Journal

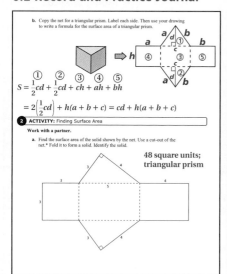

b. Copy the net for a triangular prism. Label each side. Then use your drawing to write a formula for the surface area of a triangular prism.

$$S = \frac{1}{2}cd + \frac{1}{2}cd + ch + ah + bh$$

$$= 2\left(\frac{1}{2}cd\right) + h(a + b + c) = cd + h(a + b + c)$$

② ACTIVITY: Finding Surface Area

Work with a partner.

a. Find the surface area of the solid shown by the net.* Use a cut-out of the net.* Fold it to form a solid. Identify the solid.

48 square units; triangular prism

b. Which of the surfaces of the solid are bases? Why?

Triangles because they are the only faces that are congruent.

c. Double the height of the solid. Does this double the surface area? Explain your reasoning.

no

What Is Your Answer?

3. IN YOUR OWN WORDS How can you use a formula to find the surface area of a prism?

The surface area of any prism is the sum of the areas of the bases and the lateral faces.

4. Find examples of prisms in your classroom. Measure each item and determine its surface area. For each item, give an example of how finding the surface area is important in knowing how much money is needed to manufacture or build the item.

Check students' work.

Technology For the Teacher

Dynamic Classroom

The Dynamic Planning Tool
Editable Teacher's Resources at *BigIdeasMath.com*

ACTIVITY: Finding Surface Area

Work with a partner.

a. Find the surface area of the solid shown by the net. Copy the net, cut it out, and fold it to form a solid. Identify the solid.

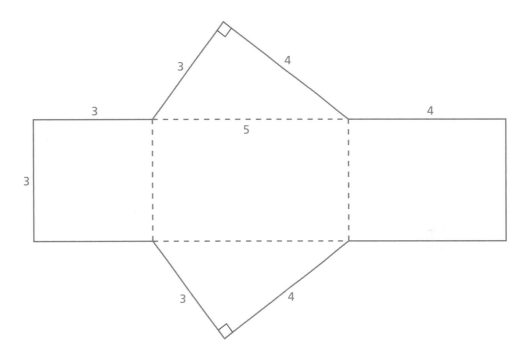

b. Which of the surfaces of the solid are bases? Why?

c. Double the height of the solid. Does this double the surface area? Explain your reasoning.

What Is Your Answer?

3. IN YOUR OWN WORDS How can you use a formula to find the surface area of a prism?

4. Find examples of prisms in your classroom. Measure each item and determine its surface area. For each item, give an example of how finding the surface area is important in knowing how much money is needed to manufacture or build the item.

Practice

Use what you learned about the surface area of a prism to complete Exercises 6–8 on page 268.

Key Vocabulary
surface area, *p. 264*
net, *p. 264*

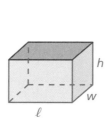 **Key Idea**

Surface Area of a Rectangular Prism

Words The surface area *S* of a rectangular prism is the sum of the areas of the bases and the lateral faces.

Algebra $S = 2\ell w + 2\ell h + 2wh$

Area of bases

Area of lateral faces

EXAMPLE 1 **Finding the Surface Area of a Rectangular Prism**

Find the surface area of the prism.

$$S = 2\ell w + 2\ell h + 2wh$$
$$= 2(5)(3) + 2(5)(6) + 2(3)(6)$$
$$= 30 + 60 + 36$$
$$= 126$$

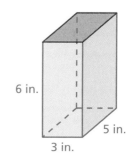

6 in.

5 in.

3 in.

∴ The surface area is 126 square inches.

On Your Own

Find the surface area of the prism.

Now You're Ready
Exercises 9–11

1.
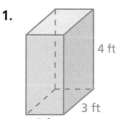
4 ft
3 ft
2 ft

2.
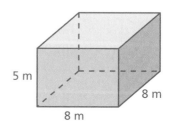
5 m
8 m
8 m

🔊 Multi-Language Glossary at BigIdeasMath✓com.

Laurie's Notes

Introduction

Connect

- **Yesterday:** Students explored surface area using the nets of prisms.
- **Today:** Students will work with a formula for the surface area of a prism.

Motivate

- Hold a rectangular prism and a triangular prism.
- **?** "How are the prisms alike?" both have 2 bases
- **?** "How are the prisms different?" The rectangular prism has rectangular bases and 4 rectangular lateral faces. The triangular prism has triangular bases and 3 rectangular lateral faces.
- **?** "How do you find the surface area of each?" Students should be able to conclude that the surface area of each solid is the sum of the areas of the bases and the areas of the lateral faces.

Lesson Notes

Key Idea

- Students found surface areas of rectangular prism in previous grades. So, they should be familiar with this concept.
- Write the formula for the surface area of a rectangular prism in words and in symbols.
- Note that the formula is color-coded.

Example 1

- **Common Error:** When students multiply (2)(5)(3), they sometimes multiply $2 \times 5 \times 2 \times 3$, similar to using the Distributive Property. Remind them that multiplication is both commutative and associative, and they can multiply in order ($2 \times 5 \times 3$) or in a different order ($2 \times 3 \times 5$).
- **Teaching Tip:** Write the equation for surface area as:
  $S =$ bases + (left and right) + (front and back). Students follow the words and find the area of each pair without thinking about the variables.

On Your Own

- **Think-Pair-Share:** Students should read each question independently and then work with a partner to answer the questions. When they have answered the questions, the pair should compare their answers with another group and discuss any discrepancies.

Goal Today's lesson is finding the **surface area** of a prism using a formula.

Lesson Materials	
Introduction	**Textbook**
• rectangular prism • triangular prism	• polygon frames

Start Thinking! and Warm Up

> **Lesson 6.2** Warm Up
> For use before Lesson 6.2
>
> **Lesson 6.2** Start Thinking!
> For use before Lesson 6.2
>
> Your uncle wants to build a shed that is 17 feet long by 13 feet wide by 8 feet high. Explain to your uncle how to find the surface area of the sides, front, and back so he knows how much paint to buy to paint the outside of the shed.

Extra Example 1

Find the surface area of a rectangular prism with a length of 6 yards, a width of 4 yards, and a height of 9 yards.
228 yd²

On Your Own

1. 52 ft²
2. 288 m²

Extra Example 2

Find the surface area of the triangular prism.

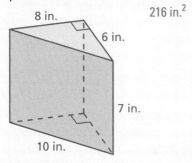

216 in.²

On Your Own

3. 150 m²

4. 60 cm²

Differentiated Instruction

Visual

Use a rectangular box to demonstrate three ways of finding surface area. The first method is to find the area of each face and then add areas. The second method is to open the box into a net and find the area of the net. The third method is to use the formula for finding surface area. Students should see that the three methods have the same result.

Laurie's Notes

Key Idea

- This is the general formula for a prism without variables. Most students are comfortable with this form.
- **?** "How many faces are there that make up the bases?" two
- **?** "How many faces are there that make up the lateral faces?" It depends on how many sides the bases have.

Example 2

- Note that the net is a visual reminder of each face whose area must be found. Color coding the faces should help students keep track of their work.
- Encourage students to write the formula in words for each new problem: S = area of bases + areas of lateral faces.

On Your Own

- Give students sufficient time to do their work before asking volunteers to share their work *and* sketch at the board.
- Students having difficulty with Question 4 may want to redraw the triangular prism with the base on the bottom.

Closure

- **Exit Ticket:** Which prism do you think has the greater surface area? Explain.

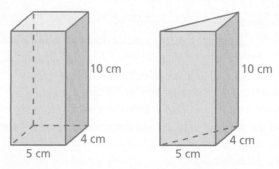

rectangular prism; *Sample answer:* In the triangular prism, the area of the bases is one-half the area of the 5 cm × 4 cm bases in the rectangular prism. So, the rectangular prism has a greater surface area.

Technology
For the Teacher

The Dynamic Planning Tool
Editable Teacher's Resources at *BigIdeasMath.com*

 **Key Idea**

Surface Area of a Prism

The surface area S of any prism is the sum of the areas of the bases and the lateral faces.

$$S = \text{areas of bases} + \text{areas of lateral faces}$$

EXAMPLE 2 **Finding the Surface Area of a Triangular Prism**

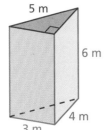

Find the surface area of the prism.

Draw a net.

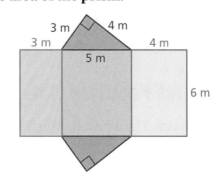

Remember

The area A of a triangle with base b and height h is $A = \frac{1}{2}bh$.

Area of a base

Red base: $\frac{1}{2} \cdot 3 \cdot 4 = 6$

Areas of lateral faces

Green lateral face: $6 \cdot 3 = 18$

Purple lateral face: $6 \cdot 5 = 30$

Blue lateral face: $6 \cdot 4 = 24$

Add the areas of the bases and the lateral faces.

$S = \text{areas of bases} + \text{areas of lateral faces}$

$= \underbrace{6 + 6} + 18 + 30 + 24$

> There are two identical bases. Count the area twice.

$= 84$

∴ The surface area is 84 square meters.

● **On Your Own**

Now You're Ready
Exercises 12–14

Find the surface area of the prism.

3.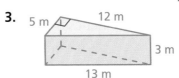

4.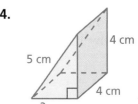

6.2 Exercises

Check It Out
Help with Homework
BigIdeasMath √com

✓ Vocabulary and Concept Check

1. **OPEN-ENDED** Describe a real-world situation in which you would want to find the surface area of a prism.

Find the indicated area for the rectangular prism.

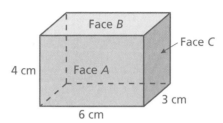

2. Area of Face A

3. Area of Face B

4. Area of Face C

5. Surface area of the prism

Practice and Problem Solving

Draw a net for the prism. Then find the surface area.

6.
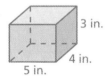
3 in.
4 in.
5 in.

7.
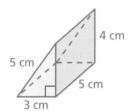
4 cm
5 cm
5 cm
3 cm

8.

7 m
6 m
3 m

Find the surface area of the prism.

① 9.
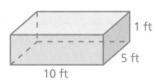
1 ft
5 ft
10 ft

10.
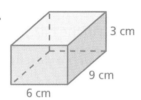
3 cm
9 cm
6 cm

11.

5 yd
4 yd
2 yd

② 12.
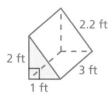
2.2 ft
2 ft
3 ft
1 ft

13.
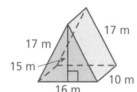
17 m
17 m
15 m
10 m
16 m

14.
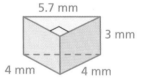
5.7 mm
3 mm
4 mm
4 mm

15. **GIFT BOX** What is the least amount of wrapping paper needed to wrap a gift box that measures 8 inches by 8 inches by 10 inches? Explain.

16. **TENT** What is the least amount of fabric needed to make the tent?

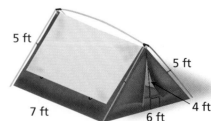
5 ft
5 ft
7 ft
6 ft
4 ft

Assignment Guide and Homework Check

Level	Day 1 Activity Assignment	Day 2 Lesson Assignment	Homework Check
Basic	6–8, 23–26	1–5, 9–15 odd, 16, 19	9, 13, 16, 19
Average	6–8, 23–26	1–5, 11–13, 16, 17, 19, 20	12, 16, 17, 19
Advanced	6–8, 23–26	1–5, 14, 16–18, 20–22	14, 16, 18, 21

For Your Information
- **Exercises 15 and 16** Students should ignore any overlap in these two exercises.

Common Errors
- **Exercises 9–11** Students may find the area of only three of the faces instead of all six. Remind them that each face is paired with another. Show students the net of a rectangular solid to remind them of the six faces.
- **Exercises 9–11** Some students may multiply length by width by height to find the surface area. Show them that the surface area is the sum of the areas of all six faces, so they must multiply and add to find the solution.
- **Exercises 12–14** Students may try to use the formula for a rectangular prism to find the surface area of a triangular prism. Show them that this will not work by focusing on the area of a triangular base. For students who are struggling to identify all the faces, draw a net of the prism and tell them to label the dimensions of each part before finding the surface area.

6.2 Record and Practice Journal

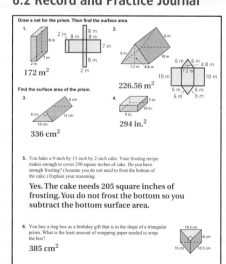

1. *Sample answer:* You want to paint a large toy chest in the form of a rectangular prism, and in order to know how much paint to buy, you need to know the surface area.

2. 24 cm^2 3. 18 cm^2

4. 12 cm^2 5. 108 cm^2

Practice and Problem Solving

6.

94 in.^2

7.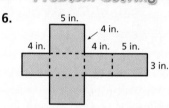

72 cm^2

8.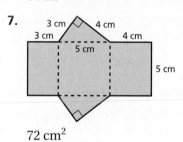

162 m^2

9. 130 ft^2 10. 198 cm^2

11. 76 yd^2 12. 17.6 ft^2

13. 740 m^2 14. 57.1 mm^2

15. 448 in.^2; The surface area of the box is 448 square inches, so that is the least amount of paper needed to cover the box.

16. 136 ft^2

17. 156 in.^{2}

18. 68 m^2

19. **a.** 83 ft^2

   b. 332 ft^2

   c. The amount of glass is 4 times greater.

20. See *Taking Math Deeper.*

21. $x = 4$ in.

22. $S = 2B + Ph$

Fair Game Review

23. 25 units

24. 48 units

25. 54 units

26. C

Mini-Assessment

Find the surface area of the prism.

1.

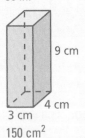
2 in.
2 in.
6 in.

56 in.^{2}

2.

9 cm
4 cm
3 cm

150 cm^2

3. Find the least amount of fabric needed to make the tent. 152 ft^2

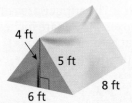
4 ft
5 ft
8 ft
6 ft

Taking Math Deeper

Exercise 20

This is a classic type of problem in manufacturing. For a given volume, what is the least amount of material I can use? The general answer is that the more cube-like, the more efficient the use of material. For instance, a cube-like tissue box is much more cost effective than a cereal box.

1 Help me see it.
Each storage box has a volume of 480 cubic inches. However, the shapes are quite different.

Box 1

Box 2

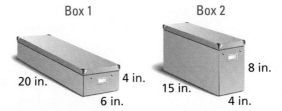

20 in.   4 in.   8 in.
6 in.   15 in.   4 in.

2 Find the surface area of each—in square feet.
Box 1
$2(20 \cdot 4) + 2(20 \cdot 6) + 2(4 \cdot 6) = 448$ in.$^2 \approx 3.11$ ft^2
Box 2
$2(15 \cdot 8) + 2(15 \cdot 4) + 2(8 \cdot 4) = 424$ in.$^2 \approx 2.94$ ft^2

Divide by 144 to get square feet.

3 Find the cost of each type and answer the question.

Rounding error

Box 1 Cost: $50(3.11 \text{ ft}^2)\left(1.25 \dfrac{\$}{\text{ft}^2}\right) \approx \$194.38$

Box 2 Cost: $50(2.94 \text{ ft}^2)\left(1.25 \dfrac{\$}{\text{ft}^2}\right) = \$183.75$

A company saves $10.63 by using Box 2.

A more exact answer of $10.42 can be found if the surface areas of the boxes are left in fraction form.

Project

Design a box that would have a volume of 480 cubic inches using the least possible amount of cardboard.

Reteaching and Enrichment Strategies

If students need help...	If students got it...
Resources by Chapter • Practice A and Practice B • Puzzle Time Record and Practice Journal Practice Differentiating the Lesson Lesson Tutorials Skills Review Handbook	Resources by Chapter • Enrichment and Extension Start the next section

Find the surface area of the prism.

17.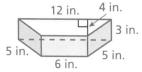
12 in. 4 in.
3 in.
5 in. 5 in.
6 in.

18.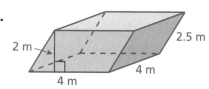
2 m
2.5 m
4 m
4 m

19. **AQUARIUM** An aquarium is in the shape of a rectangular prism.

4 ft

2.5 ft

6 ft

   a. How many square feet of glass were used to build the aquarium? (The top of the aquarium is open.)

   b. All three dimensions of a second aquarium are twice the size of the first aquarium. How much glass is needed to build this aquarium?

   c. How does doubling all of the dimensions affect the amount of glass needed to build the aquarium?

20. **STORAGE BOX** The material used to make a storage box costs $1.25 per square foot. The boxes have the same volume. How much does a company save by choosing to make 50 of Box 2 instead of 50 of Box 1?

	Length	Width	Height
Box 1	20 in.	6 in.	4 in.
Box 2	15 in.	4 in.	8 in.

21. **LABEL** A label that wraps around a box of golf balls covers 75% of its lateral surface area. What is the value of x?

3 in.
SUPER Golf Balls
SUPER Golf Balls because YOU are a super golfer
2 in.
2 in.
x

22. **Critical Thinking** Write a formula for the surface area of a rectangular prism using the height h, the perimeter P of a base, and the area B of a base.

Fair Game Review *What you learned in previous grades & lessons*

Find the perimeter. *(Skills Review Handbook)*

23.
7 8
10

24.
12
12 12
12

25.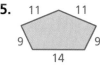
11 11
9 9
14

26. **MULTIPLE CHOICE** The class size increased 25% to 40 students. What was the original class size? *(Section 4.2)*

   A 10   **B** 30   **C** 32   **D** 50

**STANDARDS
OF LEARNING**
8.7

Essential Question How can you derive a formula for the surface area of a cylinder?

You already know that the surface area of a cylinder is the sum of the areas of the bases and the lateral surface.

$$S = 2\pi r^2 + 2\pi rh$$

Area of bases

Area of lateral surface

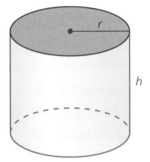

---

1 ACTIVITY: Writing an Activity

Work with a partner. Imagine that you are a math teacher and are introducing a lesson.

a. Design and write an activity in which your students can derive a formula for the surface area of a cylinder. Consider using any of the following objects. You can also use other objects, such as sheets of paper and tape.

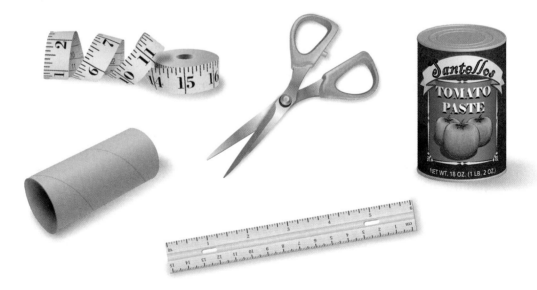

b. Perform the activity with your partner and write conclusions about your results.

Laurie's Notes

Introduction

For the Teacher
- **Goal:** Students will review the formula for surface area of a cylinder.
- Students learned to find the surface area of a cylinder in a previous grade. With that knowledge and a year's mathematical growth and maturity, the students may surprise you with their creativity today. There is value in asking students to write, and certainly the math lesson they develop could be quite interesting. In writing the lesson, they will solidify their understanding of the subject.

Motivate

- Ask students what the phrase, "like a revolving door" means, giving examples. The students may have different ideas to share.
- Revolving doors, as shown in this picture, are made up of multiple glass doors that revolve in a cylinder. The path followed by the door frames represents the surface area of the cylinder.
- Explain that today students will revisit the formula for surface area of a cylinder.

Activity Notes

Activity 1
- Be sure to have cylindrical objects, scissors, scrap paper, tape measures, and rulers available.
- Hold up a cylindrical object and review *radius* and *height*.
- Keep students focused on writing an activity for students who may not know, or remember, the formula for surface area of a cylinder. Have them write, for instance, in the context of teaching the younger students at your school.
- Give students sufficient time to work and write their conclusions. Then ask different pairs to share their ideas with the class.

Standards of Learning

8.7(a) The student will investigate and solve practical problems involving volume and surface area of prisms, cylinders, cones, and pyramids.
8.7(b) The student will describe how changing one measured attribute of the figure affects the volume and surface area.

Previous Learning

Students have found surface areas of cylinders.

Activity Materials
Textbook
• cylindrical objects
• scissors
• scrap paper
• tape measures
• rulers

Start Thinking! and Warm Up

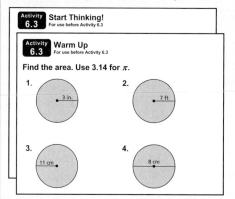

6.3 Record and Practice Journal

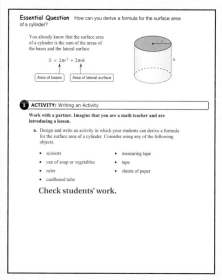

English Language Learners

Pair Activity

As a confidence booster for English learners, have students write their own math problems. Place students in pairs, one English learner and one English speaker, and ask each pair to write a problem involving the surface area of a cylinder. On a separate piece of paper, students solve their own problem. Next, students exchange their problem with another pair of students. Each pair then solves the new problem. Finally, the four students discuss the problems and the solution methods.

6.3 Record and Practice Journal

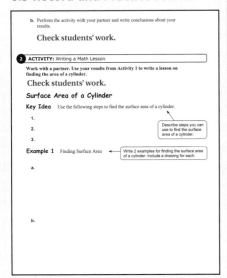

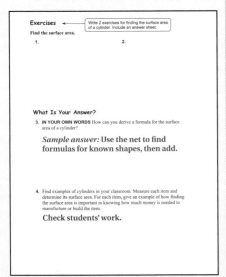

Laurie's Notes

Activity 2

- Students need to have a good understanding of the formula for the surface area of a cylinder in order to write the steps in the Key Idea.
- Point out to students that each of the examples they write needs to have a stepped out solution.
- If a document camera is available, have several volunteers share their work. If not, ask students to describe what they wrote in the Key Idea.

What Is Your Answer?

- For Question 4, students can use cylindrical objects from around the classroom or the cylindrical objects from Activity 1. Be sure to have measuring devices readily available.

Closure

- If a revolving door has a radius of 4 feet and a height of 8 feet, what is the area of the lateral surface of the cylinder in which it revolves? $64\pi \approx 201.0 \text{ ft}^2$

ACTIVITY: Writing a Math Lesson

Work with a partner. Use your results from Activity 1 to write a lesson on finding the surface area of a cylinder.

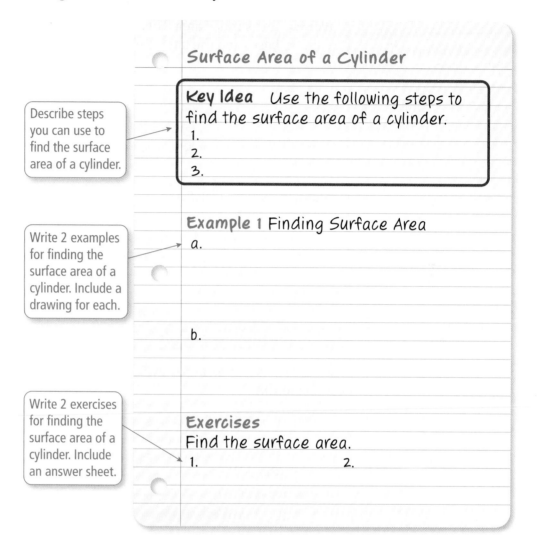

Describe steps you can use to find the surface area of a cylinder.

Write 2 examples for finding the surface area of a cylinder. Include a drawing for each.

Write 2 exercises for finding the surface area of a cylinder. Include an answer sheet.

Surface Area of a Cylinder

Key Idea   Use the following steps to find the surface area of a cylinder.
1.
2.
3.

Example 1 Finding Surface Area
a.

b.

Exercises
Find the surface area.
1.   2.

What Is Your Answer?

3. **IN YOUR OWN WORDS** How can you derive a formula for the surface area of a cylinder?

4. Find examples of cylinders in your classroom. Measure each item and determine its surface area. For each item, give an example of how finding the surface area is important in knowing how much money is needed to manufacture or build the item.

Practice   Use what you learned about the surface area of a cylinder to complete Exercises 4–6 on page 274.

Check It Out
Lesson Tutorials
BigIdeasMath ✓com

 **Key Idea**

Surface Area of a Cylinder

Words   The surface area S of a cylinder is the sum of the areas of the bases and the lateral surface.

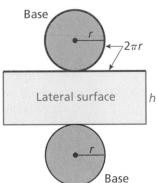

Base

$2\pi r$

Lateral surface h

Base

Algebra $S = 2\pi r^2 + 2\pi rh$

Area of bases

Area of lateral surface

EXAMPLE 1   Finding the Surface Area of a Cylinder

Find the surface area of the cylinder. Round your answer to the nearest tenth.

$$S = 2\pi r^2 + 2\pi rh$$

$$= 2\pi(8)^2 + 2\pi(8)(6.5)$$

$$= 128\pi + 104\pi$$

$$= 232\pi$$

$$\approx 728.5$$

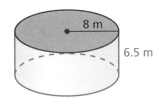

8 m

6.5 m

⁙ The surface area is about 728.5 square meters.

On Your Own

Now You're Ready
Exercises 4–9

Find the surface area of the cylinder. Round your answer to the nearest tenth.

1.

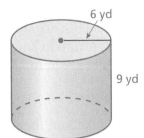

6 yd

9 yd

2.

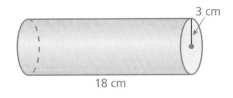

3 cm

18 cm

Laurie's Notes

Introduction

Connect

- **Yesterday:** Students reviewed the formula for surface area of a cylinder.
- **Today:** Students will explore how changing the dimensions of a cylinder affects its surface area.

Motivate

- Time for a 60-second "speed write." Pair students and tell them that on the word "go" they will have 60 seconds to list as many examples of cylindrical objects as they can. They should not list different types of essentially the same object, such as tuna fish cans and cans of peas.
- Examples include cans, new pencils, lipstick tubes, and paper towel rolls.
- Have each pair share two items from their list.

Lesson Notes

Key Idea

- **?** "How are cylinders and prisms alike?" Both have 2 congruent bases and a lateral portion. "Different?" Cylinders have circular bases, while the prisms have polygonal bases.
- Refer to the diagram with the radius marked. Review the formulas for area and circumference of a circle. $A = \pi r^2$; $C = \pi d = 2\pi r$
- Write the formula in words first. Before writing the formula in symbols, ask direct questions to help students make the connection between the words and the symbols.
- **?** "How do you find the area of the bases?" Find the area of one base, πr^2, and then multiply by 2.
- **?** "How do you find the area of the lateral portion?" The lateral portion is a rectangle whose dimensions are the height of the cylinder and a width that is the circumference of the base, so $2\pi rh$.
- Write the formula in symbols with each part identified (area of bases + lateral surface area).

Example 1

- Write the formula first to model good problem-solving techniques.
- Notice that the values of the variables are substituted, with each term being left in terms of π.
- **Common Misconception:** Students are unsure of how to perform the multiplication with π in the middle of the term. Remind students that π is a number, a factor in this case, just like the other numbers. Because of the Commutative and Associative Properties, the whole numbers can be multiplied first. Then the two like terms, 128π and 104π, are combined. The last step is to substitute 3.14 for π.
- **?** Review $\approx$. "What does this symbol mean? Why is it used?" approximately equal to; π is an irrational number and an estimate for pi is used in the calculation.

On Your Own

- Ask volunteers to share their answers.

Goal Today's lesson is describing how changing the dimensions of a cylinder affects the surface area.

Start Thinking! and Warm Up

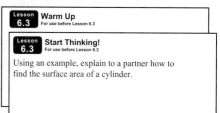

Differentiated Instruction

Visual

Students can check the surface area of a cylinder for reasonableness by finding the surface area of a rectangular prism that has square bases with side length $2r$ and height h, as illustrated below.

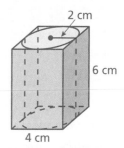

This will give an overestimate of the surface area of the cylinder. Also, it will help students remember to use the radius, not the diameter, in the given formula for surface area of a cylinder.

Extra Example 1

Find the surface area of a cylinder with a radius of 9 feet and a height of 4.5 feet. Round your answer to the nearest tenth. $243\pi \approx 763.0 \text{ ft}^2$

On Your Own

1. $180\pi \approx 565.2 \text{ yd}^2$
2. $126\pi \approx 395.6 \text{ cm}^2$

Laurie's Notes

Extra Example 2

The dimensions of an orange cylinder are four times the dimensions of the red cylinder in Example 2. How many times greater is the surface area of the orange cylinder than the surface area of the red cylinder? The surface area is 16 times greater.

Extra Example 3

Find the ratio of the amount of paper used for the label of a large can of tuna with a radius of 2 inches and a height of 3 inches to the amount of paper used for the label of a small can of tuna with a radius of 2 inches and a height of 1.5 inches. What can you conclude? The ratio of the amounts of paper is $\frac{12\pi \text{ in.}^2}{6\pi \text{ in.}^2} = 2$. So, the amount of paper used for the label of the large can is twice the amount of paper used for the label of the small can.

On Your Own

3. The surface area is 9 times greater.

4. The ratio of the amounts of paper is 1.5. So, the amount of paper used for the label of the jumbo can is 1.5 times the amount of paper used for the label of the large can.

Example 2

❓ "If you double the dimensions of a 3-inch square, how is the area of the larger square related to the area of the original square? Explain." The new dimensions are 6×6 inches and the new area is 36 square inches. The original area is 9 square inches, so the area of the larger square is four times the area of the original square.

- In this example, both dimensions, radius and height, are doubled. So, the cylinders are similar.
- Note that it is easier to compare the two surface areas when each is left in terms of π. Students should quickly recognize that 320π is four times greater than 80π.

Example 3

- Ask a volunteer to read the problem. Check to see if students understand what is being asked.
❓ "How are the two cans alike?" They are both cans of baked beans. They both have a radius of 2 inches. "Different?" The heights are different.
❓ "How is this example different from Example 2?" Only one of the dimensions is doubled in this example.
- Work through the example as shown. Point out that when finding the lateral surface area, you do not include the area of the bases in the formula.
- **Note:** Because the radii of both cylinders are equal, the lateral surface areas are different only because of the different heights. If the radius had also been doubled, the lateral surface area would have quadrupled, just as the total surface area did in Example 2.

On Your Own

- Before students try Question 3, ask them to predict the results.
- Give students sufficient time to work through these problems. Then ask volunteers to share their work at the board.

Closure

- Compare the surface area of Cylinder A, which has a radius of 2 and a height of 4, to the surface area of Cylinder B, which has a radius of 4 and a height of 2. The surface area of Cylinder B is twice the surface area of Cylinder A.

Technology
For the Teacher

The Dynamic Planning Tool
Editable Teacher's Resources at *BigIdeasMath.com*

EXAMPLE ② **Changing Dimensions of a Cylinder**

The dimensions of the red cylinder are twice the dimensions of the blue cylinder. How many times greater is the surface area of the red cylinder than the surface area of the blue cylinder?

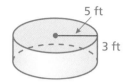

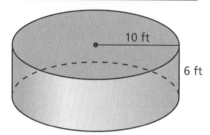

Find the surface area of each cylinder.

Blue Cylinder	**Red Cylinder**
$S = 2\pi r^2 + 2\pi rh$	$S = 2\pi r^2 + 2\pi rh$
$= 2\pi(5)^2 + 2\pi(5)(3)$	$= 2\pi(10)^2 + 2\pi(10)(6)$
$= 50\pi + 30\pi = 80\pi \text{ ft}^2$	$= 200\pi + 120\pi = 320\pi \text{ ft}^2$

⋮⋅ The ratio of the surface areas is $\dfrac{320\pi\,\cancel{\text{ft}^2}}{80\pi\,\cancel{\text{ft}^2}} = 4$. So, the surface area of the red cylinder is 4 times greater than the surface area of the blue cylinder.

EXAMPLE ③ **Real-Life Application**

Find the ratio of the amount of paper used for the label of the large can to the amount of paper used for the label of the small can. What can you conclude?

Find the *lateral* surface area of each can.

Small Can	**Large Can**
$S = 2\pi rh$	$S = 2\pi rh$
$= 2\pi(2)(3)$	$= 2\pi(2)(6)$
$= 12\pi \text{ in.}^2$	$= 24\pi \text{ in.}^2$

⋮⋅ The ratio of the amounts of paper is $\dfrac{24\pi\,\cancel{\text{in.}^2}}{12\pi\,\cancel{\text{in.}^2}} = 2$. So, the amount of paper used for the label of the large can is twice the amount of paper used for the label of the small can.

● **On Your Own**

Now You're Ready
Exercises 13 and 14

3. WHAT IF? The dimensions of a green cylinder are three times the dimensions of the blue cylinder in Example 2. How many times greater is the surface area of the green cylinder than the surface area of the blue cylinder?

4. WHAT IF? A jumbo can of beans has a height of 6 inches and a radius of 3 inches. Find the ratio of the amount of paper used for the label of the jumbo can to the amount of paper used for the label of the large can in Example 3. What can you conclude?

 Vocabulary and Concept Check

REASONING Decide whether the statement is *true* or *false*. If false, explain your reasoning.

1. The net for a cylinder consists of two circles and a rectangle.
2. Doubling the height of a cylinder doubles its surface area.
3. The area of the bases of a cylinder is always greater than its lateral surface area.

 Practice and Problem Solving

Find the surface area of the cylinder. Round your answer to the nearest tenth.

1 **4.**

1 cm
7 cm

5.
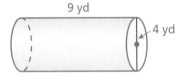
9 yd
4 yd

6.

2 in.
6 in.

7.
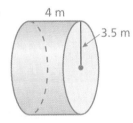
4 m
3.5 m

8.

1.5 ft
3 ft

9.
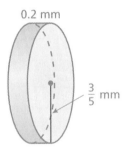
0.2 mm
$\frac{3}{5}$ mm

10. ERROR ANALYSIS Describe and correct the error in finding the surface area of the cylinder.

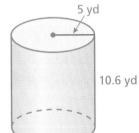
5 yd
10.6 yd

$$
\begin{aligned}
S &= \pi r^2 + 2\pi rh \\
&= \pi(5)^2 + 2\pi(5)(10.6) \\
&= 25\pi + 106\pi \\
&= 131\pi \approx 411.3 \, \text{yd}^2
\end{aligned}
$$
✗

11 in.
12 in.
7.5 in.
8 in.

11. FRUITCAKE A cylindrical fruitcake container has a radius of 10 centimeters and a height of 5.3 centimeters. What is the surface area of the container?

12. POPCORN Which popcorn canister has the greater surface area? Explain.

Assignment Guide and Homework Check

Level	Day 1 Activity Assignment	Day 2 Lesson Assignment	Homework Check
Basic	4–6, 18–20	1–3, 7–13 odd, 10	3, 7, 10, 13
Average	4–6, 18–20	1–3, 7, 9, 10–16 even	3, 7, 10, 14
Advanced	4–6, 18–20	1–3, 8–16 even, 17	3, 8, 10, 16

Common Errors

- **Exercises 4–9** Students may add the area of only one base. Remind them of the net for a cylinder and that there are two circles as bases.
- **Exercises 4–9** Students may double the radius instead of squaring it, or forget the correct order of operations when using the formula for the surface area of a cylinder. Remind them of the formula, and remind them of the order of operations.
- **Exercises 5 and 8** Students may use the diameter instead of the radius. Remind them that the radius is in the formula, so they should find the radius before finding the surface area.
- **Exercises 13 and 14** Students may not perform any analysis on these problems and simply say that because the dimensions are doubled, the surface area is doubled as well. Point out that these problems are very similar to Example 2, so they should study the Example 2 solution to approach Exercises 13 and 14 correctly.
- **Exercise 15** Students may multiply the height of the cylinder by the area of the circle instead of the circumference. Review the formula for the lateral surface area.

6.3 Record and Practice Journal

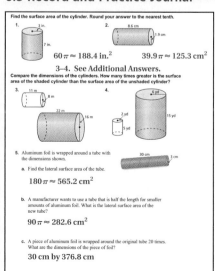

Vocabulary and Concept Check

1. true

2. false; Doubling the height of a cylinder doubles its lateral surface area but does not change the area of the bases.

3. false; The area of the bases of a cylinder can be less than, equal to, or greater than its lateral surface area.

Practice and Problem Solving

4. $16\pi \approx 50.2$ cm^2

5. $44\pi \approx 138.2$ yd^2

6. $32\pi \approx 100.5$ in.^{2}

7. $52.5\pi \approx 164.9$ m^2

8. $5.625\pi \approx 17.7$ ft^2

9. $0.96\pi \approx 3.0$ mm^2

10. The area of only one base is added. The first term should have a factor of 2;
$$S = 2\pi r^2 + 2\pi rh$$
$$= 2\pi(5)^2 + 2\pi(5)(10.6)$$
$$= 50\pi + 106\pi$$
$$= 156\pi \approx 489.8 \text{ yd}^2$$

11. $306\pi \approx 960.8$ cm^2

12. the canister on the right; The canister on the left has a surface area of 192.5π in.^{2} and the canister on the right has a surface area of 232.5π in.^{2}

13. The dimensions of the red cylinder are 4 times greater than the dimensions of the blue cylinder. The surface area is 16 times greater.

14. The dimensions of the red cylinder are 1.4 times greater than the dimensions of the blue cylinder. The surface area is 1.96 times greater.

15. See Additional Answers.

16. See *Taking Math Deeper*.

17. a. 4 times greater;
9 times greater;
25 times greater;
100 times greater

b. When both dimensions are increased by a factor of k, the surface area increases by a factor of k^2; 400 times greater

 Fair Game Review

18. $y = -x + 3$

19. $y = 2x - 1$

20. B

Mini-Assessment

Find the surface area of the cylinder. Round your answer to the nearest tenth.

1.
6 ft
7 ft

$156\pi \approx 489.8 \text{ ft}^2$

2.
12 cm
6 cm

$90\pi \approx 282.6 \text{ cm}^2$

3. Compare the dimensions of the cylinders. How many times greater is the surface area of the red cylinder than the surface area of the blue cylinder? The dimensions of the red cylinder are 3 times greater than the dimensions of the blue cylinder. So, the surface area is 9 times greater.

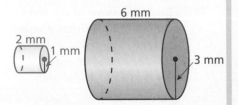
6 mm
2 mm
1 mm
3 mm

T-275

Taking Math Deeper

Exercise 16

This is a nice two-step problem in which "finding the volume of each cylinder" is not the answer to the question.

2 cm
4 cm

1 Make a table.

Block	Radius	Height	Surface Area	Surface Area of 50	Paint for 50
	2 cm	4 cm	$24\pi \text{ cm}^2$	$1200\pi \text{ cm}^2$	1 oz
	1 cm	2 cm	$6\pi \text{ cm}^2$	$300\pi \text{ cm}^2$	$\frac{1}{4}$ oz
	6 cm	12 cm	$216\pi \text{ cm}^2$	$10{,}800\pi \text{ cm}^2$	9 oz

2 **a.** You need $\frac{1}{4}$ ounce of paint to paint 50 red blocks.

b. You need 9 ounces of paint to paint 50 orange blocks.

3 It is interesting that you don't actually need to compute the surface areas to answer the question. When the scale factor is $\frac{1}{2}$, the surface area is $\left(\frac{1}{2}\right)^2$ times the original surface area. So, you need $\frac{1}{4}$ the amount of paint. When the scale factor is 3, the surface area is 3^2 times the original surface area. So, you need 9 times the amount of paint.

Scale factor

Reteaching and Enrichment Strategies

If students need help. . .	If students got it. . .
Resources by Chapter • Practice A and Practice B • Puzzle Time Record and Practice Journal Practice Differentiating the Lesson Lesson Tutorials Skills Review Handbook	Resources by Chapter • Enrichment and Extension • School-to-Work Start the next section

Compare the dimensions of the cylinders. How many times greater is the surface area of the red cylinder than the surface area of the blue cylinder?

13.

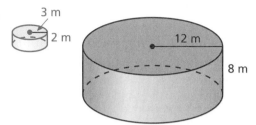

3 m
2 m
12 m
8 m

14.

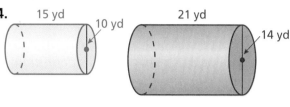

15 yd
10 yd
21 yd
14 yd

15. HAMSTER A hamster cage has a cylindrical tube for a hamster to crawl through and hide.

a. Find the lateral surface area of the tube.

b. You replace the tube. The new tube is three times longer. How does tripling the length affect the lateral surface area?

2 in.
4 in.

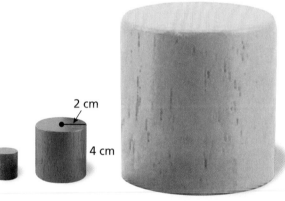

2 cm
4 cm

16. TOY BLOCKS You are painting toy blocks. You need 1 ounce of paint to paint 50 blue blocks.

a. The dimensions of the red block are one-half the dimensions of the blue block. How much paint do you need to paint 50 red blocks?

b. The dimensions of the orange block are triple the dimensions of the blue block. How much paint do you need to paint 50 orange blocks?

17. *Critical Thinking* A cylinder has radius *r* and height *h*.

a. How many times greater is the surface area of a cylinder when both dimensions are multiplied by a factor of 2? 3? 5? 10?

b. Describe the pattern in part (a). How many times greater is the surface area of a cylinder when both dimensions are multiplied by a factor of 20?

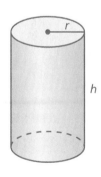

r
h

Fair Game Review What you learned in previous grades & lessons

Use the table to write a linear function that relates *y* to *x*. *(Section 3.3)*

18.

x	−2	−1	0	1
y	5	4	3	2

19.

x	−1	0	1	2
y	−3	−1	1	3

20. MULTIPLE CHOICE What is the solution of $2x - 4 = 18$? *(Section 1.2)*

Ⓐ 7   Ⓑ 11   Ⓒ 14   Ⓓ 22

You can use a **four square** to organize information about a topic. Each of the four squares can be a category, such as *definition, vocabulary, example, non-example, words, algebra, table, numbers, visual, graph,* or *equation.* Here is an example of a four square for a solid.

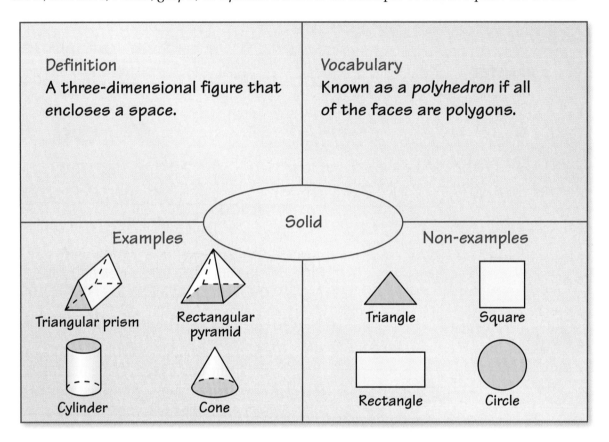

On Your Own

Make a four square to help you study these topics.

1. polyhedron   2. prism

3. pyramid   4. cylinder

5. cone   6. drawing a solid

7. surface area

    a. of a prism   **b.** of a cylinder

After you complete this chapter, make four squares for the following topics.

8. surface area

    a. of a pyramid   **b.** of a cone   **c.** of a composite solid

"I'm taking a survey for my four square.
How many fleas do you have?"

Sample Answers

1.

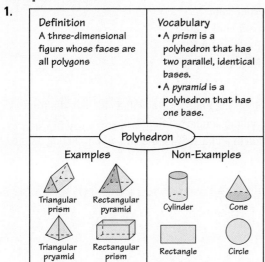

Definition	Vocabulary
A three-dimensional figure whose faces are all polygons	• A prism is a polyhedron that has two parallel, identical bases. • A pyramid is a polyhedron that has one base.

Polyhedron

Examples	Non-Examples
Triangular prism Rectangular pyramid Triangular pryamid Rectangular prism	Cylinder Cone Rectangle Circle

2.

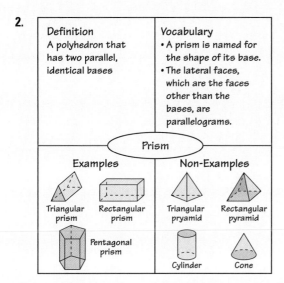

Definition	Vocabulary
A polyhedron that has two parallel, identical bases	• A prism is named for the shape of its base. • The lateral faces, which are the faces other than the bases, are parallelograms.

Prism

Examples	Non-Examples
Triangular prism Rectangular prism Pentagonal prism	Triangular pryamid Rectangular pyramid Cylinder Cone

3.

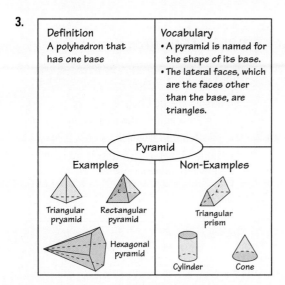

Definition	Vocabulary
A polyhedron that has one base	• A pyramid is named for the shape of its base. • The lateral faces, which are the faces other than the base, are triangles.

Pyramid

Examples	Non-Examples
Triangular pryamid Rectangular pyramid Hexagonal pyramid	Triangular prism Cylinder Cone

4–7. Available at *BigIdeasMath.com*.

List of Organizers

Available at *BigIdeasMath.com*

Comparison Chart
Concept Circle
Definition (Idea) and Example Chart
Example and Non-Example Chart
Formula Triangle
Four Square
Information Frame
Information Wheel
Notetaking Organizer
Process Diagram
Summary Triangle
Word Magnet
Y Chart

About this Organizer

A **Four Square** can be used to organize information about a topic. Students write the topic in the "bubble" in the middle of the four square. Then students write concepts related to the topic in the four squares surrounding the bubble. Any concept related to the topic can be used. Encourage students to include concepts that will help them learn the topic. Students can place their four squares on note cards to use as a quick study reference.

Technology
For the Teacher

Vocabulary Puzzle Builder

Answers

1. Front: Side:

   Top:

2. Front: Side:

   Top:

3. Front: Side:

   Top:

4. 132 cm^2

5. 52 in.^2

6. $40\pi \approx 125.6 \text{ ft}^2$

7. $162\pi \approx 508.7 \text{ m}^2$

8. 390 cm^2

9. The surface area is 9 times greater.

10. no; The amount of metal needed is 4 times greater.

Assessment Book

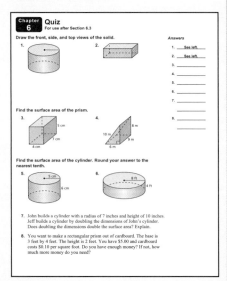

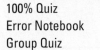

Alternative Quiz Ideas

100% Quiz	**Math Log**
Error Notebook	Notebook Quiz
Group Quiz	Partner Quiz
Homework Quiz	Pass the Paper

Math Log

Ask students to keep a math log for the chapter. Have them include diagrams, definitions, and examples. Everything should be clearly labeled. It might be helpful if they put the information in a chart. Students can add to the log as they are introduced to new topics.

Reteaching and Enrichment Strategies

If students need help. . .	If students got it. . .
Resources by Chapter • Study Help • Practice A and Practice B • Puzzle Time Lesson Tutorials *BigIdeasMath.com* Practice Quiz Practice from the Test Generator	Resources by Chapter • Enrichment and Extension • School-to-Work Game Closet at *BigIdeasMath.com* Start the next section

Technology for the Teacher

Answer Presentation Tool
Big Ideas Test Generator

Draw the front, side, and top views of the solid. *(Section 6.1)*

1.

2.

3.

Find the surface area of the prism. *(Section 6.2)*

4.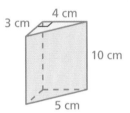

3 cm   4 cm   10 cm   5 cm

5.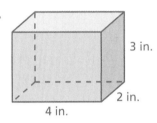

3 in.   2 in.   4 in.

Find the surface area of the cylinder. Round your answer to the nearest tenth. *(Section 6.3)*

6.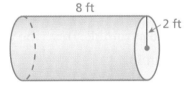

8 ft   2 ft

7.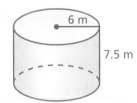

6 m   7.5 m

8. GIFT BOX Find the surface area of the gift box. *(Section 6.2)*

6.5 cm   6.5 cm   6 cm   20 cm   5 cm

9. PILLOW A cylindrical pillow has a height of 14 inches and a radius of 2 inches. Triple the dimensions of the pillow. How many times greater is the surface area of the new pillow? *(Section 6.3)*

2.6 cm   3 cm

10. CAT FOOD Does doubling both dimensions of the can of cat food double the amount of metal needed to make the can? Explain. *(Section 6.3)*

6.4 Surface Areas of Pyramids

STANDARDS OF LEARNING
8.7

Essential Question How can you find the surface area of a pyramid?

Even though many well-known **pyramids** have square bases, the base of a pyramid can be any polygon.

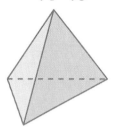

Triangular Base

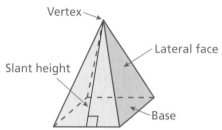

Vertex

Slant height

Lateral face

Base

Square Base

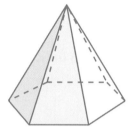

Hexagonal Base

1 ACTIVITY: Making a Scale Model

Work with a partner. Each pyramid has a square base.

- **Draw a net for a scale model of one of the pyramids. Describe your scale.**
- **Cut out the net and fold it to form a pyramid.**
- **Find the lateral surface area of the real-life pyramid.**

a. Cheops Pyramid in Egypt

Side = 230 m, Slant height ≈ 186 m

b. Muttart Conservatory in Edmonton

Side = 26 m, Slant height ≈ 27 m

c. Louvre Pyramid in Paris

Side = 35 m, Slant height ≈ 28 m

d. Pyramid of Caius Cestius in Rome

Side = 22 m, Slant height ≈ 29 m

Laurie's Notes

Introduction

For the Teacher

- **Goal:** Students will develop an intuitive understanding about how to find the surface area of a pyramid.
- **Big Idea:** In this section and the next, you want students to see the connection between the pyramid and cone—*structurally they are the same*! The pyramid and cone each have a base and a lateral portion.
- Discuss the vocabulary of pyramids and how they are named according to the base. Make a distinction between the slant height and the height.

Motivate

- Share information about the Great Pyramid of Egypt, also known as Cheops Pyramid.
- The Great Pyramid is the largest of the original *Seven Wonders of the World*. It was built in the 5th century B.C. and is estimated to have taken 100,000 men over 20 years to build it.
- The Great Pyramid is a square pyramid. It covers an area of 13 acres. The original height of the Great Pyramid was 485 feet, but due to erosion its height has declined to 450 feet. Each side of the square base is 755.5 feet in length (about 2.5 football field lengths).
- The Great Pyramid consists of approximately 2.5 million blocks that weigh from 2 tons to over 70 tons. The stones are cut so precisely that a credit card cannot fit between them.

Activity Notes

Activity 1

- This activity connects scale drawings with the study of pyramids.
- **?** "To make a net for a square pyramid, how many pieces will you need to make? Explain." 5 pieces; a square base and 4 congruent triangles
- To ensure a variety, assign one pyramid to each pair of students and make sure about $\frac{1}{4}$ of the class makes each pyramid.
- Students will need to decide on the scale they will use.
  Example: To make a scale model for pyramid A, assume the scale selected is 1 cm = 20 m.

  $$\frac{1\ cm}{20\ m} = \frac{x\ cm}{230\ m} \rightarrow x = 11.5 \qquad \frac{1\ cm}{20\ m} = \frac{x\ cm}{186\ m} \rightarrow x = 9.3$$

- Students will use their eyesight and knowledge of squares and isosceles triangles to construct the square and four isosceles triangles.
- When groups have finished, have several groups explain what scale they used and how they found the lateral surface area. Multiply the area of one triangular lateral face by 4.
- This hands-on experience of making the pyramid and finding the lateral surface area will help students remember the process and understand the formula.

Standards of Learning

8.7(a) The student will investigate and solve practical problems involving volume and surface area of prisms, cylinders, cones, and pyramids.

8.7(b) The student will describe how changing one measured attribute of the figure affects the volume and surface area.

Previous Learning

Students should know how to find the area of a triangle and should know the general properties of squares and isosceles triangles.

Activity Materials	
Introduction	**Textbook**
• models of pyramids	• scissors • tape • scrap paper • rulers • polygon frames

Start Thinking! and Warm Up

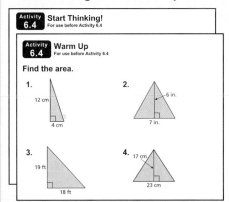

Activity 6.4 Start Thinking!
For use before Activity 6.4

Activity 6.4 Warm Up
For use before Activity 6.4

Find the area.

1. 12 cm, 4 cm
2. 6 in., 7 in.
3. 19 ft, 18 ft
4. 17 cm, 23 cm

6.4 Record and Practice Journal

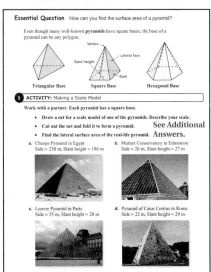

Essential Question How can you find the surface area of a pyramid?

Even though many well-known **pyramids** have square bases, the base of a pyramid can be any polygon.

Triangular Base   Square Base   Hexagonal Base

1 ACTIVITY: Making a Scale Model

Work with a partner. Each pyramid has a square base.

- Draw a net for a scale model of one of the pyramids. Describe your scale.
- Cut out the net and fold it to form a pyramid. See Additional
- Find the lateral surface area of the real-life pyramid. Answers.

a. Cheops Pyramid in Egypt
   Side = 230 m, Slant height = 186 m
b. Muttart Conservatory in Edmonton
   Side = 26 m, Slant height = 27 m
c. Louvre Pyramid in Paris
   Side = 35 m, Slant height = 28 m
d. Pyramid of Caius Cestius in Rome
   Side = 22 m, Slant height = 29 m

English Language Learners

Vocabulary

English learners may struggle with understanding the *slant height* of a pyramid. Use a skateboard ramp as an example. Ask students to find the length of the ramp. Most likely students will find the length of the slanted portion of the ramp. Compare this length to the slant height of a pyramid.

Activity 2

- Note that students are only asked to find the lateral surface area. This means that they are finding the surface area of 8 congruent isosceles triangles.

- **FYI:** The prefix octa- means eight. An octopus has 8 arms; when October was named in the Roman calendar, it was the 8th month; an octave on the piano has 8 notes; an octad is a group of 8 things.

- **?** "What common road sign is an octagon?" Stop sign

- The net includes the octagonal base, but the surface area of the base is not needed for this problem.

- Ask a volunteer to sketch his or her net at the board. If you have the appropriate snap together polygon frames, make the net.

Activity 3

- Again, only the lateral surface area is needed. Once students have found the area of one triangle, they need to multiply by 12.

What Is Your Answer?

- Have students work in pairs to answer the question.

6.4 Record and Practice Journal

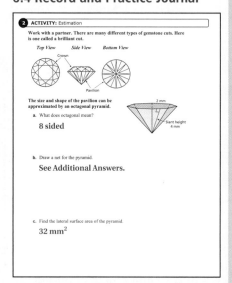

2 ACTIVITY: Estimation

Work with a partner. There are many different types of gemstone cuts. Here is one called a brilliant cut.

Top View *Side View* *Bottom View*

The size and shape of the pavilion can be approximated by an octagonal pyramid.

a. What does octagonal mean?

8 sided

b. Draw a net for the pyramid.

See Additional Answers.

c. Find the lateral surface area of the pyramid.

32 mm²

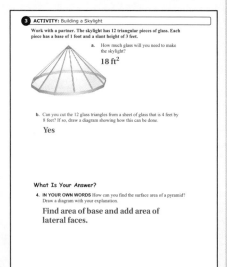

3 ACTIVITY: Building a Skylight

Work with a partner. The skylight has 12 triangular pieces of glass. Each piece has a base of 1 foot and a slant height of 3 feet.

a. How much glass will you need to make the skylight?

18 ft²

b. Can you cut the 12 glass triangles from a sheet of glass that is 4 feet by 8 feet? If so, draw a diagram showing how this can be done.

Yes

What Is Your Answer?

4. **IN YOUR OWN WORDS** How can you find the surface area of a pyramid? Draw a diagram with your explanation.

Find area of base and add area of lateral faces.

Closure

- **Exit Ticket:** Sketch a net for a hexagonal pyramid and describe how to find the lateral surface area. Find the area of one of the lateral faces and multiply by 6.

Technology For the Teacher

Dynamic Classroom

The Dynamic Planning Tool
Editable Teacher's Resources at *BigIdeasMath.com*

Work with a partner. There are many different types of gemstone cuts. Here is one called a brilliant cut.

Top View   *Side View*   *Bottom View*

Crown

Pavilion

The size and shape of the pavilion can be approximated by an octagonal pyramid.

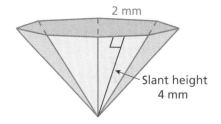

2 mm

Slant height 4 mm

   a. What does octagonal mean?

   b. Draw a net for the pyramid.

   c. Find the lateral surface area of the pyramid.

3 **ACTIVITY: Building a Skylight**

Work with a partner. The skylight has 12 triangular pieces of glass. Each piece has a base of 1 foot and a slant height of 3 feet.

   a. How much glass will you need to make the skylight?

   b. Can you cut the 12 glass triangles from a sheet of glass that is 4 feet by 8 feet? If so, draw a diagram showing how this can be done.

What Is Your Answer?

   4. IN YOUR OWN WORDS How can you find the surface area of a pyramid? Draw a diagram with your explanation.

Practice

Use what you learned about the surface area of a pyramid to complete Exercises 4–6 on page 282.

Key Vocabulary 🔊
regular pyramid,
    p. 280
slant height, *p. 280*

A **regular pyramid** is a pyramid whose base is a regular polygon. The lateral faces are triangles. The height of each triangle is the **slant height** of the pyramid.

 **Key Idea**

Remember

In a regular polygon, all of the sides have the same length and all of the angles have the same measure.

Surface Area of a Pyramid

The surface area *S* of a pyramid is the sum of the areas of the base and the lateral faces.

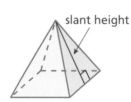

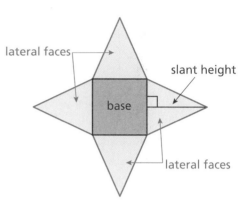

$$S = \text{area of base} + \text{areas of lateral faces}$$

EXAMPLE 1   **Finding the Surface Area of a Square Pyramid**

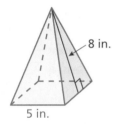

Find the surface area of the regular pyramid.

Draw a net.

Area of base   ***Area of a lateral face***

$5 \cdot 5 = 25$ $\dfrac{1}{2} \cdot 5 \cdot 8 = 20$

Find the sum of the areas of the base and the lateral faces.

$S = \text{area of base} + \text{areas of lateral faces}$

$ = 25 + \underbrace{20 + 20 + 20 + 20}$

$ = 105$

There are 4 identical lateral faces. Count the area 4 times.

∴ The surface area is 105 square inches.

On Your Own

1. What is the surface area of a square pyramid with a base side length of 9 centimeters and a slant height of 7 centimeters?

Laurie's Notes

Introduction

Connect

- **Yesterday:** Students discovered how to find the surface area of a pyramid by examining the net that makes up a pyramid.
- **Today:** Students will work with a formula for the surface area of a pyramid.

Motivate

- Ask students where they have heard about pyramids or have seen them before. Give groups of students 3–4 minutes to brainstorm a list. They may mention the pyramid on the back of U.S. dollar bills, camping tents, roof designs, tetrahedral dice, and of course, Egyptian pyramids.

Lesson Notes

Key Idea

- Introduce the vocabulary: regular pyramid, regular polygon, slant height.
- **?** "What information does the type of base give you about the lateral faces?"
  number of sides in the base = number of congruent isosceles triangles for the lateral surface area
- **?** "If you know the length of each side of the base, what else do you know?"
  the length of the base of the triangular lateral faces

Example 1

- Draw the net and label the known information. This should remind students of the work they did yesterday making a scale model of a pyramid.
- Write the formula in words first to model good problem-solving techniques.
- Continue to ask questions as you find the total surface area: "How do you find the area of the base? How many lateral faces are there? What is the area of just one lateral face? How do you find the area of a triangle?"
- **Common Error:** In using the area formula for a triangle, the $\frac{1}{2}$ often produces a computation mistake. In this instance, students must multiply $\frac{1}{2} \times 5 \times 8$. Remind students that it's okay to change the order of the factors (Commutative Property). Rewriting the problem as $\frac{1}{2} \times 8 \times 5$ means that you can work with whole numbers: $\frac{1}{2} \times 8 \times 5 = 4 \times 5 = 20$.

On Your Own

- Encourage students to sketch a three-dimensional model of the pyramid and the net for the pyramid. Label the net with the known information.
- Ask a volunteer to share his or her work at the board.

Goal Today's lesson is finding the surface area of a pyramid using a formula.

Start Thinking! and Warm Up

Lesson **6.4** Warm Up
For use before Lesson 6.4

Lesson **6.4** Start Thinking!
For use before Lesson 6.4

Your neighbor needs to put a new roof on his gazebo. The roof is an octagonal pyramid. Why would knowing the surface area of the roof be useful information?

Extra Example 1

What is the surface area of a square pyramid with a base side length of 3 meters and a slant height of 6 meters?
45 m^2

On Your Own

1. 207 cm^2

Extra Example 2

Find the surface area of the regular pyramid.

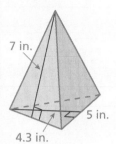

7 in.

5 in.

4.3 in.

63.25 in.^{2}

Extra Example 3

The slant height of the roof in Example 3 is 13 feet. One bundle of shingles covers 30 square feet. How many bundles of shingles should you buy to cover the roof? 16 bundles of shingles

 On Your Own

2. 105.6 ft^2

3. 17 bundles

Differentiated Instruction

Kinesthetic

Photocopy nets of solids for students to cut out and assemble. Then have students draw their own nets to cut out and assemble.

Laurie's Notes

Example 2

- Remind students of the definition of a regular pyramid. This is important because the base, as drawn, doesn't look like an equilateral triangle. This is the challenge of representing a 3-dimensional figure on a flat 2-dimensional sheet of paper.
- Drawing the net is an important step. It allows the key dimensions to be labeled in a way that can be seen.
- Encourage mental math when multiplying $\frac{1}{2} \times 10 \times 8.7$ and $\frac{1}{2} \times 10 \times 14$. Ask students to share their strategies with other students.

Example 3

? "How does the lateral surface area of the roof relate to the bundles of shingles needed?" *Lateral surface area divided by the area covered per bundle gives the number of bundles needed.*

- Have students compute the lateral surface area. Some students may need to draw the triangular lateral face first before performing the computation.
- **FYI:** When shingles are placed on a roof, they need to overlap the shingle below. The coverage given per bundle takes into account the overlap.
- **Extension:** If a bundle of shingles sells for $34.75, what will the total cost be for the shingles? $764.50

On Your Own

- Give students sufficient time to do their work for each problem before asking volunteers to share their work at the board.

Closure

- **Exit Ticket:** Sketch a square pyramid with a slant height of 4 centimeters and a base side length of 3 centimeters. Sketch the net and find the surface area. 33 cm²

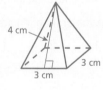 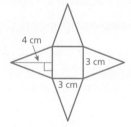

4 cm

3 cm

3 cm

4 cm

3 cm

3 cm

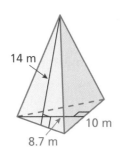

14 m
10 m
8.7 m

Find the surface area of the regular pyramid.

Draw a net.

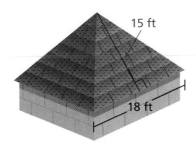

10 m
8.7 m
14 m

Area of base

$$\frac{1}{2} \cdot 10 \cdot 8.7 = 43.5$$

Area of a lateral face

$$\frac{1}{2} \cdot 10 \cdot 14 = 70$$

Find the sum of the areas of the base and the lateral faces.

S = area of base + areas of lateral faces

$= 43.5 + \underbrace{70 + 70 + 70}$

$= 253.5$

> There are 3 identical lateral faces. Count the area 3 times.

∴ The surface area is 253.5 square meters.

A roof is shaped like a square pyramid. One bundle of shingles covers 25 square feet. How many bundles should you buy to cover the roof?

15 ft
18 ft

The base of the roof does not need shingles. So, find the sum of the areas of the lateral faces of the pyramid.

Area of a lateral face

$$\frac{1}{2} \cdot 18 \cdot 15 = 135$$

There are four identical lateral faces. So, the sum of the areas of the lateral faces is

$$135 + 135 + 135 + 135 = 540.$$

Because one bundle of shingles covers 25 square feet, it will take $540 \div 25 = 21.6$ bundles to cover the roof.

∴ So, you should buy 22 bundles of shingles.

On Your Own

Now You're Ready
Exercises 4–12

2. What is the surface area of the pyramid at the right?

3. **WHAT IF?** In Example 3, one bundle of shingles covers 32 square feet. How many bundles should you buy to cover the roof?

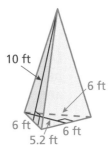

10 ft
6 ft
6 ft
6 ft
5.2 ft

Check It Out
Help with Homework
BigIdeasMath com

 ## Vocabulary and Concept Check

1. **VOCABULARY** Which of the polygons could be the base for a regular pyramid?

2. **VOCABULARY** Can a pyramid have rectangles as lateral faces? Explain.

3. **CRITICAL THINKING** Why is it helpful to know the slant height of a pyramid to find its surface area?

 ## Practice and Problem Solving

Use the net to find the surface area of the regular pyramid.

4.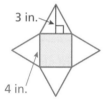
3 in.
4 in.

5.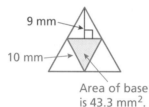
9 mm
10 mm
Area of base is 43.3 mm².

6.
6 m
6 m
Area of base is 61.9 m².

In Exercises 7–11, find the surface area of the regular pyramid.

 7.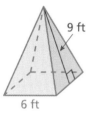
9 ft
6 ft

8.
6 cm
4 cm

9.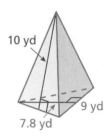
10 yd
9 yd
7.8 yd

10.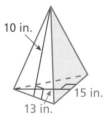
10 in.
15 in.
13 in.

11.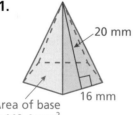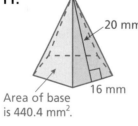
20 mm
16 mm
Area of base is 440.4 mm².

10 in.

3 12. **LAMPSHADE** The base of the lampshade is a regular hexagon with a side length of 8 inches. Estimate the amount of glass needed to make the lampshade.

13. **GEOMETRY** The surface area of a square pyramid is 85 square meters. The base length is 5 meters. What is the slant height?

Assignment Guide and Homework Check

Level	Day 1 Activity Assignment	Day 2 Lesson Assignment	Homework Check
Basic	4–6, 19–22	1–3, 7–13 odd, 12, 14	2, 9, 13, 14
Average	4–6, 19–22	1–3, 7–15 odd, 14	2, 9, 13, 14
Advanced	4–6, 19–22	1–3, 10, 11, 13, 15–18	10, 13, 16, 17

Common Errors

- **Exercises 7–11** Students may forget to add on the area of the base when finding the surface area. Remind them that when asked to find the surface area, the base is included.
- **Exercises 7–11** Students may add the wrong number of lateral face areas to the area of the base. Examine several different pyramids with different bases and ask if they can find a relationship between the number of sides of the base and the number of lateral faces. (They are the same.) Remind students that the number of sides on the base determines how many triangles make up the lateral surface area.
- **Exercise 12** Students may think that there is not enough information to solve the problem because it is not all labeled in the picture. Tell them to use the information in the word problem to finish labeling the picture. Also ask students to identify how many lateral faces are part of the lamp before they find the area of one face.

6.4 Record and Practice Journal

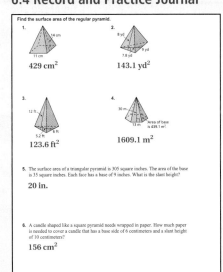

Find the surface area of the regular pyramid.

1. 429 cm²

2. 143.1 yd²

3. 123.6 ft²

4. 1609.1 m²

5. The surface area of a triangular pyramid is 305 square inches. The area of the base is 35 square inches. Each face has a base of 9 inches. What is the slant height?
   20 in.

6. A candle shaped like a square pyramid needs wrapped in paper. How much paper is needed to cover a candle that has a base side of 6 centimeters and a slant height of 10 centimeters?
   156 cm²

Technology For the Teacher
Answer Presentation Tool
Quiz*Show*

1. the triangle and the hexagon

2. no; The lateral faces of a pyramid are triangles.

3. Knowing the slant height helps because it represents the height of the triangle that makes up each lateral face. So, the slant height helps you to find the area of each lateral face.

 ### Practice and Problem Solving

4. 40 in.²

5. 178.3 mm²

6. 151.9 m²

7. 144 ft²

8. 64 cm²

9. 170.1 yd²

10. 322.5 in.²

11. 1240.4 mm²

12. 240 in.²

13. 6 m

14. 34 ft²

15. See *Taking Math Deeper*.

16. The slant height is greater. The height is the distance between the top and the point on the base directly beneath it. The distance from the top to any other point on the base is greater than the height.

17. 124 cm²

18. greater than; If it is less than or equal to, then the lateral face could not meet at a vertex to form a solid.

 Fair Game Review

19. $A \approx 452.16$ units²;
$C \approx 75.36$ units

20. $A \approx 200.96$ units²;
$C \approx 50.24$ units

21. $A \approx 572.265$ units²;
$C \approx 84.78$ units

22. B

Mini-Assessment

Find the surface area of the regular pyramid.

1.
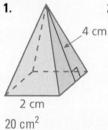

4 cm
2 cm
20 cm²

2.
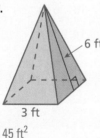
6 ft
3 ft
45 ft²

3. Find the surface area of the roof of the doll house. 480 in.²

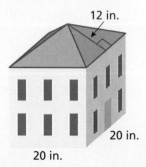
12 in.
20 in.
20 in.

Taking Math Deeper

Exercise 15

If you have ever sewn clothing from a pattern, you know that *on the bias* means that you are cutting against the weave of the fabric. Most patterns, like this one, don't allow cutting on the bias. The pieces must be cut with the weave.

 a. Find the area of the 8 pieces.

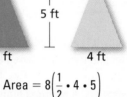
5 ft
4 ft   4 ft

Four of each

$$\text{Area} = 8\left(\frac{1}{2} \cdot 4 \cdot 5\right)$$
$$= 80 \text{ ft}^2$$

 b. Draw a diagram.

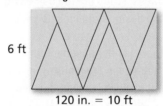
6 ft
120 in. = 10 ft

 Answer the question.
For each color, you cut the four pieces from fabric that is 72 inches (6 ft) wide and 120 inches (10 ft) long.
Fabric Area = 2(6 · 10) = 120 ft²
Area of 8 Pieces = 80 ft²

c. Area of Waste = 120 − 80 = 40 ft²

Project

Use construction paper and a pencil to create an "umbrella" using the least possible amount of paper. The umbrella should be similar to the one in the exercise, using a scale of 1 inch to 1 foot.

Reteaching and Enrichment Strategies

If students need help...	If students got it...
Resources by Chapter • Practice A and Practice B • Puzzle Time Record and Practice Journal Practice Differentiating the Lesson Lesson Tutorials Skills Review Handbook	Resources by Chapter • Enrichment and Extension • School-to-Work Start the next section

14. BMX You are building a bike ramp that is shaped like a square pyramid. You use two 4-foot by 8-foot sheets of plywood. How much plywood do you have left over?

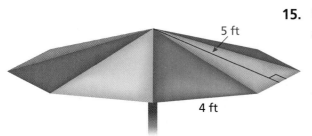

15. UMBRELLA You are making an umbrella that is shaped like a regular octagonal pyramid.

a. Estimate the amount of fabric that is needed to make the umbrella.

b. The fabric comes in rolls that are 72 inches wide. You don't want to cut the fabric "on the bias." Find out what this means. Then, draw a diagram of how you can cut the fabric most efficiently.

c. How much fabric is wasted?

16. REASONING The *height* of a pyramid is the perpendicular distance between the base and the top of the pyramid. Which is greater, the height of a pyramid or the slant height? Explain your reasoning.

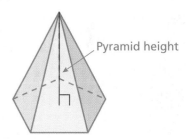
Pyramid height

17. TETRAHEDRON A tetrahedron is a triangular pyramid whose four faces are identical equilateral triangles. The total lateral surface area is 93 square centimeters. Find the surface area of the tetrahedron.

18. **Reasoning** Is the total area of the lateral faces of a pyramid *greater than*, *less than*, or *equal to* the area of the base? Explain.

Fair Game Review What you learned in previous grades & lessons

Find the area and circumference of the circle. Use 3.14 for π. *(Skills Review Handbook)*

19.

12

20.

8

21.

27

22. MULTIPLE CHOICE A youth baseball diamond is similar to a professional baseball diamond. The ratio of the perimeters is 2 : 3. The distance between bases on a youth diamond is 60 feet. What is the distance between bases on a professional diamond? *(Skills Review Handbook)*

Ⓐ 40 ft   Ⓑ 90 ft   Ⓒ 120 ft   Ⓓ 180 ft

STANDARDS
OF LEARNING
8.7

Essential Question How can you find the surface area of a cone?

A cone is a solid with one circular base and one vertex.

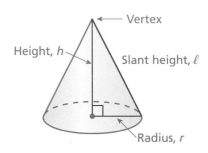

1 ACTIVITY: Finding the Surface Area of a Cone

Work with a partner.

- Draw a circle with a radius of 3 inches.

- Mark the circumference of the circle into six equal parts.

- The circumference of the circle is $2(\pi)(3) = 6\pi$. So each of the six parts on the circle has a length of π. Label each part.

- Cut out one part as shown. Then, make a cone.

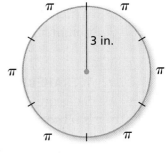

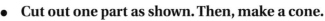

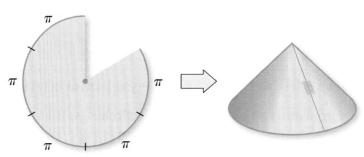

a. The base of the cone should be a circle. Explain why the circumference of the base is 5π.

b. Find the radius of the base.

c. What is the area of the original circle?

d. What is the area of the circle with one part missing?

e. Describe the surface area of the cone. Use your description to find the surface area, including the base.

Laurie's Notes

Introduction

For the Teacher

- **Goal:** Students will develop an intuitive understanding about how to find the surface area of a cone.
- **Big Idea:** Recall the connection between the pyramid and cone—*structurally they are the same.*
- Today's investigation will likely be a real surprise to students for several reasons. First, it's not obvious what the lateral portion of a cone is when it is opened up and placed flat. Secondly, it is very unusual to try to develop the formula for the surface area of a cone. Often it is simply stated and students are told to accept it as being true.
- There will be many computations. Caution students to be patient, write neatly, and keep their work organized.

Motivate

- Hold a paper cone (wrapper of an ice cream cone or homemade).
- Discuss with students the nets that they have seen in this chapter.
- **?** "What do you think the net for a cone is?" Students generally guess (incorrectly) that it's a triangle of some sort.

Activity Notes

Activity 1

- Discuss the vocabulary of cones. Make a distinction between the slant height and the height of the cone.
- **Common Error:** Students think height and slant height have the same length. In the diagram shown at the top of the page, the right triangle may help to explain the difference in length even though the Pythagorean Theorem is taught in a later chapter.
- **?** "How do you find the circumference of a circle? What is the circumference for this circle?" $C = 2\pi r = 2\pi(3) = 6\pi$
- It should seem reasonable to students that because the circumference is 6π and there are six equal pieces, each piece has a length of π inches.
- Students could use a ruler to approximate the radius of the base, *or,* substitute the circumference of the base (5π) in the circumference formula and solve for r.

$$5\pi = 2\pi r$$
$$5 = 2r \qquad \text{Divide both sides by } \pi.$$
$$\frac{5}{2} = r \qquad \text{Divide both sides by 2.}$$

- Have students talk through their work for finding the surface area. They should recognize the two components of finding the surface area of a cone. There is a circular base, so use the area of a circle formula, and there is the lateral surface that is a circle with a sector missing. The slant height of the cone is the radius of the flattened circle with a sector removed.

Standards of Learning

8.7(a) The student will investigate and solve practical problems involving volume and surface area of prisms, cylinders, cones, and pyramids.
8.7(b) The student will describe how changing one measured attribute of the figure affects the volume and surface area.

Previous Learning

Students should know how to find the area and circumference of a circle.

Activity Materials	
Introduction	**Textbook**
• paper cone	• scissors
	• tape
	• scrap paper
	• rulers

Start Thinking! and Warm Up

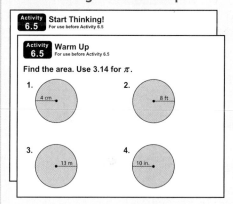

Activity 6.5 Start Thinking! For use before Activity 6.5

Activity 6.5 Warm Up For use before Activity 6.5

Find the area. Use 3.14 for π.

1. 4 cm
2. 8 ft
3. 13 m
4. 10 in.

6.5 Record and Practice Journal

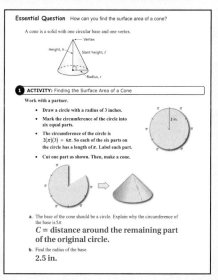

Essential Question How can you find the surface area of a cone?

A cone is a solid with one circular base and one vertex.

1 ACTIVITY: Finding the Surface Area of a Cone

Work with a partner.

- Draw a circle with a radius of 3 inches.
- Mark the circumference of the circle into six equal parts.
- The circumference of the circle is $2(\pi)(3) = 6\pi$. So each of the six parts on the circle has a length of π. Label each part.
- Cut one part as shown. Then, make a cone.

a. The base of the cone should be a circle. Explain why the circumference of the base is 5π.
$C =$ **distance around the remaining part of the original circle.**

b. Find the radius of the base.
2.5 in.

Kinesthetic

Place models of prisms, cylinders, pyramids, and cones around the room. Encourage students to sketch the objects from different points of view, such as from the floor or from above the object. Ask for volunteers to show their sketches of the objects. Discuss how the sketches differ depending on the position and the perspective of the drawer.

6.5 Record and Practice Journal

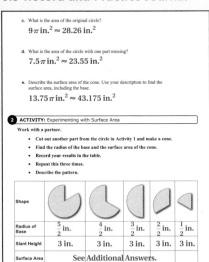

c. What is the area of the original circle?

9π in.$^2 \approx 28.26$ in.^{2}

d. What is the area of the circle with one part missing?

7.5π in.$^2 \approx 23.55$ in.^{2}

e. Describe the surface area of the cone. Use your description to find the surface area, including the base.

13.75π in.$^2 \approx 43.175$ in.^{2}

2 ACTIVITY: Experimenting with Surface Area

Work with a partner.

- Cut out another part from the circle in Activity 1 and make a cone.
- Find the radius of the base and the surface area of the cone.
- Record your results in the table.
- Repeat this three times.
- Describe the pattern.

Shape					
Radius of Base	$\frac{5}{2}$ in.	$\frac{4}{2}$ in.	$\frac{3}{2}$ in.	$\frac{2}{2}$ in.	$\frac{1}{2}$ in.
Slant Height	3 in.	3 in.	3 in.	3 in.	3 in.
Surface Area	See Additional Answers.				

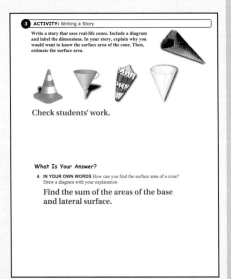

3 ACTIVITY: Writing a Story

Write a story that uses real-life cones. Include a diagram and label the dimensions. In your story, explain why you would want to know the surface area of the cone. Then, estimate the surface area.

Check students' work.

What Is Your Answer?

4. IN YOUR OWN WORDS How can you find the surface area of a cone? Draw a diagram with your explanation.

Find the sum of the areas of the base and lateral surface.

Laurie's Notes

Activity 2

- **Big Idea:** To understand what happens when additional sectors of the circle are cut out, think of surface area of a cone in the following way:

  Surface Area = Area of Base + Lateral Area

  $= \pi r^2$ + a fraction of the original circle

  The radius of the base decreases each time. The lateral area decreases by one-sixth of the original circle each time. The original area was $\pi r^2 = 9\pi$. Review the pattern in the answer key.

- Students may need assistance in recording their work for each subsequent sector that is removed. They should record their answers in terms of π and leave fractions as improper fractions.

- The radius of the base can be measured (approximated) or calculated from knowing the circumference.

- The slant height stays fixed. It is the original 3-inch radius.

- The surface area has two parts, the base and the lateral portion.

? "What patterns do you observe in the table?" This may be difficult depending upon how the students record their work. Encourage students to leave their answers in terms of π.

? "Each time a sector is removed, what happens to the area of the base?" decreases "What happens to the height of the cone?" It increases.

- Make sure students understand that you are asking about the *height* of the cone and not the *slant height* in the previous question.

Activity 3

- **Writing:** This activity allows students to display their creative writing skills.

What Is Your Answer?

- **Think-Pair-Share:** Students should read each question independently and then work with a partner to answer the questions. When they have answered the questions, the pair should compare their answers with another group and discuss any discrepancies.

Closure

- **Exit Ticket:** Sketch a net for a cone. What are the components of the net? circular base and a portion of a circle for the lateral surface

Technology
For the Teacher

Dynamic Classroom

The Dynamic Planning Tool
Editable Teacher's Resources at *BigIdeasMath.com*

Work with a partner.

- Cut out another part from the circle in Activity 1 and make a cone.
- Find the radius of the base and the surface area of the cone.
- Record your results in the table.
- Repeat this three times.
- Describe the pattern.

Shape					
Radius of Base					
Slant Height					
Surface Area					

③ **ACTIVITY: Writing a Story**

Write a story that uses real-life cones. Include a diagram and label the dimensions. In your story, explain why you would want to know the surface area of the cone. Then, estimate the surface area.

What Is Your Answer?

4. **IN YOUR OWN WORDS** How can you find the surface area of a cone? Draw a diagram with your explanation.

Practice ➤ Use what you learned about the surface area of a cone to complete Exercises 4–6 on page 288.

Check It Out
Lesson Tutorials
BigIdeasMath ✓com

Key Vocabulary 🔊
slant height, *p. 286*

The distance from the vertex of a cone to any point on the edge of its base is called the **slant height** of the cone.

🔑 Key Idea

Surface Area of a Cone

Words The surface area S of a cone is the sum of the areas of the base and the lateral surface.

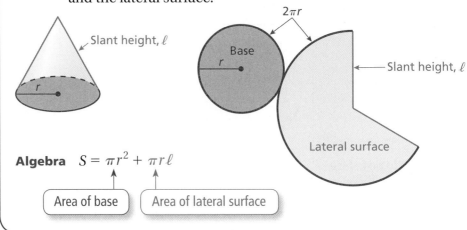

Algebra $S = \pi r^2 + \pi r \ell$

Area of base — Area of lateral surface

EXAMPLE ① **Finding the Surface Area of a Cone**

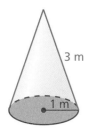

Find the surface area of the cone. Round your answer to the nearest tenth.

Draw a net.

$$S = \pi r^2 + \pi r \ell$$
$$= \pi(1)^2 + \pi(1)(3)$$
$$= \pi + 3\pi$$
$$= 4\pi \approx 12.6$$

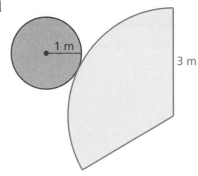

∴ The surface area is about 12.6 square meters.

⬤ On Your Own

Now You're Ready
Exercises 4–9

Find the surface area of the cone. Round your answer to the nearest tenth.

1.

2.

🔊 Multi-Language Glossary at BigIdeasMath✓com.

Laurie's Notes

Introduction

Connect

- **Yesterday:** Students discovered how to find the surface area of a cone by constructing a series of cones from a circle with a sector removed.
- **Today:** Students will work with a formula for the surface area of a cone.

Motivate

- Wear a party hat (or a dunce cap) to class.
- Tell a story as to why you might be wearing the hat.
- **?** "How much paper was used to make my hat?" Students should distinguish between the base (which is missing) and the lateral surface area.
- **?** "What information would you need in order to find the amount of paper used?" This is open ended, as the formula hasn't been given yet.

Lesson Notes

- Introduce the vocabulary: slant height.

Key Idea

- Write the formula in words. Draw the cone and net, labeled with the known information. Notice that the circumference of the base equals the arc length of the lateral surface.
- Write the symbolic formula. The area of the base is πr^2, which is no surprise. The area of the lateral surface may not be obvious to students. If your class has good numeric skills, you can show that the formula works for each case in the table they made yesterday. Otherwise, the manipulation is beyond the scope of most middle school students.
- Be sure that students recognize that in finding the lateral surface area, the r in the formula is the radius of the base.

Example 1

- Draw the net first and label the known information.
- **?** Continue to ask questions as you find the total surface area. "How do you find the area of the base? What is the slant height? What is the area of the lateral surface?"
- Notice that the work is done in terms of π. It is not until the last step that 3.14 is substituted for π.
- **Representation:** Encourage students to use parentheses to represent multiplication. Using the $\times$ symbol would make the expression confusing.
- **?** "Why can π be added to 3π?" like terms Students forget that the coefficient of π is 1.
- **Common Error:** Students may say $\pi + 3\pi = 3\pi^2$.

On Your Own

- Encourage students to sketch a three-dimensional model of the cone, and the net for the cone. Label the net with the known information.

Goal Today's lesson is finding the surface area of a cone using a formula.

Lesson Materials
Introduction
• party hat (cone shaped)

Start Thinking! and Warm Up

> **Lesson 6.5** Warm Up
> For use before Lesson 6.5
>
> **Lesson 6.5** Start Thinking!
> For use before Lesson 6.5
>
> Use what you learned from the activity to explain to a partner how to find the lateral surface area of a cone.

Extra Example 1

Find the surface area of a cone with a radius of 6 inches and a slant height of 8 inches. Round your answer to the nearest tenth. $84\pi \approx 263.8$ in.^{2}

On Your Own

1. $16\pi \approx 50.2$ ft^2
2. $48\pi \approx 150.7$ cm^2

Laurie's Notes

Extra Example 2

The surface area of a cone is 48π square feet. The radius of the cone is 4 feet. What is the slant height ℓ of the cone? 8 ft

Extra Example 3

In Example 3, suppose the slant height of the party hat is 7 inches. How much paper do you need to make the hat? $24.5\pi \approx 77$ in.^{2}

On Your Own

3. 5 m

4. yes; The surface area changes from $\pi r \ell$ to $\pi r(2\ell) = 2(\pi r \ell)$, so the amount of paper doubles.

English Language Learners

Auditory

Have students work in groups and give each group a model of a prism, cylinder, pyramid, or cone. Ask students questions about the solids. "How many faces, edges, and vertices does a pyramid have?" "Which solid rolls?" "How would you describe a cone?" "How are a cone and cylinder alike?" "How are they different?"

Example 2

- Work through the problem with your students, annotating the steps as you go, as shown in the book.
- **?** "What information is known to solve the problem?" Listen for not only the dimensions, but also the formula for the surface area of a cone.
- Substitute for the known variables, then give students time to work through the problem on their own. This will help you determine their comfort with manipulating an expression involving π.
- **Representation:** π and 5 are both factors in each expression, 75π and $5\pi\ell$. Sometimes it is helpful to represent the equation in the following way before dividing.

$$75\pi = 5\pi\ell$$
$$(15)(5\pi) = (5\pi)(\ell)$$

Now divide both sides by 5π.

Example 3

- If you have a party hat, use it to help students visualize the problem.

On Your Own

- Give students sufficient time to do their work for each problem before asking volunteers to share their work at the board.

Closure

- **Exit Ticket**: Have students find the amount of paper used to make your party hat. Answers will vary depending upon the party hat.

The Dynamic Planning Tool
Editable Teacher's Resources at *BigIdeasMath.com*

EXAMPLE ② **Finding the Slant Height of a Cone**

The surface area of the cone is 100π square meters. What is the slant height ℓ of the cone?

$S = \pi r^2 + \pi r \ell$	Write formula.
$100\pi = \pi(5)^2 + \pi(5)(\ell)$	Substitute.
$100\pi = 25\pi + 5\pi\ell$	Simplify.
$75\pi = 5\pi\ell$	Subtract 25π from each side.
$15 = \ell$	Divide each side by 5π.

∴ The slant height is 15 meters.

EXAMPLE ③ **Real-Life Application**

You design a party hat. You attach a piece of elastic along a diameter. (a) How long is the elastic? (b) How much paper do you need to make the hat?

a. To find the length of the elastic, find the diameter of the base.

$C = \pi d$	Write formula.
$22 \approx (3.14)d$	Substitute.
$7.0 \approx d$	Solve for d.

∴ The elastic is about 7 inches long.

5 in.

$C = 22$ in.

b. To find how much paper you need, find the lateral surface area.

$S = \pi r \ell$ ← Do not include the area of the base in the formula.

$= \pi(3.5)(5)$ Substitute.

$= 17.5\pi \approx 55$ Multiply.

∴ You need about 55 square inches of paper to make the hat.

> **Remember**
>
> The diameter d of a circle is two times the radius r.
>
> $d = 2r$

On Your Own

Now You're Ready
Exercises 10–14

3. **WHAT IF?** In Example 2, the surface area is 50π square meters. What is the slant height of the cone?

4. **WHAT IF?** In Example 3, the slant height of the party hat is doubled. Does the amount of paper used double? Explain.

Vocabulary and Concept Check

1. **VOCABULARY** Is the base of a cone a polygon? Explain.

2. **CRITICAL THINKING** In the formula for the surface area of a cone, what does $\pi r \ell$ represent? What does πr^2 represent?

3. **REASONING** Write an inequality comparing the slant height ℓ and the radius r of a cone.

Practice and Problem Solving

Find the surface area of the cone. Round your answer to the nearest tenth.

4.

6 in.
3 in.

5.

5 m
4 m

6.

9 mm
5 mm

7.
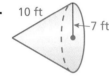
10 ft
7 ft

8.
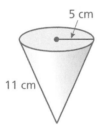
5 cm
11 cm

9.
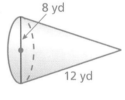
8 yd
12 yd

Find the slant height ℓ of the cone.

10. $S = 33\pi \text{ in.}^2$

ℓ
3 in.

11. $S = 126\pi \text{ cm}^2$

12 cm
ℓ

12. $S = 60\pi \text{ ft}^2$
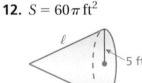
ℓ
5 ft

13. NÓN LÁ How much material is needed to make the Nón Lá Vietnamese leaf hat?

14. PAPER CUP A paper cup shaped like a cone has a diameter of 6 centimeters and a slant height of 7.5 centimeters. How much paper is needed to make the cup?

13 in.
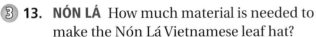
20 in.

Assignment Guide and Homework Check

Level	Day 1 Activity Assignment	Day 2 Lesson Assignment	Homework Check
Basic	4–6, 23–26	1–3, 7–11, 13–16	8, 10, 14, 16
Average	4–6, 23–26	1–3, 7–11, 16–19	8, 10, 16, 18
Advanced	4–6, 23–26	1–3, 8, 10, 12, 16, 18–22	8, 10, 16, 20

Common Errors

- **Exercises 4–9** Students may forget to add the area of the base to the area of the lateral surface. Remind them of the net and the different parts for which they need to find the areas.
- **Exercises 4–12** Students may square the radius when finding the lateral surface area.
- **Exercises 9, 11, and 13–17** Students may use the diameter to find the surface area instead of the radius. Remind them to make sure they know the radius before finding the surface area.
- **Exercise 13** Students may include the surface area of the base when finding the amount of material needed for the hat. Ask them to describe how they would make the hat. Lead this discussion toward making the point that there is no base for the hat.
- **Exercises 15–17** Students may forget to convert the dimensions to the same unit of measure. Remind them to convert one dimension to the other unit of measure before finding the surface area.

6.5 Record and Practice Journal

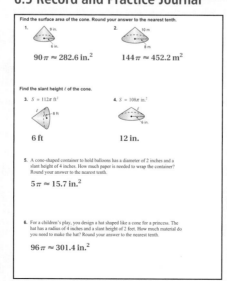

Find the surface area of the cone. Round your answer to the nearest tenth.

1. $90\pi \approx 282.6$ in.^{2}
2. $144\pi \approx 452.2$ m^2

Find the slant height ℓ of the cone.

3. $S = 112\pi$ ft^2 — 6 ft
4. $S = 108\pi$ in.^{2} — 12 in.

5. A cone-shaped container to hold balloons has a diameter of 2 inches and a slant height of 4 inches. How much paper is needed to wrap the container? Round your answer to the nearest tenth.
$5\pi \approx 15.7$ in.^{2}

6. For a children's play, you design a hat shaped like a cone for a princess. The hat has a radius of 4 inches and a slant height of 2 feet. How much material do you need to make the hat? Round your answer to the nearest tenth.
$96\pi \approx 301.4$ in.^{2}

Technology For the Teacher
Answer Presentation Tool
QuizShow

1. no; The base of a cone is a circle. A circle is not a polygon.

2. $\pi r \ell$ is the lateral surface area and πr^2 is the area of the base.

3. $\ell > r$

 Practice and Problem Solving

4. $27\pi \approx 84.8$ in.^{2}

5. $36\pi \approx 113.0$ m^2

6. $70\pi \approx 219.8$ mm^2

7. $119\pi \approx 373.7$ ft^2

8. $80\pi \approx 251.2$ cm^2

9. $64\pi \approx 201.0$ yd^2

10. 8 in.

11. 15 cm

12. 7 ft

13. $130\pi \approx 408.2$ in.^{2}

14. $22.5\pi \approx 70.65$ cm^2

15. $360\pi \approx 1130.4$ in.^{2}; $2.5\pi \approx 7.85$ ft^2

16. $8700\pi \approx 27{,}318$ mm^2; $87\pi \approx 273.18$ cm^2

17. $96\pi \approx 301.44$ ft^2; $\frac{32}{3}\pi \approx 33.49\overline{3}$ yd^2

18. See *Taking Math Deeper*.

19. 12%

20. The slant height is greater. The height is the shortest distance from the vertex to the point on the base directly beneath the vertex. So, the distance from the vertex to any other point on the base is greater than the height.

21. the lateral surface area

22. the pyramid; The pyramid's surface area is $x^2 + 2xy$. The cone's surface area is $\frac{\pi}{4}x^2 + \frac{\pi}{2}xy$. Because $x^2 > \frac{\pi}{4}x^2$ and $2xy > \frac{\pi}{2}xy$, the pyramid's surface area is greater.

 Fair Game Review

23. 45 in.^{2}

24. about 28.345 m^2

25. 16 ft^2

26. B

Mini-Assessment

**Find the surface area of the cone.
Round your answer to the nearest tenth.**

1.

5 in.

2 in.

$14\pi \approx 44.0$ in.^{2}

2.

6 yd

3 yd

$11.25\pi \approx 35.3$ yd^2

3. How much paper was used to make the party hat? Round your answer to the nearest square inch.

$21\pi \approx 66$ in.^{2}

6 in.

7 in.

Taking Math Deeper

Exercise 18

The terminology for the shingle packaging varies a little. It usually depends on the country in which the shingles are manufactured. The standard is usually that there are 3 bundles in a "square" and a square of shingles covers 100 square feet. (For some manufacturers, there are 4 bundles in a square.)

A bundle of asphalt shingles weighs about 70 pounds.

1 Find the surface area of the roof.

$S = \pi r \ell$

$\quad = \pi \cdot 6 \cdot 13$

$\quad = 78\pi$

$\quad \approx 245$ ft^2

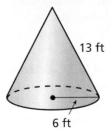
13 ft

6 ft

2 Do the math.

$\dfrac{245 \text{ ft}^2}{32 \text{ ft}^2 \text{ per bundle}} \approx 7.66$ bundles

3 Answer the question (in a real-life context).

Because you can't buy parts of bundles, you should buy 8 bundles of shingles to cover the roof.

Maybe 9 to be safe

Reteaching and Enrichment Strategies

If students need help. . .	If students got it. . .
Resources by Chapter • Practice A and Practice B • Puzzle Time Record and Practice Journal Practice Differentiating the Lesson Lesson Tutorials Skills Review Handbook	Resources by Chapter • Enrichment and Extension • School-to-Work • Financial Literacy Start the next section

Find the surface area of the cone with diameter *d* and slant height *ℓ*.

15. $d = 2$ ft

$ℓ = 18$ in.

16. $d = 12$ cm

$ℓ = 85$ mm

17. $d = 4$ yd

$ℓ = 10$ ft

18. ROOF A roof is shaped like a cone with a diameter of 12 feet. One bundle of shingles covers 32 square feet. How many bundles should you buy to cover the roof?

19. MEGAPHONE Two stickers are placed on opposite sides of the megaphone. Estimate the percent of the surface area of the megaphone covered by the stickers. Round your answer to the nearest percent.

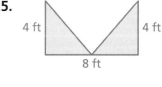

20. REASONING The *height* of a cone is the perpendicular distance from the base to the vertex. Which is greater, the height of a cone or the slant height? Explain your reasoning.

21. GEOMETRY The surface area of a cone is also given as $S = \frac{1}{2}Cℓ + B$, where C is the circumference and $ℓ$ is the slant height. What does $\frac{1}{2}Cℓ$ represent?

22. **Critical Thinking** A cone has a diameter of *x* millimeters and a slant height of *y* millimeters. A square pyramid has a base side length of *x* millimeters and a slant height of *y* millimeters. Which has the greater surface area? Explain.

 Fair Game Review What you learned in previous grades & lessons

Find the area of the figure. *(Section 5.7)*

23.

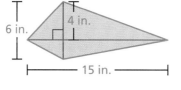

24.

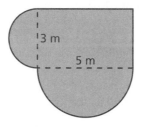

25.

4 ft   4 ft

8 ft

26. MULTIPLE CHOICE Which best describes a translation? *(Section 5.5)*

(A) a flip

(B) a slide

(C) a turn

(D) an enlargement

STANDARDS OF LEARNING
8.7

Essential Question How can you find the surface area of a composite solid?

Share Your Work at...
My.BigIdeasMath.com

1 ACTIVITY: Finding a Surface Area

Work with a partner. You are manufacturing scale models of old houses.

a. Name the four basic solids of this composite figure.

b. Determine a strategy for finding the surface area of this model. Would you use a scale drawing? Would you use a net? Explain.

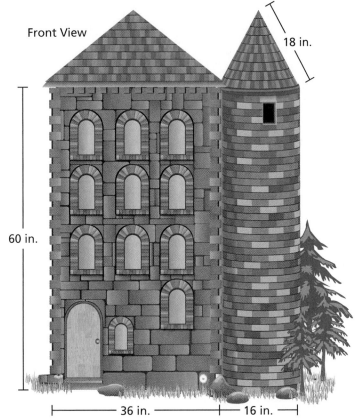

Front View

18 in.

60 in.

36 in.   16 in.

Many castles have cylindrical towers with conical roofs. These are called turrets.

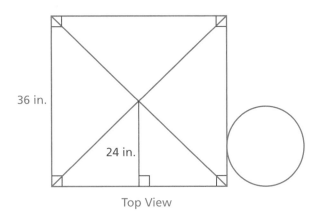

36 in.

24 in.

Top View

Laurie's Notes

Introduction

For the Teacher

- **Goal:** Students will explore strategies for finding the surface area of a composite figure.
- Look through the lesson and select one or more of the activities to focus on, depending upon the class time available and the depth to which one or more of the activities are explored.

Motivate

- **Story Time:** Coral Castle is a stone structure created out of love for a woman by the Latvian-American eccentric Edward Leedskalnin. The structure is comprised of numerous megalithic stones (mostly coral), each weighing several tons. The question remains, how could he have carved and moved over 1100 tons of rock without any human assistance? Coral Castle has baffled scientists, engineers, and scholars since its opening in 1923.

Activity Notes

Activity 1

- This activity is very open-ended in terms of what strategy is used (i.e., using a net or a scale drawing) and any extensions you might pursue.
- Discuss with students models of buildings (replicas) that they have seen. These replicas are made of metal, wood, plastic, or lightweight cardboard.
- If you have examples of building replicas, bring them in to share with the class.
- The context of the activity requires the student to determine building expenses. One expense is the material for constructing the model, therefore they need to know the surface area involved.
- ❓ "What are the four basic solids in this composite figure?" square prism, square pyramid, cylinder, and cone
- Be sure that students observe that the base of the pyramid fits on (is congruent to) one face of the prism. The base of the cone fits on (is congruent to) the base of the cylinder.
- When students have computed the surface area of each portion and have the total surface area, ask a few questions.
- ❓ "How many surfaces of each solid did you find?" prism: 4 lateral faces; pyramid: 4 lateral faces; cylinder: only the lateral portion; cone: only the lateral portion
- ❓ "How did the scale drawing or net help you in finding the surface area?" Answers will vary.
- ❓ "Was it more difficult to find the surface area of one figure than another?" Answers will vary.
- ❓ "Can you think of alternative ways to find the surface area of the composite figure?" Answers will vary.

Standards of Learning

8.7(a) The student will investigate and solve practical problems involving volume and surface area of prisms, cylinders, cones, and pyramids.

Previous Learning

Students should know how to find surface areas of prisms, cylinders, pyramids, and cones.

Start Thinking! and Warm Up

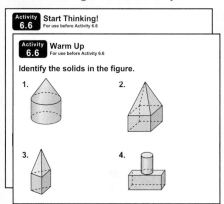

6.6 Record and Practice Journal

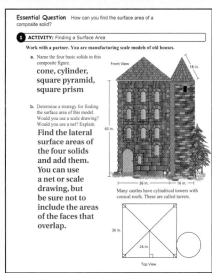

Differentiated Instruction

Kinesthetic

Provide blocks for students to use. Students can build their own composite figures and then calculate the surface areas.

6.6 Record and Practice Journal

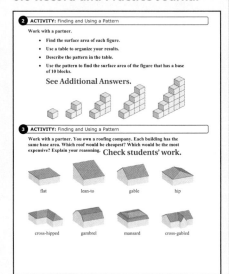

Laurie's Notes

Activity 2

- Encourage students to use a table to organize their findings. Have students gather data on each of the three views. For example:

Figure	Top	Front	Side	Total
1	1	1	1	6
2	2	2	3	14
3	3	3	6	24
4	4	4	10	36
5	5	5	15	50

- The top and front views are increasing by 1. The side view is increasing by consecutive whole numbers (2, 3, 4, 5, ...). The total is increasing by consecutive even numbers (8, 10, 12, 14, ...). Students often have difficulty describing the pattern when the amount of change is not a constant number.
- **Extension:** Have students add a column to the table and look at the number of cubes used in each figure (volume).

Activity 3

- Ask a student to read the problem.
- "What does it mean that *each building has the same base area*?" same area but not necessarily the same dimensions
- This is a difficult concept for students to understand. Two bases with the same area might be 8×10 and 5×16.
- Students need to think about the design and the areas of various faces. They need to reason and explain. For instance, depending on the slopes of the lean-to and gable, it's reasonable to think that each of these could have the same amount of roofing. Students will need to talk about slope (pitch) of the roofs.

What Is Your Answer?

- Have students work in pairs to answer the questions.

Closure

- **Exit Ticket:** Identify at least 3 composite solids in the classroom. Answers will vary.

The Dynamic Planning Tool
Editable Teacher's Resources at *BigIdeasMath.com*

2 **ACTIVITY: Finding and Using a Pattern**

Work with a partner.

- **Find the surface area of each figure.**

- **Use a table to organize your results.**

- **Describe the pattern in the table.**

- **Use the pattern to find the surface area of the figure that has a base of 10 blocks.**

  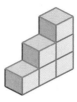 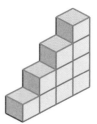 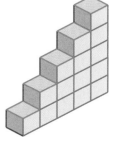

3 **ACTIVITY: Finding and Using a Pattern**

Work with a partner. You own a roofing company. Each building has the same base area. Which roof would be cheapest? Which would be the most expensive? Explain your reasoning.

   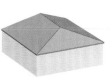

flat   lean-to   gable   hip

cross-hipped   gambrel   mansard   cross-gabled

What Is Your Answer?

4. **IN YOUR OWN WORDS** How can you find the surface area of a composite solid?

5. Design a building that has a turret and also has a mansard roof. Find the surface area of the roof.

Practice Use what you learned about the surface area of a composite solid to complete Exercises 6–8 on page 294.

6.6 Lesson

Check It Out
Lesson Tutorials
BigIdeasMath.com

Key Vocabulary 🔊
composite solid,
    p. 292

A **composite solid** is a figure that is made up of more than one solid.

composite solid

cylinder   cone

EXAMPLE ① **Identifying Solids**

Identify the solids that make up Fort Matanzas.

Rectangular prism

Cylinder

Approximately a rectangular prism

EXAMPLE ② **Standardized Test Practice**

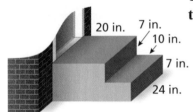

20 in. 7 in.
        10 in.
        7 in.
        24 in.

You painted the steps to an apartment green. What is the surface area that you painted?

 Ⓐ 210 in.^{2} Ⓑ 408 in.^{2} Ⓒ 648 in.^{2} Ⓓ 1056 in.^{2}

Find the area of each green face.

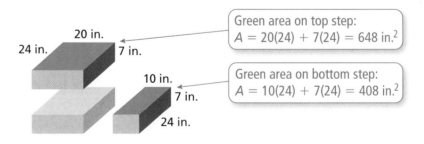

20 in.
24 in.   7 in.

10 in.
7 in.
24 in.

Green area on top step:
$A = 20(24) + 7(24) = 648$ in.^{2}

Green area on bottom step:
$A = 10(24) + 7(24) = 408$ in.^{2}

You painted $648 + 408 = 1056$ square inches.

∴ The correct answer is Ⓓ.

🌑 On Your Own

Now You're Ready
Exercises 3–5

1. **WHAT IF?** In Example 2, you also painted the sides of the steps green. What is the surface area that you painted?

Laurie's Notes

Introduction

Connect

- **Yesterday:** Students explored the surface area of composite figures.
- **Today:** Students will work with formulas for the surface area of prisms, cylinders, pyramids, and cones to find the surface area of composite figures.

Motivate

- Share some tall building facts with students.
- The tallest building in England and the United Kingdom is the Canary Wharf Tower at 235 meters (771 feet) above ground level. The pyramid roof is 40 meters tall and is 30 meters square at the base.
- The Sears Tower in Chicago is a series of rectangular prisms with an antenna at the top rising to a total height of 1725 feet (526 meters). The Sears Tower is the tallest building in North America and is about twice as tall as the Canary Wharf Tower.

Lesson Notes

Example 1

- Ask if any students have visited a fortress.
- Discuss the purpose of the cylindrical portion, and why the rectangular prism is added to the height of the fortress, instead of the height being uniform. In other words, discuss form and function.
- **Big Idea:** Students should understand that when composite solids are made, certain portions of the original surface area may be covered up, meaning the area is no longer exposed. Students need to examine the solid and decide what surfaces are actually exposed.

Example 2

- ❓ How many faces will you paint?" four
- ❓ "Do you know the dimensions needed for each face?" yes
- Work through the problem as shown by computing the area of all four faces.
- ❓ "Is there another way you can find the area of the four steps that is more efficient?" Perhaps students notice that the length of each step is 24 inches so adding the widths together first and then multiplying by 24 is more efficient. $24(20 + 7 + 10 + 7) = 24(44)$
- ❓ "What property did you use?" Distributive Property

On Your Own

- Did students find the area of a 20×14 rectangle and then subtract a 7×10 rectangle or did they divide the gray region into two rectangles?

Goal Today's lesson is using previously learned formulas to find the surface area of a **composite solid**.

Start Thinking! and Warm Up

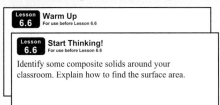

Lesson 6.6 Warm Up
For use before Lesson 6.6

Lesson 6.6 Start Thinking!
For use before Lesson 6.6

Identify some composite solids around your classroom. Explain how to find the surface area.

Extra Example 1

Identify the solids in the figure.

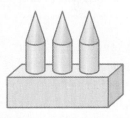

rectangular prism, cylinder, and cone

Extra Example 2

You painted the steps to your apartment yellow. What is the surface area that you painted?

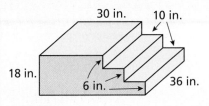

30 in.   10 in.

18 in.

6 in.   36 in.

2448 in.^{2}

On Your Own

1. 1756 in.^{2}

Extra Example 3

Find the surface area of the composite solid. Round your answer to the nearest tenth.

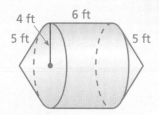

$88\pi \approx 276.3$ ft^2

 On Your Own

2. cone, cylinder;
   $54\pi \approx 169.6$ yd^2

3. rectangular prism,
   triangular prism; 120 cm^2

English Language Learners

Vocabulary

Students should understand the meaning of face and base when dealing with solids. You may need to help them understand the concept of overlapping faces. Use models to help explain this concept.

Example 3

- Discuss the problem, and note the fact that faces overlap. If the face is not exposed, it is not included in the surface area.
- **?** "Why does the surface area formula for the prism begin with ℓw instead of $2\ell w$?" One of the bases is covered by the pyramid.
- **Common Error:** Students may only find the area of 4 faces instead of 5 for the prism. They think that it looks like a house and a house would be sitting on the ground with the bottom face not exposed. Make it clear that there is no context for this problem. It was not stated to be a house so consider all faces not covered by another solid when finding the surface area.

On Your Own

- **Neighbor Check:** Have students work independently and then have their neighbor check their work. Have students discuss any discrepancies.

Closure

- **Exit Ticket:** Draw a sketch of a house that is a square prism with a square pyramid sitting on top of it. The edge length of the square is 10 meters, the height is 10 meters, and the slant height of the pyramid is 8 meters. Find the surface area of the house and roof. (Exclude the base of the house.) 560 m^2

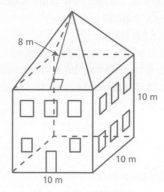

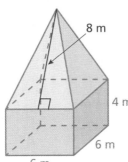

Find the surface area of the composite solid.

The solid is made up of a square prism and a square pyramid. Use the surface area formulas for a prism and a pyramid, but do not include the areas of the sides that overlap.

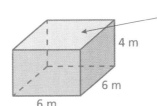

Do not include the top base of the prism in the surface area.

Do not include the base of the pyramid in the surface area.

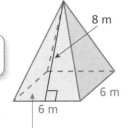

Square prism

$$S = \ell w + 2\ell h + 2wh \qquad \text{Write formula.}$$

$$= 6(6) + 2(6)(4) + 2(6)(4) \qquad \text{Substitute.}$$

$$= 36 + 48 + 48 \qquad \text{Multiply.}$$

$$= 132 \qquad \text{Add.}$$

Square pyramid

$$S = \text{areas of lateral faces} \qquad \text{Write formula.}$$

$$= 4\left(\frac{1}{2} \cdot 6 \cdot 8\right) \qquad \text{Substitute.}$$

$$= 96 \qquad \text{Multiply.}$$

Find the sum of the surface areas: $132 + 96 = 228$.

⋮• The surface area is 228 square meters.

● **On Your Own**

Exercises 6–11

Identify the solids that make up the composite solid. Then find the surface area. Round your answer to the nearest tenth.

2.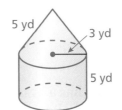

3.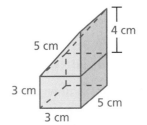

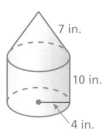

Vocabulary and Concept Check

1. **OPEN-ENDED** Draw a composite solid formed by a triangular prism and a cone.

2. **REASONING** Explain how to find the surface area of the composite solid.

7 in.
10 in.
4 in.

Practice and Problem Solving

Identify the solids that form the composite solid.

3.

4.

5.

Identify the solids that form the composite solid. Then find the surface area. Round your answer to the nearest tenth.

6.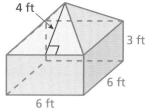
4 ft
3 ft
6 ft
6 ft

7.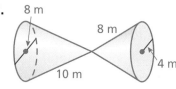
8 m
8 m
4 m
10 m

8.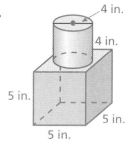
4 in.
4 in.
5 in.
5 in.
5 in.

9.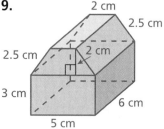
2 cm
2.5 cm
2.5 cm
2 cm
3 cm
6 cm
5 cm

10.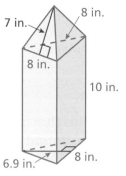
7 in.
8 in.
8 in.
10 in.
6.9 in.
8 in.

11.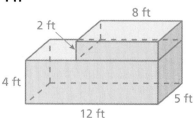
8 ft
2 ft
4 ft
12 ft
5 ft

12. **OPEN-ENDED** The solid is made using eight cubes with side lengths of 1 centimeter.

a. Draw a new solid using eight cubes that has a surface area less than that of the original solid.

b. Draw a new solid using eight cubes that has a surface area greater than that of the original solid.

Assignment Guide and Homework Check

Level	Day 1 Activity Assignment	Day 2 Lesson Assignment	Homework Check
Basic	6–8, 19–22	1, 2, 3, 5, 9, 11, 12, 13	5, 9, 12, 13
Average	6–8, 19–22	1, 2, 9–15 odd, 12, 14	9, 12, 13, 14
Advanced	6–8, 19–22	1, 2, 12–18	12, 13, 14, 16

For Your Information

- **Exercise 18** Ask students to determine how many of the 27 cubes have three faces painted (8), have two faces painted (12), one face painted (6), and no faces painted (1).

Common Errors

- **Exercises 3–5** Students may have difficulty recognizing which solids are put together to form the shape. Tell them to trace the object and then draw lines that will break the object into parts of solids that are familiar to them.
- **Exercises 6–11** When finding the surface area of composite solids, students may include the parts that are no longer surface areas. Tell them to draw the solids without those parts and then find the area.
- **Exercises 8 and 11** Students will struggle finding the surface area of the portions that intersect. First, have them find the surface area that they know how to find. Next, draw pictures of what is remaining to be found and ask questions about how to find the area.

6.6 Record and Practice Journal

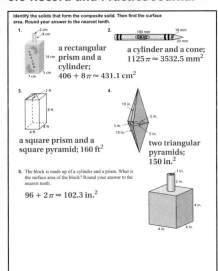

Technology For the Teacher
Answer Presentation Tool
QuizShow

Vocabulary and Concept Check

1. *Sample answer:*

2. Find the lateral surface area and the area of one base of the cylinder, and then find the area of the lateral surface of the cone. Add up all of these areas.

Practice and Problem Solving

3. three cylinders

4. rectangular prism, triangular prism

5. rectangular prism, half of a cylinder

6. square prism, square pyramid; 156 ft²

7. cones; $104\pi \approx 326.6$ m²

8. cylinder, rectangular prism; $150 + 16\pi \approx 200.2$ in.²

9. trapezoidal prism, rectangular prism; 152 cm²

10. triangular prism, triangular pyramid; 351.6 in.²

11. two rectangular prisms; 308 ft²

12. a. *Sample answer:*

   b. *Sample answer:*

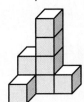

Practice and Problem Solving

13. 63.4%

14. See *Taking Math Deeper*.

15. $144\pi \approx 452.2$ in.^{2}

16. 226 ft^2

17. $806\pi \approx 2530.8$ mm^2

18. less than; Removing the purple cubes reduces the surface area by the areas of 2 cube faces. Removing the green cubes does not change the total surface area.

Fair Game Review

19. 10 ft^2

20. 16 cm^2

21. 47.5 in.^{2}

22. A

Mini-Assessment

Find the surface area of the composite solid. Round your answer to the nearest tenth.

1.

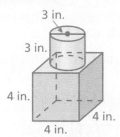

3 in.

3 in.

4 in.

4 in.

4 in.

$96 + 9\pi \approx 124.3$ in.^{2}

2.

12 ft

20 ft

10 ft

$520\pi \approx 1632.8$ ft^2

Taking Math Deeper

Exercise 14

The barbell is made up of two hexagonal prisms and one cylinder. This problem has a lot of decimal calculations. Part of the skill is to learn to keep each part organized.

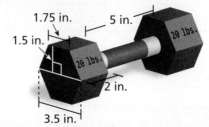

1.75 in.   5 in.

1.5 in.

20 lbs.   20 lbs.

2 in.

3.5 in.

① Find the area of each type of surface.

Figure	How many?	Area
2 ■ 1.75	12	$12(1.75 \cdot 2) = 42.0$
1.75 ▱ 1.5 3.5	8	$8\left[\frac{1}{2}(3.5 + 1.75)(1.5)\right] = 31.5$
1 ●	2	$2(\pi \cdot 0.5^2) \approx 1.57$ Subtract 1" circular handle.
π ▮ 5	1	$5\pi \approx 15.7$

Total: 87.63 in.^{2}

② Find the total.

③ Help me see it. Draw a net for each hexagonal end of the barbell.

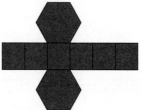

I see it.

Reteaching and Enrichment Strategies

If students need help...	If students got it...
Resources by Chapter • Practice A and Practice B • Puzzle Time Record and Practice Journal Practice Differentiating the Lesson Lesson Tutorials Skills Review Handbook	Resources by Chapter • Enrichment and Extension • School-to-Work • Financial Literacy • Technology Connection Start the next section

13. BATTERIES What is the percent increase in the surface area of the AAA battery to the AA battery? Round your answer to the nearest tenth of a percent.

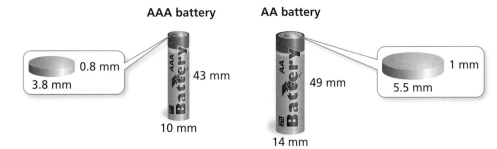

AAA battery   AA battery

14. BARBELL The diameter of the handle of a barbell is 1 inch. The hexagonal weights are identical. What is the surface area of the barbell?

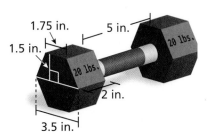

REASONING Find the surface area of the solid. Round your answer to the nearest tenth.

15.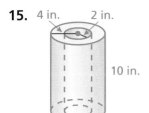

16.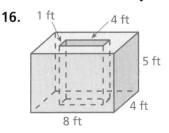

17.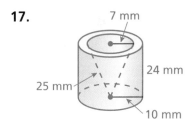

18. *Critical Thinking* The cube is made with 27 identical cubes. All cubes that cannot be seen are orange. Is the surface area of the solid formed without the purple cubes *greater than*, *less than*, or *equal to* the surface area of the solid formed without the green cubes? Explain your reasoning.

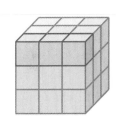

 Fair Game Review What you learned in previous grades & lessons

Find the area. *(Skills Review Handbook)*

19.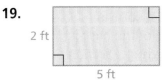

20.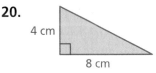

21.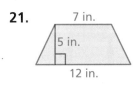

22. MULTIPLE CHOICE A cliff swallow nest is 86 meters above a canyon floor. The elevation of the nest is −56 meters. What is the elevation of the canyon floor? *(Section 1.1)*

    (A) −142   **(B)** −30   **(C)** 30   **(D)** 142

6.4 – 6.6   Quiz

Check It Out
Progress Check
BigIdeasMath √com

Identify the solids that form the composite solid. *(Section 6.6)*

1.

2.

3.

Find the surface area of the regular pyramid. *(Section 6.4)*

4.
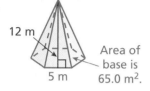

12 m

5 m

Area of base is 65.0 m².

5.

6 cm

2 cm

Find the surface area of the cone. Round your answer to the nearest tenth.
(Section 6.5)

6.
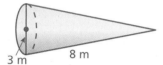

3 m   8 m

7.

7 mm

6 mm

Find the surface area of the composite solid. Round your answer to the nearest tenth. *(Section 6.6)*

8.

3 m   1 m

2 m

9.
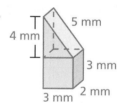

5 mm

4 mm

3 mm

3 mm   2 mm

99 cm

12 cm

12 cm

25 cm

10. TRAFFIC CONE A square reflective sticker is placed on a traffic cone to make it more visible at night. Estimate the percent of the surface area of the traffic cone covered by the sticker to the nearest percent. *(Section 6.5)*

11. GEOMETRY The surface area of a cone is 150π square inches. The radius of the base is 10 inches. What is the slant height? *(Section 6.5)*

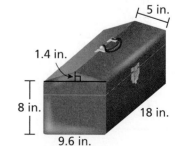

5 in.

1.4 in.

8 in.

18 in.

9.6 in.

12. TOOLBOX Find the surface area of the toolbox. *(Section 6.6)*

Alternative Assessment Options

Math Chat	Student Reflective Focus Question
Structured Interview	Writing Prompt

Math Chat

- Have students work in pairs. Assign Quiz Exercises 10–12 to each pair. Each student works through all three problems. After the students have worked through the problems, they take turns talking through the processes that they used to get each answer. Students analyze and evaluate the mathematical thinking and strategies used.
- The teacher should walk around the classroom listening to the pairs and ask questions to ensure understanding.

Study Help Sample Answers

Remind students to complete Graphic Organizers for the rest of the chapter.

8a.

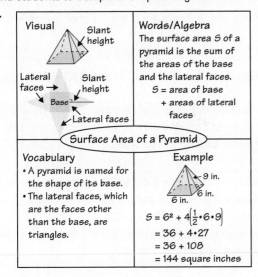

8b, c. Available at *BigIdeasMath.com*

Reteaching and Enrichment Strategies

If students need help. . .	If students got it. . .

Resources by Chapter
  • Study Help
  • Practice A and Practice B
  • Puzzle Time
Lesson Tutorials
BigIdeasMath.com Practice Quiz
Practice from the Test Generator
	Resources by Chapter
	  • Enrichment and Extension
	  • School-to-Work
	Game Closet at *BigIdeasMath.com*
	Start the Chapter Review

Technology For the Teacher
Answer Presentation Tool

Answers

1. cylinder, cone
2. rectangular prism, triangular prism
3. three rectangular prisms
4. 245 m^2 5. 28 cm^2
6. $14.25\pi \approx 44.7 \text{ m}^2$
7. $30\pi \approx 94.2 \text{ mm}^2$
8. $8\pi \approx 25.1 \text{ m}^2$
9. 66 mm^2
10. 4%
11. about 5 in.
12. 807.84 in.^2

Assessment Book

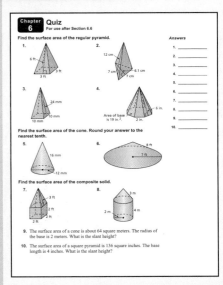

Answers

1.

2.

3.

4. 100 in.^2

5. 400 cm^2

6. 108 m^2

Review of Common Errors

Exercises 1–3

- Students may mix up the different types of solids. Remind them of the definition of each solid and give them a few real-life examples of each.

Exercises 4–6

- Students may sum the areas of only 3 of the faces of the rectangular prism instead of all 6. Remind them that a rectangular prism has 6 faces.
- Students may try to use the formula for the surface area of a rectangular prism to find the surface area of a triangular prism. Show them that this will not work by comparing the nets of the two types of prisms.

Exercises 7–9

- Students may add the area of only one base. Remind them that a cylinder has *two* bases.
- Students may double the radius instead of squaring it, or forget the correct order of operations when using the formula for the surface area of a cylinder. Remind them of the formula, and remind them of the order of operations.

Exercises 10–12

- Students may forget to include the area of the base when finding the surface area of a pyramid. Remind them that when asked to find the surface area, the base is included.
- Students may add the wrong number of lateral face areas to the area of the base. Remind them that they must add the area of a lateral face as many times as there are sides on the base of the pyramid.

Exercises 13–15

- Students may forget to add the area of the base to the area of the lateral surface. Remind them of the net for a cone and the two areas that they must find and add together to determine the surface area.
- Students may square the radius when finding the lateral surface area. Remind them of the formula for the surface area of a cone.

Exercises 16–18

- When finding the surface area of a composite solid, students may include areas of the sides that overlap. Remind them that the overlapping sides are not part of the surface area.

6 Chapter Review

Check It Out
Vocabulary Help
BigIdeasMath com

Review Key Vocabulary

solid, *p. 260*
polyhedron, *p. 260*
lateral face, *p. 260*

surface area, *p. 264*
net, *p. 264*
regular pyramid, *p. 280*

slant height, *pp. 280, 286*
composite solid, *p. 292*

Review Examples and Exercises

6.1 Drawing 3-Dimensional Figures *(pp. 258–263)*

Draw a triangular prism.

Draw identical
triangular bases.

Connect corresponding
vertices.

Change any *hidden*
lines to dashed lines.

Exercises

Draw the solid.

1. Square pyramid   **2.** Hexagonal prism   **3.** Cylinder

6.2 Surface Areas of Prisms *(pp. 264–269)*

Find the surface area of the prism.

Draw a net.

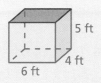

$$S = 2\ell w + 2\ell h + 2wh$$
$$= 2(6)(4) + 2(6)(5) + 2(4)(5)$$
$$= 48 + 60 + 40$$
$$= 148$$

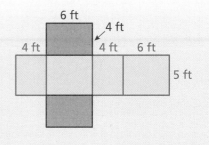

∴ The surface area is 148 square feet.

Exercises

Find the surface area of the prism.

4.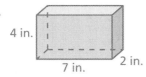

5.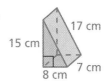

6.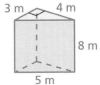

Surface Areas of Cylinders *(pp. 270–275)*

Find the surface area of the cylinder. Round your answer to the nearest tenth.

Draw a net.

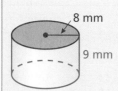

$$S = 2\pi r^2 + 2\pi rh$$
$$= 2\pi(8)^2 + 2\pi(8)(9)$$
$$= 128\pi + 144\pi$$
$$= 272\pi \approx 854.1$$

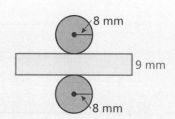

The surface area is about 854.1 square millimeters.

Exercises

Find the surface area of the cylinder. Round your answer to the nearest tenth.

7.

8.
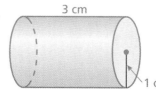

9.
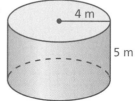

Surface Areas of Pyramids *(pp. 278–283)*

Find the surface area of the regular pyramid.

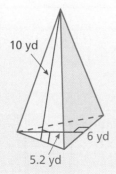

Draw a net.

Area of base

$$\frac{1}{2} \cdot 6 \cdot 5.2 = 15.6$$

Area of a lateral face

$$\frac{1}{2} \cdot 6 \cdot 10 = 30$$

Find the sum of the areas of the base and all 3 lateral faces.

$$S = 15.6 + 30 + 30 + 30 = 105.6$$

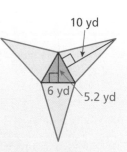

The surface area is 105.6 square yards.

Exercises

Find the surface area of the regular pyramid.

10.
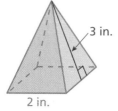

11.
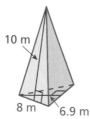

12.
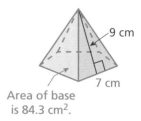

Area of base is 84.3 cm².

Review Game

3-Dingo

Big Ideas
Game Closet

Materials per Group:

- one 3-Dingo card*
- objects to cover the 3-Dingo card squares, such as bingo chips

Directions:

This activity is played like bingo. Divide the class into groups. Call out a three-dimensional figure and all of the dimensions necessary to calculate the surface area. The group calculates the surface area and if that value is in a square on their card under the correct figure, they cover it. Keep calling out figures and their dimensions until a group wins.

Who Wins?

Just like bingo, the first group to get a row, column, or diagonal of covered squares wins. The winning team yells 3-Dingo!

*A 3-Dingo card has 5 columns of 5 squares and a three-dimensional figure (prism, cylinder, pyramid, cone, and composite solid) with variable dimensions shown at the top of each column of squares. Different values for the surface area of each figure are shown in each of the 5 squares below the figure. Different cards show the values in different orders, so no two 3-Dingo cards in a set are the same. A 3-Dingo card set is available at *BigIdeasMath.com*.

For the Student
Additional Practice

- Lesson Tutorials
- Study Help (textbook)
- Student Website
  Multi-Language Glossary
  Practice Assessments

Answers

7. $126\pi \approx 395.6$ in.^{2}

8. $8\pi \approx 25.1$ cm^2

9. $72\pi \approx 226.1$ m^2

10. 16 in.^{2}

11. 147.6 m^2

12. 241.8 cm^2

13. $5\pi \approx 15.7$ in.^{2}

14. $21\pi \approx 65.9$ cm^2

15. $48\pi \approx 150.7$ m^2

16. 228 ft^2

17. 116 yd^2

18. $45\pi \approx 141.3$ m^2

My Thoughts on the Chapter

What worked. . .

What did not work. . .

What I would do differently. . .

6.5 **Surface Areas of Cones** *(pp. 284–289)*

Find the surface area of the cone. Round your answer to the nearest tenth.

Draw a net.

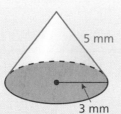

$$S = \pi r^2 + \pi r \ell$$
$$= \pi(3)^2 + \pi(3)(5)$$
$$= 9\pi + 15\pi$$
$$= 24\pi \approx 75.4$$

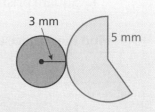

The surface area is about 75.4 square millimeters.

Exercises

Find the surface area of the cone. Round your answer to the nearest tenth.

13.

14.

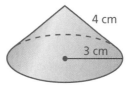

15.

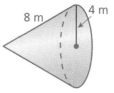

6.6 **Surface Areas of Composite Solids** *(pp. 290–295)*

Find the surface area of the composite solid. Round your answer to the nearest tenth.

The solid is made of a cone and a cylinder. Use the surface area formulas. Do not include the areas of the bases that overlap.

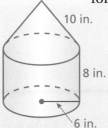

Cone

$$S = \pi r \ell$$
$$= \pi(6)(10)$$
$$= 60\pi \approx 188.4$$

Cylinder

$$S = \pi r^2 + 2\pi r h$$
$$= \pi(6)^2 + 2\pi(6)(8)$$
$$= 36\pi + 96\pi$$
$$= 132\pi \approx 414.5$$

The surface area is about $188.4 + 414.5 = 602.9$ square inches.

Exercises

Find the surface area of the composite solid. Round your answer to the nearest tenth.

16.

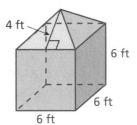

17.

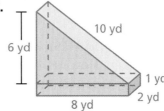

18.

Check It Out
Test Practice
BigIdeasMath ✓com

Draw the solid.

1. Square prism

2. Pentagonal pyramid

3. Cone

Find the surface area of the prism or regular pyramid.

4.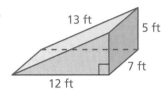
13 ft
5 ft
7 ft
12 ft

5.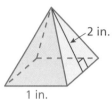
2 in.
1 in.

6.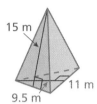
15 m
11 m
9.5 m

Find the surface area of the cylinder or cone. Round your answer to the nearest tenth.

7.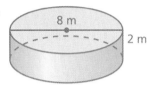
8 m
2 m

8.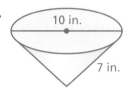
10 in.
7 in.

9. Draw the front, side, and top views of the solid in Exercise 8.

Identify the solids that form the composite solid. Then find the surface area. Round your answer to the nearest tenth.

10.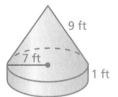
9 ft
7 ft
1 ft

11.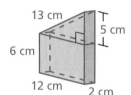
13 cm
5 cm
6 cm
12 cm
2 cm

12. **CORN MEAL** A cylindrical corn meal container has a height of 5 inches and a diameter of 4 inches. How much paper is used for the label of the corn meal container?

13. **COSTUME** The cone-shaped hat will be part of a costume for a school play. What is the least amount of material needed to make this hat?

11 in.
6 in.

14. **GEOMETRY** A cylinder has a surface area of 80 square inches. You double both dimensions. What is the surface area of the new cylinder?

15. **SKATEBOARD RAMP** A quart of paint covers 80 square feet. How many quarts should you buy to paint the ramp with two coats? (Assume you will not paint the bottom of the ramp.)

15.2 ft
19.5 ft
6 ft
14 ft

Test Item References

Chapter Test Questions	Section to Review
1–3, 9	6.1
4, 13, 15	6.2
7, 12	6.3
5, 6	6.4
8, 14	6.5
10, 11	6.6

Test-Taking Strategies

Remind students to quickly look over the entire test before they start so that they can budget their time. This test is very visual and requires that students remember many terms. It might be helpful for them to jot down some of the terms on the back of their test before they start.

Common Assessment Errors

- **Exercises 5 and 6** Students may forget to include the area of the base or add the wrong number of lateral face areas when finding the surface area of a pyramid. Remind them that the base is included as part of the surface area, and that they must add the area of each lateral face.
- **Exercises 7 and 8** Students may use the diameter instead of the radius, or double the radius instead of squaring it. Remind them to halve the given diameter to find the radius and how to properly evaluate an exponent.
- **Exercises 10 and 11** When finding the surface area of a composite solid, students may include areas of the sides that overlap. Remind them that the overlapping sides are not part of the surface area.
- **Exercises 12 and 14** Students may include the area of the base(s) when calculating the amount of material. Point out that the container's label is only on the lateral surface and that the hat does not have a base.
- **Exercise 13** Students may sum the areas of only 3 of the faces or find the product of the length, width, and height to find the surface area of a rectangular prism. Showing them a net of the prism will help them see that it has 6 faces, and that they must multiply and add to find the surface area.

Reteaching and Enrichment Strategies

If students need help...	If students got it...
Resources by Chapter • Practice A and Practice B • Puzzle Time Record and Practice Journal Practice Differentiating the Lesson Lesson Tutorials Practice from the Test Generator Skills Review Handbook	Resources by Chapter • Enrichment and Extension • School-to-Work • Financial Literacy • Technology Connection Game Closet at *BigIdeasMath.com* Start Standardized Test Practice

Answers

1. 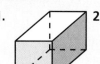   2.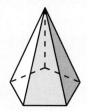

3.    4. 270 ft^2

5. 5 in.^{2} 6. 299.8 m^2

7. 48π m$^2 \approx 150.7$ m^2

8. 60π in.$^2 \approx 188.4$ in.^{2}

9. Front: Side: Top:

10. cylinder, cone;
    126π ft$^2 \approx 395.6$ ft^2

11. Rectangular prism,
    Triangular prism; 288 cm^2

12. 20π in.$^2 \approx 62.8$ in.^{2}

13. 33π in.$^2 \approx 103.62$ in.^{2}

14. 320 in.^{2}

15. 13 quarts of paint

Assessment Book

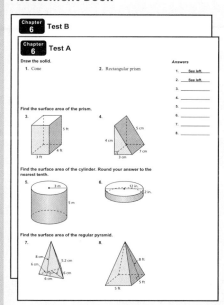

After Answering Easy Questions, Relax
Answer Easy Questions First
Estimate the Answer
Read All Choices before Answering
Read Question before Answering
Solve Directly or Eliminate Choices
Solve Problem before Looking at
   Choices
Use Intelligent Guessing
Work Backwards

About this Strategy

When taking a multiple choice test, be sure to read each question carefully and thoroughly. When taking a timed test, it is often best to skim the test and answer the easy questions first. Be careful that you record your answer in the correct position on the answer sheet.

Answers

1. C
2. F
3. 190 in.^{2}

Item Analysis

1. **A.** The student does not correctly match corresponding side lengths, instead using the proportion $\dfrac{PQ}{QR} = \dfrac{US}{ST}$.

   B. The student does not correctly match corresponding side lengths, instead using the proportion $\dfrac{PQ}{QR} = \dfrac{TU}{ST}$.

   C. Correct answer

   D. The student does not correctly match corresponding side lengths, instead using the proportion $\dfrac{PQ}{QR} = \dfrac{ST}{US}$.

2. **F.** Correct answer

   G. The student thinks that half of the entire rectangle is shaded and finds half the entire rectangle's area.

   H. The student finds the area of the part of the figure that is not shaded.

   I. The student finds the perimeter of the entire rectangle.

3. **Gridded Response:** Correct answer: 190 in.^{2}

   Common Error: The student finds the areas of only one face of each size, getting an answer of 95 square inches.

4. **A.** The student incorrectly thinks that the y-intercept is 6.

   B. Correct answer

   C. The student inverts the slope and incorrectly thinks that the y-intercept is 6.

   D. The student inverts the slope.

5. **F.** The student includes the area of only one triangular face.

   G. The student includes the area of only three triangular faces.

   H. Correct answer

   I. The student does not multiply by $\dfrac{1}{2}$ when determining the area of a triangular face.

Technology
For the Teacher

Big Ideas Test Generator

1. In the figure below, $\triangle PQR \sim \triangle STU$.

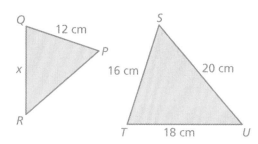

What is the value of x?

A. 9.6 cm

B. $10\frac{2}{3}$ cm

C. 13.5 cm

D. 15 cm

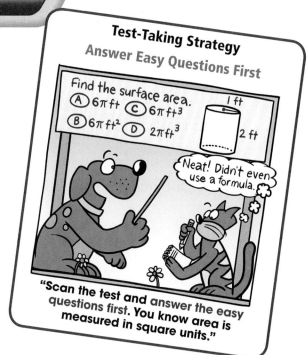
2. The rectangle below is divided into six regions.

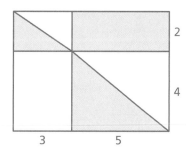

What is the area of the part of the figure that is shaded?

F. 23 units^2

G. 24 units^2

H. 25 units^2

I. 28 units^2

3. A right rectangular prism and its dimensions are shown below.

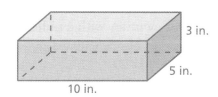

3 in.

5 in.

10 in.

What is the total surface area, in square inches, of the right rectangular prism?

4. You ride 6 miles on your bicycle in 15 minutes and 18 miles in 45 minutes. Which equation represents the distance y (in miles) you ride in x minutes?

A. $y = \dfrac{2}{5}x + 6$ 　　　　　　　　**C.** $y = \dfrac{5}{2}x + 6$

B. $y = \dfrac{2}{5}x$ 　　　　　　　　　　**D.** $y = \dfrac{5}{2}x$

5. A right square pyramid is shown below.

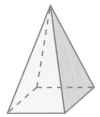

The square base and one of the triangular faces of the right square pyramid are shown below with their dimensions.

 　　　　　　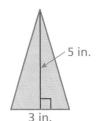 5 in.

3 in. 　　　　　　　　　3 in.

Square Base 　　　　　**A Triangular Face**

What is the total surface area of the right square pyramid?

F. 16.5 in.^{2} 　　　　　　　　　　**H.** 39 in.^{2}

G. 31.5 in.^{2} 　　　　　　　　　　**I.** 69 in.^{2}

6. A right circular cylinder with a radius of 3 centimeters and a height of 7 centimeters will be carved out of wood.

Part A　Draw and label a right circular cylinder with a radius of 3 centimeters and a height of 7 centimeters.

The two bases of the right circular cylinder will be painted blue. The rest of the cylinder will be painted red.

Part B　What is the surface area, in square centimeters, that will be painted blue? Show your work and explain your reasoning. (Use 3.14 for π.)

Part C　What is the surface area, in square centimeters, that will be painted red? Show your work and explain your reasoning. (Use 3.14 for π.)

Item Analysis (continued)

6. **4 points** The student demonstrates a thorough understanding of drawing and working with the surface area of right circular cylinders. In Part A, the student correctly draws and labels a right circular cylinder. In Part B, the student correctly find the area, in square centimeters, of the two bases, getting an answer of 56.52. In Part C, the student correctly finds the lateral area, in square centimeters, of the cylinder, getting an answer of 131.88.

3 points The student demonstrates an understanding of drawing and working with the surface area of right circular cylinders, but the student's work demonstrates an essential but less than thorough understanding.

2 points The student demonstrates a partial understanding of drawing and working with the surface area of right circular cylinders. The student's work demonstrates a lack of essential understanding.

1 point The student demonstrates a limited understanding of drawing and working with the surface area of right circular cylinders. The student's response is incomplete and exhibits many flaws.

0 points The student provided no response, a completely incorrect or incomprehensible response, or a response that demonstrates insufficient understanding of drawing and working with the surface area of right circular cylinders.

7. **A.** The student forgets the inverse operation of addition.

   B. The student forgets the inverse operation of multiplication.

   C. Correct answer

   D. The student forgets to include the negative sign when dividing.

8. **F.** The student divides by 2 in the equation in answer choice H, getting a solution of 3, thereby making answer choice F the equation with the greatest solution.

   G. The student divides by 2 in the equation in answer choice H, getting a solution of 3. The student makes a sign error in the equation in answer choice F, getting a solution of −8. The student makes a sign error in the equation in answer choice G, getting a solution of 8.

   H. Correct answer

   I. The student makes a sign error in the equation in answer choice H, getting a solution of −12. The student makes a sign error in the equation in answer choice I, getting a solution of 12.

9. **Gridded Response:** Correct answer: 10 in.

   Common Error: The student finds the area of each face, getting an answer of 100 inches.

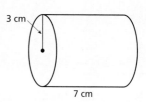

7. C

8. H

9. 10 in.

10. B

Answers for Extra Examples

1. **A.** Correct answer

    B. The student subtracts 36 from 75.

    C. The student finds 75% of 36.

    D. The student finds 75% of 36 and subtracts this result from 36.

2. **F.** The student reflects the figure in the *x*-axis.

    G. Correct answer

    H. The student translates the figure 7 units right.

    I. The student translates the figure 6 units up.

3. **A.** The student multiplies 0.04 by -0.2 instead of -0.02.

    B. Correct answer

    C. The student multiplies 0.04 by 0.02 instead of -0.02.

    D. The student multiplies 0.04 by 0.2 instead of -0.02.

Item Analysis (continued)

10. **A.** The student inverts the slope.

    B. Correct answer

    C. The student inverts the slope and incorrectly adds a negative sign.

    D. The student incorrectly adds a negative sign to the slope.

Extra Examples for Standardized Test Practice

1. Of the people at a party, 75% brought food to share. The host thanked all 36 people who brought food to share. How many people were at the party?

    A. 48   **C.** 27

    B. 39   **D.** 9

2. In the coordinate plane below, $\triangle XYZ$ is plotted and its vertices are labeled.

    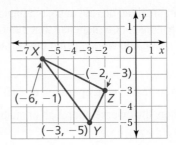

    Which of the following shows $\triangle X'Y'Z'$, the image of $\triangle XYZ$ after it is reflected in the *y*-axis?

    F.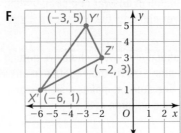

    H.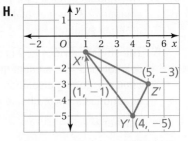

    G.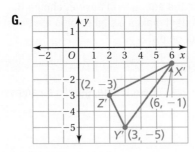

    I.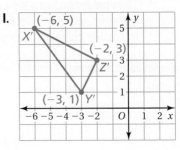

3. What is the next term in the sequence below?

    $$100, -2, 0.04$$

    A. -0.008 **C.** 0.0008

    B. -0.0008 **D.** 0.008

7. Anna was solving the inequality in the box below.

$$18 > -5x + 3$$
$$\underline{-3 \qquad\quad -3}$$
$$15 > -5x$$
$$\frac{15}{-5} > \frac{-5x}{-5}$$
$$-3 > x$$

What should Anna do to correct the error that she made?

A. Add 3 to both sides.

B. Multiply both sides by -5.

C. Reverse the inequality symbol when dividing by -5.

D. Divide both sides by 5.

8. Which equation has the greatest solution?

F. $-3x + 9 = -15$

G. $12 = 2x + 28$

H. $\frac{x}{2} - 13 = -7$

I. $6 = \frac{x}{3} + 10$

9. A cube has a total surface area of 600 square inches. What is the length, in inches, of each edge of the cube?

10. A line contains the two points plotted in the coordinate plane below.

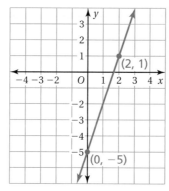

What is the slope of the line?

A. $\frac{1}{3}$

B. 3

C. $-\frac{1}{3}$

D. -3

7 Volumes of Solids

"I petitioned my owner for a dog house with greater volume."

"Add a bunk bed and we can have a sleep over."

"And this is what he built for me."

"This setup is too good to be true."

"Do you know why the volume of a cone is one-third the volume of the cylinder with the same height and base?"

Strands Development

6th Grade
• Define pi as the ratio of circumference to diameter.
• Describe and determine the volume and surface area of a rectangular prism.

7th Grade
• Solve problems involving volume and surface area of rectangular prisms and cylinders.
• Describe how changing one dimension of a rectangular prism affects the surface area and volume.

8th Grade
• Investigate and solve problems involving volume and surface area of prisms, cylinders, cones, and pyramids.
• Describe how changing one dimension of a figure affects the surface area and volume.

Math in History

For over 2500 years, mathematicians have been using the properties of similar triangles to indirectly measure things that were too difficult to measure directly.

★ Thales of Miletus (about 580 B.C.) was visiting the Great Pyramid of Egypt. When he saw the pyramid, he compared the length of its shadow to the length of his own shadow and was able to calculate the height of the pyramid.

★ In ancient China, properties of similar triangles were used in surveying, including the surveying that was used to build the Great Wall of China.

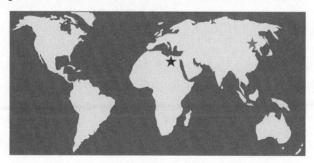

Pacing Guide for Chapter 7

Chapter Opener	1 Day
Section 1 Activity Lesson	 1 Day 1 Day
Section 2 Activity Lesson	 1 Day 1 Day
Section 3 Activity Lesson	 1 Day 1 Day
Section 4 Activity Lesson	 1 Day 1 Day
Study Help / Quiz	1 Day
Section 5 Activity Lesson	 1 Day 1 Day
Section 6 Activity Lesson	 1 Day 2 Days
Chapter Review / Tests	2 Days
Total Chapter 7	17 Days
Year-to-Date	118 Days

Check Your Resources

- Record and Practice Journal
- Resources by Chapter
- Skills Review Handbook
- Assessment Book
- Worked-Out Solutions

Technology For the Teacher

The Dynamic Planning Tool
Editable Teacher's Resources at
BigIdeasMath.com

Standards of Learning

7.6 The student will determine whether plane figures—quadrilaterals and triangles—are similar and write proportions to express the relationships between corresponding sides of similar figures.

Additional Topics for Review

- Simplifying fractions
- Naming similar figures
- Perimeter and area of figures
- Finding volumes of figures without formulas

Try It Yourself

1. *Answer should include, but is not limited to:* drawings of two rectangles with length-to-width ratios of 9 to 4

2. 35 cm

Record and Practice Journal

1. yes; $\dfrac{10}{5} = \dfrac{6}{3}$

2. no; $\dfrac{7}{4} \ne \dfrac{10}{7}$

3. no; $\dfrac{24}{12} \ne \dfrac{7}{5}$

4. yes; $\dfrac{2}{3} = \dfrac{6}{9}$

5. yes; $\dfrac{5}{10} = \dfrac{6}{12}$

6. yes; $\dfrac{12}{9} = \dfrac{20}{15}$

7. no; $\dfrac{3}{1} \ne \dfrac{2}{0.5}$

8. 4   9. 2.4

10. 12   11. 10

12. 20   13. 25

14. $2\dfrac{5}{8}$ in.

Math Background Notes

Vocabulary Review

- Similar
- Cross Products Property
- Corresponding Parts
- Proportional
- Ratio

Identifying Similar Figures

- Students should be able to identify similar figures.
- Remind students that they should check the orientation of the figures before writing ratios. The figures should be oriented in the same way so that corresponding sides are in the same place.
- **Teaching Tip:** Allow students to color code corresponding parts of figures. This will help visual learners to correctly orient and identify similar figures.
- **Teaching Tip:** Tactile learners may struggle with the concept of similar figures. Cut out and laminate several of the same type of polygons with the side measures marked. First, challenge students to orient all the figures in the same direction. Then, ask them to make groups of the polygons that they believe to be similar. Ask them to justify their choices by writing the appropriate ratios and checking the proportionality of the polygons.
- **Common Error:** Students may attempt to write ratios comparing Rectangle B to Rectangle C. Remind them that the goal of the example is to decide which rectangle is similar to Rectangle A, so one measure of Rectangle A should appear in the ratio.

Finding Measures in Similar Figures

- Students should be able to find missing measures in similar figures.
- You may wish to review the corresponding parts of similar figures with students. In Example 2, students need to realize that the figures are not oriented the same. Encourage them to re-draw and re-label one of the figures so that it is oriented in the same fashion as the other.
- **Common Error:** Students may try to write a proportion using the longest side and the base of each triangle, only to realize there are two variables in the proportion. Encourage them to identify the sides of the figure containing the most given information, and then try to write one ratio using this information first.

Reteaching and Enrichment Strategies

If students need help...	If students got it...
Record and Practice Journal • Fair Game Review Skills Review Handbook Lesson Tutorials	Game Closet at *BigIdeasMath.com* Start the next section

What You Learned Before

Number one on America's list of 10 worst ideas.

"I just figured out how to find your volume. We'll immerse you in a barrel of water and measure the water that overflows."

Identifying Similar Figures

Example 1 Which rectangle is similar to Rectangle A?

Rectangle A — 8, 18

Rectangle B — 8, 27

Rectangle C — 12, 27

Rectangle A and Rectangle B

$$\frac{\text{Length of A}}{\text{Length of B}} = \frac{18}{27} = \frac{2}{3} \qquad \frac{\text{Width of A}}{\text{Width of B}} = \frac{8}{8} = 1 \qquad \text{Not proportional}$$

Rectangle A and Rectangle C

$$\frac{\text{Length of A}}{\text{Length of C}} = \frac{18}{27} = \frac{2}{3} \qquad \frac{\text{Width of A}}{\text{Width of C}} = \frac{8}{12} = \frac{2}{3} \qquad \text{Proportional}$$

∴ So, Rectangle C is similar to Rectangle A.

Finding Measures in Similar Figures

Example 2 The two triangles are similar. Find the value of *x*.

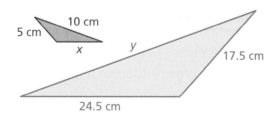

10 cm
5 cm
x
y
17.5 cm
24.5 cm

$$\frac{5}{17.5} = \frac{x}{24.5} \qquad \text{Write a proportion.}$$

$$122.5 = 17.5x \qquad \text{Use Cross Products Property.}$$

$$7 = x \qquad \text{Divide each side by 17.5.}$$

∴ So, *x* is 7 centimeters.

Try It Yourself

1. Construct two more rectangles that are similar to Rectangle A in Example 1.

2. Find the value of *y* in Example 2.

**STANDARDS
OF LEARNING**
8.7

Essential Question How can you find the volume of any prism?

1 ACTIVITY: A Famous Discovery

A famous story tells how Archimedes used volume to solve a royal mystery.

A king had a special gold crown made for himself. Afterward, he suspected that the jeweler had not used 100% gold to make the crown, but had mixed less valuable silver into the molten gold.

The king asked Archimedes if he could prove that the crown was not pure gold without destroying the crown.

When he was taking a bath, it occurred to Archimedes that the amount of water that overflowed out of the tub must have the same volume as his body. With this realization, he jumped out of the tub and ran home shouting "Eureka, I have found it!"

Archimedes (c. 287 B.C.–c. 212 B.C.)

King's Crown

After Archimedes got home, he made two crowns that each had exactly the same weight as the king's new crown.

100% Gold Crown

100% Silver Crown

Work with a partner. Explain how Archimedes used the three crowns to solve the mystery.

Laurie's Notes

Introduction

For the Teacher

- **Goal:** Students will develop an intuitive understanding of how to measure the volume of a prism.
- **Connection:** Students have explored volume and surface area of a prism. They should have a sense that volume is a *filling process* and that it can be found by stacking equal layers on top of one another.

Motivate

- Hold up a variety of common containers and ask what is commonly found inside. Examples: egg carton (12 eggs); playing cards box (52 cards; If you include jokers, then there are 2 additional cards.); crayon box (8 crayons)
- Discuss with students these examples of volume. Each container is filled with objects of the same size. How many eggs fit in the egg carton, or how many crayons fit in the crayon box? Because the units are different (eggs, cards, crayons), you can't compare the volumes.
- Each of the objects (egg, playing card, and crayon) has a volume. When objects are common geometric shapes, their volumes can be found by using a formula. What if the object is not a common geometric shape? This was the problem faced by Archimedes as presented in today's first activity.
- Archimedes was a mathematician who greatly contributed to the subject of geometry. He invented a wide variety of machines including pulleys and the Archimedean screw for pumping water.
- Archimedes was supposedly killed during the capture of Syracuse by the Romans. As the story goes, Archimedes was intently focused on a math problem when a Roman soldier entered his room and commanded him to follow. Archimedes declined, wanting to finish his problem. Then the soldier killed Archimedes with his sword.

Activity Notes

Activity 1

- Give sufficient time for students to write their explanation of what Archimedes discovered.
- **FYI:** The atomic weight of gold is 197.0 and the atomic weight of silver is 107.9. Because gold weighs more than silver, the gold crown is smaller than the silver crown.
- All three crowns shown have the same weight. Students should observe that the silver crown is the largest, followed by the king's crown, and the gold crown is smallest. So, the king's crown must contain a mixture of both gold and silver.
- **?** "Have you measured the volume of an object using a graduated cylinder?"
- **Extension:** Have students write a report about Archimedes that includes a discussion of one of his inventions.

Standards of Learning

8.7(a) The student will investigate and solve practical problems involving volume and surface area of prisms, cylinders, cones, and pyramids.

8.7(b) The student will describe how changing one measured attribute of a figure affects the volume and surface area.

Previous Learning

Students should know how to evaluate expressions and solve one-step equations.

Activity Materials
Introduction
<ul><li>egg carton</li><li>crayon box</li><li>playing cards box</li></ul>

Start Thinking! and Warm Up

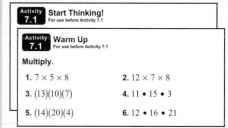

Activity 7.1 Start Thinking!
For use before Activity 7.1

Activity 7.1 Warm Up
For use before Activity 7.1

Multiply.

1. $7 \times 5 \times 8$ 2. $12 \times 7 \times 8$
3. $(13)(10)(7)$ 4. $11 \bullet 15 \bullet 3$
5. $(14)(20)(4)$ 6. $12 \bullet 16 \bullet 21$

7.1 Record and Practice Journal

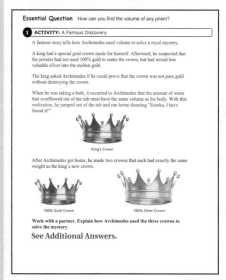

Essential Question How can you find the volume of any prism?

1 ACTIVITY: A Famous Discovery

A famous story tells how Archimedes used volume to solve a royal mystery.

A king had a special gold crown made for himself. Afterward, he suspected that the jeweler had not used 100% gold to make the crown, but had mixed less valuable silver into the molten gold.

The king asked Archimedes if he could prove that the crown was not pure gold without destroying the crown.

When he was taking a bath, it occurred to Archimedes that the amount of water that overflowed out of the tub must have the same volume as his body. With this realization, he jumped out of the tub and ran home shouting "Eureka, I have found it!"

King's Crown

After Archimedes got home, he made two crowns that each had exactly the same weight as the king's new crown.

100% Gold Crown   100% Silver Crown

Work with a partner. Explain how Archimedes used the three crowns to solve the mystery.
See Additional Answers.

Differentiated Instruction

Visual

Students may think that prisms with the same volume have the same surface area. Have them work together to find prisms with the same volume, but different dimensions. Then direct the students to find the surface areas of each of the prisms. Ask them to share their results.

7.1 Record and Practice Journal

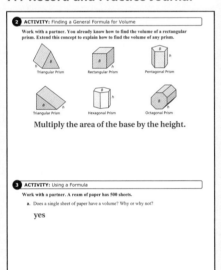

2 ACTIVITY: Finding a General Formula for Volume

Work with a partner. You already know how to find the volume of a rectangular prism. Extend this concept to explain how to find the volume of any prism.

Triangular Prism   Rectangular Prism   Pentagonal Prism

Triangular Prism   Hexagonal Prism   Octagonal Prism

Multiply the area of the base by the height.

3 ACTIVITY: Using a Formula

Work with a partner. A ream of paper has 500 sheets.

a. Does a single sheet of paper have a volume? Why or why not?

yes

b. If so, explain how you can find the volume of a single sheet of paper.
Find the volume of a ream of paper and divide by 500.

What Is Your Answer?

4. IN YOUR OWN WORDS How can you find the volume of any prism? Give examples with your explanation.
Find the area of the base and multiply it by the height of the prism.

5. Draw a prism that has a trapezoid as its base. Use your formula to find the volume of the prism.
Check students' work.

Laurie's Notes

Activity 2

- Students know that the volume V of a rectangular prism is $V = Bh$, where B is the area of the base and h is the height of the prism. Students may or may not be able to reason that the volume of all prisms is $V = Bh$.
- The right triangular prism (lower left) may be one where students can make sense of extending the concept. Putting two of these prisms together would form a rectangular prism with which they already know how to work.
- Having models of these prisms for students to manipulate is very helpful.
- Give students time to discuss the solids in this activity. If you have physical models of each of these, ask six volunteers to describe how to find the volume of each solid. Expect the student volunteer to point to the base and the height of the prism as they give the formula for volume.

Activity 3

- **Common Misconception:** Students may believe a sheet of paper has no height and so, no volume, only area. It may be difficult to measure the height with tools available to us, but a sheet of paper does have a height.
- The ream of copy paper is a good visual model.

What Is Your Answer?

- **Think-Pair-Share:** Students should read each question independently and then work with a partner to answer the questions. When they have answered the questions, the pair should compare their answers with another group and discuss any discrepancies.

Closure

- **Writing Prompt:** To find the volume of a tissue box ...

Technology For the Teacher

Dynamic Classroom

The Dynamic Planning Tool
Editable Teacher's Resources at *BigIdeasMath.com*

2 ACTIVITY: Finding a General Formula for Volume

Work with a partner. You already know how to find the volume of a rectangular prism. Extend this concept to explain how to find the volume of any prism.

Triangular Prism

Rectangular Prism

Pentagonal Prism

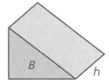

Triangular Prism

Hexagonal Prism

Octagonal Prism

3 ACTIVITY: Using a Formula

Work with a partner. A ream of paper has 500 sheets.

a. Does a single sheet of paper have a volume? Why or why not?

b. If so, explain how you can find the volume of a single sheet of paper.

What Is Your Answer?

4. **IN YOUR OWN WORDS** How can you find the volume of any prism? Give examples with your explanation.

5. Draw a prism that has a trapezoid as its base. Use your formula to find the volume of the prism.

Practice

Use what you learned about the volumes of prisms to complete Exercises 4–6 on page 310.

Key Vocabulary
volume, *p. 308*

The **volume** of a three-dimensional figure is a measure of the amount of space that it occupies. Volume is measured in cubic units.

 Key Idea

Volume of a Prism

Words The volume *V* of a prism is the product of the area of the base and the height of the prism.

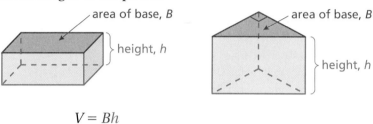

Algebra $V = Bh$

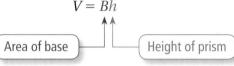

EXAMPLE ① **Finding the Volume of a Prism**

Find the volume of the prism.

> **Study Tip**
>
> The area of the base of a rectangular prism is the product of the length ℓ and the width *w*.
>
> You can use $V = \ell wh$ to find the volume of a rectangular prism.

$V = Bh$	Write formula for volume.
$= 8(6) \cdot 15$	Substitute.
$= 48 \cdot 15$	Simplify.
$= 720$	Multiply.

∴ The volume is 720 cubic yards.

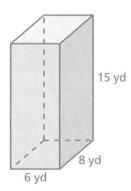

EXAMPLE ② **Finding the Volume of a Prism**

Find the volume of the prism.

$V = Bh$	Write formula for volume.
$= \dfrac{1}{2}(5.5)(2) \cdot 4$	Substitute.
$= 5.5 \cdot 4$	Simplify.
$= 22$	Multiply.

∴ The volume is 22 cubic inches.

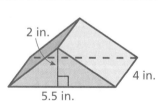

Multi-Language Glossary at BigIdeasMath√com.

Laurie's Notes

Introduction

Connect

- **Yesterday:** Students explored how to find the volume of a prism.
- **Today:** Students will use the formula for the volume of a prism to solve problems.

Motivate

- Display a shoe box and a one-dollar bill.
- ❓ "What is the volume of a million dollars in one dollar bills? Is the volume greater than or less than the shoe box?" Have students discuss before giving them the dimensions.
- The dimensions of a dollar bill are 6.15 inches long, 2.61 inches wide, and 0.0043 inches thick. The dimensions of your shoe box will vary.
- Give students time to determine the volume of a million dollars and compare it to the volume of a shoe box.
- Discuss students' solutions as a class. Students should find that the volume of a million dollars is significantly larger than a shoe box.

Lesson Notes

Key Idea

- ❓ "What is a prism?" three-dimensional solid with two congruent bases and lateral faces that are rectangles
- ❓ "What are cubic units? Give an example." Cubic units are cubes which fill a space completely without overlapping or leaving gaps. Cubic inches and cubic centimeters are common examples.
- Point out to students that the bases of the prisms have been shaded differently. The height will be perpendicular to the two congruent bases.
- **Teaching Tip:** Use words (area of base, height) and symbols (B, h) when writing the formula.
- **Review Vocabulary:** *Product* is the answer to a multiplication problem.

Example 1

- Discuss the *Study Tip* with students.
- ❓ "Could the face measuring 8 yards by 15 yards be the base?" Yes, the height would then be 6 yards.
- **Extension:** Point out to students that all of the measurements are in terms of yards. "What if the 6 yard edge had been labeled 18 feet. Now how would you find the volume?" Convert all 3 dimensions to yards or to feet.

Example 2

- Ask a volunteer to describe the base of this triangular prism.
- ❓ "What property is used to simplify the area of the base?" Commutative Property of Multiplication
- Caution students to distinguish between the height of the base and the height of the prism.

Goal Today's lesson is finding the **volumes** of prisms.

Lesson Materials
Introduction
• shoe box
• $1 bill

Start Thinking! and Warm Up

Lesson 7.1 **Warm Up** For use before Lesson 7.1

Lesson 7.1 **Start Thinking!** For use before Lesson 7.1

You are sending a gift to a friend. Explain how volume would be helpful in figuring out which size box to use to send the gift to your friend.

Extra Example 1

Find the volume of a rectangular prism with a length of 2 meters, a width of 6 meters, and a height of 3 meters. 36 m³

Extra Example 2

Find the volume of the prism.

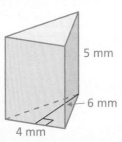

5 mm

6 mm

4 mm

60 mm³

Laurie's Notes

 On Your Own

1. 80 ft³

2. 270 m³

Extra Example 3

Two rectangular prisms each have a volume of 120 cubic centimeters. The base of Prism A is 2 centimeters by 4 centimeters. The base of Prism B is 4 centimeters by 6 centimeters.

a. Find the height of each prism.
   Prism A: 15 cm, Prism B: 5 cm

b. Which prism has the lesser surface area? Prism B

 On Your Own

3. yes; Because it has the same volume as the other two bags, but its surface area is 107.2 square inches which is less than both Bag A and Bag B.

English Language Learners

Vocabulary
Discuss the meaning of the words *volume* and *cubic units*. Have students add these words to their notebooks.

On Your Own

• Ask volunteers to share their work at the board.

Example 3

• This example connects volume, surface area, and solving equations.
• Ask a student to read the example.
 "What type of measurement is 96 cubic inches?" volume
? "What concept does part (b) refer to?" surface area
• Work through part (a).
• Before beginning part (b), ask students to review the formula for surface area of a rectangular prism. Note that only five of the six faces are considered.
• Work through part (b).
? "Both bags hold the same amount of popcorn. Are there any practical advantages of one bag over the other?" Bag A: can grip it in your hand more easily; Bag B: less likely to tip over and uses less paper

On Your Own

• Given the discussion of the practical features of Bags A and B, students should have a sense of the problems in the design of Bag C.

Closure

• Sketch a rectangular prism. Label the dimensions 4 centimeters, 6 centimeters, and 10 centimeters. Find the volume of the prism.
$V = 4 \cdot 6 \cdot 10 = 240$ cm³

The Dynamic Planning Tool
Editable Teacher's Resources at *BigIdeasMath.com*

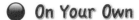

On Your Own

Now You're Ready
Exercises 4–12

Find the volume of the prism.

1.

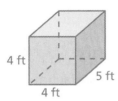

4 ft

5 ft

4 ft

2.

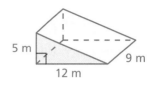

5 m

9 m

12 m

EXAMPLE 3 Real-Life Application

A movie theater designs two bags to hold 96 cubic inches of popcorn. (a) Find the height of each bag. (b) Which bag should the theater choose to reduce the amount of paper needed? Explain.

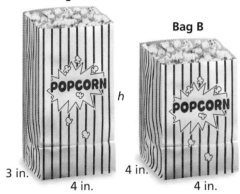

Bag A

Bag B

h

h

3 in.

4 in.

4 in.

4 in.

a. Find the height of each bag.

Bag A	**Bag B**
$V = Bh$	$V = Bh$
$96 = 4(3)(h)$	$96 = 4(4)(h)$
$96 = 12h$	$96 = 16h$
$8 = h$	$6 = h$
∴ The height is 8 inches.	∴ The height is 6 inches.

b. To determine the amount of paper needed, find the surface area of each bag. Do not include the top base.

Bag A	**Bag B**
$S = \ell w + 2\ell h + 2wh$	$S = \ell w + 2\ell h + 2wh$
$= 4(3) + 2(4)(8) + 2(3)(8)$	$= 4(4) + 2(4)(6) + 2(4)(6)$
$= 12 + 64 + 48$	$= 16 + 48 + 48$
$= 124 \text{ in.}^2$	$= 112 \text{ in.}^2$

∴ The surface area of Bag B is less than the surface area of Bag A. So, the theater should choose Bag B.

On Your Own

Bag C

3. You design Bag C that has a volume of 96 cubic inches. Should the theater in Example 3 choose your bag? Explain.

h

4 in.

4.8 in.

 ## Vocabulary and Concept Check

1. **VOCABULARY** What types of units are used to describe volume?

2. **CRITICAL THINKING** How are volume and surface area different?

3. **CRITICAL THINKING** You are ordering packaging for a product. Should you be more concerned with volume or surface area? Explain.

 ## Practice and Problem Solving

Find the volume of the prism.

 4.
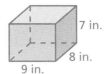
7 in.
8 in.
9 in.

5.
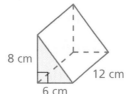
8 cm
12 cm
6 cm

6.

8 m
7 m
4 m

7.
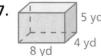
5 yd
4 yd
8 yd

8.

6 ft
9 ft
4.5 ft

9.
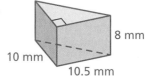
8 mm
10 mm
10.5 mm

10.
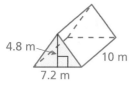
4.8 m
10 m
7.2 m

11.
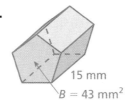
15 mm
$B = 43 \text{ mm}^2$

12.
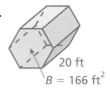
20 ft
$B = 166 \text{ ft}^2$

13. **ERROR ANALYSIS** Describe and correct the error in finding the volume of the triangular prism.

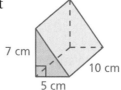
7 cm
10 cm
5 cm

$$
\begin{aligned}
V &= Bh \\
&= 10(5)(7) \\
&= 50 \cdot 7 \\
&= 350 \text{ cm}^3
\end{aligned}
$$

School Locker

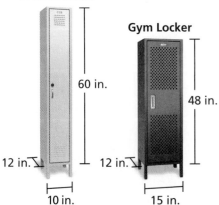
60 in.
Gym Locker
48 in.
12 in.
12 in.
10 in.
15 in.

14. **LOCKER** Each locker is shaped like a rectangular prism. Which has more storage space? Explain.

15. **CEREAL BOX** A cereal box is 9 inches by 2.5 inches by 10 inches. What is the volume of the box?

Assignment Guide and Homework Check

Level	Day 1 Activity Assignment	Day 2 Lesson Assignment	Homework Check
Basic	4–6, 25–28	1–3, 7–15, 17	7, 10, 14, 17
Average	4–6, 25–28	1–3, 7–15 odd, 16–20	7, 9, 16, 18
Advanced	4–6, 25–28	1–3, 13, 16–24	16, 18, 22, 23

Common Errors

- **Exercises 4–12** Students may write the units incorrectly, often writing square units instead of cubic units. Remind them that they are working in three dimensions, so the units are cubed. Give an example showing the formula for the base as three units multiplied together. For example, write the volume of Exercise 5 as $V = \frac{1}{2}(6\text{ cm})(8\text{ cm})(12\text{ cm})$.

7.1 Record and Practice Journal

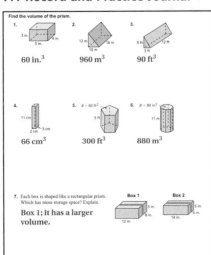

Vocabulary and Concept Check

1. cubic units

2. The volume of an object is the amount of space it occupies. The surface area of an object is the sum of the areas of all its faces.

3. *Sample answers:* Volume because you want to make sure the product will fit inside the package. Surface area because of the cost of packaging.

Practice and Problem Solving

4. 504 in.³   5. 288 cm³

6. 224 m³   7. 160 yd³

8. 121.5 ft³   9. 420 mm³

10. 172.8 m³   11. 645 mm³

12. 3320 ft³

13. The area of the base is wrong.
$$V = \frac{1}{2}(7)(5) \cdot 10$$
$$= 175 \text{ cm}^3$$

14. The gym locker has more storage space because it has a greater volume.

15. 225 in.³

16. 1440 in.³

17. 7200 ft³

18. sometimes; The prisms in Example 3 have different surface areas, but the same volume. Two prisms that are exactly the same will have the same surface area.

Practice and Problem Solving

19. 1728 in.³

$1 \times 1 \times 1 = 1$ ft³

$12 \times 12 \times 12 = 1728$ in.³

20. 48 packets

21. 20 cm

22. *Sample answer:* gas about $3 per gallon; $36

23. See *Taking Math Deeper.*

24. The volume is 2 times greater; The volume is 8 times greater.

Fair Game Review

25. reflection

26. translation

27. rotation   **28.** D

Mini-Assessment

Find the volume of the prism.

1.   **2.**

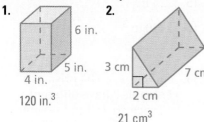

120 in.³   21 cm³

3. Find the volume of the fish tank.

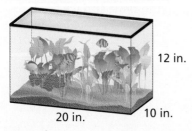

2400 in.³

T-311

Taking Math Deeper

Exercise 23

This problem gives students a chance to relate dimensions of a solid with the volume of a solid. It also gives students an opportunity to work with prime factorization. Although aquariums are traditionally the shape of a rectangular prism, remember that other shapes are also possible.

1 Find the volume of the aquarium in cubic inches.

$$\text{Volume} = (450 \text{ gal})\left(231 \frac{\text{in.}^3}{\text{gal}}\right) = 103{,}950 \text{ in.}^3$$

2 You could choose two of the dimensions and solve for the third, or you can use prime factorization to find whole number solutions.

Find the prime factorization of 103,950.

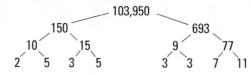

The prime factorization is $2 \times 3 \times 3 \times 3 \times 5 \times 5 \times 7 \times 11$.

3 Rearrange the factors to find one set of possible dimensions.

Length: $2 \times 3 \times 5 \times 5 = 150$ in.
Width: $3 \times 7 = 21$ in.
Height: $3 \times 11 = 33$ in.

A long tank

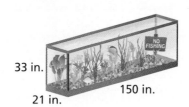

33 in.   150 in.
21 in.

Project

Research a local aquarium. Write a short report about one of the exhibits. Include a picture of the exhibit.

Reteaching and Enrichment Strategies

If students need help. . .	If students got it. . .
Resources by Chapter • Practice A and Practice B • Puzzle Time Record and Practice Journal Practice Differentiating the Lesson Lesson Tutorials Skills Review Handbook	Resources by Chapter • Enrichment and Extension Start the next section

Find the volume of the prism.

16.

12 in.

12 in.   10 in.

17.

24 ft

30 ft

20 ft

18. **REASONING** Two prisms have the same volume. Do they *always*, *sometimes*, or *never* have the same surface area? Explain.

19. **CUBIC UNITS** How many cubic inches are in a cubic foot? Use a sketch to explain your reasoning.

20. **CAPACITY** As a gift, you fill the calendar with packets of chocolate candy. Each packet has a volume of 2 cubic inches. Find the maximum number of packets you can fit inside the calendar.

6 in.

8 in.   4 in.

21. **HEIGHT** Two liters of water are poured into an empty vase shaped like an octagonal prism. The base area is 100 square centimeters. What is the height of the water? (1 L = 1000 cm^3)

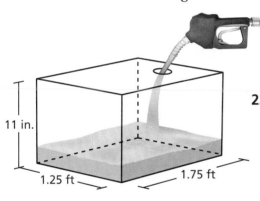

11 in.

1.25 ft   1.75 ft

22. **GAS TANK** The gas tank is 20% full. Use the current price of gas in your community to find the cost to fill the tank. (1 gal = 231 in.^{3})

23. **OPEN-ENDED** You visit an aquarium. One of the tanks at the aquarium holds 450 gallons of water. Draw a diagram to show one possible set of dimensions of the tank. (1 gal = 231 in.^{3})

24. **Critical Thinking** How many times greater is the volume of a triangular prism when one of its dimensions is doubled? when all three dimensions are doubled?

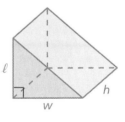

ℓ h

w

Fair Game Review What you learned in previous grades & lessons

Identify the transformation. *(Skills Review Handbook)*

25.   **26.**   **27.**

28. **MULTIPLE CHOICE** What is the approximate surface area of a cylinder with a radius of 3 inches and a height of 10 inches? *(Section 6.3)*

Ⓐ 30 in.^{2} Ⓑ 87 in.^{2} Ⓒ 217 in.^{2} Ⓓ 245 in.^{2}

STANDARDS OF LEARNING

8.7

Essential Question How can you find a pattern for changes in volume that occur in nature?

1   ACTIVITY: A Research Project by Descartes

The French mathematician René Descartes was fascinated by the shell of a chambered nautilus.

In one of his experiments, Descartes measured the volumes of several of the chambers to try to find a pattern for the changes in volume.

Work with a partner.

a. Explain how Descartes might have measured the volumes of the different chambers.

b. What is meant by "using mathematics to model a real-life situation"?

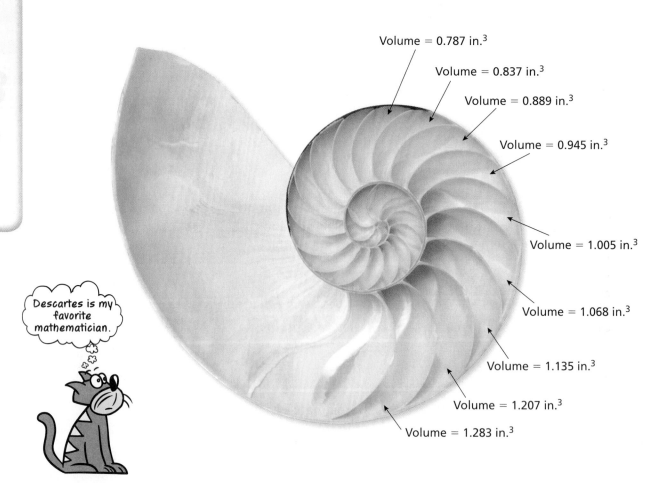

Volume = 0.787 in.^{3}

Volume = 0.837 in.^{3}

Volume = 0.889 in.^{3}

Volume = 0.945 in.^{3}

Volume = 1.005 in.^{3}

Volume = 1.068 in.^{3}

Volume = 1.135 in.^{3}

Volume = 1.207 in.^{3}

Volume = 1.283 in.^{3}

Descartes is my favorite mathematician.

Laurie's Notes

Introduction

For the Teacher

- **Goal:** Students will review the formula for volume of a cylinder.

Motivate

- To pique student interest, share a bit of the history of René Descartes.
- Descartes lived from 1596 to 1650. One of his important contributions to mathematics was the development of Cartesian geometry, which connects algebra and geometry.
- Because of his delicate health, he would lie in bed until late in the morning. This was a custom that he always followed. When he visited Blaise Pascal, another French mathematician, Descartes told him that the only way he could do good work in mathematics and preserve his health is to never get up in the morning before he felt inclined to do so.
- One popular story about Descartes is that while in bed, he noticed a fly crawling around on the ceiling. He watched the fly for a long time. He wondered how he could tell someone else where the fly was. Finally, he realized that he could describe the position of the fly by its distance from the walls of the room. When he got out of bed, Descartes wrote down what he had discovered. Then he described the positions of points in the same way he described the position of the fly. Descartes had invented the coordinate plane!

Activity Notes

Activity 1

- If you have a chambered nautilus shell, display it for students to see.
- The photo of the graduated cylinder is a clue to help students answer part (a).
- **?** "How big is a cubic inch?" Students should be able to model the approximate size of a 1-inch cube with their fingers.
- **?** After students have discussed and shared their ideas ask, "Besides water, what else might Descartes have used to measure the volumes of the different chambers?" Students may suggest to fill the chambers with sand.
- Knowing the topic for tomorrow's lesson, some students may comment that the volume can be measured using a *cylindrical* measuring device! Certainly the volume of a cylinder can be measured using a quantity of liquid and then convert it to cubic units.

Standards of Learning

8.7(a) The student will investigate and solve practical problems involving volume and surface area of prisms, cylinders, cones, and pyramids.

8.7(b) The student will describe how changing one measured attribute of a figure affects the volume and surface area.

Previous Learning

Students have found volumes of cylinders.

Activity Materials
Textbook
• chambered nautilus shell

Start Thinking! and Warm Up

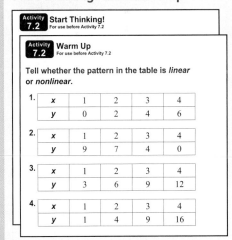

| **Activity 7.2** | **Start Thinking!** For use before Activity 7.2 |

| **Activity 7.2** | **Warm Up** For use before Activity 7.2 |

Tell whether the pattern in the table is *linear* or *nonlinear*.

1.

x	1	2	3	4
y	0	2	4	6

2.

x	1	2	3	4
y	9	7	4	0

3.

x	1	2	3	4
y	3	6	9	12

4.

x	1	2	3	4
y	1	4	9	16

7.2 Record and Practice Journal

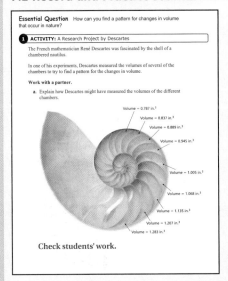

Essential Question How can you find a pattern for changes in volume that occur in nature?

1 ACTIVITY: A Research Project by Descartes

The French mathematician René Descartes was fascinated by the shell of a chambered nautilus.

In one of his experiments, Descartes measured the volumes of several of the chambers to try to find a pattern for the changes in volume.

Work with a partner.

a. Explain how Descartes might have measured the volumes of the different chambers.

Volume = 0.787 in.³
Volume = 0.837 in.³
Volume = 0.889 in.³
Volume = 0.945 in.³
Volume = 1.005 in.³
Volume = 1.068 in.³
Volume = 1.135 in.³
Volume = 1.207 in.³
Volume = 1.283 in.³

Check students' work.

Money

Have students bring in round coins of different denominations. If possible, have English learners bring in coins from their country of origin. Have students find the volume of a stack of each type of coin. Ask volunteers to discuss how they obtained their results, and how their results are related to the volume of a cylinder with the same dimensions as the stack.

7.2 Record and Practice Journal

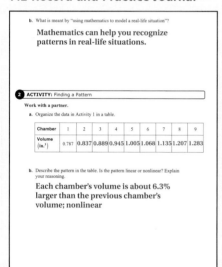

b. What is meant by "using mathematics to model a real-life situation"?

Mathematics can help you recognize patterns in real-life situations.

2 ACTIVITY: Finding a Pattern

Work with a partner.

a. Organize the data in Activity 1 in a table.

Chamber	1	2	3	4	5	6	7	8	9
Volume (in.³)	0.787	0.837	0.889	0.945	1.005	1.068	1.135	1.207	1.283

b. Describe the pattern in the table. Is the pattern linear or nonlinear? Explain your reasoning.

Each chamber's volume is about 6.3% larger than the previous chamber's volume; nonlinear

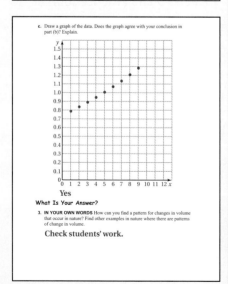

c. Draw a graph of the data. Does the graph agree with your conclusion in part (b)? Explain.

Yes

What Is Your Answer?

3. **IN YOUR OWN WORDS** How can you find a pattern for changes in volume that occur in nature? Find other examples in nature where there are patterns of change in volume.

Check students' work.

Laurie's Notes

Activity 2

? "What do you notice about the scales on the axes?" They are different.

? "Why should different scales be used?" The *y*-coordinates (range values) of the data points are very close. Using a smaller scale spreads out the data.

- Form two groups of students—those who believe that the pattern is linear and those who do not. Give each group a chance to explain their reasoning.

- From the table of values, students may only check a couple of points and conclude that the volume is increasing by about 0.08 or 0.07 cubic inch each time. If they find the difference in volume between each successive pair of chambers, they will find that the volumes increase by greater and greater amounts.

- If students plot the data by hand, they will likely say that the data are linear. If they use a graphing calculator or spreadsheet application, they may say that the data form a slight curve.

- Remind students that functions can be linear or nonlinear. Although the graph may appear linear, there is a curve. Furthermore, the rate of change can be calculated and if students do so, they will see that the rate of change is increasing.

What Is Your Answer?

- Question 3 can be assigned for homework.

Closure

- Describe how you might find the volume of a clam shell. Answers will vary.

Technology For the Teacher

The Dynamic Planning Tool
Editable Teacher's Resources at *BigIdeasMath.com*

ACTIVITY: Finding a Pattern

Work with a partner.

a. Organize the data in Activity 1 in a table.

Chamber	1	2	3	4	5	6	7	8	9
Volume (in.³)	0.787								

b. Describe the pattern in the table. Is the pattern linear or nonlinear? Explain your reasoning.

c. Draw a graph of the data. Does the graph agree with your conclusion in part (b)? Explain.

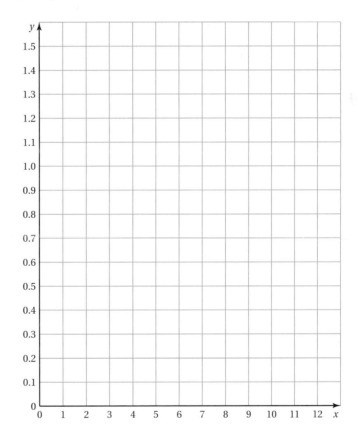

What Is Your Answer?

3. How can you find a pattern for changes in volume that occur in nature? Find other examples in nature where there are patterns of change in volume.

Practice

Use what you learned about volumes of cylinders to complete Exercises 3–5 on page 316.

Key Idea

Volume of a Cylinder

Words   The volume *V* of a cylinder is the
product of the area of the base
and the height of the cylinder.

area of base, *B*

height, *h*

Algebra $V = Bh$

Area of base   Height of cylinder

EXAMPLE 1   Finding the Volume of a Cylinder

Find the volume of the cylinder. Round your answer to the nearest tenth.

Study Tip

Because $B = \pi r^2$,
you can use $V = \pi r^2 h$
to find the volume of
a cylinder.

$V = Bh$ Write formula for volume.

$\quad = \pi(8)^2(4)$ Substitute.

$\quad = 256\pi \approx 803.8$ Simplify.

8 cm

4 cm

∴ The volume is about 803.8 cubic centimeters.

EXAMPLE 2   Finding the Height of a Cylinder

**Find the height of the cylinder. Round your answer to the nearest
whole number.**

The diameter is 5 inches. So, the radius is 2.5 inches.

$V = Bh$ Write formula for volume.

$157 = \pi(2.5)^2(h)$ Substitute.

$157 = 6.25\pi h$ Simplify.

$\quad 8 \approx h$ Divide each side by 6.25π.

h

5 in.

Volume = 157 in.³

∴ The height is about 8 inches.

On Your Own

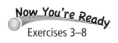

Exercises 3–8

**Find the volume *V* or height *h* of the cylinder. Round your answer to
the nearest tenth.**

1.

9 yd

8 yd

$V \approx$

2.

4 m

$h \approx$

Volume = 62.8 m³

Laurie's Notes

Introduction

Connect

- **Yesterday:** Students explored a method of finding the volume of a non-standard shape.
- **Today:** Students will work with a formula for the volume of a cylinder.

Motivate

- A national magazine named the University of Virginia the second best public university in the country. The university has ranked either first or second since 1992, and among the top 25 since the rankings first came out.
- The Commons is a cylindrical building at the University of Virginia. The Commons features a lecture hall and a coffee shop. A grassy terrace that stretches over Jefferson Park Avenue connects it to New Cabell Hall.
- ❓ "Why do you think the university would build a cylindrical building?"

Lesson Notes

Key Idea

- ❓ "How are cylinders and rectangular prisms alike?" two congruent bases and a lateral portion
- ❓ "How are cylinders and rectangular prisms different?" Cylinders have circular bases while rectangular prisms have rectangular bases.
- Write the formula in words and symbols.

Example 1

- Model good problem solving by writing the formula first.
- Notice that the values of the variables are substituted, simplified, and left in terms of π. The last step is to substitute 3.14 for π.
- ❓ Write "≈" on the board. "What does this symbol mean?" approximately equal to "Why do you use this symbol?" π is an irrational number.

Example 2

- Students may not remember how to divide 157 by 6.25π. One way is to find the product 6.25π, and then divide 157 by the product. The other way is to divide 157 by π, 3.14, and then divide that answer by 6.25.

On Your Own

- Students should work the problems alone and then check with a neighbor.

Goal Today's lesson is describing how changing the dimensions of a cylinder affects the volume.

Activity Materials
Textbook
• tennis ball can • soft drink can

Start Thinking! and Warm Up

 Lesson 7.2 Warm Up For use before Lesson 7.2

 Lesson 7.2 Start Thinking! For use before Lesson 7.2

Suppose you had two cans of corn. The net weight of one can is 14.7 ounces. The net weight of the other can is 29 ounces. Net weight is the weight of the contents and does not include the weight of the can.

Would you expect the volume of one can to be about twice that of the other can? Explain.

If two cans with the same net weight contained two different products, would you expect them to have equal volumes?

Extra Example 1

Find the volume of a cylinder with a radius of 3 feet and a height of 6 feet. Round your answer to the nearest tenth. $54\pi \approx 169.6 \text{ ft}^3$

Extra Example 2

Find the height of a cylinder with a diameter of 10 yards and a volume of 325 cubic yards. Round your answer to the nearest whole number. $\frac{13}{\pi} \approx 4 \text{ yd}$

On Your Own

1. $648\pi \approx 2034.7 \text{ yd}^3$

2. $\frac{15.7}{\pi} \approx 5.0 \text{ m}$

Laurie's Notes

Extra Example 3

In Example 3, does doubling the *radius* of Cylinder *A* (a) double its volume? (b) double its surface area? Explain.

a. no; The volume is 4 times greater.

b. no; The surface area is about 2.7 times greater.

Extra Example 4

In Example 4, how many times greater is the volume of the bottom layer than the volume of the top layer? The volume of the bottom layer is 64 times greater than the volume of the top layer.

On Your Own

3. a. yes; The volume is 3 times greater.

b. no; The surface area is about 2.3 times greater.

4. The volume of the bottom layer is 8 times greater than the volume of the middle layer.

English Language Learners

Vocabulary

Discuss the differences in the meanings of the words *volume, capacity,* and *cubic units*. *Volume* is the amount of space an object occupies. All solid objects have a volume, and it is measured in *cubic units*. *Capacity* is the amount of material a container can hold and it is measured in liquid measures, such as *liters* or *gallons*.

Example 3

- Students should be familiar with this type of problem. They solved similar problems involving the effect of changing dimensions on surface area only.
- **Representation:** If you have a tennis ball can and a soft drink can, use them as models. These cans have approximately the same radius, and a tennis ball can is about twice the height of a soft drink can.
- **?** "What should the units be for the volumes?" cubic millimeters "surface areas?" square millimeters
- In each case, write the formula first, and then substitute the variables.
- Note that it may be easier for students to compare the volumes and surface areas when each is left in terms of π, as shown.
- **?** "Why can the units be divided out in each ratio?" They are the same.
- Point out that the lateral surface area doubled, but the surface area of the bases did not change. So, the total surface area did not double.

Example 4

- **FYI:** A Quinceañera is a fifteenth birthday celebration for girls of Hispanic descent. Long ago, the celebration signaled a girl's readiness for marriage. Now it is a more of a celebration of the journey into adulthood. A religious ceremony is typically followed by a reception with a catered meal and, of course, a cake.
- Ask a volunteer to read the problem. Check for student understanding.
- **?** "How do you find the dimensions of the middle and top layers?" Divide the dimensions of the bottom layer by 2 to find the dimensions of the middle layer. Then divide the dimensions of the middle layer by 2 to find the dimensions of the top layer.
- As in Example 3, the volumes are left in terms of π.

On Your Own

- Give students sufficient time to work through these problems. Then ask volunteers to share their work at the board.

Closure

- Compare the volume of Cylinder A, which has a radius of 2 and a height of 4, to the volume of Cylinder B, which has a radius of 4 and a height of 2. The volume of Cylinder B is twice the volume of Cylinder A.

Technology **F**or the **T**eacher

The Dynamic Planning Tool
Editable Teacher's Resources at *BigIdeasMath.com*

EXAMPLE 3 **Changing One Dimension of a Cylinder**

Does doubling the height of the cylinder (a) double its volume?
(b) double its surface area? Explain.

Cylinder A

10 mm

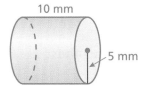

5 mm

Cylinder B

20 mm

5 mm

Cylinder A

a. $V = Bh = \pi(5)^2(10)$
    $= 250\pi \text{ mm}^3$

 The ratio of the volumes is $\dfrac{500\pi \text{ mm}^2}{250\pi \text{ mm}^2} = 2$. So, doubling
the height of the cylinder doubles the volume.

b. $S = 2\pi r^2 + 2\pi rh$
    $= 2\pi(5)^2 + 2\pi(5)(10)$
    $= 50\pi + 100\pi = 150\pi \text{ mm}^2$

Cylinder B

$V = Bh = \pi(5)^2(20)$
$= 500\pi \text{ mm}^3$

$S = 2\pi r^2 + 2\pi rh$
$= 2\pi(5)^2 + 2\pi(5)(20)$
$= 50\pi + 200\pi = 250\pi \text{ mm}^2$

The ratio of the surface areas is $\dfrac{250\pi \text{ mm}^2}{150\pi \text{ mm}^2} \approx 1.7$. So, doubling
the height of the cylinder does *not* double the surface area.

EXAMPLE 4 **Real-Life Application**

The cylindrical bottom layer of a Quinceañera cake has a radius of
8 inches and a height of 4 inches. The dimensions of each of the other
layers are one-half of the dimensions of the layer beneath. How many
times greater is the volume of the middle layer than the volume of the
top layer?

Middle Layer

$r = 8\left(\dfrac{1}{2}\right) = 4,\ h = 4\left(\dfrac{1}{2}\right) = 2$

$V = Bh$
$= \pi(4)^2(2)$
$= 32\pi \text{ in.}^3$

Top Layer

$r = 4\left(\dfrac{1}{2}\right) = 2,\ h = 2\left(\dfrac{1}{2}\right) = 1$

$V = Bh$
$= \pi(2)^2(1)$
$= 4\pi \text{ in.}^3$

The ratio of the volumes is $\dfrac{32\pi \text{ in.}^3}{4\pi \text{ in.}^3} = 8$. So, the volume of the middle
layer is 8 times greater than the volume of the top layer.

On Your Own

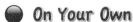

Now You're Ready
Exercises 11 and 12

3. In Example 3, does tripling the height (a) triple the volume?
    (b) triple the surface area? Explain.

4. In Example 4, how many times greater is the volume of the
    bottom layer than the volume of the middle layer?

 Vocabulary and Concept Check

1. **VOCABULARY** How are the formulas for surface area and volume of a cylinder the same? different?

2. **WHICH ONE DOESN'T BELONG?** Which formula does *not* belong with the other three? Explain your reasoning.

$$V = \pi r^2 h \qquad V = Bh \qquad V = \ell w h \qquad V = \pi\left(\frac{d}{2}\right)^2 h$$

 Practice and Problem Solving

Find the volume of the cylinder. Round your answer to the nearest tenth.

 3.

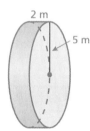
2 m
5 m

4.

9.5 in.
11 in.

5.

4 mm
0.5 mm

Find the volume V or height h of the cylinder. Round your answer to the nearest tenth.

6.

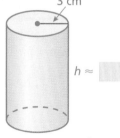
3 cm
$h \approx$ ▢
Volume = 254.3 cm³

7.

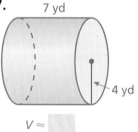
7 yd
4 yd
$V \approx$ ▢

8.

9 in.
$h \approx$ ▢
Volume = 890.2 in.³

9. **ERROR ANALYSIS** Describe and correct the error in finding the volume of the cylinder.

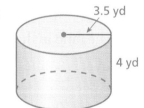
3.5 yd
4 yd

✗ $V = Bh$
$= (3.5)^2(4)$
$= 49 \text{ yd}^3$

5 in.
2.75 in.

10. **BLANK CDS** You purchase a case of blank CDs.

   a. Find the volume of the case.

   b. Each CD has a volume of about 1.2 cubic inches. How many CDs can fit into the case?

Assignment Guide and Homework Check

Level	Day 1 Activity Assignment	Day 2 Lesson Assignment	Homework Check
Basic	3–5, 17–20	1, 2, 6, 7, 9–12, 14	7, 9, 12, 14
Average	3–5, 17–20	1, 2, 6, 8, 9, 11–15	8, 9, 13, 14
Advanced	3–5, 17–20	1, 2, 6, 8, 9, 11–16	8, 9, 13, 16

Common Errors

- **Exercises 3–5, 7, 9, 10, and 14** Students may write the incorrect units for volume or surface area. Remind them that volume is measured in cubic units and surface area is measured in square units.
- **Exercises 3–8, 10–14** Students may forget to square the radius when finding the area of the base. Remind them of the formula for the area of a circle.
- **Exercises 8, 10, and 14** Students may use the diameter in the formula for the area of a circle instead of finding the radius. Encourage them to write the dimensions that are given. For instance, a student could write: diameter = 5 in., height = 2.75 in.
- **Exercise 14** Students may correctly determine the volume of each jar, but write inverted unit rates, that is, they may find cubic inches per dollar instead of dollars per cubic inch. Point out that because they are being asked to find the better buy, students should determine which jar has the lower price per unit volume.

7.2 Record and Practice Journal

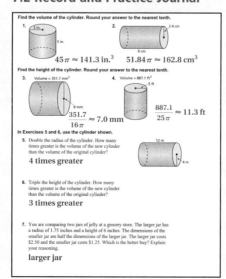

Vocabulary and Concept Check

1. Both formulas use the cylinder height and area of the base; In the formula for volume, the area of the base is multiplied by the height, but in the formula for surface area, the area of the base is doubled and added to the lateral surface area.

2. $V = \ell wh$ does not belong because it is the only formula of the four that cannot be used to find the volume of a cylinder.

Practice and Problem Solving

3. $50\pi \approx 157.0 \text{ m}^3$

4. $992.75\pi \approx 3117.2 \text{ in.}^3$

5. $\pi \approx 3.1 \text{ mm}^3$

6. $\dfrac{254.3}{9\pi} \approx 9.0 \text{ cm}$

7. $112\pi \approx 351.7 \text{ yd}^3$

8. $\dfrac{890.2}{20.25\pi} \approx 14.0 \text{ in.}$

9. The area of the base should have a factor of π.
   $$\begin{aligned} V &= Bh \\ &= \pi(3.5)^2(4) \\ &= 49\pi \approx 153.9 \text{ yd}^3 \end{aligned}$$

10. **a.** $17.1875\pi \approx 54.0 \text{ in.}^3$
    b. 44 CDs

11. The volume is 4 times greater.

12. The volume is 3 times greater.

13. Yes, the ratio of the volumes is a constant. No, depending on the values of r and h, the ratio of the surface areas may *not* be a constant.

14. The first jar; The price of the first jar is about $0.08 per cubic inch, and the price of the second jar is about $0.11 per cubic inch.

15. See *Taking Math Deeper.*

16. See *Additional Answers.*

Fair Game Review

17. $x \geq 3$;

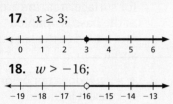

18. $w > -16$;

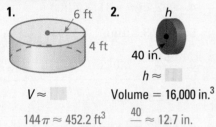

19. See *Additional Answers.*

20. D

Mini-Assessment

Find the volume *V* or height *h* of the cylinder. Round your answer to the nearest tenth.

1. 6 ft

4 ft

$V \approx$ ▭

$144\pi \approx 452.2 \text{ ft}^3$

2. h

40 in.

$h \approx$ ▭

Volume = 16,000 in.³

$\dfrac{40}{\pi} \approx 12.7$ in.

3. Does doubling the height of the cylinder (a) double its volume? (b) double its surface area? Explain.

7 cm

5 cm

a. yes; The volume is 2 times greater.
b. no; The surface area is about 1.4 times greater.

4. A wedding cake has three cylindrical layers. The bottom layer has a radius of 16 inches and a height of 8 inches. The dimensions of each of the other layers are one-half of the dimensions of the layer beneath. How many times greater is the volume of the middle layer than the volume of the top layer? The volume of the middle layer is 8 times greater than the volume of the top layer.

Taking Math Deeper

Exercise 15

The difficulty in this problem is (1) remembering to keep the two systems of measurement distinct (cubic inches and fluid ounces) and (2) keeping all of the information organized.

① Find the volume of the cooler.

$$V = \pi r^2 h$$
$$= \pi (4.5)^2 (16)$$
$$= 324\pi$$
$$\approx 1017.4 \text{ in.}^3$$
$$\approx 610.4 \text{ fl oz } (1 \text{ in.}^3 \approx 0.6 \text{ fl oz})$$
$$\approx 76.3 \text{ cups } (1 \text{ cup} = 8 \text{ fl oz})$$

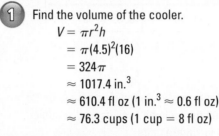
4.5 in.

16 in.

② a. One scoop of mix is needed for 8 cups of water. Because the cooler holds about 76 cups, you need almost 10 scoops of mix.

Water   Mix

b. After using one-fourth of the drink in the cooler, you have used about 19 cups. When you refill the cooler with 19 cups of water, you should add about 2 more scoops of the mix.

③ A cooler that has one-half the dimensions of the cooler shown is a *much smaller* cooler. With a scale factor of one-half, the volume is reduced to $\left(\dfrac{1}{2}\right)^3$ or one-eighth of the volume of the original cooler.

Too small

So, you need to fill the smaller cooler 8 times to have as much of the drink as you had with the larger cooler.

Reteaching and Enrichment Strategies

If students need help. . .	If students got it. . .
Resources by Chapter • Practice A and Practice B • Puzzle Time Record and Practice Journal Practice Differentiating the Lesson Lesson Tutorials Skills Review Handbook	Resources by Chapter • Enrichment and Extension Start the next section

In Exercises 11 and 12, use the cylinder shown.

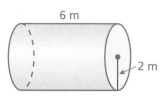

6 m

③ **11.** Double the radius of the cylinder. How many times greater is the volume of the new cylinder than the volume of the original cylinder?

2 m

12. Triple the height of the cylinder. How many times greater is the volume of the new cylinder than the volume of the original cylinder?

13. REASONING Are your results in Exercises 11 and 12 true for any cylinder? Are these results true for surface area? Explain.

5 in.

1.5 in.

6 in.

5 in.

14. PEANUT BUTTER You are comparing two jars of peanut butter at the grocery store. Which is the better buy? Explain your reasoning.

$8.99

$3.99

4.5 in.

15. SPORTS COOLER You are making a sports drink for a soccer game. (1 in.^{3} ≈ 0.6 fluid ounce)

a. Each scoop of drink mix needs to be combined with 8 cups of water. Approximately how many scoops of mix do you need to fill the cooler with the sports drink?

b. Halfway through the game, $\frac{1}{4}$ of the sports drink is gone. Approximately how many scoops of mix are needed to refill the cooler with the sports drink?

16 in.

c. At the next game, you use a smaller cooler with dimensions that are one-half the dimensions of the cooler shown. How many times do you need to fill the smaller cooler to have the same amount of sports drink as in part (a)?

16. *Critical Thinking* How does the given change affect the volume and surface area of a cylinder?

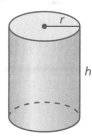

r

h

a. Height doubles
b. Height triples
c. Both dimensions double
d. Both dimensions triple

Fair Game Review *What you learned in previous grades & lessons*

Solve the inequality. Graph the solution. *(Section 1.7)*

17. $2x + 8 \geq 14$

18. $\frac{w}{-4} + 7 < 11$

19. $17.5 \leq -1.5 - 3y$

20. MULTIPLE CHOICE What is the surface area of the regular pyramid? *(Section 6.4)*

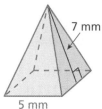

7 mm

5 mm

Ⓐ 42.5 mm^2
Ⓑ 60 mm^2
Ⓒ 77.5 mm^2
Ⓓ 95 mm^2

7.3 Volumes of Pyramids

STANDARDS
OF LEARNING
8.7

Essential Question How can you find the volume of a pyramid?

1 ACTIVITY: Finding a Formula Experimentally

Work with a partner.

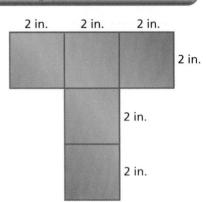

2 in.   2 in.   2 in.

2 in.

2 in.

2 in.

- Draw the two nets on cardboard and cut them out.

2.25 in.

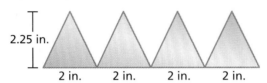

2 in.   2 in.   2 in.   2 in.

- Fold and tape the nets to form an open square box and an open pyramid.

- Both figures should have the same size square base and the same height.

- Fill the pyramid with pebbles. Then pour the pebbles into the box. Repeat this until the box is full. How many pyramids does it take to fill the box?

- Use your result to find a formula for the volume of a pyramid.

2 ACTIVITY: Comparing Volumes

Work with a partner. You are an archeologist studying two ancient pyramids. What factors would affect how long it took to build each pyramid? Given similar conditions, which pyramid took longer to build? Explain your reasoning.

Cholula Pyramid in Mexico
Height: about 217 ft
Base: about 1476 ft by 1476 ft

Cheops Pyramid in Egypt
Height: about 480 ft
Base: about 755 ft by 755 ft

Laurie's Notes

Introduction

For the Teacher

- **Goal:** Students will develop an intuition of how to find the volume of a pyramid.

Motivate

- Share information about two well known pyramid-shaped buildings.
- The Luxor Resort and Casino in Las Vegas reaches 350 feet into the sky and is 36 stories tall. Luxor has over 4400 guest rooms, making it one of the top ten largest hotels in the world.
- The Rock and Roll Hall of Fame in Cleveland was designed by architect I. M. Pei. The design of the glass-faced main building uses a pyramid shape to invoke the image of a guitar neck rising to the sky.

Activity Notes

Activity 1

- Have students cut out the nets and make the shapes.
- ❓ "How are the two shapes alike?" same base, same height "How are they different?" One is a square pyramid. The other is a square prism.
- ❓ "How do you think their volumes compare?" Most students guess that the prism has twice the volume as the pyramid.
- ❓ "How can you test your hunch about the volumes?" If students have looked at the activity, they'll want to fill the pyramid.
- After the first pour, students should start to suspect that their guess might be off.
- After the second pour, students are pretty sure the relationship is 3 to 1.
- This hands-on experience of making and filling the prism will help students remember the factor of $\frac{1}{3}$. The formula should now make sense to them. The volume of a pyramid should be $\frac{1}{3}$ the volume of a prism with the same base and height as the pyramid.

Activity 2

- ❓ "What do you know about the pyramids from looking only at the pictures?" They look like square pyramids.
- ❓ "What do you know about the pyramids from looking at their dimensions?" Cholula has the larger base. Cheops is taller.
- Give time for students to calculate the volume. From the first activity, they should feel comfortable finding the area of the base and multiplying by the height (this would be the prism's volume), and then taking $\frac{1}{3}$ of this answer.
- ❓ "Which pyramid has the greater volume, and by how much?" Cholula is about 66 million cubic feet greater in volume.
- **FYI:** Cholula is about 5 football fields long on each edge.

Standards of Learning

8.7(a) The student will investigate and solve practical problems involving volume and surface area of prisms, cylinders, cones, and pyramids.

8.7(b) The student will describe how changing one measured attribute of a figure affects the volume and surface area.

Activity Materials
Textbook
<ul><li>nets of pyramid and prism</li><li>scissors</li><li>tape</li><li>uncooked popcorn, rice, dried beans, mini uncooked pasta</li></ul>

Start Thinking! and Warm Up

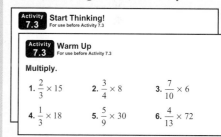

Activity 7.3 Start Thinking! For use before Activity 7.3

Activity 7.3 Warm Up For use before Activity 7.3

Multiply.

1. $\frac{2}{3} \times 15$ 2. $\frac{3}{4} \times 8$ 3. $\frac{7}{10} \times 6$

4. $\frac{1}{3} \times 18$ 5. $\frac{5}{9} \times 30$ 6. $\frac{4}{13} \times 72$

7.3 Record and Practice Journal

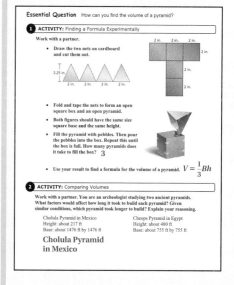

Essential Question How can you find the volume of a pyramid?

1 ACTIVITY: Finding a Formula Experimentally

Work with a partner.

- Draw the two nets on cardboard and cut them out.
- Fold and tape the nets to form an open square box and an open pyramid.
- Both figures should have the same size square base and the same height.
- Fill the pyramid with pebbles. Then pour the pebbles into the box. Repeat this until the box is full. How many pyramids does it take to fill the box? 3
- Use your result to find a formula for the volume of a pyramid. $V = \frac{1}{3}Bh$

2 ACTIVITY: Comparing Volumes

Work with a partner. You are an archeologist studying two ancient pyramids. What factors would affect how long it took to build each pyramid? Given similar conditions, which pyramid took longer to build? Explain your reasoning.

Cholula Pyramid in Mexico
Height: about 217 ft
Base: about 1476 ft by 1476 ft

Cheops Pyramid in Egypt
Height: about 480 ft
Base: about 755 ft by 755 ft

Cholula Pyramid in Mexico

Visual

Students may confuse pyramids and triangular prisms. Show the students models and point out the following characteristics. A pyramid has one base, which can be any polygon. The remaining faces are triangles. A triangular prism has two bases, which are triangles. The remaining faces are rectangles.

7.3 Record and Practice Journal

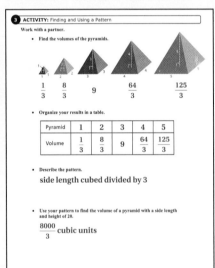

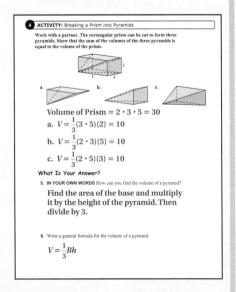

Laurie's Notes

Activity 3

- Ask a student to describe the five pyramids shown. You want to make sure that students recognize that the bases are all squares, and the height of the pyramid is the same as the length of the base edge.
- Reinforce good problem solving by having students organize their data in a table.
- Allow time for students to record the volume of each pyramid.
- **?** "What was the volume of the smallest pyramid and how did you find it?"
$$V = \frac{1}{3} \cdot 1^3 = \frac{1}{3}$$
- **?** "What was the volume of the next pyramid and how did you find it?"
$$V = \frac{1}{3} \cdot 2^3 = \frac{8}{3}$$
- Repeat this for several pyramids and ask a student to summarize the pattern. $V = \frac{1}{3} \cdot s^3$, where s is the side length and the height.
- **?** "Does the height of a pyramid have to equal the side length of the base?" No. They are equal in this problem, but they do not need to be.

Activity 4

- Discuss with students how to follow the color coding so that correct dimensions can be matched up.

What Is Your Answer?

- **Neighbor Check:** Have students work independently and then have their neighbor check their work. Have students discuss any discrepancies.

Closure

- Does the volume formula you wrote for Question 5 need to have a square base? Explain your thinking. No; Students should try to sketch or make pyramids with other polygonal bases.

Technology
For
the **T**eacher

Dynamic Classroom

The Dynamic Planning Tool
Editable Teacher's Resources at *BigIdeasMath.com*

ACTIVITY: Finding and Using a Pattern

Work with a partner.

- Find the volumes of the pyramids.
- Organize your results in a table.
- Describe the pattern.
- Use your pattern to find the volume of a pyramid with a side length and height of 20.

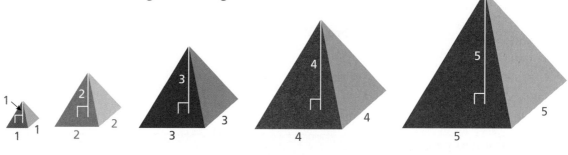

4 **ACTIVITY: Breaking a Prism into Pyramids**

Work with a partner. The rectangular prism can be cut to form three pyramids. Show that the sum of the volumes of the three pyramids is equal to the volume of the prism.

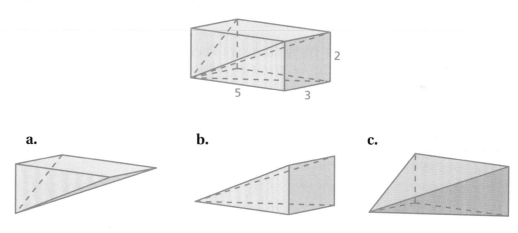

a.   b.   c.

What Is Your Answer?

5. **IN YOUR OWN WORDS** How can you find the volume of a pyramid?

6. Write a general formula for the volume of a pyramid.

Use what you learned about the volumes of pyramids to complete Exercises 4–6 on page 322.

 **Key Idea**

Volume of a Pyramid

Words The volume V of a pyramid is one-third the product of the area of the base and the height of the pyramid.

Area of base

Algebra $V = \dfrac{1}{3}Bh$

Height of pyramid

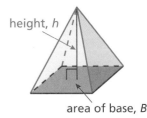

height, h

area of base, B

EXAMPLE 1   Finding the Volume of a Pyramid

Find the volume of the pyramid.

$V = \dfrac{1}{3}Bh$ Write formula for volume.

$\quad = \dfrac{1}{3}(48)(9)$ Substitute.

$\quad = 144$ Multiply.

∴ The volume is 144 cubic millimeters.

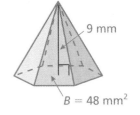

9 mm

$B = 48$ mm^2

EXAMPLE 2   Finding the Volume of a Pyramid

Find the volume of the pyramid.

a.

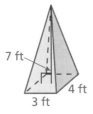

7 ft
4 ft
3 ft

$V = \dfrac{1}{3}Bh$

$\quad = \dfrac{1}{3}(4)(3)(7)$

$\quad = 28$

∴ The volume is 28 cubic feet.

b.

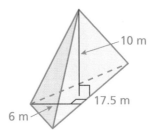

10 m
17.5 m
6 m

$V = \dfrac{1}{3}Bh$

$\quad = \dfrac{1}{3}\left(\dfrac{1}{2}\right)(17.5)(6)(10)$

$\quad = 175$

∴ The volume is 175 cubic meters.

Laurie's Notes

Introduction

Connect
- **Yesterday:** Students discovered how to find the volume of a pyramid by comparing it to the volume of a prism with the same base area and same height.
- **Today:** Students will work with a formula for the volume of a pyramid.

Lesson Notes

Key Idea
- Write the Key Idea.
- Write the formula in words.
- Write the formula in symbols.
- **?** "How will you find the area of the base?" It depends upon what type of polygon the base is.

Example 1
- Work through the example.
- Model good problem solving. Write the formula in words. Write the symbols underneath the words. Substitute the values for the symbols.
- **Common Error:** In using this volume formula, the $\frac{1}{3}$ often produces a computational mistake. In this problem, students must multiply $\frac{1}{3} \times 48 \times 9$.

  A common error is to take $\frac{1}{3}$ of both numbers $\left(\frac{1}{3}\text{ of }48\text{ and }\frac{1}{3}\text{ of }9\right)$ as if the Distributive Property were at work. I explain to students that if it had been a whole number, such as 2, they wouldn't think to multiply 2×48 and 2×9. They should only use $\frac{1}{3}$ as a factor once.

Example 2
- **?** "Describe the base of each pyramid." part (a): rectangular base; part (b): triangular base
- **?** "How do you find the area of the base in part (b)?" $\frac{1}{2} \times 17.5 \times 6$
- **FYI:** Be careful in using language, such as "one-half base times height." You may know that in this context, *base* refers to an edge of the base of a triangle and not the area of the base of the pyramid. This can be confusing to students.
- Students may need help with multiplying the fractions in each problem.

  In part (a), students should recognize that $\frac{1}{3} \times 3 = 1$. They are multiplying reciprocals. In part (b), $\frac{1}{3} \times \frac{1}{2} \times 6 = 1$. The Commutative Property allows the order of the factors to be rearranged.

Goal Today's lesson is finding the volumes of pyramids.

Start Thinking! and Warm Up

| Lesson 7.3 | Warm Up |
| For use before Lesson 7.3 |

| Lesson 7.3 | Start Thinking! |
| For use before Lesson 7.3 |

Give a real-life example of how knowing the volume of a pyramid would be beneficial.

Extra Example 1

Find the volume of a pentagonal pyramid with a base area of 24 square feet and a height of 8 feet. 64 ft^3

Extra Example 2

a. Find the volume of a rectangular pyramid with a base of 2 meters by 6 meters, and a height of 3 meters. 12 m^3

b. Find the volume of a triangular pyramid with a height of 8 inches, and where the triangular base has a width of 4 inches and an altitude of 9 inches. 48 in.^3

Laurie's Notes

On Your Own

1. 42 ft^3

2. $186\frac{2}{3} \text{ in.}^3$

3. 231 cm^3

Extra Example 3

a. The volume of lotion in Bottle B is how many times the volume in Bottle A? $1\frac{2}{3}$

b. Which is the better buy? Bottle B

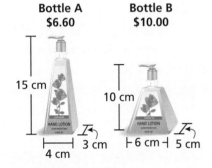

Bottle A
$6.60

Bottle B
$10.00

15 cm

10 cm

4 cm

3 cm

6 cm

5 cm

HAND LOTION

HAND LOTION

On Your Own

4. yes; Bottles B and C have the same volume, but Bottle C has a unit cost of $2.20.

English Language Learners

Forming Answers

Encourage English learners to form complete sentences in their responses. Students can use the question to help them form the answer.

Question: If you know the area of the base of a pyramid, what else do you need to know to find the volume?

Response: If you know the area of the base of a pyramid, you need to know the height of the pyramid to find the volume.

On Your Own

- Have students name each pyramid and describe what they know about each base. Note that for the pentagonal pyramid, the area of the base has already been computed.
- In Question 2, none of the dimensions contain factors of 3. In computing the volume, $V = \frac{1}{3} \times 10 \times 8 \times 7$, suggest to students that they multiply the whole numbers for a product of 560 and then multiply by $\frac{1}{3}$. Remind students how to rewrite the improper fraction $\frac{560}{3}$ as a mixed number, $186\frac{2}{3}$.

Example 3

- If you have any lotion or shampoo that is in a pyramidal bottle, use it as a model.
- Work through the computation of volume for each bottle.
- Explain different approaches to multiplying the factors in Bottle A: (1) multiply in order left to right or (2) use the Commutative Property to multiply the whole numbers, and then multiply by $\frac{1}{3}$.
- Discuss the phrase "how many times." Because the volume of Bottle B is not a multiple of the volume of Bottle A, students are uncertain how to compare the volumes.
- **?** "How do you decide which bottle is the better buy?" Students will try to describe how to find the cost for one cubic inch. This is the unit price.
- Use the language, cost per volume or cost per cubic inch.

On Your Own

- Give students time to complete this problem. Ask volunteers to share their work at the board.

Closure

- **Exit Ticket:** Sketch a rectangular pyramid with base 3 units by 4 units, and a height of 5 units. What is the volume? 20 units^3

Technology For the Teacher

Dynamic Classroom

The Dynamic Planning Tool
Editable Teacher's Resources at *BigIdeasMath.com*

On Your Own

Find the volume of the pyramid.

1.

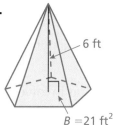

6 ft

$B = 21 \text{ ft}^2$

2.

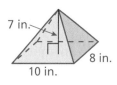

7 in.

8 in.

10 in.

3.

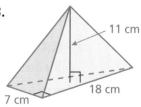

11 cm

18 cm

7 cm

EXAMPLE ③ **Real-Life Application**

a. The volume of sunscreen in Bottle B is how many times the volume in Bottle A?

b. Which is the better buy?

Bottle A
$9.96

6 in.

2 in.

1 in.

Bottle B
$14.40

4 in.

3 in.

1.5 in.

a. Use the formula for the volume of a pyramid to estimate the amount of sunscreen in each bottle.

Bottle A	*Bottle* B
$V = \dfrac{1}{3}Bh$	$V = \dfrac{1}{3}Bh$
$= \dfrac{1}{3}(2)(1)(6)$	$= \dfrac{1}{3}(3)(1.5)(4)$
$= 4 \text{ in.}^3$	$= 6 \text{ in.}^3$

So, the volume of sunscreen in Bottle B is $\dfrac{6}{4}$, or 1.5 times the volume in Bottle A.

b. Find the unit cost for each bottle.

Bottle A	*Bottle* B
$\dfrac{\text{cost}}{\text{volume}} = \dfrac{\$9.96}{4 \text{ in.}^3}$	$\dfrac{\text{cost}}{\text{volume}} = \dfrac{\$14.40}{6 \text{ in.}^3}$
$= \dfrac{\$2.49}{1 \text{ in.}^3}$	$= \dfrac{\$2.40}{1 \text{ in.}^3}$

The unit cost of Bottle B is less than the unit cost of Bottle A. So, Bottle B is the better buy.

Bottle C

3 in.

2 in.

3 in.

On Your Own

4. Bottle C is on sale for $13.20. Is Bottle C a better buy than Bottle B in Example 3? Explain.

 Vocabulary and Concept Check

1. **WRITING** How is the formula for the volume of a pyramid different from the formula for the volume of a prism?

2. **OPEN-ENDED** Describe a real-life situation that involves finding the volume of a pyramid.

3. **REASONING** A triangular pyramid and a triangular prism have the same base and height. The volume of the prism is how many times the volume of the pyramid?

 Practice and Problem Solving

Find the volume of the pyramid.

 4.

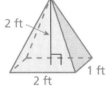
2 ft
2 ft
1 ft

5.
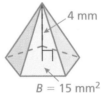
4 mm
$B = 15$ mm²

6.
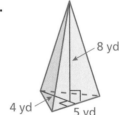
8 yd
4 yd
5 yd

7.
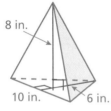
8 in.
10 in.
6 in.

8.
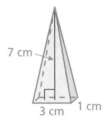
7 cm
3 cm
1 cm

9.
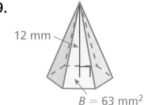
12 mm
$B = 63$ mm²

10.
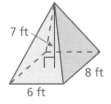
7 ft
8 ft
6 ft

11.
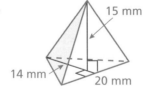
15 mm
14 mm
20 mm

12. **PARACHUTE** In 1483, Leonardo da Vinci designed a parachute. It is believed that this was the first parachute ever designed. In a notebook, he wrote "If a man is provided with a length of gummed linen cloth with a length of 12 yards on each side and 12 yards high, he can jump from any great height whatsoever without injury." Find the volume of air inside Leonardo's parachute.

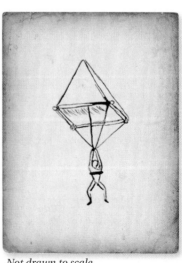

Not drawn to scale

Assignment Guide and Homework Check

Level	Day 1 Activity Assignment	Day 2 Lesson Assignment	Homework Check
Basic	4–6, 21–25	1–3, 7–12, 17	3, 7, 10, 12
Average	4–6, 21–25	1–3, 7–17 odd, 18	3, 7, 13, 17
Advanced	4–6, 21–25	1–3, 9–11, 14–20 even, 19	10, 14, 16, 18

For Your Information

- **Exercise 12** Skydiver Adrian Nicholas tested the design, jumping from a hot-air balloon at 3000 meters. The parachute weighed over 90 kilograms.

Common Errors

- **Exercises 4–11** Students may write the units incorrectly, often writing square units instead of cubic units. This is especially true when the area of the base is given. Remind them that the units are cubed because there are three dimensions.

- **Exercises 4–11** Students may forget to multiply by one of the measurements, especially when finding the area of the base. Encourage them to find the area of the base separately and then substitute it into the equation. Using colored pencils for each part can also assist students. Tell them to write the formula using different colors for the base and height, as in the lesson. When they substitute values into the equation for volume, they will be able to clearly see that they have accounted for all of the dimensions.

Vocabulary and Concept Check

1. The volume of a pyramid is $\frac{1}{3}$ times the area of the base times the height. The volume of a prism is the area of the base times the height.

2. *Sample answer:* You are comparing the sizes of two tents and want to know which one has more space inside of it.

3. 3 times

Practice and Problem Solving

4. $1\frac{1}{3}$ ft^3

5. 20 mm^3

6. $26\frac{2}{3}$ yd^3

7. 80 in.^{3}

8. 7 cm^3

9. 252 mm^3

10. 112 ft^3

11. 700 mm^3

12. 576 yd^3

7.3 Record and Practice Journal

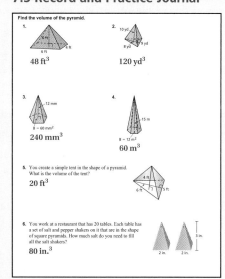

13. 30 in.^{2}

14. 9 cm

15. 7.5 ft

16. See *Taking Math Deeper*.

17. 12,000 in.^{3}; The volume of one paperweight is 12 cubic inches. So, 12 cubic inches of glass is needed to make one paperweight. So, it takes $12 \times 1000 = 12{,}000$ cubic inches to make 1000 paperweights.

18. Spire B; 4 in.^{3}

19. *Sample answer:* 5 ft by 4 ft

20. yes; Prism: $V = xyz$

    Pyramid: $V = \frac{1}{3}(xy)(3z) = xyz$

Fair Game Review

21. 28   22. 72

23. 60   24. 20

25. B

Mini-Assessment

Find the volume of the pyramid.

1.

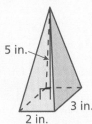

5 in.

3 in.

2 in.

10 in.^{3}

2.

3 ft

3 ft

3 ft

1 ft

3 ft^3

3. Find the volume of the paper weight.

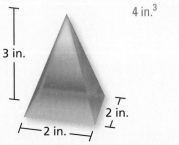

4 in.^{3}

3 in.

2 in.

2 in.

T-323

Taking Math Deeper

Exercise 16

Students have to think a bit about this question. At first it seems like you can't tell the shape of the base. However, you can count the number of support sticks to find the shape of the base.

① Count the supports.
   a. There are 12. So, the base is a dodecagon (a 12-sided polygon).

I see 12

② Using a ruler, the base of the teepee appears to be about the same as its height. So, estimate the width of the base to be 10 feet.

③ Use a 10 by 10 grid to estimate the area of the base. It appears to have an area of about 80 square feet.

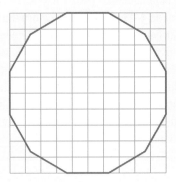

   b. $V = \frac{1}{3}Bh$

   $= \frac{1}{3} \cdot 80 \cdot 10$

   ≈ 267 ft^3

You need to give some leeway in the answers. Anything from 250 cubic feet to 300 cubic feet is a reasonable answer.

Project

Write a report about what you think were the pros and cons of living in a teepee.

Reteaching and Enrichment Strategies

If students need help...	If students got it...
Resources by Chapter • Practice A and Practice B • Puzzle Time Record and Practice Journal Practice Differentiating the Lesson Lesson Tutorials Skills Review Handbook	Resources by Chapter • Enrichment and Extension • School-to-Work Start the next section

Copy and complete the table to find the area of the base *B* or the height *h* of the pyramid.

	Volume, *V*	Area of Base, *B*	Height, *h*
13.	60 in.³		6 in.
14.	144 cm³	48 cm²	
15.	135 ft³	54 ft²	

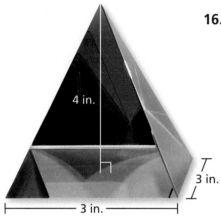

4 in.

3 in.

3 in.

Paperweight

16. TEEPEE Use the photo of the teepee.

  a. What is the shape of the base? How can you tell?

  b. The teepee's height is about 10 feet. Estimate the volume of the teepee.

17. PAPERWEIGHT How much glass is needed to manufacture 1000 paperweights? Explain your reasoning.

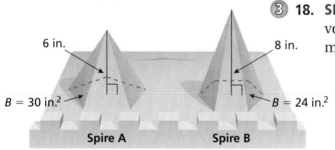

6 in.

8 in.

$B = 30$ in.² $B = 24$ in.²

Spire A   Spire B

③ **18. SPIRE** Which sandcastle spire has a greater volume? How much more sand is required to make the spire with the greater volume?

19. OPEN-ENDED A pyramid has a volume of 40 cubic feet and a height of 6 feet. Find one possible set of dimensions of the rectangular base.

20. *Reasoning* Do the two solids have the same volume? Explain.

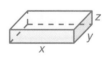

Fair Game Review What you learned in previous grades & lessons

Simplify the expression. *(Skills Review Handbook)*

21. $\frac{1}{3} \times 12 \times 7$ **22.** $\frac{1}{3} \times 8 \times 27$ **23.** $\frac{1}{3} \times 6^2 \times 5$ **24.** $\frac{1}{3} \times 2^2 \times 15$

25. MULTIPLE CHOICE You spend 25% of your money on a shirt. Then you spend $\frac{1}{6}$ of the remainder on lunch. Lunch costs $8. What percent of your money is spent on lunch? *(Section 4.1)*

  Ⓐ 4.2%   Ⓑ 12.5%   Ⓒ 16.7%   Ⓓ 32%

STANDARDS
OF LEARNING
8.7

Essential Question How can you remember the formulas for surface area and volume?

You discovered that the volume of a pyramid is one-third the volume of a prism that has the same base and same height. You can use a similar activity to discover that the volume of a cone is one-third the volume of a cylinder that has the same base and height.

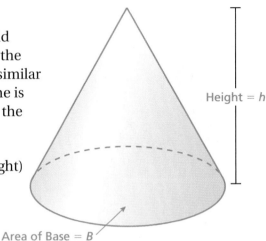

Height = h

Area of Base = B

$$\text{Volume of a Cone} = \frac{1}{3}(\text{Area of Base}) \times (\text{Height})$$

---

① ACTIVITY: Summarizing Volume Formulas

Work with a partner. You can remember the volume formulas for all of the solids shown with just two concepts.

Volumes of Prisms and Cylinders

$$\text{Volume} = \boxed{(\text{Area of Base})} \times \boxed{(\text{Height})}$$

Volumes of Pyramids and Cones

$$\text{Volume} = \boxed{\frac{1}{3}} \boxed{(\text{Volume of Prism or Cylinder with same base and height})}$$

Make a list of all the formulas you need to remember to find the area of a base. Talk about strategies for remembering these formulas.

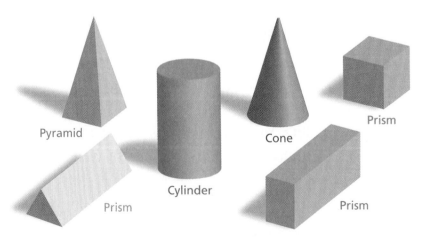

Pyramid

Prism

Cylinder

Cone

Prism

Prism

Laurie's Notes

Introduction

For the Teacher

- **Goal:** Students will develop a strategy to summarize volume and surface area formulas.
- **Big Idea:** It is not a big stretch for students to accept that the volume relationship between the cone and cylinder is the same as the volume relationship between the pyramid and prism.

    Volume of a Cylinder = (Area of Base) × (Height)

    Volume of a Cone = $\frac{1}{3}$ × (Area of Base) × (Height)

- **Common Error:** Students think height and slant height have the same measure. The slant height is used in finding the surface area of a cone, while the height is used in finding volume. In the diagram, the height is shown.

Motivate

- Give pairs of students two minutes to look around the classroom and make a list of all the geometric solids they see that are prisms, cylinders, pyramids, or cones.
- Make a column on the board for each type of solid. Ask one pair of students to list an item in each column. Continue to have pairs of students add to the lists, but only items that are not in the lists already.
- Was every group able to list 4 new items? If your classroom is like most, there are fewer pyramids and cones than prisms and cylinders.

Activity Notes

Activity 1

- **Connection:** Recall the connection between the pyramid and the cone—*structurally they are the same.* Each has a single base and a lateral portion that contains a vertex.
- **FYI:** You do not want students to think that it is necessary to memorize a lot of formulas. Instead, students need to consider the structure of the shape. Prisms and cylinders have the same structure (two congruent bases and a lateral portion) and pyramids and cones have the same structure (one base and a lateral portion that contains a vertex). There is one general formula for each pair of solids. Moreover, the two general formulas have a 1 : 3 relationship.
- **Teaching Tip:** Make a poster of each of the two volume formulas for your classroom, or ask a student to make them.
- ❓ "How many general volume formulas are there?" two
- ❓ "In each formula, you need to find the area of a base. What types of bases have you studied?" most were squares, rectangles, triangles, or circles
- Have pairs of students share their lists and strategies. Collect information at the board.

Standards of Learning

8.7(a) The student will investigate and solve practical problems involving volume and surface area of prisms, cylinders, cones, and pyramids.
8.7(b) The student will describe how changing one measured attribute of a figure affects the volume and surface area.

Previous Learning

Students should know how to find the surface area of a cone.

Activity Materials
Textbook
<ul><li>models of cones</li><li>deck of cards or stack of scrap paper</li></ul>

Start Thinking! and Warm Up

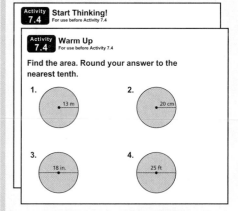

7.4 Record and Practice Journal

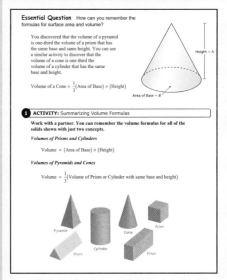

English Language Learners

Visual

Show students models of a pyramid and a prism. Then show them models of a cone and a cylinder. Have students note that the relationship between the volume of a cone and the volume of a cylinder with the same base and height is the same as the relationship between the volume of a pyramid and the volume of a prism with the same base and height.

7.4 Record and Practice Journal

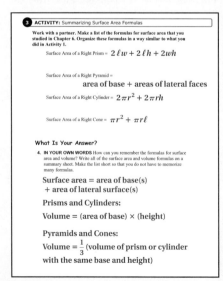

Laurie's Notes

Activity 2

- It is helpful to have a stack of scrap paper or a deck of cards to model this activity.
- Give students time to discuss their thinking and then have them share their thoughts with the rest of the class.
- **Common Misconception:** Students may believe that the height decreases as the stack of paper is slid to one side. The thickness doesn't change, so the height remains the same. The volume remains the same because no sheets are removed.
- ❓ "What is changing in this problem?" Some students may recognize that the surface area is changing because more area is being exposed. Model this with the cards or scrap paper.

Activity 3

- **FYI:** Remember, prisms and cylinders have the same structure (two congruent bases and a lateral portion) and pyramids and cones have the same structure (one base and a lateral portion that contains a vertex). There is one general formula for each pair of solids.
- **Teaching Tip:** Make a poster of each of the two surface area formulas for your classroom, or ask a student to make them.

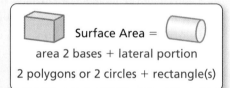

Surface Area =
area 2 bases + lateral portion
2 polygons or 2 circles + rectangle(s)

- Students should refer back in their notes and book as needed to complete this activity.
- Have pairs of students share their lists. Collect information at the board.

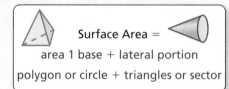

Surface Area =
area 1 base + lateral portion
polygon or circle + triangles or sector

What Is Your Answer?

- Have students work in pairs.

Closure

- Sketch a cube with edge length 2 centimeters, and a cylinder with height and diameter each 2 centimeters. Compare the volumes of the cube and cylinder.
- Sketch a cylinder and a cone, each with height and diameter of 3 centimeters. Compare the volumes of the cylinder and cone.

Technology For the Teacher

The Dynamic Planning Tool
Editable Teacher's Resources at *BigIdeasMath.com*

2 ACTIVITY: Volumes of Oblique Solids

Work with a partner. Think of a stack of paper. If you adjust the stack so that the sides are oblique (slanted), do you change the volume of the stack? If the volume of the stack does not change, then the formulas for volumes of right solids also apply to oblique solids.

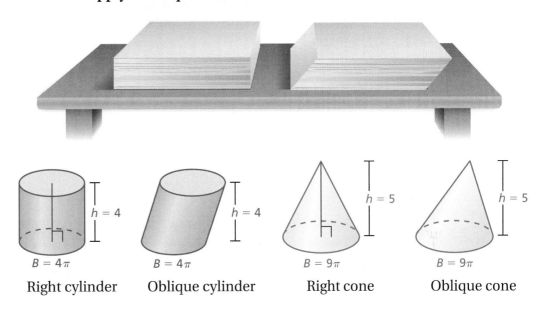

Right cylinder	Oblique cylinder	Right cone	Oblique cone
$h = 4$	$h = 4$	$h = 5$	$h = 5$
$B = 4\pi$	$B = 4\pi$	$B = 9\pi$	$B = 9\pi$

3 ACTIVITY: Summarizing Surface Area Formulas

Work with a partner. Make a list of the formulas for surface area that you studied in Chapter 6. Organize these formulas in a way similar to what you did in Activity 1.

Surface Area of a Right Prism =

Surface Area of a Right Pyramid =

Surface Area of a Right Cylinder =

Surface Area of a Right Cone =

What Is Your Answer?

4. **IN YOUR OWN WORDS** How can you remember the formulas for surface area and volume? Write all of the surface area and volume formulas on a summary sheet. Make the list short so that you do not have to memorize many formulas.

Practice

Use what you learned about the volumes of cones to complete Exercises 4–6 on page 328.

Key Idea

Volume of a Cone

Words　The volume V of a cone is one-third the product of the area of the base and the height of the cone.

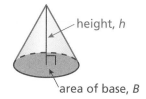

height, h

area of base, B

Area of base

Algebra　$V = \dfrac{1}{3}Bh$

Height of cone

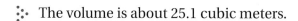

EXAMPLE　1　Finding the Volume of a Cone

Find the volume of the cone. Round your answer to the nearest tenth.

The diameter is 4 meters. So, the radius is 2 meters.

$V = \dfrac{1}{3}Bh$　　　　　Write formula.

$= \dfrac{1}{3}\pi(2)^2(6)$　　　Substitute.

$= 8\pi \approx 25.1$　　　　Simplify.

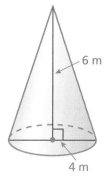

6 m

4 m

∴ The volume is about 25.1 cubic meters.

EXAMPLE　2　Finding the Height of a Cone

Find the height of the cone. Round your answer to the nearest tenth.

$V = \dfrac{1}{3}Bh$　　　　　　　Write formula.

$956 = \dfrac{1}{3}\pi(9)^2(h)$　　　Substitute.

$956 = 27\pi h$　　　　　　Simplify.

$11.3 \approx h$　　　　　　　Divide each side by 27π.

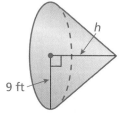

h

9 ft

Volume $= 956$ ft^3

∴ The height is about 11.3 feet.

Laurie's Notes

Introduction

Connect

- **Yesterday:** Students developed a strategy to summarize volume and surface area formulas.
- **Today:** Students will work with the formula for the volume of a cone.

Motivate

- Bring an ice cream cone and ice cream scoop to class.
- **FYI:** An ice cream scoop with a radius of 1 inch will make a round (sphere) scoop of ice cream that is a little more than 4 cubic inches. Share this information with students.
- ❔ "If I place a scoop of ice cream (with a 1 inch radius) on this cone, and the ice cream melts (because I received a phone call from a parent), will the ice cream overflow the cone?" This question is posed only to get students thinking about the volume of a cone. The volume of the cone will be found at the end of the lesson.

Lesson Notes

Key Idea

- Write the Key Idea.
- Write the formula in words. Draw the cone with the dimensions labeled.
- Write the symbolic formula.
- ❔ "What is the base?" a circle. "How do you find its area?" $A = \pi r^2$

Example 1

- Notice that the work is done in terms of π. It is not until the last step that 3.14 is substituted for π.
- **Representation:** Encourage students to use the parentheses to represent multiplication. Using the $\times$ symbol would make the expression confusing.
- **Common Misconception:** Remind students that π is a number and because multiplication is commutative and associative, this expression could be rewritten as $\frac{1}{3}(6)(2)^2\pi$, making the computation less confusing.
- ❔ "What is being squared in this expression?" only the 2

Example 2

- This example requires students to solve an equation for a variable.
- Work through the problem, annotating the steps as shown in the book.
- ❔ "How does $\frac{1}{3}\pi(9)^2 h$ equal $27\pi h$?" Only the 9 is being squared, which is 81. One-third of 81 is 27. The order of the factors doesn't matter.
- Students may have difficulty with the last step, dividing by 27π. It can be done in two steps—divide by 27 then divide by 3.14. Or, divide 956 by the product 27π, which is about 84.78.

Goal
Today's lesson is finding the volume of a cone.

Lesson Materials	
Introduction	**Textbook**
• ice cream cone • ice cream scoop	• sand timer
Closure	
• ice cream cone	

Start Thinking! and Warm Up

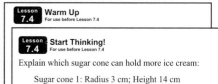

> **Lesson 7.4** Warm Up
> For use before Lesson 7.4
>
> **Lesson 7.4** Start Thinking!
> For use before Lesson 7.4
>
> Explain which sugar cone can hold more ice cream:
>
> Sugar cone 1: Radius 3 cm; Height 14 cm
>
> Sugar cone 2: Diameter 7 cm; Height 13 cm

Extra Example 1

Find the volume of a cone with a diameter of 6 feet and a height of 3 feet. Round your answer to the nearest tenth. $9\pi \approx 28.3 \text{ ft}^3$

Extra Example 2

Find the height of a cone with a radius of 6 yards and a volume of 75 cubic yards. Round your answer to the nearest whole number. $\frac{75}{12\pi} \approx 2 \text{ yd}$

On Your Own

1. $180\pi \approx 565.2 \text{ cm}^3$

2. $\dfrac{96}{\pi} \approx 30.6 \text{ yd}$

Extra Example 3

In Example 3, the height of the sand is 36 millimeters and the radius is 15 millimeters. The sand falls at a rate of 150 cubic millimeters per second. How much time do you have to answer the question? about 57 sec

 On Your Own

3. about 42 sec

4. about 6 sec

Differentiated Instruction

Organization

Some students might benefit from finding the area of the base B of the cone first. Then they can substitute this value into the formula, $V = \dfrac{1}{3}Bh$.

Laurie's Notes

On Your Own

- Ask volunteers to share their work at the board.

Example 3

- If you have a timer of this type, use it as a model.
- Ask a student volunteer to read the problem. Ask for ideas as to how the problem can be solved.
- "How long is 30 millimeters?" 30 millimeters is equal to 3 centimeters, which is a little more than 1 inch. This helps students form a visual image of the actual size of the sand timer.
- **Teaching Tip:** Again, explain that $\dfrac{1}{3} \times 24$ is a whole number. Then multiply $8 \times 10^2 = 800$.
- Be sure to use units in labeling answers. The dimensional analysis technique shows that the answer will have units of seconds.
- **Extension:** I have a sand timer in my classroom. Students calculate the volume, measure the amount of time it takes to fall to the bottom, and use this information to calculate the rate at which the sand is falling.

On Your Own

- **Extension:** Question 4 is a preview of an upcoming lesson. The height and radius have each been decreased by a factor of 2. (They are $\dfrac{1}{2}$ the original dimensions). What happens to the volume? It is decreased by a factor of 8, or 2^3.

Closure

- **Exit Ticket:** Have students find the volume of the ice cream cone used to motivate the lesson.

Technology
For
the **T**eacher

The Dynamic Planning Tool
Editable Teacher's Resources at *BigIdeasMath.com*

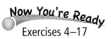
Now You're Ready
Exercises 4–17

On Your Own

Find the volume V or height h of the cone. Round your answer to the nearest tenth.

1.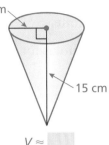

6 cm

15 cm

$V \approx$

2.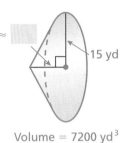

$h \approx$

15 yd

Volume $= 7200 \text{ yd}^3$

EXAMPLE 3 Real-Life Application

30 mm

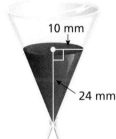
10 mm

24 mm

You must answer a trivia question before the sand in the timer falls to the bottom. The sand falls at a rate of 50 cubic millimeters per second. How much time do you have to answer the question?

Use the formula for the volume of a cone to find the volume of the sand in the timer.

$$V = \frac{1}{3}Bh \qquad\qquad \text{Write formula.}$$

$$= \frac{1}{3}\pi(10)^2(24) \qquad \text{Substitute.}$$

$$= 800\pi \approx 2512 \qquad \text{Simplify.}$$

The volume of the sand is about 2512 cubic millimeters. To find the amount of time you have to answer the question, multiply the volume by the rate at which the sand falls.

$$2512 \text{ mm}^3 \times \frac{1 \text{ sec}}{50 \text{ mm}^3} = 50.24 \text{ sec}$$

∴ You have about 50 seconds to answer the question.

On Your Own

3. **WHAT IF?** In Example 3, the sand falls at a rate of 60 cubic millimeters per second. How much time do you have to answer the question?

4. **WHAT IF?** In Example 3, the height of the sand in the timer is 12 millimeters and the radius is 5 millimeters. How much time do you have to answer the question?

Vocabulary and Concept Check

1. **VOCABULARY** Describe the height of a cone.

2. **WRITING** Compare and contrast the formulas for the volume of a pyramid and the volume of a cone.

3. **REASONING** You know the volume of a cylinder. How can you find the volume of a cone with the same base and height?

Practice and Problem Solving

Find the volume of the cone. Round your answer to the nearest tenth.

① 4.

4 in.
2 in.

5.
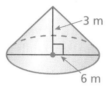
3 m
6 m

6.

10 mm
5 mm

7.
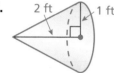
2 ft   1 ft

8.
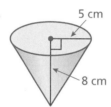
5 cm
8 cm

9.
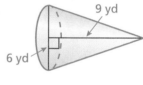
9 yd
6 yd

10.
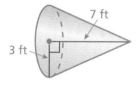
7 ft
3 ft

11.

10 in.
5 in.

12.

4 cm
8 cm

13. **ERROR ANALYSIS** Describe and correct the error in finding the volume of the cone.

8 m
6 m

$$\times \quad V = \frac{1}{3}Bh$$
$$= \frac{1}{3}(\pi)(6)^2(8)$$
$$= 96\pi\ m^3$$

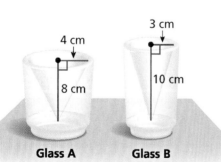
4 cm
8 cm
3 cm
10 cm
Glass A   Glass B

14. **GLASS** The inside of each glass is shaped like a cone. Which glass can hold more liquid? How much more?

Assignment Guide and Homework Check

Level	Day 1 Activity Assignment	Day 2 Lesson Assignment	Homework Check
Basic	4–6, 23–26	1–3, 7–17 odd, 14	2, 7, 14, 15
Average	4–6, 23–26	1–3, 7–19 odd, 20	2, 7, 15, 19
Advanced	4–6, 23–26	1–3, 13, 16–22	2, 16, 18, 21

For Your Information

- **Exercise 15** Because the volume is given in terms of π, students should not substitute 3.14 for π.

Common Errors

- **Exercises 4–12** Students may forget to cube the dimensions for the volume. Remind them that the volume of the cone is in three dimensions.
- **Exercises 4–12** Students may forget to square the radius when finding the area of the base. Remind them of the formula for the area of a circle. Encourage them to color-code the formula for volume as they solve for each part so that they do not forget to include one of the dimensions.
- **Exercises 5, 9, 11, 12** Students may use the diameter instead of the radius to find the area of the base. Remind them that the area of a circle is found using the radius.
- **Exercises 15–17** Students may try to use the Distributive Property before solving for h. For example, a student may incorrectly write $225 = \frac{1}{3}\pi(5^2) \cdot \frac{1}{3}h$. Remind them that factors are multiplied.

7.4 Record and Practice Journal

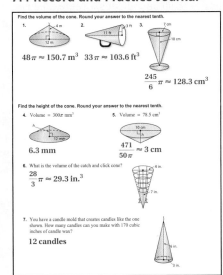

Find the volume of the cone. Round your answer to the nearest tenth.

1. $48\pi \approx 150.7 \text{ m}^3$ 2. $33\pi \approx 103.6 \text{ ft}^3$ 3. $\frac{245}{6}\pi \approx 128.3 \text{ cm}^3$

Find the height of the cone. Round your answer to the nearest tenth.

4. Volume = 300π mm³   6.3 mm

5. Volume = 78.5 cm³ $\frac{471}{50\pi} \approx 3 \text{ cm}$

6. What is the volume of the catch and click cone? $\frac{28}{3}\pi \approx 29.3 \text{ in.}^3$

7. You have a candle mold that creates candles like the one shown. How many candles can you make with 170 cubic inches of candle wax?   **12 candles**

Technology For the Teacher

Answer Presentation Tool
QuizShow

 Vocabulary and Concept Check

1. The height of a cone is the distance from the vertex to the center of the base.

2. Both formulas are $\frac{1}{3}Bh$, but the base of a cone is always a circle.

3. Divide by 3.

Practice and Problem Solving

4. $\frac{16\pi}{3} \approx 16.7 \text{ in.}^3$

5. $9\pi \approx 28.3 \text{ m}^3$

6. $\frac{250\pi}{3} \approx 261.7 \text{ mm}^3$

7. $\frac{2\pi}{3} \approx 2.1 \text{ ft}^3$

8. $\frac{200\pi}{3} \approx 209.3 \text{ cm}^3$

9. $27\pi \approx 84.8 \text{ yd}^3$

10. $21\pi \approx 65.9 \text{ ft}^3$

11. $\frac{125\pi}{6} \approx 65.4 \text{ in.}^3$

12. $\frac{32\pi}{3} \approx 33.5 \text{ cm}^3$

13. The diameter was used instead of the radius.
$$V = \frac{1}{3}(\pi)(3)^2(8)$$
$$= 24\pi \text{ m}^3$$

14. Glass A; $\frac{38\pi}{3} \approx 39.8 \text{ cm}^3$

Practice and Problem Solving

15. 1.5 ft

16. $\frac{27}{\pi} \approx 8.6$ cm

17. $\frac{40}{3\pi} \approx 4.2$ in.

18. 60π m^3

19. 24.1 min

20. See *Taking Math Deeper*.

21. $3y$

22. $4:1$

Fair Game Review

23. 315 m^3

24. 400 cm^3

25. $152\pi \approx 477.28$ ft^3

26. C

Mini-Assessment

Find the volume of the cone. Round your answer to the nearest tenth.

1.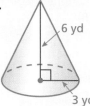
6 yd, 3 yd

$18\pi \approx 56.5$ yd^3

2.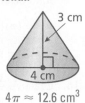
3 cm, 4 cm

$4\pi \approx 12.6$ cm^3

3. The volume of the ice cream cone is 4.71 cubic inches. Find the height of the cone.

⊢2 in.⊣ $\frac{14.13}{\pi} \approx 4.5$ in.

Taking Math Deeper

Exercise 20

This is a great type of problem to help students understand the importance of *planning ahead*. Also, in planning, remind students that you can't plan *exactly* how many cups will be used, nor can you plan how full each cup will be. So, the answers to the questions are just "ball park" figures.

 How many paper cups will you need?

$$\text{Volume of Cup} = \frac{1}{3}\pi(4)^2(11)$$
$$\approx 184.2 \text{ cm}^3$$

$$\text{Amount of Lemonade} = (10 \text{ gal})\left(3785 \frac{\text{cm}^3}{\text{gal}}\right)$$
$$= 37{,}850 \text{ cm}^3$$

$$\text{Number of Cups} \approx \frac{37{,}850}{184.2} \approx 205.5$$

a. You need about 206 cups.

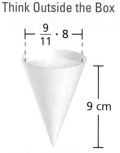
⊢ 8 cm ⊣
11 cm

Think Outside the Box

⊢ $\frac{9}{11} \cdot 8$ ⊣
9 cm

 How many packs of 50 cups?

b. You should order 5 packs of 50 cups. This will give you 250 cups.

Suppose each cup is not filled to the brim, but only to a height of 9 centimeters. This could mean each cup has a volume of 101 cubic centimeters, which would imply that you would use about 375 cups... so 5 packs would *not* be enough.

 How many cups are left over if you sell only 80% of the lemonade? 80% of 37,850 = 30,280 cm^3

$$\text{Number of Cups} \approx \frac{30{,}280}{184.2} \approx 164.4$$

c. You would have about 250 − 165 = 85 cups left over.

Sell 80%

Project

You open a lemonade stand. The lemonade costs you $5.00 per gallon and cups are $6.00 per 50 cups. Create an advertisement including the price of your lemonade. How did you determine the price to charge customers?

Reteaching and Enrichment Strategies

If students need help...	If students got it...
Resources by Chapter • Practice A and Practice B • Puzzle Time Record and Practice Journal Practice Differentiating the Lesson Lesson Tutorials Skills Review Handbook	Resources by Chapter • Enrichment and Extension • School-to-Work Start the next section

Find the height of the cone. Round your answer to the nearest tenth.

2 **15.** Volume = $\frac{1}{18}\pi$ ft³

16. Volume = 225 cm³

17. Volume = 3.6 in.³

1.8 in.

18. REASONING The volume of a cone is 20π cubic meters. What is the volume of a cylinder having the same base and same height?

4.8 in.

10 in.

19. VASE Water leaks from a crack in a vase at a rate of 0.5 cubic inch per minute. How long does it take for 20% of the water to leak from a full vase?

20. LEMONADE STAND You have 10 gallons of lemonade to sell. (1 gal ≈ 3785 cm³)

a. Each customer uses one paper cup. How many paper cups will you need?

b. The cups are sold in packages of 50. How many packages should you buy?

c. How many cups will be left over if you sell 80% of the lemonade?

8 cm

11 cm

21. REASONING The cylinder and the cone have the same volume. What is the height of the cone?

x

y

2x

?

22. *Critical Thinking* Cone A has the same height but twice the radius of Cone B. What is the ratio of the volume of Cone A to the volume of Cone B?

Fair Game Review *What you learned in previous grades & lessons*

Find the volume of the solid. *(Section 7.1, Section 7.2, and Section 7.3)*

23.

9 m

7 m

5 m

24.

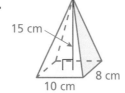

15 cm

8 cm

10 cm

25. 4 ft

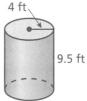

9.5 ft

26. MULTIPLE CHOICE A triangle has angle measures of 55.4°, 23.4°, and $x°$. What is the value of x? *(Section 5.2)*

(A) 11.2 **(B)** 12.2 **(C)** 101.2 **(D)** 281.2

You can use a **formula triangle** to arrange variables and operations of a formula. Here is an example of a formula triangle for volume of a prism.

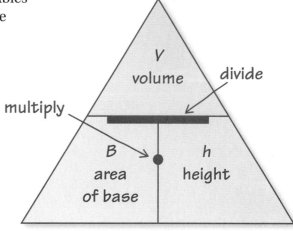

To find an unknown variable, use the other variables and the operation between them. For example, to find the area B of the base, cover up the B. Then you can see that you divide the volume V by the height h.

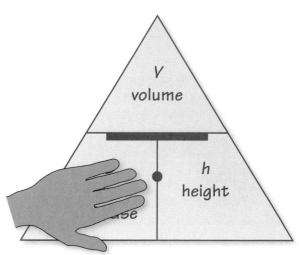

On Your Own

Make a formula triangle to help you study these topics. *Hint:* **Your formula triangles may have a different form than what is shown in the example.**

  1. volume of a cylinder

  2. volume of a pyramid

  3. volume of a cone

After you complete this chapter, make formula triangles for the following topics.

  4. volume of a composite solid

  5. surface areas of similar solids

  6. volumes of similar solids

"See how a formula triangle works? Cover any variable and you get its formula."

Sample Answers

1. Volume of a cylinder

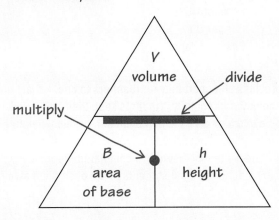

2. Volume of a pyramid

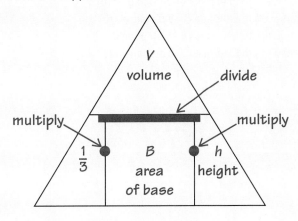

3. Volume of a cone

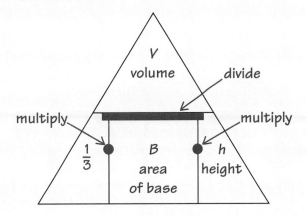

About this Organizer

A **Formula Triangle** can be used to arrange variables and operations of a formula. Students divide a triangle into the same number of parts as there are variables and factors in a formula. Then students write the variables and factors in the parts of the triangle and place either a multiplication or a division symbol, as appropriate, between the parts. This type of organizer can help students learn the formulas as well as see how the variables in the formulas are related. Students can place their formula triangles on note cards to use as a quick study reference.

Technology
For the Teacher

Vocabulary Puzzle Builder

Answers

1. 168 in.^{3}

2. 360 ft^3

3. 4925 mm^3

4. $120\pi \approx 376.8$ yd^3

5. 5 m^3

6. 664 ft^3

7. $50\pi \approx 157$ cm^3

8. $\dfrac{28.26}{\pi} \approx 9$ cm

9. 10,666.7 ft^3

10. 27 ft^3

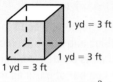

1 yd = 3 ft

1 yd = 3 ft

1 yd = 3 ft

$3 \times 3 \times 3 = 27$ ft^3

11. The volume is 27 times greater.

12. 42.39 in.^{3}

Assessment Book

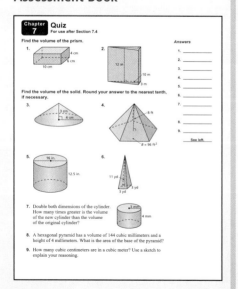

Alternative Quiz Ideas

100% Quiz	Math Log
Error Notebook	Notebook Quiz
Group Quiz	Partner Quiz
Homework Quiz	Pass the Paper

Homework Quiz

A homework notebook provides an opportunity for teachers to check that students are doing their homework regularly. Students keep their homework in a notebook. They should be told to record the page number, problem number, and copy the problem exactly in their homework notebook. Each day the teacher walks around and visually checks that homework is completed. Periodically, without advance notice, the teacher tells the students to put everything away except their homework notebook.

Questions are from students' homework.

1. What are the answers to Exercises 4–6 on page 310?
2. What are the answers to Exercises 6–8 on page 316?
3. What are the answers to Exercises 4–6 on page 322?
4. What are the answers to Exercises 7–9 on page 328?

Reteaching and Enrichment Strategies

If students need help. . .	If students got it. . .
Resources by Chapter • Study Help • Practice A and Practice B • Puzzle Time Lesson Tutorials *BigIdeasMath.com* Practice Quiz Practice from the Test Generator	Resources by Chapter • Enrichment and Extension • School-to-Work Game Closet at *BigIdeasMath.com* Start the next section

Technology For the Teacher

Answer Presentation Tool
Big Ideas Test Generator

Check It Out
Progress Check
BigIdeasMath ✓com

Find the volume of the prism. *(Section 7.1)*

1.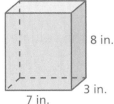

8 in.

3 in.

7 in.

2.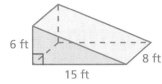

6 ft

8 ft

15 ft

3.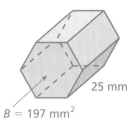

25 mm

$B = 197$ mm^2

Find the volume of the solid. Round your answer to the nearest tenth, if necessary. *(Section 7.2, Section 7.3, and Section 7.4)*

4.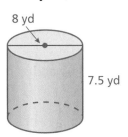

8 yd

7.5 yd

5.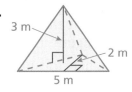

3 m

2 m

5 m

6.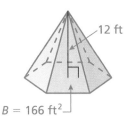

12 ft

$B = 166$ ft^2

7.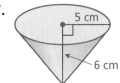

5 cm

6 cm

8. PAPER CONE The paper cone can hold 84.78 cubic centimeters of water. What is the height of the cone? *(Section 7.4)*

6 cm

h

9. ROOF A pyramid hip roof is a good choice for a house in a hurricane area. What is the volume of the roof to the nearest tenth? *(Section 7.3)*

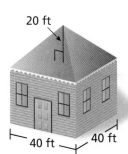

20 ft

40 ft   40 ft

10. CUBIC UNITS How many cubic feet are there in a cubic yard? Use a sketch to explain your reasoning. *(Section 7.1)*

11. GEOMETRY Triple both dimensions of the cylinder. How many times greater is the volume of the new cylinder than the volume of the original cylinder? *(Section 7.2)*

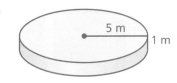

5 m

1 m

1.5 in.

16 in.

12. SAND ART There are 42.39 cubic inches of blue sand and 28.26 cubic inches of red sand in the cylindrical container. How many cubic inches of white sand are in the container? *(Section 7.2)*

7.5 Volumes of Composite Solids

Essential Question How can you estimate the volume of a composite solid?

1 ACTIVITY: Estimating Volume

Work with a partner. You work for a toy company and need to estimate the volume of a Minifigure that will be molded out of plastic.

a. Estimate the number of cubic inches of plastic that is needed to mold the Minifigure's head. Show your work.

b. Estimate the number of cubic inches of plastic that is needed to mold one of the Minifigure's legs. Show your work.

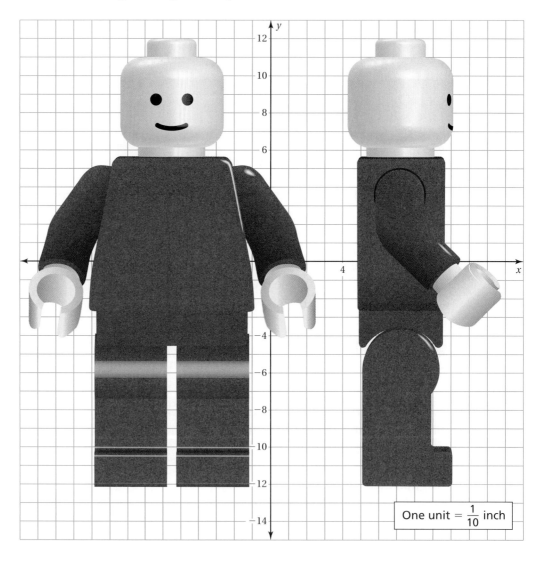

One unit = $\frac{1}{10}$ inch

Laurie's Notes

Introduction

For the Teacher

- **Goal:** Students will explore strategies for finding the volumes of composite figures.
- Each activity can be expanded enough to require the entire class period to complete. Therefore, decide in advance how far you want students to take each activity, or if you want students to investigate each activity.

Motivate

- Start looking at home for items that are composites of at least two solids, such as a jar of balsamic vinegar that is a square prism and a cylinder. Ask students to identify the various solids that form each item.

Activity Notes

Activity 1

- This activity is very open-ended. Students are asked to estimate the volume of the Minifigure's head (two cylinders) and one leg (approximately 2 prisms and 1 cylinder). Part of the challenge today will be keeping their work neat and organized. The answers provided are just one of many ways students can approach the activity.
- As the lead graphic engineer of a toy manufacturer, you have been asked to estimate the amount of plastic needed for the Minifigure. These *deluxe* pieces are solid plastic!
- **?** "What are the basic solids in this composite figure?" square prism, rectangular prism, and cylinder
- Once students understand the context, it is time for them to work with a partner and decide how to proceed. The figure is drawn on a coordinate grid with a scale provided. Students worked with scale drawings previously.
- After students have computed the volume of the head and a leg, ask a few questions.
- **?** "What did you use for the dimensions of the head?" *Sample answer:* a cylinder with an approximate height of 0.5 inch and a radius of 0.3 inch, and a cylinder with a height of 0.1 inch and a radius of 0.15 inch; The volume of the head $= \pi(0.3)^2(0.5) + \pi(0.15)^2(0.1) \approx 0.15$ in.^{3}
- **?** "What solids did you work with to find the volume of one leg?" foot: rectangular prism; leg portion: square prism; hip portion: cylinder
- **?** "What dimensions did you find for each solid?" *Sample answer:*

rectangular prism	square prism	cylinder
$V = (0.5)(0.4)(0.2)$	$V = (0.4)(0.4)(0.3)$	$V = \pi(0.2)^2(0.4)$
$V = 0.04$ in.^{3}	$V = 0.048$ in.^{3}	$V \approx 0.05$ in.^{3}

The sum of the 3 composite parts of one leg ≈ 0.138 in.^{3}
- **?** "Can you think of alternative ways to find the volume of the composite figure?" Students may mention displacement of water.
- **?** "Did any group work in fractions instead of decimals?" open-ended
- **Extension:** Compute the volume of other body parts.

Standards of Learning

8.7(a) The student will investigate and solve practical problems involving volume and surface area of prisms, cylinders, cones, and pyramids.

8.7(b) The student will describe how changing one measured attribute of a figure affects the volume and surface area.

Previous Learning

Students should know how to find volumes of prisms, cylinders, pyramids, and cones.

Activity Materials	
Introduction	**Closure**
• composite solids from home	• composite solids

Start Thinking! and Warm Up

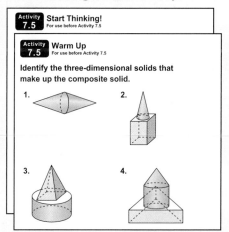

Activity 7.5 Start Thinking!
For use before Activity 7.5

Activity 7.5 Warm Up
For use before Activity 7.5

Identify the three-dimensional solids that make up the composite solid.

1.
2.
3.
4.

7.5 Record and Practice Journal

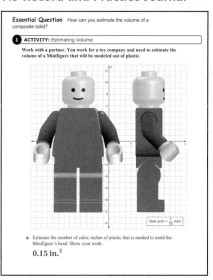

Essential Question How can you estimate the volume of a composite solid?

① ACTIVITY: Estimating Volume

Work with a partner. You work for a toy company and need to estimate the volume of a Minifigure that will be modeled out of plastic.

One unit $= \frac{1}{10}$ inch

a. Estimate the number of cubic inches of plastic that is needed to mold the Minifigure's head. Show your work.

0.15 in.^{3}

Auditory

Discuss with students the limits of measuring tools. What if you only had a 12-inch ruler? How could you measure the height of a ceiling or the length of a hall? For the ceiling, you might have a long stick to use as the measuring device and then measure the stick. For the hallway, you could measure the length of your foot and then walk the distance. A curved object could be measured using a piece of string. Have students measure different objects or distances and compare their results.

7.5 Record and Practice Journal

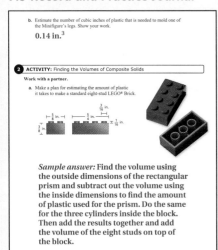

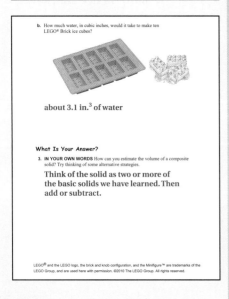

Laurie's Notes

Activity 2

- Part (a) asks students to make a plan for how much plastic would be needed. It does not ask students to do any computation, although they could, given a few assumptions.
- From the photos, it is known that the pieces are not solid. The thickness of plastic forming the cylinders and prisms varies. One would have to decide the thickness of the plastic, knowing that the outer walls appear to be thicker than the cylindrical walls.
- You might want to work through finding the volume of one top stud so that fractions can be discussed and reviewed.
- This is not a trivial problem. Precision is required so that when the LEGO® Bricks are stacked, the 3 bottom cylinders are centered among the 8 top cylinders (studs).
- **Alternate Approach:** You can fill a LEGO® Brick with water and measure how much water is contained. Then subtract the volume of water from the estimated volume of the brick to find the amount of plastic needed.
- Part (b) asks about a solid composite figure.
- There are 10 rectangular prisms measuring $\frac{5}{4}$ in. $\times \frac{5}{8}$ in. $\times \frac{3}{8}$ in.
$$V = 2\frac{119}{128} \text{ in.}^3 = 2.9296875 \text{ in.}^3$$
- There are 80 cylinders with a height of $\frac{1}{16}$ in. and a radius of $\frac{3}{32}$ in.
$V \approx 0.138 \text{ in.}^3$
- The volume could also be found by filling the ice cube tray with water and measuring the volume of the water!

What Is Your Answer?

- **Think-Pair-Share:** Students should read the question independently and then work with a partner to answer the question. When they have answered the question, the pair should compare their answer with another group and discuss any discrepancies.

Closure

- Use one of the composite solids from home (or distribute items to different pairs of students) and have students measure and compute the volume of the item.

The Dynamic Planning Tool
Editable Teacher's Resources at *BigIdeasMath.com*

ACTIVITY: Finding the Volumes of Composite Solids

Work with a partner.

a. Make a plan for estimating the amount of plastic it takes to make a standard eight-stud LEGO® Brick.

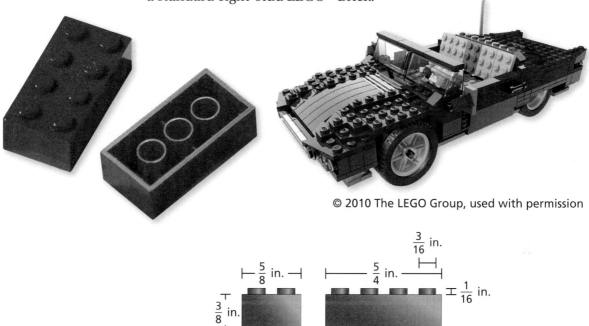

© 2010 The LEGO Group, used with permission

b. How much water, in cubic inches, would it take to make ten LEGO® Brick ice cubes?

What Is Your Answer?

3. IN YOUR OWN WORDS How can you estimate the volume of a composite solid? Try thinking of some alternative strategies.

Practice Use what you learned about the volumes of composite solids to complete Exercises 4–6 on page 336.

LEGO® and the LEGO logo, the brick and knob configuration, and the Minifigure™ are trademarks of the LEGO Group, and are used here with permission. ©2010 The LEGO Group. All rights reserved.

Check It Out
Lesson Tutorials
BigIdeasMath com

EXAMPLE 1 Finding the Volume of a Composite Solid

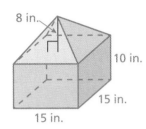

Find the volume of the composite solid.

The solid is made up of a square prism and a square pyramid. Find each volume.

Square prism

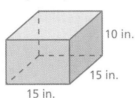

Square pyramid

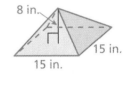

$$V = Bh$$
$$= 15(15)(10)$$
$$= 2250$$

$$V = \frac{1}{3}Bh$$
$$= \frac{1}{3}(15)(15)(8)$$
$$= 600$$

Find the sum: $2250 + 600 = 2850$ in.^{3}.

∴ The volume of the composite solid is 2850 cubic inches.

EXAMPLE 2 Finding the Volume of a Composite Solid

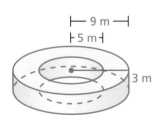

Find the volume of the composite solid. Round your answer to the nearest tenth.

The solid is a cylinder with a cylinder-shaped hole. Find each volume.

Entire Cylinder

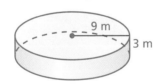

Cylinder-Shaped Hole

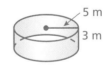

$$V = Bh$$
$$= \pi(9)^2(3)$$
$$= 243\pi$$

$$V = Bh$$
$$= \pi(5)^2(3)$$
$$= 75\pi$$

Find the difference: $243\pi - 75\pi = 168\pi \approx 527.5$ m^3.

∴ The volume of the composite solid is about 527.5 cubic meters.

Laurie's Notes

Introduction

Connect

- **Yesterday:** Students explored the volumes of composite figures.
- **Today:** Students will work with formulas to find the volume of a composite solid.

Motivate

- Discuss examples of composite solids. They could be items that are in your classroom, in your school, some portion of your school building, or a particular building in your town/city. Buildings are often made up of more than one solid. For the item(s) selected, discuss a strategy for how the volume would be found.

Lesson Notes

Example 1

- Work through the example, discussing the components of the solid.
- Model good problem solving techniques by writing the formula first, and then showing the substitution of the known variables.
- Remind students to show all of their work neatly and to label their answer with the correct units.
- **Connection:** Unlike working with the surface areas of composite figures, the composite volume is simply the sum of the individual volumes. In working with the surface areas of composite figures, recall that the areas of certain faces are in the interior of the solid and therefore the areas are subtracted or simply not computed.

Example 2

? "How is this solid made?" Students may describe it as a donut. A cylinder has been removed from the center of a cylinder.

- Work through the problem as shown by computing the volume of each cylinder and then subtracting. Note that each answer is left in terms of π and in the last step π is replaced by 3.14.

? "Is there another way to find the volume? Is it okay to subtract the two radii (9 m − 5 m) and find the volume of a cylinder with radius 4 meters? Explain." No. The answer is different. A cylinder with radius 4 and height 3 has a volume of 48π, which is quite different from 168π. This is actually a common student error.

Goal Today's lesson is finding the volumes of composite solids.

Start Thinking! and Warm Up

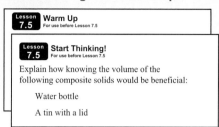

Extra Example 1

Find the volume of the composite solid. Round your answer to the nearest tenth.

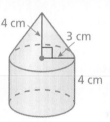

$48\pi \approx 150.7 \text{ cm}^3$

Extra Example 2

Find the volume of the composite solid. Round your answer to the nearest tenth.

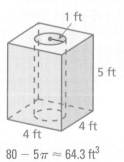

$80 - 5\pi \approx 64.3 \text{ ft}^3$

Laurie's Notes

On Your Own

1. 4.7 ft^3
2. $1680 - 48\pi \approx 1529.3 \text{ in.}^3$

Extra Example 3

Find the volume of the metal washer. Round your answer to the nearest tenth.

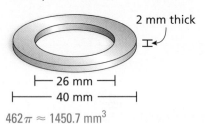

2 mm thick

├── 26 mm ──┤

├──── 40 mm ────┤

$462\pi \approx 1450.7 \text{ mm}^3$

On Your Own

3. The volume of the silver ring would be half the volume of the silver ring in Example 3.

4. $\frac{27}{4}\pi \approx 21.2 \text{ ft}^3$

English Language Learners

Visual

Have students make a table to organize the different solids within a composite solid. Have a row for each solid, with columns that include a diagram and the volume. They can then add the column with the volume of each solid to find the total volume of the composite solid.

On Your Own

- Discuss each solid before students begin so they understand the dimensions. The dotted lines are needed to convey the three-dimensional structure, however it may confuse some students.
- Encourage students to use words to label each part of the problem so their work is readable. Example: top pyramid; rectangular prism; cylindrical hole
- If enough board space is available, have two different students share their work for each problem.

Example 3

? "Have you solved a problem similar to this before?" Yes, Example 2

? Walk students through the example by asking the following questions.
- "What is the height of the coin?" 2.2 mm
- "What is the radius of the coin?" 11.5 mm
- "What is the radius of the inner portion?" 8.5 mm
- "What is the width of the silver ring portion?" 3 mm
- "Is this number used in computing the volume?" no
- Work through the problem as shown. Students will need to remember how to multiply decimals.

On Your Own

- Note that in Question 3, only the thickness is decreased. The radius stays the same.

Closure

- **Exit ticket:** Draw a sketch of a farm silo composed of a cylinder with a cone on top. The cylinder is 24 feet in height and 16 feet in diameter. The cone is also 16 feet in diameter and 9 feet in height. Find the volume of the silo. $1728\pi \approx 5425.92 \text{ ft}^3$

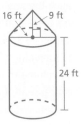

16 ft ⟋⟍ 9 ft

24 ft

Technology For the Teacher

The Dynamic Planning Tool
Editable Teacher's Resources at *BigIdeasMath.com*

On Your Own

Find the volume of the composite solid. Round your answer to the nearest tenth.

1.

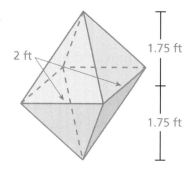

2 ft

1.75 ft

1.75 ft

2.

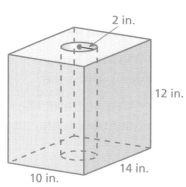

2 in.

12 in.

10 in.

14 in.

EXAMPLE ③ **Real-Life Application**

8.5 mm

11.5 mm

2.2 mm

What is the volume of the silver ring in an Argentine peso? Round your answer to the nearest tenth.

The coin is a cylinder. The silver ring is the portion remaining when the inner cylinder is removed. Find the volume of each cylinder.

Entire cylinder

11.5 mm

2.2 mm

Inner cylinder

8.5 mm

2.2 mm

$V = Bh$

$= \pi(11.5)^2(2.2)$

$= 290.95\pi$

$V = Bh$

$= \pi(8.5)^2(2.2)$

$= 158.95\pi$

Subtract the volume of the inner cylinder from the volume of the entire cylinder: $290.95\pi - 158.95\pi = 132\pi \approx 414.5 \text{ mm}^3$.

∴ The volume of the silver ring is about 414.5 cubic millimeters.

On Your Own

3. **WHAT IF?** In Example 3, how would the volume of the silver ring change if the coin were only half as thick?

4. Find the volume of the composite solid. Round your answer to the nearest tenth.

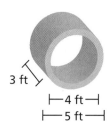

3 ft

4 ft

5 ft

Vocabulary and Concept Check

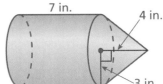
7 in.   4 in.
3 in.

1. **VOCABULARY** What is a composite solid?

2. **WRITING** Explain how to find the volume of the composite solid.

3. **CRITICAL THINKING** Explain how finding the volume in Example 2 is different from finding the volume in Example 1.

Practice and Problem Solving

Find the volume of the composite solid. Round your answer to the nearest tenth.

 4.
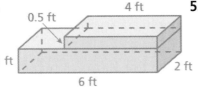
0.5 ft   4 ft
1 ft
6 ft   2 ft

5.
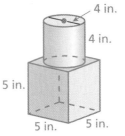
4 in.
4 in.
5 in.
5 in.   5 in.

6.
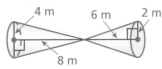
4 m   6 m   2 m
8 m

7.
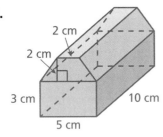
2 cm
2 cm
3 cm   10 cm
5 cm

8.
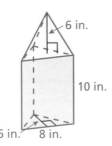
6 in.
10 in.
6 in.   8 in.

9.
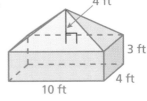
4 ft
3 ft
10 ft   4 ft

10.
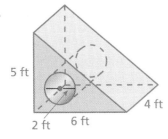
5 ft
4 ft
2 ft   6 ft

11.
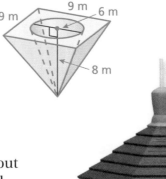
9 m   9 m   6 m
8 m

12. **BIRD FEEDER** The cedar waxwing measures about 6 inches from head to tail. The green hexagonal part of the bird feeder has a base area of 18 square inches. Estimate how much bird seed the bird feeder will hold. Explain how you found your estimate.

Assignment Guide and Homework Check

Level	Day 1 Activity Assignment	Day 2 Lesson Assignment	Homework Check
Basic	4–6, 17–19	1–3, 7–11, 13	2, 7, 10, 13
Average	4–6, 17–19	1–3, 7–11, 13, 14	2, 7, 10, 13
Advanced	4–6, 17–19	1–3, 8–16 even, 15	2, 10, 12, 14

Common Errors

- **Exercises 4–11** Students may find the volumes of the two figures and choose one as the final volume instead of adding (or subtracting) the volumes. Remind them that finding the volumes of both solids is only the first step. They must then determine whether to add or subtract the volumes for the final volume of the composite solid.
- **Exercises 4–11** Some students may continue to make the same mistakes as in previous sections when finding the volumes of different solids. Remind them of the mistakes they have made before and work through the corrections so that they understand what they did wrong.
- **Exercise 12** Students may think that there is not enough information to solve the problem. Ask them what the height of the bird is and how the bird's height relates to the volume of the birdfeeder.

7.5 Record and Practice Journal

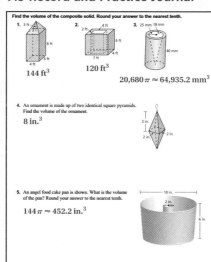

 Vocabulary and Concept Check

1. A composite solid is a solid that is made up of more than one solid.

2. Find the volume of the cylinder and the cone. Then add them together.

3. In Example 2, you had to subtract the volume of the cylinder-shaped hole from the volume of the entire cylinder. In Example 1, you had to find the volumes of the square prism and the square pyramid and add them together.

 **Practice and Problem Solving**

4. 16 ft^3

5. $125 + 16\pi \approx 175.2 \text{ in.}^3$

6. $\dfrac{56}{3}\pi \approx 58.6 \text{ m}^3$

7. 220 cm^3

8. 288 in.^3

9. 173.3 ft^3

10. $60 - 4\pi \approx 47.4 \text{ ft}^3$

11. $216 - 24\pi \approx 140.6 \text{ m}^3$

12. 126 in.^3; The height of the green hexagonal part is about 6 inches. The height of the hexagonal pyramid is about 3 inches. Then find the volume of each solid and add them together.

Practice and Problem Solving

13. a. *Sample answer:* 80%

   b. *Sample answer:*
$100\pi \approx 314$ in.^{3}

14. a. $159 + 18.00625\pi$
     ≈ 215.5 in.^{3}

   b. 1.5 lb

15. 13.875 in.^{3}; The volume
of the hexagonal prism is
10.5(0.75) and the volume of
the hexagonal pyramid is
$\frac{1}{3}(6)(3)$.

16. See *Taking Math Deeper*.

Fair Game Review

17. $\frac{25}{9}$ **18.** $\frac{81}{49}$

19. B

Mini-Assessment

**Find the volume of the composite solid.
Round your answer to the nearest tenth.**

1.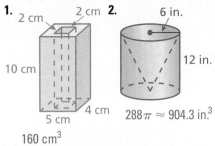

160 cm^3

2 cm, 2 cm, 10 cm, 5 cm, 4 cm

2. 6 in., 12 in. $288\pi \approx 904.3$ in.^{3}

3. Find the volume of the wedding cake.
Round your answer to the nearest
tenth.

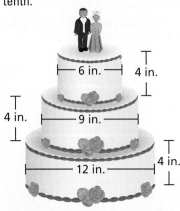

6 in., 4 in., 4 in., 9 in., 4 in., 12 in., 4 in.

$261\pi \approx 819.5$ in.^{3}

Taking Math Deeper

Exercise 16

This is a logic puzzle. It gives students a chance to use deductive reasoning to
determine the volume of each type of solid.

①   This one   than this
     is 8 more   one.

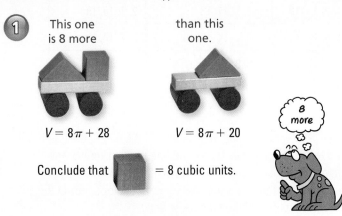

$V = 8\pi + 28$ $V = 8\pi + 20$

8 more

Conclude that ▪ = 8 cubic units.

② Note that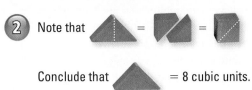

Conclude that ▲ = 8 cubic units.

③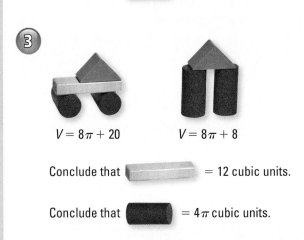

$V = 8\pi + 20$ $V = 8\pi + 8$

Conclude that ▭ = 12 cubic units.

Conclude that ⬤ = 4π cubic units.

Reteaching and Enrichment Strategies

If students need help...	If students got it...

Resources by Chapter
  • Practice A and Practice B
  • Puzzle Time
Record and Practice Journal Practice
Differentiating the Lesson
Lesson Tutorials
Skills Review Handbook
	Resources by Chapter
	  • Enrichment and Extension
	  • School-to-Work
	  • Financial Literacy
	Start the next section

13. CAKE The raspberry layer cake has a diameter of 10 inches and a height of 5 inches.

   a. About what percent of the cake is remaining?

   b. Estimate the volume of the remaining cake.

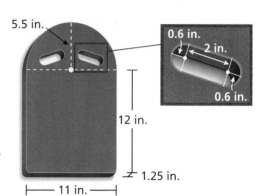

14. KICKBOARD A foam kickboard used for swimming has two identical hand grips.

   a. Find the volume of the kickboard.

   b. One cubic inch of foam weighs about 0.007 pound. How much does the kickboard weigh?

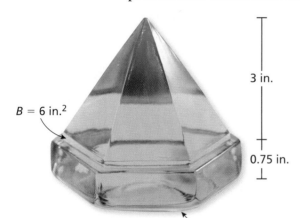

15. PAPERWEIGHT Estimate the amount of glass in the paperweight. Explain how you found your estimate.

16. ✸**Puzzle**✸ The volume of each group of solids is given. Find the volume of each of the four types of blocks.

$V = 8\pi + 8$

$V = 8\pi + 28$

$V = 8\pi + 20$

 Fair Game Review What you learned in previous grades & lessons

The two figures are similar. Find the ratio (red to blue) of the areas. *(Skills Review Handbook)*

17.
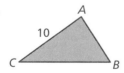

18.
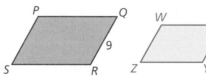

19. MULTIPLE CHOICE A fire hydrant releases 1200 gallons of water in 4 minutes. What is the rate of release in gallons per second? *(Skills Review Handbook)*

   Ⓐ 3 gal/sec   Ⓑ 5 gal/sec   Ⓒ 30 gal/sec   Ⓓ 300 gal/sec

STANDARDS OF LEARNING
8.7

Essential Question When the dimensions of a solid increase by a factor of k, how does the surface area change? How does the volume change?

1 ACTIVITY: Comparing Volumes and Surface Areas

Work with a partner. Copy and complete the table. Describe the pattern. Are the solids similar? Explain your reasoning.

a.

Radius	1	1	1	1	1
Height	1	2	3	4	5
Surface Area					
Volume					

b.

Radius	1	2	3	4	5
Height	1	2	3	4	5
Surface Area					
Volume					

Laurie's Notes

Introduction

For the Teacher

- **Goal:** Students will explore what happens to the surface areas and volumes of solids whose dimensions are increased by a factor of k.
- In this lesson, students will investigate similar figures in space. You may want to begin with a few review questions about similar figures.

Motivate

- **Story Time:** Retell a portion of the story of *Goldilocks and the 3 Bears*. Focus on the 3 sizes of porridge bowls, chairs, and beds.
- Share with students that Papa Bear's mattress was twice as long, twice as wide, and twice as high as Baby Bear's mattress. So, are there twice as many feathers in Papa Bear's feather bed mattress?
- This question will be answered at the end of the class.

Activity Notes

Activity 1

- Remind students to leave their answers in terms of π.
- **?** To help students see the pattern in the first table, ask the following questions.
    - "Describe the changes in the dimensions." radius same, height increases by 1
    - "How does the surface area change?" increases by 2π
    - "How does the volume change?" increases by π
    - "Compare each figure's height to the original figure's height. Do the same for surface areas and volumes. What do you notice?" The volumes are multiplied by the same number as the heights.
- **?** To help students see the pattern in the second table, ask the following questions.
    - "Describe the changes in the dimensions." radius and height each increase by 1
    - "Compare each figure's height to the original figure's height. Do the same for radii, surface areas, and volumes. What do you notice?" The heights and radii are multiplied by the same number. The surface areas are multiplied by the square of this number and the volumes are multiplied by the cube of this number.
- **?** "Are the cylinders similar in part (a)? Explain." No, only the height increased, not the radius.
- **?** "Are the cylinders similar in part (b)? Explain." Yes, both the radius and height are increasing by the same factor.

Standards of Learning

8.7(a) The student will investigate and solve practical problems involving volume and surface area of prisms, cylinders, cones, and pyramids.

Previous Learning

Students should be familiar with similar figures, surface area formulas, and volume formulas.

Start Thinking! and Warm Up

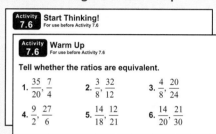

7.6 Record and Practice Journal

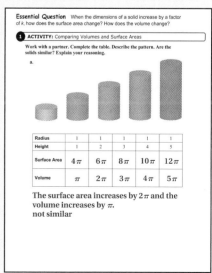

Differentiated Instruction

In the examples, check to be sure that students are correctly identifying corresponding sides. Remind them that they have to identify corresponding linear measures to write proportions before solving them.

7.6 Record and Practice Journal

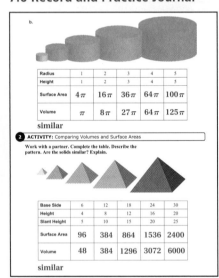

Radius	1	2	3	4	5
Height	1	2	3	4	5
Surface Area	4π	16π	36π	64π	100π
Volume	π	8π	27π	64π	125π

similar

2 ACTIVITY: Comparing Volumes and Surface Areas

Work with a partner. Complete the table. Describe the pattern. Are the solids similar? Explain.

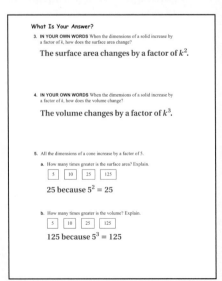

Base Side	6	12	18	24	30
Height	4	8	12	16	20
Slant Height	5	10	15	20	25
Surface Area	96	384	864	1536	2400
Volume	48	384	1296	3072	6000

similar

What Is Your Answer?

3. IN YOUR OWN WORDS When the dimensions of a solid increase by a factor of k, how does the surface area change?

The surface area changes by a factor of k^2.

4. IN YOUR OWN WORDS When the dimensions of a solid increase by a factor of k, how does the volume change?

The volume changes by a factor of k^3.

5. All the dimensions of a cone increase by a factor of 5.

a. How many times greater is the surface area? Explain.

25 because $5^2 = 25$

b. How many times greater is the volume? Explain.

125 because $5^3 = 125$

Laurie's Notes

Activity 2

- You want students to see a pattern. It may be helpful for students to use a calculator.
- Ask students to describe patterns they see. Remind them to think about factors (multiplication) versus addition. The first pyramid should be referred to as the original pyramid. Describe any patterns in terms of the original pyramid.
- **?** "Are the pyramids similar? Explain." yes; The three dimensions are all changing by factors of 2, 3, 4, and 5 times the original dimensions.
- To help students see the factor by which the surface areas and volumes are multiplied, they should divide the new surface area (or volume) by the original surface area (or volume).

Example for Pyramid 4

Base Side	$24 \div 6 = 4$	Multiplied by a scale factor of 4
Height	$16 \div 4 = 4$	Multiplied by a scale factor of 4
Slant Height	$20 \div 5 = 4$	Multiplied by a scale factor of 4
Surface Area	$1536 \div 96 = 16$	Multiplied by a scale factor of 4^2
Volume	$3072 \div 48 = 64$	Multiplied by a scale factor of 4^3

- **Big Idea:** When the dimensions of a solid are all multiplied by a scale factor of k, the surface area is multiplied by a scale factor of k^2 and the volume is multiplied by a scale factor of k^3.

What Is Your Answer?

- **Think-Pair-Share:** Students should read each question independently and then work with a partner to answer the questions. When they have answered the questions, the pair should compare their answers with another group and discuss any discrepancies.

Closure

- Refer to Papa Bear's feather bed mattress. If the dimensions are all double Baby Bear's mattress, how many times more feathers are there? 8 times more feathers

Technology For the Teacher

Dynamic Classroom

The Dynamic Planning Tool
Editable Teacher's Resources at *BigIdeasMath.com*

ACTIVITY: Comparing Volumes and Surface Areas

Work with a partner. Copy and complete the table. Describe the pattern. Are the solids similar? Explain.

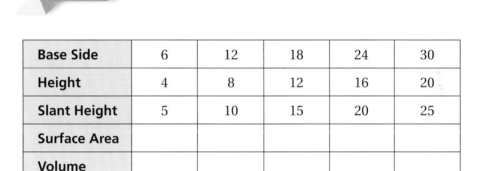

Base Side	6	12	18	24	30
Height	4	8	12	16	20
Slant Height	5	10	15	20	25
Surface Area					
Volume					

What Is Your Answer?

3. **IN YOUR OWN WORDS** When the dimensions of a solid increase by a factor of k, how does the surface area change?

4. **IN YOUR OWN WORDS** When the dimensions of a solid increase by a factor of k, how does the volume change?

5. All the dimensions of a cone increase by a factor of 5.

   a. How many times greater is the surface area? Explain.

   | 5 | 10 | 25 | 125 |

   b. How many times greater is the volume? Explain.

   | 5 | 10 | 25 | 125 |

Practice

Use what you learned about the surface areas and volumes of similar solids to complete Exercises 4–6 on page 343.

Check It Out
Lesson Tutorials
BigIdeasMath.com

Key Vocabulary 🔊
similar solids, *p. 340*

Solids of the same type that have proportional corresponding linear measures are **similar solids**.

EXAMPLE 1 Identifying Similar Solids

Cylinder B
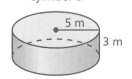
5 m
3 m

Cylinder C
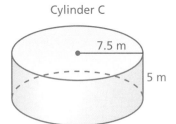
7.5 m
5 m

Which cylinder is similar to Cylinder A?

Check to see if corresponding linear measures are proportional.

Cylinder A
6 m
4 m

Cylinder A and Cylinder B

$$\frac{\text{Height of A}}{\text{Height of B}} = \frac{4}{3} \qquad \frac{\text{Radius of A}}{\text{Radius of B}} = \frac{6}{5}$$

Not proportional

Cylinder A and Cylinder C

$$\frac{\text{Height of A}}{\text{Height of C}} = \frac{4}{5} \qquad \frac{\text{Radius of A}}{\text{Radius of C}} = \frac{6}{7.5} = \frac{4}{5}$$

Proportional

∴ So, Cylinder C is similar to Cylinder A.

EXAMPLE 2 Finding Missing Measures in Similar Solids

Cone X

13 yd
5 yd

Cone Y

ℓ
7 yd

The cones are similar. Find the missing slant height ℓ.

$$\frac{\text{Radius of X}}{\text{Radius of Y}} = \frac{\text{Slant height of X}}{\text{Slant height of Y}}$$

$$\frac{5}{7} = \frac{13}{\ell} \qquad \text{Substitute.}$$

$$5\ell = 91 \qquad \text{Use Cross Products Property.}$$

$$\ell = 18.2 \qquad \text{Divide each side by 5.}$$

∴ The slant height is 18.2 yards.

On Your Own

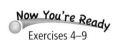
Now You're Ready
Exercises 4–9

1. Cylinder D has a radius of 7.5 meters and a height of 4.5 meters. Which cylinder in Example 1 is similar to Cylinder D?

2. The prisms are similar. Find the missing width and length.

Prism A
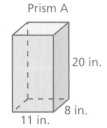
20 in.
8 in.
11 in.

Prism B
8 in.
ℓ
w

🔊 Multi-Language Glossary at BigIdeasMath.com.

Laurie's Notes

Introduction

Connect
- **Yesterday:** Students explored what happens to the surface areas and volumes of solids when the dimensions are multiplied by a factor of *k*.
- **Today:** Students will use properties of similar solids to solve problems.

Motivate
- **Movie Time:** Hold an object that is miniature in size (model car, doll house item, statue, and so on). Tell students that this is a prop from a movie set. The movie plot is about giants. In order to make people look large, all of the props have been shrunk proportionally.
- Spend some time talking about movie making. Creating props larger than normal will make real people appear smaller than normal, and vice versa.

Lesson Notes

Example 1
- Note that the definition simply states that the corresponding linear measures must be in the same proportion. This means that solids can increase or decrease proportionally.
- **?** "What is a proportion?" an equation of two equal ratios
- **?** "How do you know if two ratios are equal?" Students might say by eyesight; by simple arithmetic, like $\frac{1}{2} = \frac{2}{4}$; that the ratios simplify to the same ratio. Students should recall the Cross Products Property.
- Work through the example.
- Be sure to write the words and the numbers. Use language such as "The ratio of the height of A to the height of B is 4 to 3."
- **?** "How do you know $\frac{6}{7.5} = \frac{4}{5}$?" Answers may vary depending upon students' number sense. By the Cross Products Property $6 \times 5 = 7.5 \times 4$.

Example 2
- **?** "By the definition of similar solids, what can you determine about two similar cones?" Corresponding linear measures are proportional.
- Set up the proportion and solve for the missing slant height.

On Your Own
- **Think-Pair-Share:** Students should read each question independently and then work with a partner to answer the questions. When they have answered the questions, the pair should compare their answers with another group and discuss any discrepancies.
- Ask volunteers to put their work on the board.

Goal Today's lesson is finding the surface areas and volumes of **similar solids**.

Lesson Materials	
Introduction	**Closure**
• miniature object	• miniature object

Start Thinking! and Warm Up

Lesson 7.6 Warm Up
For use before Lesson 7.6

Lesson 7.6 Start Thinking!
For use before Lesson 7.6

Explain to a partner how to determine if two figures are similar.

Extra Example 1
Which prism is similar to Prism A?

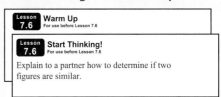

Prism A   Prism B   Prism C

Prism B

Extra Example 2
The square pyramids are similar. Find the length of the base of Pyramid E.

Pyramid D   Pyramid E

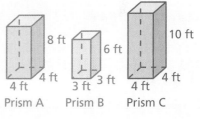

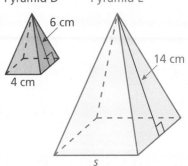

$9\frac{1}{3}$ cm

On Your Own
1. Cylinder B
2. $w = 3.2$ in.
   $\ell = 4.4$ in.

Laurie's Notes

Key Ideas

- Write the Key Ideas.
- **Example:** If the linear dimensions of B are double A, dimensions would be in the ratio of $\frac{1}{2}$, and the surface areas would be in the ratio of $\left(\frac{1}{2}\right)^2$ or $\frac{1}{4}$.
- Refer to yesterday's activity to confirm that this relationship was found in Activity 1, part (b) and Activity 2.

Example 3

? "Do you have enough information to solve this problem? Explain." Yes; The heights are in the ratio of $\frac{6}{10}$, so the surface areas are in the ratio of $\left(\frac{6}{10}\right)^2$.

- Set up the problem and solve.
- **FYI:** Notice that the problem is solved using the Multiplication Property of Equality. It could also be solved using the Cross Products Property.
- **Connection:** The ratio:

$$\frac{\text{original dimension}}{\text{new dimension}}$$

is the scale factor. The square of the scale factor is used to find the new surface area.

On Your Own

- Students should first identify the ratio of the corresponding linear measurements. Question 3: $\frac{5}{8}$; Question 4: $\frac{5}{4}$
- Ask student volunteers to share their work at the board.

Extra Example 3

The cones are similar. What is the surface area of Cone G? Round your answer to the nearest tenth.

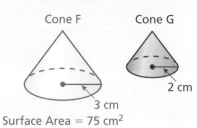

Cone F   Cone G

3 cm

2 cm

Surface Area = 75 cm²

about 33.3 cm²

On Your Own

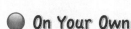

3. 237.5 m²

4. 171.9 cm²

English Language Learners

Vocabulary

Have students add the key vocabulary *similar solids* to their notebooks with a description of the meaning in their own words.

 **Key Ideas**

Linear Measures

 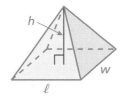 

Surface Areas of Similar Solids

If two solids are similar, then the ratio of their surface areas is equal to the square of the ratio of their corresponding linear measures.

Solid A 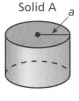 Solid B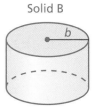

$$\frac{\text{Surface Area of A}}{\text{Surface Area of B}} = \left(\frac{a}{b}\right)^2$$

EXAMPLE 3 Finding Surface Area

Pyramid A

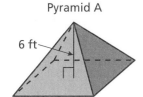

6 ft

Pyramid B

10 ft

Surface Area = 600 ft²

The pyramids are similar. What is the surface area of Pyramid A?

$$\frac{\text{Surface Area of A}}{\text{Surface Area of B}} = \left(\frac{\text{Height of A}}{\text{Height of B}}\right)^2$$

$$\frac{S}{600} = \left(\frac{6}{10}\right)^2 \qquad \text{Substitute.}$$

$$\frac{S}{600} = \frac{36}{100} \qquad \text{Evaluate power.}$$

$$\frac{S}{600} \cdot 600 = \frac{36}{100} \cdot 600 \qquad \text{Multiply each side by 600.}$$

$$S = 216 \qquad \text{Simplify.}$$

∴ The surface area of Pyramid A is 216 square feet.

⬤ **On Your Own**

The solids are similar. Find the surface area of the red solid. Round your answer to the nearest tenth.

3.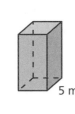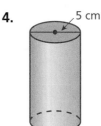

8 m 5 m

Surface Area = 608 m²

4.

5 cm 4 cm

Surface Area = 110 cm²

 **Key Idea**

Volumes of Similar Solids

If two solids are similar, then the ratio of their volumes is equal to the cube of the ratio of their corresponding linear measures.

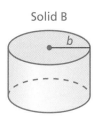

Solid A a

Solid B b

$$\frac{\text{Volume of A}}{\text{Volume of B}} = \left(\frac{a}{b}\right)^3$$

EXAMPLE ④ **Standardized Test Practice**

Original Tank

Volume = 2000 ft³

The dimensions of the touch tank at an aquarium are doubled. What is the volume of the new touch tank?

(A) 150 ft³   (B) 4000 ft³

(C) 8000 ft³   (D) 16,000 ft³

The dimensions are doubled, so the ratio of the dimensions in the original tank to the dimensions in the new tank is 1 : 2.

$$\frac{\text{Original volume}}{\text{New volume}} = \left(\frac{\text{Original dimension}}{\text{New dimension}}\right)^3$$

$\dfrac{2000}{V} = \left(\dfrac{1}{2}\right)^3$ Substitute.

$\dfrac{2000}{V} = \dfrac{1}{8}$ Evaluate power.

$16{,}000 = V$ Use Cross Products Property.

Study Tip

When the dimensions of a solid are multiplied by k, the surface area is multiplied by k^2 and the volume is multiplied by k^3.

∴ The volume of the new tank is 16,000 cubic feet. The correct answer is (D).

● **On Your Own**

Now You're Ready
Exercises 10–13

The solids are similar. Find the volume of the red solid. Round your answer to the nearest tenth.

5.

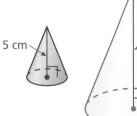

5 cm

12 cm

Volume = 288 cm³

6.

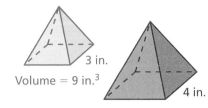

3 in.

Volume = 9 in.³

4 in.

Laurie's Notes

Key Idea

- Write the Key Idea.
- **Example:** If the linear dimensions of B are double A, dimensions would be in the ratio of $\frac{1}{2}$, and the volumes would be in the ratio of $\left(\frac{1}{2}\right)^3$ or $\frac{1}{8}$.
- Refer to yesterday's activity to confirm that this relationship was found in Activity 1, part (b) and Activity 2.

Example 4

- Write the problem in words to help students recognize how the numbers are being substituted.
- **Common Misconception:** Many students think that when you double the dimensions, the surface area and volume also double. This Big Idea takes time for students to fully understand.
- **Connection:** The ratio:

$$\frac{\text{original dimension}}{\text{new dimension}}$$

is the scale factor. The cube of the scale factor is used to find the new volume.

On Your Own

- Students should first identify the ratio of the corresponding linear measurements. Question 5: $\frac{5}{12}$; Question 6: $\frac{4}{3}$
- Ask student volunteers to share their work at the board.

Closure

- Use one of the miniature items used to motivate the lesson and ask a question related to surface area or volume. Some miniature items have a scale printed on the item.

Extra Example 4

The cylinders are similar. Find the volume of Cylinder J. Round your answer to the nearest tenth.

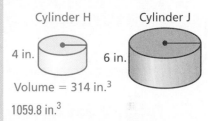

Cylinder H   Cylinder J

4 in.   6 in.

Volume = 314 in.³

1059.8 in.³

On Your Own

5. 20.8 cm³

6. 21.3 in.³

Vocabulary and Concept Check

1. Similar solids are solids of the same type that have proportional corresponding linear measures.

2. *Sample answer:*

 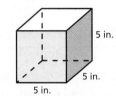

3. a. $\frac{4}{9}$

   b. $\frac{8}{27}$

Practice and Problem Solving

4. yes

5. no

6. yes

7. no

8. 25 in.

9. $b = 18$ m
   $c = 19.5$ m
   $h = 9$ m

Assignment Guide and Homework Check

Level	Day 1 Activity Assignment	Day 2 Lesson Assignment	Homework Check
Basic	4–6, 20–23	1–3, 7–16	7, 8, 10, 16
Average	4–6, 20–23	1–3, 7–14, 16, 18	7, 8, 10, 16
Advanced	4–6, 20–23	1–3, 7, 8–14 even, 16–19	7, 8, 10, 16

Common Errors

- **Exercises 4–7** Students may only compare two sets of measurements instead of all three. The bases of two figures may be similar, but the heights may not be proportional to the length or width. Remind them to check all of the corresponding linear measures when determining if two solids are similar. Ask them how many sets of ratios they need to write for each type of solid.

- **Exercises 8 and 9** Students may write the proportion incorrectly.

  For example, in Exercise 8, a student may write $\frac{10}{4} = \frac{10}{d}$ which gives $d = 4$ instead of $d = 25$. Remind them to write the proportion with the dimensions of one solid in the numerator and the dimensions of the other solid in the denominator.

7.6 Record and Practice Journal

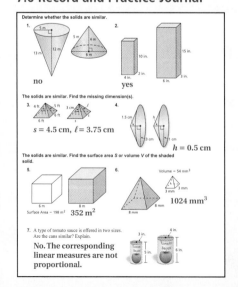

✓ Vocabulary and Concept Check

1. **VOCABULARY** What are similar solids?

2. **OPEN-ENDED** Draw two similar solids and label their corresponding linear measures.

3. **REASONING** The ratio of the corresponding linear measures of Cube A to Cube B is $\frac{2}{3}$.

   a. Find the ratio of the area of one face of Cube A to the area of one face of Cube B.

   b. Find the ratio of the volume of Cube A to the volume of Cube B.

 ## Practice and Problem Solving

Determine whether the solids are similar.

① **4.**

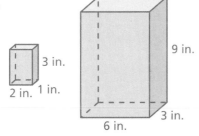

3 in.
2 in. 1 in.
9 in.
6 in. 3 in.

5.

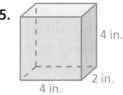

4 in.
4 in. 2 in.
4 in.
2 in. 1 in.

6.

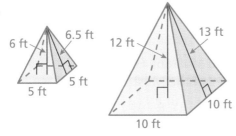

6 ft 6.5 ft
5 ft
5 ft
12 ft 13 ft
10 ft
10 ft

7.

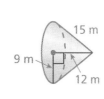 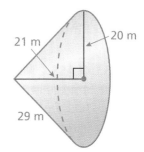

15 m
9 m
12 m
21 m 20 m
29 m

The solids are similar. Find the missing dimension(s).

② **8.**

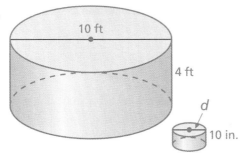

10 ft
4 ft
d
10 in.

9.

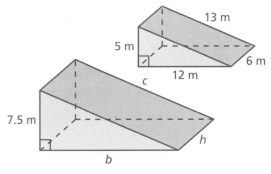

13 m
5 m
6 m
12 m
c
7.5 m
b
h

The solids are similar. Find the surface area *S* or volume *V* of the red solid. Round your answer to the nearest tenth.

③ ④ 10.

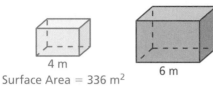

4 m
Surface Area = 336 m²

6 m

11.

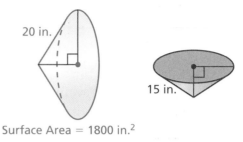

20 in.

15 in.

Surface Area = 1800 in.²

12.

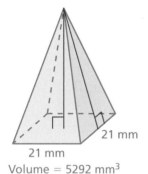

21 mm

21 mm
Volume = 5292 mm³

7 mm
7 mm

13.

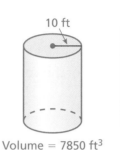

12 ft

10 ft

Volume = 7850 ft³

14. **ERROR ANALYSIS** The ratio of the corresponding linear measures of two similar solids is 3 : 5. The volume of the smaller solid is 108 cubic inches. Describe and correct the error in finding the volume of the larger solid.

$$\frac{108}{V} = \left(\frac{3}{5}\right)^2$$

$$\frac{108}{V} = \frac{9}{25}$$

$$300 = V$$

The volume of the larger solid is 300 cubic inches.

15. **MIXED FRUIT** The ratio of the corresponding linear measures of two similar cans of fruit is 4 to 7. The smaller can has a surface area of 220 square centimeters. Find the surface area of the larger can.

16. **CLASSIC MUSTANG** The volume of a 1968 Ford Mustang GT engine is 390 cubic inches. Which scale model of the Mustang has the greater engine volume, a 1 : 18 scale model or a 1 : 24 scale model? How much greater?

Common Errors

- **Exercises 10–13** Students may forget to square or cube the ratio of the corresponding linear measures when finding the surface area or volume of the red solid. Remind them of the Key Ideas.
- **Exercises 10–13** Students may cube the ratio of corresponding linear measures when finding surface area, or square the ratio of corresponding linear measures when finding volume. Remind them of the Key Ideas. The ratio of corresponding linear measures is squared for surface area and cubed for volume.
- **Exercise 15** Students may invert the ratio of the surface area when writing the proportion. When they look at the ratio of corresponding linear measures as a fraction, ask whether the numerator or denominator corresponds to the smaller figure. This will help them know where to place the surface area in the proportion.

Practice and Problem Solving

10. 756 m^2

11. 1012.5 in.^2

12. 196 mm^3

13. $13{,}564.8 \text{ ft}^3$

14. The ratio of the volumes of two similar solids is equal to the cube of the ratio of their corresponding linear measures.

$$\frac{108}{V} = \left(\frac{3}{5}\right)^3$$

$$\frac{108}{V} = \frac{27}{125}$$

$$V = 500 \text{ in.}^3$$

15. 673.75 cm^2

16. $1 : 18$ scale model; about 0.04 in.^3

Practice and Problem Solving

17. a. yes; Because all circles are similar, the slant height and the circumference of the base of the cones are proportional.

b. no; because the ratio of the volumes of similar solids is equal to the cube of the ratio of their corresponding linear measures

18. See Additional Answers.

19. See *Taking Math Deeper*.

 ### Fair Game Review

20. 39   **21.** 1

22. 0   **23.** C

Mini-Assessment

The solids are similar. Find the surface area S of the red solid. Round your answer to the nearest tenth.

1. 288 m²

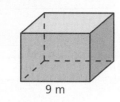

3 m   9 m

Surface Area = 32 m²

2. 37.8 in.²

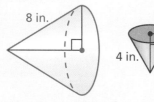

8 in.   4 in.

Surface Area = 151 in.²

3. The candles are similar. Find the volume of the larger candle. 600 in.³

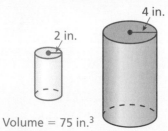

2 in.   4 in.

Volume = 75 in.³

Taking Math Deeper

Exercise 19

This problem is a straightforward application of the two main concepts of the lesson. That is, with similar solids, surface area is proportional to the square of the scale factor and volume is proportional to the cube of the scale factor. Even so, students have trouble with this problem because they don't see that enough information is given to create the table. The thing to learn here is that it is possible to compare two surfaces without knowing either one of them.

① Make a table. Include the height of each doll.

Heights go up by 1

Height	1	2	3	4	5	6	7
Surface Area	S	$4S$	$9S$	$16S$	$25S$	$36S$	$49S$
Volume	V	$8V$	$27V$	$64V$	$125V$	$216V$	$343V$

② Compare the surface areas of the dolls.

③ Compare the volumes of the dolls.

Matryoshka dolls, or Russian nested dolls, are also called stacking dolls. A set of matryoshkas consists of a wooden figure which can be pulled apart to reveal another figure of the same sort inside. It has, in turn, another figure inside, and so on. The number of nested figures is usually five or more.

Reteaching and Enrichment Strategies

If students need help...	If students got it...
Resources by Chapter • Practice A and Practice B • Puzzle Time Record and Practice Journal Practice Differentiating the Lesson Lesson Tutorials Skills Review Handbook	Resources by Chapter • Enrichment and Extension • School-to-Work • Financial Literacy • Technology Connection Start the next section

17. **Critical Thinking** You and a friend make paper cones to collect beach glass. You cut out the largest possible three-fourths circle from each piece of paper.

a. Are the cones similar? Explain your reasoning.

b. Your friend says that because your sheet of paper is twice as large, your cone will hold exactly twice the volume of beach glass. Is this true? Explain your reasoning.

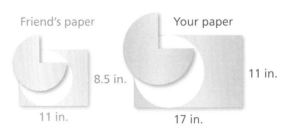

Friend's paper
Your paper
8.5 in.
11 in.
11 in.
17 in.

18. **MARBLE STATUE** You have a small marble statue of Wolfgang Mozart that is 10 inches tall and weighs 16 pounds. The original statue in Vienna is 7 feet tall.

a. Estimate the weight of the original statue. Explain your reasoning.

b. If the original statue were 20 feet tall, how much would it weigh?

Wolfgang Mozart

19. **RUSSIAN DOLLS** The largest doll is 7 inches tall. Each of the other dolls is 1 inch shorter than the next larger doll. Make a table that compares the surface areas and volumes of the seven dolls.

 Fair Game Review *What you learned in previous grades & lessons*

Add. *(Skills Review Handbook)*

20. $69 + (-31) + 7 + (-6)$ 21. $-2 + (-5) + (-12) + 20$ 22. $10 + (-6) + (-5) + 1$

23. **MULTIPLE CHOICE** What is the mean of the numbers below? *(Skills Review Handbook)*

   14, 6, 21, 8, 14, 19, 30

   Ⓐ 6   Ⓑ 15   Ⓒ 16   Ⓓ 56

1. Determine whether the solids are similar. *(Section 7.6)*

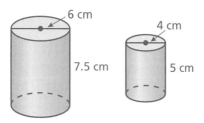

2. The prisms are similar. Find the missing width and height. *(Section 7.6)*

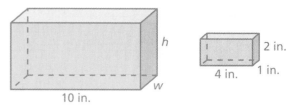

Find the volume of the composite solid. Round your answer to the nearest tenth.
(Section 7.5)

3.

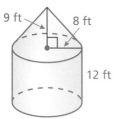

4.

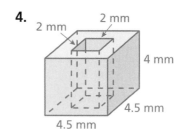

5. The solids are similar. Find the surface area of the red solid. *(Section 7.6)*

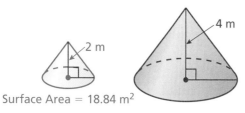

Surface Area = 18.84 m²

6. **ARCADE** You win a token after playing an arcade game. What is the volume of the gold ring? Round your answer to the nearest tenth. *(Section 7.5)*

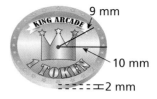

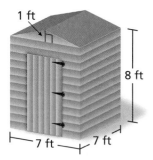

7. **SHED** What is the volume of the storage shed? *(Section 7.5)*

8. **JEWELRY BOXES** The ratio of the corresponding linear measures of two similar jewelry boxes is 2 to 3. The larger box has a volume of 162 cubic inches. Find the volume of the smaller jewelry box. *(Section 7.6)*

9. **GELATIN** You make a dessert with lemon gelatin and lime gelatin. What percent of the dessert is lime-flavored? Explain. *(Section 7.5)*

Alternative Assessment Options

Math Chat   Student Reflective Focus Question
Structured Interview   Writing Prompt

Math Chat
Ask students to use their own words to summarize what they know about finding volumes of composite solids and similar solids. Be sure that they include examples. Select students at random to present their summary to the class.

Study Help Sample Answers
Remind students to complete Graphic Organizers for the rest of the chapter.

4. Volume of a composite solid

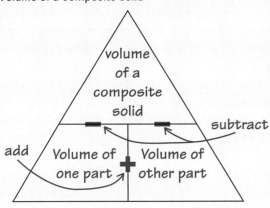

5. Surface areas of similar solids

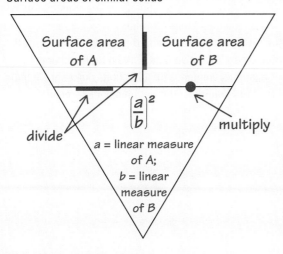

6. Available at *BigIdeasMath.com.*

Reteaching and Enrichment Strategies

If students need help. . .	If students got it. . .

Resources by Chapter
  • Study Help
  • Practice A and Practice B
  • Puzzle Time
Lesson Tutorials
BigIdeasMath.com Practice Quiz
Practice from the Test Generator
	Resources by Chapter
	  • Enrichment and Extension
	  • School-to-Work
	Game Closet at *BigIdeasMath.com*
	Start the Chapter Review

Technology For the Teacher
Answer Presentation Tool

Assessment Book

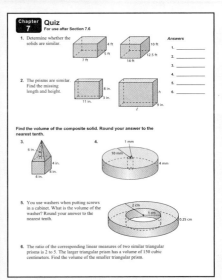

For the Teacher
Additional Review Options
- **Quiz**Show
- Big Ideas Test Generator
- Game Closet at *BigIdeasMath.com*
- Vocabulary Puzzle Builder
- Resources by Chapter
  Puzzle Time
  Study Help

Answers

1. 96 in.^{3}
2. 120 m^3
3. 607.5 mm^3
4. $40\pi \approx 125.6$ in.^{3}
5. $\dfrac{75}{8\pi} \approx 3.0$ m
6. $393.75\pi \approx 1236.4$ ft^3

Review of Common Errors

Exercises 1–3
- Students may write linear or square units for volume rather than cubic units. Remind them that volume is measured in cubic units.

Exercises 4–6
- Students may forget to square the radius when finding the area of the base. Remind them of the formula for area of a circle.
- Students may use the diameter instead of the radius.

Exercises 7–9
- Students may forget to multiply the area of the base by the height and/or the factor of $\dfrac{1}{3}$ when finding the volume of a pyramid. Encourage them to find the area of the base separately and then substitute it into the volume formula.
- Students may write the units incorrectly, often writing square units instead of cubic units. This is especially true when the area of the base is given.

Exercises 10–12
- Students may forget to square the radius when finding the area of the base. Remind them of the formula for area of a circle. Encourage them to write the parts of the formula for volume using different colors so that it is easier for them to keep track of their work.

Exercises 13–15
- Students may find the volumes of the solids that make up the composite solid and choose one as the volume of the composite solid, instead of adding or subtracting volumes as appropriate.

Exercises 16 and 17
- Students may forget to square or cube the ratio of the linear measures when finding the surface area or volume of the red solid.
- Students may cube the ratio of the linear measures when finding surface area, or square the ratio when finding volume. Take a few moments to examine the units. For example, volume is in cubic units, so it should make sense to cube the ratio of the heights of the pyramids in Exercise 16.

Check It Out
Vocabulary Help
BigIdeasMath.com

Review Key Vocabulary

volume, *p. 308*   similar solids, *p. 340*

Review Examples and Exercises

7.1 Volumes of Prisms (pp. 306–311)

Find the volume of the prism.

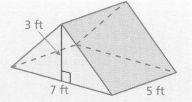

$V = Bh$	Write formula for volume.
$= \dfrac{1}{2}(7)(3) \cdot 5$	Substitute.
$= 52.5$	Multiply.

∴ The volume is 52.5 cubic feet.

Exercises

Find the volume of the prism.

1.
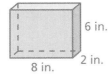

6 in.
8 in.   2 in.

2.
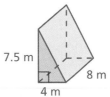

7.5 m
4 m   8 m

3.
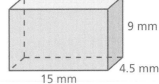

9 mm
15 mm   4.5 mm

7.2 Volumes of Cylinders (pp. 312–317)

Find the height of the cylinder. Round your answer to the nearest whole number.

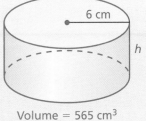

6 cm
h
Volume = 565 cm³

$V = Bh$	Write formula for volume.
$565 = \pi(6)^2(h)$	Substitute.
$565 = 36\pi h$	Simplify.
$5 \approx h$	Divide each side by 36π.

∴ The height is about 5 centimeters.

Exercises

Find the volume V or height h of the cylinder. Round your answer to the nearest tenth.

4.
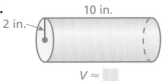

2 in.   10 in.
$V \approx$ ▨

5.
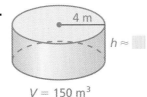

4 m
$h \approx$ ▨
$V = 150$ m³

6.
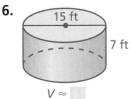

15 ft
7 ft
$V \approx$ ▨

7.3 **Volumes of Pyramids** *(pp. 318–323)*

Find the volume of the pyramid.

$$V = \frac{1}{3}Bh \qquad \text{Write formula for volume.}$$

$$= \frac{1}{3}(6)(5)(10) \qquad \text{Substitute.}$$

$$= 100 \qquad \text{Multiply.}$$

∴ The volume is 100 cubic yards.

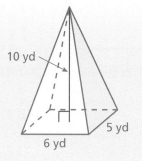

Exercises

Find the volume of the pyramid.

7.

8.

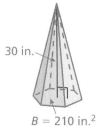

9.

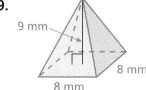

7.4 **Volumes of Cones** *(pp. 324–329)*

Find the height of the cone. Round your answer to the nearest tenth.

$$V = \frac{1}{3}Bh \qquad \text{Write formula for volume.}$$

$$900 = \frac{1}{3}\pi(6)^2(h) \qquad \text{Substitute.}$$

$$900 = 12\pi h \qquad \text{Simplify.}$$

$$23.9 \approx h \qquad \text{Divide each side by } 12\pi.$$

∴ The height is about 23.9 millimeters.

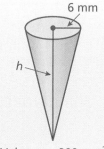

Exercises

Find the volume _V_ or height _h_ of the cone. Round your answer to the nearest tenth.

10.

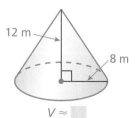

11.

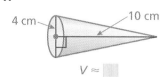

12.

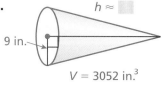

Review Game

Volume

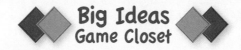

Materials

- a variety of containers of different shapes and sizes
- liquid measuring devices
- water

For the Student

Additional Practice

- Lesson Tutorials
- Study Help (textbook)
- Student Website
  Multi-Language Glossary
  Practice Assessments

Directions

At the start of the chapter, have students bring in containers of different shapes and sizes. The containers should be shaped the same as the solids being studied in the chapter, they should be able to hold water, and they should be small enough so that they do not require a lot of water to fill. Collect containers until you have a sufficient variety of shapes and enough for the number of groups you want to have.

Work in groups. Give each group a container. Each group calculates the volume of the container and passes it to another group. Continue until all groups have calculated the volumes of the containers. When calculations are completed, each group measures the volume of a container using water. Measured volumes are shared with the class and compared to the calculated volumes.

Who Wins?

The group whose calculated volume is closest to the correct measured volume receives 1 point. The group with the most points wins.

Answers

7. 850 ft^3

8. 2100 in.^3

9. 192 mm^3

10. $256\pi \approx 803.8 \text{ m}^3$

11. $\frac{40}{3}\pi \approx 41.9 \text{ cm}^3$

12. $\frac{3052}{27\pi} \approx 36.0 \text{ in.}$

13. $360\pi \approx 1130.4 \text{ m}^3$

14. 132 ft^3

15. $12\pi \approx 37.7 \text{ cm}^3$

16. 576 m^3

17. 86.625 yd^2

My Thoughts on the Chapter

What worked. . .

What did not work. . .

What I would do differently. . .

7.5 Volumes of Composite Solids (pp. 332–337)

Find the volume of the composite solid. Round your answer to the nearest tenth.

Square Prism	Cylinder
$V = Bh$	$V = Bh$
$= (12)(12)(9)$	$= \pi(5)^2(9)$
$= 1296$	$= 225\pi \approx 706.5$

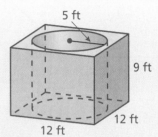

Find the difference: $1296 - 706.5 = 589.5$.

∴ The volume of the composite solid is about 589.5 cubic feet.

Exercises

Find the volume of the composite solid. Round your answer to the nearest tenth.

13.

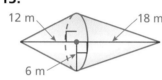

14.

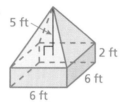

15.

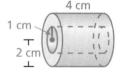

7.6 Surface Areas and Volumes of Similar Solids (pp. 338–345)

The cones are similar. What is the volume of the red cone? Round your answer to the nearest tenth.

$$\frac{\text{Volume of A}}{\text{Volume of B}} = \left(\frac{\text{Height of A}}{\text{Height of B}}\right)^3$$

$\dfrac{V}{157} = \left(\dfrac{4}{6}\right)^3$ Substitute.

$\dfrac{V}{157} = \dfrac{64}{216}$ Evaluate power.

$V \approx 46.5$ Multiply each side by 157.

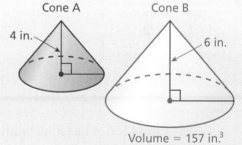

∴ The volume is about 46.5 cubic inches.

Exercises

The solids are similar. Find the surface area S or volume V of the red solid.

16.

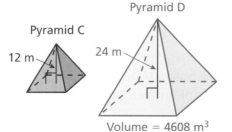

17.

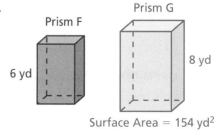

Check It Out
Test Practice
BigIdeasMath ✓com

Find the volume of the solid. Round your answer to the nearest tenth.

1.

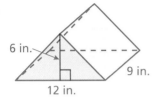

6 in.
9 in.
12 in.

2.

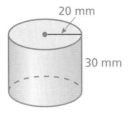

20 mm
30 mm

3.

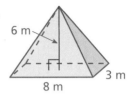

6 m
8 m
3 m

4.

6 cm
3 cm

5.

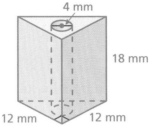

4 mm
18 mm
12 mm   12 mm

6.

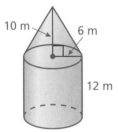

10 m
6 m
12 m

7. The pyramids are similar.

   a. Find the missing dimension.

   b. Find the surface area of the red pyramid.

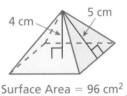

4 cm   5 cm

Surface Area = 96 cm²

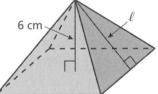

6 cm   ℓ

6 in.   4 in.
5 in.   5.5 in.

8. SMOOTHIES You are making smoothies. You will use either the cone-shaped glass or the cylindrical glass. Which glass holds more? About how much more?

9. CAPACITY A baseball team uses a heated tub to treat injuries. What is the capacity of the tub in liters? (1 L = 1000 cm³)

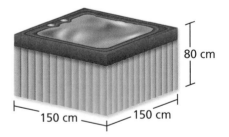

80 cm
150 cm   150 cm

10. WAFFLE CONES The ratio of the corresponding linear measures of two similar waffle cones is 3 to 4. The smaller cone has a volume of about 18 cubic inches. Find the volume of the larger cone. Round your answer to the nearest tenth.

11. OPEN-ENDED Draw two different composite solids that have the same volume, but different surface areas. Explain your reasoning.

Test Item References

Chapter Test Questions	Section to Review
1, 9	7.1
2, 8	7.2
3	7.3
4, 8	7.4
5, 6, 11	7.5
7, 10	7.6

Test-Taking Strategies

Remind students to quickly look over the entire test before they start so that they can budget their time. This test is very visual and requires that students remember many terms. It might be helpful for them to jot down some of the terms on the back of their test before they start. Students should make sketches and diagrams to help them.

Common Assessment Errors

- **Exercises 1–6, 8–11** Students may write linear or square units for volume rather than cubic units.
- **Exercises 1–6, 8–11** Students may forget to multiply the area of the base by the height and/or the factor of $\frac{1}{3}$ (if appropriate) when finding volume. Encourage them to find the area of the base separately and then substitute it into the volume formula.
- **Exercises 2, 4, 5, 6, 8** When finding the area of the circular base of a cylinder or a cone, students may not square the radius, or they may use the diameter instead of the radius.
- **Exercises 5 and 6** Students may forget to add or subtract the volumes as appropriate to find the volume of the composite solid.
- **Exercises 7 and 10** Students may raise the ratio of the linear measures to the wrong power, or forget to square or cube the ratio altogether. Discuss why squaring or cubing the ratio makes sense.

Reteaching and Enrichment Strategies

If students need help. . .	If students got it. . .
Resources by Chapter • Practice A and Practice B • Puzzle Time Record and Practice Journal Practice Differentiating the Lesson Lesson Tutorials Practice from the Test Generator Skills Review Handbook	Resources by Chapter • Enrichment and Extension • School-to-Work • Financial Literacy Game Closet at *BigIdeasMath.com* Start Standardized Test Practice

Answers

1. 324 in.^{3}
2. $12,000\pi \approx 37,680$ mm^3
3. 48 m^3
4. $4.5\pi \approx 14.1$ cm^3
5. $1296 - 72\pi \approx 1069.9$ mm^3
6. $552\pi \approx 1733.3$ m^3
7. **a.** $\ell = 7.5$ cm
   b. 216 cm^2
8. cylindrical glass; about 22 in.^{3}
9. 1800 L
10. 42.7 in.^{3}
11. See Additional Answers.

Assessment Book

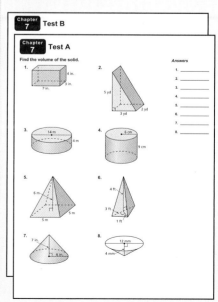

After Answering Easy Questions, Relax
Answer Easy Questions First
Estimate the Answer
Read All Choices before Answering
Read Question before Answering
Solve Directly or Eliminate Choices
Solve Problem before Looking at Choices
Use Intelligent Guessing
Work Backwards

About this Strategy

When taking a multiple choice test, be sure to read each question carefully and thoroughly. After skimming the test and answering the easy questions, stop for a few seconds, take a deep breath, and relax. Work through the remaining questions carefully, using your knowledge and test-taking strategies. Remember, you already completed many of the questions on the test!

Answers

1. D
2. H
3. 480 in.^{3}

Item Analysis

1. **A.** The student subtracts 20 from the right side instead of adding 20.

   B. The student did not distribute the 5 to both terms of $(x - 4)$.

   C. The student adds $3x$ to the left side instead of subtracting $3x$.

   D. Correct answer

2. **F.** The student incorrectly uses half the radius.

   G. The student incorrectly uses half the radius and also uses the formula for a right circular cylinder, neglecting to multiply by $\frac{1}{3}$.

   H. Correct answer

   I. The student uses the formula for a right circular cylinder, neglecting to multiply by $\frac{1}{3}$.

3. **Gridded Response:** Correct answer: 480 in.^{3}

   Common Error: The student finds the base area to be the product of 8 and 6, not half the product, and gets an answer of 960 cubic inches.

4. **A.** The student chooses a graph that represents wind speeds that are less than or equal to 39 miles per hour or greater than 74 miles per hour.

   B. The student chooses a graph that represents wind speeds that are less than 39 miles per hour or greater than or equal to 74 miles per hour.

   C. Correct answer

   D. The student chooses a graph that represents wind speeds that are greater than 39 miles per hour and at most 74 miles per hour.

5. **F.** Correct answer

   G. The student does not correctly apply the concept of slope and does not determine that answer choice F does not lie on the line.

   H. The student does not correctly apply the concept of slope and does not determine that answer choice F does not lie on the line.

   I. The student does not correctly apply the concept of slope and does not determine that answer choice F does not lie on the line.

Technology
For the **T**eacher

Big Ideas Test Generator

1. What is the value of x?

$$5(x - 4) = 3x$$

A. -10

C. $2\frac{1}{2}$

B. 2

D. 10

2. A right circular cone and its dimensions are shown below.

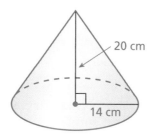

20 cm

14 cm

What is the volume of the right circular cone? $\left(\text{Use } \dfrac{22}{7} \text{ for } \pi.\right)$

F. $1,026\frac{2}{3}$ cm³

H. $4,106\frac{2}{3}$ cm³

G. $3,080$ cm³

I. $12,320$ cm³

3. A right triangular prism and its dimensions are shown below.

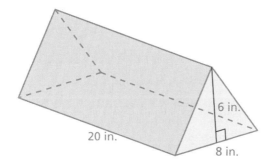

6 in.

20 in.

8 in.

What is the volume of the right triangular prism?

4. A tropical storm has maximum sustained surface winds of at least 39 miles per hour but less than 74 miles per hour. Which graph correctly represents the possible wind speeds of a tropical storm?

A.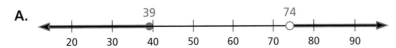

B.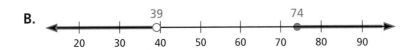

C.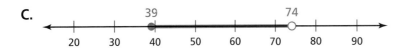

D.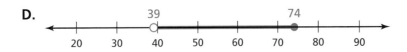

5. Use the coordinate plane to answer the question below.

Which point does *not* lie on the same line as the other three?

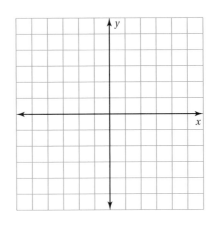

F. $(-5, 3)$ **H.** $(-1, -1)$

G. $(-3, 2)$ **I.** $(1, -4)$

6. Olga was solving an equation in the box shown.

What should Olga do to correct the error that she made?

A. Multiply both sides by $-\dfrac{5}{2}$ instead of $-\dfrac{2}{5}$.

B. Multiply both sides by $\dfrac{2}{5}$ instead of $-\dfrac{2}{5}$.

C. Distribute $-\dfrac{2}{5}$ to get $-4x - 6$.

D. Add 15 to -30.

$$-\frac{2}{5}(10x - 15) = -30$$

$$10x - 15 = -30\left(-\frac{2}{5}\right)$$

$$10x - 15 = 12$$

$$10x - 15 + 15 = 12 + 15$$

$$10x = 27$$

$$\frac{10x}{10} = \frac{27}{10}$$

$$x = \frac{27}{10}$$

Item Analysis (continued)

6. **A.** Correct answer

    B. The student thinks that multiplying by $\frac{2}{5}$ is the inverse operation of multiplying by $-\frac{2}{5}$.

    C. The student does not distribute the negative sign to the second term.

    D. The student makes an order of operations error by not first distributing the multiplication.

7. **F.** The student divides the number of inches per hour by the number of hours.

    G. Correct answer

    H. The student divides the number of hours by the number of inches per hour and makes a place value error.

    I. The student thinks that $2\frac{1}{2}$ is equivalent to 0.25 and adds this number to 0.08.

8. **Gridded Response:** Correct answer: 9 in.^{3}

    Common Error: The student divides the volume by r instead of r^2, getting an answer of 108 cubic inches.

9. **A.** The student finds $\frac{6}{9}$ of 240 and subtracts this result from 240.

    B. The student uses direct variation and finds $\frac{6}{9}$ of 240.

    C. Correct answer

    D. The student finds $\frac{6}{9}$ of 240 and adds this result to 240.

10. **F.** The student thinks that 12 students are equivalent to 12%.

    G. Correct answer

    H. The student finds what percent 12 is of 20.

    I. The student finds the percent of students who prefer to write with a pen.

Answers

4. C

5. F

6. A

Item Analysis (continued)

11. **2 points** The student demonstrates a thorough understanding of finding the composite volume of a right circular cylinder and a right circular cone. The student correctly finds a composite volume of 113.04 cubic inches. The student provides clear and complete work and explanations.

    1 point The student demonstrates a partial understanding of finding the composite volume of a right circular cylinder and a right circular cone. The student provides some correct work and explanation toward finding the composite volume.

    0 points The student demonstrates insufficient understanding of finding the composite volume of a right circular cylinder and a right circular cone. The student is unable to make any meaningful progress toward finding the composite volume.

Extra Examples for Standardized Test Practice

1. On the grid below, Rectangle *EFGH* is plotted and its vertices are labeled.

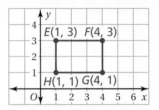

Which of the following shows Rectangle *E′F′G′H′*, the image of Rectangle *EFGH* after it is reflected in the *x*-axis?

A.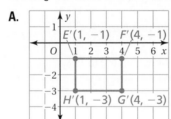

C.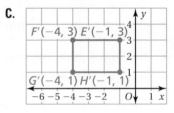

B.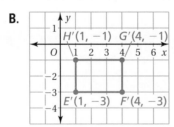

D.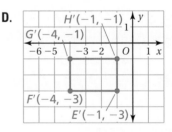

2. There are 72 singers in a choir. The conductor determined that $\frac{2}{3}$ of the singers are women and that $\frac{3}{8}$ of the women are sopranos. How many women in the choir are sopranos?

   F. 18

   G. 21

   H. 48

   I. 54

7. It has been raining at a rate of 0.08 inch per hour. At this rate, how much rain will fall in $2\frac{1}{2}$ hours?

   F. 0.032 in.   **H.** 0.3125 in.

   G. 0.2 in.   **I.** 0.33 in.

8. A right circular cylinder has a volume of 1296 cubic inches. If the radius of the cylinder is divided by 12, what would be the volume, in cubic inches, of the smaller cylinder?

9. If 9 friends share equally a large box of baseball cards, each friend gets 240 cards. If 6 friends share equally the same box of cards, how many cards does each friend get?

   A. 80   **C.** 360

   B. 160   **D.** 400

10. All students in a class were surveyed to find out their preferences for writing instruments. The survey found that 12 students prefer to write with a pencil and 20 students prefer to write with a pen. What percent of students in the class prefer to write with a pencil?

   F. 12%   **H.** 60%

   G. 37.5%   **I.** 62.5%

11. The figure below is a diagram for making a tin lantern.

Think
Solve
Explain

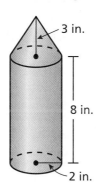

The figure consists of a right circular cylinder without its top base and a right circular cone without its base. What is the volume, in cubic inches, of the entire lantern? Show your work and explain your reasoning. (Use 3.14 for π.)

8 Square Roots and the Pythagorean Theorem

"I'm pretty sure that Pythagoras was a Greek."

"I said 'Greek', not 'Geek'."

"Leonardo da Vinci claimed that the human face is made up of golden ratios."

"Let's see if the same is true of a cat's face."

Strands Development

6th Grade

- Investigate and describe positive exponents and perfect squares.
- Evaluate numerical expressions using order of operations.

7th Grade

- Determine square roots.

8th Grade

- Simplify numerical expressions involving positive exponents using properties of operations with real numbers.
- Determine whether a given number is a perfect square.
- Find two consecutive whole numbers between which a square root lies.
- Verify and apply the Pythagorean Theorem.

Math in History

Early cultures were aware of square roots. For instance, they were aware that a square with side lengths of 1 unit has a diagonal whose length is $\sqrt{2}$.

★ The following representation of the square root of 2 was found on an old Babylonian tablet.

The symbols are 1, 24, 51, and 10. Because the Babylonians used a base 60 system, this number is $1 + \dfrac{24}{60} + \dfrac{51}{60^2} + \dfrac{10}{60^3} \approx 1.41421$.

★ Another early approximation of the square root of 2 is given in an Indian mathematical text, the Sulbasutras (c. 800–200 B.C.), as follows "Increase the length by its third and this third by its own fourth less the thirty-fourth part of that fourth."

$$1 + \frac{1}{3} + \frac{1}{3 \cdot 4} - \frac{1}{3 \cdot 4 \cdot 34} \approx 1.41422$$

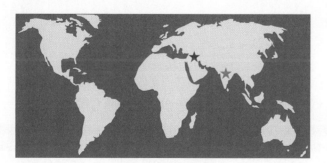

Pacing Guide for Chapter 8

Chapter Opener	1 Day
Section 1 Activity Lesson	 1 Day 1 Day
Section 2 Activity Lesson	 1 Day 1 Day
Study Help / Quiz	1 Day
Section 3 Activity Lesson	 1 Day 1 Day
Section 4 Activity Lesson	 2 Days 1 Day
Section 5 Activity Lesson	 1 Day 1 Day
Chapter Review / Tests	2 Days
Total Chapter 8	15 Days
Year-to-Date	133 Days

Check Your Resources

- Record and Practice Journal
- Resources by Chapter
- Skills Review Handbook
- Assessment Book
- Worked-Out Solutions

Technology For the Teacher

Dynamic Classroom

The Dynamic Planning Tool
Editable Teacher's Resources at
BigIdeasMath.com

Standards of Learning

6.8 The student will evaluate whole number numerical expressions, using the order of operations.

7.1(c) The student will compare and order fractions, decimals, percents and numbers written in scientific notation.

Additional Topics for Review

- Number line
- Converting decimals to fractions
- Order of Operations
- Exponents
- Compare and order decimals and fractions

Try It Yourself

1. =   **2.** <

3. <

4. $-0.009, -0.001, 0.01$

5. $-1.75, -1.74, 1.74$

6. $-0.75, 0.74, 0.75$

7. -3 **8.** 181

9. 99

Record and Practice Journal

1. <   **2.** >

3. =   **4.** >

5–8. Sample answers are given.

5. $-5.2, -5.3, -6.5$

6. $2.56, 2.3, -3.2$

7. $-3.18, -3.1, -2.05$

8. $0.05, 0.3, 1.55$

9. $12.49; 12.495; 12.55; 12.60; 12.63$

10. 167 **11.** 3

12. 63 **13.** 116

14. -51 **15.** 1

16. $\dfrac{24 + 32 + 30 + 28}{2}; 57$

Math Background Notes

Vocabulary Review

- Greater Than
- Less Than
- Order of Operations

Comparing Decimals

- Students should know how to compare decimals.
- **Teaching Tip:** Some students will have difficulty determining which decimal is greater simply by looking. Encourage these students to convert the decimals to fractions with a common denominator and compare the numerators. The fraction with the greater (positive) numerator was produced by the greater decimal.
- **Common Error:** Some students will have difficulty with Example 3 because there is not one "right" answer. Remind them that any number that makes the comparison true is a correct answer. Encourage creativity and remind students their answers will not always match the teacher's answers!

Using Order of Operations

- Students should know how to use the order of operations.
- You may want to review the correct order of operations with students. Many students probably learned the pneumonic device *Please Excuse My Dear Aunt Sally*. Ask a volunteer to explain why this phrase is helpful.
- You may want to review exponents with students. Remind students that the exponent tells you how many times the base is a factor. Exponents express repeated multiplication.

Reteaching and Enrichment Strategies

If students need help. . .	If students got it. . .
Record and Practice Journal • Fair Game Review Skills Review Handbook Lesson Tutorials	Game Closet at *BigIdeasMath.com* Start the next section

What You Learned Before

"Here's how I remember the square root of 2. February is the 2nd month. It has 28 days. Split 28 into 14 and 14. Move the decimal to get 1.414."

Can't I just use a calculator?

Comparing Decimals

Complete the number sentence with <, >, or =.

Example 1 1.1 [ ] 1.01

Because $\frac{110}{100}$ is greater than $\frac{101}{100}$, 1.1 is greater than 1.01.

∴ So, $1.1 > 1.01$.

Example 2 −0.3 [ ] −0.003

```
        -0.3              -0.003
  ←——+————+————+————+————+————→
   -0.5  -0.4  -0.3  -0.2  -0.1   0
```

∴ Because −0.3 is to the left of −0.003, $-0.3 < -0.003$.

Example 3   **Find three decimals that make the number sentence −5.12 > [ ] true.**

Any decimal less than −5.12 will make the sentence true.

∴ *Sample answer:* −10.1, −9.05, −8.25

Try It Yourself
Complete the number sentence with <, >, or =.

1. 2.10 [ ] 2.1

2. −4.5 [ ] −4.25

3. π [ ] 3.2

Find three decimals that make the number sentence true.

4. −0.01 ≤ [ ]

5. 1.75 > [ ]

6. 0.75 ≥ [ ]

Using Order of Operations

Example 4   **Evaluate $8^2 \div (32 \div 2) + 2(3 - 5)$.**

$$8^2 \div (32 \div 2) + 2(3 - 5) = 8^2 \div 16 + 2(-2)$$ Perform operations in parentheses.

$$= 64 \div 16 + 2(-2)$$ Evaluate the power.

$$= 4 + (-4)$$ Multiply and divide from left to right.

$$= 0$$ Add.

Try It Yourself
Evaluate the expression.

7. $15\left(\dfrac{12}{3}\right) - 7^2 - 2 \cdot 7$

8. $3^2 \cdot 4 \div 18 + 30 \cdot 6 - 1$

9. $-1 + \left(\dfrac{4}{2}(6 - 1)\right)^2$

STANDARDS OF LEARNING

8.5

Essential Question How can you find the dimensions of a square or circle when you are given its area?

1 ACTIVITY: Finding Square Roots

Work with a partner. Use a square root symbol to write the side length of the square. Then find the square root. Check your answer by multiplying.

a. **Sample:** $s = \sqrt{144} = 12$ ft

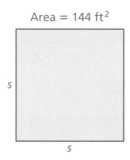

Area = 144 ft²

Check

$$\begin{array}{r} 12 \\ \times\ 12 \\ \hline 24 \\ 120 \\ \hline 144 \ \checkmark \end{array}$$

∴ The side length of the square is 12 feet.

b. Area = 225 mi²   s   s

c. Area = 2.89 in.²   s   s

d. Area = $\frac{4}{9}$ ft²   s   s

2 ACTIVITY: Using Square Roots

Work with a partner. Find the radius of each circle.

a.

$A = 36\pi$ in.²

b.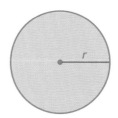

$A = 81\pi$ yd²

c.

$A = 0.25\pi$ ft²

Laurie's Notes

Introduction

For the Teacher

- **Goal:** Students will develop an understanding of perfect squares.
- In this section, square roots of perfect squares are considered. Knowledge of perfect squares will be used in decimal problems. For example, knowing that $12^2 = 144$, you would expect students to know that $1.2^2 = 1.44$.

Motivate

- **Preparation:** Make two (or more) pendulums of different lengths.
- Swing the two pendulums back and forth a few times while telling a story.
- ❓ "Does it take the same amount of time for the pendulum to go back and forth for each length?" Answers will vary.
- **Extension:** Have a student time you as you swing the pendulum through 10 periods. Divide the total time by 10 to find the time of one period. Repeat for a different length pendulum.

Activity Notes

Activity 1

- Students were introduced to square roots in a previous grade. A short introduction will tell you immediately what students remember.
- **Preparation:** Cut a number of squares from paper. Calculate the areas of several and write the areas on the figures. Make one of the squares 6 cm by 6 cm.
- ❓ "Can you find the area of any of these squares? Explain." Yes, multiply length by width.
- ❓ "There are no dimensions marked on the square, so how do you find the area?" Measure the side lengths, then multiply to find the area.
- Hold up one of the squares and show students that it has Area $= 36$ cm^2 recorded on it.
- ❓ "If you know the area, how do you find the dimensions?" Ideas will vary.
- **Common Error:** Students will say to divide by 4 (perimeter) or divide by 2. Remind students that the side lengths are the same and they are multiplied together to get 36. So, the side lengths must be 6 because 6(6) = 36.
- At this point, students should remember what they learned last year. Write $6^2 = 36 \rightarrow$ undo $\rightarrow \sqrt{36} = 6$.
- Students should be ready to begin the activity with a partner.
- When students have finished, discuss the answers and the strategies they used.

Activity 2

- ❓ "How do you find the area of a circle?" $A = \pi r^2$
- ❓ "If you know the area of a circle, can you solve for the radius?" yes
- Do not give away too much at this point. Let students think through the problems. The first two problems are obvious perfect squares.
- **Common Error:** For part (c), students will often answer 0.05, forgetting how decimals are multiplied.

Standards of Learning

8.5(a) The student will determine whether a given number is a perfect square.

Previous Learning

Students learned about square roots in a previous grade.

Activity Materials	
Introduction	**Textbook**
• string; weight • stop watch	• different sized squares

Start Thinking! and Warm Up

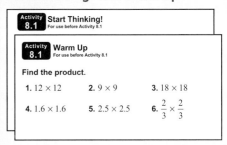

Activity 8.1 Start Thinking!
For use before Activity 8.1

Activity 8.1 Warm Up
For use before Activity 8.1

Find the product.

1. 12×12 2. 9×9 3. 18×18

4. 1.6×1.6 5. 2.5×2.5 6. $\dfrac{2}{3} \times \dfrac{2}{3}$

8.1 Record and Practice Journal

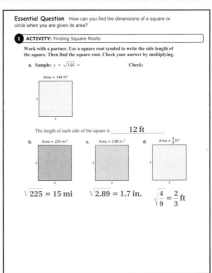

Essential Question How can you find the dimensions of a square or circle when you are given its area?

1 ACTIVITY: Finding Square Roots

Work with a partner. Use a square root symbol to write the side length of the square. Then find the square root. Check your answer by multiplying.

a. **Sample:** $s = \sqrt{144} =$ Check:

Area $= 144$ ft^2

The length of each side of the square is   **12 ft**

b. Area $= 225$ mi^2 c. Area $= 2.89$ in.^{2} d. Area $= \frac{4}{9}$ ft^2

$\sqrt{225} = 15$ mi $\sqrt{2.89} = 1.7$ in. $\sqrt{\dfrac{4}{9}} = \dfrac{2}{3}$ ft

English Language Learners

Build on Past Knowledge

Remind students of inverse operations. Addition and subtraction are inverse operations, as are multiplication and division. Taking the square root of a number is the inverse of squaring a number and squaring a number is the inverse of taking the square root of a number.

8.1 Record and Practice Journal

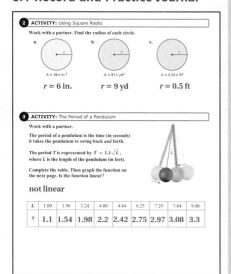

2 ACTIVITY: Using Square Roots

Work with a partner. Find the radius of each circle.

a. $A = 36\pi$ in.^{2} $r = 6$ in.

b. $A = 81\pi$ yd^2 $r = 9$ yd

c. $A = 0.25\pi$ ft^2 $r = 0.5$ ft

3 ACTIVITY: The Period of a Pendulum

Work with a partner.

The period of a pendulum is the time (in seconds) it takes the pendulum to swing back *and* forth.

The period T is represented by $T = 1.1\sqrt{L}$, where L is the length of the pendulum (in feet).

Complete the table. Then graph the function on the next page. Is the function linear?

not linear

L	1.00	1.96	3.24	4.00	4.84	6.25	7.29	7.84	9.00
T	1.1	1.54	1.98	2.2	2.42	2.75	2.97	3.08	3.3

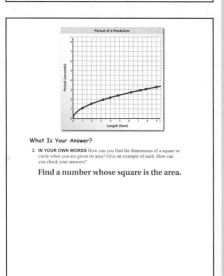

Period of a Pendulum

Period (seconds) / Length (feet)

What Is Your Answer?

3. **IN YOUR OWN WORDS** How can you find the dimensions of a square or circle when you are given its area? Give an example of each. How can you check your answers?

Find a number whose square is the area.

Laurie's Notes

Activity 3

- Define and model the period of a pendulum.
- Write the formula, $T = 1.1\sqrt{L}$. Explain that if the length is 9 feet, you can find out the time of one period by evaluating the equation for $L = 9$. So, $T = 1.1\sqrt{9} = 1.1(3) = 3.3$ seconds.
- For each of the values in the table, remind students to think about the whole numbers 100, 196, 324, 400, and so on, to help find $\sqrt{1.00}$, $\sqrt{1.96}$, $\sqrt{3.24}$, $\sqrt{4.00}$, and so on.
- When plotting the ordered pairs, students will need to be precise to see the curvature in the graph.
- **Connection:** The equation they are graphing is the function $y = 1.1\sqrt{x}$. This is not a linear function, so the graph is not a line. Find the slope between two different pairs of points on the graph. For (1, 1.1) and (4, 2.2), the slope is $\frac{1.1}{3} = 0.3\overline{6}$. For (4, 2.2) and (9, 3.3), the slope is $\frac{1.1}{5} = 0.22$. The slopes are not the same, so the graph cannot be a line.

What Is Your Answer?

- **Neighbor Check:** Have students work independently and then have their neighbor check their work. Have students discuss any discrepancies.

Closure

- **Matching Activity:** Match each square root with the correct answer.

  1. $\sqrt{1600}$ D   **A.** 12
  2. $\sqrt{400}$ B   **B.** 20
  3. $\sqrt{144}$ A   **C.** 6
  4. $\sqrt{36}$ C   **D.** 40

Technology For the Teacher

Dynamic Classroom

The Dynamic Planning Tool
Editable Teacher's Resources at *BigIdeasMath.com*

3 ACTIVITY: The Period of a Pendulum

Work with a partner.

The period of a pendulum is the time (in seconds) it takes the pendulum to swing back *and* forth.

The period T is represented by $T = 1.1\sqrt{L}$, where L is the length of the pendulum (in feet).

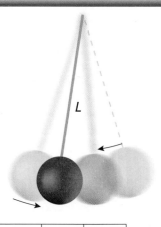

Copy and complete the table. Then graph the function. Is the function linear?

L	1.00	1.96	3.24	4.00	4.84	6.25	7.29	7.84	9.00
T									

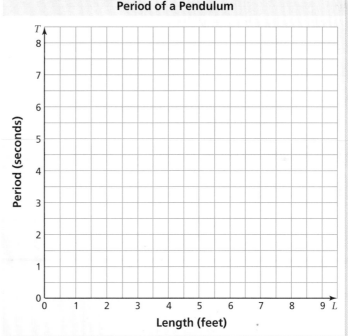

Period of a Pendulum

Period (seconds) vs. *Length (feet)*

What Is Your Answer?

4. IN YOUR OWN WORDS How can you find the dimensions of a square or circle when you are given its area? Give an example of each. How can you check your answers?

Practice ⟶ Use what you learned about finding square roots to complete Exercises 4–6 on page 360.

Key Vocabulary
square root, *p. 358*
perfect square,
   p. 358
radical sign, *p. 358*
radicand, *p. 358*

A **square root** of a number is a number that when multiplied by itself, equals the given number. Every positive number has a positive *and* a negative square root. A **perfect square** is a number with integers as its square roots.

EXAMPLE 1   Finding Square Roots of a Perfect Square

Find the two square roots of 49.

$$7 \cdot 7 = 49 \text{ and } (-7) \cdot (-7) = 49$$

⋮ So, the square roots of 49 are 7 and -7.

Study Tip

Zero has one square root, which is 0.

The symbol $\sqrt{}$ is called a **radical sign**. It is used to represent a square root. The number under the radical sign is called the **radicand**.

Positive Square Root $\sqrt{}$	Negative Square Root $-\sqrt{}$	Both Square Roots $\pm\sqrt{}$
$\sqrt{16} = 4$	$-\sqrt{16} = -4$	$\pm\sqrt{16} = \pm4$

EXAMPLE 2   Finding Square Roots

Find the square root(s).

a. $\sqrt{25}$

> $\sqrt{25}$ represents the *positive* square root.

⋮ Because $5^2 = 25$, $\sqrt{25} = \sqrt{5^2} = 5$.

b. $-\sqrt{\dfrac{9}{16}}$

> $-\sqrt{\dfrac{9}{16}}$ represents the *negative* square root.

⋮ Because $\left(\dfrac{3}{4}\right)^2 = \dfrac{9}{16}$, $-\sqrt{\dfrac{9}{16}} = -\sqrt{\left(\dfrac{3}{4}\right)^2} = -\dfrac{3}{4}$.

c. $\pm\sqrt{2.25}$

> $\pm\sqrt{2.25}$ represents both the *positive and negative* square roots.

⋮ Because $1.5^2 = 2.25$, $\pm\sqrt{2.25} = \pm\sqrt{1.5^2} = 1.5$ and -1.5.

On Your Own

Now You're Ready
Exercises 7–16

Find the two square roots of the number.

1. 36   **2.** 100   **3.** 121

Find the square root(s).

4. $-\sqrt{1}$ **5.** $\pm\sqrt{\dfrac{4}{25}}$ **6.** $\sqrt{12.25}$

Laurie's Notes

Introduction

Connect

- **Yesterday:** Students explored square roots in the context of finding the side length of a square when the area was known.
- **Today:** Students will find the square roots of a perfect square.

Motivate

- Play the game *Keep it Going!*
- Give the students the first 3 to 4 numbers in a sequence and have them *Keep it Going.* If students are sitting in a row, each person in the row says the next number in the pattern. Keep the pattern going until it becomes too difficult to continue. For example, use the sequence 4, 400, 40,000, … (4,000,000, 400,000,000…)

Lesson Notes

Discuss

- Write and discuss the definitions of square root of a number and perfect squares. Mention the *Study Tip.*
- Students are often confused when you say "every positive number has a positive and a negative square root." Use Example 1 to explain.

Example 1

- Note that the direction line is written in words without the square root symbol.
- **?** "What is the product of two positives? two negatives?" Both are positive.

Discuss

- The square root symbol is called a **radical sign** and the number under the radical sign is the **radicand**.
- Write and discuss the three examples in the table. Explain to students that the symbol $\pm$ is read as *plus or minus.*
- **Representation:** Students will need to pay attention to how the problem is written, especially if they are asked for more than the positive square root.

Example 2

- Remind students to pay attention to the signs that may precede the radical sign.
- **?** "How do you multiply fractions?" Write the product of the numerators over the product of the denominators.
- **?** "What fraction is multiplied by itself to get $\frac{9}{16}$?" $\frac{3}{4}$

On Your Own

- **Think-Pair-Share:** Students should read each question independently and then work with a partner to answer the questions. When they have answered the questions, the pair should compare their answers with another group and discuss any discrepancies.

Goal Today's lesson is finding the **square root** of a **perfect square**.

Start Thinking! and Warm Up

Lesson 8.1	Warm Up
	For use before Lesson 8.1

Lesson 8.1 Start Thinking! For use before Lesson 8.1

Shelley says that there are two solutions to the equation $x^2 = 400$. Gina says that there is only one solution. Who is correct? Explain.

Extra Example 1

Find the two square roots of 64.
8 and -8

Extra Example 2

Find the square root(s) of $-\sqrt{81}$. -9

On Your Own

1. 6 and -6
2. 10 and -10
3. 11 and -11
4. -1
5. $\pm\dfrac{2}{5}$
6. 3.5

T-358

Laurie's Notes

Extra Example 3

Evaluate $2\sqrt{144} - 10$. 14

Example 3

- **Teaching Tip:** In these examples, remind students that square roots are numbers, so you can evaluate numerical expressions that include square roots. Students see a *symbol*, think *variable*, and suddenly they forget things like the order of operations. In part (a), some students think of this as $5x + 7$ and will not know what to do.
- Write the expression in part (a).
- **?** "What operations are involved in this problem?" square root, multiplication, and addition
- Work through parts (a) and (b) as shown.
- **?** "Can you name inverse operations?" addition and subtraction, multiplication and division, squaring and taking the square root
- Write and discuss that squaring and taking the square root are inverse operations. Use $\sqrt{4^2}$ as an example.

Example 4

- **?** "How do you find the area of a circle?" $A = \pi r^2$
- The numbers involved may be overwhelming to students. Reassure them that this is an equation with one variable and that they know how to solve equations!
- Use a calculator or long division.
- When you get to the step $14{,}400 = r^2$, remind students that whatever you do to one side of an equation, you must do to the other side. So, to get r by itself, you need to undo the squaring. This is called taking the square root.
- Discuss with students why a negative square root does not make sense in this context. You cannot have a negative radius, so there will be no negative square root.

Extra Example 4

What is the radius of the circle? Use 3.14 for π. about 4 in.

Area = 50.24 in.^{2}

On Your Own

7. -3
8. 4.4
9. -15
10. $3.14r^2 = 2826$; about 30 ft

On Your Own

- Ask volunteers to share their work at the board for each of the problems.
- Question 8 looks more difficult because of the fraction. You may want to point out that $\dfrac{28}{7} = 4$.

Closure

- Write 3 numbers of which you know how to take the square root.
- Write 3 numbers of which you do not know how to take the square root.

Differentiated Instruction

Auditory

Ask students to use mental math to answer the following verbal questions.
- "What is the sum of the square root of 9 and 3?" 6
- "What is the difference of 12 and the square root of 144?" 0
- "What is twice the square root of 16?" 8
- "What is one-fourth of the square root of 64?" 2

Technology For the Teacher

The Dynamic Planning Tool
Editable Teacher's Resources at *BigIdeasMath.com*

EXAMPLE 3 **Evaluating Expressions Involving Square Roots**

Evaluate the expression.

a. $5\sqrt{36} + 7$

$$5\sqrt{36} + 7 = 5(6) + 7 \qquad \text{Evaluate the square root.}$$

$$= 30 + 7 \qquad \text{Multiply.}$$

$$= 37 \qquad \text{Add.}$$

b. $\dfrac{1}{4} + \sqrt{\dfrac{18}{2}}$

$$\dfrac{1}{4} + \sqrt{\dfrac{18}{2}} = \dfrac{1}{4} + \sqrt{9} \qquad \text{Simplify.}$$

$$= \dfrac{1}{4} + 3 \qquad \text{Evaluate the square root.}$$

$$= 3\dfrac{1}{4} \qquad \text{Add.}$$

Squaring a positive number and finding a square root are inverse operations. Use this relationship to solve equations involving squares.

EXAMPLE 4 **Real-Life Application**

The area of a crop circle is 45,216 square feet. What is the radius of the crop circle? Use 3.14 for π.

$$A = \pi r^2 \qquad \text{Write the formula for the area of a circle.}$$

$$45{,}216 \approx 3.14 r^2 \qquad \text{Substitute 45,216 for } A \text{ and 3.14 for } \pi.$$

$$14{,}400 = r^2 \qquad \text{Divide each side by 3.14.}$$

$$\sqrt{14{,}400} = \sqrt{r^2} \qquad \text{Take positive square root of each side.}$$

$$120 = r \qquad \text{Simplify.}$$

⋰ The radius of the crop circle is about 120 feet.

On Your Own

Now You're Ready
Exercises 18–23

Evaluate the expression.

7. $12 - 3\sqrt{25}$ **8.** $\sqrt{\dfrac{28}{7}} + 2.4$ **9.** $5\left(\sqrt{49} - 10\right)$

10. The area of a circle is 2826 square feet. Write and solve an equation to find the radius of the circle. Use 3.14 for π.

 ## Vocabulary and Concept Check

1. **VOCABULARY** Is 26 a perfect square? Explain.

2. **REASONING** Can the square of an integer be a negative number? Explain.

3. **NUMBER SENSE** Does $\sqrt{256}$ represent the positive square root of 256, the negative square root of 256, or both? Explain.

 ## Practice and Problem Solving

Find the dimensions of the square or circle. Check your answer.

4. Area = 441 cm²

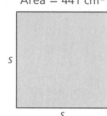

5. Area = 1.69 km²

6.

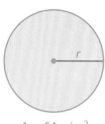

$A = 64\pi$ in.²

Find the two square roots of the number.

7. 9

8. 64

9. 4

10. 144

Find the square root(s).

11. $\sqrt{625}$

12. $-\sqrt{\dfrac{9}{100}}$

13. $\pm\sqrt{\dfrac{1}{961}}$

14. $\sqrt{7.29}$

15. $\pm\sqrt{4.84}$

16. $-\sqrt{361}$

17. **ERROR ANALYSIS** Describe and correct the error in finding the square roots.

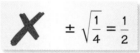

$$\times \quad \pm\sqrt{\dfrac{1}{4}} = \dfrac{1}{2}$$

Evaluate the expression.

18. $3\sqrt{16} - 5$

19. $10 - 4\sqrt{\dfrac{1}{16}}$

20. $\sqrt{6.76} + 5.4$

21. $8\sqrt{8.41} + 1.8$

22. $2\left(\sqrt{\dfrac{80}{5}} - 5\right)$

23. $4\left(\sqrt{\dfrac{147}{3}} + 3\right)$

24. **NOTEPAD** The area of the base of a square notepad is 9 square inches. What is the length of one side of the base of the notepad?

25. **CRITICAL THINKING** There are two square roots of 25. Why is there only one answer for the radius of the button?

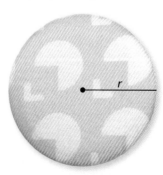

$A = 25\pi$ mm²

Assignment Guide and Homework Check

Level	Day 1 Activity Assignment	Day 2 Lesson Assignment	Homework Check
Basic	4–6, 35–39	1–3, 7–27 odd, 24	2, 7, 11, 13, 19, 24
Average	4–6, 35–39	1–3, 15–25 odd, 27–32	15, 19, 28, 30, 32
Advanced	4–6, 35–39	1–3, 17, 22, 23, 25, 27–34	22, 28, 30, 32

Common Errors

- **Exercises 7–10** Students may only find the positive square root of the number given. Remind them that a square root can be positive or negative, and the question is asking for both answers.
- **Exercises 11–16** Students may divide the number by two instead of finding a number that, when multiplied by itself, gives the radicand. Remind them that taking the square root of a number is the inverse of squaring a number.
- **Exercises 18–23** Students may not follow the order of operations when evaluating the expression. Remind them of the order of operations. Because taking a square root is the inverse of squaring, it is evaluated before multiplication and division.

8.1 Record and Practice Journal

Find the two square roots of the number.

1. 16 — 4 and −4
2. 100 — 10 and −10
3. 196 — 14 and −14

Find the square root(s).

4. $\sqrt{169}$ — 13
5. $\sqrt{\frac{4}{225}}$ — $\frac{2}{15}$
6. $-\sqrt{12.25}$ — −3.5

Evaluate the expression.

7. $2\sqrt{36} + 9$ — 21
8. $8 - 11\sqrt{\frac{25}{121}}$ — 3
9. $3\left(\sqrt{\frac{125}{5}} - 8\right)$ — −9

10. A trampoline has an area of 49π square feet. What is the diameter of the trampoline?
14 ft

11. The volume of a cylinder is 75π cubic inches. The cylinder has a height of 3 inches. What is the radius of the base of the cylinder?
5 in.

Vocabulary and Concept Check

1. no; There is no integer whose square is 26.

2. no; A positive number times a positive number is a positive number, and a negative number times a negative number is a positive number.

3. $\sqrt{256}$ represents the positive square root because there is not a − or a ± in front.

Practice and Problem Solving

4. $s = 21$ cm

5. $s = 1.3$ km

6. $r = 8$ in.

7. 3 and −3

8. 8 and −8

9. 2 and −2

10. 12 and −12

11. 25   12. $-\frac{3}{10}$

13. $\frac{1}{31}$ and $-\frac{1}{31}$

14. 2.7

15. 2.2 and −2.2

16. −19

17. The positive and negative square roots should have been given.

$\pm\sqrt{\frac{1}{4}} = \frac{1}{2}$ and $-\frac{1}{2}$

18. 7   19. 9

20. 8   21. 25

22. −2   23. 40

24. 3 in.

25. because a negative radius does not make sense

26. >

27. =

28. <

29. 9 ft

30. yes; *Sample answer:* Consider the perfect squares, a^2 and b^2. Their product can be written as $a^2b^2 = a \cdot a \cdot b \cdot b = (a \cdot b) \cdot (a \cdot b) = (a \cdot b)^2$.

31. 8 m/sec

32. See *Taking Math Deeper*.

33. 2.5 ft

34. 8 cm

Fair Game Review

35. 25   **36.** 289

37. 144   **38.** 49

39. B

Mini-Assessment

Find the square root(s).

1. $\sqrt{169}$ 13

2. $\sqrt{225}$ 15

3. $\pm\sqrt{4.41}$ 2.1 and −2.1

4. $-\sqrt{\dfrac{16}{25}}$ $-\dfrac{4}{5}$

5. $\sqrt{\dfrac{512}{2}}$ 16

Taking Math Deeper

Exercise 32

In this problem, students are given the area of the smaller watch face and are asked to find the radius of the larger watch face.

 Summarize the given information.

Area = 4π cm^2
Ratio of areas is 16 to 25.

 Answer the question. The two watch faces are similar, so the ratio of their areas is equal to the square of the ratio of their radii.

$$\frac{\text{Area of small}}{\text{Area of large}} = \left(\frac{\text{radius of small}}{\text{radius of large}}\right)^2$$

$$\frac{16}{25} = \left(\frac{\text{radius of small}}{\text{radius of large}}\right)^2$$

$$\sqrt{\frac{16}{25}} = \frac{\text{radius of small}}{\text{radius of large}}$$

$$\frac{4}{5} = \frac{\text{radius of small}}{\text{radius of large}}$$

a. The ratio of the radius of the smaller watch face to the radius of the larger watch face is $\dfrac{4}{5}$.

b. Solve the proportion for R.

$$\frac{4}{5} = \frac{r}{R}$$

$$\frac{4}{5} = \frac{2}{R}$$

$$R = \frac{10}{4}, \text{ or } \frac{5}{2}$$

The radius of the larger watch face is $\dfrac{5}{2}$ or 2.5 centimeters.

Reteaching and Enrichment Strategies

If students need help...	If students got it...
Resources by Chapter • Practice A and Practice B • Puzzle Time Record and Practice Journal Practice Differentiating the Lesson Lesson Tutorials Skills Review Handbook	Resources by Chapter • Enrichment and Extension Start the next section

Copy and complete the statement with <, >, or =.

26. $\sqrt{81}$ ▢ 8

27. 0.5 ▢ $\sqrt{0.25}$

28. $\dfrac{3}{2}$ ▢ $\sqrt{\dfrac{25}{4}}$

29. SAILBOAT The area of a sail is $40\dfrac{1}{2}$ square feet. The base and the height of the sail are equal. What is the height of the sail (in feet)?

30. REASONING Is the product of two perfect squares always a perfect square? Explain your reasoning.

31. ENERGY The kinetic energy K (in joules) of a falling apple is represented by $K = \dfrac{v^2}{2}$, where v is the speed of the apple (in meters per second). How fast is the apple traveling when the kinetic energy is 32 joules?

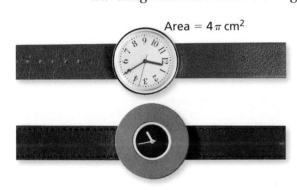

Area = 4π cm²

32. WATCHES The areas of the two watch faces have a ratio of $16:25$.

    a. What is the ratio of the radius of the smaller watch face to the radius of the larger watch face?

    b. What is the radius of the larger watch face?

33. WINDOW The cost C (in dollars) of making a square window with a side length of n inches is represented by $C = \dfrac{n^2}{5} + 175$. A window costs \$355. What is the length (in feet) of the window?

34. ⚡Geometry⚡ The area of the triangle is represented by the formula $A = \sqrt{s(s - 21)(s - 17)(s - 10)}$, where s is equal to half the perimeter. What is the height of the triangle?

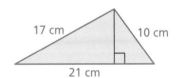

17 cm   10 cm   21 cm

Fair Game Review *What you learned in previous grades & lessons*

Evaluate the expression. *(Skills Review Handbook)*

35. $3^2 + 4^2$

36. $8^2 + 15^2$

37. $13^2 - 5^2$

38. $25^2 - 24^2$

39. MULTIPLE CHOICE Which of the following describes the triangle? *(Section 5.2)*

    A Acute   **B** Right

    C Obtuse   **D** Equiangular

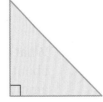

8.2 The Pythagorean Theorem

STANDARDS OF LEARNING

8.10

Essential Question How are the lengths of the sides of a right triangle related?

Pythagoras was a Greek mathematician and philosopher who discovered one of the most famous rules in mathematics. In mathematics, a rule is called a **theorem**. So, the rule that Pythagoras discovered is called the Pythagorean Theorem.

Pythagoras
(c. 570 B.C.–c. 490 B.C.)

1 ACTIVITY: Discovering the Pythagorean Theorem

Work with a partner.

a. On grid paper, draw any right triangle. Label the lengths of the two shorter sides (the **legs**) a and b.

b. Label the length of the longest side (the **hypotenuse**) c.

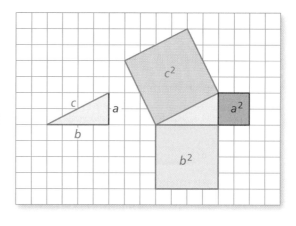

c. Draw squares along each of the three sides. Label the areas of the three squares a^2, b^2, and c^2.

d. Cut out the three squares. Make eight copies of the right triangle and cut them out. Arrange the figures to form two identical larger squares.

e. What does this tell you about the relationship among a^2, b^2, and c^2?

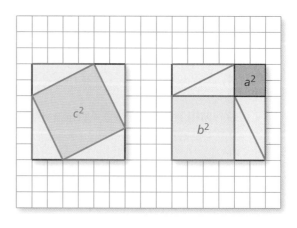

Laurie's Notes

Introduction

For the Teacher

- **Goal:** Students will explore a geometric proof of the Pythagorean Theorem.
- **Management Tip:** To help keep the room clean, cluster 4 to 6 desks together in a circle and tape a plastic bag to the front edge of one of the desks. Students are expected to put scraps of paper in the bag when they are finished with the investigation.

Motivate

- Share information about Pythagoras, who was born in Greece in 569 B.C.
  - He is known as the *Father of Numbers*.
  - He traveled extensively in Egypt, learning math, astronomy, and music.
  - Pythagoras urged the citizens of Cretona to follow his religious, political, and philosophical goals.
  - His followers were known as Pythagoreans. They observed a rule of silence called *echemythia*. One had to remain silent for *five years* before he could contribute to the group. Breaking this silence was punishable by death!

Activity Notes

Activity 1

- **Suggestions:** Use centimeter grid paper for ease of manipulating the cut pieces. Suggest to students that they draw their original triangle in the upper left of the grid paper, and then make a working copy of the triangle towards the middle of the paper. This gives enough room for the squares to be drawn on each side of the triangle.
- Vertices of the triangle need to be on lattice points. You do not want every student in the room to use the same triangle. Suggest other leg lengths (3 and 4, 3 and 6, 2 and 4, 2 and 3, and so on).
- **Model:** Drawing the square on the side of the hypotenuse is the challenging step. Model one technique for accomplishing the task using a triangle with legs 2 units and 5 units.
  - Notice that the hypotenuse has a slope of "right 5 units, up 2 units."
  - Place your pencil on the upper right endpoint and rotate the paper 90° clockwise. Move your pencil right 5 units and up 2 units. Mark a point.
  - Repeat rotating and moving the slope of the hypotenuse until you end at the endpoint of the original hypotenuse.
  - Use a straightedge to connect the four points (two that you marked and two on the endpoints of the hypotenuse) to form the square.
- Before students cut anything, check that they have 3 squares of the correct size.
- **Big Idea:** The two squares formed do have equal area. Referring to areas, if $c^2 + (4$ triangles$) = a^2 + b^2 + (4$ triangles$)$, then $c^2 = a^2 + b^2$ by subtracting the 4 triangles from each side of the equation.

Standards of Learning

8.10(a) The student will verify the Pythagorean Theorem.
8.10(b) The student will apply the Pythagorean Theorem.

Previous Learning

Students should know how to multiply fractions and decimals.

Activity Materials	
Textbook	
• scissors	• plastic bags
• grid paper	• transparency grid

Start Thinking! and Warm Up

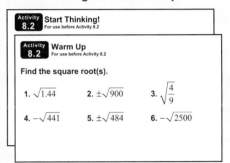

Activity 8.2 Start Thinking! For use before Activity 8.2

Activity 8.2 Warm Up For use before Activity 8.2

Find the square root(s).

1. $\sqrt{1.44}$ 2. $\pm\sqrt{900}$ 3. $\sqrt{\dfrac{4}{9}}$

4. $-\sqrt{441}$ 5. $\pm\sqrt{484}$ 6. $-\sqrt{2500}$

8.2 Record and Practice Journal

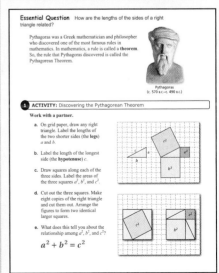

Essential Question How are the lengths of the sides of a right triangle related?

Pythagoras was a Greek mathematician and philosopher who discovered one of the most famous rules in mathematics. In mathematics, a rule is called a **theorem**. So, the rule that Pythagoras discovered is called the Pythagorean Theorem.

Pythagoras
(c. 570 B.C.–c. 490 B.C.)

1 ACTIVITY: Discovering the Pythagorean Theorem

Work with a partner.

a. On grid paper, draw any right triangle. Label the lengths of the two shorter sides (the **legs**) a and b.

b. Label the length of the longest side (the **hypotenuse**) c.

c. Draw squares along each of the three sides. Label the areas of the three squares a^2, b^2, and c^2.

d. Cut out the three squares. Make eight copies of the right triangle and cut them out. Arrange the figures to form two identical larger squares.

e. What does this tell you about the relationship among a^2, b^2, and c^2?

$$a^2 + b^2 = c^2$$

English Language Learners

Vocabulary

Help English learners understand the meanings of the words that make up a definition. Provide students with statements containing blanks and a list of the words used to fill in the blanks.

- In any right ___, the ___ is the side ___ the right ___.
  Word list: angle, hypotenuse, opposite, triangle
  triangle, hypotenuse, opposite, angle

- In any right ___, the ___ are the ___ sides and the ___ is always the ___ side.
  Word list: hypotenuse, legs, longest, shorter, triangle
  triangle, legs, shorter, hypotenuse, longest

8.2 Record and Practice Journal

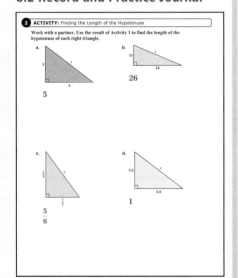

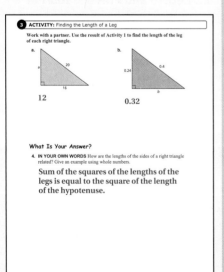

Activity 2

- **Part (a):** This triangle is known as a 3-4-5 right triangle. Using the property from the investigation, $3^2 + 4^2 = 9 + 16 = 25$. Students will recognize that $25 = 5^2$, so the length of the hypotenuse is 5.

- **Part (d):** This is related to a 3-4-5 right triangle: $3 \times 0.2 = 0.6$; $4 \times 0.2 = 0.8$; $5 \times 0.2 = 1.0$. Check: $0.6^2 + 0.8^2 = 0.36 + 0.64 = 1.0$ and $\sqrt{1} = 1$.

- Have students share their work for each of these problems.

- **Common Error:** In part (c), when students square a fraction, they sometimes double the numerator and denominator instead of squaring each number. In other words, $\left(\frac{2}{3}\right)^2 \neq \frac{4}{6}$, but $\left(\frac{2}{3}\right)^2 = \frac{4}{9}$.

Activity 3

- The two triangles in this activity have a leg length missing. Building squares on the two legs of the triangle and finding their areas would give a^2 and 16^2 for part (a). The area of the square built on the hypotenuse would be 20^2. The result of Activity 1 says that $a^2 + 16^2 = 20^2$. Students should recognize this as an opportunity to solve an equation.

- ❓ "What is the first step in solving the equation $a^2 + 16^2 = 20^2$?" Evaluate 16^2 and 20^2.

- ❓ "What is the next step in solving $a^2 + 256 = 400$?" Subtract 256 from each side.

- ❓ "Finally, what number squared is 144?" 12

What Is Your Answer?

- **Neighbor Check:** Have students work independently and then have their neighbor check their work. Have students discuss any discrepancies.

Closure

- **Exit Ticket:** If you drew a right triangle with legs of 4 and 6 on grid paper, what would be the area of the square drawn on the hypotenuse of the triangle? 52 square units

ACTIVITY: Finding the Length of the Hypotenuse

Work with a partner. Use the result of Activity 1 to find the length of the hypotenuse of each right triangle.

a.
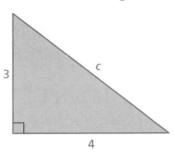

b.
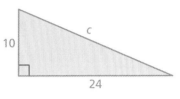

c.
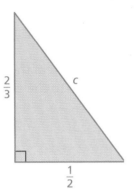

d.
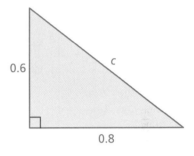

3 **ACTIVITY: Finding the Length of a Leg**

Work with a partner. Use the result of Activity 1 to find the length of the leg of each right triangle.

a.
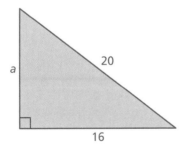

b.
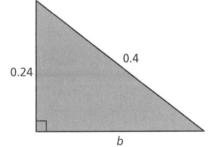

What Is Your Answer?

4. **IN YOUR OWN WORDS** How are the lengths of the sides of a right triangle related? Give an example using whole numbers.

Practice

Use what you learned about the Pythagorean Theorem to complete Exercises 3–5 on page 366.

Key Vocabulary 🔊))
theorem, *p. 362*
legs, *p. 364*
hypotenuse, *p. 364*
Pythagorean
    Theorem, *p. 364*

🔑⊙ Key Ideas

Sides of a Right Triangle

The sides of a right triangle have special names.

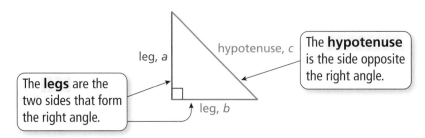

The **legs** are the two sides that form the right angle.

leg, *a*

hypotenuse, *c*

The **hypotenuse** is the side opposite the right angle.

leg, *b*

The Pythagorean Theorem

Words   In any right triangle, the sum of the squares of the lengths of the legs is equal to the square of the length of the hypotenuse.

Algebra $a^2 + b^2 = c^2$

Study Tip

In a right triangle, the legs are the shorter sides and the hypotenuse is always the longest side.

EXAMPLE ① **Finding the Length of a Hypotenuse**

Find the length of the hypotenuse of the triangle.

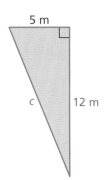

5 m

c

12 m

$a^2 + b^2 = c^2$	Write the Pythagorean Theorem.
$5^2 + 12^2 = c^2$	Substitute 5 for a and 12 for b.
$25 + 144 = c^2$	Evaluate powers.
$169 = c^2$	Add.
$\sqrt{169} = \sqrt{c^2}$	Take positive square root of each side.
$13 = c$	Simplify.

∴∙ The length of the hypotenuse is 13 meters.

⚫ **On Your Own**

Find the length of the hypotenuse of the triangle.

1.

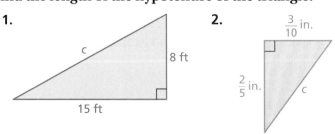

c

8 ft

15 ft

2.

$\frac{3}{10}$ in.

$\frac{2}{5}$ in.

c

Laurie's Notes

Introduction

Connect

- **Yesterday:** Students investigated a visual proof of the Pythagorean Theorem.
- **Today:** Students will use the Pythagorean Theorem to find the missing lengths of a right triangle.

Motivate

- **Preparation:** Cut coffee stirrers (or carefully break spaghetti) so that triangles with the following side lengths can be made: 2-3-4; 3-4-5; 4-5-6.
- **?** "What are consecutive numbers?" numbers in sequential order
- With student aid, use the coffee stirrers to make three triangles: 2-3-4; 3-4-5; and 4-5-6 on the overhead projector. If arranged carefully, all 3 will fit on the screen.
- Ask students to make observations about the 3 triangles. Students may mention that all triangles are scalene; one triangle appears to be acute, one right, one obtuse.
- They should observe that just a small change in the side lengths seems to have made a big change in the angle measures.

Lesson Notes

Key Ideas

- Draw a picture of a right triangle and label the *legs* and the *hypotenuse*. The **hypotenuse** is always opposite the right angle and is the longest side of a right triangle.
- Try not to have all right triangles in the same orientation.
- Write the Pythagorean Theorem.
- **Common Error:** Students often forget that the Pythagorean Theorem is a relationship that is *only* true for right triangles.

Example 1

- Draw and label the triangle. Review the symbol used to show that an angle is a right angle.
- **?** "What information is known for this triangle?" The legs are 5 m and 12 m.

On Your Own

- Give time for students to work the problems. Knowing their perfect squares is helpful.

Goal

Today's lesson is using the **Pythagorean Theorem** to solve for lengths of a right triangle.

Lesson Materials
Introduction
<ul><li>coffee stirrers</li><li>scissors</li></ul>

Start Thinking! and Warm Up

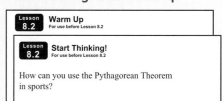

Lesson 8.2 — **Warm Up** For use before Lesson 8.2

Lesson 8.2 — **Start Thinking!** For use before Lesson 8.2

How can you use the Pythagorean Theorem in sports?

Extra Example 1

Find the length of the hypotenuse of the triangle. 5 in.

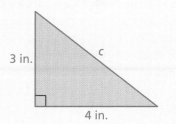

3 in.   c   4 in.

On Your Own

1. 17 ft
2. $\frac{1}{2}$ in.

Extra Example 2

Find the missing length of the triangle.
24 ft

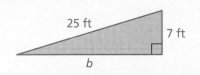

Extra Example 3

In Example 3, Group C leaves the station and hikes 3 kilometers west then 4 kilometers south. How far apart are Group B and Group C? 10 km

⬤ On Your Own

3. 30 yd   **4.** 4 m

5. 20 km

Differentiated Instruction

Kinesthetic

Have students verify the Pythagorean Theorem by drawing right triangles with legs of a given length, measuring the hypotenuse, and then calculating the hypotenuse using the Pythagorean Theorem. Use Pythagorean triples so that students work only with whole numbers.

Leg Lengths	Hypotenuse Length
3, 4	5
6, 8	10
5, 12	13
8, 15	17

Laurie's Notes

Example 2

❓ "What information is known for this triangle?" One leg is 2.1 centimeters and the hypotenuse is 2.9 centimeters.

• Substitute and solve as shown.
• **Common Error:** Students need to be careful with decimal multiplication. It is very common for students to multiply the decimal by 2 instead of multiplying the decimal by itself.
• **FYI:** The side lengths are a scale factor of the triple 20-21-29.

Example 3

• Ask a student to read the example.
❓ "Given the compass directions stated, what is a reasonable way to represent this information?" coordinate plane
• Explain that east and west are in the *x*-direction and north and south are in the *y*-direction. Draw the situation in a coordinate plane.
❓ "How can you be sure that the segments representing the hypotenuses of the smaller triangles can be connected to form a straight line?"

The segments forming the hypotenuses each have a slope of $\frac{4}{3}$.

• Students may claim that the hypotenuses of the smaller triangles can always be connected to form a straight line. To dispute this claim, draw a hiking group that travels 6 miles east and 4 miles north.

Closure

• **Exit Ticket:** Solve for the missing side. $x = 15$ cm, $y = 0.5$ m

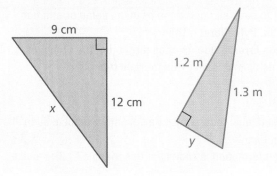

The Dynamic Planning Tool
Editable Teacher's Resources at *BigIdeasMath.com*

Find the missing length of the triangle.

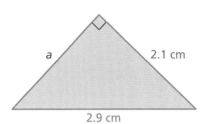

$$a^2 + b^2 = c^2$$ Write the Pythagorean Theorem.

$$a^2 + 2.1^2 = 2.9^2$$ Substitute 2.1 for b and 2.9 for c.

$$a^2 + 4.41 = 8.41$$ Evaluate powers.

$$a^2 = 4$$ Subtract 4.41 from each side.

$$a = 2$$ Take positive square root of each side.

⋮· The length of the leg is 2 centimeters.

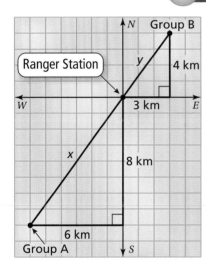

Hiking Group A leaves a ranger station and hikes 8 kilometers south then 6 kilometers west. Group B leaves the station and hikes 3 kilometers east then 4 kilometers north. Using the figure, how far apart are the two groups of hikers?

Ⓐ 5 km   Ⓑ 10 km   Ⓒ 15 km   Ⓓ 21 km

The distance between the groups is the sum of the hypotenuses, *x* and *y*. Use the Pythagorean Theorem to find *x* and *y*.

$$a^2 + b^2 = c^2$$ Write the Pythagorean Theorem. $$a^2 + b^2 = c^2$$

$$6^2 + 8^2 = x^2$$ Substitute. $$3^2 + 4^2 = y^2$$

$$36 + 64 = x^2$$ Evaluate powers. $$9 + 16 = y^2$$

$$100 = x^2$$ Add. $$25 = y^2$$

$$10 = x$$ Take positive square root of each side. $$5 = y$$

⋮· The distance between the groups of hikers is 10 + 5 = 15 kilometers. So, the correct answer is Ⓒ.

● **On Your Own**

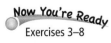
Now You're Ready
Exercises 3–8

Find the missing length of the triangle.

3.
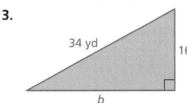

4.
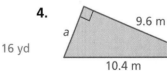

5. **WHAT IF?** In Example 3, Group A hikes 12 kilometers south and 9 kilometers west. How far apart are the hikers?

 Vocabulary and Concept Check

1. **VOCABULARY** In a right triangle, how can you tell which sides are the legs and which side is the hypotenuse?

2. **DIFFERENT WORDS, SAME QUESTION** Which is different? Find "both" answers.

Which side is the hypotenuse?

Which side is the longest?

Which side is a leg?

Which side is opposite the right angle?

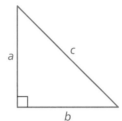

Practice and Problem Solving

Find the missing length of the triangle.

  3.

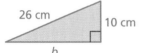

4.

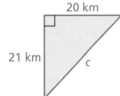

5.

6.

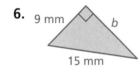

7.

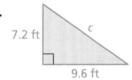

8.

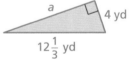

9. **ERROR ANALYSIS** Describe and correct the error in finding the missing length of the triangle.

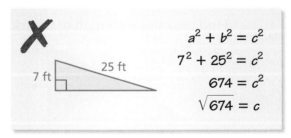

$$a^2 + b^2 = c^2$$
$$7^2 + 25^2 = c^2$$
$$674 = c^2$$
$$\sqrt{674} = c$$

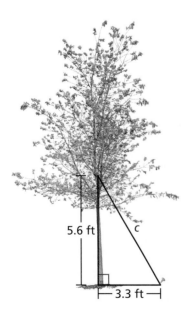

10. **TREE SUPPORT** How long is the wire that supports the tree?

Assignment Guide and Homework Check

Level	Day 1 Activity Assignment	Day 2 Lesson Assignment	Homework Check
Basic	3–5, 19–23	1, 2, 6–11, 14, 15	2, 6, 10, 14
Average	3–5, 19–23	1, 2, 7–11, 14–16	8, 10, 14, 16
Advanced	3–5, 19–23	1, 2, 9, 12–18	12, 14, 16, 17

For Your Information

- **Exercise 17** There is more than one correct drawing for this exercise. Encourage students to start at the origin and move along an axis to begin.

Common Errors

- **Exercises 3–8** Students may substitute the given lengths in the wrong part of the formula. For example, if they are finding one of the legs, they may write $5^2 + 13^2 = c^2$ instead of $5^2 + b^2 = 13^2$. Remind them that the side opposite the right angle is the hypotenuse c.
- **Exercises 3–8** Students may multiply each side length by two instead of squaring the side length. Remind them of the definition of exponents.
- **Exercises 11–13** Students may think that there is not enough information to find the value of x. Tell them that it is possible to find x; however, they may have to make an extra calculation before writing an equation for x.

Vocabulary and Concept Check

1. The hypotenuse is the longest side and the legs are the other two sides.

2. Which side is a leg?; a or b; c

Practice and Problem Solving

3. 24 cm

4. 29 km

5. 9 in.

6. 12 mm

7. 12 ft

8. $11\frac{2}{3}$ yd

9. The length of the hypotenuse was substituted for the wrong variable.
$$a^2 + b^2 = c^2$$
$$7^2 + b^2 = 25^2$$
$$49 + b^2 = 625$$
$$b^2 = 576$$
$$b = 24$$

10. 6.5 ft

8.2 Record and Practice Journal

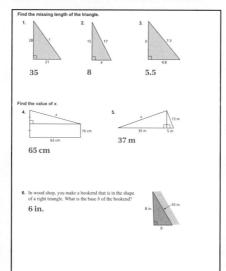

11. 16 cm

12. 37 mm

13. 10 ft

14. yes; The diagonal of the television is 40 inches.

15. 8.4 cm

16. See *Taking Math Deeper*.

17. **a.** *Sample answer:*

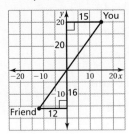

    b. 45 ft

18. 7

 Fair Game Review

19. 6 and −6   **20.** −11

21. 13   **22.** −15

23. C

Mini-Assessment

Find the missing length of the triangle.

1. 50 ft

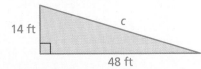

2. 24 mm

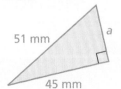

3. 12 in.

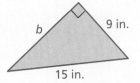

Taking Math Deeper

Exercise 16

The challenging part of this problem is realizing that the hypotenuse of the right triangle is given as 181 yards above the diagram.

 Find the hypotenuse of the right triangle.

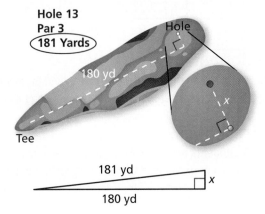

 Use the Pythagorean Theorem.

$$180^2 + x^2 = 181^2$$
$$32{,}400 + x^2 = 32{,}761$$
$$x^2 = 361$$
$$x = 19$$

19 yards

 Answer the question.

The ball is 19 yards from the hole. Using the relationship of

3 feet = 1 yard, 19 yd $\times \dfrac{3 \text{ ft}}{1 \text{ yd}}$ = 57 ft. So, the ball is **57** feet from the hole.

Reteaching and Enrichment Strategies

If students need help...	If students got it...

Resources by Chapter
  • Practice A and Practice B
  • Puzzle Time
Record and Practice Journal Practice
Differentiating the Lesson
Lesson Tutorials
Skills Review Handbook
	Resources by Chapter
	  • Enrichment and Extension
	Start the next section

Find the value of x.

11.

20 cm

12 cm   x

12.

5 mm

13 mm

x

35 mm

13.

x   10 ft

16 ft

14. FLAT SCREEN Televisions are advertised by the lengths of their diagonals. A store has a sale on televisions 40 inches and larger. Is the television on sale? Explain.

24 in.   d

32 in.

15. BUTTERFLY Approximate the wingspan of the butterfly.

Wingspan

4 cm

5.8 cm

Hole 13
Par 3
181 Yards

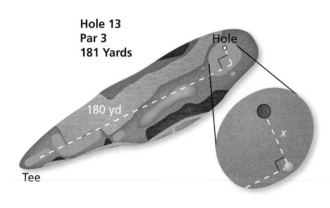

Hole

180 yd

x

Tee

16. GOLF The figure shows the location of a golf ball after a tee shot. How many feet from the hole is the ball?

17. SNOWBALLS You and a friend stand back-to-back. You run 20 feet forward then 15 feet to your right. At the same time, your friend runs 16 feet forward then 12 feet to her right. She stops and hits you with a snowball.

   a. Draw the situation in a coordinate plane.

   b. How far does your friend throw the snowball?

18. **Algebra** The legs of a right triangle have lengths of 28 meters and 21 meters. The hypotenuse has a length of $5x$ meters. What is the value of x?

Fair Game Review *What you learned in previous grades & lessons*

Find the square root(s). *(Section 8.1)*

19. $\pm\sqrt{36}$ **20.** $-\sqrt{121}$ **21.** $\sqrt{169}$ **22.** $-\sqrt{225}$

23. MULTIPLE CHOICE Which type of triangle can have an obtuse angle? *(Section 5.2)*

   (A) equiangular   **(B)** right   **(C)** isosceles   **(D)** equilateral

You can use a **summary triangle** to explain a topic. Here is an example of a summary triangle for finding the length of the hypotenuse of a triangle.

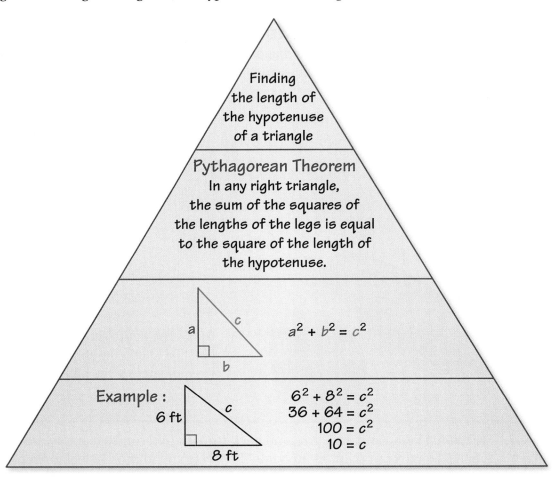

Finding the length of the hypotenuse of a triangle

Pythagorean Theorem
In any right triangle, the sum of the squares of the lengths of the legs is equal to the square of the length of the hypotenuse.

$a^2 + b^2 = c^2$

Example:

$$6^2 + 8^2 = c^2$$
$$36 + 64 = c^2$$
$$100 = c^2$$
$$10 = c$$

On Your Own

Make a summary triangle to help you study these topics.

1. finding square roots

2. evaluating expressions involving square roots

3. finding the length of a leg of a right triangle

After you complete this chapter, make summary triangles for the following topics.

4. approximating square roots

5. simplifying square roots

Cheese
Doggy treat
Good pet reward
Example: 4 Newton

Nacho cheese

"What do you call a cheese summary triangle that isn't yours?"

Sample Answers

1.

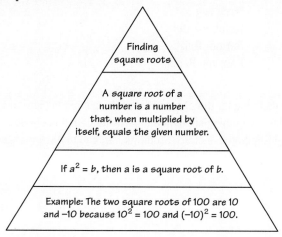

Finding square roots

A square root of a number is a number that, when multiplied by itself, equals the given number.

If $a^2 = b$, then a is a square root of b.

Example: The two square roots of 100 are 10 and −10 because $10^2 = 100$ and $(-10)^2 = 100$.

2.

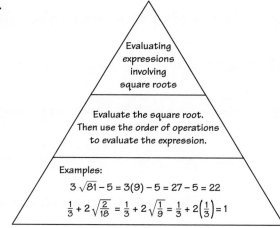

Evaluating expressions involving square roots

Evaluate the square root. Then use the order of operations to evaluate the expression.

Examples:

$3\sqrt{81} - 5 = 3(9) - 5 = 27 - 5 = 22$

$\frac{1}{3} + 2\sqrt{\frac{2}{18}} = \frac{1}{3} + 2\sqrt{\frac{1}{9}} = \frac{1}{3} + 2\left(\frac{1}{3}\right) = 1$

3.

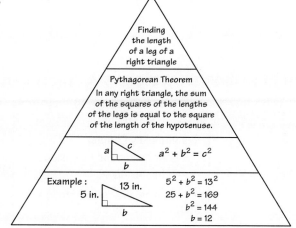

Finding the length of a leg of a right triangle

Pythagorean Theorem
In any right triangle, the sum of the squares of the lengths of the legs is equal to the square of the length of the hypotenuse.

$a^2 + b^2 = c^2$

Example:

$5^2 + b^2 = 13^2$
$25 + b^2 = 169$
$b^2 = 144$
$b = 12$

List of Organizers
Available at *BigIdeasMath.com*

Comparison Chart
Concept Circle
Definition (Idea) and Example Chart
Example and Non-Example Chart
Formula Triangle
Four Square
Information Frame
Information Wheel
Notetaking Organizer
Process Diagram
Summary Triangle
Word Magnet
Y Chart

About this Organizer

A **Summary Triangle** can be used to explain a concept. Typically, the summary triangle is divided into 3 or 4 parts. In the top part, students write the concept being explained. In the middle part(s), students write any procedure, explanation, description, definition, theorem, and/or formula(s). In the bottom part, students write an example to illustrate the concept. A summary triangle can be used as an assessment tool, in which blanks are left for students to complete. Also, students can place their summary triangles on note cards to use as a quick study reference.

Technology For the Teacher
Vocabulary Puzzle Builder

Answers

1. 14 and -14

2. 7 and -7

3. 20 and -20

4. -2

5. $\dfrac{4}{5}$

6. 2.5 and -2.5

7. 26

8. -6

9. $5\dfrac{1}{4}$

10. 41 ft

11. 28 in.

12. 6.3 cm

13. $\dfrac{1}{2}$ yd

14. $3.14r^2 = 314$; about 20 feet

15. 1000 ft

16. 53 in.

Assessment Book

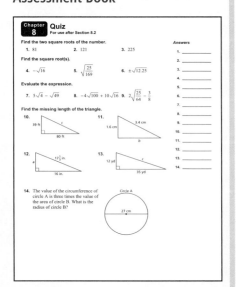

Alternative Quiz Ideas

100% Quiz	Math Log
Error Notebook	Notebook Quiz
Group Quiz	Partner Quiz
Homework Quiz	Pass the Paper

Math Log

Ask students to keep a math log for the chapter. Have them include diagrams, definitions, and examples. Everything should be clearly labeled. It might be helpful if they put the information in a chart. Students can add to the log as they are introduced to new topics.

Reteaching and Enrichment Strategies

If students need help. . .	If students got it. . .
Resources by Chapter • Study Help • Practice A and Practice B • Puzzle Time Lesson Tutorials *BigIdeasMath.com* Practice Quiz Practice from the Test Generator	Resources by Chapter • Enrichment and Extension • School-to-Work Game Closet at *BigIdeasMath.com* Start the next section

Technology For the Teacher

Answer Presentation Tool
Big Ideas Test Generator

Check It Out
Progress Check
BigIdeasMath ✓com

Find the two square roots of the number. *(Section 8.1)*

1. 196

2. 49

3. 400

Find the square root(s). *(Section 8.1)*

4. $-\sqrt{4}$

5. $\sqrt{\dfrac{16}{25}}$

6. $\pm\sqrt{6.25}$

Evaluate the expression. *(Section 8.1)*

7. $3\sqrt{49} + 5$

8. $10 - 4\sqrt{16}$

9. $\dfrac{1}{4} + \sqrt{\dfrac{100}{4}}$

Find the missing length of the triangle. *(Section 8.2)*

10.
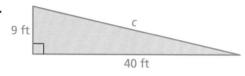
9 ft   c   40 ft

11.
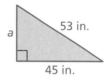
a   53 in.   45 in.

12.
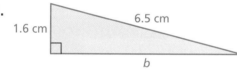
1.6 cm   6.5 cm   b

13.
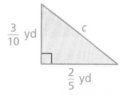
$\dfrac{3}{10}$ yd   c $\dfrac{2}{5}$ yd

14. POOL The area of a circular pool cover is 314 square feet. Write and solve an equation to find the diameter of the pool cover. Use 3.14 for π. *(Section 8.1)*

15. LAND A square parcel of land has an area of 1 million square feet. What is the length of one side of the parcel? *(Section 8.1)*

16. FABRIC You are cutting a rectangular piece of fabric in half along the diagonal. The fabric measures 28 inches wide and $1\dfrac{1}{4}$ yards long. What is the length (in inches) of the diagonal? *(Section 8.2)*

STANDARDS
OF LEARNING
8.2
8.5

Essential Question How can you find decimal approximations of square roots that are irrational?

You already know that a rational number is a number that can be written as the ratio of two integers. Numbers that cannot be written as the ratio of two integers are called **irrational**.

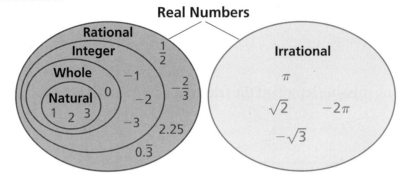

1 ACTIVITY: Approximating Square Roots

Work with a partner.

Archimedes was a Greek mathematician, physicist, engineer, inventor, and astronomer.

a. Archimedes tried to find a rational number whose square is 3. Here are two that he tried.

$$\frac{265}{153} \text{ and } \frac{1351}{780}$$

Are either of these numbers equal to $\sqrt{3}$? How can you tell?

Archimedes
(c. 287 B.C.–c. 212 B.C.)

b. Use a calculator with a square root key to approximate $\sqrt{3}$.

Write the number on a piece of paper. Then enter it into the calculator and square it. Then subtract 3. Do you get 0? Explain.

c. Calculators did not exist in the time of Archimedes. How do you think he might have approximated $\sqrt{3}$?

Square
Root Key

Laurie's Notes

Introduction

For the Teacher

- **Goal:** Students will investigate the irrational number $\sqrt{3}$ both numerically and geometrically.

Motivate

- Make a large Venn diagram based on student characteristics.
- The diagram can be made on the floor with yarn. Have students write their names on index cards.
- Use the diagram shown for students to place themselves. Sample labels for the groups: A = girls in our class, B = boys in our class, C = wears glasses/contacts, D = brown hair, E = taller than 5' 4", F = wearing a short sleeved T-shirt

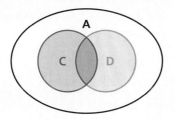
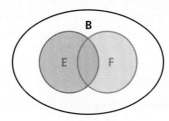

- Discuss what it means to be in certain sets and not in other sets.

Activity Notes

Activity 1

- Draw the Venn diagram shown and write the sets of numbers.
- **FYI:** Archimedes wanted a number x, such that $x^2 = 3$. Students often think $x = 1.5$ or $\frac{3}{2}$ because they are not used to squaring and think of doubling instead. If $x^2 = 3$, then $x = \pm\sqrt{3}$. Archimedes wanted to find a rational number that equaled $\sqrt{3}$.
- Frame this question in the context of what students know: $\sqrt{1} = 1$ and $\sqrt{4} = 2$, so $\sqrt{3}$ will be a decimal between 1 and 2.
- **Part (a):** To square this fraction using a calculator, you can (1) change $\frac{265}{153}$ into a decimal by dividing, then square the decimal, or (2) write the fraction inside parentheses (if available on the calculator), then use the exponent key (if available on the calculator).
- **Part (b):** If students are using their personal calculators, be aware that some calculators have you enter the number and then the square root key, while other calculators have you enter the square root key and then the number.
- **Note:** In part (b), if you get anything other than 0, it means you did not have the exact value for $\sqrt{3}$, because $\sqrt{3}$ is irrational.

Standards of Learning

8.2 The student will describe orally and in writing the relationships between the subsets of the real number system.
8.5(b) The student will find the two consecutive whole numbers between which a square root lies.

Previous Learning

Students should know how to find square roots of perfect squares.

Activity Materials	
Introduction	**Textbook**
- yarn - index cards	- calculators - compasses

Start Thinking! and Warm Up

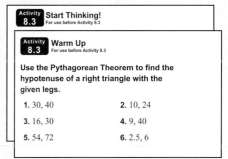

Activity 8.3 Start Thinking! For use before Activity 8.3

Activity 8.3 Warm Up For use before Activity 8.3

Use the Pythagorean Theorem to find the hypotenuse of a right triangle with the given legs.

1. 30, 40   2. 10, 24
3. 16, 30   4. 9, 40
5. 54, 72   6. 2.5, 6

8.3 Record and Practice Journal

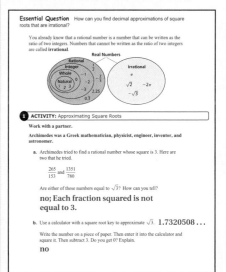

Essential Question How can you find decimal approximations of square roots that are irrational?

You already know that a rational number is a number that can be written as the ratio of two integers. Numbers that cannot be written as the ratio of two integers are called **irrational**.

1 ACTIVITY: Approximating Square Roots

Work with a partner.

Archimedes was a Greek mathematician, physicist, engineer, inventor, and astronomer.

a. Archimedes tried to find a rational number whose square is 3. Here are two that he tried.

$$\frac{265}{153} \text{ and } \frac{1351}{780}$$

Are either of these numbers equal to $\sqrt{3}$? How can you tell?

no; Each fraction squared is not equal to 3.

b. Use a calculator with a square root key to approximate $\sqrt{3}$. **1.7320508 . . .**

Write the number on a piece of paper. Then enter it into the calculator and square it. Then subtract 3. Do you get 0? Explain.

no

Differentiated Instruction

Visual

On the board, create a large Venn diagram similar to the one shown in the activity. Have students place given rational and irrational numbers in the correct spaces on the Venn diagram. Emphasize that a rational number cannot be irrational and an irrational number cannot be rational. You should also reinforce that a number such as 5 is a natural number, as well as a whole number, an integer, and a rational number.

8.3 Record and Practice Journal

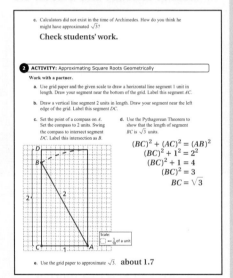

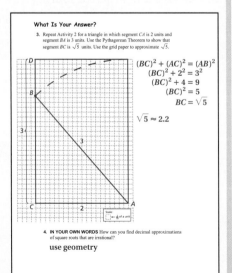

Laurie's Notes

Activity 2

- In Activity 1, students looked at $\sqrt{3}$ as a number. In this activity, students will look at $\sqrt{3}$ geometrically, as a length of a line segment.
- Students should be able to follow the written directions to construct segment *BC*.
- ❓ "Why does swinging the compass make *AB* equal 2 units?" *AB* is a radius of a circle that you know equals 2.
- ❓ "What type of triangle is *ABC*?" right
- ❓ "What information do you know about the triangle?" The hypotenuse equals 2 and one leg equals 1.
- Ask a volunteer to show how they used the Pythagorean Theorem.
- ❓ "Is $\sqrt{3}$ greater than or less than 1.5?" greater than

What Is Your Answer?

- **Think-Pair-Share:** Students should read each question independently and then work with a partner to answer the questions. When they have answered the questions, the pair should compare their answers with another group and discuss any discrepancies.

Closure

- **Exit Ticket:** Describe how you would approximate $\sqrt{2}$.

  Listen for students to describe a procedure similar to that used in Activity 2, except with segments 1 unit in length.

Technology For the Teacher

Dynamic Classroom

The Dynamic Planning Tool
Editable Teacher's Resources at *BigIdeasMath.com*

Work with a partner.

a. Use grid paper and the given scale to draw a horizontal line segment 1 unit in length. Label this segment *AC*.

b. Draw a vertical line segment 2 units in length. Label this segment *DC*.

c. Set the point of a compass on *A*. Set the compass to 2 units. Swing the compass to intersect segment *DC*. Label this intersection as *B*.

d. Use the Pythagorean Theorem to show that the length of segment *BC* is $\sqrt{3}$ units.

e. Use the grid paper to approximate $\sqrt{3}$.

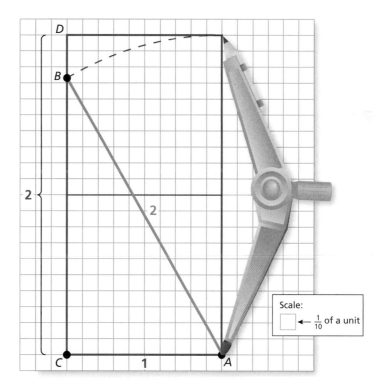

Scale:
▢ ← $\frac{1}{10}$ of a unit

What Is Your Answer?

3. Repeat Activity 2 for a triangle in which segment *CA* is 2 units and segment *BA* is 3 units. Use the Pythagorean Theorem to show that segment *BC* is $\sqrt{5}$ units. Use the grid paper to approximate $\sqrt{5}$.

4. **IN YOUR OWN WORDS** How can you find decimal approximations of square roots that are irrational?

Practice ➤ Use what you learned about approximating square roots to complete Exercises 5–8 on page 375.

A rational number is a number that can be written as the ratio of two integers. An **irrational number** cannot be written as the ratio of two integers.

- The square root of any whole number that is not a perfect square is irrational.
- The decimal form of an irrational number neither terminates nor repeats.

 **Key Idea**

Real Numbers

Rational numbers and irrational numbers together form the set of **real numbers**.

Remember

Decimals that *terminate* or *repeat* are rational.

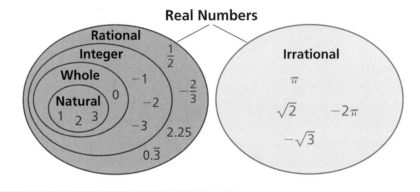

EXAMPLE (1) **Classifying Real Numbers**

Classify each real number.

Study Tip

When classifying a real number, list all the subsets in which the number belongs.

	Number	Subset(s)	Reasoning
a.	$\sqrt{12}$	Irrational	12 is not a perfect square.
b.	$-0.36\overline{4}$	Rational	$-0.36\overline{4}$ is a repeating decimal.
c.	$-\sqrt{9}$	Integer, Rational	$-\sqrt{9}$ is equal to -3.
d.	$\dfrac{72}{4}$	Natural, Whole, Integer, Rational	$\dfrac{72}{4}$ is equal to 18.
e.	π	Irrational	The decimal form of π neither terminates nor repeats.

⬤ **On Your Own**

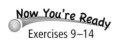
Now You're Ready
Exercises 9–14

Classify the real number.

1. $0.121221222\ldots$ **2.** $-\sqrt{196}$ **3.** $\sqrt{2}$

Laurie's Notes

Introduction

Connect

- **Yesterday:** Students investigated $\sqrt{3}$ numerically and geometrically.
- **Today:** Students will approximate square roots as being between two integers.

Motivate

- Discuss applications of a periscope and share the following information.
  - A periscope is an optical device for conducting observations from a concealed or protected position.
  - Simple periscopes consist of reflecting mirrors and/or prisms at opposite ends of a tube container. The reflecting surfaces are parallel to each other and at a 45° angle to the axis of the tube.
  - The Navy attributes the invention of the periscope (1902) to Simon Lake and the perfection of the periscope to Sir Howard Grubb.

Lesson Notes

Key Idea

- Explain the definitions of *rational* and *irrational* numbers. Use the Venn diagram to give several examples of each.
- Write the Key Idea. Students saw this Venn diagram yesterday. It is important for students to understand that any real number is either rational or irrational. The two sets do not intersect.
- Explain that a *subset* is a set in which every element is contained within a larger set. The sets of rational numbers and irrational numbers are subsets of the set of real numbers. The sets of natural numbers, whole numbers, and integers are subsets of the set of rational numbers.
- Natural numbers are also called counting numbers because they are used to count objects. Whole numbers include the natural numbers and 0. Integers include the natural numbers, 0, and the opposites of the natural numbers.
- Mention that all square roots of perfect squares are rational.
- **?** "Can you think of a repeating decimal and its fractional equivalent?"

  Sample answer: $0.\overline{3} = \dfrac{1}{3}$

- **?** "Can you think of a terminating decimal and its fractional equivalent?"

  Sample answer: $0.5 = \dfrac{1}{2}$

Example 1

- Students will gain a better understanding of how to classify real numbers in this example.
- Discuss the Study Tip with students. Point out in part (c), for instance, that because $-\sqrt{9} = -3 = \dfrac{-3}{1}$, $-\sqrt{9}$ is an integer *and* a rational number.

On Your Own

- **Think-Pair-Share:** Students should read each question independently and then work with a partner to answer the questions. When they have answered the questions, the pair should compare their answers with another group and discuss any discrepancies.

Goal Today's lesson is approximating square roots.

Lesson Materials
Textbook
• calculators

Start Thinking! and Warm Up

Lesson 8.3 **Warm Up** For use before Lesson 8.3

Lesson 8.3 **Start Thinking!** For use before Lesson 8.3

How can you find the side length of a square that has the same area as an 8.5-inch by 11-inch piece of paper?

Extra Example 1

Classify each real number.

a. $\sqrt{15}$ irrational

b. 0.35 rational

 On Your Own

1. irrational

2. integer, rational

3. irrational

T-372

Extra Example 2

Estimate $\sqrt{23}$ to the nearest integer.
Because 23 is closer to 25 than to 16, $\sqrt{23}$ is closer to 5 than to 4. So, $\sqrt{23} \approx 5$.

 On Your Own

4. 6   **5.** 9

6. 14   **7.** −3

Extra Example 3

Which is greater, $\sqrt{0.49}$ or 0.71? 0.71

 On Your Own

8. $\sqrt{23}$; $\sqrt{23}$ is to the right of $4\frac{1}{5}$.

9. $\sqrt{10}$; $\sqrt{10}$ is positive and $-\sqrt{5}$ is negative.

10. $-\sqrt{2}$; $-\sqrt{2}$ is to the right of −2.

English Language Learners

Vocabulary

Point out to students that the prefix *ir-* means *not*. An *irrational* number is a number that is not rational. Here are other common prefixes that also mean *not*.

dis-   disadvantage, disagree
il-   illiterate, illogical
im-   impolite, improper
in-   independent, indirect
ir-   irrational, irregular
un-   unfair, unfriendly

Example 2

? "What are the first 10 perfect squares?" 1, 4, 9, 16, 25, 36, 49, 64, 81, 100

? "What type of number do you get if you take the square root of any of these perfect squares?" integer

- Write this list on the board as a reference for students. Connect this list to the Venn diagram.
- The integer 52 is not a perfect square. It falls between 49 and 64.
- Draw the number line and work the problem as shown.

On Your Own

- **Question 6:** Students may need help recognizing perfect squares greater than 100.
- **Question 7:** Students should estimate $\sqrt{7}$ first, and then consider the negative sign.

Example 3

- The number line is used as a visual model in each part.
- In part (a), students will ask where to place $\sqrt{5}$. Knowing that $\sqrt{5}$ is between $\sqrt{4}$ and $\sqrt{9}$ does not tell you where to graph it on the number line. Explain that you know it has to be closer to $\sqrt{4}$ than $\sqrt{9}$ because 5 is closer to 4.
- The fraction $2\frac{3}{4}$ is greater than $2\frac{1}{2}$, so it is closer to $\sqrt{9}$.

? "In part (b), what is 0.36 as a fraction?" $\frac{36}{100}$

- Because 36 and 100 are both perfect squares, their square roots are integers. The rational number $\frac{6}{10}$ is equivalent to the decimal 0.6.

On Your Own

- **Question 9:** A positive number is always greater than a negative number.
- **Question 10:** A number line is helpful for this question.

EXAMPLE **2**   **Approximating Square Roots**

Estimate $\sqrt{52}$ to the nearest integer.

Use a number line and the square roots of the perfect squares nearest to the radicand. The nearest perfect square less than 52 is 49. The nearest perfect square greater than 52 is 64.

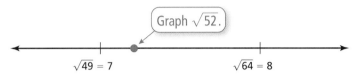

Graph $\sqrt{52}$.

$\sqrt{49} = 7$ $\sqrt{64} = 8$

Because 52 is closer to 49 than to 64, $\sqrt{52}$ is closer to 7 than to 8.

∴ So, $\sqrt{52} \approx 7$.

On Your Own

Now You're Ready
Exercises 18–23

Estimate to the nearest integer.

4. $\sqrt{33}$ **5.** $\sqrt{85}$ **6.** $\sqrt{190}$ **7.** $-\sqrt{7}$

EXAMPLE **3**   **Comparing Real Numbers**

a. Which is greater, $\sqrt{5}$ or $2\frac{3}{4}$?

Graph the numbers on a number line.

$2\frac{3}{4} = 2.75$

$\sqrt{5}$

$\sqrt{4} = 2$ $\sqrt{9} = 3$

∴ $2\frac{3}{4}$ is to the right of $\sqrt{5}$. So, $2\frac{3}{4}$ is greater.

b. Which is greater, $0.\overline{6}$ or $\sqrt{0.36}$?

Graph the numbers on a number line.

$\sqrt{0.36} = 0.6$ $0.\overline{6}$

0.6   0.7

∴ $0.\overline{6}$ is to the right of $\sqrt{0.36}$. So, $0.\overline{6}$ is greater.

On Your Own

Now You're Ready
Exercises 25–30

Which number is greater? Explain.

8. $4\frac{1}{5}, \sqrt{23}$ **9.** $\sqrt{10}, -\sqrt{5}$ **10.** $-\sqrt{2}, -2$

EXAMPLE 4 **Approximating an Expression**

The radius of a circle with area A is approximately $\sqrt{\dfrac{A}{3}}$. The area of a circular mouse pad is 51 square inches. Estimate its radius.

$$\sqrt{\dfrac{A}{3}} = \sqrt{\dfrac{51}{3}} \qquad \text{Substitute 51 for } A.$$

$$= \sqrt{17} \qquad \text{Divide.}$$

The nearest perfect square less than 17 is 16. The nearest perfect square greater than 17 is 25.

Because 17 is closer to 16 than to 25, $\sqrt{17}$ is closer to 4 than to 5.

∴ The radius is about 4 inches.

On Your Own

11. **WHAT IF?** The area of a circular mouse pad is 64 square inches. Estimate its radius.

EXAMPLE 5 **Real-Life Application**

The distance (in nautical miles) you can see with a periscope is $1.17\sqrt{h}$, where h is the height of the periscope above the water. Can a periscope that is 6 feet above the water see twice as far as a periscope that is 3 feet above the water? Explain.

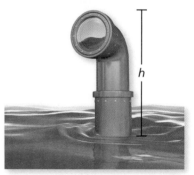

Use a calculator to find the distances.

3 feet above water

$$1.17\sqrt{h} = 1.17\sqrt{3} \qquad \text{Substitute for } h.$$

$$\approx 2.03 \qquad \text{Use a calculator.}$$

6 feet above water

$$1.17\sqrt{h} = 1.17\sqrt{6}$$

$$\approx 2.87$$

You can see $\dfrac{2.87}{2.03} \approx 1.41$ times farther with the periscope that is 6 feet above the water than with the periscope that is 3 feet above the water.

∴ No, the periscope that is 6 feet above the water cannot see twice as far.

On Your Own

12. You use a periscope that is 10 feet above the water. Can you see farther than 4 nautical miles? Explain.

Laurie's Notes

Example 4

- A simple diagram of a circle helps students focus on what is being asked.
- ❓ "What is the formula for the area of a circle?" $A = \pi r^2$
- Review with students how to solve this formula for r.

$$A = \pi r^2 \qquad \text{Write the area formula.}$$

$$\frac{A}{\pi} = r^2 \qquad \text{Divide each side by } \pi.$$

$$\sqrt{\frac{A}{\pi}} = r \qquad \text{Take positive square root of each side.}$$

Because π is close to 3, when approximating the radius, you can replace π with 3. This is the formula presented in this example.

- ❓ "What information is known in this problem?" You have a circle with an area of 51 square inches.
- ❓ "What are you trying to find?" an estimate for the radius
- Radicands that are fractions can be intimidating to students.
- Draw the number line and work the problem as shown.

On Your Own

- The quotient $\frac{64}{3}$ is not a whole number, but the question is still completed in the same fashion.

Example 5

- Ask a student to read through the problem.
- You want to compare the distances for a periscope at two different heights above water, so the equation is used twice.
- ❓ "Do you think you can see twice as far at 6 feet than at 3 feet?" Most will say yes.
- Write the expression $1.17\sqrt{h}$ on the board and evaluate it for each height, as shown.

On Your Own

- Ask volunteers to share their work at the board.

Closure

- Order the numbers from least to greatest: $\sqrt{38}, \sqrt{\frac{100}{3}}, 6.\overline{5}$ $\sqrt{\frac{100}{3}}, \sqrt{38}, 6.\overline{5}$

Technology **F**or the **T**eacher

Dynamic Classroom

The Dynamic Planning Tool
Editable Teacher's Resources at *BigIdeasMath.com*

Extra Example 4

In Example 4, estimate the radius of a circular mouse pad with an area of 45 square inches. about 4 in.

On Your Own

11. 5 in.

Extra Example 5

In Example 5, a periscope is 8 feet above the water. Can you see farther than 3 nautical miles? Explain. yes; You can see about 3.3 nautical miles.

On Your Own

12. no; You can only see about 3.7 nautical miles.

1. A rational number can be written as the ratio of two integers. An irrational number cannot be written as the ratio of two integers.

2. 32 is between the perfect squares 25 and 36, but is closer to 36, so $\sqrt{32} \approx 6$.

3. all rational and irrational numbers; *Sample answer:* $-2, \frac{1}{8}, \sqrt{7}$

4. $\sqrt{8}$; $\sqrt{8}$ is irrational and the other three numbers are rational.

Practice and Problem Solving

5. yes

6. no

7. no

8. yes

9. whole, integer, rational

10. irrational

11. integer, rational

12. rational

13. natural, whole, integer, rational

14. irrational

15. 144 is a perfect square. So, $\sqrt{144}$ is rational.

16. no; 52 is not a perfect square.

17. **a.** If the last digit is 0, it is a whole number. Otherwise, it is a natural number.

    b. irrational number

    c. irrational number

Assignment Guide and Homework Check

Level	Day 1 Activity Assignment	Day 2 Lesson Assignment	Homework Check
Basic	5–8, 41–44	1–4, 9–31 odd, 16, 24, 32	16, 24, 27, 32
Average	5–8, 41–44	1–4, 13–17, 22–24, 25–33 odd, 32, 37	16, 24, 27, 32
Advanced	5–8, 41–44	1–4, 15, 23, 24, 29–40	24, 30, 34, 38

Common Errors

- **Exercises 9–14** Students may not classify the real number in as many ways as possible. For instance, they may classify $\frac{52}{13}$ as rational only, because it is written as a fraction. Remind students that real numbers can have more than one classification. Point out that they should simplify the number, if possible, before classifying it.
- **Exercises 11 and 12** Students may think that all negative numbers are irrational. Remind them of the integers and that negative numbers can be rational or irrational.
- **Exercises 11 and 14** Students may think that all square roots are irrational. Remind them that square roots of perfect squares are rational.

8.3 Record and Practice Journal

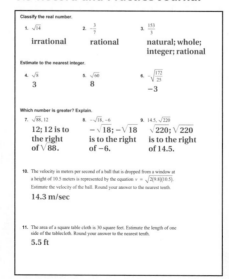

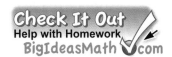

Vocabulary and Concept Check

1. **VOCABULARY** How are rational numbers and irrational numbers different?

2. **WRITING** Describe a method of approximating $\sqrt{32}$.

3. **VOCABULARY** What are real numbers? Give three examples.

4. **WHICH ONE DOESN'T BELONG?** Which number does *not* belong with the other three? Explain your reasoning.

$$-\frac{11}{12} \qquad 25.075 \qquad \sqrt{8} \qquad -3.\overline{3}$$

Practice and Problem Solving

Tell whether the rational number is a reasonable approximation of the square root.

5. $\frac{559}{250}, \sqrt{5}$

6. $\frac{3021}{250}, \sqrt{11}$

7. $\frac{678}{250}, \sqrt{28}$

8. $\frac{1677}{250}, \sqrt{45}$

Classify the real number.

9. 0

10. $\frac{\pi}{6}$

11. $-\sqrt{81}$

12. -1.125

13. $\frac{52}{13}$

14. $\sqrt{15}$

15. **ERROR ANALYSIS** Describe and correct the error in classifying the number.

$\sqrt{144}$ is irrational.

16. **SCRAPBOOKING** You cut a picture into a right triangle for your scrapbook. The lengths of the legs of the triangle are 4 inches and 6 inches. Is the length of the hypotenuse a rational number? Explain.

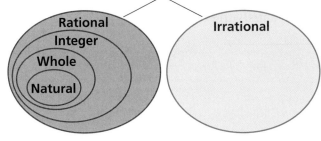
Real Numbers

Rational

Integer

Whole

Natural

Irrational

17. **VENN DIAGRAM** Place each number in the correct area of the Venn Diagram.

   a. The last digit of your phone number

   b. The square root of any prime number

   c. The ratio of the circumference of a circle to its diameter

Estimate to the nearest integer.

② 18. $\sqrt{24}$

19. $\sqrt{685}$

20. $-\sqrt{61}$

21. $-\sqrt{105}$

22. $\sqrt{\dfrac{27}{4}}$

23. $-\sqrt{\dfrac{335}{2}}$

24. CHECKERS A checkerboard is 8 squares long and 8 squares wide. The area of each square is 14 square centimeters. Estimate the perimeter of the checkerboard.

Which number is greater? Explain.

③ 25. $\sqrt{20}$, 10

26. $\sqrt{15}$, -3.5

27. $\sqrt{133}$, $10\dfrac{3}{4}$

28. $\dfrac{2}{3}$, $\sqrt{\dfrac{16}{81}}$

29. $-\sqrt{0.25}$, -0.25

30. $-\sqrt{182}$, $-\sqrt{192}$

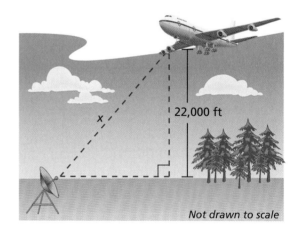

31. FOUR SQUARE The area of a four square court is 66 square feet. Estimate the length s of one of the sides of the court.

32. RADIO SIGNAL The maximum distance (in nautical miles) that a radio transmitter signal can be sent is represented by the expression $1.23\sqrt{h}$, where h is the height (in feet) above the transmitter.

Estimate the maximum distance x (in nautical miles) between the plane that is receiving the signal and the transmitter. Round your answer to the nearest tenth.

33. OPEN-ENDED Find two numbers a and b that satisfy the diagram.

Common Errors

- **Exercises 18–23** Students may struggle with knowing what integer is closest to the given number. To help make comparisons, encourage them to write the first 10 perfect squares. If the number under the radical is greater than 100, then students should use *Guess, Check, and Revise* to find two integers on either side of the number. When determining which integer is closer to the rational number, encourage students to use a number line.

- **Exercises 25–30** Students may guess which is greater just by looking at the numbers. Encourage them to use a number line to compare the numbers. Also remind them to simplify and/or estimate the numbers so that they are easier to compare.

- **Exercises 34–36** Students may struggle estimating the square roots because of the decimals. Remind them of the method they used in Exercises 18–23. Tell them to use the list they wrote, but with the decimal points moved two places to the left. These new perfect squares will help to estimate the square roots.

Practice and Problem Solving

18. 5

19. 26

20. -8

21. -10

22. 3

23. -13

24. 128 cm

25. 10; 10 is to the right of $\sqrt{20}$.

26. $\sqrt{15}$; $\sqrt{15}$ is positive and -3.5 is negative.

27. $\sqrt{133}$; $\sqrt{133}$ is to the right of $10\frac{3}{4}$.

28. $\frac{2}{3}$; $\frac{2}{3}$ is to the right of $\sqrt{\frac{16}{81}}$.

29. -0.25; -0.25 is to the right of $-\sqrt{0.25}$.

30. $-\sqrt{182}$; $-\sqrt{182}$ is to the right of $-\sqrt{192}$.

31. 8 ft

32. 182.4 nautical miles

33. *Sample answer:* $a = 82$, $b = 97$

34. 0.6

35. 1.1

36. 1.2

37. 30.1 m/sec

38. yes; $\left(\dfrac{1}{2}\right)^2 = \dfrac{1}{4}$, so $\sqrt{\dfrac{1}{4}} = \dfrac{1}{2}$.

no; $\left(\dfrac{\sqrt{3}}{4}\right)^2 = \dfrac{3}{16}$, and $\sqrt{3}$

is irrational.

39. See *Taking Math Deeper*.

40. Sample answers are given.

  a. always; The product of two fractions is a fraction.

    $\dfrac{2}{3} \cdot \dfrac{3}{4} = \dfrac{1}{2}$

  b. sometimes; $\pi \cdot 0 = 0$ is rational, but $2 \cdot \sqrt{3}$ is irrational.

  c. sometimes; $\sqrt{2} \cdot \pi$ is irrational, but $\pi \cdot \dfrac{1}{\pi}$ is rational.

Fair Game Review

  41. $-3x + 3y$ **42.** $4t - 5\pi$

  43. $40k - 9$ **44.** D

Mini-Assessment
Estimate to the nearest integer.

1. $\sqrt{65}$ about 8

2. $\sqrt{99}$ about 10

3. $\sqrt{\dfrac{15}{2}}$ about 3

Which number is greater?

4. $2\dfrac{11}{12}, -\sqrt{8}$ $2\dfrac{11}{12}$

5. $\dfrac{5}{4}, \sqrt{\dfrac{49}{64}}$ $\dfrac{5}{4}$

Taking Math Deeper

Exercise 39

This is a nice science problem. Students learn from this problem that objects do not fall at a linear rate. Their speed increases with each second they are falling.

1 Understand the problem.

  A water balloon is dropped from a height of 14 meters. How long does it take the balloon to fall to the ground?

2 Use the given formula.

$$t = \sqrt{\dfrac{d}{4.9}}$$
$$= \sqrt{\dfrac{14}{4.9}}$$
$$\approx \sqrt{2.86}$$
$$\approx 1.7$$

Fall 14 meters.

3 Answer the question.

  The water balloon will hit the ground in about 1.7 seconds.

Project

Use a stop watch, a metric tape measure, and several water balloons. Measure the distance from the top of the bleachers at your school. Drop a balloon and record the time it takes to fall to the ground. Use the formula in the problem to calculate the time it should take. Compare.

Reteaching and Enrichment Strategies

If students need help. . .	If students got it. . .
Resources by Chapter • Practice A and Practice B • Puzzle Time Record and Practice Journal Practice Differentiating the Lesson Lesson Tutorials Skills Review Handbook	Resources by Chapter • Enrichment and Extension • School-to-Work Start the next section

Estimate to the nearest tenth.

34. $\sqrt{0.39}$

35. $\sqrt{1.19}$

36. $\sqrt{1.52}$

37. ROLLER COASTER The velocity v (in meters per second) of a roller coaster is represented by the equation $v = 3\sqrt{6r}$, where r is the radius of the loop. Estimate the velocity of a car going around the loop. Round your answer to the nearest tenth.

$r = 16.764$ m

38. Is $\sqrt{\dfrac{1}{4}}$ a rational number? Is $\sqrt{\dfrac{3}{16}}$ a rational number? Explain.

39. WATER BALLOON The time t (in seconds) it takes a water balloon to fall d meters is represented by the equation $t = \sqrt{\dfrac{d}{4.9}}$. Estimate the time it takes the balloon to fall to the ground from a window that is 14 meters above the ground. Round your answer to the nearest tenth.

40. Determine if the statement is *sometimes*, *always*, or *never* true. Explain your reasoning and give an example of each.

    a. A rational number multiplied by a rational number is rational.

    b. A rational number multiplied by an irrational number is rational.

    c. An irrational number multiplied by an irrational number is rational.

Fair Game Review What you learned in previous grades & lessons

Simplify the expression. *(Skills Review Handbook)*

41. $2x + 3y - 5x$

42. $3\pi + 8(t - \pi) - 4t$

43. $17k - 9 + 23k$

44. MULTIPLE CHOICE What is the ratio (red to blue) of the corresponding side lengths of the similar triangles? *(Skills Review Handbook)*

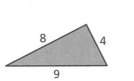

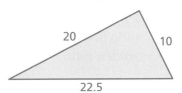

   (A) $1:3$

   (B) $5:2$

   (C) $3:4$

   (D) $2:5$

8.4 Simplifying Square Roots

STANDARDS OF LEARNING

8.1

Essential Question
How can you use a square root to describe the golden ratio?

Two quantities are in the *golden ratio* if the ratio between the sum of the quantities and the greater quantity is the same as the ratio between the greater quantity and the lesser quantity.

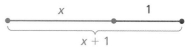

$$\frac{x+1}{x} = \frac{x}{1}$$

In a future algebra course, you will be able to prove that the golden ratio is

$$\frac{1 + \sqrt{5}}{2} \qquad \text{Golden ratio.}$$

---

1   ACTIVITY: Constructing a Golden Rectangle

Work with a partner.

a. Use grid paper and the given scale to draw a square that is 1 unit by 1 unit (blue).

b. Draw a line from midpoint C of one side of the square to the opposite corner D, as shown.

c. Use the Pythagorean Theorem to find the length of segment CD.

d. Set the point of a compass on C. Set the compass radius to the length of segment CD. Swing the compass to intersect line BC at point E.

e. The rectangle $ABEF$ is called a *golden rectangle* because the ratio of its side lengths is the golden ratio.

f. Use a calculator to find a decimal approximation of the golden ratio. Round your answer to two decimal places.

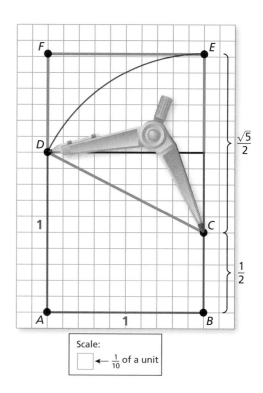

Scale:
⬜ ← $\frac{1}{10}$ of a unit

Laurie's Notes

Introduction

For the Teacher

- **Goal:** Students will explore a classic example of a computation that involves a radical, the golden ratio, $\frac{1 + \sqrt{5}}{2} \approx 1.62$.

Motivate

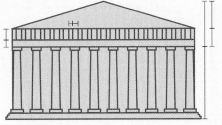

- Share information with students about the Parthenon in Athens. The Parthenon was a great example of a mathematical approach to art. Many of its attributes were based on the golden ratio.
- If possible, show lengths that are in the golden ratio using photographs and diagrams.

Activity Notes

Activity 1

- Note that the midpoint C is not constructed. It is located by knowing the side length is 1 unit. So, the midpoint is 0.5 unit from B.
- **Extension:** "What type of quadrilateral is $ABCD$? What is the area of this quadrilateral?" trapezoid; $A = \frac{1}{2}\left(1 + \frac{1}{2}\right)1 = \frac{3}{4}$ units^2
- Students may need help with part (c). Set up the Pythagorean Theorem for the right triangle with legs 1 unit and $\frac{1}{2}$ unit. Segment CD is the hypotenuse of the triangle. Let x be the length of segment CD. So, $x^2 = 1^2 + \left(\frac{1}{2}\right)^2$ and $x = \sqrt{\frac{5}{4}}$.
- The last step involves a property which students will learn formally tomorrow. At this point, you are asking students to accept that $\sqrt{\frac{5}{4}} = \frac{\sqrt{5}}{\sqrt{4}} = \frac{\sqrt{5}}{2}$. In other words, the square root of a quotient is equal to the quotient of the square roots.
- To find the length of the rectangle, find $BC + CE = \frac{1}{2} + \frac{\sqrt{5}}{2} = \frac{1 + \sqrt{5}}{2}$. The width of the rectangle is 1 unit, so the ratio of the side lengths is $\frac{1 + \sqrt{5}}{2}$. This is known as the golden ratio.
- "From the grid paper, approximate BE, the golden ratio." about 1.6 units

Standards of Learning

8.1(a) The student will simplify numerical expressions involving positive exponents, using rational numbers, order of operations, and properties of operations with real numbers.

Activity Materials
Textbook

- compasses
- calculators
- tape measures, yard sticks, or meter sticks

Start Thinking! and Warm Up

Activity 8.4 Start Thinking!
For use before Activity 8.4

Activity 8.4 Warm Up
For use before Activity 8.4

Use a calculator to find a decimal approximation of the expression. Round your answer to the nearest thousandth.

1. $\frac{\sqrt{7}}{7}$
2. $\frac{\sqrt{3}}{2}$
3. $\frac{1 + \sqrt{3}}{2}$
4. $\frac{\sqrt{3} - 1}{3}$
5. $\frac{2 + \sqrt{2}}{3}$
6. $\frac{2 - \sqrt{2}}{4}$

8.4 Record and Practice Journal

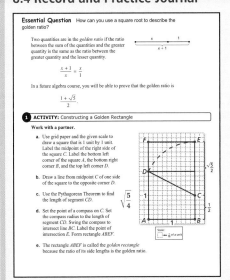

Essential Question How can you use a square root to describe the golden ratio?

Two quantities are in the *golden ratio* if the ratio between the sum of the quantities and the greater quantity is the same as the ratio between the greater quantity and the lesser quantity.

$$\frac{x + 1}{x} = \frac{x}{1}$$

In a future algebra course, you will be able to prove that the golden ratio is

$$\frac{1 + \sqrt{5}}{2}$$

1 ACTIVITY: Constructing a Golden Rectangle

Work with a partner.

a. Use grid paper and the given scale to draw a square that is 1 unit by 1 unit. Label the midpoint of the right side of the square C. Label the bottom left corner of the square A, the bottom right corner B, and the top left corner D.

b. Draw a line from midpoint C of one side of the square to the opposite corner D.

c. Use the Pythagorean Theorem to find the length of segment CD. $\sqrt{\frac{5}{4}}$

d. Set the point of a compass on C. Set the compass radius to the length of segment CD. Swing the compass to intersect line BC. Label the point of intersection E. Form rectangle $ABEF$.

e. The rectangle $ABEF$ is called the *golden rectangle* because the ratio of its side lengths is the golden ratio.

8.4 Record and Practice Journal

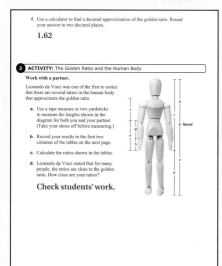

Activity 2

- In this activity, you need to be sensitive to students' feelings about measuring body parts. If you believe there are students in your class who, for whatever reason, will be uncomfortable with having their partner measure certain body parts, you should probably speak to them privately. Refer to the diagram and reassure them that their privacy will not be violated.

- My experience has been that students enjoy this activity and find the results fascinating. Give ample time for students to measure and compute.

- **Teaching Tip:** Have students measure in metric units so that they are using decimals instead of fractions.

- When discussing the results, it is possible that some students are not very *golden* and that is okay. Leonardo da Vinci only implied that it was true for *many* people.

What Is Your Answer?

- **Think-Pair-Share:** Students should read the question independently and then work with a partner to answer the question. When they have answered the question, the pair should compare their answer with another group and discuss any discrepancies.

Closure

- Compute the length to width ratio for each rectangle. Which ratio is closer to the golden ratio? Second rectangle is closer to the golden ratio.

- **FYI:** Most people say that rectangles with dimensions in the ratio close to 1.6 to 1 are more pleasing to look at.

The Dynamic Planning Tool
Editable Teacher's Resources at *BigIdeasMath.com*

ACTIVITY: The Golden Ratio and the Human Body

Work with a partner.

Leonardo da Vinci was one of the first to notice that there are several ratios in the human body that approximate the golden ratio.

a. Use a tape measure or two yardsticks to measure the lengths shown in the diagram for both you and your partner. (Take your shoes off before measuring.)

b. Copy the tables below. Record your results in the first two columns.

c. Calculate the ratios shown in the tables.

d. Leonardo da Vinci stated that for many people, the ratios are close to the golden ratio. How close are your ratios?

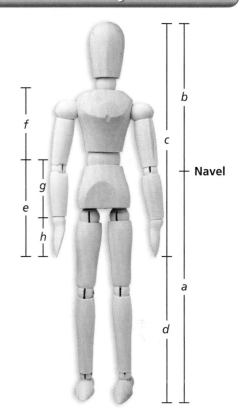

You		
$a =$ ▢	$b =$ ▢	$\dfrac{a}{b} =$ ▢
$c =$ ▢	$d =$ ▢	$\dfrac{c}{d} =$ ▢
$e =$ ▢	$f =$ ▢	$\dfrac{e}{f} =$ ▢
$g =$ ▢	$h =$ ▢	$\dfrac{g}{h} =$ ▢

Partner		
$a =$ ▢	$b =$ ▢	$\dfrac{a}{b} =$ ▢
$c =$ ▢	$d =$ ▢	$\dfrac{c}{d} =$ ▢
$e =$ ▢	$f =$ ▢	$\dfrac{e}{f} =$ ▢
$g =$ ▢	$h =$ ▢	$\dfrac{g}{h} =$ ▢

What Is Your Answer?

3. IN YOUR OWN WORDS How can you use a square root to describe the golden ratio? Use the Internet or some other reference to find examples of the golden ratio in art and architecture.

Practice

Use what you learned about square roots to complete Exercises 3–5 on page 382.

Check It Out
Lesson Tutorials
BigIdeasMathcom

You can add or subtract radical expressions the same way you combine like terms, such as $5x + 4x = 9x$.

EXAMPLE 1 **Adding and Subtracting Square Roots**

Reading

Do not assume that radicals that have different radicands cannot be simplified.

An expression such as $2\sqrt{4} + \sqrt{1}$ can easily be simplified.

a. Simplify $5\sqrt{2} + 4\sqrt{2}$.

$$5\sqrt{2} + 4\sqrt{2} = (5 + 4)\sqrt{2} \qquad \text{Use the Distributive Property.}$$
$$= 9\sqrt{2} \qquad \text{Simplify.}$$

b. Simplify $2\sqrt{3} - 7\sqrt{3}$.

$$2\sqrt{3} - 7\sqrt{3} = (2 - 7)\sqrt{3} \qquad \text{Use the Distributive Property.}$$
$$= -5\sqrt{3} \qquad \text{Simplify.}$$

On Your Own

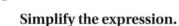
Now You're Ready
Exercises 6–14

Simplify the expression.

1. $\sqrt{5} + \sqrt{5}$ 2. $6\sqrt{10} + 4\sqrt{10}$ 3. $2\sqrt{7} - \sqrt{7}$

To simplify square roots that are not perfect squares, use the following property.

Key Idea

Product Property of Square Roots

Algebra $\sqrt{xy} = \sqrt{x} \cdot \sqrt{y}$, where $x, y \geq 0$

Numbers $\sqrt{4 \cdot 3} = \sqrt{4} \cdot \sqrt{3} = 2\sqrt{3}$

EXAMPLE 2 **Simplifying Square Roots**

Study Tip

A square root is simplified when the radicand has no perfect square factors other than 1.

Simplify $\sqrt{50}$.

$$\sqrt{50} = \sqrt{25 \cdot 2} \qquad \text{Factor using the greatest perfect square factor.}$$
$$= \sqrt{25} \cdot \sqrt{2} \qquad \text{Use the Product Property of Square Roots.}$$
$$= 5\sqrt{2} \qquad \text{Simplify.}$$

On Your Own

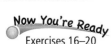
Now You're Ready
Exercises 16–20

Simplify the expression.

4. $\sqrt{24}$ 5. $\sqrt{45}$ 6. $\sqrt{98}$

Laurie's Notes

Introduction

Connect
- **Yesterday:** Students investigated the golden ratio.
- **Today:** Students will use properties of square roots to simplify expressions.

Motivate
- To connect today's lesson to variable expressions, have students work with a partner to simplify the following.

  1. $12x - 9x$ $3x$ 2. $8m + 6m$ $14m$

  3. $2x(3x)$ $6x^2$ 4. $\dfrac{12m}{4m}$ 3

Lesson Notes

Example 1
- ❓ "What are like terms?" terms that have the same variables raised to the same exponents
- Explain that square root expressions are treated the same as like terms.
- **Teaching Tip:** Write a parallel problem involving x side-by-side with the square root problem.

$5\sqrt{2} + 4\sqrt{2}$	$5x + 4x$
$9\sqrt{2}$	$9x$

- The radicals can be combined because they have the same radicand. You cannot combine $3x + 2y$, so you cannot combine $3\sqrt{5} + 2\sqrt{7}$.

On Your Own
- ❓ "How many square roots of 5 are being added together in $\sqrt{5} + \sqrt{5}$?"
  two; $\sqrt{5} + \sqrt{5} = 2\sqrt{5}$

Key Idea
- **Teaching Tip:** An example that students find helpful is the following.

  $$\sqrt{9 \cdot 4} = \sqrt{9} \cdot \sqrt{4}$$
  $$\sqrt{36} = 3 \cdot 2$$
  $$6 = 6$$

Example 2
- ❓ "What are the factors of 50?" 1, 2, 5, 10, 25, 50
- The only square roots that simplify to whole numbers are those which are perfect squares. Write 50 as $25 \cdot 2$.
- Some students might write 50 as $2 \cdot 25$ (Commutative Property). The result will be $\sqrt{50} = \sqrt{2}\sqrt{25} = \sqrt{2} \cdot 5$. Tell students to write the constant first followed by the square root in the same way that you write the coefficient before the variable.
- **Big Idea:** To simplify the square root, find the greatest perfect square factor.

Start Thinking! and Warm Up

Lesson **8.4** Warm Up For use before Lesson 8.4

Lesson **8.4** Start Thinking! For use before Lesson 8.4

In previous courses, you have learned how to simplify fractions. When is a fraction simplified?

Square roots can also be simplified.

A square root is simplified when the number under the radical sign has no perfect square factors other than 1.

Which of the following expressions are simplified? Explain why.

$$\sqrt{2}, \sqrt{4}, \sqrt{10}, \sqrt{50}, 3\sqrt{5}, 3\sqrt{8}$$

Extra Example 1
a. Simplify $6\sqrt{7} + 2\sqrt{7}$. $8\sqrt{7}$
b. Simplify $14\sqrt{13} - 17\sqrt{13}$. $-3\sqrt{13}$

 On Your Own

  1. $2\sqrt{5}$ 2. $10\sqrt{10}$

  3. $\sqrt{7}$

Extra Example 2
Simplify $\sqrt{162}$. $9\sqrt{2}$

 On Your Own

  4. $2\sqrt{6}$ 5. $3\sqrt{5}$

  6. $7\sqrt{2}$

Laurie's Notes

Extra Example 3

Simplify $\sqrt{\dfrac{17}{25}}$. $\dfrac{\sqrt{17}}{5}$

Extra Example 4

Find the volume of the rectangular prism. $12\ \text{m}^3$

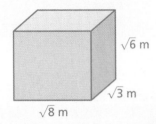

$\sqrt{6}\ \text{m}$

$\sqrt{3}\ \text{m}$

$\sqrt{8}\ \text{m}$

On Your Own

7. $\dfrac{\sqrt{35}}{6}$ **8.** $\dfrac{\sqrt{13}}{2}$

9. $\dfrac{\sqrt{5}}{b}$ **10.** $20\ \text{m}^3$

Differentiated Instruction

Visual

Students may have a difficult time understanding that the square root of a number between 0 and 1 is greater than the number. They may think that $\sqrt{\dfrac{1}{4}} = \dfrac{1}{16}$, when actually $\sqrt{\dfrac{1}{16}} = \dfrac{1}{4}$. Help students to understand this concept by using a 10 by 10 grid to represent the number 1. A square of $\dfrac{49}{100}$ square units has a side length of $\dfrac{7}{10}$. Because $\sqrt{\dfrac{49}{100}} = \dfrac{7}{10}$, $\dfrac{7}{10} > \dfrac{49}{100}$ ($0.7 > 0.49$).

Key Idea

- Write the Key Idea.
- **Teaching Tip:** An example that students find helpful is the following.

$$\sqrt{\dfrac{64}{16}} = \dfrac{\sqrt{64}}{\sqrt{16}}$$
$$\sqrt{4} = \dfrac{8}{4}$$
$$2 = 2$$

Example 3

? "How can this problem be rewritten?" Listen for the Quotient Property.
- Note that only the denominator is a perfect square, so the numerator is left as a square root.

Example 4

? "What is the definition of volume and how do you find the volume of a prism?" Volume is space inside a solid. $V = \ell w h$.
- Write the formula and substitute the variables.
- **Common Misconception:** Students do not always recognize that these expressions can be multiplied. This is the reverse of what was done when they simplified expressions at the beginning of class. Remind students that the Product Property of Square Roots has an equal sign. The left side equals the right side and the right side equals the left side.
- Using the Product Property of Square Roots, multiply the three expressions.
- Finish working through the example as shown.

On Your Own

- For Question 9, remind students that the square root of a squared number is the number. So, the square root of b^2 is b. At this level, you are assuming that $b > 0$. In future math courses, students will learn that $\sqrt{b^2} = |b|$.

Closure

- Simplify the expression.
  $\sqrt{48}$ $4\sqrt{3}$ $\sqrt{10} + 5\sqrt{10}$ $6\sqrt{10}$ $\sqrt{\dfrac{25}{4}}$ $\dfrac{5}{2}$

 **Key Idea**

Quotient Property of Square Roots

Algebra $\sqrt{\dfrac{x}{y}} = \dfrac{\sqrt{x}}{\sqrt{y}}$, where $x \geq 0$ and $y > 0$

Numbers $\sqrt{\dfrac{7}{9}} = \dfrac{\sqrt{7}}{\sqrt{9}} = \dfrac{\sqrt{7}}{3}$

EXAMPLE ③ **Simplifying Square Roots**

Simplify $\sqrt{\dfrac{11}{16}}$.

$\sqrt{\dfrac{11}{16}} = \dfrac{\sqrt{11}}{\sqrt{16}}$ Use the Quotient Property of Square Roots.

$\qquad\quad = \dfrac{\sqrt{11}}{4}$ Simplify.

EXAMPLE ④ **Finding a Volume**

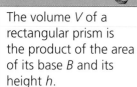 **Remember**

The volume V of a rectangular prism is the product of the area of its base B and its height h.

$V = Bh$

Find the volume of the rectangular prism.

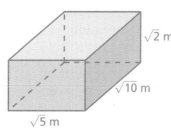

√2 m

√10 m

√5 m

$V = Bh$ Write formula for volume.

$\quad = (\sqrt{5})(\sqrt{10})(\sqrt{2})$ Substitute.

$\quad = \sqrt{5 \cdot 10 \cdot 2}$ Use the Product Property of Square Roots.

$\quad = \sqrt{100}$ Multiply.

$\quad = 10$ Simplify.

⋮⋅ The volume is 10 cubic meters.

⬤ **On Your Own**

 *Now You're Ready*
Exercises 21–24

Simplify the expression.

7. $\sqrt{\dfrac{35}{36}}$ **8.** $\sqrt{\dfrac{13}{4}}$ **9.** $\sqrt{\dfrac{5}{b^2}}$

10. WHAT IF? In Example 4, the height of the rectangular prism is $\sqrt{8}$ meters. Find the volume of the prism.

 ## Vocabulary and Concept Check

1. **WRITING** Describe how combining like terms is similar to adding and subtracting square roots.

2. **WRITING** How are the Product Property of Square Roots and the Quotient Property of Square Roots similar?

 ## Practice and Problem Solving

Find the ratio of the side lengths. Is the ratio close to the golden ratio?

3.

544 ft

336 ft

4.

21 yd

34 yd

5.

50 m

45 m

Simplify the expression.

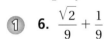

① 6. $\dfrac{\sqrt{2}}{9} + \dfrac{1}{9}$

7. $\dfrac{\sqrt{7}}{3} + \dfrac{1}{3}$

8. $\dfrac{1}{4} + \dfrac{\sqrt{13}}{4}$

9. $2\sqrt{3} + 4\sqrt{3}$

10. $6\sqrt{7} - 2\sqrt{7}$

11. $\dfrac{3}{4}\sqrt{5} + \dfrac{5}{4}\sqrt{5}$

12. $\sqrt{6} - 4\sqrt{6}$

13. $1.5\sqrt{15} - 9.2\sqrt{15}$

14. $\dfrac{7}{8}\sqrt{11} + \dfrac{3}{8}\sqrt{11}$

15. **ERROR ANALYSIS** Describe and correct the error in simplifying the expression.

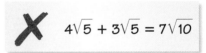

$$4\sqrt{5} + 3\sqrt{5} = 7\sqrt{10}$$

Simplify the expression.

  16. $\sqrt{18}$

17. $\sqrt{200}$

18. $\sqrt{12}$

19. $\sqrt{48}$

20. $\sqrt{125}$

21. $\sqrt{\dfrac{23}{64}}$

22. $\sqrt{\dfrac{65}{121}}$

23. $\sqrt{\dfrac{17}{49}}$

24. $\sqrt{\dfrac{22}{c^2}}$

25. **RAIN GUTTER** A rain gutter is made from a single sheet of metal. What is the length of the red cross-section?

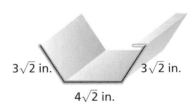

$3\sqrt{2}$ in. $3\sqrt{2}$ in.

$4\sqrt{2}$ in.

Assignment Guide and Homework Check

Level	Day 1 Activity Assignment	Day 2 Lesson Assignment	Homework Check
Basic	3–5, 34–37	1, 2, 7–29 odd	7, 11, 17, 21, 27
Average	3–5, 34–37	1, 2, 11–31 odd, 30	11, 17, 21, 27, 30
Advanced	3–5, 34–37	1, 2, 13–15, 22–28 even, 29–33	14, 22, 26, 30, 32

Common Errors

- **Exercises 6–14** Students may add the radicands as well as the coefficients, or they may only add the coefficients even if the operation is subtraction. Remind students that they only add the coefficients. Also remind them to perform the correct operation on the numbers.
- **Exercises 16–24** Students may still have difficulty identifying perfect squares to use to simplify the expression. Encourage them to write the first 10 perfect squares at the top of their paper as a reminder and a reference.
- **Exercises 26–28** Students may not know where to start with these problems. Remind them of the order of operations and relate it to the Key Ideas that they learned. They should use the Product Property or the Quotient Property first, and then add or subtract the square roots.

8.4 Record and Practice Journal

Simplify the expression.

1. $\frac{\sqrt{3}}{8} + \frac{1}{8}$
$\frac{1+\sqrt{3}}{8}$

2. $\frac{2}{9} - \frac{\sqrt{11}}{9}$
$\frac{2-\sqrt{11}}{9}$

3. $7\sqrt{7} + 3\sqrt{7}$
$10\sqrt{7}$

4. $\frac{3}{2}\sqrt{15} + \frac{1}{2}\sqrt{15}$
$2\sqrt{15}$

5. $12\sqrt{42} - 5\sqrt{42}$
$7\sqrt{42}$

6. $16.4\sqrt{21} - 15.1\sqrt{21}$
$1.3\sqrt{21}$

7. $\sqrt{20}$
$2\sqrt{5}$

8. $\sqrt{32}$
$4\sqrt{2}$

9. $\sqrt{75}$
$5\sqrt{3}$

10. $\sqrt{\frac{29}{81}}$
$\frac{\sqrt{29}}{9}$

11. $\sqrt{\frac{17}{a^2}}$
$\frac{\sqrt{17}}{a}$

12. $\sqrt{40} + 3\sqrt{10}$
$5\sqrt{10}$

13. You build a shed in your backyard.

a. What is the perimeter of the shed?
$28\sqrt{3}$ ft

b. What is the volume of the shed?
$576\sqrt{3}$ ft³

48 ft
108 ft
192 ft

Technology
For
the **T**eacher

Answer Presentation Tool
QuizShow

Vocabulary and Concept Check

1–2. Sample answers are given.

1. The square root is like a variable. So, you add or subtract the number in front to simplify.

2. Both allow you to take the square roots of the numbers inside the radical to simplify.

Practice and Problem Solving

3. about 1.62; yes

4. about 1.62; yes

5. about 1.11; no

6. $\frac{\sqrt{2}+1}{9}$

7. $\frac{\sqrt{7}+1}{3}$

8. $\frac{1+\sqrt{13}}{4}$

9. $6\sqrt{3}$

10. $4\sqrt{7}$

11. $2\sqrt{5}$

12. $-3\sqrt{6}$

13. $-7.7\sqrt{15}$

14. $\frac{5}{4}\sqrt{11}$

15. You do not add the radicands.
$4\sqrt{5} + 3\sqrt{5} = 7\sqrt{5}$

16. $3\sqrt{2}$

17. $10\sqrt{2}$

18. $2\sqrt{3}$

19. $4\sqrt{3}$

20. $5\sqrt{5}$

21. $\frac{\sqrt{23}}{8}$

22. $\frac{\sqrt{65}}{11}$

23. $\frac{\sqrt{17}}{7}$

24. $\frac{\sqrt{22}}{c}$

25. $10\sqrt{2}$ in.

26. 0

27. $6\sqrt{6}$

28. $\dfrac{10}{3}\sqrt{7}$

29. 210 ft^3

30. $\sqrt{15}$ or $-\sqrt{15}$

31. a. $88\sqrt{2} \text{ ft}$

    b. 680 ft^2

32. $5\sqrt{15} \approx 19.36 \text{ km}$

33. See *Taking Math Deeper.*

 Fair Game Review

34. 40 m

35. 24 in.

36. 9 cm

37. C

Taking Math Deeper

Exercise 33

This problem basically comes down to trying to inscribe a square inside a circle. The square has sides of length s and the circle has a radius of r.

 Draw a diagram to be sure that students understand the question.

 Solve the given equation for r.

$$s^2 = 2r^2$$
$$\frac{s^2}{2} = r^2$$
a. $\dfrac{s}{\sqrt{2}} = r$

Note: $s^2 = 2r^2$ came from the Pythagorean Theorem.
$$s^2 + s^2 = (2r)^2$$
$$2s^2 = 4r^2$$

 Find r when $s = \sqrt{98}$ inches.

$$r = \frac{s}{\sqrt{2}}$$
$$= \frac{\sqrt{98}}{\sqrt{2}}$$
$$= \sqrt{\frac{98}{2}}$$
$$= \sqrt{49}$$
$$= 7$$

At least 7 in.

b. The cooler must have a radius of 7 inches (or more) to hold the block of ice.

Project

Compare the time it takes for an ice cube to melt inside a cooler with the time it takes for it to melt outside the cooler. Draw a picture to go with your comparison.

Mini-Assessment

Simplify the expression.

1. $9\sqrt{3} - \sqrt{3}$ $8\sqrt{3}$

2. $\dfrac{2}{3}\sqrt{5} + \dfrac{2}{3}\sqrt{5}$ $\dfrac{4}{3}\sqrt{5}$

3. $\sqrt{18}$ $3\sqrt{2}$

4. $\sqrt{125}$ $5\sqrt{5}$

5. $\sqrt{\dfrac{21}{196}}$ $\dfrac{\sqrt{21}}{14}$

Reteaching and Enrichment Strategies

If students need help. . .	If students got it. . .
Resources by Chapter • Practice A and Practice B • Puzzle Time Record and Practice Journal Practice Differentiating the Lesson Lesson Tutorials Skills Review Handbook	Resources by Chapter • Enrichment and Extension • School-to-Work Start the next section

Simplify the expression.

26. $3\sqrt{5} - \sqrt{45}$

27. $\sqrt{24} + 4\sqrt{6}$

28. $\dfrac{4}{3}\sqrt{7} + \sqrt{28}$

29. VOLUME What is the volume of the aquarium (in cubic feet)?

30. RATIO The ratio $3:x$ is equivalent to the ratio $x:5$. What are the possible values of x?

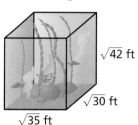
$\sqrt{42}$ ft
$\sqrt{30}$ ft
$\sqrt{35}$ ft

$34\sqrt{2}$ ft
$10\sqrt{2}$ ft

Physics of a SLAM DUNK
See Science Put to the Test
Call Now for Tickets!

31. BILLBOARD The billboard has the shape of a rectangle.

   a. What is the perimeter of the billboard?

   b. What is the area of the billboard?

32. MT. FUJI Mt. Fuji is in the shape of a cone with a volume of about 475π cubic kilometers. What is the radius of the base of Mt. Fuji?

The height of Mt. Fuji is 3.8 kilometers.

33. **Geometry** A block of ice is in the shape of a square prism. You want to put the block of ice in a cylindrical cooler. The equation $s^2 = 2r^2$ represents the minimum radius r needed for the block of ice with side length s to fit in the cooler.

   a. Solve the equation for r.

   b. Use the equation in part (a) to find the minimum radius needed when the side length of the block of ice is $\sqrt{98}$ inches.

s
r

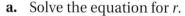
Fair Game Review What you learned in previous grades & lessons

Find the missing length of the triangle. *(Section 8.2)*

34.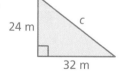
24 m
c
32 m

35.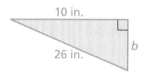
10 in.
26 in.
b

36.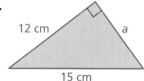
12 cm
a
15 cm

37. MULTIPLE CHOICE Where is $-\sqrt{110}$ on a number line? *(Section 8.3)*

   (A) Between -9 and -10

   (B) Between 9 and 10

   (C) Between -10 and -11

   (D) Between 10 and 11

STANDARDS
OF LEARNING
8.10

Essential Question How can you use the
Pythagorean Theorem to solve real-life problems?

1 ACTIVITY: Using the Pythagorean Theorem

Work with a partner.

a. A baseball player throws a ball
from second base to home plate.
How far does the player throw the
ball? Include a diagram showing
how you got your answer. Decide
how many decimal points of
accuracy are reasonable. Explain
your reasoning.

b. The distance from the pitcher's
mound to home plate is 60.5 feet.
Does this form a right triangle
with first base? Explain your
reasoning.

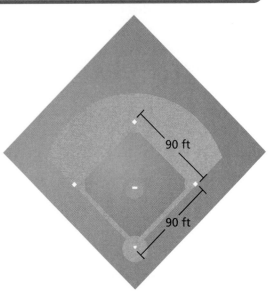

90 ft

90 ft

2 ACTIVITY: Firefighting and Ladders

Work with a partner.

**The recommended angle for a firefighting
ladder is 75°.**

**When a 110-foot ladder is put up against a
building at this angle, the base of the ladder
is about 28 feet from the building.**

**The base of the ladder is 8 feet above
the ground.**

**How high on the building will the
ladder reach? Round your answer
to the nearest tenth.**

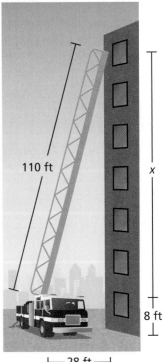

110 ft

x

8 ft

⊢— 28 ft —⊣

Laurie's Notes

Introduction

For the Teacher

- **Goal:** Students will explore solving real-life problems that can be modeled by a right triangle.

Motivate

- ❓ "How many of you have ridden on a fire truck?" anticipate a small number
- ❓ "Did you know that you can hire a fire truck for a party, reunion, or other special events?" unlikely

Activity Notes

Activity 1

- ❓ "In baseball, which is farther, home to first base or home to second base? How do you know?" Home to second is the hypotenuse of a right triangle and home to first is a leg.
- Not all students will realize there is a right triangle because the third side of the triangle is not drawn.
- ❓ "What are the dimensions of a major league *diamond*?" 90 feet between the bases
- The baseball *diamond* is a square. Draw and label the right triangle. Students should be ready to work the problem with their partner.
- ❓ "What is the exact distance from second to home?" $\sqrt{16{,}200}$ ft
- In discussing the approximate distance, round to the nearest whole number, 127 feet.
- **Part (b):** Have students share their reasoning. If students use the Pythagorean Theorem to find the distance from the pitcher's mound to first base, remind them that you need to know it is a right triangle first. You cannot use the theorem to find the length, and then use the length to prove it is a right triangle. That is circular reasoning.

Activity 2

- In this activity, the right angle is not drawn. Ask students to make a sketch of the problem. Check to see that they represent the base of the triangle 8 feet off the ground.
- ❓ "What are the measures of the three angles of this triangle?" 90°, 75°, 15°
- ❓ "What is the relationship between the two acute angles?" complementary
- Students should use the Pythagorean Theorem to solve for x, a leg of the right triangle.

Standards of Learning

8.10(b) The student will apply the Pythagorean Theorem.

Activity Materials
Textbook
• calculators

Start Thinking! and Warm Up

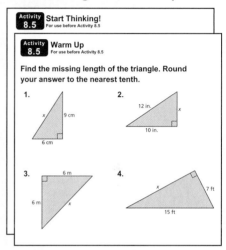

8.5 Record and Practice Journal

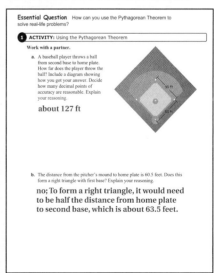

Create a poster to display the connections between a right triangle and the Pythagorean Theorem. Use color to indicate corresponding parts of the triangle and the equation. Give examples of solving for the hypotenuse and solving for a leg of the triangle.

8.5 Record and Practice Journal

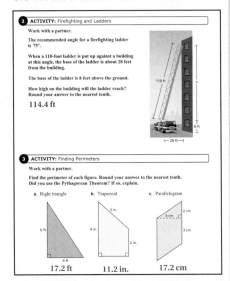

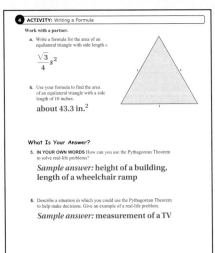

Laurie's Notes

Activity 3

? "How do you find the perimeter of a polygon?" Sum the lengths of the sides.

? "Do you know, or can you find, the lengths of all sides of the polygons? Explain." Yes; Use the Pythagorean Theorem to solve for the missing hypotenuse in parts (a) and (c) and for the missing leg in part (b).

Activity 4

? "How do you find the area of a triangle?" $A = \frac{1}{2}bh$

? "Can you sketch in a height for this triangle? Do you know anything about the height and where it intersects the base?" Answers vary.

- Students need to recognize that for an equilateral triangle, the height is perpendicular to the base and intersects it at its midpoint. The height will make the two right triangles shown. You may need to work through the mathematics of this problem. The use of variables in the general case is very challenging for students.

$$\left(\frac{s}{2}\right)^2 + h^2 = s^2$$

$$h^2 = s^2 - \left(\frac{s}{2}\right)^2$$

$$h^2 = s^2 - \frac{s^2}{4}$$

$$h^2 = \frac{3}{4}s^2$$

$$h = \sqrt{\frac{3}{4}s^2}$$

$$h = \frac{\sqrt{3}}{2}s$$

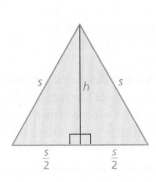

- Once students know the height of an equilateral triangle in terms of its side length s, they can write the formula for the area.
- Give students time to work part (b) with their partner.

Closure

- A little league baseball diamond is 60 feet between the bases. What is the distance from home to second base? about 85 feet

The Dynamic Planning Tool
Editable Teacher's Resources at *BigIdeasMath.com*

ACTIVITY: Finding Perimeters

Work with a partner.

Find the perimeter of each figure. Round your answer to the nearest tenth. Did you use the Pythagorean Theorem? If so, explain.

a. Right triangle

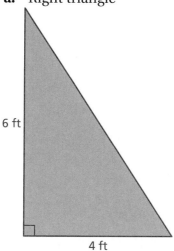

6 ft

4 ft

b. Trapezoid

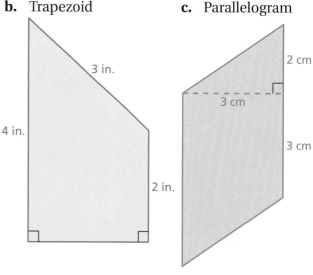

3 in.

4 in.

2 in.

c. Parallelogram

2 cm

3 cm

3 cm

4 **ACTIVITY: Writing a Formula**

Work with a partner.

a. Write a formula for the area of an equilateral triangle with side length *s*.

b. Use your formula to find the area of an equilateral triangle with a side length of 10 inches.

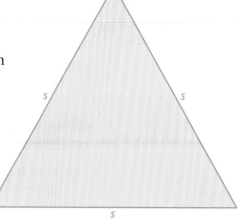

s   *s*

s

What Is Your Answer?

5. **IN YOUR OWN WORDS** How can you use the Pythagorean Theorem to solve real-life problems?

6. Describe a situation in which you could use the Pythagorean Theorem to help make decisions. Give an example of a real-life problem.

Practice

Use what you learned about using the Pythagorean Theorem to complete Exercises 3–5 on page 388.

EXAMPLE 1 Finding a Distance in a Coordinate Plane

Key Vocabulary
Pythagorean triple, p. 387

The park is 5 miles east of your home. The library is 4 miles north of the park. How far is your home from the library? Round your answer to the nearest tenth.

Plot a point for your home at the origin in a coordinate plane. Then plot points for the locations of the park and the library to form a right triangle.

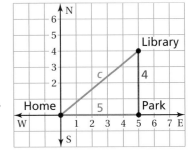

$a^2 + b^2 = c^2$ Write the Pythagorean Theorem.

$4^2 + 5^2 = c^2$ Substitute 4 for a and 5 for b.

$16 + 25 = c^2$ Evaluate powers.

$41 = c^2$ Add.

$\sqrt{41} = \sqrt{c^2}$ Take positive square root of each side.

$6.4 \approx c$ Use a calculator.

:•: Your home is about 6.4 miles from the library.

On Your Own

Now You're Ready
Exercises 6–8

1. The post office is 3 miles west of your home. Your school is 2 miles north of the post office. How far is your home from your school? Round your answer to the nearest tenth.

EXAMPLE 2 Real-Life Application

Find the height of the firework. Round your answer to the nearest tenth.

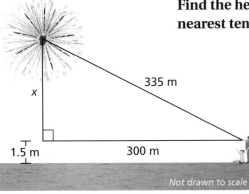

335 m
x
1.5 m   300 m
Not drawn to scale

$a^2 + b^2 = c^2$ Write the Pythagorean Theorem.

$x^2 + 300^2 = 335^2$ Substitute.

$x^2 + 90{,}000 = 112{,}225$ Evaluate powers.

$x^2 = 22{,}225$ Subtract 90,000 from each side.

$\sqrt{x^2} = \sqrt{22{,}225}$ Take positive square root of each side.

$x \approx 149.1$ Use a calculator.

:•: The height of the firework is about $149.1 + 1.5 = 150.6$ meters.

Laurie's Notes

Introduction

Connect

- **Yesterday:** Students investigated real-life problems that required the Pythagorean Theorem to solve.
- **Today:** Students will solve right triangle problems and determine if three side lengths form a right triangle.

Motivate

- Explain the converse of an if-then statement. The converse of *if p then q* is *if q then p*. Example:

  Original—If all sides of the triangle are congruent, then the triangle is equilateral.

  Converse—If the triangle is equilateral, then all three sides are congruent.

- Both the statement and its converse are true. Putting the two statements together gives the definition of an equilateral triangle.
- ? "If an if-then statement is true, do you think the converse is always true?" Answers will vary.
- The converse of a true statement is not always true.
- Ask students to think of an example (not related to math) where the converse is true and an example where the converse is false. Something related to your school would be helpful. Converse true: If the doors are closed, then you must open them to get in. Converse not true: If it is snowing, then it is cold outside.

Goal Today's lesson is using the Pythagorean Theorem to find distances.

Lesson Materials
Textbook
• calculators

Start Thinking! and Warm Up

Lesson **8.5** Warm Up
For use before Lesson 8.5

Lesson **8.5** Start Thinking!
For use before Lesson 8.5

Write a word problem that can be solved using the Pythagorean Theorem. Be sure to include a sketch of the situation.

Lesson Notes

Example 1

- Ask a volunteer to read the problem.
- Draw a coordinate plane and sketch the example.
- ? "What are you solving for, a leg or the hypotenuse?" hypotenuse
- Set up the problem and solve.
- Before using a calculator, ask students to estimate $\sqrt{41}$ using a number line.
- ? **Extension:** "If your house had been located at $(-2, 3)$, what would be the coordinates of the park and the library?" $(3, 3)$ and $(3, 7)$ "What would be the distance to the library?" the same, 6.4 miles

On Your Own

- ? "Does it matter where you locate your house?" no

Example 2

- Information to solve the problem is given in the illustration.
- ? "What are you solving for, a leg or the hypotenuse?" leg
- Set up the problem and solve.
- ? "Why do you add 1.5 to the answer?" to account for height of person

Extra Example 1

In Example 1, your friend's house is 6 miles east of the library. A grocery store is 5 miles north of your friend's house. How far is the grocery store from the library? Round your answer to the nearest tenth. about 7.8 mi

On Your Own

1. 3.6 mi

Extra Example 2

In Example 2, the distance between you and the firework is 370 meters. Estimate the height of the firework. Round your answer to the nearest tenth.
about 218.1 m

T-386

Laurie's Notes

On Your Own

2. 181.8 m

Extra Example 3

Tell whether the triangle is a right triangle. *not* a right triangle

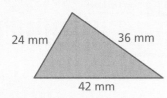

24 mm   36 mm

42 mm

On Your Own

3. yes   **4.** no

5. no   **6.** yes

Differentiated Instruction

Kinesthetic

Give students copies of the diagram. Have them cut out and physically move the pieces of the two smaller squares to create the larger square. A hands-on approach will help kinesthetic learners remember the relationship.

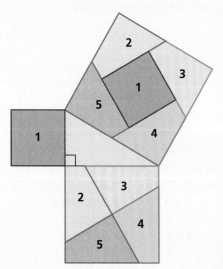

On Your Own

- **Neighbor Check:** Have students work independently and then have their neighbor check their work. Have students discuss any discrepancies.

Key Idea

- **Pythagorean Triple:** A **Pythagorean triple** is three positive integers, a, b, and c, where $a^2 + b^2 = c^2$. Remembering the basic triples, and knowing that multiplying each number by the same scalar produces another triple, can be very helpful.
  Example: $3^2 + 4^2 = 5^2 \rightarrow$ multiply by 2 $\rightarrow 6^2 + 8^2 = 10^2$
- The Converse of the Pythagorean Theorem says that when the relationship $a^2 + b^2 = c^2$ is true, you have a right triangle.
- Previously, you were given a right triangle and concluded that $a^2 + b^2 = c^2$ was true. Now you are given side lengths of a triangle. If $a^2 + b^2 = c^2$ is true, then the triangle is a right triangle.

Example 3

- If the three numbers satisfy the theorem, then it is a right triangle. Explain that you are not using eyesight to decide if it is a right triangle.
- Substitute the side lengths for each triangle. Remind students that the longest side is substituted for c.
- Because 9, 40, and 41 satisfy the theorem, they are Pythagorean triples and the triangle is a right triangle.
- Because 12, 18, and 24 do not satisfy the theorem, it is not a right triangle.
- **Extension:** The 12, 18, 24 triangle is similar to a triangle with side lengths 2, 3, and 4 (scale factor is 6). The 2, 3, 4 triangle is not a right triangle either.

On Your Own

- **Common Error:** Students may not substitute the longest side for c. This is particularly true for Question 6 because the measures are listed longest to shortest.

Closure

- **Writing Prompt:** To determine if three lengths are the sides of a right triangle, …

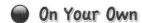 **On Your Own**

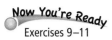
Now You're Ready
Exercises 9–11

2. WHAT IF? In Example 2, the distance between you and the firework is 350 meters. Find the height of the firework. Round your answer to the nearest tenth.

A **Pythagorean triple** is a set of three positive integers a, b, and c where $a^2 + b^2 = c^2$.

 **Key Idea**

Converse of the Pythagorean Theorem

If the equation $a^2 + b^2 = c^2$ is true for the side lengths of a triangle, then the triangle is a right triangle.

When using the converse of the Pythagorean Theorem, always substitute the length of the longest side for c.

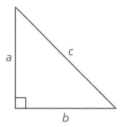

EXAMPLE ③ **Identifying a Right Triangle**

Tell whether the given triangle is a right triangle.

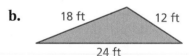

a. (triangle: 9 cm, 41 cm, 40 cm)

$$a^2 + b^2 = c^2$$
$$9^2 + 40^2 \overset{?}{=} 41^2$$
$$81 + 1600 \overset{?}{=} 1681$$
$$1681 = 1681 \quad ✓$$

∴ It *is* a right triangle.

b. (triangle: 18 ft, 12 ft, 24 ft)

$$a^2 + b^2 = c^2$$
$$12^2 + 18^2 \overset{?}{=} 24^2$$
$$144 + 324 \overset{?}{=} 576$$
$$468 \neq 576 \quad ✗$$

∴ It is *not* a right triangle.

 On Your Own

Now You're Ready
Exercises 13–18

Tell whether the triangle with the given side lengths is a right triangle.

3. 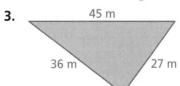 (triangle: 45 m, 36 m, 27 m)

4. 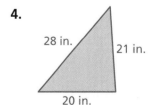 (triangle: 28 in., 21 in., 20 in.)

5. $1\frac{1}{2}$ yd, $2\frac{1}{2}$ yd, $3\frac{1}{2}$ yd

6. 1.25 mm, 1 mm, 0.75 mm

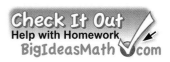
 ## Vocabulary and Concept Check

1. **WRITING** How can the Pythagorean Theorem be used to find distances in a coordinate plane?

2. **WHICH ONE DOESN'T BELONG?** Which set of numbers does *not* belong with the other three? Explain your reasoning.

| 3, 6, 8 | 6, 8, 10 | 5, 12, 13 | 7, 24, 25 |

 ## Practice and Problem Solving

Find the perimeter of the figure. Round your answer to the nearest tenth.

3. Right triangle

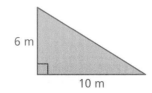

6 m

10 m

4. Parallelogram

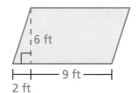

6 ft

9 ft

2 ft

5. Square

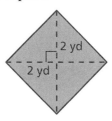

2 yd

2 yd

Find the distance d. Round your answer to the nearest tenth.

① 6.

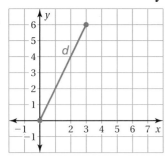

7.

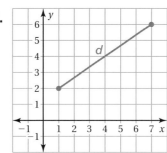

8.

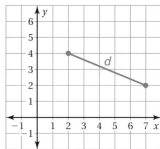

Find the height x. Round your answer to the nearest tenth.

② 9.

30 ft

x

12 ft

10.

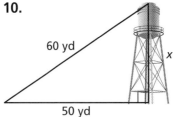

60 yd

x

50 yd

11.

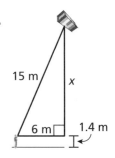

15 m

x

6 m   1.4 m

12. **BICYCLE** You ride your bicycle along the outer edge of a park. Then you take a shortcut back to where you started. Find the length of the shortcut. Round your answer to the nearest tenth.

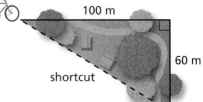

100 m

60 m

shortcut

Assignment Guide and Homework Check

Level	Day 1 Activity Assignment	Day 2 Lesson Assignment	Homework Check
Basic	3–5, 23–26	1, 2, 6–13, 15, 16	6, 10, 12, 16
Average	3–5, 23–26	1, 2, 6–11, 13–19 odd, 20	6, 10, 17, 20
Advanced	3–5, 23–26	1, 2, 8–18 even, 19–22	8, 10, 14, 20

Common Errors

- **Exercises 6–8** Students may not know how to find the distance because there are no triangles drawn. Remind them of the arrows that they drew for change in *x* and change in *y* when finding the slope of a line. Encourage them to use a similar technique to find the distance of the line. Instead of writing a ratio, they will use the Pythagorean Theorem.
- **Exercise 11** Students may only find the value of *x* and forget to add the additional height labeled in the picture. Remind them that they are not solving for *x*, but they are finding the height of the object. So, they need to include any additional heights after using the Pythagorean Theorem.
- **Exercises 13–15** Students may substitute the wrong value for *c* in the Pythagorean Theorem. Remind them that *c* will be the longest side, so they should substitute the greatest value for *c*.

Vocabulary and Concept Check

1. *Sample answer:* You can plot a point at the origin and then draw lengths that represent the legs. Then, you can use the Pythagorean Theorem to find the hypotenuse of the triangle.

2. 3, 6, 8; It is the only set that is not a Pythagorean triple.

Practice and Problem Solving

3. 27.7 m
4. 34.6 ft
5. 11.3 yd
6. 6.7 units
7. 7.2 units
8. 5.4 units
9. 27.5 ft
10. 33.2 yd
11. 15.1 m
12. 116.6 m
13. yes
14. yes
15. no
16. no
17. yes
18. yes

8.5 Record and Practice Journal

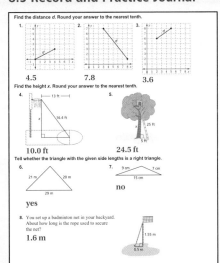

Technology For the Teacher
Answer Presentation Tool
QuizShow

T-388

Practice and Problem Solving

19. 12.8 ft

20. See *Taking Math Deeper*.

21. a. *Sample answer:* 5 in., 7 in., 3 in.

   b. *Sample answer:* $BC \approx 8.6$ in.; $AB \approx 9.1$ in.

   c. Check students' work.

22. See Additional Answers.

Fair Game Review

23. mean: 13; median: 12.5; mode: 12

24. mean: 21; median: 21; no mode

25. mean: 58; median: 59; mode: 59

26. B

Taking Math Deeper

Exercise 20

At first this seems like a simple question. Plane A is 5 kilometers from the tower and Plane B is 7 kilometers from the tower. So, Plane A seems closer. However, on second glance, you see that Plane A is much higher than Plane B. So, to see which is closer, you need to compute the diagonal distance of each.

 Find the distance for Plane A.

$$x^2 = 5^2 + 6.1^2$$
$$x^2 = 62.21$$
$$x \approx 7.89 \text{ km}$$

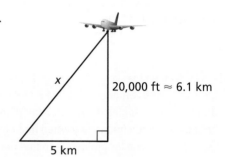

20,000 ft ≈ 6.1 km

5 km

 Find the distance for Plane B.

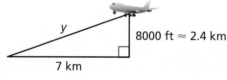

8000 ft ≈ 2.4 km

7 km

$$y^2 = 7^2 + 2.4^2$$
$$y^2 = 54.76$$
$$y = 7.4 \text{ km}$$

A little closer

 Answer the question.

Plane B is slightly closer to the tower.

Mini-Assessment

Estimate the height. Round your answer to the nearest tenth.

1. about 39.8 ft

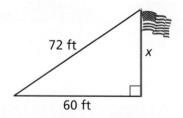

72 ft

x

60 ft

2. about 20.5 ft

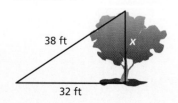

38 ft

x

32 ft

Reteaching and Enrichment Strategies

If students need help...	If students got it...
Resources by Chapter • Practice A and Practice B • Puzzle Time Record and Practice Journal Practice Differentiating the Lesson Lesson Tutorials Skills Review Handbook	Resources by Chapter • Enrichment and Extension • School-to-Work • Financial Literacy Start the next section

Tell whether the triangle with the given side lengths is a right triangle.

3 **13.**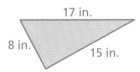
17 in.
8 in.
15 in.

14.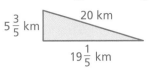
20 km
$5\frac{3}{5}$ km
$19\frac{1}{5}$ km

15.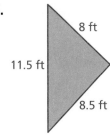
8 ft
11.5 ft
8.5 ft

16. 14 mm, 19 mm, 23 mm

17. $\frac{9}{10}$ mi, $1\frac{1}{5}$ mi, $1\frac{1}{2}$ mi

18. 1.4 m, 4.8 m, 5 m

19. STAIRS There are 12 steps in the staircase. Find the distance from point *A* to point *B* (in feet). Round your answer to the nearest tenth.

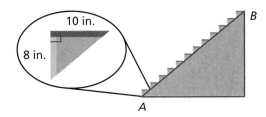
10 in.
8 in.
B
A

20. AIRPORT Which plane is closer to the tower? Explain.

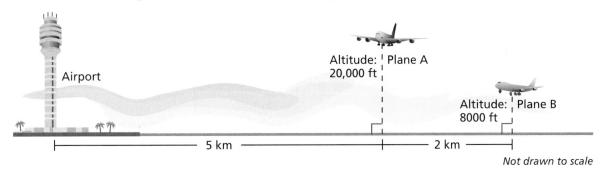
Airport
Altitude: Plane A
20,000 ft
Altitude: Plane B
8000 ft
5 km
2 km
Not drawn to scale

21. PROJECT Find a shoebox or some other small box.

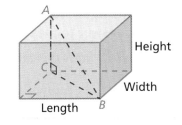
A
Height
C
Width
Length
B

    a. Measure the dimensions of the box.

    b. Without measuring, find length *BC* and length *AB*.

    c. Use a piece of string and a ruler to check the lengths you found in part (b).

22. **Critical Thinking** Plot the points $(-1, -2)$, $(2, 1)$, and $(-3, 6)$ in a coordinate plane. Are the points the vertices of a right triangle? Explain.

Fair Game Review *What you learned in previous grades & lessons*

Find the mean, median, and mode of the data. *(Skills Review Handbook)*

23. 12, 9, 17, 15, 12, 13

24. 21, 32, 16, 27, 22, 19, 10

25. 67, 59, 34, 71, 59

26. MULTIPLE CHOICE What is the sum of the angle measures of an octagon? *(Section 5.3)*

    Ⓐ 720°   Ⓑ 1080°   Ⓒ 1440°   Ⓓ 1800°

Classify the real number. *(Section 8.3)*

1. $-\sqrt{225}$

2. $-1\dfrac{1}{9}$

3. $\sqrt{41}$

Estimate to the nearest integer. *(Section 8.3)*

4. $\sqrt{38}$

5. $-\sqrt{99}$

6. $\sqrt{172}$

Which number is greater? Explain. *(Section 8.3)*

7. $\sqrt{11}, 3\dfrac{3}{5}$

8. $\sqrt{1.44}, 1.1\overline{8}$

Simplify the expression. *(Section 8.4)*

9. $\sqrt{2} + 2\sqrt{2}$

10. $3\sqrt{15} - 7\sqrt{15}$

11. $\sqrt{\dfrac{6}{25}}$

Find the volume of the rectangular prism. *(Section 8.4)*

12.

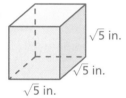

$\sqrt{5}$ in.
$\sqrt{5}$ in.
$\sqrt{5}$ in.

13.

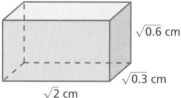

$\sqrt{0.6}$ cm
$\sqrt{0.3}$ cm
$\sqrt{2}$ cm

Use the figure to answer Exercises 14–17. Round your answer to the nearest tenth. *(Section 8.5)*

14. How far is the cabin from the peak?

15. How far is the fire tower from the lake?

16. How far is the lake from the peak?

17. You are standing at $(-5, -6)$. How far are you from the lake?

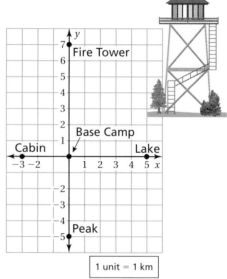

1 unit = 1 km

Tell whether the triangle with the given side lengths is a right triangle. *(Section 8.5)*

18.

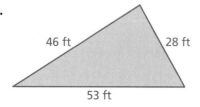

46 ft
28 ft
53 ft

19.

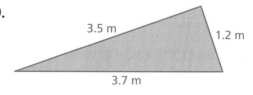

3.5 m
1.2 m
3.7 m

Alternative Assessment Options

Math Chat   **Student Reflective Focus Question**

Structured Interview   Writing Prompt

Student Reflective Focus Question

Ask students to summarize approximating square roots, simplifying square roots, and using the Pythagorean Theorem. Be sure that they include examples. Select students at random to present their summary to the class.

Study Help Sample Answers

Remind students to complete Graphic Organizers for the rest of the chapter.

4.

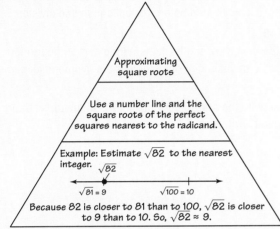

5. Available at *BigIdeasMath.com*.

Reteaching and Enrichment Strategies

If students need help...	If students got it...

Resources by Chapter
  • Study Help
  • Practice A and Practice B
  • Puzzle Time
Lesson Tutorials
BigIdeasMath.com Practice Quiz
Practice from the Test Generator
	Resources by Chapter
	  • Enrichment and Extension
	  • School-to-Work
	Game Closet at *BigIdeasMath.com*
	Start the Chapter Review

Answers

1. integer, rational

2. rational

3. irrational

4. 6   5. -10

6. 13

7. $3\dfrac{3}{5}$; $3\dfrac{3}{5}$ is to the right of $\sqrt{11}$.

8. $\sqrt{1.44}$; $\sqrt{1.44}$ is to the right of $1.1\overline{8}$.

9. $3\sqrt{2}$

10. $-4\sqrt{15}$

11. $\dfrac{\sqrt{6}}{5}$

12. $5\sqrt{5}$ in.^{3} 13. 0.6 cm^3

14. 5.8 km   15. 8.6 km

16. 7.1 km   17. 11.7 km

18. no   19. yes

```
┌─────────────────────────────┐
│ Technology                   │
│ For the Teacher              │
│                              │
│ Answer Presentation Tool     │
└─────────────────────────────┘
```

Assessment Book

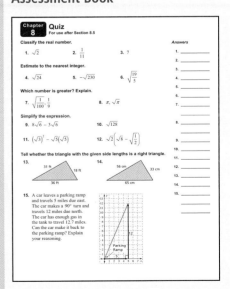

Answers

1. 4 and -4

2. 30 and -30

3. 50 and -50

4. 1

5. $-\dfrac{3}{5}$

6. 1.3 and -1.3

7. -1

8. $3\dfrac{2}{3}$

9. -30

Review of Common Errors

Exercises 1–3

- Students may only find the positive square root of the number given. Remind them that a square root can be positive or negative, and the question is asking for both answers.

Exercises 4–6

- Students may divide the number by two instead of finding a number that, when multiplied by itself, gives the radicand. Remind them that taking the square root of a number is the inverse of squaring a number.

Exercises 7–9

- Remind students of the order of operations. Because taking a square root is the inverse of squaring, it is evaluated before multiplication and division.

Exercises 10, 11, 18, and 19

- Students may substitute the given lengths in the wrong part of the formula. Remind them that the side opposite the right angle is the hypotenuse c.

Exercises 12–17

- Encourage students to write the first 10 perfect squares at the top of their papers as a reminder and a reference.

Check It Out
Vocabulary Help
BigIdeasMath com

Review Key Vocabulary

square root, *p. 358*
perfect square, *p. 358*
radical sign, *p. 358*
radicand, *p. 358*

theorem, *p. 362*
legs, *p. 364*
hypotenuse, *p. 364*
Pythagorean Theorem, *p. 364*

irrational number, *p. 372*
real numbers, *p. 372*
Pythagorean triple, *p. 387*

Review Examples and Exercises

8.1 Finding Square Roots *(pp. 356–361)*

Find the square root(s).

a. $-\sqrt{36}$

> $-\sqrt{36}$ represents the *negative* square root.

∴ Because $6^2 = 36$, $-\sqrt{36} = -\sqrt{6^2} = -6$.

b. $\sqrt{1.96}$

> $\sqrt{1.96}$ represents the *positive* square root.

∴ Because $1.4^2 = 1.96$, $\sqrt{1.96} = \sqrt{1.4^2} = 1.4$.

c. $\pm\sqrt{\dfrac{16}{81}}$

> $\pm\sqrt{\dfrac{16}{81}}$ represents both the *positive and negative* square roots.

∴ Because $\left(\dfrac{4}{9}\right)^2 = \dfrac{16}{81}$, $\pm\sqrt{\dfrac{16}{81}} = \pm\sqrt{\left(\dfrac{4}{9}\right)^2} = \dfrac{4}{9}$ and $-\dfrac{4}{9}$.

Exercises

Find the two square roots of the number.

1. 16

2. 900

3. 2500

Find the square root(s).

4. $\sqrt{1}$

5. $-\sqrt{\dfrac{9}{25}}$

6. $\pm\sqrt{1.69}$

Evaluate the expression.

7. $15 - 4\sqrt{16}$

8. $\sqrt{\dfrac{54}{6}} + \dfrac{2}{3}$

9. $10\left(\sqrt{81} - 12\right)$

8.2 The Pythagorean Theorem (pp. 362–367)

Find the length of the hypotenuse of the triangle.

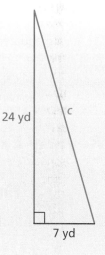

$$a^2 + b^2 = c^2 \qquad \text{Write the Pythagorean Theorem.}$$
$$7^2 + 24^2 = c^2 \qquad \text{Substitute.}$$
$$49 + 576 = c^2 \qquad \text{Evaluate powers.}$$
$$625 = c^2 \qquad \text{Add.}$$
$$\sqrt{625} = \sqrt{c^2} \qquad \text{Take positive square root of each side.}$$
$$25 = c \qquad \text{Simplify.}$$

24 yd c 7 yd

⋰ The length of the hypotenuse is 25 yards.

Exercises

Find the missing length of the triangle.

10.

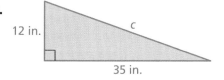

12 in. c 35 in.

11.

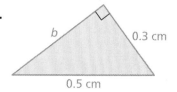

b 0.3 cm   0.5 cm

8.3 Approximating Square Roots (pp. 370–377)

Estimate $\sqrt{34}$ to the nearest integer.

Use a number line and the square roots of the perfect squares nearest to the radicand. The nearest perfect square less than 34 is 25. The nearest perfect square greater than 34 is 36.

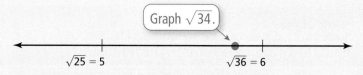

Graph $\sqrt{34}$.

$\sqrt{25} = 5$ $\sqrt{36} = 6$

Because 34 is closer to 36 than to 25, $\sqrt{34}$ is closer to 6 than to 5.

⋰ So, $\sqrt{34} \approx 6$.

Exercises

Estimate to the nearest integer.

12. $\sqrt{14}$ **13.** $\sqrt{90}$ **14.** $\sqrt{175}$

Review Game

Significant Square Roots

Big Ideas
Game Closet

For the Student
Additional Practice
• Lesson Tutorials
• Study Help (textbook)
• Student Website
   Multi-Language Glossary
   Practice Assessments

Materials per Group
• piece of paper
• pencil

Directions
Divide the class into groups of 3 or 4.

Each group is to come up with 5 significant numbers and compute the exact square root of each number.

Examples of significant numbers:
   School address: 1764 Knowledge Road; $\sqrt{1764} = 42$
   Year of presidential election: 1936—Franklin D. Roosevelt elected to his second term; $\sqrt{1936} = 44$
   Age for driver's license: 16 years old; $\sqrt{16} = 4$

Who wins?
The first group to come up with five significant numbers and correct square roots wins.

Answers

10. 37 in.
11. 0.4 cm
12. 4
13. 9
14. 13
15. $\dfrac{3\sqrt{11}}{10}$
16. $4\sqrt{6}$
17. $5\sqrt{3}$
18. 32.2 ft
19. 36 ft

My Thoughts on the Chapter

What worked. . .

Teacher Tip

Not allowed to write in your teaching edition? Use sticky notes to record your thoughts.

What did not work. . .

What I would do differently. . .

8.4 Simplifying Square Roots *(pp. 378–383)*

Simplify $\sqrt{28}$.

$$\sqrt{28} = \sqrt{4 \cdot 7} \qquad \text{Factor using the greatest perfect square factor.}$$
$$= \sqrt{4} \cdot \sqrt{7} \qquad \text{Use the Product Property of Square Roots.}$$
$$= 2\sqrt{7} \qquad \text{Simplify.}$$

Simplify $\sqrt{\dfrac{13}{64}}$.

$$\sqrt{\frac{13}{64}} = \frac{\sqrt{13}}{\sqrt{64}} \qquad \text{Use the Quotient Property of Square Roots.}$$
$$= \frac{\sqrt{13}}{8} \qquad \text{Simplify.}$$

Exercises

Simplify the expression.

15. $\sqrt{\dfrac{99}{100}}$ **16.** $\sqrt{96}$ **17.** $\sqrt{75}$

8.5 Using the Pythagorean Theorem *(pp. 384–389)*

Find the height of the stilt walker. Round your answer to the nearest tenth.

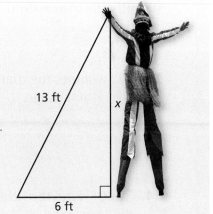

$$a^2 + b^2 = c^2 \qquad \text{Write the Pythagorean Theorem.}$$
$$6^2 + x^2 = 13^2 \qquad \text{Substitute.}$$
$$36 + x^2 = 169 \qquad \text{Evaluate powers.}$$
$$x^2 = 133 \qquad \text{Subtract 36 from each side.}$$
$$\sqrt{x^2} = \sqrt{133} \qquad \text{Take positive square root of each side.}$$
$$x \approx 11.5 \qquad \text{Use a calculator.}$$

13 ft   x   6 ft

⋮ The height of the stilt walker is about 11.5 feet.

Exercises

Find the height x. Round your answer to the nearest tenth, if necessary.

18.

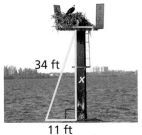

34 ft

x

11 ft

19.

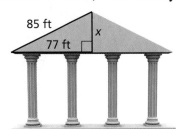

85 ft

77 ft

x

Check It Out
Test Practice
BigIdeasMath✓com

Find the square root(s).

1. $-\sqrt{1600}$

2. $\sqrt{\dfrac{25}{49}}$

3. $\pm\sqrt{\dfrac{100}{9}}$

Evaluate the expression.

4. $12 + 8\sqrt{16}$

5. $\dfrac{1}{2} + \sqrt{\dfrac{72}{2}}$

6. Find the missing length of the triangle.

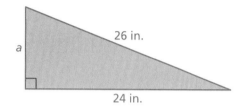

Classify the real number.

7. 16π

8. $-\sqrt{49}$

Which number is greater? Explain.

9. $\sqrt{0.16}$, $\dfrac{1}{2}$

10. $\sqrt{45}$, $6.\overline{3}$

Simplify the expression.

11. $6\sqrt{5} + 5\sqrt{5}$

12. $\sqrt{250}$

13. Tell whether the triangle is a right triangle.

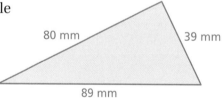

14. ROBOT Find the height of the dinosaur robot.

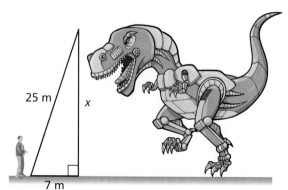

15. SUPERHERO Find the altitude of the superhero balloon.

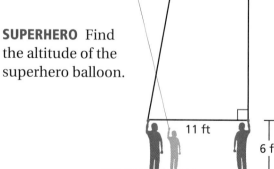

Test Item References

Chapter Test Questions	Section to Review
1–5	8.1, 8.4
6	8.2
7–10	8.3
11, 12	8.4
13–15	8.5

Test-Taking Strategies

Remind students to quickly look over the entire test before they start so that they can budget their time. Students should estimate and check their answers for reasonableness as they work through the test. Teach the students to use the Stop and Think strategy before answering. **Stop** and carefully read the question, and **Think** about what the answer should look like.

Common Assessment Errors

- **Exercises 1–3** Remind students that a square root can be positive or negative.
- **Exercises 4 and 5** Remind students of the order of operations. Because taking a square root is the inverse of squaring, it is evaluated before multiplication and division.
- **Exercises 6, 13–15** Students may substitute the given lengths in the wrong part of the formula. Remind them that the side opposite the right angle is the hypotenuse c.
- **Exercises 7 and 8** Students may not classify the real number in as many ways as possible. Remind students that real numbers can have more than one classification.
- **Exercise 11** Students may add the radicands as well as the coefficients. Remind them to only add the coefficients because the square roots are like terms.
- **Exercise 12** Students may still have difficulty identifying perfect squares to use to simplify the expression. Encourage them to write the first 10 perfect squares at the top of their papers as a reminder and a reference.

Reteaching and Enrichment Strategies

If students need help. . .	If students got it. . .
Resources by Chapter • Practice A and Practice B • Puzzle Time Record and Practice Journal Practice Differentiating the Lesson Lesson Tutorials Practice from the Test Generator Skills Review Handbook	Resources by Chapter • Enrichment and Extension • School-to-Work • Financial Literacy Game Closet at *BigIdeasMath.com* Start Standardized Test Practice

Answers

1. -40
2. $\dfrac{5}{7}$
3. $\dfrac{10}{3}$ and $-\dfrac{10}{3}$
4. 44
5. $6\dfrac{1}{2}$
6. 10 in.
7. irrational
8. integer, rational
9. $\dfrac{1}{2}; \dfrac{1}{2}$ is to the right of $\sqrt{0.16}$.
10. $\sqrt{45}; \sqrt{45}$ is to the right of $6.\overline{3}$.
11. $11\sqrt{5}$
12. $5\sqrt{10}$
13. yes
14. 24 m
15. 66 ft

Assessment Book

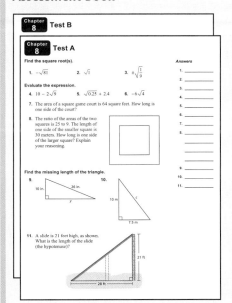

T-394

After Answering Easy Questions, Relax
Answer Easy Questions First
Estimate the Answer
Read All Choices before Answering
Read Question before Answering
Solve Directly or Eliminate Choices
Solve Problem before Looking at
 Choices
Use Intelligent Guessing
Work Backwards

About this Strategy

When taking a multiple choice test, be sure to read each question carefully and thoroughly. When taking a timed test, it is often best to skim the test and answer the easy questions first. Be careful that you record your answer in the correct position on the answer sheet.

Answers

1. D
2. H
3. A
4. G

Item Analysis

1. **A.** The student adds 1.1 and 4.

   B. The student multiplies 1.1 by 4.

   C. The student adds 1.1 and 2.

   D. Correct answer

2. **F.** The student misunderstands what the question is asking.

   G. The student misunderstands what the question is asking and incorrectly identifies the slope formula.

   H. Correct answer

   I. The student misunderstands the slope-intercept form of an equation.

3. **A.** Correct answer

   B. The student adds 60 and 8 together.

   C. The student interchanges the roles of 60 and 8 in the equation.

   D. The student adds 8 and y together instead of multiplying them.

4. **F.** The student misunderstands the meaning of continuous and discrete.

   G. Correct answer

   H. The student makes an error by assuming the function is linear from the information given.

   I. The student assumes that range will be the same as domain.

5. **2 points** The student demonstrates a thorough understanding of how to apply the Pythagorean Theorem to the problem, explains the work fully, and calculates the distance accurately. The distance between opposite corners is $\sqrt{16,000} = 40\sqrt{10} \approx 126.5$ yards.

   1 point The student's work and explanations demonstrate a lack of essential understanding. The Pythagorean Theorem is misstated or, if stated correctly, is applied incorrectly to the problem.

   0 points The student provides no response, a completely incorrect or incomprehensible response, or a response that demonstrates insufficient understanding of the Pythagorean Theorem.

6. **Gridded Response:** Correct answer: 15 hours

   Common Error: The student adds 50 to the right hand side of the equation instead of subtracting, yielding an answer of 17.5.

7. **A.** The student interchanges the roles of n and S.

   B. Correct answer

   C. The student subtracts 2 from S instead of adding it.

   D. The student adds 2 first, then divides through by 180.

Technology
For the Teacher

Big Ideas Test Generator

Test-Taking Strategy
Answer Easy Questions First

"Scan the test and answer the easy questions first. You know the square root of 4 is 2."

1. The period T of a pendulum is the time, in seconds, it takes the pendulum to swing back and forth. The period can be found using the formula $T = 1.1\sqrt{L}$, where L is the length, in feet, of the pendulum. A pendulum has a length of 4 feet. Find its period.

   A. 5.1 sec   **C.** 3.1 sec

   B. 4.4 sec   **D.** 2.2 sec

2. The steps Pat took to write the equation in slope-intercept form are shown below. What should Pat change in order to correctly rewrite the equation in slope-intercept form?

   $$3x - 6y = 1$$
   $$3x = 6y + 1$$
   $$x = 2y + \frac{1}{3}$$

   F. Use the formula $m = \dfrac{\text{rise}}{\text{run}}$.

   G. Use the formula $m = \dfrac{\text{run}}{\text{rise}}$.

   H. Subtract $3x$ from both sides of the equation and divide every term by -6.

   I. Subtract 1 from both sides of the equation and divide every term by 3.

3. A housing community started with 60 homes. In each of the following years, 8 more homes were built. Let y represent the number of years that have passed since the first year and let n represent the number of homes. Which equation describes the relationship between n and y?

   A. $n = 8y + 60$ **C.** $n = 60y + 8$

   B. $n = 68y$ **D.** $n = 60 + 8 + y$

4. The domain of a function is 0, 1, 2, 3, 4, 5. What can you conclude?

   F. The domain is continuous.   **H.** The function is linear.

   G. The domain is discrete.   **I.** The range is 0, 1, 2, 3, 4, 5.

5. A football field is 40 yards wide and 120 yards long. Find the distance between opposite corners of the football field. Show your work and explain your reasoning.

Think Solve Explain

6. A computer consultant charges $50 plus $40 for each hour she works. The consultant charged $650 for one job. This can be represented by the equation below, where h represents the number of hours worked.

$$40h + 50 = 650$$

How many hours did the consultant work?

7. The formula below can be used to find the number S of degrees in a polygon with n sides. Solve the formula for n.

$$S = 180(n - 2)$$

A. $n = 180(S - 2)$

C. $n = \dfrac{S}{180} - 2$

B. $n = \dfrac{S}{180} + 2$

D. $n = \dfrac{S}{180} + \dfrac{1}{90}$

8. The table below shows a linear pattern. Which linear function relates y to x?

x	1	2	3	4	5
y	4	2	0	-2	-4

F. $y = 2x + 2$

H. $y = -2x + 2$

G. $y = 4x$

I. $y = -2x + 6$

9. What is the value of x in the right triangle shown?

A. 16 cm

C. 24 cm

B. 18 cm

D. $\sqrt{674}$ cm

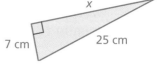

7 cm   25 cm   x

10. Find the height of the tree in the diagram.

F. 22.5 ft

H. 35 ft

G. 31.5 ft

I. 40 ft

6 ft

4.5 ft

30 ft   Not drawn to scale

Item Analysis (continued)

8. F. The student has the wrong sign for the slope and makes a mistake finding the *y*-intercept.

   G. The student bases the equation on the first column only.

   H. The student finds the correct slope, but makes a mistake finding the *y*-intercept.

   I. Correct answer

9. A. The student takes the average of the two sides.

   B. The student subtracts the shorter from the longer side.

   C. Correct answer

   D. The student treats the missing leg as the hypotenuse.

10. F. The student treats shadow length as tree height (i.e., reverses the ratio).

   G. The student adds 1.5 to the shadow length because the man is 1.5 feet taller than his shadow.

   H. The student guesses, and picks an answer slightly greater than 30.

   I. Correct answer

11. A. The student simplifies $\sqrt{24}$ correctly, but evaluates $\sqrt{4}$ as 4 instead of as 2.

   B. The student reverses the numbers.

   C. Correct answer

   D. The student adds 12 and 24 under the radical.

12. F. Correct answer

   G. The student mistakes supplement for complement.

   H. The student reverses the order of the subtraction.

   I. The student mistakes supplement for complement and reverses the order of the subtraction.

13. A. The student divides the right side of the equation by 2.5, but makes a decimal error by dividing the left side of the equation by 25.

   B. Correct answer

   C. The student sets *g* equal to 0.

   D. The student adds 3 to 18 instead of subtracting.

14. Gridded Response: Correct answer: 65 mi

Common Error: The student adds the two distances to get 89 miles as an answer.

Answers

5. about 126.5 yards

6. 15 hours

7. B

8. I

9. C

10. I

Answer for Extra Example

1. **A.** Correct answer

B. The student misreads "greatest speed a car is allowed legally" to mean strict inequality.

C. The student mistakes the inequality symbols.

D. The student mistakes the inequality symbols and assumes strict inequality.

Item Analysis (continued)

15. **F.** Correct answer

G. The student picks slope of 2 instead of −2.

H. The student picks y-intercept of 2 instead of −2.

I. The student picks y-intercept of 2 instead of −2 and slope of 2 instead of −2.

Extra Example for Standardized Test Practice

1. The sign below shows the speed limit on a highway.

The speed limit indicates the **greatest** speed a car is legally allowed. If s represents speed, how can this speed limit be written algebraically?

A. $s \leq 65$ **C.** $s \geq 65$

B. $s < 65$ **D.** $s > 65$

11. Which expression is equivalent to $12\sqrt{24}$?

A. $48\sqrt{6}$

C. $24\sqrt{6}$

B. $24\sqrt{12}$

D. 6

12. The measure of an angle is x degrees. What is the measure of its complement?

F. $(90 - x)°$

H. $(x - 90)°$

G. $(180 - x)°$

I. $(x - 180)°$

13. You fill up the gas tank of your car and begin driving on the interstate. You drive at an average speed of 60 miles per hour. The amount g, in gallons, of gas left in your car can be estimated. Use the formula shown below, where h is the number of hours you have been driving.

$$g = 18 - 2.5h$$

You will fill up when you have 3 gallons of gas left in the gas tank. How long after you start driving will you fill up again?

A. about 36 min

C. about 7.2 h

B. about 6.0 h

D. about 8.4 h

14. An airplane flies 56 miles due north and then 33 miles due east. How many miles is the plane from its starting point?

15. Which graph represents the linear equation $y = -2x - 2$?

F.

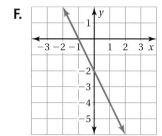

H.

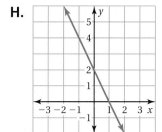

G.

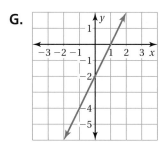

I.

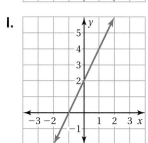

9 Data Displays and Probability

"Wow. The number of minutes I can dog paddle is growing like crazy!"

"Please hold still. I am trying to find the mean of 6, 8, and 10 by dividing their sum into three equal piles."

Strands Development

6th Grade

- Construct circle graphs.
- Draw conclusions and make predictions using circle graphs.
- Compare and contrast graphs that display information from the same data set.
- Compare and contrast dependent and independent events.
- Find the probabilities of dependent and independent events.

7th Grade

- Construct and analyze histograms.
- Compare and contrast histograms with other graphs that display information from the same data set.
- Investigate and describe the difference between experimental and theoretical probability.
- Determine the probability of compound events using the Fundamental (Basic) Counting Principle.

8th Grade

- Construct and analyze scatter plots.
- Make comparisons, predictions, and inferences using information displayed in graphs.
- Find the probabilities of independent and dependent events with and without replacement.

Math in History

Many ancient cultures used a counting frame or abacus to perform calculations. Most of these cultures used a base ten system like the Roman or Chinese system. The abacus shown below is representing the number 2786.

★ Examples of the use of an abacus in Rome date back to around the first century A.D.

★ Examples of the use of an abacus in China date back to around the 14th century A.D.

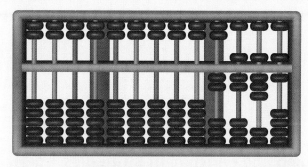

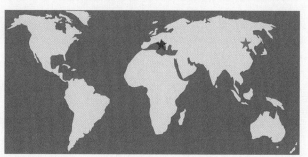

Pacing Guide for Chapter 9

Chapter Opener	1 Day
Section 1 Activity Lesson	 1 Day 1 Day
Section 2 Activity Lesson	 1 Day 1 Day
Study Help / Quiz	1 Day
Section 3 Activity Lesson	 1 Day 1 Day
Section 4 Activity Lesson	 1 Day 1 Day
Chapter Review / Tests	2 Days
Total Chapter 9	12 Days
Year-to-Date	145 Days

Check Your Resources

- Record and Practice Journal
- Resources by Chapter
- Skills Review Handbook
- Assessment Book
- Worked-Out Solutions

Technology
For the **Teacher**

Dynamic Classroom

The Dynamic Planning Tool
Editable Teacher's Resources at
BigIdeasMath.com

Standards of Learning

6.14(a) The student, given a problem situation, will construct circle graphs.

7.11(a) The student, given data in a practical situation, will construct and analyze histograms.

Additional Topics for Review

- Multiplying fractions
- Circle graphs
- Histograms
- Frequency tables
- Writing the equations of lines

Try It Yourself

1. Answers will vary.

2. Answers will vary.

Record and Practice Journal

1.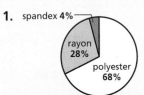

2.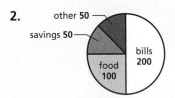

3.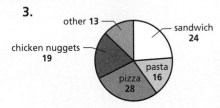

4.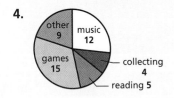

5.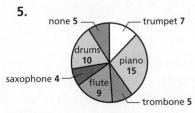

6–10. See Additional Answers.

Math Background Notes

Vocabulary Review

- Frequency Table
- Histogram
- Survey

Displaying Data

- Students have collected, analyzed, and displayed data.
- **Teaching Tip:** Example 1 provides a great opportunity for review. Remind students that a circle contains 360°. This is also a good time to review using a protractor.
- Remind students that it is helpful to know the total number of people surveyed before constructing the circle graph. This number will serve as the whole (denominator of the fraction).
- **Teaching Tip:** Example 2 provides an excellent opportunity to explore students' prerequisite knowledge. Students should be familiar with bar graphs, double bar graphs, and histograms. Consider using a Venn diagram to compare and contrast the three types of displays. This will create a nice visual representation to show which characteristics go with which display.
- **Common Error:** Students might forget that a histogram uses intervals rather than individual data values. Remind students that the horizontal axis of the graph will be labeled with intervals and the vertical axis of the graph will be labeled with frequency.
- **Common Error:** Even if an interval has a frequency of zero, it must appear on the histogram.
- You can adapt the context of the survey to personalize it to your class.

Reteaching and Enrichment Strategies

If students need help. . .	If students got it. . .
Record and Practice Journal • Fair Game Review Skills Review Handbook Lesson Tutorials	Game Closet at *BigIdeasMath.com* Start the next section

What You Learned Before

"Behind two of the doors is a doggy biscuit. Behind the other door is a mouse. Which door do you choose?"

Displaying Data

Example 1 The table shows the results of a survey. Display the data in a circle graph.

Class Trip Location	Water Park	Museum	Zoo	Other
Students	25	11	5	4

A total of 45 students took the survey.

Water park:

$$\frac{25}{45} \cdot 360° = 200°$$

Museum:

$$\frac{11}{45} \cdot 360° = 88°$$

Zoo:

$$\frac{5}{45} \cdot 360° = 40°$$

Other:

$$\frac{4}{45} \cdot 360° = 32°$$

Class Trip Locations

Example 2 The frequency table shows the number of books that 12 people read last month. Display the data in a histogram.

Books Read Last Month	Frequency
0–1	6
2–3	4
4–5	0
6–7	2

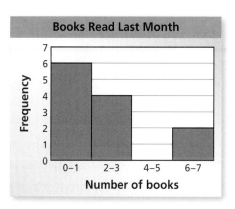

Try It Yourself

1. Conduct a survey to determine the after-school activities of students in your class. Display the results in a circle graph.

2. Conduct a survey to determine the number of pets owned by students in your class. Display the results in a histogram.

STANDARDS OF LEARNING
8.13

Essential Question How can you use data to predict an event?

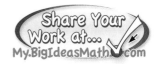

Share Your Work at...
My.BigIdeasMath.com

1 **ACTIVITY: Representing Data by a Linear Equation**

Work with a partner. You have been working on a science project for 8 months. Each month, you have measured the length of a baby alligator.

My Science Project

The table shows your measurements.

September ↓   April ↓

Month, x	0	1	2	3	4	5	6	7
Length (in.), y	22.0	22.5	23.5	25.0	26.0	27.5	28.5	29.5

Use the following steps to predict the baby alligator's length next September.

a. Graph the data in the table.

b. Draw the straight line that you think best approximates the points.

c. Write an equation of the line you drew.

d. Use the equation to predict the baby alligator's length next September.

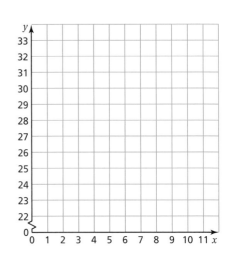

Laurie's Notes

Introduction

For the Teacher

- **Goal:** Students will gain an intuitive understanding of how to construct scatter plots and how to write an equation of the line of best fit.
- **Big Idea:** A scatter plot differs from previous data displays in that it is bi-variate (paired data). Each data point is associated with two numbers, *x* and *y*, unlike uni-variate data where each is a single value.
- My experience has been that students are comfortable with plotting ordered pairs. Summarizing the data using the *line of best fit* is challenging.

Motivate

- Solicit information about what students know about alligators. Share alligator facts with students as a warm-up. (See the next page.)
- That should be enough information to set the context for this first activity!

Activity Notes

Activity 1

- ❓ "Look at the table of values. What do the ordered pairs represent?" (month, length of alligator)
- ❓ "Does the data represent the first 7 months of growth of a baby alligator? Explain." No, it does not suggest that this is from birth to age 7 months.
- ❓ "Are there any observations about the data in the table?" Months are increasing by 1. Lengths are increasing by about one-half to an inch each month.
- Students will ask what drawing a line "that best approximates the points" means. You should explain that it is a line that passes as closely as possible to all the points. Use a straightedge to lightly draw the line.
- ❓ "What does the jagged symbol at the bottom of the *y*-axis mean?" broken axis
- ❓ "Do you think everyone in class drew the exact same line? Explain." no; They will be close, but they do not have to be exactly the same.
- ❓ "How did you write the equation for the line?" Listen for an approximation of the slope (rise over run) and the *y*-intercept (close to 22). Write the equation in slope-intercept form.
- ❓ "Does everyone have the same slope?" No, but they should be relatively close and should match the observations made about the data when looking at the table.
- Have students interpret the slope and *y*-intercept in the context of the problem.
- ❓ "How does the equation help you answer part (d)?" Substitute 12 for *x*, and find *y*.
- ❓ "Without the equation, can you predict the length of the alligator next September?" Yes, but you need to extend the graph and use eyesight to approximate the ordered pair.

Standards of Learning

8.13(b) The student will construct and analyze scatterplots.

Previous Learning

Students should know how to plot ordered pairs and write equations in slope-intercept form.

Activity Materials
Textbook
• straightedge

Start Thinking! and Warm Up

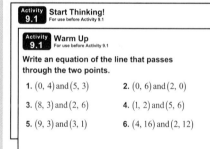

Activity 9.1 Start Thinking!
For use before Activity 9.1

Activity 9.1 Warm Up
For use before Activity 9.1

Write an equation of the line that passes through the two points.

1. $(0, 4)$ and $(5, 3)$ 2. $(0, 6)$ and $(2, 0)$

3. $(8, 3)$ and $(2, 6)$ 4. $(1, 2)$ and $(5, 6)$

5. $(9, 3)$ and $(3, 1)$ 6. $(4, 16)$ and $(2, 12)$

9.1 Record and Practice Journal

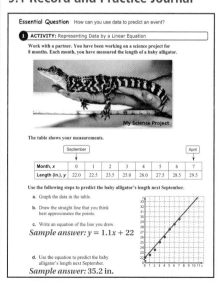

Essential Question How can you use data to predict an event?

1 ACTIVITY: Representing Data by a Linear Equation

Work with a partner. You have been working on a science project for 8 months. Each month, you have measured the length of a baby alligator.

My Science Project

The table shows your measurements.

	September							April
Month, *x*	0	1	2	3	4	5	6	7
Length (in.), *y*	22.0	22.5	23.5	25.0	26.0	27.5	28.5	29.5

Use the following steps to predict the baby alligator's length next September.

a. Graph the data in the table.

b. Draw the straight line that you think best approximates the points.

c. Write an equation of the line you drew.
Sample answer: $y = 1.1x + 22$

d. Use the equation to predict the baby alligator's length next September.
Sample answer: 35.2 in.

Class Activity

Provide English learners with an opportunity to interact while learning the concept. Draw a coordinate plane on poster board. Label the horizontal axis *shoe size* and the vertical axis *height*. Have students place a sticker on the ordered pair that represents their shoe size and height. Then have the class fit a line to the data and write an equation of the line.

9.1 Record and Practice Journal

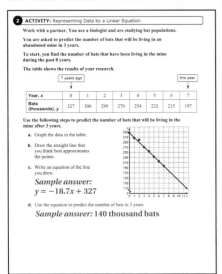

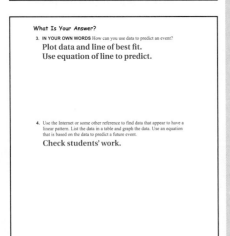

Laurie's Notes

Activity 2

- In this activity, the data has not been collected from an experiment. The data has been collected from a documented source and recorded in the table.
- Read the introduction. The purpose of making a scatter plot is stated. You want to make a prediction about the future by examining known data.
- **?** "Are there any observations about the data in the table?" Students may recognize that as the years increase, the number of bats is decreasing by about 15–20 (in thousands) per year.
- Discuss equations written by students. Record students' results on the board. There will likely be a bit more variation of results than in the first activity.
- Have students interpret what the slope and *y*-intercept mean in the context of the problem.
- Discuss how the equation allows us to make predictions about the future.

What Is Your Answer?

- Question 4 can become a project due at the conclusion of the chapter.

Closure

- **Exit Ticket:** Describe the difference in the source of data for Activity 1 versus Activity 2. The data in Activity 1 are the result of gathering actual data from an experiment. The data in Activity 2 has been collected from a documented source and recorded in a table.

More about Alligators

- The American alligator (Alligator mississippiensis) is the largest reptile in North America. The first reptiles appeared 300 million years ago. Ancestors of the American alligator appeared 200 million years ago.
- The name alligator comes from early Spanish explorers who called them "El legarto" or "big lizard" when they first saw these giant reptiles.
- Louisiana and Florida have the most alligators. There are over one million wild alligators in each state with over a quarter million more on alligator farms.
- Alligators are about 10–12 inches in length when they are hatched from eggs. Growth rates vary from 2 inches per year to 12 inches per year, depending on the habitat, sex, size, and age of the alligator.
- Females can grow to about 9 feet in length and over 200 pounds. Males can grow to about 13 feet in length and over 500 pounds.
- The largest alligator was taken in Louisiana and measured 19 feet 2 inches.
- Alligators live about as long as humans, an average of 70 years.

Technology
For
the Teacher

The Dynamic Planning Tool
Editable Teacher's Resources at *BigIdeasMath.com*

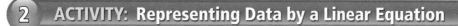

2 ACTIVITY: Representing Data by a Linear Equation

Work with a partner. You are a biologist and are studying bat populations.

You are asked to predict the number of bats that will be living in an abandoned mine in 3 years.

To start, you find the number of bats that have been living in the mine during the past 8 years.

The table shows the results of your research.

7 years ago   this year

Year, x	0	1	2	3	4	5	6	7
Bats (thousands), y	327	306	299	270	254	232	215	197

Use the following steps to predict the number of bats that will be living in the mine after 3 years.

a. Graph the data in the table.

b. Draw the straight line that you think best approximates the points.

c. Write an equation of the line you drew.

d. Use the equation to predict the number of bats in 3 years.

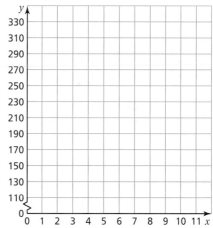

What Is Your Answer?

3. **IN YOUR OWN WORDS** How can you use data to predict an event?

4. Use the Internet or some other reference to find data that appear to have a linear pattern. List the data in a table and graph the data. Use an equation that is based on the data to predict a future event.

Practice   Use what you learned about scatter plots and lines of best fit to complete Exercise 3 on page 405.

Key Vocabulary 🔊
scatter plot, *p. 402*
line of best fit, *p. 404*

 **Key Idea**

Scatter Plot

A **scatter plot** is a graph that shows the relationship between two data sets. The two sets of data are graphed as ordered pairs in a coordinate plane.

EXAMPLE **Interpreting a Scatter Plot**

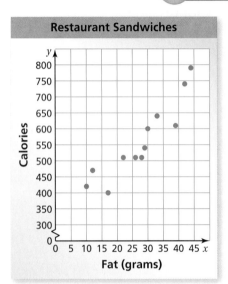

Restaurant Sandwiches

The scatter plot at the left shows the total fat (in grams) and the total calories in 12 restaurant sandwiches.

a. How many calories are in the sandwich that contains 17 grams of fat?

Draw a horizontal line from the point that has an *x*-value of 17. It crosses the *y*-axis at 400.

∴ So, the sandwich has 400 calories.

b. How many grams of fat are in the sandwich that contains 600 calories?

Draw a vertical line from the point that has a *y*-value of 600. It crosses the *x*-axis at 30.

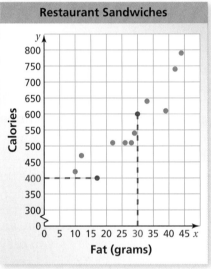

Restaurant Sandwiches

∴ So, the sandwich has 30 grams of fat.

c. What tends to happen to the number of calories as the number of grams of fat increases?

Looking at the graph, the plotted points go up from left to right.

∴ So, as the number of grams of fat increases, the number of calories increases.

On Your Own

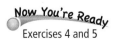
Now You're Ready
Exercises 4 and 5

1. WHAT IF? A sandwich has 650 calories. Based on the scatter plot in Example 1, how many grams of fat would you expect the sandwich to have? Explain your reasoning.

🔊 Multi-Language Glossary at BigIdeasMath√com.

Laurie's Notes

Introduction

Connect

- **Yesterday:** Students gained an intuitive understanding of how to construct scatter plots and write an equation of the line of best fit.
- **Today:** Students will construct scatter plots, draw the line of best fit, and analyze the equation.

Motivate

- **Preparation:** Stop by any fast food restaurant to pick up a pamphlet, or go online to find nutritional information about the menu items.
- ❓ "Do you think there is a relationship between the grams of fat and number of calories in the sandwich?" yes
- Share the information about a few of the sandwiches from your pamphlet or printout to confirm students' opinions.

Lesson Notes

Key Idea

- Explain that the plot they are going to make today displays the relationship, if any, between two variables, such as grams of fat and calories.
- Define scatter plot.
- Discuss the two scatter plots made yesterday. In Activity 1, the two sets of data were months and alligator length. In Activity 2, the two sets of data were years and number of bats.

Example 1

- This example helps students understand how a scatter plot is read and interpreted. Discuss the labels on the axes and what an ordered pair represents: (grams of fat, number of calories). There are 12 different sandwiches that are represented.
- To read information from the plot, move horizontally to the *x*-value, find the ordered pair, and then move to the *y*-axis to read the *y*-value. It is helpful to use your hands to demonstrate the motion.
- A scatter plot allows you to see trends in the data. You read a scatter plot from left to right. As the *x*-coordinate increases, is the *y*-coordinate increasing, decreasing, staying the same, *or* is there no pattern?

On Your Own

- This question implies that because you can see a particular trend in the data, you are able to make estimates about points which are not part of the data set but would fall within the trend in the data. Although it is possible that the 650 calorie sandwich has 10 grams of fat, you would not predict it based upon this scatter plot.

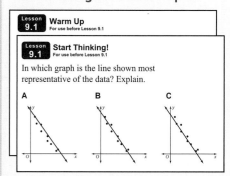
Extra Example 1

Use the scatter plot in Example 1.

a. How many grams of fat are in a sandwich that contains 740 calories? about 42 g

b. How many calories are in a sandwich that contains 33 grams of fat? about 640 calories

On Your Own

1. about 35 g; The point just below $y = 650$ has an *x*-value just below $x = 35$.

Laurie's Notes

Extra Example 2

Tell whether the data show a *positive*, a *negative*, or *no* relationship.

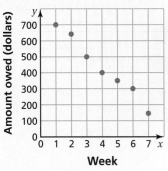

negative relationship

On Your Own

2. See Additional Answers.

3.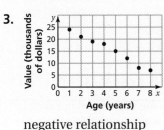

   negative relationship

Differentiated Instruction

Visual

Some students may find it easier to draw a line of best fit before determining if the data have a positive relationship, a negative relationship, or no relationship. A line with a *positive* slope means the data have a *positive* relationship. A line with a *negative* slope means the data have a *negative* relationship. If a line cannot be drawn, the data have *no* relationship.

Discuss

- There are three general cases that describe the relationship between two data sets. Draw a quick example of each case.
- The alligator data was an example of a positive relationship and the bat data was an example of a negative relationship.

Example 2

- Have students review the two scatter plots shown.
- Ask students to complete this sentence. As the size of the television increases, the price <u>increases</u>. This is an example of a positive relationship.
- **Connection:** By this point, some students have made the connection between the slope of a line and the relationship between the two data sets. A positive relationship is related to a positive slope.
- ? "Should there be a relationship between a person's age and the number of pets they own?" no
- Part (b) makes sense to students. There should be no trend in the data.

On Your Own

- Give time for students to complete these two scatter plots.
- A common difficulty for students is deciding how to scale the axes. Students should look at the range of numbers that need to be displayed, and then decide if it is necessary to start their axes at 0 or if another starting point (broken axes) makes sense.
- Have transparency grids available so that results can be shared quickly as a class.

A scatter plot can show that a relationship exists between two data sets.

Positive Relationship	*Negative Relationship*	*No Relationship*
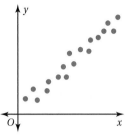	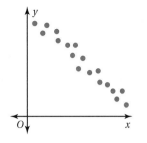	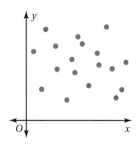
As *x* increases, *y* increases.	As *x* increases, *y* decreases.	The points show no pattern.

EXAMPLE ② **Identifying a Relationship**

Tell whether the data show a *positive*, a *negative*, or *no* relationship.

a. Television size and price

b. Age and number of pets owned

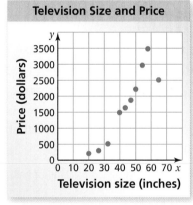

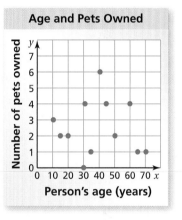

As the size of the television increases, the price increases.

The number of pets owned does not depend on a person's age.

⋮• So, the scatter plot shows a positive relationship.

⋮• So, the scatter plot shows no relationship.

On Your Own

Now You're Ready
Exercises 6–8

Make a scatter plot of the data. Tell whether the data show a *positive*, a *negative*, or *no* relationship.

2.

Study Time (min), *x*	30	20	60	90	45	10	30	75	120	80
Test Score, *y*	87	74	92	97	85	62	83	90	95	91

3.

Age of a Car (years), *x*	1	2	3	4	5	6	7	8
Value (thousands), *y*	$24	$21	$19	$18	$15	$12	$8	$7

A **line of best fit** is a line drawn on a scatter plot that is close to most of the data points. It can be used to estimate data on a graph.

EXAMPLE 3 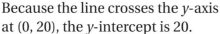 **Finding a Line of Best Fit**

Week, x	Sales (millions), y
1	$19
2	$15
3	$13
4	$11
5	$10
6	$8
7	$7
8	$5

The table shows the weekly sales of a DVD and the number of weeks since its release. (a) Make a scatter plot of the data. (b) Draw a line of best fit. (c) Write an equation of the line of best fit. (d) Predict the sales in week 9.

a. Plot the points in a coordinate plane. The scatter plot shows a negative relationship.

b. Draw a line that is close to the data points. Try to have as many points above the line as below it.

c. The line passes through (5, 10) and (6, 8).

$$\text{slope} = \frac{\text{rise}}{\text{run}} = \frac{-2}{1} = -2$$

Because the line crosses the y-axis at (0, 20), the y-intercept is 20.

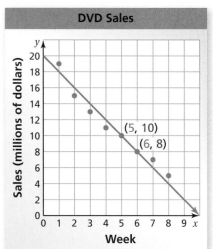

So, the equation of the line of best fit is $y = -2x + 20$.

d. To predict the sales for week 9, substitute 9 for x in the equation of the line of best fit.

$y = -2x + 20$ Line of best fit

$= -2(9) + 20$ Substitute 9 for x.

$= 2$ Evaluate.

The sales in week 9 should be about $2 million.

Study Tip

A line of best fit does not need to pass through any of the data points.

On Your Own

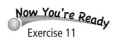
Exercise 11

4. The table shows the number of people who have attended a neighborhood festival over an 8-year period.

Year, x	1	2	3	4	5	6	7	8
Attendance, y	420	500	650	900	1100	1500	1750	2400

a. Make a scatter plot of the data.

b. Draw a line of best fit.

c. Write an equation of the line of best fit.

d. Predict the number of people who will attend the festival in year 10.

Laurie's Notes

Discuss

- **Model:** Define and discuss a line of best fit. You can model the line with a piece of spaghetti. Use a scatter plot from the previous page that was completed on the transparency. Show how the line can approximate the trend of the data.
- Move the spaghetti so that it does *not* represent the data, and then move the spaghetti so that it does. Use your eyesight when judging where to draw the line.

Example 3

? "What observations can you make about the sales of the DVD as the weeks go on?" Sales are decreasing.

- Carefully plot the ordered pairs on a transparency grid.
- When drawing a line of best fit, try to put as many points above the line as below it.
- Students may draw different lines of best fit and still get a reasonable answer.
- In this example, the line passes through two actual data points, (5, 10) and (6, 8). As noted in the *Study Tip*, a line of best fit does not need to pass through any of the data points.
- Finish working the problem as shown.
- **Big Idea:** The purpose of writing the equation of the line of best fit is to make predictions. The equation becomes a model for the data, describing its behavior.

On Your Own

- This is a nice summary problem. Students should quickly observe the positive relationship just from the table of values.
- Share results of this problem as a whole class.

Closure

- **Exit Ticket:** In Example 3, interpret the slope and *y*-intercept in the context of the problem. Why does the slope make sense for this problem? The slope, -2, represents the decrease in sales in millions of dollars per week. The *y*-intercept, 20, represents the sales in millions of dollars for week 0. The slope makes sense for this problem because interest in buying a DVD is greatest when the DVD is first released, and then sales fall. The *y*-intercept does not make sense in this problem, because there would not have been any sales before the first week.

Technology **F**or the **T**eacher

The Dynamic Planning Tool
Editable Teacher's Resources at *BigIdeasMath.com*

Extra Example 3

The table shows the weekly sales of a DVD and the number of weeks since its release.

Week, *x*	Sales (millions), *y*
1	$15
2	$13
3	$12
4	$9
5	$6
6	$4
7	$3

a. Make a scatter plot of the data.
b. Draw a line of best fit.

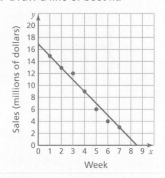

c. Write an equation of the line of best fit. $y = -2x + 17$
d. Predict the sales in week 8.
   about $1 million

On Your Own

4. a–b.

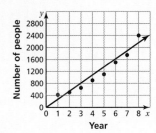

   c. *Sample answer:*
      $y = 270x$

   d. *Sample answer:*
      about 2700 people

1. They must be ordered pairs so there are equal amounts of *x*- and *y*-values.

2. You can estimate and predict values.

Practice and Problem Solving

3. **a–b.**

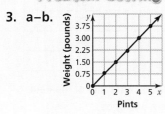

c. *Sample answer:* $y = 0.75x$

d. *Sample answer:* 7.5 lb

e. *Sample answer:* $16.88

4. **a.** 2007

b. about 875 SUVs

c. There is a negative relationship between year and number of SUVs sold.

5. **a.** 3.5 h

b. $85

c. There is a positive relationship between hours worked and earnings.

Assignment Guide and Homework Check

Level	Day 1 Activity Assignment	Day 2 Lesson Assignment	Homework Check
Basic	3, 17–19	1, 2, 4–9, 11–13	2, 4, 6, 11, 12
Average	3, 17–19	1, 2, 4–9, 11–13, 15	2, 4, 6, 11, 12
Advanced	3, 17–19	1, 2–16 even, 11, 15	2, 4, 6, 12, 14

Common Errors

- **Exercise 3** Students may use inconsistent increments or forget to label their graphs. They should use consistent increments to represent the data. Remind them to label the axes so that information can be read from the graph.
- **Exercises 4 and 5** When reading values from the graph, students may accidentally shift over or up too far and get an answer that is off by an increment. Encourage them to start at the given value on the axis and trace the graph to the point. Then trace down or left to the other axis for the answer.

9.1 Record and Practice Journal

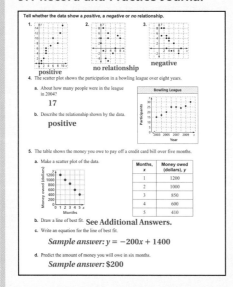

Technology For the Teacher

Answer Presentation Tool

QuizShow

Vocabulary and Concept Check

1. **VOCABULARY** What type of data is needed to make a scatter plot? Explain.

2. **WRITING** Explain why a line of best fit is helpful when analyzing data.

Practice and Problem Solving

3. **BLUEBERRIES** The table shows the weight y of x pints of blueberries.

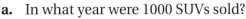

Number of Pints, x	0	1	2	3	4	5
Weight (pounds), y	0	0.8	1.50	2.20	3.0	3.75

   a. Graph the data in the table.

   b. Draw the straight line that you think best approximates the points.

   c. Write an equation of the line you drew.

   d. Use the equation to predict the weight of 10 pints of blueberries.

   e. Blueberries cost $2.25 per pound. How much do 10 pints of blueberries cost?

4. **SUVS** The scatter plot shows the number of sport utility vehicles sold in a city from 2005 to 2010.

   a. In what year were 1000 SUVs sold?

   b. About how many SUVs were sold in 2009?

   c. Describe the relationship shown by the data.

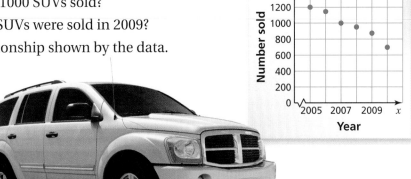

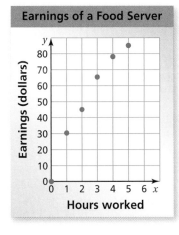

5. **EARNINGS** The scatter plot shows the total earnings (wages and tips) of a food server during 1 day.

   a. About how many hours must the server work to earn $70?

   b. About how much did the server earn for 5 hours of work?

   c. Describe the relationship shown by the data.

Tell whether the data show a *positive*, a *negative*, or *no* relationship.

6.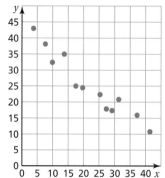

7.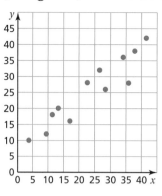

8.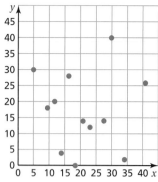

9. **HONEYBEES** The table shows the number of honeybee colonies in the United States from 2003 to 2006. What type of relationship does the data show?

Year, x	2003	2004	2005	2006
Honeybee Colonies (millions), y	2.599	2.556	2.413	2.392

10. **OPEN-ENDED** Describe a set of real-life data that has a positive relationship.

11. **VACATION** The table shows the distance you travel over a 6-hour period.

   a. Make a scatter plot of the data.

   b. Draw a line of best fit.

   c. Write an equation of the line of best fit.

   d. Predict the distance you will travel in 7 hours.

Hours, x	Distance (miles), y
1	62
2	123
3	188
4	228
5	280
6	344

12. **ERROR ANALYSIS** Describe and correct the error in drawing the line of best fit.

13. **TEST SCORES** The scatter plot shows the relationship between the number of minutes spent studying and the test scores for a science class.

   a. What type of relationship does the data show?

   b. Interpret the relationship.

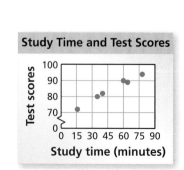

Study Time and Test Scores

Common Errors

- **Exercises 6–8** Students may confuse positive and negative relationships. Remind them about slope. The slope is positive when the line rises from left to right and negative when it falls from left to right. The same is true for relationships in a scatter plot. If the data rises from left to right, it is a positive relationship. If it falls from left to right, it is a negative relationship.

- **Exercise 11** Students may draw a line of best fit that does not accurately reflect the data trend. Remind them that the line does not have to go through any of the data points. Also remind them that the line should go through the middle of the data so that about half of the data points are above the line and half are below. One strategy is to draw an oval around the data and then draw a line through the middle of the oval. For example:

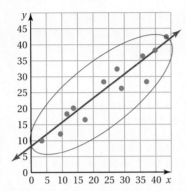

- **Exercise 11** Students may struggle writing the equation for the line of best fit. When drawing the line, encourage them to try to make the line go through a lattice point. Also, students can use lattice points that are very close to the line to help them find the slope.

Practice and Problem Solving

6. negative relationship

7. positive relationship

8. no relationship

9. negative relationship

10. *Sample answer:* age and height of a person

11. **a–b.**

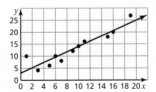

   c. *Sample answer:*
$y = 55x + 15$

   d. *Sample answer:* 400 mi

12. The line does not fit the data.

13. **a.** positive relationship

  b. The more time spent studying, the better the test score.

14. no; There is no line that lies close to most of the points.

15. See *Taking Math Deeper*.

16. See *Additional Answers*.

Fair Game Review

17. $-32, 64, -128$

18. $6, 3, \dfrac{3}{2}$

19. B

Mini-Assessment

The table shows the distance you travel over a 6-hour period.

Hours, x	Distance (miles), y
1	60
2	130
3	186
4	244
5	300
6	378

a. Make a scatter plot of the data.

b. Draw a line of best fit.

c. Write an equation of the line of best fit. *Sample answer:* $y = 60x$

d. Predict the distance traveled after 7 hours. *Sample answer:* about 420 mi

Taking Math Deeper

Exercise 15

The drawing for Exercise 15 is a stylized version of Leonardo da Vinci's famous drawing called "The Vitruvian Man." Leonardo created the drawing in 1487. It depicts a male figure in two superimposed positions with his arms and legs apart, and inscribed in a circle and square. The drawing and text are sometimes called the Proportions of Man. It is stored in the Gallerie dell'Accademia in Venice, Italy, but is only displayed on special occasions. Leonardo's drawing shows that the height and arm span of a typical human are equal.

① The project in the student text is described so that it can be assigned as homework. Another way to assign the project is to ask students to do the project in class.

② Gather the data by having students measure each other's height and arm span.

Plot the data for the entire class in a coordinate plane. Mark the x-axis and y-axis so that the heights of your students (in inches) will fit.

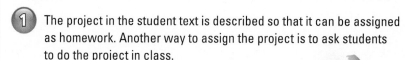

③ Ask your students to describe the relationship between height and arm span. If your class' results are similar to those described by Leonardo da Vinci, the slope of the line of best fit should be approximately equal to 1.

Height = Arm Span

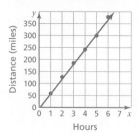

Project

Research Leonardo da Vinci's drawing of the *Vitruvian Man*. Explain the concept behind the drawing.

Reteaching and Enrichment Strategies

If students need help...	If students got it...
Resources by Chapter • Practice A and Practice B • Puzzle Time Record and Practice Journal Practice Differentiating the Lesson Lesson Tutorials Skills Review Handbook	Resources by Chapter • Enrichment and Extension Start the next section

14. REASONING A data set has no relationship. Is it possible to find a line of best fit for the data? Explain.

15. PROJECT Use a ruler or a yardstick to find the height and arm span of three people.

a. Make a scatter plot using the data you collected. Then draw a line of best fit for the data.

b. Use your height and the line of best fit to predict your arm span.

c. Measure your arm span. Compare the result with your prediction in part (b).

d. Is there a relationship between a person's height x and arm span y? Explain.

16. **Critical Thinking** The table shows the price of admission to a local theater and the yearly attendance for several years.

Price of Admission (dollars), x	Yearly Attendance, y
19.50	50,000
21.95	48,000
23.95	47,500
24.00	40,000
24.50	45,000
25.00	43,500

a. Identify the outlier.

b. How does the outlier affect a line of best fit? Explain.

c. Make a scatter plot of the data and draw a line of best fit.

d. Use the line of best fit to predict the attendance when the admission cost is $27.

 Fair Game Review *What you learned in previous grades & lessons*

Write the next three terms of the geometric sequence. *(Skills Review Handbook)*

17. $-2, 4, -8, 16, \ldots$

18. $96, 48, 24, 12, \ldots$

19. MULTIPLE CHOICE The circle graph shows the super powers chosen by a class. What percent of the students want strength as their super power? *(Skills Review Handbook)*

  Ⓐ   10.5%   Ⓑ   12.5%

  Ⓒ   15%   Ⓓ   25%

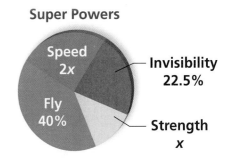

STANDARDS
OF LEARNING
8.13

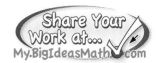

Essential Question How can you display data in a way that helps you make decisions?

1 **ACTIVITY: Displaying Data**

Work with a partner. Analyze and display each data set in a way that best describes the data. Explain your choice of display.

a. ROAD KILL A group of schools in New England participated in a 2-month study and reported 3962 dead animals.

Birds 307   Mammals 2746
Amphibians 145   Reptiles 75
Unknown 689

b. BLACK BEAR ROAD KILL The data below show the number of black bears killed on Florida roads from 1987 to 2006.

1987	30	1994	47	2001	99
1988	37	1995	49	2002	129
1989	46	1996	61	2003	111
1990	33	1997	74	2004	127
1991	43	1998	88	2005	141
1992	35	1999	82	2006	135
1993	43	2000	109		

c. RACCOON ROAD KILL A 1-week study along a 4-mile section of road found the following weights (in pounds) of raccoons that had been killed by vehicles.

13.4	14.8	17.0	12.9
21.3	21.5	16.8	14.8
15.2	18.7	18.6	17.2
18.5	9.4	19.4	15.7
14.5	9.5	25.4	21.5
17.3	19.1	11.0	12.4
20.4	13.6	17.5	18.5
21.5	14.0	13.9	19.0

d. What do you think can be done to minimize the number of animals killed by vehicles?

Laurie's Notes

Introduction

For the Teacher

- **Goal:** Students will review data displays.
- An alternative to making the visual displays in Activity 1 is for students to describe their choices for each part without actually creating the display, or to have different groups of students working on one of the first three parts simultaneously. It is an instructional decision based upon length of class time, and if you want time for students to investigate Activity 2.

Motivate

- The theme for the first activity is road kill. While students may giggle at the thought, automobile accidents involving large animals can be serious. I had my first and only accident with a deer 5 years ago. I was 2 miles from home and I was traveling 40 miles per hour. The deer was killed, my daughter and I were not injured, and repairs to my car were about $1400.
- See the next page for some statistics on animal-vehicle accidents.
- Allow time for students to share personal stories.

Activity Notes

Discuss

- Discuss the data displays with which students are familiar: pictograph, bar graph, line graph, circle graph, stem-and-leaf plot, histogram, line plot, and scatter plot. Have students describe the feature(s) of each display.
- Discuss the different numerical tools they have for describing data: mean, median, mode, range, and outlier.

Activity 1

- The data given in parts (a) and (b) are actual data. The data for part (c) is fictional; however, it is based on the average weight of raccoons.
- Students need to decide what display makes sense for the type of data that they have. There may be more than one appropriate answer.
- Discuss students' choices and their explanations.
- Possible data displays:
  - Part (a): a circle graph (what part of the whole set is each animal) or a bar graph (compare the different categories, although there is a large difference in bar heights: 75 to 2746)
  - Part (b): a scatter plot and line of best fit (pair data, show trend over time, and make predictions for the future)
  - Part (c): a stem-and-leaf plot (spread of data), along with calculating the mean (about 16.7) and median (17.1)
  - Part (d): As a class, discuss students' ideas for minimizing the number of animals killed by vehicles.

Standards of Learning

8.13(a) The student will make comparisons, predictions, and inferences, using information displayed in graphs.

Previous Learning

Students should know how to construct a variety of data displays from this year and past years.

Start Thinking! and Warm Up

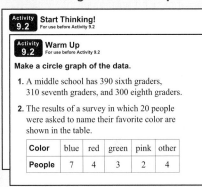

Activity 9.2 Start Thinking! For use before Activity 9.2

Activity 9.2 Warm Up For use before Activity 9.2

Make a circle graph of the data.

1. A middle school has 390 sixth graders, 310 seventh graders, and 300 eighth graders.

2. The results of a survey in which 20 people were asked to name their favorite color are shown in the table.

Color	blue	red	green	pink	other
People	7	4	3	2	4

9.2 Record and Practice Journal

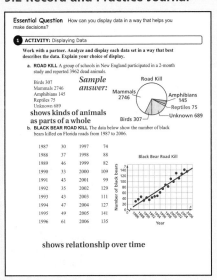

Essential Question How can you display data in a way that helps you make decisions?

1 ACTIVITY: Displaying Data

Work with a partner. Analyze and display each data set in a way that best describes the data. Explain your choice of display.

a. **ROAD KILL** A group of schools in New England participated in a 2-month study and reported 3962 dead animals.

Birds 307
Mammals 2746
Amphibians 145
Reptiles 75
Unknown 689

Sample answer:

Road Kill

shows kinds of animals as parts of a whole

b. **BLACK BEAR ROAD KILL** The data below show the number of black bears killed on Florida roads from 1987 to 2006.

1987	30	1997	74
1988	37	1998	88
1989	46	1999	82
1990	33	2000	109
1991	43	2001	99
1992	35	2002	129
1993	43	2003	111
1994	47	2004	127
1995	49	2005	141
1996	61	2006	135

shows relationship over time

Vocabulary

English learners may need help understanding the word *scale*. There are several meanings in the English language. Some of the common meanings are:

a series of musical notes,

the covering of a reptile,

a device for weighing,

a ratio,

to climb.

In bar graphs, the scale is a series of markings used for measuring. Most scales start at 0 and go to (at least) the greatest value of the data.

9.2 Record and Practice Journal

c. **RACCOON ROAD KILL** A 1-week study along a 4-mile section of road found the following weights (in pounds) of raccoons that had been killed by vehicles.

13.4	14.8	17.0	12.9	21.3	21.5	16.8	14.8
15.2	18.7	18.6	17.2	18.5	9.4	19.4	15.7
14.5	9.5	25.4	21.5	17.3	19.1	11.0	12.4
20.4	13.6	17.5	18.5	21.5	14.0	13.9	19.0

See Additional Answers.

d. What do you think can be done to minimize the number of animals killed by vehicles?

Check students' work.

2 **ACTIVITY: Statistics Project**

ENDANGERED SPECIES PROJECT Use the Internet or some other reference to write a report about an animal species that is (or has been) endangered. Include graphical displays of the data you have gathered.

Sample: Florida Key Deer In 1939, Florida banned the hunting of Key deer. The numbers of Key deer fell to about 100 in the 1940s.

About half of Key deer deaths are due to vehicles.

In 1947, public sentiment was stirred by 11-year-old Glenn Allen from Miami. Allen organized Boy Scouts and others in a letter-writing campaign that led to the establishment of the National Key Deer Refuge in 1957. The approximately 8600-acre refuge includes 2280 acres of designated wilderness.

One of two Key deer wildlife underpasses on Big Pine Key.

Key Deer Refuge has increased the population of Key deer. A recent study estimated the total Key deer population to be between 700 and 800.

Check students' work.

What Is Your Answer?

3. **IN YOUR OWN WORDS** How can you display data in a way that helps you make decisions? Use the Internet or some other reference to find examples of the following types of data displays.

- Bar graph
- Circle graph
- Stem-and-leaf plot
- Scatter plot

Data displays make it easy to interpret data and make conclusions.

Laurie's Notes

Activity 2

- Ask a volunteer to read the information presented about Key deer. Discuss how the actions of one person can often make a big difference.
- It is important that students be able to select the display based upon the data and the question you hope to answer from making the display.
- If you assign this project, students will need several days.

What Is Your Answer?

- It would be ideal if the library or computer room is available. If not, you or your students could bring in newspapers and magazines that contain graphical displays.
- The information gathered by students can be made into classroom posters.

Closure

- **Class Discussion:** Have students present their answers to Question 3. Then have students discuss features of each display, and what types of data lend itself to each data display.

Statistics on Animal-Vehicle Accidents

- Making the roads safer for humans and animals is a goal of many highway transportation agencies.
- You may wish to share additional road kill data.

4 million	miles of roads in the U.S.
226 million	number of vehicles registered in the U.S.
23 trillion	vehicle miles traveled in the U.S. in 2002
6.3 million	number of automobile accidents annually in the U.S.
253,000	number of animal-vehicle accidents annually
50	estimated percent of large animal-vehicle collisions that go unreported
90	percent of animal-vehicle collisions that involve deer
2000	average minimum cost (in dollars) for repairing a vehicle after a collision with a deer
200	number of human deaths annually resulting from vehicle-wildlife collisions
40	percent by which deer-vehicle collisions were reduced after installation of a deer crosswalk system in northeast Utah

Technology **F**or the **T**eacher

The Dynamic Planning Tool
Editable Teacher's Resources at *BigIdeasMath.com*

ACTIVITY: Statistics Project

ENDANGERED SPECIES PROJECT Use the Internet or some other reference to write a report about an animal species that is (or has been) endangered. Include graphical displays of the data you have gathered.

Sample: Florida Key Deer
In 1939, Florida banned the hunting of Key deer. The numbers of Key deer fell to about 100 in the 1940s.

In 1947, public sentiment was stirred by 11-year-old Glenn Allen from Miami. Allen organized Boy Scouts and others in a letter-writing campaign that led to the establishment of the National Key Deer Refuge in 1957. The approximately 8600-acre refuge includes 2280 acres of designated wilderness.

Key Deer Refuge has increased the population of Key deer. A recent study estimated the total Key deer population to be between 700 and 800.

About half of Key deer deaths are due to vehicles.

One of two Key deer wildlife underpasses on Big Pine Key

What Is Your Answer?

3. **IN YOUR OWN WORDS** How can you display data in a way that helps you make decisions? Use the Internet or some other reference to find examples of the following types of data displays.

- Bar graph
- Circle graph
- Stem-and-leaf plot
- Scatter plot

Practice ▶ Use what you learned about choosing data displays to complete Exercise 3 on page 413.

Key Idea

Data Display	What does it do?	
Pictograph	shows data using pictures	
Bar Graph	shows data in specific categories	
Circle Graph	shows data as parts of a whole	
Line Graph	shows how data change over time	
Histogram	shows frequencies of data values in intervals of the same size	
Stem-and-Leaf Plot	orders numerical data and shows how they are distributed	
Line Plot	shows the number of times each value occurs in a data set	
Scatter Plot	shows the relationship between two data sets using ordered pairs in a coordinate plane	

EXAMPLE 1 Choosing an Appropriate Data Display

Choose an appropriate data display for the situation. Explain your reasoning.

a. the number of students in a marching band each year

  ∴ A line graph shows change over time. So, a line graph is an appropriate data display.

b. comparison of people's shoe sizes and their heights

  ∴ You want to compare two different data sets. So, a scatter plot is an appropriate data display.

On Your Own

Now You're Ready
Exercises 4–7

Choose an appropriate data display for the situation. Explain your reasoning.

1. the population of the United States divided into age groups

2. the percents of students in your school who play basketball, football, soccer, or lacrosse

Laurie's Notes

Introduction

Connect
- **Yesterday:** Students reviewed data displays.
- **Today:** Students will choose and construct an appropriate data display.

Motivate
- Make a quick sketch of the two bar graphs shown and ask students to comment on each.

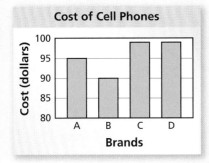

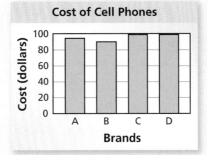

❓ "Who do you think printed the graph on the left and why?" company selling brand B; Appears to be a lot less expensive than the other brands.

Lesson Notes

Key Idea
- Write the Key Idea. This is a terrific summary of data displays that students have learned to make.
- Emphasize that *choosing an appropriate display* is more poetry than science. On the other hand, it is clearly possible to use any of the graphs in misleading ways. This is science.
- There may be examples of each of these displays around your room.

Example 1
- Read each problem. Students should not have difficulty determining the appropriate data display for each problem.

On Your Own
- **Think-Pair-Share:** Students should read each question independently and then work with a partner to answer the questions. When they have answered the questions, the pair should compare their answers with another group and discuss any discrepancies.

Goal Today's lesson is choosing and constructing an appropriate data display.

Start Thinking! and Warm Up

How are a bar graph and a histogram similar? How are they different?

How are a line graph and a line plot similar? How are they different?

Differentiated Instruction

Auditory

Ask students what data display would best represent the given data.
- the number of baseball cards each boy in the class has histogram or stem-and-leaf plot
- the number of hours studying for a test and the test scores of students in a class scatter plot

Extra Example 1

You conduct a survey at your school about insects that students fear the most. Choose an appropriate data display. Explain your reasoning.
Sample answers: Circle graph: shows data as parts of a whole; Bar graph: shows data in specific categories; Pictograph: shows data using pictures.

● On Your Own

1. *Sample answer:* histogram; Shows frequencies of ages (data values) in intervals of the same size.

2. *Sample answer:* bar graph; Shows data in specific categories.

Tell whether the data display is appropriate for representing the data in Example 2. Explain your reasoning.

a. pictograph yes; A pictograph would show the number of hits for each month using pictures.

b. scatter plot yes; A scatter plot would show the number of hits for each month, with the months numbered from 1 to 5.

On Your Own

3. no; A line plot would not show the number of hits for each month.

4. yes; A circle graph would show the fraction or percent of the total number of hits for each month.

5. no; A stem-and-leaf plot would not show the number of hits for each month.

English Language Learners

Vocabulary

Explain that a line graph and the graph of a line are *not* the same thing. A line graph is made up of line segments, each of which has endpoints. A line does not have endpoints.

Laurie's Notes

Example 2

- Write the data on the board and ask a volunteer to read the problem.

? "Looking at the data, how would you describe the change in website hits over the 5-month period?" increasing

- Remind students that they are looking for a data display that will show how the data changes during the 5 months.

? "How does the bar graph represent the change in the number of website hits?" by using different bar heights

? "Why are there only 3 bars in the histogram?" data have been grouped

? "What key information is lost in the histogram? Explain." time; You can no longer see the months.

? "How are the line graph and bar graph alike? Explain." They have the same shape. Connecting the midpoints of the tops of the bars creates a graph that looks like the line graph.

On Your Own

- Discussing the answers will provide a review of three additional data displays.

EXAMPLE 2 **Identifying an Appropriate Data Display**

You record the number of hits for your school's new website for 5 months. Tell whether the data display is appropriate for representing how the number of hits changed during the 5 months. Explain your reasoning.

Month	Hits
August	250
September	320
October	485
November	650
December	925

a.

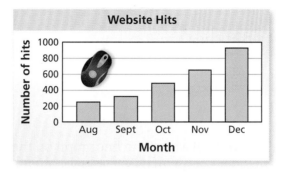

∴ The bar graph shows the number of hits for each month. So, it is an appropriate data display.

b.

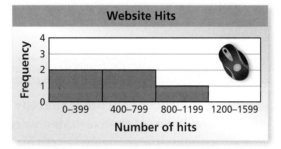

∴ The histogram does not show the number of hits for each month or how the number of hits changes over time. So, it is *not* an appropriate data display.

c.

∴ The line graph shows how the number of hits changes over time. So, it is an appropriate data display.

● **On Your Own**

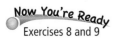
Now You're Ready
Exercises 8 and 9

Tell whether the data display is appropriate for representing the data in Example 2. Explain your reasoning.

3. line plot   4. circle graph   5. stem-and-leaf plot

EXAMPLE **3**   **Identifying a Misleading Data Display**

Which line graph is misleading? Explain.

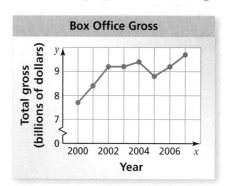

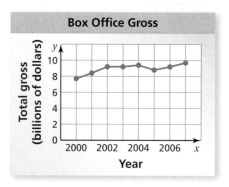

The vertical axis of the line graph on the left has a break ($\rightsquigarrow$) and begins at 7. This graph makes it appear that the total gross increased rapidly from 2000 to 2004. The graph on the right has an unbroken axis. It is more honest and shows that the total gross increased slowly.

∴ So, the graph on the left is misleading.

EXAMPLE **4**   **Analyzing a Misleading Data Display**

Food Drive Donation Totals

Canned food	
Boxed food	
Juice	

🥫 = 20 cans   🥣 = 20 boxes   🧃 = 20 bottles

A volunteer concludes that the number of cans of food and boxes of food donated were about the same. Is this conclusion accurate? Explain.

Each icon represents the same number of items. Because the box icon is larger than the can icon, it looks like the number of boxes is about the same as the number of cans, but the number of boxes is actually about half of the number of cans.

∴ So, the conclusion is not accurate.

● **On Your Own**

Now You're Ready
Exercises 11–14

Explain why the data display is misleading.

6.

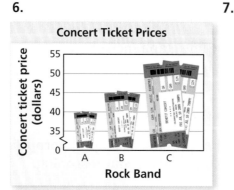

7.

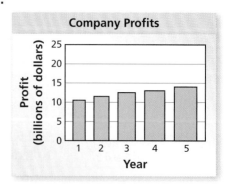

Laurie's Notes

Discuss

- Have a collection of misleading data displays. When you find a data display in the newspaper or magazine that is misleading, cut it out and save it for later use. Ask colleagues in your school to do the same.
- Often what makes a graph misleading is the scale selected for one, or both, of the axes. By spreading out or condensing the scale, the graph becomes misleading.
- Tell your students, the person who makes the data display influences how we will view it. They control the extent to which we can see, or not see, features of the data.

Example 3

- **?** "The same data is displayed in each line graph. How do the graphs differ?" The vertical scale is different.
- **?** "Which graph is misleading and why?" first graph; It makes it appear that there has been a rapid growth in box office gross.
- **Extension:** Have students pretend that both graphs appear in the newspaper with an article, and ask them what they would use for a headline for each article. What story does the author want readers to see when they look at each graph?

Example 4

- Have students "read" the pictograph and ask them to summarize what information it describes. Many students will conclude that the amount of cans and the amount of boxes is about the same due to the horizontal distance each set of icons takes up.
- **?** "Approximately how many cans of food and boxes of food have been donated?" 11 cans × 20 = 220 cans; 6 boxes × 20 = 120 boxes
- Almost twice as many cans of food have been donated as boxes, so this is misleading. The box icon is too large. It should be the same width as the can.

On Your Own

- **Think-Pair-Share:** Students should read each question independently and then work with a partner to answer the questions. When they have answered the questions, the pair should compare their answers with another group and discuss any discrepancies.

Closure

- **Exit Ticket:** Make a pictograph for the data in Example 4 that would not be misleading.

Extra Example 3

Which line graph is misleading? Explain.

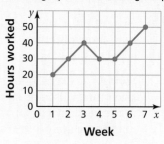

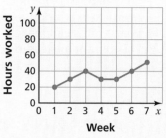

the second graph; The *y*-scale makes the change from week to week appear smaller.

Extra Example 4

Explain why the data display is misleading.

Favorite Pets

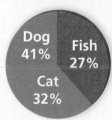

The size of each part of the circle is not proportional to the percent each choice represents.

On Your Own

6. The tickets vary in width and the break in the vertical axis makes the difference in ticket prices appear to be greater.

7. The bars become wider as the years progress, making the increase in profit appear greater.

1. yes; Different displays may show different aspects of the data.

2. *Sample answer:* Different sized intervals, a break in the vertical axis, an inappropriately large or small scale on the vertical axis, or different bar widths can make a histogram misleading.

Practice and Problem Solving

3. *Sample answer:*

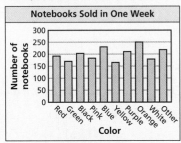

A bar graph shows the data in different color categories.

4. *Sample answer:* Stem-and-leaf plot; shows how data is distributed

5. *Sample answer:* Line graph; shows changes over time

6. *Sample answer:* Line plot; shows the number of times each outcome occurs

7. *Sample answer:* Line graph; shows changes over time

8. **a.** yes; The pictograph shows the number of hours worked each month using pictures.

   b. yes; The bar graph shows the number of hours worked each month.

Assignment Guide and Homework Check

Level	Day 1 Activity Assignment	Day 2 Lesson Assignment	Homework Check
Basic	3, 20–22	1, 2, 4–7, 9–15	4, 9, 10, 12
Average	3, 20–22	1, 2, 4–8, 10–14	4, 8, 10, 12
Advanced	3, 20–22	1, 2, 4–10, 12, 14–19	8, 10, 12, 16

Common Errors

- **Exercises 4–7** Students may confuse the names of some of the data displays. For example, they may say that a line plot should be used when they mean a line graph. Remind them to write an explanation about why they chose that data display. Students should refer to the Key Idea for the names and descriptions of data displays.

- **Exercises 8 and 9** Students may guess whether a given data display is appropriate. Encourage them to carefully read the problem, and then carefully think about whether the display is appropriate.

9.2 Record and Practice Journal

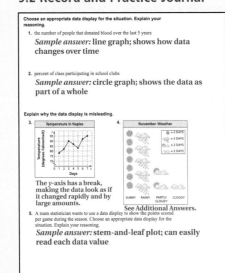

 Vocabulary and Concept Check

1. **REASONING** Can more than one display be appropriate for a data set? Explain.

2. **OPEN-ENDED** Describe how a histogram can be misleading.

 Practice and Problem Solving

3. Analyze and display the data in a way that best describes the data. Explain your choice of display.

Notebooks Sold in One Week				
192 red	170 green	203 black	183 pink	230 blue
165 yellow	210 purple	250 orange	179 white	218 other

Choose an appropriate data display for the situation. Explain your reasoning.

① 4. a student's test scores and how the scores are spread out

5. the distance a person drives each month

6. the outcome of rolling a number cube

7. number of homework problems assigned each day

② 8. The table shows how many hours you worked as a lifeguard from May to August. Tell whether the data display is appropriate for representing how the number of hours worked changed during the 4 months. Explain your reasoning.

Lifeguard Schedule	
Month	**Hours Worked**
May	40
June	80
July	160
August	120

a.

Key: = 20 hours

b.

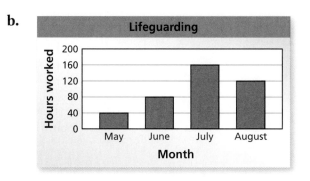

9. A survey asked 800 students to choose their favorite subject. The results are shown in the table. Tell whether the data display is appropriate for representing the portion of students who prefer math. Explain your reasoning.

Favorite School Subject	
Subject	**Number of Students**
Science	200
Math	160
Literature	240
Social Studies	120
Other	80

a.

Favorite School Subject

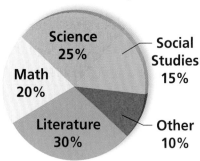

b.

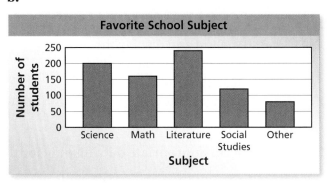

10. WRITING When should you use a histogram instead of a bar graph to display data? Use an example to support your answer.

Explain why the data display is misleading.

③ ④ **11.**

12.

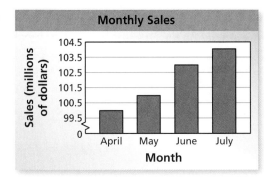

13.

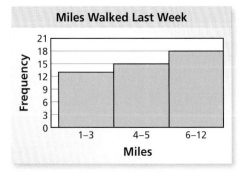

14.

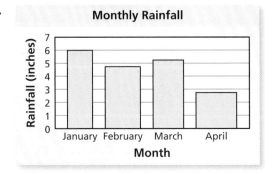

Common Errors

- **Exercises 11–14** Students may not be able to recognize why the data display is misleading. As a class, make a list of things to look for when analyzing a data display. For instance, students should check the increments or intervals for the axes, if applicable.

- **Exercise 17** Students may say that an appropriate data display for showing the mode is a stem-and-leaf plot, because the stem with the most leaves would be the mode. However, the stem with the most leaves may have data that is not part of the mode. Remind them that a line plot isolates each data value and shows the frequency of each individual number, so this would be a more appropriate data display.

Practice and Problem Solving

9. **a.** yes; The circle graph shows the data as parts of the whole.

   b. no; The bar graph shows the number of students, not the portion of students.

10. when the data is in terms of intervals of one category, as opposed to multiple categories; *Sample answer:* You can use a histogram to display the frequencies of voters in the last election by age group.

11. The pictures of the bikes are the largest on Monday and the smallest on Wednesday, which makes it seem like the distance is the same each day.

12. The break in the scale for the vertical axis makes it appear as though there is a greater difference in sales between months.

13. The intervals are not the same size.

14. The widths of the bars are different, so it looks like some months have more rainfall.

15. *Sample answer:* bar graph; Each bar can represent a different vegetable.

16. yes; The vertical axis has a scale that increases by powers of 10, which makes the data appear to have a linear relationship.

17. *Sample answer:* line plot

18. **a.** The percents do not sum to 100%.

    b. *Sample answer:* bar graph; It would show the frequency of each sport.

19. See *Taking Math Deeper.*

 Fair Game Review

20. $x + 3 = 5$

21. $8x = 24$

22. A

Mini-Assessment

Choose an appropriate data display for the situation. Explain your reasoning.

1. the outcome of flipping a coin
   Sample answers: pictograph, bar graph, or line plot; all show the number of times you get heads or tails.

2. comparison of student's test scores and how long students studied
   Sample answer: Scatter plot: you want to compare two data sets.

3. the number of students participating in after-school sports each year
   Sample answer: Line graph: shows how data change over time.

Taking Math Deeper

Exercise 19

This exercise introduces students to an amazing property of the number pi. Pi is an irrational number and therefore its decimal representation is not repeating. Even so, the ten digits from 0 to 9 each occur about 10 percent of the time, when one considers thousands of digits.

 ① Display the data in a bar graph.

a.

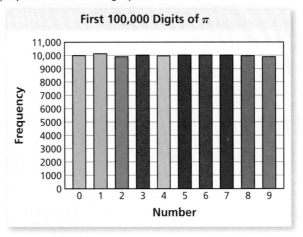

First 100,000 Digits of π

 ② Display the data in a circle graph.

b.

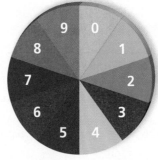

Bar and circle

③ **c. and d.** Compare the two displays.

Both graphs show that each digit occurs about 10% of the time. The bar graph has a slight advantage because it shows that some digits occur slightly more than others.

Reteaching and Enrichment Strategies

If students need help...	If students got it...
Resources by Chapter • Practice A and Practice B • Puzzle Time Record and Practice Journal Practice Differentiating the Lesson Lesson Tutorials Skills Review Handbook	Resources by Chapter • Enrichment and Extension Start the next section

15. **VEGETABLES** A nutritionist wants to use a data display to show the favorite vegetables of the students at a school. Choose an appropriate data display for the situation. Explain your reasoning.

16. **CHEMICALS** A scientist gathers data about a decaying chemical compound. The results are shown in the scatter plot. Is the data display misleading? Explain.

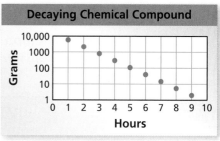

17. **REASONING** What type of data display is appropriate for showing the mode of a data set?

18. **SPORTS** A survey asked 100 students to choose their favorite sports. The results are shown in the circle graph.

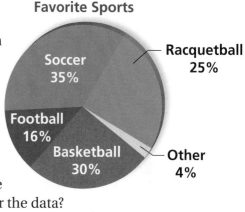

a. Explain why the graph is misleading.

b. What type of data display would be more appropriate for the data? Explain.

19. With the help of computers, mathematicians have computed and analyzed billions of digits of the irrational number π. One of the things they analyze is the frequency of each of the numbers 0 through 9. The table shows the frequency of each number in the first 100,000 digits of π.

a. Display the data in a bar graph.

b. Display the data in a circle graph.

c. Which data display is more appropriate? Explain.

d. Describe the distribution.

Number	0	1	2	3	4	5	6	7	8	9
Frequency	9999	10,137	9908	10,025	9971	10,026	10,029	10,025	9978	9902

Fair Game Review What you learned in previous grades & lessons

Write the sentence as an equation. *(Skills Review Handbook)*

20. A number plus 3 is 5.

21. 8 times a number is 24.

22. **MULTIPLE CHOICE** What is 20% of 25% of 400? *(Skills Review Handbook)*

Ⓐ 20　　　　Ⓑ 200　　　　Ⓒ 240　　　　Ⓓ 380

You can use an **information frame** to help you organize and remember concepts. Here is an example of an information frame for scatter plots.

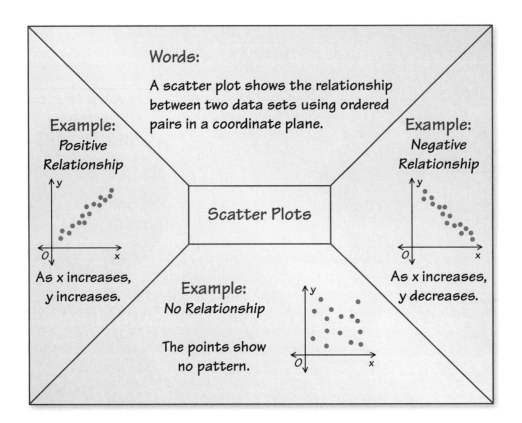

On Your Own

Make an information frame to help you study these topics.

1. lines of best fit

2. data displays

After you complete this chapter, make information frames for the following topics.

3. probability

4. independent events

5. dependent events

"Dear Teacher, I am emailing my information frame showing the characteristics of circles."

Sample Answers

1.

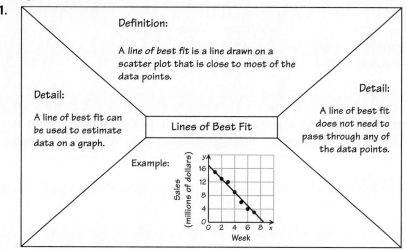

Definition:

A *line of best fit* is a line drawn on a scatter plot that is close to most of the data points.

Detail:

A line of best fit can be used to estimate data on a graph.

Detail:

A line of best fit does not need to pass through any of the data points.

Lines of Best Fit

Example:

2.

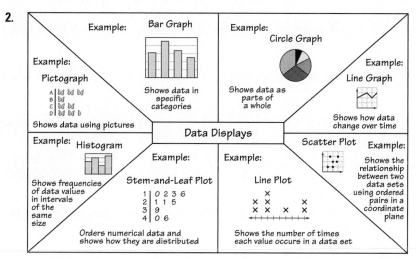

Example: Bar Graph

Shows data in specific categories

Example: Pictograph

Shows data using pictures

Example: Circle Graph

Shows data as parts of a whole

Example: Line Graph

Shows how data change over time

Data Displays

Example: Histogram

Shows frequencies of data values in intervals of the same size

Example: Stem-and-Leaf Plot

Orders numerical data and shows how they are distributed

Example: Line Plot

Shows the number of times each value occurs in a data set

Scatter Plot
Example:

Shows the relationship between two data sets using ordered pairs in a coordinate plane

About this Organizer

An **Information Frame** can be used to help students organize and remember concepts. Students write the topic in the middle rectangle. Then students write related concepts in the spaces around the rectangle. Related concepts can include *Words, Numbers, Algebra, Example, Non-Example, Formula, Symbols, Definition, Visual, Procedure, Details, Solution,* and *Vocabulary.* Students can place their information frames on note cards to use as a quick study reference.

Technology For the Teacher
Vocabulary Puzzle Builder

Answers

1. **a.** 2005   **b.** $120,000

   c. There is a negative relationship between year and amount donated.

2. negative relationship

3. no relationship

4. positive relationship

5. *Sample answer:* circle graph; shows data as parts of a whole

6. *Sample answer:* line graph; shows changes over time

7. yes; The break in the vertical axis makes it appear that the amount of money raised increased very rapidly from month to month.

8. See Additional Answers.

Assessment Book

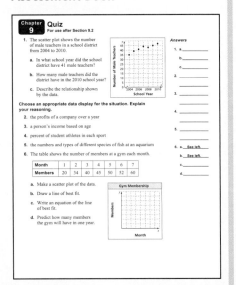

Alternative Quiz Ideas

100% Quiz	Math Log
Error Notebook	Notebook Quiz
Group Quiz	Partner Quiz
Homework Quiz	Pass the Paper

Group Quiz

Students work in groups. Give each group a large index card. Each group writes five questions that they feel evaluate the material they have been studying. On a separate piece of paper, students solve the problems. When they are finished, they exchange cards with another group. The new groups work through the questions on the card.

Reteaching and Enrichment Strategies

If students need help. . .	If students got it. . .
Resources by Chapter • Study Help • Practice A and Practice B • Puzzle Time Lesson Tutorials *BigIdeasMath.com* Practice Quiz Practice from the Test Generator	Resources by Chapter • Enrichment and Extension • School-to-Work Game Closet at *BigIdeasMath.com* Start the next section

Technology For the Teacher

Answer Presentation Tool
Big Ideas Test Generator

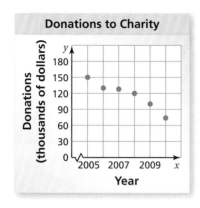

Donations to Charity

1. The scatter plot shows the amount of money donated to a charity from 2005 to 2010. *(Section 9.1)*

   a. In what year did the charity receive $150,000?

   b. How much did the charity receive in 2008?

   c. Describe the relationship shown by the data.

Tell whether the data show a *positive*, a *negative*, or *no* relationship. *(Section 9.1)*

2.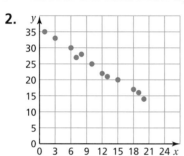

3.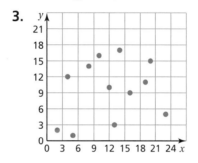

4.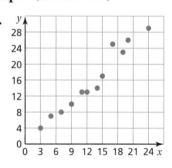

Choose an appropriate data display for the situation. Explain your reasoning. *(Section 9.2)*

5. percent of band students in each section

6. company's profit for each week

7. FUNDRAISER The graph shows the amount of money that the eighth-grade students at a school raised each month to pay for the class trip. Is the data display misleading? Explain. *(Section 9.2)*

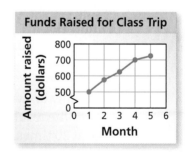

Funds Raised for Class Trip

8. CATS The table shows the number of cats adopted from an animal shelter each month. *(Section 9.1)*

   a. Make a scatter plot of the data.

   b. Draw a line of best fit.

   c. Write an equation of the line of best fit.

   d. Predict how many cats will be adopted in month 10.

Month	1	2	3	4	5	6	7	8	9
Cats	3	6	7	11	13	14	15	18	19

9.3 Probability

STANDARDS OF LEARNING
8.12

Essential Question How is probability used in the "mark-recapture" method?

1 ACTIVITY: The Mark-Recapture Method

Work with a partner. One method used by marine biologists to determine the number of whales in a population is the "mark-recapture" method. Using this method, whales are captured, marked, and released back into the environment. The population is estimated from the number of marked whales that are recaptured.

a. Fill a paper bag with several dozen packing peanuts. Don't count them. Your goal is to estimate the total number of peanuts in the bag.

b. Remove 20 peanuts from the bag and mark them with a colored marker. Put them back and shake the bag to mix the peanuts.

c. Randomly draw 1 peanut from the bag. Record the result and replace the peanut. Repeat 30 times.

d. From your results, estimate how many peanuts are in the bag. Explain your reasoning.

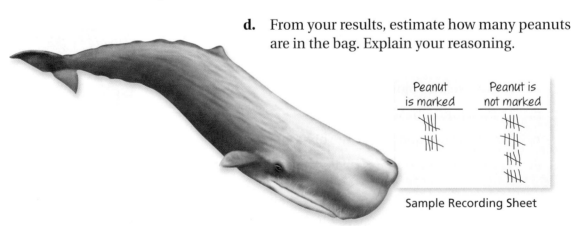

Peanut is marked	Peanut is not marked

Sample Recording Sheet

Laurie's Notes

Introduction

For the Teacher

- **Goal:** Students will develop an intuitive understanding of how a prediction can be made through experimentation.

Motivate

- Tell students that you considered being a marine biologist before deciding to be a mathematics teacher!
- **?** "What does a marine biologist do?"
- Share information about the two types of whales shown in Activity 1. A blue whale grows up to about 100 feet and is the largest animal ever known to have existed. A sperm whale grows up to about 60 feet and has the largest brain of any animal known to have existed.

Activity Notes

Activity 1

- It is important to understand how the mark-recapture method is used to estimate the size of a population. Researchers set traps to capture samples of a population. Captured animals are marked and then released. After a certain amount of time, another sample is trapped, which includes both marked and unmarked animals. This information is used to estimate the size of the entire population.
- **Example:** You capture and mark 10 animals, then release them back into the population. Next month you capture 20 animals, 5 of which are marked.

  To determine the number x of animals in the population, solve the proportion $\frac{5}{20} = \frac{10}{x}$. The mark-recapture method estimates that there are 40 animals in the total population.
- **Management Tip:** Fill paper bags with foam peanuts before class. The bags do not have to have the same number of peanuts. If foam peanuts are not available, you could use blank tiles or cubes.
- Record results from different groups on the board. Each group should explain how they estimated the number of peanuts in their bag.

Standards of Learning

8.12 The student will determine the probability of independent and dependent events with and without replacement.

Previous Learning

Students should know how to solve proportions.

Activity Materials
Textbook
• paper bags
• foam peanuts

Start Thinking! and Warm Up

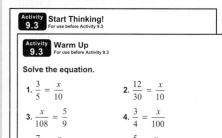

Activity 9.3 Start Thinking! For use before Activity 9.3

Activity 9.3 Warm Up For use before Activity 9.3

Solve the equation.

1. $\frac{3}{5} = \frac{x}{10}$　　　2. $\frac{12}{30} = \frac{x}{10}$

3. $\frac{x}{108} = \frac{5}{9}$　　　4. $\frac{3}{4} = \frac{x}{100}$

5. $\frac{7}{9} = \frac{x}{45}$　　　6. $\frac{5}{8} = \frac{x}{16}$

9.3 Record and Practice Journal

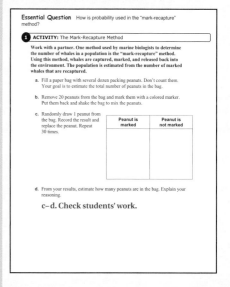

Essential Question How is probability used in the "mark-recapture" method?

1 ACTIVITY: The Mark-Recapture Method

Work with a partner. One method used by marine biologists to determine the number of whales in a population is the "mark-recapture" method. Using this method, whales are captured, marked, and released back into the environment. The population is estimated from the number of marked whales that are recaptured.

a. Fill a paper bag with several dozen packing peanuts. Don't count them. Your goal is to estimate the total number of peanuts in the bag.

b. Remove 20 peanuts from the bag and mark them with a colored marker. Put them back and shake the bag to mix the peanuts.

c. Randomly draw 1 peanut from the bag. Record the result and replace the peanut. Repeat 30 times.

Peanut is marked	Peanut is not marked

d. From your results, estimate how many peanuts are in the bag. Explain your reasoning.

c–d. Check students' work.

English Language Learners

Vocabulary

This section and the next contain new terms that may cause English learners to struggle. Students should write the key vocabulary in their notebooks along with definitions and formulas so that they become familiar and comfortable with the vocabulary.

9.3 Record and Practice Journal

② ACTIVITY: The Mark-Recapture Method

Work with a partner. Estimate each wildlife population.

	Number Marked	Number Sampled	Number of Marked Animals in Sample
a. Large mouth bass in a lake	120	500	30
b. Lynx in a national park	40	120	20
c. Snowshoe hare in a national park	150	250	25
d. Gray squirrels in a national park	255	175	5

a. 2000 bass

b. 240 lynx

c. 1500 hare

d. 8925 squirrels

What Is Your Answer?

3. IN YOUR OWN WORDS How is probability used in the "mark-recapture" method?

The experimental probability of the number of marked animals in a sample helps to determine the population.

4. BIG IDEAS SCIENCE Use the Internet or some other reference to write a report about a wildlife population that has been estimated using the "mark-recapture" method.

Check students' work.

Activity 2

? "Can you tell what percent of the sample was marked? Explain." yes; Compare the number of marked animals in the sample to the number of animals sampled.

- If students are having difficulty getting started, suggest that they focus on just part (a) to begin. The fraction of marked bass in the sample was $\frac{30}{500} = \frac{3}{50}$. Now consider the number of bass that were marked in the beginning.

- The proportion that can be used to estimate the population P for each animal is

$$\frac{\text{\# of marked animals in sample}}{\text{\# of animals sampled}} = \frac{\text{\# of animals marked}}{P}.$$

- Have different groups present their estimates for each wildlife population.

- **FYI:** The lynx and the snowshoe hare have a "predator-prey" relationship. The hare is the primary food source for the lynx. As the lynx population increases, the hare population decreases. With the decline in their food source, the lynx population decreases. With the decline in the number of predators, the hare population increases. With a more abundant food source, the lynx population increases and the cycle repeats.

What Is Your Answer?

- Talk with your science colleagues about possible co-curricular opportunities for the suggested research.

Closure

- You call a friend who was absent today. Explain how the "mark-recapture" method is used to estimate wildlife populations.

Technology For the Teacher

Dynamic Classroom

The Dynamic Planning Tool
Editable Teacher's Resources at *BigIdeasMath.com*

ACTIVITY: The Mark-Recapture Method

Work with a partner. Estimate each wildlife population.

	Number Marked	Number Sampled	Number of Marked Animals in Sample
a. Large mouth bass in a lake	120	500	30
b. Lynx in a national park	40	120	20
c. Snowshoe hare in a national park	150	250	25
d. Gray squirrels in a national park	255	175	5

What Is Your Answer?

3. **IN YOUR OWN WORDS** How is probability used in the "mark-recapture" method?

4. **BIG IDEAS SCIENCE** Use the Internet or some other reference to write a report about a wildlife population that has been estimated using the "mark-recapture" method.

Practice

Use what you learned about the "mark-recapture" method to complete Exercises 4–6 on page 423.

Check It Out
Lesson Tutorials
BigIdeasMath⊘com

Key Vocabulary ◀))
theoretical probability,
   p. 420
experimental
   probability, *p. 421*

 **Key Idea**

Theoretical Probability

When all possible outcomes are equally likely, the **theoretical probability** of an event is the ratio of the number of favorable outcomes to the number of possible outcomes. The probability of an event is written as P(event).

$$P(\text{event}) = \frac{\text{number of favorable outcomes}}{\text{number of possible outcomes}}$$

EXAMPLE ① **Finding a Theoretical Probability**

You randomly choose one of the SCRABBLE tiles shown. What is the theoretical probability of choosing a tile worth more than 1 point?

$$P(\text{event}) = \frac{\text{number of favorable outcomes}}{\text{number of possible outcomes}}$$

$$P(\text{more than 1 point}) = \frac{2}{6} = \frac{1}{3}$$

There are 2 tiles worth more than 1 point.

There is a total of 6 tiles.

∴ The probability of choosing a tile worth more than 1 point is $\frac{1}{3}$, or about 33%.

EXAMPLE ② **Using a Theoretical Probability**

There are 100 tiles in a bag. The theoretical probability of randomly drawing an E from the bag is $\frac{3}{25}$. How many E's are in the bag?

$$P(\text{E}) = \frac{\text{number of E's}}{\text{total number of tiles}}$$

$$\frac{3}{25} = \frac{n}{100} \qquad \text{Substitute. Let } n \text{ be the number of E's.}$$

$$12 = n \qquad \text{Multiply each side by 100.}$$

∴ There are 12 E's in the bag.

◀) Multi-Language Glossary at BigIdeasMath⊘com.

Laurie's Notes

Introduction

Connect

- **Yesterday:** Students developed an understanding of how proportions can be used to estimate wildlife populations.
- **Today:** Students will compute probabilities of events.

Motivate

- Play *Mystery Bag*. Before students arrive, place 20 cubes of the same shape and size in a paper bag; ten of one color and ten of a second color.
- Ask a volunteer to be the detective.
- ❓ "There are 20 cubes in my bag. Can you guess what color they are?" not likely
- Let the student remove a cube and look at its color.
- ❓ "Can you guess what color my cubes are?" not likely
- *Replace the cube*. Let the student pick again and see the color. Repeat your question.
- Try this 5–8 times until the student is ready to guess. The number of trials will depend upon the results and the student. You want students to see that they are collecting data and making a prediction.

Lesson Notes

Key Idea

- Write the Key Idea on the board.
- Discuss theoretical probability and give several examples with which students would be familiar, such as cards, number cubes, or marbles in a bag. Stress that the outcomes must be equally likely.

Example 1

- Work through the example.
- ❓ "What is the probability of *not* choosing a tile worth more than 1 point?" $\frac{4}{6} = \frac{2}{3}$

Example 2

- Read the problem and ask a few questions to help students understand.
- ❓ "What does a theoretical probability of $\frac{3}{25}$ mean?" Listen for students to suggest that for every 25 tiles, 3 of them are E's.
- ❓ "What proportion can be used to solve the problem?" $\frac{3}{25} = \frac{n}{100}$
- ❓ "What property is used to solve for *n*?" Multiplication Property of Equality
- **Connection:** Think of equivalent fractions: $\frac{3}{25} = \frac{12}{100}$.
- ❓ "How many tiles are *not* E's?" 88

Goal Today's lesson is finding theoretical and experimental probabilities.

Lesson Materials	
Introduction	**Closure**
• bag	• bag
• colored cubes	• colored cubes

Start Thinking! and Warm Up

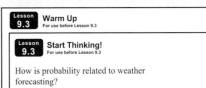

Lesson 9.3 Warm Up
For use before Lesson 9.3

Lesson 9.3 Start Thinking!
For use before Lesson 9.3

How is probability related to weather forecasting?

Describe some other instances in which you have come across probability in your daily life.

Extra Example 1

In Example 1, what is the theoretical probability of choosing a tile worth 5 points? $\frac{1}{6}$, or about 16.7%

Extra Example 2

There are 20 names in a hat. The theoretical probability of randomly drawing a name that starts with an A is 15%. How many names in the hat start with an A? 3

Differentiated Instruction

Below Level

Use Example 1 to review impossible events (choosing an X), unlikely events (choosing a Z), equally likely events (choosing a consonant), likely events (choosing a tile worth 1 point), and certain events (choosing a tile worth at least 1 point).

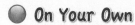

On Your Own

1. $\frac{1}{2}$, or 50%

2. 8

Extra Example 3

The bar graph shows the results of rolling a number cube 30 times. What is the experimental probability of rolling an odd number?

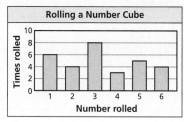

$\frac{19}{30}$, or about 63.3%

On Your Own

3. $\frac{7}{40}$, or 17.5%

Laurie's Notes

On Your Own

- **Think-Pair-Share:** Students should read each question independently and then work with a partner to answer the questions. When they have answered the questions, the pair should compare their answers with another group and discuss any discrepancies.

Key Idea

- Discuss experimental probability and give several examples, such as the "mark-recapture" procedure used in yesterday's activity.

? "How are theoretical probability and experimental probability different?" Listen for an understanding that theoretical is what *should* happen and experimental is what *does* happen in an experiment.

Example 3

? "If the number of spins had not been given in the first sentence, could you still answer the question? Explain." yes; You can add the number of spins for each color in the bar graph: $11 + 7 + 14 + 8 = 40$ spins.

- Work through the example.

? "Explain how you know $\frac{8}{40}$ is 20%." Listen for any number of correct answers. One could be $\frac{8}{40} = \frac{1}{5} = 0.2 = 20\%$.

? "What is the probability of *not* spinning green?" $\frac{32}{40}$, or 80%

On Your Own

Now You're Ready
Exercises 7–18

1. **WHAT IF?** In Example 1, what is the theoretical probability of choosing a consonant?

2. **WHAT IF?** In Example 2, the theoretical probability of randomly drawing an O is $\frac{2}{25}$. How many O's are in the bag?

Key Idea

Experimental Probability

Probability that is based on repeated trials of an experiment is called **experimental probability**.

$$P(\text{event}) = \frac{\text{number of times the event occurs}}{\text{total number of trials}}$$

EXAMPLE ③ **Finding an Experimental Probability**

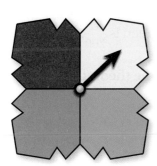

The bar graph shows the results of spinning the spinner 40 times. What is the experimental probability of spinning green?

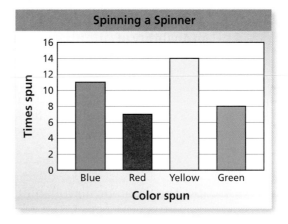

$$P(\text{event}) = \frac{\text{number of times the event occurs}}{\text{total number of trials}}$$

Green was spun 8 times.

$$P(\text{green}) = \frac{8}{40} = \frac{1}{5}$$

There was a total of 40 spins.

The experimental probability of spinning green is $\frac{1}{5}$, or 20%.

On Your Own

Now You're Ready
Exercises 21–24

3. What is the experimental probability of spinning red?

EXAMPLE 4 **Comparing Theoretical and Experimental Probabilities**

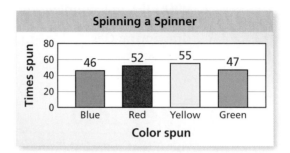

The bar graph shows the results of spinning the spinner 200 times.

Spinning a Spinner

Color spun	Times spun
Blue	46
Red	52
Yellow	55
Green	47

a. What is the experimental probability of spinning green?

$$P(\text{event}) = \frac{\text{number of times the event occurs}}{\text{total number of trials}}$$

$$P(\text{green}) = \frac{47}{200}$$
  ← Green was spun 47 times.
  ← There was a total of 200 spins.

∴ The experimental probability of spinning green is $\frac{47}{200}$, or 23.5%.

b. How does the result of part (a) compare with the theoretical probability of spinning green?

$$P(\text{event}) = \frac{\text{number of favorable outcomes}}{\text{number of possible outcomes}}$$

$$P(\text{green}) = \frac{1}{4}$$
  ← There is 1 green section.
  ← There is a total of 4 sections.

∴ The theoretical probability of spinning green is $\frac{1}{4}$, or 25%.

The experimental probability is close to the theoretical probability.

c. Compare the experimental probabilities in Example 3 and Example 4 part (a).

∴ As the number of trials increased, the experimental probability increased from 20% to 23.5%. So, it became closer to the theoretical probability of 25%.

● **On Your Own**

4. What is the experimental probability of spinning red? How does this compare with the theoretical probability of spinning red?

Laurie's Notes

Example 4

- Work through the example.
- **Representation:** Have students gather data by spinning a 4-section spinner 200 times or, if available, run a computer simulation.
- **?** "Compare the experimental and theoretical probabilities." Listen for the fact that they are close to each other.
- Discuss with students that the greater the number of trials used to compute an experimental probability, the closer that probability will be to the theoretical probability.

On Your Own

- **Neighbor Check:** Have students work independently and then have their neighbor check their work. Have students discuss any discrepancies.

Closure

- Use the colored cubes in the Mystery Bag. Reveal the contents, or use a different color ratio if you wish.
- **?** "If the contents of the Mystery Bag came from a bag of 1000 colored cubes, how many of each color would you predict is in the bag of 1000?" Answers will vary depending upon materials.

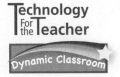
Extra Example 4

The bar graph shows the results of rolling a number cube 300 times.

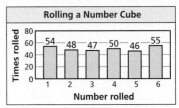

a. What is the experimental probability of rolling an odd number? $\frac{147}{300}$, or 49%

b. How does the result of part (a) compare with the theoretical probability of rolling an odd number? It is close to the theoretical probability of 50%.

c. Compare the experimental probabilities in Extra Example 3 and Extra Example 4 part (a). As the number of trials increased, the experimental probability decreased from about 63.3% to 49%. So, it became closer to the theoretical probability of 50%.

On Your Own

4. $\frac{13}{50}$, or 26%; It is close to the theoretical probability of 25%.

1. Perform an experiment several times. Count how often the event occurs and divide by the number of trials.

2. *Sample answer:* flipping heads on a coin

3. Experimental probability is based on actual results of an experiment, so it will not always equal the theoretical probability.

Practice and Problem Solving

4. 1000   5. 1950

6. 8700

7. $\frac{1}{6}$, or about 16.7%

8. $\frac{1}{2}$, or 50%

9. $\frac{1}{3}$, or about 33.3%

10. $\frac{1}{2}$, or 50%

11. 0, or 0%

12. $\frac{5}{6}$, or about 83.3%

13. 30   14. 20

15. 24   16. 10

17. 0   18. 36

19. $\frac{1}{6}$, or about 16.7%

20. $\frac{2}{5}$, or 40%; $\frac{1}{2}$, or 50%

Assignment Guide and Homework Check

Level	Day 1 Activity Assignment	Day 2 Lesson Assignment	Homework Check
Basic	4–6, 37–40	1–3, 7–15 odd, 19–25 odd, 29, 32	7, 15, 19, 21, 25, 29, 32
Average	4–6, 37–40	1–3, 10–20 even, 21–31 odd, 32, 34, 35	10, 16, 20, 23, 25, 29, 34
Advanced	4–6, 37–40	1–3, 10, 12, 16–24 even, 25–31 odd, 32–36	12, 18, 24, 25, 27, 31, 33, 35

Common Errors

- **Exercises 7–12** Students may write a different probability than what is asked, or count favorable outcomes incorrectly. For instance, they may include 1 in a list of prime numbers. The prime numbers on a number cube are 2, 3, and 5.

9.3 Record and Practice Journal

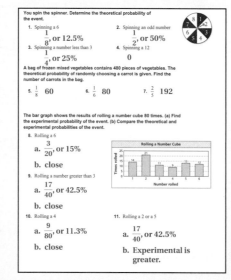

Check It Out
Help with Homework
BigIdeasMath ✓com

✓ Vocabulary and Concept Check

1. **VOCABULARY** Describe how to find the experimental probability of an event.

2. **OPEN-ENDED** Describe an event that has a theoretical probability of 0.5.

3. **WRITING** Explain why the theoretical probability and the experimental probability of the same event are *not* always equal.

 ## Practice and Problem Solving

Estimate the wildlife population.

	Number Marked	Number Sampled	Number of Marked Animals in Sample
4.	50	200	10
5.	75	650	25
6.	180	725	15

You roll a number cube. Determine the theoretical probability of the event.

7. Rolling a 2

8. Rolling an odd number

9. Rolling a multiple of 3

10. Rolling a prime number

11. Rolling an 8

12. Rolling a number less than 6

A bag contains 120 marbles. The theoretical probability of randomly drawing a blue marble is given. Find the number of blue marbles in the bag.

13. $\frac{1}{4}$

14. $\frac{1}{6}$

15. $\frac{1}{5}$

16. $\frac{1}{12}$

17. 0

18. $\frac{3}{10}$

19. **VENDING MACHINE** You randomly choose a button on the vending machine. What is the theoretical probability of choosing water?

20. **GUESS 1 TO 10** Your friend is holding up fingers behind his back. What is the theoretical probability that the number of fingers is even if he is using one hand? both hands?

The bar graph shows the results of spinning the spinner 40 times. Find the experimental probability of the event.

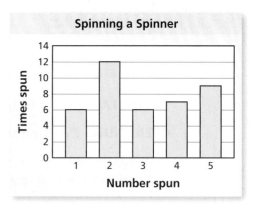

Spinning a Spinner

③ **21.** Spinning a 4

22. Spinning a 3

23. Spinning a number greater than 4

24. Spinning a 1 or a 2

25. ERROR ANALYSIS Describe and correct the error in finding $P(2)$ using the bar graph shown above.

✗ $\quad P(2) = \dfrac{\text{number of times the event occurs}}{\text{total number of trials}} = \dfrac{12}{28} = \dfrac{3}{7}$

26. DONATIONS You randomly remove 10 bills from a donation box. Eight of them are \$1 bills. How many of the next 25 bills can you expect to be \$1 bills?

27. MUSIC You have 80 songs on your MP3 player. Seven of the last 16 songs played were pop songs. How many of the 80 songs can you expect to be pop songs?

The bar graph shows the results of spinning the spinner 200 times. Compare the theoretical and experimental probabilities of the event.

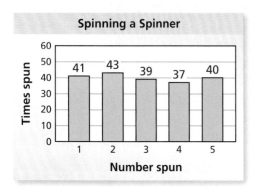

Spinning a Spinner

④ **28.** Spinning a 4

29. Spinning a 3

30. Spinning a number greater than 4

31. You spin the spinner 10,000 times. How many 3's can you expect to spin?

32. The table shows the results of flipping 2 coins 12 times each.

HH	HT	TH	TT
2	6	3	1

   a. What is the experimental probability of flipping two tails?

   b. Using your answer to part (a), how many times can you expect to flip two tails in 600 trials?

   c. Use a tree diagram to find the theoretical probability of flipping two tails.

   d. Using your answer to part (c), how many times can you expect to flip two tails in 600 trials?

   e. Why is it important to use a large number of trials when using experimental probability to predict results?

Common Errors

- **Exercises 28–30** Students may try to use information given for the experimental probability when finding the theoretical probability. Remind them that the theoretical probability does not use information from the experiment.

21. $\frac{7}{40}$, or 17.5%

22. $\frac{3}{20}$, or 15%

23. $\frac{9}{40}$, or 22.5%

24. $\frac{9}{20}$, or 45%

25. The total number of trials, 40, should be in the denominator, not 28.

$$P(2) = \frac{12}{40} = \frac{3}{10}$$

26. 20   **27.** 35

28. theoretical: $\frac{1}{5}$, or 20%;

experimental: $\frac{37}{200}$, or 18.5%;

The experimental probability is close to the theoretical probability.

29. theoretical: $\frac{1}{5}$, or 20%;

experimental: $\frac{39}{200}$, or 19.5%;

The experimental probability is close to the theoretical probability.

30. theoretical: $\frac{1}{5}$, or 20%;

experimental: $\frac{1}{5}$, or 20%;

The probabilities are equal.

31. 2000

32. **a.** $\frac{1}{12}$, or about 8.3%

b. 50 times

c. $\frac{1}{4}$, or 25%

d. 150 times

e. A larger number of trials should result in a more accurate probability, which gives a more accurate prediction.

Practice and Problem Solving

33. a. $\frac{5}{8}$, or 62.5%

   b. 15

34. experimental probability; The population is too large to survey every person, so a sample will be used to predict the outcome.

35. See *Taking Math Deeper*.

36. The theoretical probability increases from $\frac{1}{3} \approx 33.3\%$ to $\frac{2}{5} = 40\%$.

Fair Game Review

37. 26 m   **38.** 46 ft

39. about 46.84 in.

40. B

Mini-Assessment

A bag contains 7 red marbles, 6 white marbles, and 3 blue marbles. Find the theoretical probability of the event.

1. drawing a blue marble

   $\frac{3}{16}$, or 18.75%

2. drawing a white marble

   $\frac{3}{8}$, or 37.5%

You draw a marble 20 times from the bag in Exercises 1 and 2 and record the results. Use the table to find the experimental probability of the event.

Outcome	red	white	blue
Frequency	8	8	4

3. drawing a blue marble

   $\frac{1}{5}$, or 20%

4. drawing a white marble

   $\frac{2}{5}$, or 40%

Taking Math Deeper

Exercise 35

The easiest way to answer the questions is to rewrite the table showing all 102 cards.

Card Rank	Red	Brown	Purple	Yellow	Black
0	1	1	1	1	1
1	2	2	2	2	1
2	2	2	2	2	1
3	2	2	2	2	1
4	2	2	2	2	1
5	2	2	2	2	1
6	2	2	2	2	1
7	2	2	2	2	1
8	2	2	2	2	1
9	2	2	2	2	1
Joker	1	1	1	1	0
Wild	2	2	2	2	4
Totals	22	22	22	22	14

 a. There are 22 yellow cards in the deck.

 b. Of the 6 cards dealt, the magician dealt 2 yellow cards. So, the experimental probability of dealing a yellow card is $\frac{2}{6} = \frac{1}{3}$, or about 33.3%.

The theoretical probability of dealing a yellow card is $\frac{22}{102} = \frac{11}{51}$, or about 21.6%.

 c. After the 6 cards are dealt, the deck has more brown cards than any other color. So, a brown card is most likely to be dealt next.

Reteaching and Enrichment Strategies

If students need help...	If students got it...
Resources by Chapter • Practice A and Practice B • Puzzle Time Record and Practice Journal Practice Differentiating the Lesson Lesson Tutorials Skills Review Handbook	Resources by Chapter • Enrichment and Extension • School-to-Work Start the next section

33. FISHING You go on a fishing trip. The ratio of the number of bass you catch to the number of other fish you catch is 5 : 3.

    a. What is the experimental probability that you catch a bass?

    b. How many of the next 24 fish you catch can you expect to be bass?

34. REASONING A pollster surveys randomly selected individuals about an upcoming election. Do you think the pollster will use experimental probability or theoretical probability to make predictions? Explain.

35. MAGICIAN There are 102 cards in a magician's deck. The table shows the distribution of the cards among the colors.

Card Rank	Red	Brown	Purple	Yellow	Black
0	1	1	1	1	1
1, 2, 3, 4, 5, 6, 7, 8, 9	2	2	2	2	1
Joker	1	1	1	1	0
Wild	2	2	2	2	4

    a. How many yellow cards are in the deck?

    b. The magician deals the cards shown. What is the experimental probability of dealing a yellow card? What is the theoretical probability of dealing a yellow card?

    c. What color is most likely to be dealt next? Explain.

36. **Critical Thinking** Describe how the theoretical probability of randomly choosing a red apple changes when a green apple is removed from the plate.

 Fair Game Review What you learned in previous grades & lessons

Find the perimeter of the figure. *(Section 5.6)*

37.

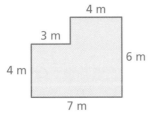

38.

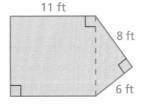

39.

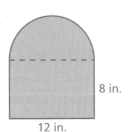

40. MULTIPLE CHOICE What is the surface area of the cone? *(Section 6.5)*

    (A) $14\pi \, cm^2$ **(B)** $18\pi \, cm^2$

    (C) $28\pi \, cm^2$ **(D)** $44\pi \, cm^2$

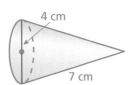

STANDARDS OF LEARNING

8.12

Essential Question How can you use probability to help you win a game show?

1 ACTIVITY: Analyzing a Game

Work with a partner. You are a contestant on a television game show. You are asked to pick one of three doors. Behind two of the doors are goats. Behind the other door is a luxury car.

Use three cards to simulate this game. One student acts as the host. The other acts as the contestant. The host mixes up the cards and lays them face down. The contestant chooses a card and wins the prize on the card.

Play the game 30 times as the host and 30 times as the contestant. Record your results.

Write a summary of your results. Include a discussion of experimental probability and theoretical probability.

Laurie's Notes

Introduction

For the Teacher

- **Goal:** Students will explore the difference between independent and dependent events.
- Activity 2 is known as "The Monty Hall Problem." This famous problem is fun to explore because it is counter-intuitive.
- Video explanations and computer simulations of the problem can be found on the Internet. You can show these to students after they have completed Activity 2.
- The experimentation today helps students realize that their intuitions cannot always be trusted when finding probabilities.

Motivate

- Greet students today as if you are a game show host. Welcome them and ask if they are ready to win fabulous prizes.
- ❓ "Who wants to be the first contestant?" Hopefully everyone wants to participate, but select just one student.
- Tell students that before they came to class today, you placed a treat (a piece of candy or a cookie) under one of the three cups. Have the contestant point to one of the cups. Do not reveal what is under it. Instead, reveal one of the two remaining cups that you know has nothing under it.
- ❓ "Do you want to switch?" Answers will vary.
- Instead of finishing this game, have students work through the activities. Return to the game at the end of class.

Activity Notes

Activity 1

- Before class, cut enough index cards in half so that each pair of students has 3 cards. Be sure that they are the same size and that there is no way to tell what is written on them by looking at the blank side.
- Distribute the cards. Have students write a prize name on one side of each card.
- Read through the directions and make sure students understand. Students need to collect data for this activity.
- Gather data from the class after everyone plays the game 60 times.
- Experimental probabilities should be about $\frac{1}{3}$ for picking the car and about $\frac{2}{3}$ for picking a goat.

Standards of Learning

8.12 The student will determine the probability of independent and dependent events with and without replacement.

Previous Learning

Students should know how to find theoretical and experimental probabilities.

Activity Materials	
Introduction	**Textbook**
• 3 paper cups • piece of candy or a cookie	• index cards

Start Thinking! and Warm Up

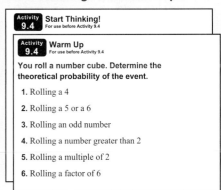

Activity 9.4 Start Thinking!
For use before Activity 9.4

Activity 9.4 Warm Up
For use before Activity 9.4

You roll a number cube. Determine the theoretical probability of the event.

1. Rolling a 4
2. Rolling a 5 or a 6
3. Rolling an odd number
4. Rolling a number greater than 2
5. Rolling a multiple of 2
6. Rolling a factor of 6

9.4 Record and Practice Journal

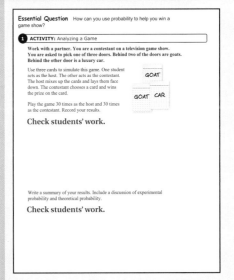

Essential Question How can you use probability to help you win a game show?

1 ACTIVITY: Analyzing a Game

Work with a partner. You are a contestant on a television game show. You are asked to pick one of three doors. Behind two of the doors are goats. Behind the other door is a luxury car.

Use three cards to simulate this game. One student acts as the host. The other acts as the contestant. The host mixes up the cards and lays them face down. The contestant chooses a card and wins the prize on the card.

Play the game 30 times as the host and 30 times as the contestant. Record your results.

Check students' work.

Write a summary of your results. Include a discussion of experimental probability and theoretical probability.

Check students' work.

English Language Learners

Visual

English learners are better able to understand verbal and written instruction if it is accompanied by visual clues, such as models, as much as possible.

9.4 Record and Practice Journal

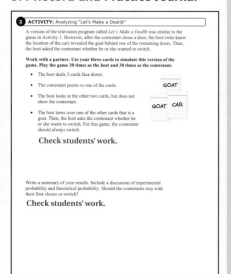

2 ACTIVITY: Analyzing "Let's Make a Deal®"

A version of the television program called *Let's Make a Deal®* was similar to the game in Activity 1. However, after the contestant chose a door, the host (who knew the location of the car) revealed the goat behind one of the remaining doors. Then, the host asked the contestant whether he or she wanted to switch.

Work with a partner. Use your three cards to simulate this version of the game. Play the game 30 times as the host and 30 times as the contestant.

- The host deals 3 cards face down.
- The contestant points to one of the cards.
- The host looks at the other two cards, but does not show the contestant.
- The host turns over one of the other cards that is a goat. Then, the host asks the contestant whether he or she wants to switch. For this game, the contestant should always switch.

Check students' work.

Write a summary of your results. Include a discussion of experimental probability and theoretical probability. Should the contestants stay with their first choice or switch?

Check students' work.

What Is Your Answer?

3. IN YOUR OWN WORDS How can you use probability to help you win a game show?

Probability helps you make decisions that will increase your chances of winning.

4. CONCLUSION Compare your results from Activities 1 and 2. In which activity did the contestant win more? Explain your reasoning.

Sample answer: **The contestant won more in Activity 2 because the probability of choosing the correct door increased.**

Laurie's Notes

Activity 2

- This activity puts a little twist on the game. It is similar to the game played at the beginning of class.
- **?** "After you make your choice and the game show host reveals that a goat is behind one of the other two doors, should you switch?" Answers will vary.
- Give students time to discuss the question before they simulate the problem. Most students will say that it does not matter if you switch. That is the common intuition!
- Read through the directions. Students need to collect data for this activity as well. Be sure students understand that they should always switch when the host offers them the opportunity.
- Gather data from the class after everyone plays the game 60 times.
- Switching should lead to a car about two-thirds of the time. This is counter-intuitive because once one of the doors is eliminated, it seems that you now have a 50-50 chance of getting the car.
- Make sure students understand that Activity 1 and Activity 2 are different. In Activity 1, all of the door choices are independent events. If you had been given the opportunity to switch in Activity 1, the probability of picking the car would still have been $\frac{1}{3}$. In Activity 2, you are given additional information before you are offered the opportunity to switch.

Closure

- Return to the game from the beginning of class and offer the contestant the opportunity to switch. Ask the class what they think the contestant should do. Hopefully everyone recommends that the contestant should switch!

ACTIVITY: Analyzing "Let's Make a Deal®"

A version of the television program called *Let's Make a Deal*® was similar to the game in Activity 1. However, after the contestant chose a door, the host (who knew the location of the car) revealed the goat behind one of the remaining doors. Then, the host asked the contestant whether he or she wanted to switch.

Work with a partner. Use your three cards to simulate this version of the game. Play the game 30 times as the host and 30 times as the contestant.

- The host deals 3 cards face down.
- The contestant points to one of the cards.
- The host looks at the other two cards, but does not show the contestant.
- The host turns over one of the other cards that is a goat. Then, the host asks the contestant whether he or she wants to switch. For this game, the contestant should always switch.

Write a summary of your results. Include a discussion of experimental probability and theoretical probability. Should contestants stay with their first choice or switch?

What Is Your Answer?

3. **IN YOUR OWN WORDS** How can you use probability to help you win a game show?

4. **CONCLUSION** Compare your results from Activities 1 and 2. In which activity did the contestant win more? Explain your reasoning.

Practice Use what you learned about independent and dependent events to complete Exercises 3–7 on page 430.

Check It Out
Lesson Tutorials
BigIdeasMath ✓com

Key Vocabulary
independent events, p. 428
dependent events, p. 429

Events are **independent events** if the occurrence of one event *does not* affect the likelihood that the other event(s) will occur.

🔑 Key Idea

Probability of Independent Events

Words The probability of two or more independent events is the product of the probabilities of the events.

Symbols $P(A \text{ and } B) = P(A) \cdot P(B)$

$P(A \text{ and } B \text{ and } C) = P(A) \cdot P(B) \cdot P(C)$

EXAMPLE 1   Finding the Probability of Independent Events

You flip three quarters. What is the probability that you flip three tails?

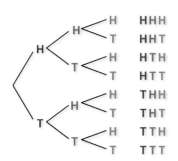

The outcome of flipping one quarter does not affect the outcome of flipping the other quarters. So, the events are independent.

Method 1: Use a tree diagram to find the probability.

Let H = Heads and T = Tails.

$$P(\text{three tails}) = \frac{\text{number of times three tails occur}}{\text{total number of outcomes}} = \frac{1}{8}$$

∴ The probability that you flip three tails is $\frac{1}{8}$, or 12.5%.

Method 2: Use the formula for the probability of independent events.

$P(A \text{ and } B \text{ and } C) = P(A) \cdot P(B) \cdot P(C)$

$P(\text{three tails}) = P(\text{tails}) \cdot P(\text{tails}) \cdot P(\text{tails})$

$= \dfrac{1}{2} \cdot \dfrac{1}{2} \cdot \dfrac{1}{2}$ Substitute.

$= \dfrac{1}{8}$ Multiply.

∴ The probability that you flip three tails is $\frac{1}{8}$, or 12.5%.

⬤ On Your Own

Now You're Ready
Exercises 8–12

1. You flip two coins and roll a number cube. What is the probability of flipping heads, flipping tails, then rolling a 3?

🔊 Multi-Language Glossary at BigIdeasMath✓com.

Laurie's Notes

Introduction

Connect

- **Yesterday:** Students developed an understanding of the difference between independent and dependent events.
- **Today:** Students will use formal definitions to compute the theoretical probabilities of independent and dependent events.

Motivate

- **?** "Playing a game with number cubes, do you roll two ones very often?" no
- **?** "What is the probability of rolling two ones?" Students may quickly say $\frac{1}{6}$ before realizing that it is $\frac{1}{36}$.
- **?** "Does the roll on the first number cube affect what you roll on the second number cube?" no
- **?** "Are rolling two number cubes independent or dependent events?" independent
- Explain that today they will compute the probability of independent and dependent events.

Lesson Notes

Discuss

- Write the definition of independent events on the board.
- Relate the definition to drawing cards from a deck. If you replace a drawn card before drawing again, the events are independent.

Key Idea

- Write the Key Idea on the board. Note that the probability of independent events is not defined in terms of two events only, as it was in a previous grade.
- The formulas may seem daunting to students because of all the symbols. Be sure to use the words along with the notation.

Example 1

- Use three quarters to model the problem. They should have different dates so that they are easier to identify.
- Students may ask if you can flip the coins at the same time or if you have to flip one after another. It does not matter, but for recording purposes, it is easier to flip one after another.
- Work through Method 1, which uses a tree diagram.
- **?** "How do you know that $\frac{1}{8} = 12.5\%$?" $\frac{1}{8} = 0.125 = 12.5\%$
- Work through Method 2, which uses one of the given formulas.
- **?** "What is the theoretical probability of flipping tails on one coin? Explain." $\frac{1}{2}$; Tails is one of only two possible outcomes.

On Your Own

- Have students solve this problem using both methods.

Lesson Materials	
Introduction	**Textbook**
• number cubes	• 3 quarters with different dates • deck of cards
Closure	
• number cube • coin	

Start Thinking! and Warm Up

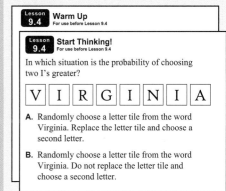

Lesson 9.4 Warm Up
For use before Lesson 9.4

Lesson 9.4 Start Thinking!
For use before Lesson 9.4

In which situation is the probability of choosing two I's greater?

| V | I | R | G | I | N | I | A |

A. Randomly choose a letter tile from the word Virginia. Replace the letter tile and choose a second letter.

B. Randomly choose a letter tile from the word Virginia. Do not replace the letter tile and choose a second letter.

Extra Example 1

In Example 1, what is the probability that you flip three heads? $\frac{1}{8}$, or 12.5%

On Your Own

1. $\frac{1}{24}$, or about 4.2%

Laurie's Notes

Discuss

- Write the definition of dependent events on the board.
- Relate the definition to drawing cards from a deck. If you do *not* replace a drawn card before drawing again, the events are dependent.
- You can simulate this using four cards, two with even numbers and two with odd numbers. Ask what the probability of randomly drawing two even-numbered cards would be without replacement. The size of the sample space is 4 for the first draw but only 3 for the second draw. The occurrence of the first event (drawing an even-numbered card) affects the likelihood of the second event (drawing another even-numbered card). So, the probability of drawing both even-numbered cards would be $\frac{2}{4} \cdot \frac{1}{3} = \frac{1}{6}$.

Key Idea

- Write the Key Idea on the board. Again, be sure to use the words along with the notation.
- Explain that this formula is similar to the formula for the probability of independent events, except that the probability of the second event has been affected by the occurrence of the first event.

Example 2

- **Representation:** Give five students a card marked with an R (for relative) and give six students a card marked with an F (for friend). The whole class is the audience. Find the probability of choosing a relative. Then find the probability of choosing a friend after a relative is chosen. Finally, multiply the two probabilities.

On Your Own

? "Of the 100 audience members, how many are *not* you, your relatives, or your friends?" $100 - 12 = 88$

Closure

- Use a number cube and a coin.

  Find the probability of rolling a four and flipping heads. $\frac{1}{12}$

  Find the probability of rolling an even number and flipping tails. $\frac{1}{4}$

Extra Example 2

In Example 2, what is the probability that one of your friends is chosen first, and then you are chosen second? $\frac{1}{1650}$, or about 0.061%

On Your Own

2. $\frac{58}{75}$, or about 77.3%

Differentiated Instruction

Vocabulary

Some students may have difficulty understanding how the independence or dependence of events affects probability. Allow students to experiment with bags containing similar small objects, such as number tiles or crayons. Have them find probabilities with and without replacement. Ask volunteers to present their results to the class.

Events are **dependent events** if the occurrence of one event *does* affect the likelihood that the other event(s) will occur.

 **Key Idea**

Probability of Dependent Events

Words The probability of two dependent events A and B is the probability of A times the probability of B after A occurs.

Symbols $P(A \text{ and } B) = P(A) \cdot P(B \text{ after } A)$

EXAMPLE 2 **Finding the Probability of Dependent Events**

People are randomly chosen to be game show contestants from an audience of 100 people. You are with 5 of your relatives and 6 other friends. What is the probability that one of your relatives is chosen first, and then one of your friends is chosen second?

Choosing an audience member changes the number of audience members left. So, the events are dependent.

$$P(\text{relative}) = \frac{5}{100} = \frac{1}{20}$$

There are 5 relatives.

There is a total of 100 audience members.

$$P(\text{friend}) = \frac{6}{99} = \frac{2}{33}$$

There are 6 friends.

There is a total of 99 audience members left.

Use the formula for the probability of dependent events.

$$P(A \text{ and } B) = P(A) \cdot P(B \text{ after } A)$$

$$P(\text{relative and friend}) = P(\text{relative}) \cdot P(\text{friend after relative})$$

$$= \frac{1}{20} \cdot \frac{2}{33} \qquad \text{Substitute.}$$

$$= \frac{1}{330} \qquad \text{Simplify.}$$

∴ The probability is $\frac{1}{330}$, or about 0.3%.

On Your Own

Now You're Ready
Exercises 13–18

2. What is the probability that you, your relatives, and your friends are *not* chosen to be either of the first two contestants?

Vocabulary and Concept Check

1. **VOCABULARY** Events *A*, *B*, and *C* are independent. Describe two ways to find $P(A \text{ and } B \text{ and } C)$.

2. **OPEN-ENDED** Describe a real-life example of three independent events. Describe a real-life example of two dependent events.

Practice and Problem Solving

Tell whether the events are *independent* or *dependent*. Explain.

3. You randomly draw a marble from a bag containing 5 yellow marbles and 7 blue marbles. You replace the marble and then draw a second marble.

       First Draw: Yellow   Second Draw: Yellow

4. You and two friends are in a drawing for five door prizes. You can only win one prize.

       First Draw: Your first friend's name is drawn.
       Second Draw: Your name is drawn.
       Third Draw: Your second friend's name is drawn.

5. You randomly draw a marble from a bag containing 10 black marbles, 5 gold marbles, and 4 white marbles. You keep the first marble, draw and keep a second marble, and then draw a third marble.

       First Draw: White   Second Draw: Black   Third Draw: Black

6. You flip a coin three times.

   First Flip: Heads
   Second Flip: Tails
   Third Flip: Tails

7. You roll a number cube three times.

   First Roll: You roll a 4.
   Second Roll: You roll an odd number.
   Third Roll: You roll an even number.

You spin the spinner, flip a coin, then spin the spinner again. Find the probability of the events.

8. Spinning a 4, flipping heads, then spinning a 7

9. Spinning an odd number, flipping heads, then spinning a 3

10. Spinning an even number, flipping tails, then spinning an odd number

11. *Not* spinning a 5, flipping heads, then spinning a 1

12. Spinning an odd number, *not* flipping heads, then *not* spinning a 6

Assignment Guide and Homework Check

Level	Day 1 Activity Assignment	Day 2 Lesson Assignment	Homework Check
Basic	3–7, 22–25	1, 2, 9–19 odd	5, 9, 17, 19
Average	3–7, 22–25	1, 2, 9, 11, 14–18 even, 19, 20	5, 9, 18, 19, 20
Advanced	3–7, 22–25	1, 2, 8–18 even, 19–21	5, 10, 18, 19, 21

Common Errors

- **Exercises 3–7** Students may confuse independent and dependent events or may have difficulty determining which type of event it is. Remind them that independent events are similar to doing two different things, or an event where you *start over* before the next trial. Dependent events have at least one less possible outcome after the first draw, roll, or flip.
- **Exercises 8–12** If students use the formula, they may find the probability of the second spin as if the experiment was dependent. Remind them that these are independent events.
- **Exercises 13–18** Students may forget to subtract one from the total number of possible outcomes when finding the probability of choosing the second coin. Remind them that the second draw has one less possible outcome because you have removed one of the coins.

9.4 Record and Practice Journal

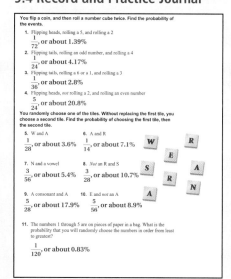

Vocabulary and Concept Check

1. Draw a tree diagram or multiply $P(A)$, $P(B)$, and $P(C)$.

2. *Sample answer:* independent events: a traffic jam, a sunny day, and your birthday; dependent events: temperatures below freezing and ice

Practice and Problem Solving

3. independent; The marble from the first draw is replaced so it does not affect the outcome of the second draw.

4. dependent; There is one less person to choose from on the second draw and two less people to choose from on the third draw.

5. dependent; There is one less marble to choose from on the second draw and two less marbles to choose from on the third draw.

6. independent; The outcome of one coin flip does not affect the outcome of the other coin flips.

7. independent; The outcome of one roll does not affect the outcome of the other rolls.

8. $\frac{1}{162}$, or about 0.62%

9. $\frac{5}{162}$, or about 3.1%

10. $\frac{10}{81}$, or about 12.3%

11. $\frac{4}{81}$, or about 4.9%

12. $\frac{20}{81}$, or about 24.7%

13. $\frac{2}{15}$, or about 13.3%

14. $\frac{1}{15}$, or about 6.7%

15. $\frac{1}{45}$, or about 2.2%

16. $\frac{2}{45}$, or about 4.4%

17. $\frac{4}{15}$, or about 26.7%

18. $\frac{14}{45}$, or about 31.1%

19–20. See Additional Answers.

21. See *Taking Math Deeper*.

Fair Game Review

22. $-3\sqrt{2}$ 23. $-1.5\sqrt{11}$

24. 0   25. D

Mini-Assessment

You roll a number cube three times. Find the probability of the events.

1. Rolling three odd numbers

   $\frac{1}{8}$, or 12.5%

2. Rolling a 3, a number less than 3, then a number greater than 3

   $\frac{1}{36}$, or about 2.8%

You randomly choose one of the tiles. Without replacing the first tile, you randomly choose a second tile. Find the probability of the events.

3. Choosing two even numbers

   $\frac{1}{12}$, or about 8.3%

4. Choosing a number less than 9 and then a multiple of 3

   $\frac{1}{4}$, or 25%

Taking Math Deeper

Exercise 21

To answer this question, students need to know that the letters spell the name "Norfolk."

 You are choosing the 7 letters in order without replacement. Begin by finding the probability of choosing each letter.

$\frac{1}{7}$ $\frac{2}{6}$ $\frac{1}{5}$ $\frac{1}{4}$ $\frac{1}{3}$ $\frac{1}{2}$ $\frac{1}{1}$

Notice that there are 2 O's. So, the probability of choosing the first O is $\frac{2}{6}$, not $\frac{1}{6}$.

 Use the formula for the probability of dependent events to find the probability of choosing the letters in order.

$$P = \frac{1}{7} \cdot \frac{2}{6} \cdot \frac{1}{5} \cdot \frac{1}{4} \cdot \frac{1}{3} \cdot \frac{1}{2} \cdot \frac{1}{1}$$

$$= \frac{2}{5040}$$

$$= \frac{1}{2520}, \text{ or about } 0.04\%$$

So, it is very unlikely that you would spell "Norfolk" when choosing the 7 letters at random.

 In 1622, Adam Thoroughgood came to Virginia from Norfolk, England, as an indentured servant. Eventually he became a leading citizen of the settlement that was later called Norfolk.

Reteaching and Enrichment Strategies

If students need help. . .	If students got it. . .
Resources by Chapter • Practice A and Practice B • Puzzle Time Record and Practice Journal Practice Differentiating the Lesson Lesson Tutorials Skills Review Handbook	Resources by Chapter • Enrichment and Extension • School-to-Work Start the next section

You randomly choose one of the coins. Without replacing the first coin, you choose a second coin. Find the probability of choosing the first coin, then the second coin.

13. Nickel and dime

14. Quarter and nickel

15. Quarter and penny

16. Penny and dime

17. Nickel and *not* a penny

18. Dime and *not* a quarter

19. ERROR ANALYSIS Describe and correct the error in finding the probability.

You have 5 pairs of white socks and 10 pairs of black socks in a drawer. You randomly choose two pairs. What is the probability that both pairs are black?

$$P(\text{black and black}) = P(\text{black}) \cdot P(\text{black})$$
$$= \frac{10}{15} \cdot \frac{10}{15}$$
$$= \frac{2}{3} \cdot \frac{2}{3} = \frac{4}{9}$$

20. WRITING A jar contains 12 purple straws and 12 blue straws. You randomly choose two straws. Is the probability of choosing two purple straws greater if you replace the first straw after you choose it, or if you keep the first straw after you choose it? Explain.

21. **Critical Thinking** If you randomly choose all seven tiles in order, what is the probability that you will spell the name of a city in Virginia?

 Fair Game Review *What you learned in previous grades & lessons*

Simplify the expression. *(Section 8.4)*

22. $4\sqrt{2} - 7\sqrt{2}$

23. $-2.7\sqrt{11} + 1.2\sqrt{11}$

24. $2\sqrt{5} - \sqrt{20}$

25. MULTIPLE CHOICE What is the surface area of the prism? *(Section 6.2)*

   (A) 48.6 cm²

   (B) 54 cm²

   (C) 61.6 cm²

   (D) 88.6 cm²

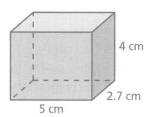

You randomly choose a marble. Determine the theoretical probability of the event. *(Section 9.3)*

1. Choosing red

2. Choosing blue

3. *Not* choosing yellow

4. Choosing green

Color	Times Chosen
Red	50
Green	52
Yellow	45
Blue	53

The table shows the results of randomly choosing one of the marbles shown above 200 times. Find the experimental probability of the event. *(Section 9.3)*

5. Choosing green

6. Choosing yellow

7. Choosing red or blue

8. Choosing red or green

9. Use the marbles and the table shown above. Compare the experimental and theoretical probabilities of randomly choosing a red marble. *(Section 9.3)*

You flip a coin, spin the spinner, then flip a coin again. Find the probability of the events. *(Section 9.4)*

10. Flipping tails, spinning a 6, then flipping heads

11. Flipping heads, spinning an even number, then *not* flipping heads

You randomly choose one of the buttons. Without replacing the first button, you choose a second button. Find the probability of choosing the first button, then the second button. *(Section 9.4)*

12. Green and yellow

13. Yellow and black

14. Black and *not* green

15. Green and *not* black

16. **MONEY** You randomly remove 150 coins from a jar. Thirty of them are quarters. How many of the next 200 coins can you expect to be quarters? *(Section 9.3)*

17. **STICKERS** You randomly choose one of the stickers. Without replacing the first sticker, you choose a second sticker. Find the probability of choosing two hearts. *(Section 9.4)*

Alternative Assessment Options

Math Chat   **Student Reflective Focus Question**
Structured Interview   Writing Prompt

Student Reflective Focus Question
Ask students to summarize the similarities and differences between finding probabilities of independent events and finding probabilities of dependent events. Be sure that they include examples. Select students at random to present their summary to the class.

Study Help Sample Answers
Remind students to complete Graphic Organizers for the rest of the chapter.

3.
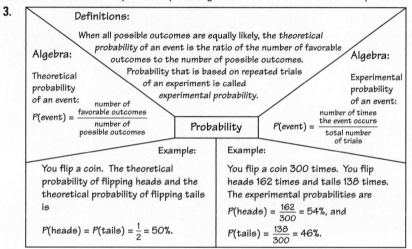

4.
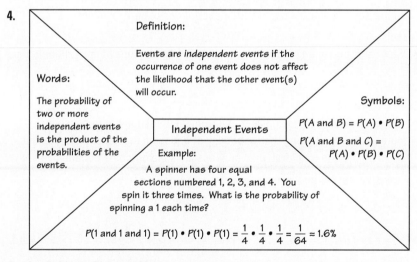

5. Available at *BigIdeasMath.com*.

Reteaching and Enrichment Strategies

If students need help. . .	If students got it. . .
Resources by Chapter • Study Help • Practice A and Practice B • Puzzle Time Lesson Tutorials *BigIdeasMath.com* Practice Quiz Practice from the Test Generator	Resources by Chapter • Enrichment and Extension • School-to-Work Game Closet at *BigIdeasMath.com* Start the Chapter Review

Answers

1. $\frac{1}{4}$, or 25%   2. $\frac{3}{8}$, or 37.5%

3. $\frac{3}{4}$, or 75%   4. $\frac{1}{8}$, or 12.5%

5. $\frac{13}{50}$, or 26%   6. $\frac{9}{40}$, or 22.5%

7. $\frac{103}{200}$, or 51.5%

8. $\frac{51}{100}$, or 51%

9. The experimental and theoretical probabilities are both $\frac{1}{4}$, or 25%.

10. $\frac{1}{32}$, or 3.125%

11. $\frac{1}{8}$, or 12.5%

12. $\frac{2}{11}$, or about 18.2%

13. $\frac{4}{55}$, or about 7.3%

14. $\frac{1}{11}$, or about 9.1%

15–17. See Additional Answers.

Technology For the Teacher
Answer Presentation Tool

Assessment Book

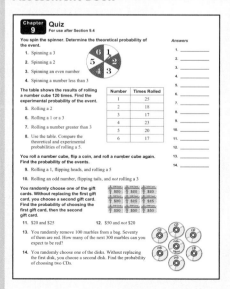

T-432

For the Teacher
Additional Review Options

- **Quiz**Show
- Big Ideas Test Generator
- Game Closet at *BigIdeasMath.com*
- Vocabulary Puzzle Builder
- Resources by Chapter
  Puzzle Time
  Study Help

Answers

1. **a.** 2009

   b. 225 geese

   c. positive relationship

2. negative relationship

3. no relationship

4. **a.**

   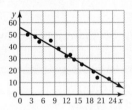

   b. *Sample answer:*
   $y = -1.9x + 56$

Review of Common Errors

Exercise 1

- When reading values from the graph, students may accidentally shift over or up too far and get an answer that is off by an increment. Encourage them to start at the given value on the axis and trace the graph to the point. Then trace down or left to the other axis for the answer.

Exercises 2 and 3

- Students may confuse positive and negative relationships. Remind them about slope. The slope is positive when the line rises from left to right and negative when it falls from left to right. The same is true for relationships in a scatter plot. If the data rises from left to right, it is a positive relationship. If it falls from left to right, it is a negative relationship.

Exercise 4

- Students may draw a line of best fit that does not accurately reflect the data trend. Remind them that the line does not have to go through any of the data points. Also remind them that the line should go through the middle of the data so that about half of the data points are above the line and half are below.

Exercise 4

- Students may struggle writing the equation for the line of best fit. When drawing the line, encourage them to try to make the line go through a lattice point. Also students can use lattice points that are very close to the line to help them find the slope.

Exercises 5–8

- Students may confuse the names of the data displays. Remind them to write an explanation about why they chose that data display. Students should refer to the Key Idea for the names and descriptions of data displays.

Exercise 9

- Students may count outcomes incorrectly. A student may think that because there are 3 colors, the theoretical probability of spinning blue is $\frac{1}{3}$ instead of $\frac{2}{5}$.

Exercises 10–12

- Students may forget to subtract one from the total number of possible outcomes when finding the probability of choosing the second tile. Remind them that the second draw has one less possible outcome because you have removed one of the tiles.

Check It Out
Vocabulary Help
BigIdeasMath.com

Review Key Vocabulary

scatter plot, *p. 402*
line of best fit, *p. 404*
theoretical probability, *p. 420*

experimental probability, *p. 421*
independent events, *p. 428*
dependent events, *p. 429*

Review Examples and Exercises

9.1 Scatter Plots and Lines of Best Fit *(pp. 400–407)*

Your school is ordering custom T-shirts. The scatter plot shows the number of T-shirts ordered and the cost per shirt. What tends to happen to the cost per shirt as the number of T-shirts ordered increases?

Looking at the graph, the plotted points go down from left to right.

∴ So, as the number of T-shirts ordered increases, the cost per shirt decreases.

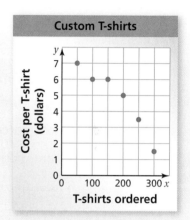

Custom T-shirts

Exercises

1. The scatter plot shows the number of geese that migrated to a park each season.

   a. In what year did 270 geese migrate?

   b. How many geese migrated in 2007?

   c. Describe the relationship shown by the data.

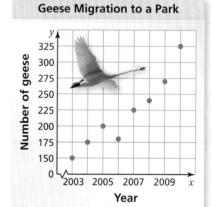

Geese Migration to a Park

Tell whether the data show a *positive*, a *negative*, or *no* relationship.

2.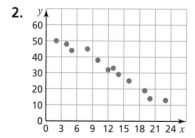

3.

4. Consider the scatter plot in Exercise 2.

   a. Draw a line of best fit.

   b. Write an equation of the line of best fit.

9.2 Choosing a Data Display *(pp. 408–415)*

Choose an appropriate data display for each situation. Explain your reasoning.

a. the percent of votes that each candidate received in an election

⋮ A circle graph shows data as parts of a whole. So, a circle graph is an appropriate data display.

b. the distribution of the ages of U.S. presidents

⋮ A stem-and-leaf plot orders numerical data and shows how they are distributed. So, a stem-and-leaf plot is an appropriate data display.

Exercises

Choose an appropriate data display for the situation. Explain your reasoning.

5. the number of pairs of shoes sold by a store each week

6. the outcomes of spinning a spinner with 3 equal sections numbered 1, 2, and 3

7. comparison of the number of cans of food donated by each eighth-grade class

8. comparison of the heights of brothers and sisters

9.3 Probability *(pp. 418–425)*

The bar graph shows the results of spinning the spinner 40 times.

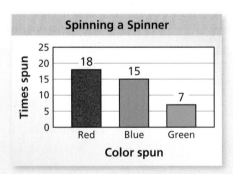

a. What is the experimental probability of spinning red?

$$P(\text{red}) = \frac{\text{number of times the event occurs}}{\text{total number of trials}} = \frac{18}{40} = \frac{9}{20}$$

⋮ The experimental probability of spinning red is $\frac{9}{20}$, or 45%.

b. What is the theoretical probability of spinning red?

$$P(\text{red}) = \frac{\text{number of favorable outcomes}}{\text{number of possible outcomes}} = \frac{2}{5}$$

⋮ The theoretical probability of spinning red is $\frac{2}{5}$, or 40%.

Review Game

Rolling for Data

Big Ideas
Game Closet

For the Student
Additional Practice
- Lesson Tutorials
- Study Help (textbook)
- Student Website
    Multi-Language Glossary
    Practice Assessments

Materials per pair
- two number cubes
- paper
- pencil

Directions
Students should work in pairs. Students in each pair take turns rolling the two number cubes one at a time. The first number they roll represents the tens digit and the second number represents the ones digit of a whole number. For example, if a 1 is rolled and then a 6, the whole number is 16. Students record the whole numbers in a stem-and-leaf plot and keep rolling until they have 10 leaves for any one stem. Once a pair acquires the 10 leaves, they race to find how their experimental probabilities of rolling 11–16, 21–26, 31–36, 41–46, 51–56, and 61–66 compare to the theoretical probability of rolling a number in each range.

Who wins?
The first pair to finish all tasks wins 10 points, the second 9 points, the third 8 points, and so on. The game can be repeated as many times as desired. The pair with the most points after a predetermined number of rounds or amount of time wins.

Answers

5. *Sample answer:* line graph; shows changes over time

6. *Sample answer:* circle graph; shows data as parts of a whole

7. *Sample answer:* pictograph; shows data using pictures

8. *Sample answer:* scatter plot; shows the relationship between two data sets

9. 200 times

10. $\frac{1}{10}$, or 10%

11. $\frac{1}{10}$, or 10%

12. $\frac{3}{20}$, or 15%

13. $\frac{1}{10}$, or 10%

My Thoughts on the Chapter

What worked. . .

What did not work. . .

What I would do differently. . .

Exercises

9. You spin the spinner 500 times. How many times can you expect to spin blue?

9.4 **Independent and Dependent Events** *(pp. 426–431)*

You randomly choose a marble without replacing it. Your friend then chooses another marble. What is the probability that you choose a red marble and your friend chooses a green marble?

Choosing a marble without replacement changes the number of marbles left. So, the events are dependent.

$P(\text{first is red}) = \dfrac{5}{12}$ ← There are 5 red marbles.
← There is a total of 12 marbles.

$P(\text{second is green}) = \dfrac{2}{11}$ ← There are 2 green marbles.
← There is a total of 11 marbles left.

Use the formula for the probability of dependent events.

$P(\text{red and green}) = P(\text{red}) \cdot P(\text{green after red})$

$= \dfrac{5}{12} \cdot \dfrac{2}{11}$ Substitute.

$= \dfrac{10}{132} = \dfrac{5}{66}$ Simplify.

❖ The probability of choosing a red marble followed by a green marble is $\dfrac{5}{66}$, or about 7.6%.

Exercises

You randomly choose one of the lettered tiles. Without replacing the first tile, you choose a second tile. Find the probability of choosing the first tile, then the second tile.

10. C and I   **11.** I and I   **12.** V and *not* L

13. You choose one of the lettered tiles and flip two coins. What is the probability of choosing an I, flipping heads, then flipping tails?

The bar graph shows the results of spinning the spinner 50 times. Find the experimental probability of the event.

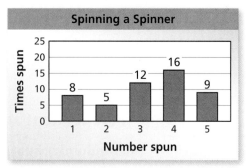

1. Spinning a 3

2. Spinning a 2 or a 5

There are 10 skateboarders and 15 bikers at a skate park. You randomly choose two of them to judge a tournament. Find the probability of the event.

3. Choosing a biker, then choosing a skateboarder

4. Choosing a skateboarder, then choosing another skateboarder

5. **NUMBER CUBE** You roll a number cube three times. What is the probability that you roll an even number all three times?

6. **POPULATION** The graph shows the population (in millions) of the United States from 1960 to 2000.

   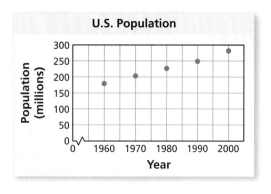

   a. In what year was the population of the United States about 180 million?

   b. What was the approximate population of the United States in 1990?

   c. Describe the trend shown by the data.

Choose an appropriate data display for the situation. Explain your reasoning.

7. magazine sales grouped by price

8. distance a person hikes each week

9. **NEWBORNS** The table shows the lengths and weights of several newborn babies.

   a. Make a scatter plot of the data.

   b. Draw a line of best fit.

   c. Write an equation of the line of best fit.

   d. Use the equation to predict the weight of a newborn that is 21.75 inches long.

Length (inches)	Weight (pounds)
19	6
19.5	7
20	7.75
20.25	8.5
20.5	8.5
22.5	11

Test Item References

Chapter Test Questions	Section to Review
6, 9	9.1
7, 8	9.2
1, 2	9.3
3–5	9.4

Test-Taking Strategies

Remind students to quickly look over the entire test before they start so that they can budget their time. When they receive their test, students should list the different types of data displays. Teach the students to use the Stop and Think strategy before answering. **Stop** and carefully read the question, and **Think** about what the answer should look like.

Common Assessment Errors

- **Exercises 1 and 2** Students may misread, or fail to read, the directions and find the theoretical probability instead of the experimental probability. Encourage them to read the directions carefully.
- **Exercises 3–5** Students may not be able to tell whether the events are independent or dependent. Ask them to think about whether the occurrence of one event affects the likelihood that the other event will occur.
- **Exercise 6** When reading values from the graph, students may accidentally shift over or up too far and get an answer that is off by an increment. Encourage them to start at the given value on the axis and trace the graph to the point. Then trace down or left to the other axis for the answer.
- **Exercises 7 and 8** Students may confuse the names of the data displays. Remind them to write an explanation about why they chose that type of data display.
- **Exercise 9** Students may use inconsistent increments on their graphs or forget to label their graphs. They should use consistent increments to represent the data. Remind them to label the axes so that information can be read from the graph.

Reteaching and Enrichment Strategies

If students need help. . .	If students got it. . .
Resources by Chapter • Practice A and Practice B • Puzzle Time Record and Practice Journal Practice Differentiating the Lesson Lesson Tutorials Practice from the Test Generator Skills Review Handbook	Resources by Chapter • Enrichment and Extension • School-to-Work Game Closet at *BigIdeasMath.com* Start Standardized Test Practice

Answers

1. $\frac{6}{25}$, or 24%

2. $\frac{7}{25}$, or 28%

3. $\frac{1}{4}$, or 25%

4. $\frac{3}{20}$, or 15%

5. $\frac{1}{8}$, or 12.5%

6. **a.** 1960

   b. about 250 million

   c. There is a positive relationship between year and population.

7. *Sample answer:* histogram; shows frequencies of data values in intervals of the same size

8. *Sample answer:* line graph; shows how data change over time

9. See Additional Answers.

Assessment Book

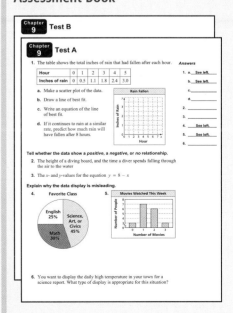

T-436

Test-Taking Strategies

Available at *BigIdeasMath.com*

After Answering Easy Questions, Relax

Answer Easy Questions First

Estimate the Answer

Read All Choices before Answering

Read Question before Answering

Solve Directly or Eliminate Choices

Solve Problem before Looking at Choices

Use Intelligent Guessing

Work Backwards

About this Strategy

When taking a multiple choice test, be sure to read each question carefully and thoroughly. It is also very important to read each answer choice carefully. Do not pick the first answer that you think is correct! If two answer choices are the same, eliminate them both. There can only be one correct answer.

Answers

1. C
2. F
3. A

Technology For the Teacher
Big Ideas Test Generator

T-437

Item Analysis

1. **A.** The student makes an error subtracting or dividing integers.

B. The student makes an error subtracting or dividing integers, and then fails to reverse the direction of the inequality symbol when dividing by a negative coefficient.

C. Correct answer

D. The student fails to reverse the direction of the inequality symbol when dividing by a negative coefficient.

2. **F.** Correct answer

G. The student finds the square root of $\frac{40}{4}$.

H. The student thinks the square root of 40 is equal to 20.

I. The student finds the square root of 40, and ignores the denominator.

3. **A.** Correct answer

B. The student triples the probability because they flip the nickel three times.

C. The student finds the probability of an outcome of flipping the nickel once.

D. The student finds the probability to be $\frac{1}{4}$ and triples the probability because they flip the nickel three times.

4. **F.** The student fails to realize that a histogram is inappropriate. The display must allow a reader to compare parts of a whole.

G. Correct answer

H. The student fails to realize that a line graph is inappropriate. The display must allow a reader to compare parts of a whole.

I. The student fails to realize that a scatter plot is inappropriate. The display must allow a reader to compare parts of a whole.

1. Which graph represents the inequality below?

$$-2x + 3 < 1$$

A.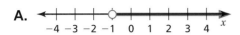

A.
-4 -3 -2 -1 0 1 2 3 4 x

B.
-4 -3 -2 -1 0 1 2 3 4 x

C.
-4 -3 -2 -1 0 1 2 3 4 x

D.
-4 -3 -2 -1 0 1 2 3 4 x

Test-Taking Strategy

Read All Choices Before Answering

What's the probability you will take a nap today?
Ⓐ 1   Ⓑ 0.5   Ⓒ 0.25   Ⓓ 0.1

ZZZZZZZ

"Reading all choices before answering can sometimes point out the obvious answer!"

2. An object dropped from a height will fall under the force of gravity. The time t, in seconds, it takes to fall a distance d, in feet, can be found using the formula below.

$$t = \frac{\sqrt{d}}{4}$$

A ball is dropped from the top of a building that is 40 feet tall. Approximately how many seconds will it take for the ball to reach the ground?

F. 1.6 sec   **H.** 5 sec

G. 3.2 sec   **I.** 6.3 sec

3. You flip three nickels. What is the probability that you flip tails, tails, then heads?

A. $\dfrac{1}{8}$ **C.** $\dfrac{1}{2}$

B. $\dfrac{3}{8}$ **D.** $\dfrac{3}{4}$

4. The director of a research lab wants to present data to donors, showing how a great deal of donated money is used for research and how only a small amount of donated money is used for other expenses. Which type of display is best suited for showing these data?

F. histogram

H. line graph

G. circle graph

I. scatter plot

5. Which value of x makes the equation below true?

$$3x - 9 = 2(x + 4)$$

6. As part of a probability experiment, students were asked to roll two number cubes and find the sum of the numbers obtained. One group of students did this 600 times and obtained the results shown in the table. What was the experimental probability of rolling a sum of 3?

Sum	2	3	4	5	6	7	8	9	10	11	12
Number of Rolls	16	30	51	66	83	98	93	64	47	35	17

A. $\dfrac{2}{75}$

C. $\dfrac{8}{75}$

B. $\dfrac{1}{20}$

D. $\dfrac{11}{100}$

7. Which expression is equivalent to $\dfrac{\sqrt{32}}{\sqrt{18}}$?

F. $\sqrt{14}$

H. $\dfrac{8}{3}$

G. $\dfrac{4}{3}$

I. $\dfrac{16}{9}$

8. Which point lies on the graph of the line given by $y = -\dfrac{1}{2}x + 7$?

A. $(5, 4)$

C. $(20, 3)$

B. $(-4, 5)$

D. $(40, -13)$

Item Analysis (continued)

5. **Gridded Response:** Correct answer: 17

   Common Error: The student may fail to distribute 2 to the expression $x + 4$, yielding an answer of 13.

6. **A.** The student finds the probability of rolling a sum of 2.

   B. Correct answer

   C. The student finds the probability of rolling a sum of 9.

   D. The student finds the probability of rolling a sum of 5.

7. **F.** The student subtracts 18 from 32.

   G. Correct answer

   H. The student makes a mistake dividing out $\dfrac{\sqrt{2}}{\sqrt{2}}$, yielding 2 instead of 1.

   I. The student factors correctly, but leaves $\dfrac{16}{9}$ as the answer instead of taking its square root.

8. **A.** The student reverses the roles of x and y.

   B. The student makes a mistake operating with signed integers.

   C. The student makes a mistake operating with signed integers.

   D. Correct answer

9. **F.** The student confuses positive and negative relationships.

   G. The student confuses no relationship with a negative relationship.

   H. The student confuses a constant function with a negative relationship.

   I. Correct answer

10. **Gridded Response:** Correct answer: 17 cm

    Common Error: The student adds the legs for an answer of 23 centimeters.

Answers

4. G

5. 17

6. B

7. G

8. D

T-438

Answers

9. I

10. 17 cm

11. B

12. No. For example, the inequality is not true when $x = 0.5$.

Answers for Extra Examples

1. **A.** The student thinks mean is mode.

   B. The student finds the mean of the four scores (91) and adds 1 to 92 because 91 is 1 less than 92.

   C. Correct answer

   D. The student makes an arithmetic error finding the sum.

2. **F.** The student omits (overlooks) the point on the y-axis.

   G. Correct answer

   H. The student reports the domain.

   I. The student combines the domain and range.

Item Analysis (continued)

11. **A.** The student does not realize that the underlying idea here is to show change over time, something of which a circle graph is not capable.

    B. Correct answer

    C. The student does not realize that the underlying idea here is to show change over time, something of which a histogram is not capable.

    D. The student does not realize that the underlying idea here is to show change over time, something of which a stem-and-leaf plot is not capable.

12. **2 points** The student demonstrates a thorough understanding of how to read and interpret an inequality, and then finds a value of x for which the inequality is not true (for example, $x = 0.5$). A clear and complete explanation is provided.

    1 point The student demonstrates a partial understanding of how to read and interpret an inequality. He or she is able to see what the inequality means, but fails to go far enough to provide a value of x for which it is false.

    0 points The student provides no response, a completely incorrect or incomprehensible response, or a response that demonstrates insufficient understanding of inequalities.

Extra Examples for Standardized Test Practice

1. A student took five tests this marking period and had a mean score of 92. Her scores on the first four tests were 90, 96, 86, and 92. What was her score on the fifth test?

   A. 92

   B. 93

   C. 96

   D. 98

2. What is the range of the function represented by the graph?

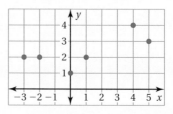

   F. 2, 3, 4

   G. 1, 2, 3, 4

   H. −3, −2, 0, 1, 4, 5

   I. −3, −2, 0, 1, 2, 3, 4, 5

9. Which scatter plot shows a negative relationship between x and y?

F.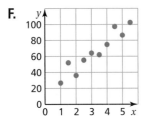

H.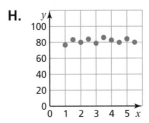

G.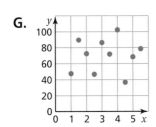

I.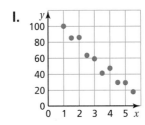

10. The legs of a right triangle have the lengths of 8 centimeters and 15 centimeters. What is the length of the hypotenuse, in centimeters?

11. A store has recorded total dollar sales each month for the past three years. Which type of graph would best show how sales have increased over this time period?

A. circle graph

C. histogram

B. line graph

D. stem-and-leaf plot

12. Does squaring a number always make it greater? Is the inequality shown below true for all numbers?

$$x^2 > x$$

Show your work and explain your reasoning.

10 Exponents and Scientific Notation

"Descartes, do you prefer the original *binary* definition that 1 kilobyte = 2^{10} bytes?"

"Or do you prefer the newer decimal definition that 1 kilobyte = 10^3 bytes?"

"The Mayans used base 20 for their number system."

"And the Babylonians used base 60 for their number system."

"Can you name an ancient culture that used base 10 for its number system?"

Strands Development

6th Grade
• Investigate and describe positive exponents and perfect squares.
• Compare and order fractions, decimals, and percents.
• Compare and order integers.

7th Grade
• Investigate and describe the concept of negative exponents for powers of ten.
• Determine scientific notation for numbers greater than zero.
• Compare and order fractions, decimals, percents, and numbers written in scientific notation.

8th Grade
• Simplify numerical expressions involving positive exponents, using rational numbers, order of operations, and properties of operations with real numbers.
• Compare and order fractions, decimals, percents, and numbers written in scientific notation.

Math in History

Primitive cultures from all over the world tended to develop counting methods—often before the culture developed a written language. It was possible to count without naming many different numbers.

★ The Aboriginal Australians were able to count even though they had only a few names for numbers.

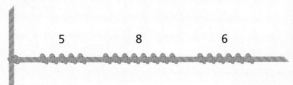

> 1 = Neecha
> 2 = Boolia
> 3 = Boolia Neecha (2 + 1)
> 4 = Boolia Boolia (2 + 2)
> 5 = *Hand* (not spoken)

With this system, a person could communicate the number 23 by saying "boolia neecha" and holding up both hands twice.

★ The ancient Incas used a knotted string called a *quipu* to record numbers. A number was represented by knots in the string, using a base 10 system. For example, the number 586 was represented as shown at the right.

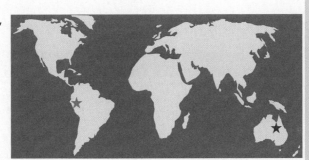

Pacing Guide for Chapter 10

Chapter Opener	1 Day
Section 1 Activity Lesson	1 Day 1 Day
Section 2 Activity Lesson	1 Day 1 Day
Study Help / Quiz	1 Day
Section 3 Activity Lesson	1 Day 1 Day
Section 4 Activity Lesson	1 Day 1 Day
Chapter Review / Tests	2 Days
Total Chapter 10	12 Days
Year-to-Date	157 Days

Check Your Resources

- Record and Practice Journal
- Resources by Chapter
- Skills Review Handbook
- Assessment Book
- Worked-Out Solutions

Technology For the Teacher

The Dynamic Planning Tool Editable Teacher's Resources at *BigIdeasMath.com*

Standards of Learning

7.3(b) The student will add, subtract, multiply, and divide integers.

Additional Topics for Review

- Absolute value
- Ordering and comparing integers
- Adding and subtracting on a number line

Try It Yourself

1. 8
2. 2
3. −13
4. −4
5. 6
6. 19

Record and Practice Journal

1. −1	**2.** 4
3. −20	**4.** 36
5. −8	**6.** 12
7. −16	**8.** −41
9. −6	**10.** 7
11. 19	**12.** 14
13. $18 + (−11)$; 7th floor	
14. −9	**15.** 1
16. 17	**17.** −3
18. 14	**19.** 69
20. 23	**21.** −21
22. −5	**23.** −22
24. 48	**25.** −24
26. −$6	

Math Background Notes

Vocabulary Review

- Integer
- Opposite
- Sum
- Difference

Adding Integers

- Students should know how to add integers.
- **Common Error:** Students may attempt to find the sum mentally and not always get the correct answer. Encourage them to use the method shown in Example 1.
- **Teaching Tip:** Students can also use a number line to find a sum. For many students, using a number line helps them to visualize the correct answer.

Subtracting Integers

- Students should know how to subtract integers.
- Subtracting integers is more difficult for students than adding. They need to be comfortable with addition in order to be comfortable with subtraction.
- **Teaching Tip:** Remind students that addition and subtraction are inverse operations. They can turn any subtraction problem into an addition problem by adding the opposite of the second integer.
- **Common Error:** As with adding integers, students may attempt to find the difference mentally and not always get the correct answer. Encourage them to use the method shown in Example 2.
- **Teaching Tip:** Students can use a number line to find a difference.

Reteaching and Enrichment Strategies

If students need help. . .	If students got it. . .
Record and Practice Journal • Fair Game Review Skills Review Handbook Lesson Tutorials	Game Closet at *BigIdeasMath.com* Start the next section

What You Learned Before

"For my dog biscuit order, my calculator switched to scientific notation. I'm in ecstasy!"

You mean bankruptcy, right?

Adding Integers

Example 1 Find each sum.

a. $-3 + (-6)$

The integers have the *same* sign.

$$-3 + (-6) = -9$$

1. Add the absolute values: $|-3| + |-6| = 9$
2. Use the common sign: negative

b. $4 + (-12)$

The integers have *different* signs.

$$4 + (-12) = -8$$

1. Subtract the lesser absolute value from the greater absolute value: $|-12| - |4| = 8$
2. Use the sign of the greater absolute value: negative

Subtracting Integers

Example 2 Find each difference.

a. $5 - 9$

$$5 - 9 = 5 + (-9) \qquad \text{Add the opposite of 9.}$$
$$= -4 \qquad \text{Add.}$$

b. $6 - (-2)$

$$6 - (-2) = 6 + 2 \qquad \text{Add the opposite of } -2.$$
$$= 8 \qquad \text{Add.}$$

c. $-7 - (-13)$

$$-7 - (-13) = -7 + 13 \qquad \text{Add the opposite of } -13.$$
$$= 6 \qquad \text{Add.}$$

Try It Yourself

Find the sum or difference.

1. $-2 + 10$

2. $11 + (-9)$

3. $-8 + (-5)$

4. $7 - 11$

5. $-2 - (-8)$

6. $9 - (-10)$

STANDARDS
OF LEARNING
8.1

Essential Question How can you use carbon dating to estimate the age of an object?

1 ACTIVITY: Carbon Dating

When a living thing dies, its carbon-14 content begins to decay with a half-life of about 5700 years. This means that after 5700 years, half of the carbon-14 will have decayed.

Work with a partner. The fraction of remaining carbon-14 is given for each object. Use the fraction to estimate the age of each object. Explain your reasoning.

Sample: $\frac{1}{8}$ means that $\frac{7}{8}$ of the carbon-14 has decayed and only $\frac{1}{8}$ remains.

$\frac{1}{8}$ represents 3 half-lives because $\frac{1}{8} = \frac{1}{2} \cdot \frac{1}{2} \cdot \frac{1}{2}$.

So, the object is about $3 \cdot 5700 = 17{,}100$ years old.

a. Carbon-14 remaining: $\left(\frac{1}{2}\right)^2$

b. Carbon-14 remaining: 2^{-1}

Sea Shell

Chinese Ivory Carving

c. Carbon-14 remaining: 2^0

d. Carbon-14 remaining: $\left(\frac{1}{2}\right)^6$

Clothes Pin

Petrified Wood

Laurie's Notes

Introduction

For the Teacher

- **Goal:** Students will explore the ages of objects using carbon dating.

Motivate

- Before class, place about 64 pennies in a container. You're going to model what *half-life* means.
- Shake the container as you tell students what is in the container. Pour out the contents and remove all of the pennies that land heads up. About one-half of the pennies should land heads up, but do not say this aloud to the students.
- Place the rest of the pennies back in the container and repeat the process several times. Try to space the trials so that they are about one minute apart.
- Make a table to record how many pennies you have after each trial. You *might* have results similar to the following.

Trial	0	1	2	3	4
Pennies Remaining	64	35	16	7	4

- ❓ "About what fraction of the pennies remained after the first trial?" $\frac{1}{2}$

  "Is $\frac{1}{2}$ the same as 2^{-1}?" yes

- ❓ "About what fraction of the 64 pennies remained after the second trial?" $\frac{1}{4}$

  "What is another way to write $\frac{1}{4}$?" $\left(\frac{1}{2}\right)^2$ or 2^{-2}

- Explain that the trials in this example were about a minute apart. Having $\frac{1}{4}$ of the objects remaining means that two *half-lives* have occurred and in that case, the trials began two minutes ago.

Activity Notes

Activity 1

- Before students begin, explain what decaying means (a material is decomposing) and relate it to the Motivate that simulated half-life.
- **FYI:** Carbon-14 dating is a way of determining the age of biological objects. For example, it can be used to determine the age of a bone or the age of an artifact made of wood.
- If possible, show students a video on the Internet about how carbon-14 is used to determine the age of an object.
- Remind students that $a^0 = 1$, so the clothespin is not very old!

Standards of Learning

8.1(a) The student will simplify numerical expressions involving positive exponents, using rational numbers, order of operations, and properties of operations with real numbers.

Previous Learning

Students should know how to evaluate expressions involving exponents.

Activity Materials
Introduction
- 64 pennies or two-color counters

Start Thinking! and Warm Up

Activity 10.1 Start Thinking! For use before Activity 10.1

Activity 10.1 Warm Up For use before Activity 10.1

Find the product.

1. $5 \times 5 \times 5$
2. $10 \times 10 \times 10$
3. $(-3) \times (-3) \times (-3)$
4. $10 \times 10 \times 10 \times 10 \times 10$
5. $4 \times 4 \times 4 \times 4$
6. $(-2) \times (-2) \times (-2) \times (-2)$

10.1 Record and Practice Journal

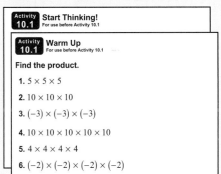

Essential Question How can you use carbon dating to estimate the age of an object?

1 ACTIVITY: Carbon Dating

When a living thing dies, its carbon-14 content begins to decay with a half-life of about 5700 years. This means that after 5700 years, half of the carbon-14 will have decayed.

Work with a partner. The fraction of remaining carbon-14 is given for each object. Use the fraction to estimate the age of each object. Explain your reasoning.

Sample: $\frac{1}{8}$ means that $\frac{7}{8}$ of the carbon-14 has decayed and only $\frac{1}{8}$ remains.

$\frac{1}{8}$ represents 3 half-lives because $\frac{1}{8} = \frac{1}{2} \cdot \frac{1}{2} \cdot \frac{1}{2}$

So, the object is about $3 \cdot 5700 = 17,100$ years old.

a. Carbon-14 remaining: $\left(\frac{1}{2}\right)^2$

b. Carbon-14 remaining: 2^{-1}

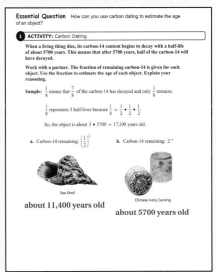

Sea Shell

about 11,400 years old

Chinese Ivory Carving

about 5700 years old

English Language Learners

Vocabulary

Remind English learners that when they see a negative exponent, they should think *reciprocal*. Review the meaning of the word reciprocal. Students often think that because the exponent is negative, the expression is negative. Remind them that a number of the form x^a cannot be negative unless the base is negative.

10.1 Record and Practice Journal

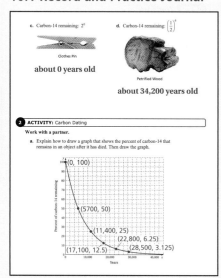

c. Carbon-14 remaining: 2^0

Clothes Pin

about 0 years old

d. Carbon-14 remaining: $\left(\frac{1}{2}\right)^6$

Petrified Wood

about 34,200 years old

2 ACTIVITY: Carbon Dating

Work with a partner.

a. Explain how to draw a graph that shows the percent of carbon-14 that remains in an object after it has died. Then draw the graph.

(0, 100)
(5700, 50)
(11,400, 25)
(17,100, 12.5)
(22,800, 6.25)
(28,500, 3.125)

b. Use your graph on the previous page to estimate the age of an object that has 80% of its carbon-14 remaining.

about 2000 years old

c. Use your graph on the previous page to estimate the age of an object that has 40% of its carbon-14 remaining.

about 7500 years old

What Is Your Answer?

3. **IN YOUR OWN WORDS** How can you use carbon dating to estimate the age of an object?

Use the amount of carbon-14 remaining to estimate the age of the object.

4. **RESEARCH** Use the Internet or some other reference to write a report about other methods that are used to estimate the age of an object.

Check students' work.

Laurie's Notes

Activity 2

- Discuss the labels on the axes before students begin. The ordered pairs relate to the answers in Activity 1.

- ? "How do you write $\frac{1}{8}$ as a percent? Explain." $\frac{1}{8}$ = 12.5%; One possible explanation is to write $\frac{1}{8}$ as a decimal and then write the decimal as a percent.

- Have students connect their ordered pairs with a smooth curve. It should make sense that the graph is continuous.

- Students will have to use their eyesight to read the graph to answer parts (b) and (c).

- **Extension:** This activity can lead students to think about exponents that are not integers.

    - $100\% = 1 = 2^0$

    - $80\% = \frac{4}{5} = 2^x$ $x \approx -0.3$

    - $50\% = \frac{1}{2} = 2^{-1}$

    - $25\% = \frac{1}{4} = 2^{-2}$

Closure

- **Exit Ticket:** If $\frac{1}{32}$ of the carbon-14 remains in a bone, approximately how old is the bone? 28,500 years old

Technology For the Teacher

Dynamic Classroom

The Dynamic Planning Tool
Editable Teacher's Resources at *BigIdeasMath.com*

ACTIVITY: Carbon Dating

Work with a partner.

a. Explain how to draw a graph that shows the percent of carbon-14 that remains in an object after it has died. Then draw the graph.

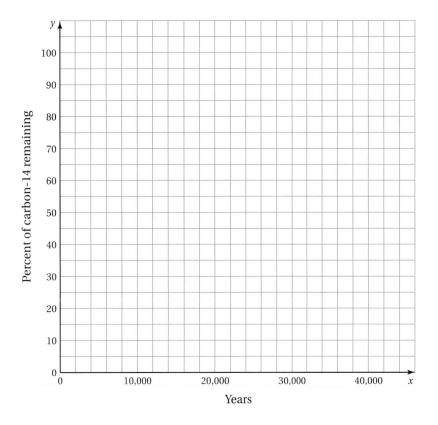

b. Use your graph to estimate the age of an object that has 80% of its carbon-14 remaining.

c. Use your graph to estimate the age of an object that has 40% of its carbon-14 remaining.

What Is Your Answer?

3. IN YOUR OWN WORDS How can you use carbon dating to estimate the age of an object?

4. RESEARCH Use the Internet or some other reference to write a report about other methods that are used to estimate the age of an object.

Practice

Use what you learned about carbon dating to complete Exercises 5 and 6 on page 446.

Key Vocabulary
power, *p. 444*
base, *p. 444*
exponent, *p. 444*

A **power** is a product of repeated factors. The **base** of a power is the common factor. The **exponent** of a power indicates the number of times the base is used as a factor.

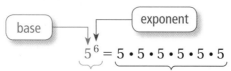

$$5^6 = 5 \cdot 5 \cdot 5 \cdot 5 \cdot 5 \cdot 5$$

power   5 is used as a factor 6 times.

EXAMPLE 1 Evaluating Expressions

Evaluate each expression.

a. $\left(-\dfrac{1}{2}\right)^4$

$\left(-\dfrac{1}{2}\right)^4 = \left(-\dfrac{1}{2}\right) \cdot \left(-\dfrac{1}{2}\right) \cdot \left(-\dfrac{1}{2}\right) \cdot \left(-\dfrac{1}{2}\right)$ Write as repeated multiplication.

> The base is $-\dfrac{1}{2}$.

$\qquad\qquad = \dfrac{1}{16}$ Simplify.

b. -8^3

$-8^3 = -(8 \cdot 8 \cdot 8)$ Write as repeated multiplication.

> The base is 8.

$\qquad = -512$ Simplify.

On Your Own

Now You're Ready
Exercises 7–11

Evaluate the expression.

1. $\left(-\dfrac{1}{3}\right)^2$ **2.** $(-4)^3$ **3.** -5^4 **4.** 2.5^2

Key Ideas

Zero Exponents

Words For any nonzero number a, $a^0 = 1$. The power 0^0 is *undefined*.

Numbers $7^0 = 1$ **Algebra** $a^0 = 1$, where $a \neq 0$

Negative Exponents

Words For any integer n and any nonzero number a, a^{-n} is the reciprocal of a^n.

Numbers $5^{-3} = \dfrac{1}{5^3}$ **Algebra** $a^{-n} = \dfrac{1}{a^n}$, where $a \neq 0$

Laurie's Notes

Introduction

Connect
- **Yesterday:** Students explored zero and negative exponents.
- **Today:** Students will use the definitions of zero and negative exponents to evaluate expressions.

Motivate
- ❓ "Have any of you toured the White House in Washington, D.C.?"
- One room in the White House is called the Blue Room. The President often receives guests there. Unlike most rooms that are rectangular, the Blue Room is *elliptical*. Like circles, ellipses have a circumference. Today students will find the circumference of the Blue Room.
- You can learn more about rooms in the White House at *www.whitehouse.gov/about/history/rooms*.

Lesson Notes

Discuss
- Write a power, such as 5^6, on the board. Use this expression to discuss the vocabulary *power, base,* and *exponent*.
- ❓ "What is the base?" 5 "What is the exponent?" 6 "What is the power?" 5^6

Example 1
- It is important for students to recognize the difference between these two problems. The base in part (a) includes everything in the parentheses.
- ❓ "What is the base in part (a)?" $-\dfrac{1}{2}$
- Explain that because of the parentheses, the negative sign is part of the base. The negative sign is part of the factor that is repeated when the expression is written as repeated multiplication.
- ❓ "What is the base in part (b)?" 8
- Stress that the negative sign is *not* part of the factor that is repeated when the expression is written as repeated multiplication.
- **Teaching Tip:** -8^3 is read "the opposite of 8 cubed" and $(-8)^3$ is read "negative 8 cubed." Students should understand that while $-8^3 = (-8)^3$, this is not the case when the exponent is even: $-8^4 \neq (-8)^4$.

On Your Own
- **Think-Pair-Share:** Students should read each question independently and then work with a partner to answer the questions. When they have answered the questions, the pair should compare their answers with another group and discuss any discrepancies.
- **Common Error:** Students may evaluate Question 3 as if it were $(-5)^4$.

Key Ideas
- Work through the definitions of zero and negative exponents. Students should be familiar with these from the activity and from last year.

Goal Today's lesson is to evaluate expressions involving **exponents**.

Start Thinking! and Warm Up

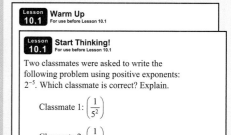

Two classmates were asked to write the following problem using positive exponents: 2^{-5}. Which classmate is correct? Explain.

Classmate 1: $\left(\dfrac{1}{5^2}\right)$

Classmate 2: $\left(\dfrac{1}{2^5}\right)$

Extra Example 1
Evaluate each expression.

a. $\left(-\dfrac{3}{2}\right)^3$ $-\dfrac{27}{8}$

b. -1.2^2 -1.44

On Your Own
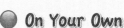

1. $\dfrac{1}{9}$ 2. -64

3. -625 4. 6.25

Laurie's Notes

Extra Example 2

Evaluate each expression.

a. -9^{-2} $-\dfrac{1}{81}$

b. $\left(-\dfrac{7}{9}\right)^0 - 10^{-1}$ $\dfrac{9}{10}$

 On Your Own

5. $\dfrac{1}{32}$ **6.** -125

7. $-\dfrac{13}{16}$

Extra Example 3

Use the formula in Example 3 to estimate the circumference of the figure to the nearest inch.

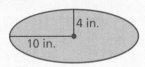

4 in.

10 in.

about 48 in.

On Your Own

8. about 83 ft

Differentiated Instruction

Visual

Help students to understand zero and negative exponents using methods already known to them.
Evaluate and then simplify.

$$\dfrac{3^2}{3^3} = \dfrac{9}{27} = \dfrac{9 \div 9}{27 \div 9} = \dfrac{1}{3}$$

Divide out common factors.

$$\dfrac{3^2}{3^3} = \dfrac{\cancel{3} \cdot \cancel{3}}{\cancel{3} \cdot \cancel{3} \cdot 3} = \dfrac{1}{3}$$

Example 2

- **Part (a):** This is a direct application of the definition of negative exponents. The last step may not be obvious to students. One way to explain the last step is to multiply the numerator and denominator by 1000:

$$\dfrac{1}{-0.125} \cdot \dfrac{1000}{1000} = \dfrac{1000}{-125} = -8.$$

- **Part (a):** An alternative approach is

$$(-0.5)^{-3} = \left(-\dfrac{1}{2}\right)^{-3} = \dfrac{1}{\left(-\dfrac{1}{2}\right)^3} = \dfrac{1 \cdot 8}{-\dfrac{1}{8} \cdot 8} = \dfrac{8}{-1} = -8.$$

- **Part (b):** There are three terms in this expression. Begin by identifying the three terms. Evaluate each and simplify.

On Your Own

- Ask for volunteers to show their solutions at the board. Be sure that Question 6 is simplified completely, meaning that the answer is not left as a fraction with a decimal.

Example 3

- Draw two concentric circles and label the radii as 15 feet and 20 feet.

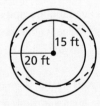

15 ft

20 ft

- **?** "Can you find the circumference of each circle? Explain." yes; Substitute each radius into the formula $C = 2\pi r$ to obtain $C = 30\pi$ ft and $C = 40\pi$ ft.
- Draw an ellipse inside the concentric circles.
- **?** "How do you think the circumference of the ellipse compares to the circumference of the two circles?" Students should suggest that the circumference of the ellipse is between the circumferences of the two circles.
- Work through the example as shown. Be sure students know how to use their calculators to multiply by π and take the square root of a decimal.
- **Connection:** Notice that a and b are legs of a right triangle. Using the Pythagorean Theorem, you can determine that the length of the hypotenuse is 25 feet. This makes sense, as one-fourth of the circumference of the ellipse is 27.75 feet.
- **Extension:** Use a calculator to show that 111 feet is greater than 30π feet and less than 40π feet.

Closure

- **Writing Prompt:** To evaluate $8^0 - 2^{-2} + 4^{-1}$, you . . .

Technology For the Teacher

Dynamic Classroom

The Dynamic Planning Tool
Editable Teacher's Resources at *BigIdeasMath.com*

EXAMPLE ② **Evaluating Expressions**

a. $(-0.5)^{-3} = \dfrac{1}{(-0.5)^3}$ Definition of negative exponent

$= \dfrac{1}{-0.125} = -8$ Simplify.

b. $4^0 - 2^{-4} + \left(\dfrac{1}{4}\right)^2 = 4^0 - \dfrac{1}{2^4} + \left(\dfrac{1}{4}\right)^2$ Definition of negative exponent

$= 1 - \dfrac{1}{16} + \dfrac{1}{16}$ Evaluate the powers.

$= 1$ Simplify.

● **On Your Own**

Now You're Ready
Exercises 12–18

Evaluate the expression.

5. 2^{-5} **6.** $(-0.2)^{-3}$ **7.** $4^{-2} + \left(\dfrac{1}{2}\right)^3 - 8^0$

EXAMPLE ③ **Real-Life Application**

The circumference C of the Blue Room in the White House is given by the formula $C = 2\pi\sqrt{\dfrac{a^2 + b^2}{2}}$. Estimate the circumference to the nearest foot.

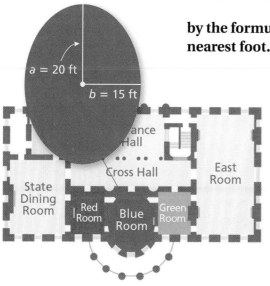

$a = 20$ ft
$b = 15$ ft

$C = 2\pi\sqrt{\dfrac{a^2 + b^2}{2}}$ Write formula.

$= 2\pi\sqrt{\dfrac{20^2 + 15^2}{2}}$ Substitute.

$= 2\pi\sqrt{\dfrac{400 + 225}{2}}$ Evaluate the powers.

$= 2\pi\sqrt{312.5}$ Simplify.

≈ 111 Use a calculator.

∴ The circumference of the room is about 111 feet.

● **On Your Own**

8. Use the formula in Example 3 to estimate the circumference of the figure to the nearest foot.

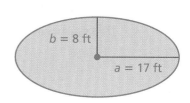

$b = 8$ ft
$a = 17$ ft

 ## Vocabulary and Concept Check

1. **VOCABULARY** Identify the base and exponent of each power in the expression below.

$$5^0 + 2^{-8}$$

Copy and complete the statement using < or >.

2. 3.2^2 ▢ 6^{-3}

3. $\left(-\dfrac{1}{4}\right)^0$ ▢ 5^4

4. 7^0 ▢ 8^{-1}

 ## Practice and Problem Solving

The fraction of remaining carbon-14 is given for an object. Use the fraction to estimate the age of the object. Explain your reasoning.

5. Carbon-14 remaining: $\left(\dfrac{1}{2}\right)^5$

6. Carbon-14 remaining: 2^{-4}

Evaluate the expression.

① ② 7. 4^3

8. $(-3)^4$

9. -2^3

10. $\left(-\dfrac{1}{5}\right)^2$

11. 2.8^2

12. 3^{-3}

13. $(-7)^{-2}$

14. $\left(-\dfrac{1}{6}\right)^0$

15. 9.8^0

16. $2^{-3} - 8^{-1} + \left(\dfrac{1}{2}\right)^0$

17. $(-2.5)^0 - 5^0 - 10^{-3}$

18. $10^{-2} - \left(\dfrac{2}{5}\right)^2 + 2^{-2}$

19. **ERROR ANALYSIS** Describe and correct the error in evaluating the expression.

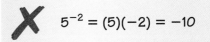
✗ $5^{-2} = (5)(-2) = -10$

20. **BINOCULARS** You are 600 meters from a boat. When you look through the binoculars, the boat appears to be $600 \cdot 10^{-1}$ meters away. Evaluate this expression.

10x magnification:
objects will appear 10 times closer

Assignment Guide and Homework Check

Level	Day 1 Activity Assignment	Day 2 Lesson Assignment	Homework Check
Basic	5, 6, 27–30	1–4, 7–19 odd, 20	9, 11, 17, 19, 20
Average	5, 6, 27–30	1–4, 8–12 even, 13–19 odd, 21–24	12, 13, 17, 19, 21, 23
Advanced	5, 6, 27–30	1–4, 8–18 even, 19, 23–26	10, 14, 18, 19, 24, 26

Common Errors

- **Exercises 7–18** Students may think that any nonzero number with an exponent of zero is zero instead of one. Remind them of the definition of zero exponents.
- **Exercises 7–18** Students may simplify parts of the expression, but forget to evaluate the exponents or leave a decimal in a fraction. Remind them that there should be no exponents, other than 1, in their answers and fractions should be in simplified form.

10.1 Record and Practice Journal

Evaluate the expression.

1. 6^4

1296

2. $(-5)^3$

-125

3. -7^2

-49

4. $\left(\frac{1}{4}\right)^6$

$\frac{1}{4096}$

5. 3.2^2

10.24

6. 2^{-7}

$\frac{1}{128}$

7. $(-3)^{-5}$

$-\frac{1}{243}$

8. 7.9^0

1

9. $\left(-\frac{3}{4}\right)^0$

1

10. $(-4)^{-3} + 8^{-1} - \left(\frac{1}{5}\right)^0$

$-\frac{57}{64}$

11. $6.1^0 - 12^{-2} + 7^0$

$1\frac{143}{144}$

12. $3^{-4} + \left(\frac{2}{3}\right)^2 - 9^{-2}$

$\frac{4}{9}$

13. The strongest animal on Earth is the rhinoceros beetle. It can lift up to 850 times its own weight. A rhinoceros beetle weighs about $2 \cdot 10^{-2}$ kilogram. What is the maximum weight a rhinoceros beetle can lift?

17 kg

14. The maximum volume of a container of liquid allowed as a carry-on onto an airplane is 3.4 fluid ounces. You put six 3.4-fluid ounce containers in a bag when traveling. What is the total volume of the liquid in your carry-on in liters? $(3.4 \text{ fl oz} = 10^{-1} \text{ L})$

0.6 L

Vocabulary and Concept Check

1. power: 5^0, base: 5, exponent: 0;
   power: 2^{-8}, base: 2, exponent: -8

2. $3.2^2 > 6^{-3}$

3. $\left(-\frac{1}{4}\right)^0 < 5^4$

4. $7^0 > 8^{-1}$

Practice and Problem Solving

5. 28,500 years old

6. 22,800 years old

7. 64

8. 81

9. -8

10. $\frac{1}{25}$

11. 7.84

12. $\frac{1}{27}$

13. $\frac{1}{49}$

14. 1

15. 1

16. 1

17. $-\frac{1}{1000}$

18. $\frac{1}{10}$

19. The exponent should not be used as a factor.
    $5^{-2} = \frac{1}{5^2} = \frac{1}{25}$

20. 60 m

21. yes; no; The base is 7, not -7, so the middle step should be $-\dfrac{1}{(7)(7)(7)}$.

22. -8^{-5}

23. See *Taking Math Deeper.*

24. $4737.50

25. Multiply the denominator of $\dfrac{1}{729}$ by 3 to get $\dfrac{1}{2187}$.

26.

Expression	Evaluate	Write as a power
$4^2 \cdot 4^1$	64	4^3
$4^3 \cdot 4^{-2}$	4	4^1
$4^1 \cdot 4^{-2}$	$\dfrac{1}{4}$	4^{-1}
$4^{-1} \cdot 4^{-2}$	$\dfrac{1}{64}$	4^{-3}

The sum of the exponents in the original expression is the same as the exponent of the power whose base is 4; x^{-3} or $\dfrac{1}{x^3}$.

Fair Game Review

27. yes   **28.** no

29. yes   **30.** D

Mini-Assessment

Evaluate the expression.

1. $(-0.5)^4$ 0.0625

2. $-\left(\dfrac{1}{2}\right)^6$ $-\dfrac{1}{64}$

3. -10^{-4} $-\dfrac{1}{10,000}$

4. $(0.2)^{-1} - 7.8^0$ 4

5. $-2^2 + \left(-\dfrac{1}{2}\right)^0 + 1^{-1}$ -2

Taking Math Deeper

Exercise 23

Water striders rely on the surface tension of water to stay on top of the water. Students may have been exposed to a common science experiment in which small amounts of detergent are added to water. The detergent reduces the surface tension and causes objects to break through the surface of the water.

Walking on water

① Summarize the given information.

Length of 1 hair = 50 micrometers

1 micrometer = 10^{-6} meter

= 0.000001 meter

② Find the length in meters.

Length of 1 hair = 50(1 micrometer)

= 50(10^{-6} meter)

= 0.000050 meter

③ Water striders are insects (they have 6 legs) and are not known to be harmful to humans. In fact, they are generally thought to be beneficial to humans because they eat insects and other small creatures that fall onto the surface of ponds.

Reteaching and Enrichment Strategies

If students need help...	If students got it...
Resources by Chapter • Practice A and Practice B • Puzzle Time Record and Practice Journal Practice Differentiating the Lesson Lesson Tutorials Skills Review Handbook	Resources by Chapter • Enrichment and Extension Start the next section

21. **YOU BE THE TEACHER** A classmate's work is shown. Is your classmate's final answer correct? Is the work shown correct? Explain.

$$-7^{-3} = \frac{1}{(-7)(-7)(-7)} = -\frac{1}{343}$$

22. **NUMBER SENSE** Write $-\left(\dfrac{1}{8} \cdot \dfrac{1}{8} \cdot \dfrac{1}{8} \cdot \dfrac{1}{8} \cdot \dfrac{1}{8}\right)$ using negative exponents.

23. **WATER STRIDER** A water strider has thousands of microscopic hairs on its legs which give it the ability to walk on water. The length of each hair is about 50 micrometers. What is the length of one hair in *meters*? (A micrometer is 10^{-6} meter.)

24. **INK CARTRIDGE** The black ink cartridge contains 5^{-3} liter of ink. The ink in the cartridge costs $10. About how much does a *gallon* of black ink cost? (1 gal $\approx$ 3.79 L)

25. **CRITICAL THINKING** Given that $3^{-6} = \dfrac{1}{729}$, how do you evaluate 3^{-7} without multiplying seven 3's?

26. **Reasoning** Copy and complete the table. Describe the pattern in the exponents. Use the pattern to simplify the expression $x^2 \cdot x^{-5}$.

Expression	Evaluate	Write as a power whose base is 4
$4^2 \cdot 4^1$		
$4^3 \cdot 4^{-2}$		
$4^1 \cdot 4^{-2}$		
$4^{-1} \cdot 4^{-2}$		

 Fair Game Review *What you learned in previous grades & lessons*

Tell whether the triangle with the given side lengths is a right triangle. *(Section 8.5)*

27. 5 ft, 12 ft, 13 ft

28. 9 mm, 14 mm, 17 mm

29. 7 m, 24 m, 25 m

30. **MULTIPLE CHOICE** Which data display best orders numerical data and shows how they are distributed? *(Section 9.2)*

Ⓐ bar graph

Ⓑ line graph

Ⓒ scatter plot

Ⓓ stem-and-leaf plot

10.2 Product of Powers Property

Essential Question How can you multiply two powers that have the same base?

**STANDARDS
OF LEARNING**
8.1

1 ACTIVITY: Finding Products of Powers

Work with a partner.

a. Copy and complete the table.

Product	Repeated Multiplication Form	Power
$2^2 \cdot 2^4$	$2 \cdot 2 \cdot 2 \cdot 2 \cdot 2 \cdot 2$	2^6
$(-3)^2 \cdot (-3)^4$	$(-3) \cdot (-3) \cdot (-3) \cdot (-3) \cdot (-3) \cdot (-3)$	$(-3)^6$
$7^3 \cdot 7^2$		
$5.1^1 \cdot 5.1^6$		
$(-4)^2 \cdot (-4)^2$		
$10^3 \cdot 10^5$		
$\left(\frac{1}{2}\right)^5 \cdot \left(\frac{1}{2}\right)^5$		

b. **INDUCTIVE REASONING** Describe the pattern in the table. Then write a rule for multiplying two powers that have the same base.

$$a^m \cdot a^n = a^{\boxed{}}$$

c. Use your rule to simplify the products in the first column of the table above. Does your rule give the results in the third column?

2 ACTIVITY: Using a Calculator

Work with a partner.

Some calculators have *exponent keys* that are used to evaluate powers.

Use a calculator with an exponent key to evaluate the products in Activity 1.

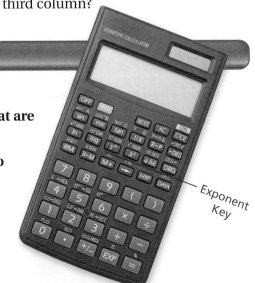

Exponent Key

Laurie's Notes

Introduction

For the Teacher

- **Goal:** Students will explore how to multiply two powers with the same base.

Motivate

- **Story Time:** Tell students that the superintendent has agreed to put you on a special salary schedule for one month. On day 1 you will receive 1¢, on day 2 you will receive 2¢, day 3 is 4¢, and so on, with your salary doubling every school day for the month. There are 23 school days this month. Should you take the new salary?
- Give time for students to start the tabulation. Let them use a calculator for speed. The table below shows the daily pay.

1	$2 = 2^1$	$4 = 2^2$	$8 = 2^3$
$16 = 2^4$	$32 = 2^5$	$64 = 2^6$	$128 = 2^7$
$256 = 2^8$	$512 = 2^9$	$1024 = 2^{10}$	$2048 = 2^{11}$
$4096 = 2^{12}$	$8192 = 2^{13}$	$16{,}384 = 2^{14}$	$32{,}768 = 2^{15}$
$65{,}536 = 2^{16}$	$131{,}072 = 2^{17}$	$262{,}144 = 2^{18}$	$524{,}288 = 2^{19}$
$1{,}048{,}576 = 2^{20}$	$2{,}097{,}152 = 2^{21}$	$4{,}194{,}304 = 2^{22}$	

- If the superintendent is looking for additional math teachers, they will be lined up at the door.
- In this penny doubling problem, each day you are paid a power of 2. Your salary is actually the *sum* of all of these amounts.

Activity Notes

Activity 1

- Have students work with their partner to complete the table. A calculator is not necessary for this activity. The first two problems have been done as examples. Notice the color coding.
- **?** "What did you notice about the number of factors in the middle column and the exponent used to write the power?" same number
- **Part (b):** Students will recognize that the exponents are added together, but it may not be obvious to them how to write this fact using variables.
- **Big Idea:** Write the summary statement: $a^m \cdot a^n = a^{m+n}$. Stress that the bases must be the same. That is why a is the base for both powers. This rule tells us nothing about how to simplify a problem such as $3^3 \cdot 4^2$.

Activity 2

- If students are going to use calculators, they need to know how to use them correctly. Different calculators have different ways in which the powers are entered.

Standards of Learning

8.1(a) The student will simplify numerical expressions involving positive exponents, using rational numbers, order of operations, and properties of operations with real numbers.

Previous Learning

Students should know how to evaluate a power.

Activity Materials	
Introduction	**Textbook**
• calculator	• calculator

Start Thinking! and Warm Up

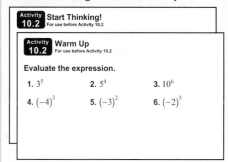

Activity 10.2 Start Thinking!
For use before Activity 10.2

Activity 10.2 Warm Up
For use before Activity 10.2

Evaluate the expression.

1. 3^5 2. 5^4 3. 10^6

4. $(-4)^3$ 5. $(-3)^2$ 6. $(-2)^5$

10.2 Record and Practice Journal

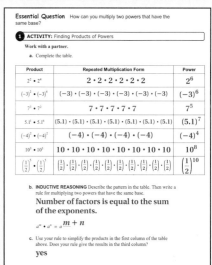

Essential Question How can you multiply two powers that have the same base?

1 ACTIVITY: Finding Products of Powers

Work with a partner.

a. Complete the table.

Product	Repeated Multiplication Form	Power
$2^2 \cdot 2^4$	$2 \cdot 2 \cdot 2 \cdot 2 \cdot 2 \cdot 2$	2^6
$(-3)^2 \cdot (-3)^4$	$(-3) \cdot (-3) \cdot (-3) \cdot (-3) \cdot (-3) \cdot (-3)$	$(-3)^6$
$7^3 \cdot 7^2$	$7 \cdot 7 \cdot 7 \cdot 7 \cdot 7$	7^5
$5.1^1 \cdot 5.1^6$	$(5.1) \cdot (5.1) \cdot (5.1) \cdot (5.1) \cdot (5.1) \cdot (5.1) \cdot (5.1)$	$(5.1)^7$
$(-4)^2 \cdot (-4)^2$	$(-4) \cdot (-4) \cdot (-4) \cdot (-4)$	$(-4)^4$
$10^5 \cdot 10^3$	$10 \cdot 10 \cdot 10 \cdot 10 \cdot 10 \cdot 10 \cdot 10 \cdot 10$	10^8
$\left(\frac{1}{2}\right)^5 \cdot \left(\frac{1}{2}\right)^5$	$\left(\frac{1}{2}\right) \cdot \left(\frac{1}{2}\right) \cdot \left(\frac{1}{2}\right) \cdot \left(\frac{1}{2}\right) \cdot \left(\frac{1}{2}\right) \cdot \left(\frac{1}{2}\right) \cdot \left(\frac{1}{2}\right) \cdot \left(\frac{1}{2}\right) \cdot \left(\frac{1}{2}\right) \cdot \left(\frac{1}{2}\right)$	$\left(\frac{1}{2}\right)^{10}$

b. **INDUCTIVE REASONING** Describe the pattern in the table. Then write a rule for multiplying two powers that have the same base.

Number of factors is equal to the sum of the exponents.

$a^m \cdot a^n = a^{m+n}$

c. Use your rule to simplify the products in the first column of the table above. Does your rule give the results in the third column?

yes

English Language Learners

Pair Activity

Have students work in pairs to simplify exponential expressions. Each student simplifies a different expression. When both students are done, they take turns explaining the solution while the other person follows along.

Activity 3

- Take time to discuss the notation. In position (1, 1), the amount of pennies is $2^1 \cdot 2^1 = 4$. In position (2, 1), the amount of pennies is $2^2 \cdot 2^1 = 8$. Answer any questions about notation or how to find the number of pennies on any square.
- There are many patterns and interesting extensions to this problem that may surface as they explore the questions presented.
- **Part (a):** There are $2^3 \cdot 2^5 = 2^8 = 256$ pennies in location (3, 5).
- **Part (b):** Because $32 = 2^5$, the exponents need to sum to 5. The locations include (1, 4), (4, 1), (2, 3), and (3, 2).
- **Part (c):** The most money will be in the location where x and y have the greatest sum. This will occur at (8, 8), where the value is $2^8 \cdot 2^8 = 2^{16} = 65,536 = \$655.36$.
- **Part (d):** Multiply the number of pennies by the thickness, $65,536 \times 0.06 = 3932.16$ inches.

What Is Your Answer?

- **Neighbor Check:** Have students work independently and then have their neighbor check their work. Have students discuss any discrepancies.

Closure

- Refer back to the penny doubling problem from the beginning of the lesson. What was the first day that your daily pay was more than $1000? day 18

10.2 Record and Practice Journal

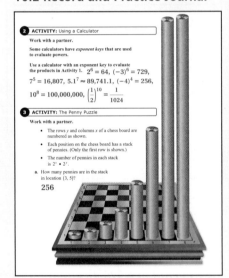

2 ACTIVITY: Using a Calculator

Work with a partner.

Some calculators have *exponent keys* that are used to evaluate powers.

Use a calculator with an exponent key to evaluate the products in Activity 1. $2^6 = 64$, $(-3)^6 = 729$, $7^5 = 16,807$, $5.1^7 \approx 89,741.1$, $(-4)^4 = 256$, $10^8 = 100,000,000$, $\left(\frac{1}{2}\right)^{10} = \frac{1}{1024}$

3 ACTIVITY: The Penny Puzzle

Work with a partner.

- The rows y and columns x of a chess board are numbered as shown.
- Each position on the chess board has a stack of pennies. (Only the first row is shown.)
- The number of pennies in each stack is $2^x \cdot 2^y$.

a. How many pennies are in the stack in location (3, 5)?

256

b. Which locations have 32 pennies in their stacks?

$(1, 4), (2, 3), (3, 2), (4, 1)$

c. How much money (in dollars) is in the location with the tallest stack?

$655.36

d. A penny is about 0.06 inch thick. About how tall (in inches) is the tallest stack?

3932.16 in.

What Is Your Answer?

4. **IN YOUR OWN WORDS** How can you multiply two powers that have the same base? Give two examples of your rule.

Add their exponents then evaluate.

Technology
For the Teacher

Dynamic Classroom

The Dynamic Planning Tool
Editable Teacher's Resources at *BigIdeasMath.com*

ACTIVITY: The Penny Puzzle

Work with a partner.

- The rows y and columns x of a chess board are numbered as shown.
- Each position on the chess board has a stack of pennies. (Only the first row is shown.)
- The number of pennies in each stack is
  $$2^x \cdot 2^y.$$

a. How many pennies are in the stack in location (3, 5)?

b. Which locations have 32 pennies in their stacks?

c. How much money (in dollars) is in the location with the tallest stack?

d. A penny is about 0.06 inch thick. About how tall (in inches) is the tallest stack?

What Is Your Answer?

4. IN YOUR OWN WORDS How can you multiply two powers that have the same base? Give two examples of your rule.

Practice Use what you learned about the Product of Powers Property to complete Exercises 3–5 on page 452.

 **Key Idea**

Product of Powers Property

Words To multiply powers with the same base, add their exponents.

Numbers $4^2 \cdot 4^3 = 4^{2+3} = 4^5$ **Algebra** $a^m \cdot a^n = a^{m+n}$

EXAMPLE ① **Multiplying Powers with the Same Base**

a. $2^4 \cdot 2^5 = 2^{4+5}$ The base is 2. Add the exponents.

$= 2^9$ Simplify.

b. $(-5.1)^{-3} \cdot (-5.1)^3 = (-5.1)^{-3+3}$ The base is -5.1. Add the exponents.

$= (-5.1)^0$ Simplify.

$= 1$ Definition of zero exponent

c. $x^3 \cdot x^7 = x^{3+7}$ The base is x. Add the exponents.

$= x^{10}$ Simplify.

EXAMPLE ② **Finding a Power of a Power**

a. $(3^4)^3 = 3^4 \cdot 3^4 \cdot 3^4$ Write as repeated multiplication.

$= 3^{4+4+4}$ The base is 3. Add the exponents.

$= 3^{12}$ Simplify.

b. $(w^{-5})^4 = w^{-5} \cdot w^{-5} \cdot w^{-5} \cdot w^{-5}$ Write as repeated multiplication.

$= w^{-5+(-5)+(-5)+(-5)}$ The base is w. Add the exponents.

$= w^{-20}$ Simplify.

$= \dfrac{1}{w^{20}}$ Definition of negative exponent

On Your Own

Now You're Ready
Exercises 3–14

Simplify. Write your answer using only positive exponents.

1. $6^2 \cdot 6^4$

2. $\left(-\dfrac{1}{2}\right)^3 \cdot \left(-\dfrac{1}{2}\right)^6$

3. $z \cdot z^{-12}$

4. $(4^{-4})^3$

5. $(y^2)^4$

6. $((-4)^3)^2$

Laurie's Notes

Introduction

Connect

- **Yesterday:** Students explored exponents.
- **Today:** Students will use the Product of Powers Property to simplify expressions.

Motivate

- More money talk! The $10,000 bill, which is no longer in circulation, would be much easier to carry than the same amount in pennies.
- ❓ Ask a few questions about money.
  - "How many pennies equal $10,000?" $100 \times 10,000 = 1,000,000$ or 10^6
  - "How many dimes equal $10,000?" $10 \times 10,000 = 100,000$ or 10^5
  - "How many $10 bills equal $10,000?" $\frac{1}{10} \times 10,000 = 1000$ or 10^3
  - "How many $100 bills equal $10,000?" $\frac{1}{100} \times 10,000 = 100$ or 10^2

Lesson Notes

Key Idea

- Write the Key Idea. Discuss the Words, Numbers, and Algebra.

Example 1

- **Part (a):** Write and simplify the expression. The base is 2 for each power, so add the exponents.
- **Part (b):** Use this problem to remind students of the definition of a zero exponent.
- ❓ "For any nonzero number a, what does a^0 equal?" 1
- ❓ "In part (c), what is the base for each power?" x "Can you still apply the Product of Powers Property?" yes

Example 2

- ❓ "In the expression $\left(3^4\right)^3$, what does the exponent of 3 tell you to do?" Use 3^4 as a factor three times.
- Expand the expression, use the Product of Powers Property and add the exponents.
- **Part (b):** Point out that in the second line of the solution, the use of parentheses in the exponent is for clarity.
- ❓ "What is the definition of a negative exponent?" For any integer n and any nonzero number a, a^{-n} is the reciprocal of a^n.

On Your Own

- Students may struggle with Questions 3 and 5. Assure them that the expressions with variables are simplified the same way as expressions with numbers.
- **Common Error:** When an exponent is 1, it is not written. Students will sometimes forget to add the exponent 1 when multiplying powers.

Goal Today's lesson is using the Product of Powers Property to simplify expressions.

Start Thinking! and Warm Up

Lesson **10.2** Warm Up For use before Lesson 10.2

Lesson **10.2** Start Thinking! For use before Lesson 10.2

Think of an example in geometry where you would need to use the Product of Powers Property.

Extra Example 1

Simplify. Write your answer using only positive exponents.

a. $6^2 \cdot 6^7$ 6^9

b. $-2 \cdot (-2)^3$ $(-2)^4$

c. $x^2 \cdot x^{-5}$ $\dfrac{1}{x^3}$

Extra Example 2

Simplify. Write your answer using only positive exponents.

a. $\left(5^2\right)^3$ 5^6

b. $\left(y^{-4}\right)^6$ $\dfrac{1}{y^{24}}$

⬤ On Your Own

1. 6^6
2. $\left(-\dfrac{1}{2}\right)^9$
3. $\dfrac{1}{z^{11}}$
4. $\dfrac{1}{4^{12}}$
5. y^8
6. $(-4)^6$

Extra Example 3

Simplify. Write your answer using only positive exponents.

a. $(4x)^2$ $16x^2$

b. $(wz)^3$ w^3z^3

On Your Own

7. $625y^4$ 8. $\dfrac{4}{n^2}$

9. a^5b^5

Extra Example 4

In Example 4, the total storage space of a computer is 32 gigabytes. How many bytes of total storage space does the computer have? 2^{35} bytes

On Your Own

10. 2^{34} bytes

Differentiated Instruction

Visual

Remind students that the Product of Powers Property can only be applied to powers having the same base. Have students highlight each unique base with a different color. Then add the exponents.

$$2^4 \cdot 2^5 - \left(3^2\right)^2 = 2^4 \cdot 2^5 - 3^2 \cdot 3^2$$
$$= 2^{4+5} - 3^{2+2}$$
$$= 2^9 - 3^4$$
$$= 512 - 81$$
$$= 431$$

Example 3

- **Common Misconception:** Students sometimes think of this as an application of the Distributive Property and distribute the exponent. Be careful and deliberate with language when simplifying these problems.
- **?** "In part (a), what does the exponent of 3 tell you to do in the expression $(2x)^3$?" Use 2x as a factor three times.
- Write the factor $2x$ three times. Properties of Multiplication (Associative and Commutative) allow you to reorder the terms. Notice that you can identify six factors: three 2's and three x's. Use exponents to write the powers. Finally, 2^3 is rewritten as 8 and the final answer is $8x^3$.
- **Part (b):** Follow the same procedure of writing xy as a factor twice. It is very common for students to write $x \cdot x = 2x$. Do not assume that students will see this error.

On Your Own

- Encourage students to write out the steps in their solution. Show each product as a factor the appropriate number of times.
- **Common Error:** $(0.5)^2 \neq 1$; $(0.5)^2 = 0.25$
- Have volunteers write their solutions on the board.

Example 4

- Writing the verbal model is necessary in this problem because the terms gigabytes and bytes may not be familiar to all students. The first sentence is a conversion fact: 1 GB = 2^{30} bytes. There are 64 GB of total storage. Students may naturally think 64×2^{30} to solve the problem.
- **?** "What is wrong with writing 64×2^{30} to solve the problem?" The answer choices have a base of 2, so try to write each factor in the product with a base of 2.
- Rewrite 64 as a power with a base of 2, $64 = 2^6$. Now you can solve the example.

On Your Own

- Students may respond with $\dfrac{1}{4}$ as much storage space and mean $\dfrac{1}{4}$ the total storage space. In fact, $\dfrac{1}{4}$ of $2^{36} = 2^{34}$. However, this is not an obvious step. Students should model the problem after Example 4.

Closure

- **Exit Ticket:** Simplify. $5^3 \cdot 5^4$ 5^7 $(-3x)^3$ $-27x^3$

Technology For the Teacher

The Dynamic Planning Tool
Editable Teacher's Resources at *BigIdeasMath.com*

EXAMPLE ③ **Finding a Power of a Product**

a. $(2x)^3 = 2x \cdot 2x \cdot 2x$ \qquad Write as repeated multiplication.

$\qquad = (2 \cdot 2 \cdot 2) \cdot (x \cdot x \cdot x)$ \quad Group like bases using properties of multiplication.

$\qquad = 2^{1+1+1} \cdot x^{1+1+1}$ \qquad The bases are 2 and x. Add the exponents.

$\qquad = 2^3 \cdot x^3 = 8x^3$ \qquad Simplify.

b. $(xy)^2 = xy \cdot xy$ \qquad Write as repeated multiplication.

$\qquad = (x \cdot x) \cdot (y \cdot y)$ \qquad Group like bases using properties of multiplication.

$\qquad = x^{1+1} \cdot y^{1+1}$ \qquad The bases are x and y. Add the exponents.

$\qquad = x^2 y^2$ \qquad Simplify.

⚫ **On Your Own**

Simplify. Write your answer using only positive exponents.

Now You're Ready
Exercises 17–22

7. $(-5y)^4$ \qquad **8.** $(0.5n)^{-2}$ \qquad **9.** $(ab)^5$

EXAMPLE ④ **Standardized Test Practice**

Details	⊗
Local Disk (C:)	
Local Disk	
Free Space: 16GB	
Total Space: 64GB	

A gigabyte (GB) of computer storage space is 2^{30} bytes. The details of a computer are shown. How many bytes of total storage space does the computer have?

Ⓐ 2^{34} \qquad Ⓑ 2^{36} \qquad Ⓒ 2^{180} \qquad Ⓓ 128^{30}

The computer has 64 gigabytes of total storage space. Notice that 64 can be written as a power, 2^6. Use a model to solve the problem.

$$\underset{\text{of bytes}}{\text{Total number}} = \underset{\text{in a gigabyte}}{\text{Number of bytes}} \cdot \underset{\text{gigabytes}}{\text{Number of}}$$

$\qquad = 2^{30} \cdot 2^6$ \qquad Substitute.

$\qquad = 2^{30+6}$ \qquad Add exponents.

$\qquad = 2^{36}$ \qquad Simplify.

∴ The computer has 2^{36} bytes of total storage space. The correct answer is Ⓑ.

⚫ **On Your Own**

10. How many bytes of free storage space does the computer have?

 Vocabulary and Concept Check

1. **REASONING** When should you use the Product of Powers Property?

2. **CRITICAL THINKING** Can you use the Product of Powers Property to multiply powers with different bases? Explain.

 Practice and Problem Solving

Simplify. Write your answer using only positive exponents.

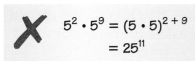

3. $3^2 \cdot 3^2$

4. $8^{10} \cdot 8^{-4}$

5. $(-4)^5 \cdot (-4)^7$

6. $a^{-3} \cdot a^3$

7. $h^6 \cdot h$

8. $\left(\frac{2}{3}\right)^{-2} \cdot \left(\frac{2}{3}\right)^6$

9. $\left(-\frac{5}{7}\right)^8 \cdot \left(-\frac{5}{7}\right)^9$

10. $(-2.9) \cdot (-2.9)^7$

11. $(5^4)^3$

12. $(b^{12})^{-3}$

13. $(3.8^{-3})^{-4}$

14. $\left(\left(-\frac{3}{4}\right)^5\right)^2$

ERROR ANALYSIS Describe and correct the error in simplifying the expression.

15.
$$\text{✗} \quad 5^2 \cdot 5^9 = (5 \cdot 5)^{2+9}$$
$$= 25^{11}$$

16.
$$\text{✗} \quad (r^6)^4 = r^{6+4}$$
$$= r^{10}$$

Simplify. Write your answer using only positive exponents.

17. $(6g)^3$

18. $(2v)^{-5}$

19. $\left(\frac{1}{5}k\right)^2$

20. $(1.2m)^4$

21. $(rt)^{-6}$

22. $\left(-\frac{3}{4}p\right)^3$

23. **CRITICAL THINKING** Is $3^2 + 3^3$ equal to 3^5? Explain.

24. **ARTIFACT** A display case for the artifact is in the shape of a cube. Each side of the display case is three times longer than the width of the artifact.

   a. Write an expression for the volume of the case. Write your answer as a power.

   b. Simplify the expression.

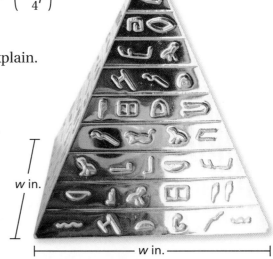

w in.

w in.

Assignment Guide and Homework Check

Level	Day 1 Activity Assignment	Day 2 Lesson Assignment	Homework Check
Basic	3–5, 33–37	1, 2, 6–13, 15–20, 23, 24	10, 12, 16, 18, 23, 24
Average	3–5, 33–37	1, 2, 6–18 even, 19–31 odd, 24, 28	10, 12, 16, 19, 25, 28
Advanced	3–5, 33–37	1, 2, 13–16, 20–23, 26–32	14, 22, 26, 30

Common Errors

- **Exercises 3–14** Students may multiply the bases as well as add the exponents. Remind them that the base stays the same and only the exponent changes when simplifying using the Product of Powers Property.
- **Exercises 11–14** Students may add the exponents when finding the power of a power. Encourage them to write the expression as repeated multiplication and then add the exponents.
- **Exercises 17–22** Students may forget to apply the exponent to the coefficient. Encourage them to write the expression as repeated multiplication and group like bases using properties of multiplication.

10.2 Record and Practice Journal

Simplify. Write your answer using only positive exponents.

1. $(-6)^5 \cdot (-6)^4$
   $(-6)^9$

2. $x^1 \cdot x^9$
   x^{10}

3. $\left(\frac{4}{5}\right)^3 \cdot \left(\frac{4}{5}\right)^{12}$
   $\left(\frac{4}{5}\right)^{15}$

4. $(-1.5)^{-11} \cdot (-1.5)^{11}$
   $(-1.5)^0$

5. $\left(y^{-10}\right)^{20}$
   $\frac{1}{y^{200}}$

6. $\left(\left(-\frac{2}{9}\right)^8\right)^7$
   $\left(-\frac{2}{9}\right)^{56}$

7. $(2a)^6$
   $64a^6$

8. $(-4b)^{-4}$
   $\frac{1}{256b^4}$

9. $\left(-\frac{9}{10}p\right)^2$
   $\frac{81}{100}p^2$

10. $(xy)^{15}$
    $x^{15}y^{15}$

11. $10^5 \cdot 10^5 - \left(10^5\right)^0$
    0

12. $7^2\left(7^{-4} \cdot 7^4\right)$
    49

13. The surface area of the sun is about $4 \times 3.141 \times \left(7 \times 10^5\right)^2$ square kilometers. Simplify the expression.
    $6,156,360,000,000 \text{ km}^2$

Technology For the Teacher
Answer Presentation Tool
QuizShow

Vocabulary and Concept Check

1. when multiplying powers with the same base

2. no; The bases must be the same.

Practice and Problem Solving

3. 3^4

4. 8^6

5. $(-4)^{12}$

6. $a^0 = 1$

7. h^7

8. $\left(\frac{2}{3}\right)^4$

9. $\left(-\frac{5}{7}\right)^{17}$

10. $(-2.9)^8$

11. 5^{12}

12. $\frac{1}{b^{36}}$

13. 3.8^{12}

14. $\left(-\frac{3}{4}\right)^{10}$

15. The bases should not be multiplied.
    $$5^2 \cdot 5^9 = 5^{2+9}$$
    $$= 5^{11}$$

16. The exponents should not be added. Write the expression as repeated multiplication.
    $$\left(r^6\right)^4 = r^6 \cdot r^6 \cdot r^6 \cdot r^6$$
    $$= r^{6+6+6+6}$$
    $$= r^{24}$$

17. $216g^3$

18. $\frac{1}{32v^5}$

19. $\frac{1}{25}k^2$

20. $2.0736m^4$

21. $\frac{1}{r^6 t^6}$

22. $-\frac{27}{64}p^3$

23. no; $3^2 + 3^3 = 9 + 27 = 36$ and $3^5 = 243$

24. a. $(3w)^3$

    b. $27w^3$

Practice and Problem Solving

25. 496

26. x^4

27. 125

28. 3^9 ft

29. a. $16\pi \approx 50.24$ in.^{3}

   b. $192\pi \approx 602.88$ in.^{3}
   Squaring each of the dimensions causes the volume to be 12 times larger.

30. $V = \dfrac{3}{4}b^2h$

31. See *Taking Math Deeper*.

32. a. 3

   b. 4

Fair Game Review

33. 4

34. 25

35. 3

36. 6

37. B

Mini-Assessment

Simplify. Write your answer using only positive exponents.

1. $b^2 \cdot b^6$ b^8

2. $(-2)^3 \cdot (-2)^{-1}$ $(-2)^2$

3. $\left(c^8\right)^3$ c^{24}

4. $(-4w)^4$ $256w^4$

5. $(st)^{11}$ $s^{11}t^{11}$

Taking Math Deeper

Exercise 31

This exercise gives students some practice in representing large numbers as powers.

1 Summarize the given information.

Mail delivered each second: $2^6 \cdot 5^3 = 8000$
Seconds in 6 days: $2^8 \cdot 3^4 \cdot 5^2 = 518{,}400$
How many pieces of mail in 6 days?

2 Multiply to find the number of pieces of mail delivered in 6 days.

$$(2^6 \cdot 5^3)(2^8 \cdot 3^4 \cdot 5^2) = 2^6 \cdot 5^3 \cdot 2^8 \cdot 3^4 \cdot 5^2$$
$$= 2^{14} \cdot 3^4 \cdot 5^5$$

A lot of mail

3 Write the number in normal decimal form.

If you expand this number, you find that the U.S. postal service delivers about 4 billion pieces of mail each week (6 days not counting Sunday). This is an average of about 13 pieces of mail per week for each person in the United States!

Project

Research the price of a postage stamp. How many times has it changed? How often has it changed? What has been the range in the cost over the last one hundred years?

Reteaching and Enrichment Strategies

If students need help...	If students got it...
Resources by Chapter • Practice A and Practice B • Puzzle Time Record and Practice Journal Practice Differentiating the Lesson Lesson Tutorials Skills Review Handbook	Resources by Chapter • Enrichment and Extension Start the next section

Simplify the expression.

25. $2^4 \cdot 2^5 - (2^2)^2$

26. $16\left(\dfrac{1}{2}x\right)^4$

27. $5^{-2}(5^3 \cdot 5^2)$

28. **CLOUDS** The lowest altitude of an altocumulus cloud is about 3^8 feet. The highest altitude of an altocumulus cloud is about 3 times the lowest altitude. What is the highest altitude of an altocumulus cloud? Write your answer as a power.

29. **PYTHON EGG** The volume V of a python egg is given by the formula $V = \dfrac{4}{3}\pi abc$. For the python egg shown, $a = 2$ inches, $b = 2$ inches, and $c = 3$ inches.

   a. Find the volume of the python egg.

   b. Square the dimensions of the python egg. Then evaluate the formula. How does this volume compare to your answer in part (a)?

30. **PYRAMID** The volume of a square pyramid is $V = \dfrac{1}{3}b^2 h$, where b is the length of one side of the base and h is the height of the pyramid. The length of each side of the base increases by 50%. Write a formula for the volume of the new pyramid.

31. **MAIL** The United States Postal Service delivers about $2^6 \cdot 5^3$ pieces of mail each second. There are $2^8 \cdot 3^4 \cdot 5^2$ seconds in 6 days. How many pieces of mail does the United States Postal Service deliver in 6 days? Write your answer as a power.

32. *Critical Thinking* Find the value of x in the equation without evaluating the power.

   a. $2^5 \cdot 2^x = 256$

   b. $\left(\dfrac{1}{3}\right)^2 \cdot \left(\dfrac{1}{3}\right)^x = \dfrac{1}{729}$

Fair Game Review What you learned in previous grades & lessons

Simplify. *(Skills Review Handbook)*

33. $\dfrac{4 \cdot 4}{4}$

34. $\dfrac{5 \cdot 5 \cdot 5}{5}$

35. $\dfrac{2 \cdot 3}{2}$

36. $\dfrac{8 \cdot 6 \cdot 6}{6 \cdot 8}$

37. **MULTIPLE CHOICE** What is the measure of each angle of the regular polygon? *(Section 5.3)*

   (A) 45°

   (B) 135°

   (C) 1080°

   (D) 1440°

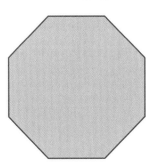

You can use an **information wheel** to organize information about a topic. Here is an example of an information wheel for exponents.

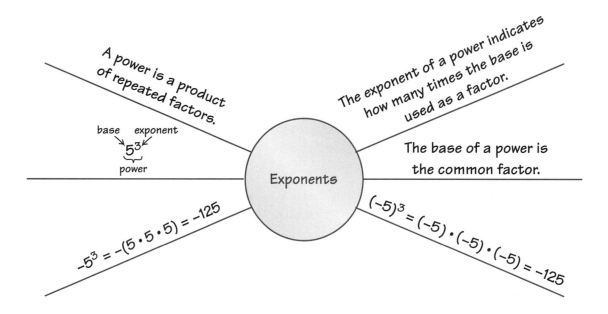

On Your Own

Make an information wheel to help you study these topics.

1. zero exponents

2. negative exponents

3. Product of Powers Property

After you complete this chapter, make information wheels for the following topics.

4. Quotient of Powers Property

5. writing numbers in standard form

6. writing numbers in scientific notation

7. Choose three other topics you studied earlier in this course. Make an information wheel for each topic.

"My information wheel **for Fluffy** has **matching adjectives and nouns.**"

Sample Answers

1.

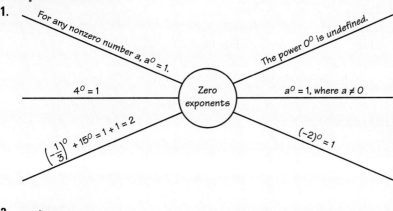

For any nonzero number a, $a^0 = 1$.

The power 0^0 is undefined.

$4^0 = 1$

Zero exponents

$a^0 = 1$, where $a \neq 0$

$\left(-\frac{1}{3}\right)^0 + 15^0 = 1 + 1 = 2$

$(-2)^0 = 1$

2.

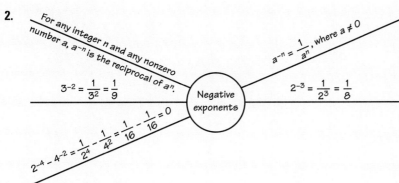

For any integer n and any nonzero number a, a^{-n} is the reciprocal of a^n.

$a^{-n} = \frac{1}{a^n}$, where $a \neq 0$

$3^{-2} = \frac{1}{3^2} = \frac{1}{9}$

Negative exponents

$2^{-3} = \frac{1}{2^3} = \frac{1}{8}$

$2^{-4} - 4^{-2} = \frac{1}{2^4} - \frac{1}{4^2} = \frac{1}{16} - \frac{1}{16} = 0$

3.

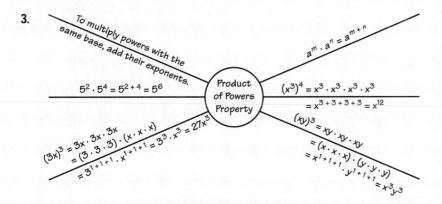

To multiply powers with the same base, add their exponents.

$a^m \cdot a^n = a^{m+n}$

$5^2 \cdot 5^4 = 5^{2+4} = 5^6$

Product of Powers Property

$(x^3)^4 = x^3 \cdot x^3 \cdot x^3 \cdot x^3$
$= x^{3+3+3+3} = x^{12}$

$(3x)^3 = 3x \cdot 3x \cdot 3x$
$= (3 \cdot 3 \cdot 3) \cdot (x \cdot x \cdot x)$
$= 3^{1+1+1} \cdot x^{1+1+1} = 3^3 \cdot x^3 = 27x^3$

$(xy)^3 = xy \cdot xy \cdot xy$
$= (x \cdot x \cdot x) \cdot (y \cdot y \cdot y)$
$= x^{1+1+1} \cdot y^{1+1+1} = x^3 y^3$

List of Organizers
Available at *BigIdeasMath.com*

Comparison Chart
Concept Circle
Definition (Idea) and Example Chart
Example and Non-Example Chart
Formula Triangle
Four Square
Information Frame
Information Wheel
Notetaking Organizer
Process Diagram
Summary Triangle
Word Magnet
Y Chart

About this Organizer

An **Information Wheel** can be used to organize information about a concept. Students write the concept in the middle of the "wheel." Then students write information related to the concept on the "spokes" of the wheel. Related information can include, but is not limited to: vocabulary words or terms, definitions, formulas, procedures, examples, and visuals. This type of organizer serves as a good summary tool because any information related to a concept can be included.

Technology
For the Teacher

Vocabulary Puzzle Builder

Answers

1. $\dfrac{1}{64}$

2. $\dfrac{1}{4}$

3. 1

4. $-\dfrac{1}{16}$

5. $(-6)^5$

6. $\left(\dfrac{6}{7}\right)^0 = 1$

7. -2.3

8. $\dfrac{1}{8^6}$

9. $0.36f^2$

10. $\dfrac{1}{64}t^3$

11. $\dfrac{1}{256z^4}$

12. $\dfrac{1}{9m^2}$

13. $\$3.00$

14. 1.728 cm^3

15. 0.1 m

16. no;
$$(ab)^2 = (ab) \cdot (ab)$$
$$= a \cdot a \cdot b \cdot b = a^2 b^2$$

17. 10^6 times greater

Assessment Book

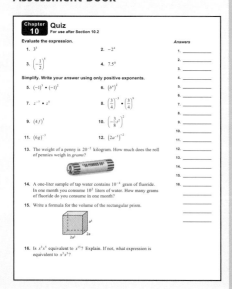

Alternative Quiz Ideas

100% Quiz	Math Log
Error Notebook	Notebook Quiz
Group Quiz	Partner Quiz
Homework Quiz	Pass the Paper

100% Quiz

This is a quiz where students are given the answers and then they have to explain and justify each answer.

Reteaching and Enrichment Strategies

If students need help. . .	If students got it. . .
Resources by Chapter • Study Help • Practice A and Practice B • Puzzle Time Lesson Tutorials *BigIdeasMath.com* Practice Quiz Practice from the Test Generator	Resources by Chapter • Enrichment and Extension • School-to-Work Game Closet at *BigIdeasMath.com* Start the next section

Technology For the Teacher

Answer Presentation Tool
Big Ideas Test Generator

Evaluate the expression. *(Section 10.1)*

1. 4^{-3}

2. $\left(-\dfrac{1}{2}\right)^2$

3. $\left(-\dfrac{2}{3}\right)^0$

4. -2^{-4}

Simplify. Write your answer using only positive exponents. *(Section 10.2)*

5. $(-6)^2 \cdot (-6)^3$

6. $\left(\dfrac{6}{7}\right)^{-4} \cdot \left(\dfrac{6}{7}\right)^4$

7. $(-2.3)^{-1} \cdot (-2.3)^2$

8. $\left(8^2\right)^{-3}$

9. $(0.6f)^2$

10. $\left(\dfrac{1}{4}t\right)^3$

11. $(4z)^{-4}$

12. $(3m)^{-2}$

13. **SHOPPING** Apricot jelly costs 2^{-2} dollar per ounce. How much does the jar of jelly cost? *(Section 10.1)*

14. **VOLUME** The volume of a cube is s^3, where s is the length of one side of the cube. A cube has a side length of 1.2 centimeters. What is the volume of the cube in cubic centimeters? *(Section 10.1)*

15. **GECKO** Find the length of the gecko in *meters*. (1 mm = 10^{-3} m) *(Section 10.2)*

16. **CRITICAL THINKING** Is $(ab)^2$ equivalent to ab^2? Explain. *(Section 10.2)*

17. **WEIGHT** The weight of a lion is 10^3 times greater than the weight of a bird. The weight of a whale is 10^3 times greater than the weight of the lion. How many times greater is the weight of the whale than the weight of the bird? *(Section 10.2)*

10.3 Quotient of Powers Property

STANDARDS
OF LEARNING
8.1

Essential Question How can you divide two powers that have the same base?

1 ACTIVITY: Finding Quotients of Powers

Work with a partner.

a. Copy and complete the table.

Quotient	Repeated Multiplication Form	Power
$\dfrac{2^4}{2^2}$	$\dfrac{\overset{1}{\cancel{2}}\cdot\overset{1}{\cancel{2}}\cdot 2\cdot 2}{\underset{1}{\cancel{2}}\cdot\underset{1}{\cancel{2}}}$	2^2
$\dfrac{(-4)^5}{(-4)^2}$	$\dfrac{\overset{1}{\cancel{(-4)}}\cdot\overset{1}{\cancel{(-4)}}\cdot(-4)\cdot(-4)\cdot(-4)}{\underset{1}{\cancel{(-4)}}\cdot\underset{1}{\cancel{(-4)}}}$	$(-4)^3$
$\dfrac{7^7}{7^3}$		
$\dfrac{8.5^9}{8.5^6}$		
$\dfrac{10^8}{10^5}$		
$\dfrac{3^{12}}{3^4}$		
$\dfrac{(-5)^7}{(-5)^5}$		
$\dfrac{11^4}{11^1}$		

b. INDUCTIVE REASONING Describe the pattern in the table. Then write a rule for dividing two powers that have the same base.

$$\frac{a^m}{a^n} = a^{\boxed{}}$$

c. Use your rule to simplify the quotients in the first column of the table above. Does your rule give the results in the third column?

456   Chapter 10   Exponents and Scientific Notation

Laurie's Notes

Introduction

For the Teacher

- **Goal:** Students will explore how to divide two powers with the same base.
- Remember to use correct vocabulary in this lesson. The numbers are not *canceling*. There is no mathematical definition of *cancel*. It is the factors that are common in the numerator and the denominator that are being divided out, similar to simplifying fractions. The fraction $\frac{2}{4} = \frac{1}{2}$ because there is a common factor of 2 in both the numerator and denominator that divide out. This same concept of dividing out common factors is why the Quotient of Powers Property works.

Motivate

- Tell students that you spent last evening working on a very long problem and you want them to give it a try. Write the problem on the board.

$$\frac{1}{2} \cdot \frac{2}{3} \cdot \frac{3}{4} \cdot \frac{4}{5} \cdot \frac{5}{6} \cdot \frac{6}{7} \cdot \frac{7}{8} \cdot \frac{8}{9} \cdot \frac{9}{10}$$

- It is likely that at least one of your students will recognize the answer immediately after you finish writing the problem. Act surprised and ask for their strategy...because you spent a long time on the problem.
- You want all students to recognize that the common factors in the numerator divide out with common factors in the denominator, leaving only $\frac{1}{10}$ as the final answer.

Activity Notes

Activity 1

- Have students work with their partner to complete the table. The first two problems have been done as examples. Notice the color coding. Also notice that integers and decimals are used as bases.
- **?** "What do you notice about the number of factors in the numerator and denominator of the middle column, and the exponent used to write the power?" When you subtract the number of factors in the denominator from the number of factors in the numerator, it equals the exponent in the power.
- Students may need help in writing the summary statement: $\frac{a^m}{a^n} = a^{m-n}$. Stress that the bases must be the same in order to use this property.

Standards of Learning

8.1(a) The student will simplify numerical expressions involving positive exponents, using rational numbers, order of operations, and properties of operations with real numbers.

Previous Learning

Students should know how to simplify fractions by dividing out common factors.

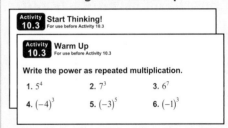

Activity Materials	
Introduction	**Textbook**
• calculator	• plastic cubes

Start Thinking! and Warm Up

Activity 10.3 Start Thinking!
For use before Activity 10.3

Activity 10.3 Warm Up
For use before Activity 10.3

Write the power as repeated multiplication.

1. 5^4 2. 7^3 3. 6^7

4. $(-4)^3$ 5. $(-3)^5$ 6. $(-1)^3$

10.3 Record and Practice Journal

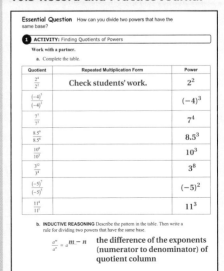

Differentiated Instruction

Kinesthetic

Use algebra tiles or slips of paper to help students understand the Quotient of Powers Property. Have students model the quotient $\dfrac{x^4}{x^2}$.

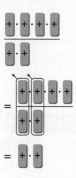

So, $\dfrac{x^4}{x^2} = x^2$.

10.3 Record and Practice Journal

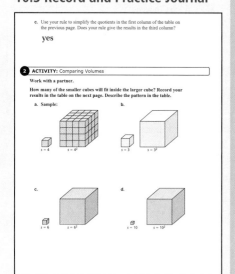

c. Use your rule to simplify the quotients in the first column of the table on the previous page. Does your rule give the results in the third column?

yes

2 **ACTIVITY: Comparing Volumes**

Work with a partner.

How many of the smaller cubes will fit inside the larger cube? Record your results in the table on the next page. Describe the pattern in the table.

	Volume of Smaller Cube	Volume of Larger Cube	Larger Volume / Smaller Volume	Answer
a.	4^3	$(4^2)^3 = 4^6$	$\dfrac{4^6}{4^3}$	4^3
b.	3^3	$(3^2)^3 = 3^6$	$\dfrac{3^6}{3^3}$	3^3
c.	6^3	$(6^2)^3 = 6^6$	$\dfrac{6^6}{6^3}$	6^3
d.	10^3	$(10^2)^3 = 10^6$	$\dfrac{10^6}{10^3}$	10^3

What Is Your Answer?

3. **IN YOUR OWN WORDS** How can you divide two powers that have the same base? Give two examples of your rule.

Subtract their exponents then evaluate.

Laurie's Notes

Activity 2

- If you have small wooden or plastic cubes available, model one of these problems or a similar problem to start.
- Point out to students that $s = 4$ means the edge (or side) length is 4. In part (a), the side length of the larger cube is 4^2 or 16, which is 4 times as long as the small red cube. You can see it is four times longer by looking at the additional lines that have been drawn on the larger cube. Those same markings do not appear on the remaining cubes.
- When completing the table, it is necessary for students to simplify a power raised to an exponent as shown in part (a). Recall,
  $$\left(4^2\right)^3 = 4^2 \cdot 4^2 \cdot 4^2 = 4^{2+2+2} = 4^6.$$
- Have students work with their partner to complete the table.
- **?** "How do you find the volume of the small cube each time?" Cube the side length; s^3.
- **?** "How do you find the volume of the larger cube each time?" Cube the side length; s^3; The side length for the larger cube, however, is a power.
- When finding the ratio of the volumes, students will need to divide out the common factors.
- **?** "What do you notice about the volume of the small cube and the answer?" The answer is always the same as the volume of the small cube.

What Is Your Answer?

- **Think-Pair-Share:** Students should read the question independently and then work with a partner to answer the question. When they have answered the question, the pair should compare their answer with another group and discuss any discrepancies.

Closure

- Simplify.

1. $\dfrac{2^2}{2} \cdot \dfrac{2^3}{2^2} \cdot \dfrac{2^4}{2^3}$ 2^3

2. $\dfrac{(-3)^7}{(-3)^4}$ $(-3)^3$

Technology For the Teacher

Dynamic Classroom

The Dynamic Planning Tool
Editable Teacher's Resources at *BigIdeasMath.com*

Work with a partner.

How many of the smaller cubes will fit inside the larger cube? Record your results in the table. Describe the pattern in the table.

a. **Sample:**

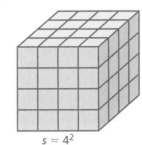

$s = 4$ $s = 4^2$

b.

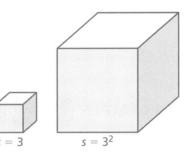

$s = 3$ $s = 3^2$

c.

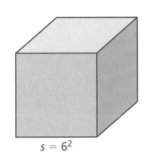

$s = 6$ $s = 6^2$

d.

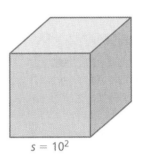

$s = 10$ $s = 10^2$

	Volume of Smaller Cube	Volume of Larger Cube	Larger Volume / Smaller Volume	Answer
a.	4^3	$(4^2)^3 = 4^6$	$\dfrac{4^6}{4^3}$	4^3
b.				
c.				
d.				

What Is Your Answer?

3. **IN YOUR OWN WORDS** How can you divide two powers that have the same base? Give two examples of your rule.

Practice

Use what you learned about the Quotient of Powers Property to complete Exercises 3–6 on page 460.

10.3 Lesson

 **Key Idea**

> **Quotient of Powers Property**
>
> **Words** To divide powers with the same base, subtract their exponents.
>
> **Numbers** $\dfrac{4^5}{4^2} = 4^{5-2} = 4^3$ **Algebra** $\dfrac{a^m}{a^n} = a^{m-n}$, where $a \neq 0$

EXAMPLE 1 Dividing Powers with the Same Base

a. $\dfrac{2^6}{2^4} = 2^{6-4}$ The base is 2. Subtract the exponents.

    $= 2^2$ Simplify.

> **Common Error** ⚠
>
> When dividing powers, do not divide the bases.
> $\dfrac{2^6}{2^4} = 2^2$, not 1^2.

b. $\dfrac{(-7)^3}{(-7)^9} = (-7)^{3-9}$ The base is -7. Subtract the exponents.

    $= (-7)^{-6}$ Simplify.

    $= \dfrac{1}{(-7)^6}$ Definition of negative exponent

c. $\dfrac{h^7}{h^6} = h^{7-6}$ The base is h. Subtract the exponents.

    $= h^1 = h$ Simplify.

⬤ **On Your Own**

Now You're Ready
Exercises 3–14

Simplify. Write your answer using only positive exponents.

1. $\dfrac{9^4}{9^7}$ 2. $\dfrac{4.2^6}{4.2^5}$ 3. $\dfrac{(-8)^8}{(-8)^4}$ 4. $\dfrac{x^3}{x^{-8}}$

EXAMPLE 2 Simplifying an Expression

Simplify $\dfrac{3^4 \cdot 3^2}{3^3}$. **Write your answer using only positive exponents.**

> The numerator is a product of powers.

$\dfrac{3^4 \cdot 3^2}{3^3} = \dfrac{3^{4+2}}{3^3}$ The base is 3. Add the exponents in the numerator.

    $= \dfrac{3^6}{3^3}$ Simplify.

    $= 3^{6-3}$ The base is 3. Subtract the exponents.

    $= 3^3$ Simplify.

Laurie's Notes

Introduction

Connect
- **Yesterday:** Students explored exponents.
- **Today:** Students will use the Quotient of Powers Property to simplify expressions.

Motivate
- **Preparation:** Find the area of your classroom in square feet. Select two smaller regions of your room that make logical sense given the shape of your room. My classroom is shown. I found the area of the entire room (A + B); the area of B; and the area of C.

- Have students stand around the room so that they are an arm's length away from everyone else.
- Ask them to stand only in region B (which includes C).
- Ask them to move into region C. It should be very tight.
- Ask them to describe the three regions and how they felt about personal space. Then discuss population density and compute it for each region.

Lesson Notes

Key Idea
- Write the Key Idea. Discuss the Words, Numbers, and Algebra.

Example 1
- **? Part (a):** Write and simplify the expression. The base is 2 for each power. Ask the following questions to help develop correct vocabulary.
  - "How many factors of 2 are in the numerator?" 6
  - "How many factors of 2 are in the denominator?" 4
  - "How many factors of 2 are common in *both* the numerator and denominator?" 4
  - "How many factors of 2 remain after you divide out the common factors?" 2
- Repeat similar questions for parts (b) and (c). Note that in part (b), the remaining factors are in the denominator.

Example 2
- **?** This example combines two properties. Ask the following questions.
  - "How many factors of 3 are in the numerator?" $4 + 2 = 6$
  - "How many factors of 3 are in the denominator?" 3
  - "How many factors of 3 are common in *both* the numerator and denominator?" 3
  - "How many factors of 3 remain after you divide out the common factors?" 3

Goal Today's lesson is using the Quotient of Powers Property to simplify expressions.

Start Thinking! and Warm Up

Lesson 10.3	Warm Up
	For use before Lesson 10.3

Lesson 10.3 Start Thinking! For use before Lesson 10.3

Scott learned about the Quotient of Powers Property in math class, but he is not convinced that it is helpful. For example, he thinks that it is just as easy to simplify $\frac{2^5}{2^2}$ by calculating $2^5 = 32$ and dividing by $2^2 = 4$ to get 8. Do you agree or disagree with Scott? Give reasons to support your answer.

Extra Example 1

Simplify. Write your answer using only positive exponents.

a. $\frac{3^7}{3^4}$ 3^3

b. $\frac{(-2)^3}{(-2)^{10}}$ $\frac{1}{(-2)^7}$

c. $\frac{p^7}{p^6}$ p

On Your Own

1. $\frac{1}{9^3}$ 2. 4.2

3. $(-8)^4$ 4. x^{11}

Extra Example 2

Simplify $\frac{5^6 \cdot 5^2}{5^4}$. Write your answer using only positive exponents. 5^4

Extra Example 3

Simplify $\dfrac{z^6}{z^2} \cdot \dfrac{z^8}{z^5}$. Write your answer using only positive exponents. z^7

 On Your Own

   5. 2^7 **6.** d^3

Extra Example 4

The projected population of Hawaii in 2020 is about $5.48 \cdot 2^{18}$. The land area of Hawaii is about 2^{14} square kilometers. Predict the average number of people per square kilometer in 2020. about 88 people per km^2

 On Your Own

   7. about 36 people per km^2

English Language Learners

Organization

Have students organize the *Key Ideas* of this chapter in their notebooks. This will provide them with easy access to the material and concepts of the chapter.

Key Idea	Product of Powers Property	Quotient of Powers Property
Example	$(-3)^2(-3)^4$	$\dfrac{5^3}{5^2}$
Answer	$(-3)^6 = 729$	5
Method	Add exponents: $2 + 4$	Subtract exponents: $3 - 2$

Example 3

- This example also combines two properties.
- Work through the problem as shown.
- Discuss the approach with students. Each quotient was simplified first and then the product of the two expressions was found.
- **?** "Will the answer be the same if the product of the two expressions is found and then the quotient is simplified? Explain." yes; It is the same as multiplying two fractions and then simplifying the answer.
- Simplify the expression using the alternate approach in the Study Tip.

$$\frac{a^{10}}{a^6} \cdot \frac{a^7}{a^4} = \frac{a^{10} \cdot a^7}{a^6 \cdot a^4} = \frac{a^{10+7}}{a^{6+4}} = \frac{a^{17}}{a^{10}} = a^{17-10} = a^7$$

On Your Own

- There is more than one way to simplify these expressions. Remind students to think about the number of factors as they work the problems.
- **Question 6:** Students may forget that $d = d^1$.
- Have volunteers write their solutions on the board.

Example 4

- This problem is about population density, the number of people per square unit. In this case, it is the projected number of people in Tennessee per square mile in 2030.
- When working through this problem, notice that the factor 5 in the numerator is not the same base as the other two factors.
- **?** "Why can you move 5 out of the numerator and write it as a whole number times the quotient of $(5.9)^8$ and $(5.9)^6$?" definition of multiplying fractions
- Simplify the quotient and multiply by 5.
- Use local landmarks to help students visualize the size of a square mile.

Closure

- Explain how the Quotient of Powers Property is related to simplifying fractions. You divide out the common factors.

Technology For the Teacher

Dynamic Classroom

The Dynamic Planning Tool
Editable Teacher's Resources at *BigIdeasMath.com*

Study Tip

You can also simplify the expression in Example 3 as follows.

$$\frac{a^{10}}{a^6} \cdot \frac{a^7}{a^4} = \frac{a^{10} \cdot a^7}{a^6 \cdot a^4}$$

$$= \frac{a^{17}}{a^{10}}$$

$$= a^{17-10}$$

$$= a^7$$

Simplify $\dfrac{a^{10}}{a^6} \cdot \dfrac{a^7}{a^4}$. Write your answer using only positive exponents.

$$\frac{a^{10}}{a^6} \cdot \frac{a^7}{a^4} = a^{10-6} \cdot a^{7-4} \qquad \text{Subtract the exponents.}$$

$$= a^4 \cdot a^3 \qquad\qquad \text{Simplify.}$$

$$= a^{4+3} \qquad\qquad \text{Add the exponents.}$$

$$= a^7 \qquad\qquad\quad \text{Simplify.}$$

● **On Your Own**

Now You're Ready
Exercises 16–21

Simplify. Write your answer using only positive exponents.

5. $\dfrac{2^{15}}{2^3 \cdot 2^5}$

6. $\dfrac{d^5}{d} \cdot \dfrac{d^8}{d^9}$

EXAMPLE ④ **Real-Life Application**

The projected population of Tennessee in 2030 is about $5 \cdot 5.9^8$. Predict the average number of people per square mile in 2030.

Use a model to solve the problem.

$$\frac{\text{People per}}{\text{square mile}} = \frac{\text{Population in 2030}}{\text{Land area}}$$

Land Area: about 5.9^6 mi²

$$= \frac{5 \cdot 5.9^8}{5.9^6} \qquad \text{Substitute.}$$

$$= 5 \cdot \frac{5.9^8}{5.9^6} \qquad \text{Rewrite.}$$

$$= 5 \cdot 5.9^2 \qquad \text{Subtract the exponents.}$$

$$= 174.05 \qquad \text{Evaluate.}$$

∴ There will be about 174 people per square mile in Tennessee in 2030.

● **On Your Own**

Now You're Ready
Exercises 23–28

7. The projected population of Alabama in 2020 is about $2.25 \cdot 2^{21}$. The land area of Alabama is about 2^{17} square kilometers. Predict the average number of people per square kilometer in 2020.

 Vocabulary and Concept Check

1. **WRITING** Explain what it means to divide powers.

2. **WHICH ONE DOESN'T BELONG?** Which quotient does *not* belong with the other three? Explain your reasoning.

$$\dfrac{(-10)^7}{(-10)^2} \qquad \dfrac{6^3}{6^2} \qquad \dfrac{(-4)^8}{(-3)^4} \qquad \dfrac{5^6}{5^3}$$

 Practice and Problem Solving

Simplify. Write your answer using only positive exponents.

 **3.** $\dfrac{6^{10}}{6^4}$ **4.** $\dfrac{8^7}{8^9}$ **5.** $\dfrac{(-3)^4}{(-3)^1}$ **6.** $\dfrac{4.5^{-5}}{4.5^{-5}}$

7. $\dfrac{5^9}{5^3}$ **8.** $\dfrac{64^4}{64^3}$ **9.** $\dfrac{(-17)^{-5}}{(-17)^{-2}}$ **10.** $\dfrac{(-7.9)^{10}}{(-7.9)^4}$

11. $\dfrac{(-6.4)^8}{(-6.4)^{-6}}$ **12.** $\dfrac{\pi^{11}}{\pi^7}$ **13.** $\dfrac{b^{11}}{b^{24}}$ **14.** $\dfrac{n^{18}}{n^7}$

15. **ERROR ANALYSIS** Describe and correct the error in simplifying the quotient.

$$\cancel{\qquad} \quad \dfrac{6^{15}}{6^5} = 6^{\frac{15}{5}}$$
$$= 6^3$$

Simplify. Write your answer using only positive exponents.

16. $\dfrac{7^5 \cdot 7^3}{7^8}$ **17.** $\dfrac{2^{19} \cdot 2^5}{2^{12} \cdot 2^3}$ **18.** $\dfrac{(-8.3)^8}{(-8.3)^7} \cdot \dfrac{(-8.3)^4}{(-8.3)^3}$

19. $\dfrac{\pi^{30}}{\pi^{18} \cdot \pi^{24}}$ **20.** $\dfrac{c^{22}}{c^8 \cdot c^9}$ **21.** $\dfrac{k^{13}}{k^5} \cdot \dfrac{k^{11}}{k^{20}}$

22. **SOUND INTENSITY** The sound intensity of a normal conversation is 10^6 times greater than the quietest noise a person can hear. The sound intensity of a jet at takeoff is 10^{14} times greater than the quietest noise a person can hear. How many times more intense is the sound of a jet at takeoff than the sound of a normal conversation?

Assignment Guide and Homework Check

Level	Day 1 Activity Assignment	Day 2 Lesson Assignment	Homework Check
Basic	3–6, 33–37	1, 2, 7–21 odd, 22, 23–27 odd	9, 17, 21, 22, 25
Average	3–6, 33–37	1, 2, 7–27 odd, 29, 30	9, 17, 21, 25, 30
Advanced	3–6, 33–37	1, 2, 13–15, 20, 21, 26–32	14, 20, 26, 30, 31

Common Errors

- **Exercises 3–14** Students may divide the exponents instead of subtracting the exponents. Remind them that the Quotient of Powers Property states that the exponents are subtracted.
- **Exercises 16–21** Students may multiply and/or divide the bases when simplifying the expression. Remind them that the base does not change when using the Product of Powers or Quotient of Powers Properties to simplify an expression.
- **Exercises 23–28** Students may try to combine powers that do not have the same base. Remind them that the Product of Powers and Quotient of Powers Properties can only be used with powers that have the same base.

10.3 Record and Practice Journal

Simplify. Write your answer using only positive exponents.

1. $\frac{7^6}{7^5}$

7^1

2. $\frac{(-21)^{11}}{(-21)^5}$

$(-21)^6$

3. $\frac{8.6^{11}}{8.6^4}$

$(8.6)^7$

4. $\frac{(3.9)^{20}}{(3.9)^{-10}}$

$(3.9)^{30}$

5. $\frac{t^{-7}}{t^{-3}}$

$\frac{1}{t^4}$

6. $\frac{d^{32}}{d^{16}}$

d^{16}

7. $\frac{8^7 \cdot 8^4}{8^9}$

8^2

8. $\frac{(-1.1)^{15} \cdot (-1.1)^{12}}{(-1.1)^{10} \cdot (-1.1)^3}$

$(-1.1)^{14}$

9. $\frac{m^{30}}{m^{22}} \cdot \frac{m^{-17}}{m^{15}}$

$\frac{1}{m^4}$

10. $\frac{k \cdot 3^5}{3^1}$

$81k$

11. $\frac{x^4 \cdot y^{30} \cdot 2^{11}}{y^{10} \cdot 2^7}$

$16x^4y^{20}$

12. $\frac{a^{15}b^{19}}{a^6b^{12}}$

a^9b^7

13. The radius of a basketball is about 3.6 times greater than the radius of a tennis ball. How many times greater is the volume of a basketball than the volume of a tennis ball? (Note: The volume of a sphere is $V = \frac{4}{3}\pi r^3$.)

46.656

Vocabulary and Concept Check

1. *Sample answer:* To divide powers with the same base, write the power with the common base and the exponent found by subtracting the exponent in the denominator from the exponent in the numerator.

2. $\frac{(-4)^8}{(-3)^4}$; The other quotients have powers with the same base.

Practice and Problem Solving

3. 6^6

4. $\frac{1}{8^2}$

5. $(-3)^3$

6. $4.5^0 = 1$

7. 5^6

8. 64

9. $\frac{1}{(-17)^3}$

10. $(-7.9)^6$

11. $(-6.4)^{14}$

12. π^4

13. $\frac{1}{b^{13}}$

14. n^{11}

15. You should subtract the exponents instead of dividing them.

$$\frac{6^{15}}{6^5} = 6^{15-5}$$
$$= 6^{10}$$

16. $7^0 = 1$

17. 2^9

18. $(-8.3)^2$

19. $\frac{1}{\pi^{12}}$

20. c^5

21. $\frac{1}{k}$

22. 10^8 times

Practice and Problem Solving

23. $64x$

24. $6w$

25. $125a^3b^2$

26. $125cd^2$

27. $\dfrac{x^7}{y^6}$

28. m^9

29. See *Taking Math Deeper*.

30. a. *Sample answer:* $m = 5$, $n = 3$

   b. yes; Any two numbers that satisfy the equation $m - n = 2$.

31. 10^{13} galaxies

32. 10; The difference in the exponents needs to be 9. To find x, solve the equation $3x - (2x + 1) = 9$.

Fair Game Review

33. -9

34. -8

35. 61

36. -4

37. B

Mini-Assessment

Simplify. Write your answer using only positive exponents.

1. $\dfrac{(-4)^1}{(-4)^3}$ $\dfrac{1}{(-4)^2}$

2. $\dfrac{9.7^7}{9.7^3}$ 9.7^4

3. $\dfrac{5^4 \cdot 5^2}{5^3}$ 5^3

4. $\dfrac{m^{10}}{m^5 \cdot m^2}$ m^3

5. $\dfrac{y^{17}}{y^{10}} \cdot \dfrac{y^3}{y^6}$ y^4

Taking Math Deeper

Exercise 29

In this problem, the memory in the different styles of MP3 players increases exponentially, but the price increases linearly.

 Compare Player D with Player B.

   a. $\dfrac{2^4}{2^2} = 2^2 = 4$ times more memory

4 times as much

 Compare the memory with the price.

If you plot the five points representing the memory and the prices, you get the following graph.

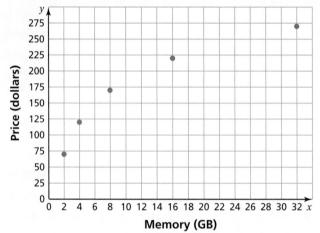

③ Answer the question.

   b. This graph does not show a constant rate of change. In other words, the relationship between price and memory is not linear. However, the differences in price between consecutive sizes reflect a constant rate of change.

Project

What changes in technology have occurred over the past 50 years? What do you predict will change over the next 50 years?

Reteaching and Enrichment Strategies

If students need help...	If students got it...
Resources by Chapter • Practice A and Practice B • Puzzle Time Record and Practice Journal Practice Differentiating the Lesson Lesson Tutorials Skills Review Handbook	Resources by Chapter • Enrichment and Extension • School-to-Work Start the next section

Simplify. Write your answer using only positive exponents.

4 **23.** $\dfrac{x \cdot 4^8}{4^5}$

24. $\dfrac{6^3 \cdot w}{6^2}$

25. $\dfrac{a^3 \cdot b^4 \cdot 5^4}{b^2 \cdot 5}$

26. $\dfrac{5^{12} \cdot c^{10} \cdot d^2}{5^9 \cdot c^9}$

27. $\dfrac{x^{15} y^3}{x^8 y^9}$

28. $\dfrac{m^{10} n^7}{m^1 n^7}$

MP3 Player	Memory (GB)	Price
A	2^1	$70
B	2^2	$120
C	2^3	$170
D	2^4	$220
E	2^5	$270

29. MEMORY The memory capacities and prices of five MP3 players are shown in the table.

  a. How many times more memory does MP3 Player D have than MP3 Player B?

  b. Do the differences in price between consecutive sizes reflect a constant rate of change?

30. CRITICAL THINKING Consider the equation $\dfrac{9^m}{9^n} = 9^2$.

  a. Find two numbers m and n that satisfy the equation.

  b. Are there any other pairs of numbers that satisfy the equation? Explain.

Milky Way Galaxy
$10 \cdot 10^{10}$ stars

31. STARS There are about 10^{24} stars in the Universe. Each galaxy has approximately the same number of stars as the Milky Way Galaxy. About how many galaxies are in the Universe?

32. **Number Sense** Find the value of x that makes $\dfrac{8^{3x}}{8^{2x+1}} = 8^9$ true. Explain how you found your answer.

 Fair Game Review What you learned in previous grades & lessons

Subtract. *(Skills Review Handbook)*

33. $-4 - 5$

34. $-23 - (-15)$

35. $33 - (-28)$

36. $18 - 22$

37. MULTIPLE CHOICE What is the value of x? *(Section 5.1)*

  A 20

  B 30

  C 45

  D 60

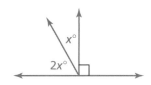

STANDARDS
OF LEARNING
8.1

Essential Question How did people in ancient cultures represent large numbers?

1 ACTIVITY: Hieroglyphics

Ancient Egyptians used hieroglyphics to represent numbers.

1	10	100	1000	10,000	100,000	1,000,000
vertical stroke	arch	coil of rope	lotus flower	pointing finger	tadpole	astonished man

Work with a partner. Write each Egyptian number in standard form.

a.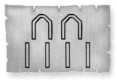

b.

c.

d.

e.

f.

Write each number using hieroglyphics.

g. 58

h. 608

i. 1501

j. 27,900

k. 404,000

l. 2,500,000

Laurie's Notes

Introduction

For the Teacher

- **Goal:** Students will explore how people in ancient cultures represented large numbers.

Motivate

- Explain that a *rebus* is a puzzle that uses pictures or words to symbolize other words or phrases. Draw a few examples on the board.

print	STA4NCE	SHOW
small print	for instance	sideshow

- After students have guessed them, have a discussion about hieroglyphics and how ancient people communicated.
- **Background:** The English language is based on 26 letters which are combined to form words and sentences. Ancient Egyptian hieroglyphics use a much larger set of characters.

Activity Notes

Activity 1

- Students will enjoy the first portion of the activity. They only need to count how many of each symbol is shown. In the second portion, students may feel like they can't draw well enough to "write" each number. Encourage students to do their best.
- **Big Idea:** To represent *seventy* in the base 10 system, you write a 7 in the tens position and a 0 in the ones position. Ancient Egyptians did not have a place value system so they repeated the symbol for 10 seven times.
- Have students share some of their answers for parts (g) through (l) at the board.
- **Extension:** Have students create symbols for a new number system and write a few numbers using their symbols. Then have students exchange papers with their partner and write their partner's numbers in standard form.

Standards of Learning

8.1(b) The student will compare and order decimals, fractions, percents, and numbers written in scientific notation.

Previous Learning

Students should know the base 10 place value system.

Start Thinking! and Warm Up

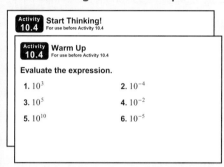

10.4 Record and Practice Journal

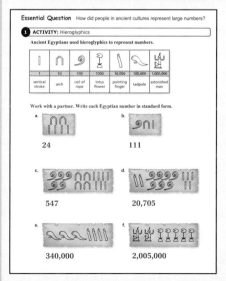

English Language Learners

Group Activity

Have students work in groups that include both English learners and English speakers. Assign each group a scientific notation application problem. Have each group solve their problem showing all of the steps. English learners will benefit by having the opportunity to restate the problem and gain a deeper understanding of the concept.

Activity 2

- Students may be familiar with Roman numerals, as they are on buildings and at the end of television programs.
- Students may ask how Roman numerals were used in calculations and to form fractions. These and similar questions could be researched for extra credit. You might want to share some information about Roman civilization as an introduction.
- **Background:** Romans used math in architecture applications, such as constructing buildings, roads, bridges, and aqueducts. Aqueducts were used to transport water to cities in the Roman Empire. The remains of many ancient Roman aqueducts still stand today!
- Before students begin the activity, explain that the order in which the numerals are written does matter. When a symbol for a smaller number is written after the symbol for a larger number, it means to add. When a symbol for a smaller number is written before the symbol for a larger number, it means to subtract.
  - Example: XI means $10 + 1 = 11$
  - Example: IX means $10 - 1 = 9$
- Some "rules" for subtracting:
  - Only subtract powers of 10. $(\text{I}, \text{X}, \text{C}, \text{M}, \overline{\text{X}}, \overline{\text{C}}, \overline{\text{M}})$
  - Only subtract one symbol from another.
  - Do not subtract a symbol from one that is more than 10 times greater.

10.4 Record and Practice Journal

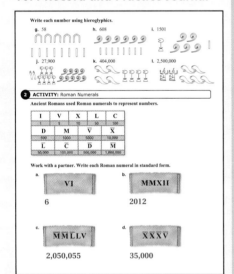

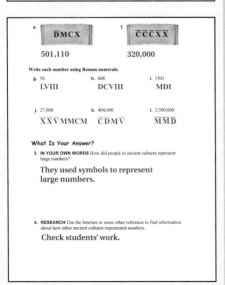

Closure

- **Exit Ticket:** Write a number in hieroglyphic form between and  that is divisible by ∩∩. Write a Roman numeral between M and $\overline{\text{X}}$ that is divisible by II.

  Sample answer: ◎◎◎◎ $(400 \div 20 = 20)$

  $\overline{\text{V}}\text{M}$ $(6000 \div 2 = 3000)$

Ancient Romans used Roman numerals
to represent numbers.

I	V	X	L	C
1	5	10	50	100

D	M	$\overline{V}$	$\overline{X}$
500	1000	5000	10,000

$\overline{L}$	$\overline{C}$	$\overline{D}$	$\overline{M}$
50,000	100,000	500,000	1,000,000

Work with a partner. Write each Roman numeral in standard form.

a.

VI

b.

MMXII

c.

$\overline{MM}$LLV

d.

$\overline{XXXV}$

e.

$\overline{D}$MCX

f.

$\overline{CCCXX}$

Write each number using Roman numerals.

g. 58   h. 608   i. 1501

j. 27,900   k. 404,000   l. 2,500,000

What Is Your Answer?

3. **IN YOUR OWN WORDS** How did people in ancient cultures represent large numbers?

4. **RESEARCH** Use the Internet or some other reference to find information about how other ancient cultures represented numbers.

10.4 Lesson

Key Vocabulary
scientific notation, *p. 464*

A number is written in **scientific notation** when it is represented as the product of a factor and a power of 10. The factor must be greater than or equal to 1 and less than 10.

> The factor is greater than or equal to 1 and less than 10. → 1.5×10^6 ← The power of 10 has an integer exponent.

EXAMPLE 1 — Identifying Numbers Written in Scientific Notation

Tell whether the number is written in scientific notation. Explain.

a. 8.4×10^{-4}

⋮ The factor is greater than or equal to 1 and less than 10. The power of 10 has an integer exponent. So, the number is written in scientific notation.

b. 10.7×10^2

⋮ The factor is greater than 10. So, the number is not written in scientific notation.

 **On Your Own**

Now You're Ready
Exercises 3–8

Tell whether the number is written in scientific notation. Explain.

1. 0.9×10^{-2} **2.** 12×10^{-3} **3.** 7.25×10^8

🔑 Key Idea

Writing Numbers in Standard Form

The absolute value of the exponent indicates how many places to move the decimal point.

- If the exponent is negative, move the decimal point to the left.
- If the exponent is positive, move the decimal point to the right.

EXAMPLE 2 — Writing Numbers in Standard Form

a. Write 4.17×10^{-3} in standard form.

$$4.17 \times 10^{-3} = 0.00417$$
     Move decimal point $|-3| = 3$ places to the left.
     3

b. Write 2.2×10^6 in standard form.

$$2.2 \times 10^6 = 2,200,000$$
     Move decimal point $|6| = 6$ places to the right.
     6

🔊 Multi-Language Glossary at BigIdeasMath.com.

Laurie's Notes

Introduction

Connect

- **Yesterday:** Students explored how people in ancient cultures represented large numbers.
- **Today:** Students will read and write numbers in scientific notation and standard form.
- This lesson extends students' knowledge of scientific notation to include multiplying numbers written in scientific notation.

Motivate

- **Preparation:** Make a model of one square foot by taping four rulers together.
- ❓ "What does one square foot look like?" Students should use their hands to model one square foot.
- Hold up the square foot model. Now, share information about Virginia.
- The land area of Virginia is about 39,493 square miles, or about 1.1×10^{12} square feet. Today, students will identify numbers written in scientific notation and write them in standard form.

Lesson Notes

Discuss

- Write the definition of scientific notation on the board. There are two parts to the definition; the factor is a number n, with $1 \le n < 10$, and it is multiplied by a power of 10 with an integer exponent.

Example 1

- Work through each example as described.

On Your Own

- Student explanations should reference the definition of scientific notation.

Key Idea

- Write the Key Idea. Students should recall that the exponent of 10 is connected to place value. If the exponent is positive, the number will be larger, so the decimal point moves to the right. Conversely, if the exponent is negative, the number will be smaller, so the decimal point moves to the left.
- ❓ Have students fill in the blank with less than or greater than.
  - "A power of 10 with a positive exponent is _____ 1." greater than
  - "A power of 10 with a negative exponent is _____ 1." less than

Example 2

- **Part (a):** 4.17 is the factor and -3 is the exponent. The number in standard form will be less than 4.17, so the decimal point moves to the left 3 places.
- **Part (b):** 2.2 is the factor and 6 is the exponent. The number in standard form will be greater than 2.2, so the decimal point moves to the right 6 places.

Goal Today's lesson is reading and writing numbers in **scientific notation**.

Lesson Materials
Introduction
• 4 rulers
• tape

Start Thinking! and Warm Up

Lesson **10.4** **Warm Up** For use before Lesson 10.4

Lesson **10.4** **Start Thinking!** For use before Lesson 10.4

Estimate the population of the world.

Go to *www.census.gov* to find the actual world population.

Write the population in scientific notation. How did you choose to round the number and why?

Extra Example 1

Tell whether the number is written in scientific notation. Explain.

a. 10×10^{-5} no; The factor is not less than 10.

b. 2.12×10^{15} yes; The factor is greater than or equal to 1 and less than 10. The power of 10 has an integer exponent.

🔵 On Your Own

1. no; The factor is less than 1.

2. no; The factor is greater than 10.

3. yes; The factor is greater than or equal to 1 and less than 10. The power of 10 has an integer exponent.

Extra Example 2

Write the number in standard form.

a. 9.1×10^{-4} 0.00091

b. 8.73×10^3 8730

Laurie's Notes

On Your Own

4. 510,000

5. 0.0002

6. 0.000000357

Extra Example 3

Write the number in scientific notation.

a. 62,100,000 6.21×10^7

b. 0.00009 9×10^{-5}

On Your Own

7. 3×10^5

8. 7.25×10^7

9. 9.01×10^{-4}

Differentiated Instruction

Kinesthetic

When writing a number in scientific notation, have students underline the first two nonzero digits. The decimal point will be placed between these two digits to create the factor.

27,000 = 2.7×10^4

0.0000048 = 4.8×10^{-6}

On Your Own

- **Think-Pair-Share:** Students should read the questions independently and then work with a partner to answer the questions. When they have answered the questions, the pair should compare their answers with another group and discuss any discrepancies.

Key Idea

- Reference the definition of scientific notation again, and then write the Key Idea.
- The leading nonzero digit is the leftmost digit that is not zero. In the number 8600, this digit is 8. In the number 0.0024, this digit is 2. Because the decimal point moves to the right of this digit, the factor is a number greater than or equal to 1 and less than 10.
- ❓ "Why is the decimal point moved to the right of the leading nonzero digit?" The factor must be greater than or equal to 1 and less than 10.

Example 3

- ❓ "How do you read the number of photons?" one hundred twenty-five million

"How do you read the amount of time?" six hundred twenty-five millionths

- **Teaching Tip:** Have students place an arrow where the decimal point will be placed in the factor. Then have students count the number of places the decimal point moves.
- **FYI:** Drawing the movement of the decimal point under the numbers helps students keep track of their counting.
- ❓ "How do you know if the exponent for the power of 10 will be positive or negative?" If the standard form of the number is 10 or greater, the exponent is positive. If the standard form of the number is between 0 and 1, the exponent is negative.

On Your Own

- **Think-Pair-Share:** Students should read the questions independently and then work with a partner to answer the questions. When they have answered the questions, the pair should compare their answers with another group and discuss any discrepancies.

T-465

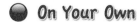

On Your Own

Now You're Ready
Exercises 9–17

Write the number in standard form.

4. 5.1×10^5 **5.** 2×10^{-4} **6.** 3.57×10^{-7}

🔑 Key Idea

Writing Numbers in Scientific Notation

Step 1: Move the decimal point to the right of the leading nonzero digit.

Step 2: Count the number of places you moved the decimal point. This indicates the exponent of the power of 10, as shown below.

Study Tip

When you write a number greater than or equal to 1 and less than 10 in scientific notation, use zero as the exponent.

$7 = 7 \times 10^0$

Number greater than or equal to 10

Use a positive exponent when you move the decimal point to the left.

$$8600 = 8.6 \times 10^3$$
$$3$$

Number between 0 and 1

Use a negative exponent when you move the decimal point to the right.

$$0.0024 = 2.4 \times 10^{-3}$$
$$3$$

EXAMPLE ③   **Writing Numbers in Scientific Notation**

A jellyfish emits about 125,000,000 particles of light, or photons, in 0.000625 second.

a. Write the number of photons in scientific notation.

Move the decimal point 8 places to the left. → $125{,}000{,}000 = 1.25 \times 10^8$ ← The number is greater than 10. So, the exponent is positive.

b. Write the number of seconds in scientific notation.

Move the decimal point 4 places to the right. → $0.000625 = 6.25 \times 10^{-4}$ ← The number is between 0 and 1. So, the exponent is negative.

On Your Own

Now You're Ready
Exercises 19–27

Write the number in scientific notation.

7. 300,000   **8.** 72,500,000   **9.** 0.000901

EXAMPLE 4 **Ordering Numbers in Scientific Notation**

The table shows the final sale price of three items at an auction. Order the items from least expensive to most expensive.

Item	Roman Sculpture	24.4-carat Diamond Ring	Magna Carta
Final Price (in dollars)	2.86×10^7	3.625×10^6	2.13×10^7

Step 1: Compare the powers of 10.

Because $10^6 < 10^7$,
$3.625 \times 10^6 < 2.86 \times 10^7$ and $3.625 \times 10^6 < 2.13 \times 10^7$.

Step 2: Compare the factors when the powers of 10 are the same.

Because $2.13 < 2.86$,
$2.13 \times 10^7 < 2.86 \times 10^7$.

From least to greatest, the order is 3.625×10^6, 2.13×10^7, and 2.86×10^7.

⋮• So, the items in order from least expensive to most expensive are the diamond ring, the Magna Carta, and the Roman sculpture.

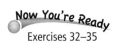 **On Your Own**

Now You're Ready
Exercises 32–35

10. WHAT IF? The final sale price of a 1933 Double Eagle coin is 7.59×10^6 dollars. Order the four items from least expensive to most expensive.

EXAMPLE 5 **Multiplying Numbers in Scientific Notation**

Find $(3 \times 10^{-5}) \times (5 \times 10^{-2})$. Write your answer in scientific notation.

$(3 \times 10^{-5}) \times (5 \times 10^{-2})$

$= 3 \times 5 \times 10^{-5} \times 10^{-2}$ Commutative Property of Multiplication

$= (3 \times 5) \times (10^{-5} \times 10^{-2})$ Associative Property of Multiplication

$= 15 \times 10^{-7}$ Simplify.

$= 1.5 \times 10^1 \times 10^{-7}$ Write 15 in scientific notation.

$= 1.5 \times 10^{-6}$ Simplify.

Study Tip

You can check your answer using standard form.
(3×10^{-5})
$\times (5 \times 10^{-2})$
$= 0.00003 \times 0.05$
$= 0.0000015$
$= 1.5 \times 10^{-6}$

 **On Your Own**

Now You're Ready
Exercises 37–42

Multiply. Write your answer in scientific notation.

11. $(2.5 \times 10^8) \times (2 \times 10^3)$ **12.** $(2 \times 10^{-4}) \times (1 \times 10^{-4})$

13. $(5 \times 10^{-4}) \times (5.4 \times 10^{-9})$ **14.** $(7 \times 10^2) \times (3 \times 10^5)$

Laurie's Notes

Example 4

- **Background:** One of the most important documents in the history of democracy is the Magna Carta. Written in 1215, it contained laws designed to limit the powers of King John (and future kings and queens) of England and granted rights to individuals. The Magna Carta was a great influence on the writers of the United States Constitution.
- Remind students that scientific notation is very useful in writing very large numbers and very small numbers.
- Work through the example as shown.
- Note that to order using the method shown, the numbers must be written in scientific notation.
- **Another Way:** Show students that you can order these numbers by first writing each of them in standard form.

Example 5

- Even though you cannot add or subtract numbers in scientific notation (unless they have the same power), you can multiply them.
- Write the problem on the board.
- **?** "How would you multiply the numbers?" Most students will immediately suggest multiplying the factors, and then multiplying the powers of 10.
- This process makes sense to them. You want to make sure that students realize that the Commutative and Associative Properties allow this to happen. Then the Product of Powers Property is used to multiply the powers of 10.

On Your Own

- These problems review mental math and properties of exponents.

Closure

- The land area of Rhode Island is about 1000 square miles. The land area of Alaska is about 570,000 square miles. The United States land area is about 3,500,000 square miles. Write each of these in scientific notation.
1×10^3, 5.7×10^5, 3.5×10^6

Extra Example 4

The final sale price of a painting is 9.52×10^7 dollars. Order the painting and the three items from Example 3 from least expensive to most expensive. diamond ring, Magna Carta, Roman sculpture, painting

On Your Own

10. diamond ring, Double Eagle coin, Magna Carta, Roman sculpture

Extra Example 5

Find $(2 \times 10^{-4}) \times (6 \times 10^{-3})$. Write your answer in scientific notation. 1.2×10^{-6}

On Your Own

11. 5×10^{11}

12. 2×10^{-8}

13. 2.7×10^{-12}

14. 2.1×10^8

Technology
For
the **T**eacher

Dynamic Classroom

The Dynamic Planning Tool
Editable Teacher's Resources at *BigIdeasMath.com*

Vocabulary and Concept Check

1. right; left
2. 11.5×10^8; It is not written in scientific notation.

Practice and Problem Solving

3. no; The factor is less than 1.

4. yes; The factor is greater than or equal to 1 and less than 10. The power of 10 has an integer exponent.

5. yes; The factor is greater than or equal to 1 and less than 10. The power of 10 has an integer exponent.

6. no; The factor is less than 1.

7. yes; The factor is greater than or equal to 1 and less than 10. The power of 10 has an integer exponent.

8. no; The factor is greater than 10.

9. 7500   10. 577

11. 0.000000389

12. 0.000116

13. 430,000   14. 2,040,000

15. 0.000000000809

16. 0.00000006332

17. 96.54

18. The decimal point should be moved 4 places left, not right.
$6.23 \times 10^{-4} = 0.000623$

19. 1.2×10^4 20. 7.89×10^2

21. 2.7×10^{-1} 22. 3.5×10^{-3}

23. 2×10^{-3} 24. 1.35×10^5

25. 1.75×10^6 26. 3.55×10^{-4}

27. 8.002×10^5

28. A very large or very small number may be written in scientific notation as a shorthand way of writing the number.

Assignment Guide and Homework Check

Level	Day 1 Activity Assignment	Day 2 Lesson Assignment	Homework Check
Basic	55–57	1, 2, 3–27 odd, 28–30, 31–39 odd, 45–51 odd	3, 9, 21, 29, 31, 33, 37, 49
Average	55–57	1, 2, 4–28 even, 31–43 odd, 46–52 even	4, 12, 18, 24, 35, 39, 46, 48
Advanced	55–57	1, 2, 4–28 even, 32–42 even, 44, 45, 47, 50–54	8, 16, 18, 26, 36, 42, 44, 50, 53

For Your Information

- **Exercise 52** Remind students that population density is the average number of people for some amount of land area. To find the population density, you divide the population by the land area.

Common Errors

- **Exercises 3–8** Students may think that the number is in scientific notation because the exponent is an integer. Remind them that the factor at the beginning of the number must be greater than or equal to 1 and less than 10.
- **Exercises 9–17** Students may move the decimal point in the wrong direction. Remind them that when the exponent is negative they move the decimal point to the left, and when the exponent is positive they move the decimal point to the right.
- **Exercises 19–27** Students may write an exponent with the opposite sign of what is correct. Remind them that large numbers have a positive exponent in scientific notation and that small numbers have a negative exponent in scientific notation.

10.4 Record and Practice Journal

Tell whether the number is written in scientific notation. Explain.

1. 8.4×10^{-3}
   Yes

2. 0.6×10^5
   No, the factor is less than 1.

3. 12.1×10^6
   No, the factor is greater than 10.

Write the number in standard form.

4. 5.3×10^{-6}
   0.0000053

5. 7.43×10^{-4}
   0.000743

6. 2.91×10^7
   29,100,000

Write the number in scientific notation.

7. 150,000
   1.5×10^5

8. 0.000000033
   3.3×10^{-8}

9. 62,500,000,000
   6.25×10^{10}

Order the numbers from greatest to least.

10. 4.5×10^6, 4.2×10^7, 4.75×10^6
    4.2×10^7, 4.75×10^6, 4.5×10^6

11. 9.2×10^{-4}, 8.82×10^5, 9.15×10^{-4}
    8.82×10^5, 9.15×10^{-4}, 9.2×10^{-4}

Multiply. Write your answer in scientific notation.

12. $(6 \times 10^9) \times (4 \times 10^5)$
    2.4×10^{15}

13. $(7 \times 10^{-7}) \times (5 \times 10^{10})$
    3.5×10^4

14. Find the area of the figure. Write your answer in scientific notation.
    8.84×10^{-9} cm^2
    3.4×10^{-5} cm
    2.6×10^{-4} cm

Technology For the Teacher

Answer Presentation Tool
QuizShow

10.4 Exercises

✓ Vocabulary and Concept Check

1. **REASONING** When writing a number in standard form, which way do you move the decimal point when the exponent is positive? negative?

2. **WHICH ONE DOESN'T BELONG?** Which number does *not* belong with the other three? Explain your reasoning.

$$4.7 \times 10^3 \qquad 7.89 \times 10^{-6} \qquad 11.5 \times 10^8 \qquad 6.025 \times 10^{-9}$$

Practice and Problem Solving

Tell whether the number is written in scientific notation. Explain.

3. 0.4×10^{-5}
4. 5.3×10^7
5. 2.65×10^{12}
6. 0.88×10^{-3}
7. 2.0×10^{-11}
8. 11.2×10^{-6}

Write the number in standard form.

9. 7.5×10^3
10. 5.77×10^2
11. 3.89×10^{-7}
12. 1.16×10^{-4}
13. 4.3×10^5
14. 2.04×10^6
15. 8.09×10^{-10}
16. 6.332×10^{-8}
17. 9.654×10^1

18. **ERROR ANALYSIS** Describe and correct the error in writing the number in standard form.

$$\times \quad 6.23 \times 10^{-4} = 62,300$$

Write the number in scientific notation.

19. 12,000
20. 789
21. 0.27
22. 0.0035
23. 0.002
24. 135,000
25. 1,750,000
26. 0.000355
27. 800,200

28. **REASONING** When is it convenient to write a number in scientific notation?

29. **DUST MITE** The length of a dust mite is 2.75×10^{-7} kilometer. Write this number in standard form.

30. **LCD TVS** An LCD flat panel television has 921,600 pixels. Write this number in scientific notation.

31. **ERROR ANALYSIS** Describe and correct the error in writing the number in scientific notation.

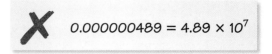
✗ $0.000000489 = 4.89 \times 10^7$

Order the numbers from greatest to least.

④ 32. $9.7 \times 10^5, 7.45 \times 10^6, 8.4 \times 10^5$

33. $1.49 \times 10^4, 2.11 \times 10^{-3}, 1.09 \times 10^4$

34. $5.27 \times 10^{-3}, 4.02 \times 10^2, 6.0 \times 10^{-3}$

35. $2.78 \times 10^{-7}, 3.49 \times 10^{-8}, 3.611 \times 10^{-7}$

36. **SALARY** The table shows the annual salary of four jobs. Order the salaries from least to greatest.

Job Title	Nurse	Dentist	Psychologist	Pharmacist
Annual Salary (in dollars)	6.2×10^4	1.4×10^5	7.8×10^4	1.1×10^5

Multiply. Write your answer in scientific notation.

⑤ 37. $(4 \times 10^4) \times (2 \times 10^6)$

38. $(3 \times 10^{-8}) \times (3 \times 10^{-2})$

39. $(5 \times 10^{-7}) \times (3 \times 10^6)$

40. $(8 \times 10^3) \times (2 \times 10^4)$

41. $(6 \times 10^8) \times (1.4 \times 10^{-5})$

42. $(7.2 \times 10^{-1}) \times (4 \times 10^{-7})$

Find the area of the figure. Write your answer in scientific notation.

43.
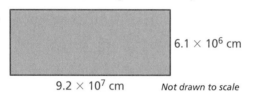
6.1×10^6 cm
9.2×10^7 cm   *Not drawn to scale*

44.
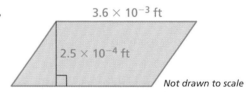
3.6×10^{-3} ft
2.5×10^{-4} ft
Not drawn to scale

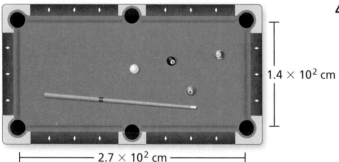
1.4×10^2 cm
2.7×10^2 cm

45. **POOL TABLE** Find the playing area of the pool table in square centimeters. Write your answer in scientific notation. How many square *meters* is the playing area?

46. **LIGHT BULB** A 100-watt light bulb emits about 800,000,000 photons in 0.0000000008 second.

a. Write the number of photons in scientific notation.

b. Write the number of seconds in scientific notation.

c. Which emits photons at a greater rate, a 100-watt light bulb or the jellyfish in Example 3? Explain.

Common Errors

- **Exercises 32–35** Students may order the numbers by the factor at the beginning of the number without taking into account the power of 10. Encourage them to follow the method in Example 4. Students can check their answers by writing the numbers in standard form.

- **Exercises 37–42** Students may find the product and leave the decimal factor greater than 10. Remind them that the factor in scientific notation must be greater than or equal to 1 and less than 10.

29. 0.000000275

30. 9.216×10^5

31. The decimal point moved 7 places to the right, so the exponent should be negative. $0.000000489 = 4.89 \times 10^{-7}$

32. 7.45×10^6, 9.7×10^5, 8.4×10^5

33. 1.49×10^4, 1.09×10^4, 2.11×10^{-3}

34. 4.02×10^2, 6.0×10^{-3}, 5.27×10^{-3}

35. 3.611×10^{-7}, 2.78×10^{-7}, 3.49×10^{-8}

36. 6.2×10^4, 7.8×10^4, 1.1×10^5, 1.4×10^5

37. 8×10^{10} **38.** 9×10^{-10}

39. 1.5×10^0 **40.** 1.6×10^8

41. 8.4×10^3 **42.** 2.88×10^{-7}

43. 5.612×10^{14} cm^2

44. 9×10^{-7} ft^2

45. 3.78×10^4 cm^2; 3.78 m^2

46. a. 8×10^8

   b. 8×10^{-10}

   c. light bulb; It emits more photons in a shorter amount of time than the jellyfish.

47. 1.5×10^1 m; 1.5×10^3 cm

48. $\frac{79,500}{10}$, 7.9×10^3, 790

49. 3.1×10^{-2}, 0.03, $\frac{6}{205}$

50. $\frac{1}{4}$, 0.235, 2.3%, 2.35×10^{-3}

51. 8922.1, 89×10^2, $\frac{2650}{3}$, 892%

52. *Answer should include, but is not limited to:* Make sure calculations using scientific notation are done correctly.

53. See *Taking Math Deeper*.

54. **a.** 2.65×10^8

   b. 2.2×10^{-4}

 Fair Game Review

55.

discrete

56.

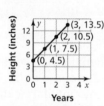

continuous

57. B

Mini-Assessment

Write the number in standard form.

1. 4×10^7 40,000,000

2. 9.9×10^{-3} 0.0099

3. 1.206×10^{-6} 0.000001206

Write the number in scientific notation.

4. 1981 1.981×10^3

5. 805,100,000 8.051×10^8

6. 0.00000336 3.36×10^{-6}

Taking Math Deeper

Exercise 53

We are all familiar with the look of a DVD (digital versatile discs), but how many of us know what the surface of a DVD looks like? This problem gives students some idea of what this digital storage device actually looks like.

 Summarize the given information.

   Width of each ridge = 0.000032 cm
   Width of each valley = 0.000074 cm
   Diameter of center portion = 4.26 cm

 Find the diameter of the DVD.

   ridges + valleys = 73,000(0.000032) + 73,000(0.000074)
   $$= 73,000(0.000032 + 0.000074)$$
   $$= 73,000(0.000106)$$
   $$= 7.738 \text{ cm}$$

   OR using scientific notation

   ridges + valleys $= (7.3 \times 10^4)(3.2 \times 10^{-5}) + (7.3 \times 10^4)(7.4 \times 10^{-5})$
   $$= (7.3 \times 10^4)(3.2 \times 10^{-5} + 7.4 \times 10^{-5})$$
   $$= (7.3 \times 10^4)(10.6 \times 10^{-5})$$
   $$= 77.38 \times 10^{-1}$$
   $$= 7.738 \text{ cm}$$

   diameter = ridges + valleys + center portion
   $$= 7.738 + 4.26$$
   $$= 11.998 \text{ cm}$$
   $$\approx 12 \text{ cm}$$

 Here's a fun fact.

   The microscopic dimensions of the bumps make the spiral track on a DVD extremely long. If you could lift the data track off a single layer of a DVD, and stretch it out into a straight line, it would be almost 7.5 miles long!

Project

Write a report on the invention of the DVD and the DVD player.

Reteaching and Enrichment Strategies

If students need help...	If students got it...
Resources by Chapter • Practice A and Practice B • Puzzle Time Record and Practice Journal Practice Differentiating the Lesson Lesson Tutorials Skills Review Handbook	Resources by Chapter • Enrichment and Extension • School-to-Work Start the next section

47. **CONVERSIONS** The length of a bridge is 1.5×10^{-2} kilometer. Write the length in *meters* and in *centimeters* using scientific notation.

Order the numbers from greatest to least.

48. $\dfrac{79,500}{10}$, 790, 7.9×10^3

49. $\dfrac{6}{205}$, 0.03, 3.1×10^{-2}

50. 2.3%, 2.35×10^{-3}, $\dfrac{1}{4}$, 0.235

51. 8922.1, 892%, $\dfrac{2650}{3}$, 8.9×10^2

52. **PROJECT** Use the Internet or some other reference to find the populations and population densities of India, China, Argentina, the United States, and Egypt. Round each population to the nearest million.

  a. Write each population in scientific notation.

  b. Find the area of each country.

H ← 0.000074 cm

H ← 0.000032 cm

4.26 cm

53. **DVDS** On a DVD, information is stored on bumps that spiral around the disk. There are 73,000 ridges (with bumps) and 73,000 valleys (without bumps) across the diameter of the DVD. What is the diameter of the DVD in centimeters?

54. **Number Sense** Simplify. Write your answer in scientific notation.

  a. $\dfrac{(53,000,000)(0.002)}{(0.0004)}$

  b. $\dfrac{(0.33)(60,000)}{(90,000,000)}$

Fair Game Review What you learned in previous grades & lessons

Graph the function. Is the domain of the graph discrete or continuous? *(Section 3.2)*

55.

Input Jars of Jelly, x	Output Cost, y (dollars)
0	0
1	3.99
2	7.98
3	11.97

56.

Input Years, x	Output Height of a Shrub, y (inches)
0	4.5
1	7.5
2	10.5
3	13.5

57. **MULTIPLE CHOICE** The triangles are similar. What is the value of x? *(Section 5.4)*

  Ⓐ 30

  Ⓑ 60

  Ⓒ 90

  Ⓓ 120

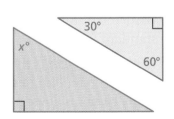

10.3–10.4 Quiz

Simplify. Write your answer using only positive exponents.
(Section 10.3)

1. $\dfrac{8^{-7}}{8^{-4}}$

2. $\dfrac{6^3 \cdot 6^7}{6^{12}}$

3. $\dfrac{\pi^{15}}{\pi^3 \cdot \pi^9}$

4. $\dfrac{t^{13}}{t^5} \cdot \dfrac{t^8}{t^6}$

Tell whether the number is written in scientific notation. Explain. *(Section 10.4)*

5. 11×10^{-8}

6. 0.1×10^3

Write the number in standard form. *(Section 10.4)*

7. 5.2×10^4

8. 4.6×10^{-2}

Write the number in scientific notation. *(Section 10.4)*

9. 45,900,000

10. 0.0000683

Order the numbers from greatest to least. *(Section 10.4)*

11. 9.2×10^5, 9.9×10^4, 9.6×10^5

12. 5.4×10^{-6}, 8.3×10^{-6}, 6.05×10^{-7}

Multiply. Write your answer in scientific notation. *(Section 10.4)*

13. $(3 \times 10^2) \times (8 \times 10^6)$

14. $(2.5 \times 10^{-4}) \times (4 \times 10^{-2})$

15. **EARTHQUAKES** An earthquake of magnitude 3.0 is 10^2 times stronger than an earthquake of magnitude 1.0. An earthquake of magnitude 8.0 is 10^7 times stronger than an earthquake of magnitude 1.0. How many times stronger is an earthquake of magnitude 8.0 than an earthquake of magnitude 3.0? *(Section 10.3)*

16. **HAIR** The human scalp contains about 100,000 hairs. Write this number in scientific notation. *(Section 10.4)*

17. **CAMERA** A retailer sold 3.5×10^5 digital cameras last year. *(Section 10.4)*

   a. Write the number of digital cameras in standard form.

   b. The retailer expects the number of cameras sold this year to be 10 times greater than last year. How many cameras does the retailer expect to sell this year? Write your answer in scientific notation.

Alternative Assessment Options

Math Chat   Student Reflective Focus Question

Structured Interview   Writing Prompt

Math Chat

- Have individual students work problems from the quiz on the board. The student explains the process used and justifies each step. Students in the class ask questions of the student presenting.
- The teacher probes the thought process of the student presenting, but does not teach or ask leading questions.

Study Help Sample Answers

Remind students to complete Graphic Organizers for the rest of the chapter.

4.

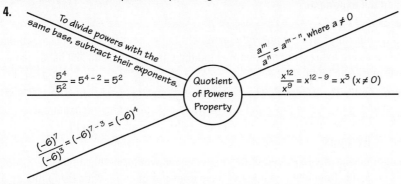

5.

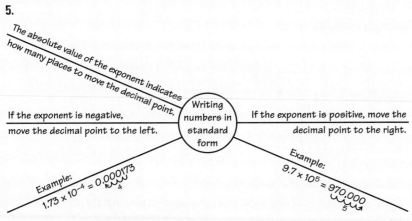

6–7. Available at *BigIdeasMath.com*

Reteaching and Enrichment Strategies

If students need help...	If students got it...
Resources by Chapter • Study Help • Practice A and Practice B • Puzzle Time Lesson Tutorials *BigIdeasMath.com* Practice Quiz Practice from the Test Generator	Resources by Chapter • Enrichment and Extension • School-to-Work Game Closet at *BigIdeasMath.com* Start the Chapter Review

Technology
For
the Teacher

Answer Presentation Tool

Assessment Book

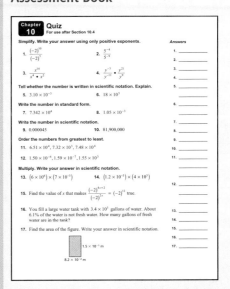

Additional Review Options
- **Quiz**Show
- Big Ideas Test Generator
- Game Closet at *BigIdeasMath.com*
- Vocabulary Puzzle Builder
- Resources by Chapter
  - Puzzle Time
  - Study Help

Answers

1. $-\dfrac{1}{216}$

2. -1

3. $-\dfrac{1}{32}$

4. $-\dfrac{4}{9}$

5. $\dfrac{15}{16}$

6. $-\dfrac{19}{20}$

Review of Common Errors

Exercises 1–6
- Students may have the wrong sign in their answer. Remind them that when a negative sign is inside the parentheses, it is part of the base.
- Students may forget the definitions of zero and negative exponents. A review of these definitions may be helpful.

Exercises 7–9
- Students may multiply the bases as well as add the exponents. Remind them that the base stays the same and only the exponent changes when simplifying using the Product of Powers Property.

Exercises 10–12
- Students may add the exponents when finding the power of a power. Encourage them to write the expression as repeated multiplication and then add the exponents.

Exercises 13–15
- Students may forget to apply the exponent to the coefficient. Encourage them to write the expression as repeated multiplication and group like bases using properties of multiplication.

Exercises 16–21
- Students may divide the exponents instead of subtracting the exponents. Remind them that the Quotient of Powers Property states that the exponents are subtracted.
- Students may multiply and/or divide the bases when simplifying the expression. Remind them that the base does not change when using the Product of Powers or Quotient of Powers Properties to simplify an expression.

Exercises 22 and 23
- Students may move the decimal point in the wrong direction. Remind them that when the exponent is negative they move the decimal point to the left, and when the exponent is positive they move the decimal point to the right.

Exercises 24 and 25
- Students may write an exponent with the opposite sign of what is correct. Remind them that large numbers have a positive exponent in scientific notation and small numbers have a negative exponent in scientific notation.

Exercises 26 and 27
- Students may order the numbers without taking into account the power of 10. Encourage them to order the numbers by powers first and then by decimal factors.

Exercises 28 and 29
- Students may find the product and leave the decimal factor greater than 10. Remind them that the factor in scientific notation must be greater than or equal to 1 and less than 10.

Check It Out
Vocabulary Help
BigIdeasMath com

Review Key Vocabulary

power, *p. 444*   exponent, *p. 444*
base, *p. 444*   scientific notation, *p. 464*

Review Examples and Exercises

10.1 Properties of Exponents *(pp. 442–447)*

a. $-5^{-3} = -\dfrac{1}{5^3}$ Definition of negative exponent

$= -\dfrac{1}{125}$ Simplify.

b. $8^0 - 3^{-2} + \left(\dfrac{1}{3}\right)^2 = 8^0 - \dfrac{1}{3^2} + \left(\dfrac{1}{3}\right)^2$ Definition of negative exponent

$= 1 - \dfrac{1}{9} + \dfrac{1}{9}$ Evaluate the powers.

$= 1$ Simplify.

Exercises

Evaluate the expression.

1. $(-6)^{-3}$

2. -1.9^0

3. $\left(-\dfrac{1}{2}\right)^5$

4. -1.5^{-2}

5. $\left(\dfrac{1}{4}\right)^2 - 2^{-3} + 4^0$

6. $5^{-2} + \left(\dfrac{1}{10}\right)^2 - \left(\dfrac{2}{3}\right)^0$

10.2 Product of Powers Property *(pp. 448–453)*

a. $\left(-\dfrac{1}{8}\right)^7 \cdot \left(-\dfrac{1}{8}\right)^{-4} = \left(-\dfrac{1}{8}\right)^{7 + (-4)}$ The base is $-\dfrac{1}{8}$. Add the exponents.

$= \left(-\dfrac{1}{8}\right)^3$ Simplify.

b. $(3m)^2 = 3m \cdot 3m$ Write as repeated multiplication.

$= (3 \cdot 3) \cdot (m \cdot m)$ Group like bases using properties of multiplication.

$= 3^{1+1} \cdot m^{1+1}$ The bases are 3 and m. Add the exponents.

$= 3^2 \cdot m^2 = 9m^2$ Simplify.

Exercises

Simplify. Write your answer using only positive exponents.

7. $7^8 \cdot 7^{-5}$

8. $(-3)^4 \cdot (-3)$

9. $\left(-\dfrac{1}{4}\right)^{-4} \cdot \left(-\dfrac{1}{4}\right)^{12}$

10. $\left(5^3\right)^2$

11. $\left(m^4\right)^5$

12. $\left(w^6\right)^{-3}$

13. $(5y)^2$

14. $(2x)^{-3}$

15. $\left(-\dfrac{1}{3}k\right)^4$

10.3 **Quotient of Powers Property** (pp. 456–461)

a. $\dfrac{(-4)^6}{(-4)^9} = (-4)^{6-9}$ The base is -4. Subtract the exponents.

        $= (-4)^{-3}$ Simplify.

        $= \dfrac{1}{(-4)^3}$ Definition of negative exponent

b. $\dfrac{5^5 \cdot 5^2}{5^3} = \dfrac{5^{5+2}}{5^3}$ The base is 5. Add the exponents in the numerator.

        $= \dfrac{5^7}{5^3}$ Simplify.

        $= 5^{7-3}$ The base is 5. Subtract the exponents.

        $= 5^4$ Simplify.

c. $\dfrac{a^6}{a^3} \cdot \dfrac{a^4}{a^5} = a^{6-3} \cdot a^{4-5}$ Subtract the exponents.

        $= a^3 \cdot a^{-1}$ Simplify.

        $= a^{3+(-1)}$ Add the exponents.

        $= a^2$ Simplify.

Exercises

Simplify. Write your answer using only positive exponents.

16. $\dfrac{(-8)^3}{(-8)^8}$

17. $\dfrac{2^2 \cdot 2^5}{2^3}$

18. $\dfrac{w^8}{w^7} \cdot \dfrac{w^5}{w^2}$

19. $\dfrac{3^2 \cdot 3^4}{3^9}$

20. $\dfrac{c^0}{c^5}$

21. $\dfrac{m^0}{m^6} \cdot \dfrac{m^{10}}{m^5}$

Review Game

Review for You

Big Ideas
Game Closet

Materials per Group
- copy of the Chapter Review from the Pupil's Edition
- chalk or dry erase marker
- eraser

Directions
Divide the class into four teams. Team members gather in groups at the board.

One member of each team works the first problem from the Chapter Review. Coaching from other team members is allowed.

Check each student's work and award 2 points to the team if the work is correct. If the work needs to be corrected, award 1 point to the team after the student makes the corrections.

Team members take turns working the problems. Repeat the process until you finish the Chapter Review or until you run out of time.

Who wins?
The team with the most points wins.

Variations
- Have students write review problems on index cards. Draw a card for students to use.
- To provide a cumulative review, write problems on index cards from anywhere in the book. Have team members select a card at random.

Answers

7. 7^3

8. $(-3)^5$

9. $\left(-\dfrac{1}{4}\right)^8$

10. 5^6

11. m^{20}

12. $\dfrac{1}{w^{18}}$

13. $25y^2$

14. $\dfrac{1}{8x^3}$

15. $\dfrac{k^4}{81}$

16. $\dfrac{1}{(-8)^5}$

17. 2^4

18. w^4

19. $\dfrac{1}{3^3}$

20. $\dfrac{1}{c^5}$

21. $\dfrac{1}{m}$

22. 40,000

23. 0.000096

24. 8.26×10^6

25. 5.07×10^{-5}

26. 8.2×10^5, 4.5×10^6, 4.8×10^6

27. 1.06×10^{-8}, 1.6×10^{-8}, 3.4×10^{-7}

28. 1.86×10^{10}

29. 2.2×10^{-12}

My Thoughts on the Chapter

What worked. . .

What did not work. . .

What I would do differently. . .

10.4 Scientific Notation (pp. 462–469)

a. Write 2.9×10^4 in standard form.

$$2.9 \times 10^4 = 29,\underset{4}{000}$$

Move decimal point $|4| = 4$ places to the right.

b. Write 3.08×10^{-6} in standard form.

$$3.08 \times 10^{-6} = 0.00000\underset{6}{308}$$

Move decimal point $|-6| = 6$ places to the left.

c. There are 1860 steps from the ground to the observatory on the 102nd floor of the Empire State Building. Write this number in scientific notation.

Move the decimal point 3 places to the left.

$$1860 = 1.\underset{3}{86} \times 10^3$$

The number is greater than 10. So, the exponent is positive.

d. The outer layer of skin is called the epidermis. On the palm of your hand, the epidermis is 0.0015 meter thick. Write this number in scientific notation.

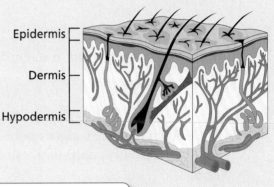

Epidermis

Dermis

Hypodermis

Move the decimal point 3 places to the right.

$$0.00\underset{3}{15} = 1.5 \times 10^{-3}$$

The number is between 0 and 1. So, the exponent is negative.

Exercises

Write the number in standard form.

22. 4×10^4

23. 9.6×10^{-5}

Write the number in scientific notation.

24. 8,260,000

25. 0.0000507

Order the numbers from least to greatest.

26. 4.5×10^6, 8.2×10^5, 4.8×10^6

27. 1.6×10^{-8}, 1.06×10^{-8}, 3.4×10^{-7}

Multiply. Write your answer in scientific notation.

28. $(6.2 \times 10^5) \times (3 \times 10^4)$

29. $(4 \times 10^{-7}) \times (5.5 \times 10^{-6})$

Check It Out
Test Practice
BigIdeasMath.com

Write the number in scientific notation.

1. 0.000258

2. 456,000

Evaluate the expression.

3. $(-5)^{-3}$

4. $\left(-\dfrac{9}{11}\right)^0$

Write the number in standard form.

5. 4.9×10^{-7}

6. 7.256×10^5

Simplify. Write your answer using only positive exponents.

7. $9^{10} \cdot 9$

8. $\left(2^{-3}\right)^2$

9. $\dfrac{(-3.5)^{-13}}{(-3.5)^9}$

10. $\dfrac{j^3}{j^5} \cdot \dfrac{j^{-5}}{j^{-2}}$

11. $(2s)^{-4}$

12. $\left(-\dfrac{1}{4}w\right)^3$

Multiply. Write your answer in scientific notation.

13. $\left(7 \times 10^3\right) \times \left(5 \times 10^2\right)$

14. $\left(3 \times 10^{-5}\right) \times \left(2 \times 10^{-3}\right)$

15. RICE A grain of rice weighs about 3^3 milligrams. About how many grains of rice are in one scoop?

16. CRITICAL THINKING Is $\left(xy^2\right)^3$ the same as $\left(xy^3\right)^2$? Explain.

One scoop of rice weighs about 3^9 milligrams.

17. LEAD From 1978 to 2008, the amount of lead allowed in the air in the United States was 1.5×10^{-6} gram per cubic meter. In 2008, the amount allowed decreased by a factor of 9×10^{-1}. What is the new amount of lead allowed in the air?

Test Item References

Chapter Test Questions	Section to Review
3, 4	10.1
7, 8, 11, 12, 16	10.2
9, 10, 15	10.3
1, 2, 5, 6, 13, 14, 17	10.4

Test-Taking Strategies

Remind students to quickly look over the entire test before they start so that they can budget their time. Have students use the **Stop** and **Think** strategy before they answer each question.

Common Assessment Errors

- **Exercises 1, 2, 5, and 6** Students may write an exponent with the incorrect sign or move the decimal point in the wrong direction. Remind them that large numbers have a positive exponent in scientific notation and small numbers have a negative exponent in scientific notation.
- **Exercises 3 and 4** Students may have the wrong sign in their answer, or forget the definitions of zero and negative exponents. Remind them that when the negative sign is inside the parentheses, it is part of the base. Also, a review of the definitions of zero and negative exponents may be helpful.
- **Exercise 7** Students may multiply the bases as well as add the exponents. Remind them that the base stays the same and only the exponent changes when using the Product of Powers Property.
- **Exercise 8** Students may add the exponents when finding the power of a power. Encourage them to write the expression as repeated multiplication and then add the exponents.
- **Exercises 9 and 10** Students may divide the exponents instead of subtracting them. Remind them of the Quotient of Powers Property.
- **Exercises 11 and 12** Students may forget to apply the exponent to the coefficient. Encourage them to write the expression as repeated multiplication.
- **Exercise 13** Students may find the product and leave the decimal factor greater than 10. Remind them that the factor in scientific notation must be greater than or equal to 1 and less than 10.

Reteaching and Enrichment Strategies

If students need help. . .	If students got it. . .
Resources by Chapter • Practice A and Practice B • Puzzle Time Record and Practice Journal Practice Differentiating the Lesson Lesson Tutorials Practice from the Test Generator Skills Review Handbook	Resources by Chapter • Enrichment and Extension • School-to-Work Game Closet at *BigIdeasMath.com* Start Standardized Test Practice

Answers

1. 2.58×10^{-4}

2. 4.56×10^{5}

3. $-\dfrac{1}{125}$ 4. 1

5. 0.00000049

6. $725{,}600$ 7. 9^{11}

8. $\dfrac{1}{2^6}$ 9. $\dfrac{1}{(-3.5)^{22}}$

10. $\dfrac{1}{j^5}$

11. $\dfrac{1}{16s^4}$ 12. $-\dfrac{1}{64}w^3$

13. 3.5×10^6

14. 6×10^{-8}

15. 3^6 or 729 grains

16. no; $(xy^2)^3 =$
$$(xy^2) \cdot (xy^2) \cdot (xy^2) =$$
$$x \cdot x \cdot x \cdot y^2 \cdot y^2 \cdot y^2 = x^3y^6$$
$$(xy^3)^2 = (xy^3) \cdot (xy^3) =$$
$$x \cdot x \cdot y^3 \cdot y^3 = x^2y^6$$

17. 1.35×10^{-6} gram per cubic meter

Assessment Book

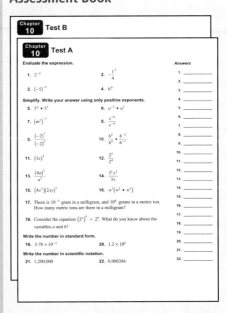

After Answering Easy Questions, Relax
Answer Easy Questions First
Estimate the Answer
Read All Choices before Answering
Read Question before Answering
Solve Directly or Eliminate Choices
Solve Problem before Looking at
  Choices
Use Intelligent Guessing
Work Backwards

About this Strategy

When taking a multiple choice test, be sure to read each question carefully and thoroughly. Sometimes you don't know the answer. So...guess intelligently! Look at the choices and choose the ones that are possible answers.

Answers

1. C
2. I
3. D
4. 7 in.
5. G

Item Analysis

1. **A.** The student assumes there should be 7 zeroes.

   B. The student miscounts when adding zeroes.

   C. Correct answer

   D. The student miscounts when adding zeroes.

2. **F.** The student is finding the sum of the angle measures of a quadrilateral.

   G. The student is finding the sum of the measures of two acute angles of a right triangle.

   H. The student finds the measure of the wrong angle.

   I. Correct answer

3. **A.** The student multiplies exponents instead of adding them.

   B. The student multiplies the bases and adds the exponents.

   C. The student multiplies all of the numbers in the expression.

   D. Correct answer

4. **Gridded Response:** Correct answer: 7 in.

   Common Error: The student divides the volume by the perimeter of the base, instead of the area, and gets a height of 12 inches.

5. **F.** The student misinterprets "never been above" to mean "always been below."

   G. Correct answer

   H. The student confuses less than and greater than symbols, and uses strict inequality inappropriately.

   I. The student confuses less than and greater than symbols.

6. **A.** The student adds $5000 to the account every ten years.

   B. The student doubles the amount every ten years, but loses track of the number of doublings needed.

   C. Correct answer

   D. The student doubles the amount every ten years, but loses track of the number of doublings needed, counting 1940 as one of the times to double.

Technology
For the Teacher

Big Ideas Test Generator

1. Mercury's distance to the Sun is approximately 5.79×10^7 kilometers. What is this distance in standard form?

   A. 5,790,000,000 km

   B. 579,000,000 km

   C. 57,900,000 km

   D. 5,790,000 km

2. The steps Jim took to answer the question are shown below. What should Jim change to correctly answer the question?

   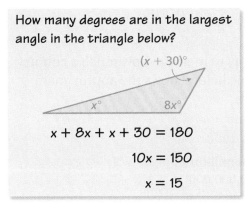

   How many degrees are in the largest angle in the triangle below?

   $(x + 30)°$

   $x°$ $8x°$

   $x + 8x + x + 30 = 180$

   $10x = 150$

   $x = 15$

   F. The left side of the equation should equal 360° instead of 180°.

   G. The sum of the acute angles should equal 90°.

   H. Evaluate the smallest angle when $x = 15$.

   I. Evaluate the largest angle when $x = 15$.

3. Which expression is equivalent to the expression below?

   $$2^4 2^3$$

   A. 2^{12}

   C. 48

   B. 4^7

   D. 128

4. The volume of a rectangular prism is 336 cubic inches. The length of the base is 8 inches and the width of the base is 6 inches. What is the height, in inches, of the rectangular prism?

5. The temperature in Frostbite Falls has never been above 38 degrees Fahrenheit. Let t represent the temperature, in degrees Fahrenheit. Write this as an inequality.

   F. $t < 38$

   H. $t > 38$

   G. $t \leq 38$

   I. $t \geq 38$

6. A bank account pays interest so that the amount in the account doubles every 10 years. The account started with $5,000 in 1940. How much would be in the account in the year 2010?

    A. $40,000   **C.** $640,000

    B. $320,000   **D.** $1,280,000

7. Which expression is equivalent to $5\sqrt{5} + 2\sqrt{5}$?

    F. $7\sqrt{5}$ **H.** $7\sqrt{10}$

    G. $10\sqrt{5}$ **I.** $10\sqrt{10}$

8. The gross domestic product (GDP) is a way to measure how much a country produces economically in a year. The table below shows the approximate population and GDP for the United States.

United States 2008	
Population	300 million (300,000,000)
GDP	14.4 trillion dollars ($14,400,000,000,000)

    Part A Find the GDP per person for the United States. Show your work and explain your reasoning.

    Part B Write the population and GDP using scientific notation.

    Part C Find the GDP per person for the United States using your answers from Part B. Write your answer in scientific notation. Show your work and explain your reasoning.

9. What is the equation of the line shown in the graph?

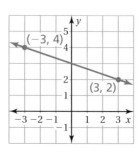

    A. $y = -\dfrac{1}{3}x + 3$ **C.** $y = -3x + 3$

    B. $y = \dfrac{1}{3}x + 1$ **D.** $y = 3x - \dfrac{1}{3}$

Item Analysis (continued)

7. **F.** Correct answer

    G. The student multiplies coefficients.

    H. The student adds the radicands.

    I. The student multiplies the coefficients and adds the radicands.

8. **4 points** The student demonstrates a thorough understanding of how to work arithmetically with large numbers both in standard form and in scientific notation. In Part A, an answer of $48,000 is obtained. In Part B, the data are written as 3×10^8 and 1.44×10^{13}. In Part C, the student works

    out the quotient $\dfrac{1.44 \times 10^{13}}{3 \times 10^8}$ step-by-step.

    3 points The student demonstrates an essential but less than thorough understanding. In particular, Parts A and B should be completed correctly, but the steps taken in Part C may show gaps or be incomplete.

    2 points The student demonstrates an understanding of how to write the data using scientific notation, but is otherwise limited in understanding how to approach the problem arithmetically.

    1 point The student demonstrates limited understanding of working with large numbers arithmetically. The student's response is incomplete and exhibits many flaws.

    0 points The student provides no response, a completely incorrect or incomprehensible response, or a response that demonstrates insufficient understanding of how to work with large numbers.

9. **A.** Correct answer

    B. The student miscalculates slope as positive, and then chooses the equation that has (3, 2) as a solution.

    C. The student reverses the roles of x and y in finding slope, and then uses the correct intercept, interpolated from the graph.

    D. The student reverses slope and y-intercept in the equation.

Answers

6. C

7. F

8. *Part A* $48,000

    Part B 3×10^8; 1.44×10^{13}

    Part C $\dfrac{1.44 \times 10^{13}}{3 \times 10^8} = 4.8 \times 10^4$

9. A

10. I

11. 0.16, or $\frac{4}{25}$

12. B

13. H

Item Analysis (continued)

10. **F.** The student makes an arithmetic mistake when adding 1.5 to both sides, and chooses strict inequality incorrectly.

G. The student chooses strict inequality incorrectly.

H. The student makes an arithmetic mistake when adding 1.5 to both sides.

I. Correct answer

11. **Gridded Response:** Correct answer: 0.16, or $\frac{4}{25}$

Common Error: The student writes the answer as a negative number.

12. **A.** The student fails to realize that a histogram is inappropriate. The display must allow a reader to compare parts of a whole.

B. Correct answer

C. The student fails to realize that a line graph is inappropriate. The display must allow a reader to compare parts of a whole.

D. The student fails to realize that a scatter plot is inappropriate. The display must allow a reader to compare parts of a whole.

13. **F.** The student uses addition where multiplication is appropriate.

G. The student incorrectly interprets "more than" as "greater than or equal to" and uses addition where multiplication is called for.

H. Correct answer

I. The student incorrectly interprets "more than" as "greater than or equal to."

Extra Example for Standardized Test Practice

Answer for Extra Example

1. **A.** The student rewrites $\frac{4^8}{4^4}$ as 2 (by dividing out the bases of 4).

B. Correct answer

C. The student multiplies and divides exponents, instead of adding and subtracting.

D. The student multiplies bases in the numerator (and adds exponents).

1. Which of the following is equivalent to $\frac{4^8 4^5}{4^4}$?

A. $2 \cdot 4^5$

C. 4^{10}

B. 4^9

D. $\frac{16^{13}}{4^4}$

10. Which graph represents the inequality shown below?

$$x - 1.5 \leq -1$$

F.
-2.5 -2.0 -1.5 -1.0 -0.5 0 0.5 1.0 1.5 2.0 2.5 x

G.
-2.5 -2.0 -1.5 -1.0 -0.5 0 0.5 1.0 1.5 2.0 2.5 x

H.
-2.5 -2.0 -1.5 -1.0 -0.5 0 0.5 1.0 1.5 2.0 2.5 x

I.
-2.5 -2.0 -1.5 -1.0 -0.5 0 0.5 1.0 1.5 2.0 2.5 x

11. Find $(-2.5)^{-2}$.

12. The director of a research lab wants to present data to donors, showing how a great deal of donated money is used for research and only a small amount of money is used for other expenses. Which type of display is best suited for showing these data?

A. histogram

B. circle graph

C. line graph

D. scatter plot

13. You earn $14.75 per hour at your job. Your goal is to earn more than $2000 next month. If you work h hours next month, which inequality represents this situation algebraically?

F. $14.75 + h > 2000$

G. $14.75 + h \geq 2000$

H. $14.75h > 2000$

I. $14.75h \geq 2000$

Appendix A
My Big Ideas Projects

About the Appendix

- The interdisciplinary projects can be used anytime throughout the year.
- The projects offer students an opportunity to build on prior knowledge, to take mathematics to a deeper level, and to develop organizational skills.
- Students will use the Essential Questions to help them form "need to knows" to focus their research.

Essential Question

- **Literature Project**
  How does the knowledge of mathematics provide you and your family with survival skills?
- **History Project**
  How have tools and knowledge from the past influenced modern day mathematics?

Additional Resources

BigIdeasMath.com

Essential Question

- **Art Project**
  How do polyhedra influence the design of games and architecture?
- **Science Project**
  How do the characteristics of a planet influence whether or not it can sustain life?

My Big Ideas Projects

A.1 Literature Project

STANDARDS
OF LEARNING
8.1–17

Swiss Family Robinson

1 Getting Started

Swiss Family Robinson is a novel about a Swiss family who was shipwrecked in the East Indies. The story was written by Johann David Wyss, and was first published in 1812.

Essential Question How does the knowledge of mathematics provide you and your family with survival tools?

Read *Swiss Family Robinson*. As you read the exciting adventures, think about the mathematics the family knew and used to survive.

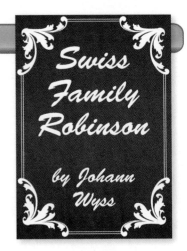

Sample: The tree house built by the family was accessed by a long rope ladder. The ladder was about 30 feet long with a rung every 10 inches. To make the ladder, the family had to plan how many rungs were needed. They decided the number was $1 + 12(30) \div 10$. Why?

Project Notes

Introduction
For the Teacher

- **Goal:** Students will read *Swiss Family Robinson* by Johann David Wyss and write a report about the mathematics they find in the story. Samples of things that could be included in students' reports are discussed below.
- **Management Tip:** You may want to have students work together in groups.

Essential Question

- How does the knowledge of mathematics provide you and your family with survival tools?

References

Go to *BigIdeasMath.com* to access links related to this project.

Things to Think About
Summary of *Swiss Family Robinson*

- A husband, wife, and four young sons, were shipwrecked as a result of a turbulent storm. Abandoned by the crew, they were left to their own ingenuity. The ship was smashed on a rock, but within sight of land. They built a raft out of barrels to transport themselves and material from the ship to the shore. After repeated trips, they removed as much as possible from the ship, which was full of livestock, equipment, and food. There were even pieces of a sailboat onboard, which they assembled and sailed.
- The family established temporary quarters in a tent made with sailcloth. They hunted, planted, and explored. They built a treehouse to use as a safe place to live. They named the tree house *Falconhurst*. It was very comfortable until the rainy season.
- The family built several other structures to serve as shelters on their various expeditions. Each structure was well furnished using either the things from the ship or furniture that they had made.
- The father was extremely innovative, able to make anything they needed from the materials at hand. He seemed to know how to use every resource for either the appropriate or improvised purpose.
- The island was lush with both flowers and animals. Vegetables and fruits from potatoes to pineapples were abundant. The family planted additional crops using the seeds obtained from the ship. Animals, from apes to kangaroos, were captured and tamed or used for food. The family established farms with animals that they captured or rescued from the ship.
- The family considered themselves very fortunate, knowing that things could have been much worse. On the one-year anniversary of the shipwreck, they observed a day of thanksgiving.

Meet with a reading or language arts teacher and review curriculum maps to identify whether students have or have yet to read *Swiss Family Robinson*. If the book has been read, you may want to discuss the work students have completed and review the book with them. If the book has not been read, perhaps you can both work simultaneously and share notes. Or, you may want to explore activities that the reading or language arts teacher has done in the past to support student learning in this particular area.

Project Notes

- Fritz, the eldest son, became restless after 10 years. So, he ventured out to explore, and discovered an albatross with a message tied to its leg. He found and rescued Jenny (Miss Montrose), an English woman who had also been shipwrecked. She lived alone on an island until Fritz noticed her signal fire. A rescue ship came shortly after Fritz found Jenny. Some of the occupants decided to stay at New Switzerland (as they liked to call their dominion). Others, including Jenny, Fritz, and Franz (the youngest son) decided to board the ship and go to England.

Mathematics Used in the Story

Some examples of mathematics used are illustrated in the following excerpts from the story.

- "This convinced me that we must not be far from the equator, for twilight results from the refraction of the sun's rays; the more obliquely these rays fall, the further does the partial light extend, while the more perpendicularly they strike the earth the longer do they continue their undiminished force, …"
- "Jack showed me where he thought the bridge should be, and I certainly saw no better place, as the banks were at that point tolerably close to each other, steep, and of about equal height. 'How shall we find out if our planks are long enough to reach across? … A surveyor's table would be useful now.' 'What do you say to a ball of string, father? … Tie one end to a stone, throw it across, then draw it back, and measure the line!' … we speedily ascertained the distance across to be eighteen feet. Then allowing three feet more at each side, I calculated twenty-four feet as the necessary length of the boards."
- In constructing the raft, they used empty water-casks, "arranging twelve of them side by side in rows of three" and placing planks on top for the floor.
- When making a canoe out of birch bark, they "cut the bark through in a circle" in two places, "took a narrow perpendicular slip of bark entirely out," and then loosened and separated the bark from the tree.
- While getting next to a whale they estimated, "the length being from sixty to sixty-five feet, and the girth between thirty and forty, while the weight could not have been less than 50,000 lbs. …the enormous head about one-third the length of the entire hulk…"

Closure

- **Rubric** An editable rubric for this project is available at *BigIdeasMath.com*.
- Students may present their reports to the class or school as a television report or public information broadcast.

2 Things to Include

- Suppose you lived in the 18th century. Plan a trip from Switzerland to Australia. Describe your route. Estimate the length of the route and the number of miles you will travel each day. About how many days will the entire trip take?

- Suppose that your family is shipwrecked on an island that has no other people. What do you need to do to survive? What types of tools do you hope to salvage from the ship? Describe how mathematics could help you survive.

- Suppose that you are the oldest of four children in a shipwrecked family. Your parents have made you responsible for the education of your younger siblings. What type of mathematics would you teach them? Explain your reasoning.

3 Things to Remember

- You can download each part of the book at *BigIdeasMath.com*.

- Add your own illustrations to your project.

- Organize your math stories in a folder, and think of a title for your report.

Mathematics in Ancient China

Share Your Work at... My.BigIdeasMath.com

1 Getting Started

Mathematics was developed in China independently of the mathematics that was developed in Europe and the Middle East. For example, the Pythagorean Theorem and the computation of pi were used in China prior to the time when China and Europe began communicating with each other.

Essential Question How have tools and knowledge from the past influenced modern day mathematics?

Sample: Here are the names and symbols that were used in ancient China to represent the digits from 1 through 10.

1	yi	一
2	er	二
3	san	三
4	si	四
5	wu	五
6	liu	六
7	qi	七
8	ba	八
9	jiu	九
10	shi	十

Life-size Terra-cotta Warriors

A Chinese Abacus

Project Notes

Introduction

For the Teacher

- **Goal:** Students will discover how mathematics was used in ancient China.
- **Management Tip:** Students can work in groups to research the required topics and generate a report.

Essential Question

- How have tools and knowledge from the past influenced modern day mathematics?

References

Go to *BigIdeasMath.com* to access links related to this project.

Things to Think About

? What is the ancient Chinese book *The Nine Chapters on the Mathematical Art* (c. 100 B.C.)?

- The book is one of the earliest surviving mathematics texts of ancient China. It is a collection of scholarly math writings that were written over a span of more than a thousand years. It assisted the ancient Chinese in solving problems dealing with trade, taxation, surveying, and engineering. It consists of 246 problems, a solution to each problem, and an explanation of how to get each solution.

? What types of mathematics are contained in *The Nine Chapters on the Mathematical Art*?

- **Chapter One:** Areas of triangles, rectangles, circles, and trapeziums; operations on fractions; finding greatest common divisor
- **Chapter Two:** Rates of exchange; proportions; percentages
- **Chapter Three:** Direct, inverse, and compound proportions
- **Chapter Four:** Keeping the area of a rectangle the same while increasing its width; square roots and cube roots
- **Chapter Five:** Volumes of prisms, pyramids, cylinders, and cones
- **Chapter Six:** Ratios and proportions
- **Chapter Seven:** Linear equations
- **Chapter Eight:** Systems of linear equations
- **Chapter Nine:** Right triangles; similar triangles; Pythagoean Theorem (called the Gougu rule)

? What is an abacus?

- The Chinese abacus consists of a wooden frame with 13 vertical rods and a horizontal wooden divider. There are seven beads on each rod. Five of the seven beads on each rod are located below the wooden divider, which the Chinese called the earth. The other two beads on each rod are located above the wooden divider, called the heaven. Earth beads are worth one point each, while the heaven beads are worth five points each.

? How is a number represented on the abacus?

- To start, all of the beads in both sections are pushed away from the divider. To represent numbers on the abacus, the beads are pushed toward the divider. The rod on the far right is the ones rod, then the one to its left is the tens rod, then the hundreds rod, then the thousands rod, etc.

Cross-Curricular Instruction

Meet with a history teacher and review curriculum maps to identify whether students have covered or have yet to discuss ancient China. If the topic has been covered, you may want to discuss the work students have completed and review prior knowledge with them. If the history teacher has not discussed these concepts, perhaps you can both work simultaneously on these concepts and share notes. Or, you may want to explore activities that the history teacher has done in the past to support student learning in this particular area.

Project Notes

- Suppose you want to represent the number 827 on the abacus. On the ones rod, move one of the heaven beads to the divider (5 points) and two of the earth beads to the divider (2 points). On the tens rod, move none of the heaven beads (0 points) and two of the earth beads (2 points). On the hundreds rod, move one of the heaven beads (5 points) and three of the earth beads (3 points).

? How is an abacus used to add or subtract numbers?

- Suppose you want to add 827 and 122. With 827 already on the abacus, add 122, digit by digit, starting with the ones rod. On the ones rod, move two more earth beads to the divider, making that rod represent a nine. On the tens rod, move two more earth beads to the divider, making that rod represent a four. On the hundreds rod, move one more earth bead to the divider, making that rod represent a nine. So, 827 + 122 = 949.

- To subtract two numbers, follow the same format, except in reverse, moving beads away from the divider instead of toward it.

? How did the ancient Chinese write numbers that are greater than 10?

- The ancient Chinese had symbols to represent each of the numbers from zero through nine.

零 一 二 三 四 五 六 七 八 九
0　1　2　3　4　5　6　7　8　9

- They also had symbols to represent 10, 100, 1000, and 10,000.

十　百　千　萬
10　100　1000　10,000

- To write a number such as 467, they had to write the number as
$4 \cdot 100 + 6 \cdot 10 + 7$.

467 = 四百六十七

Closure

- **Rubric** An editable rubric for this project is available at *BigIdeasMath.com*.
- You may hold a class debate where students can compare, defend, and discuss their findings with another student or group of students.

② Things to Include

- Describe the ancient Chinese book *The Nine Chapters on the Mathematical Art* (c. 100 B.C.). What types of mathematics are contained in this book?

- How did the ancient Chinese use the abacus to add and subtract numbers? How is the abacus related to base 10?

- How did the ancient Chinese use mathematics to build large structures, such as the Great Wall and the Forbidden City?

- How did the ancient Chinese write numbers that are greater than 10?

- Describe how the ancient Chinese used mathematics. How does this compare with the ways in which mathematics is used today?

Ancient Chinese Teapot

The Great Wall of China

③ Things to Remember

- Add your own illustrations to your project.

- Organize your math stories in a folder, and think of a title for your report.

Chinese Guardian Fu Lions

STANDARDS OF LEARNING
8.1–17

Polyhedra in Art

Share Your Work at...
My.BigIdeasMath.com

1 Getting Started

Polyhedra is the plural of *polyhedron*. Polyhedra have been used in art for many centuries, in cultures all over the world.

Essential Question Do polyhedra influence the design of games and architecture?

Some of the most famous polyhedra are the five Platonic solids. They have faces that are congruent, regular, convex polygons.

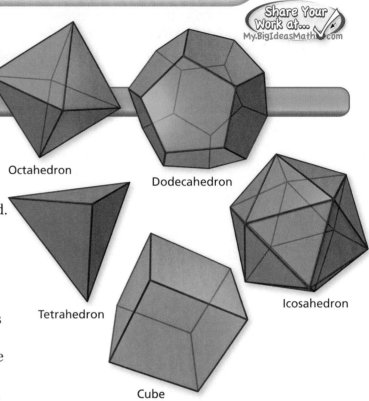

Octahedron

Dodecahedron

Tetrahedron

Icosahedron

Cube

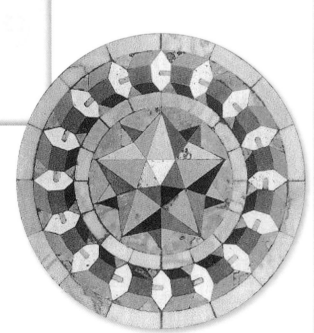

Mosaic by Paolo Uccello, 1430 A.D.

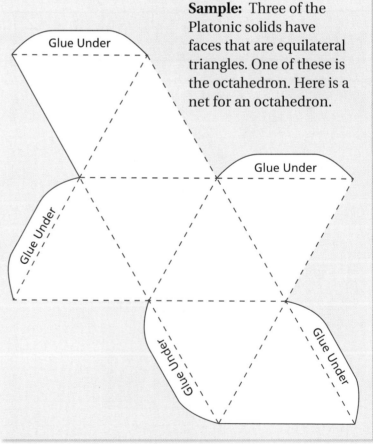

Glue Under

Glue Under

Glue Under

Glue Under

Glue Under

Sample: Three of the Platonic solids have faces that are equilateral triangles. One of these is the octahedron. Here is a net for an octahedron.

Project Notes

Introduction

For the Teacher

- **Goal:** Students will research and discover how polyhedra are used in games and architecture. They will also create their own polyhedra.
- **Management Tip:** Students may wish to search online or visit *BigIdeasMath.com* for links to websites containing instructions on how to make their own icosahedron or dodecahedron.

Essential Question

- Do polyhedra influence the design of games and architecture?

Things to Think About

? What are polyhedra?

- Polyhedra are three-dimensional shapes that have faces (sides) that are polygons. The polygons meet along straight line segments (edges) and the edges meet at vertices.

? What did Plato associate with the five Platonic solids?

- The Platonic solids, named for Plato, are a prominent feature of his philosophy. In his dialogue *Timaeus c. 360 B.C.*, Plato associated each of the four classical elements with a regular solid.

  "There was intuitive justification for these associations: the heat of fire feels sharp and stabbing (like little tetrahedra). Air is made of the octahedron; its minuscule components are so smooth that one can barely feel it. Water the icosahedron, flows out of one's hand when picked up, as if it is made of tiny little balls. By contrast, a highly un-spherical solid, the hexahedron (cube) represents earth. These clumsy little solids cause dirt to crumble and break when picked up, in stark difference to the smooth flow of water."

- Because there were only the four elements, there was need for only the four polyhedra. However, a fifth polyhedra, the dodecahedron, was used for the universe. Plato remarked, *"...the god used for arranging the constellations on the whole heaven."*

? Why are polyhedra used in architecture?

- From the Renaissance to present time, many artists saw the use of polyhedra as a challenging way to demonstrate the mastery of perspective. Others, such as Plato, thought that polyhedra symbolized philosophical truths or religious beliefs. Other artists used polyhedra simply because of their symmetrical beauty. From the Great Pyramids in Egypt to the Spaceship Earth geosphere at Epcot, polyhedra have been a part of architecture since prehistoric times.

Materials

- List of materials needed to construct a polyhedron is available at *BigIdeasMath.com*

References

Go to *BigIdeasMath.com* to access links related to this project.

Cross-Curricular Instruction

Meet with an art teacher and review curriculum maps to identify whether students have covered or have yet to discuss polyhedra. If the topic has been covered, you may want to discuss the work students have completed and review prior knowledge with them. If the art teacher has not discussed these concepts, perhaps you can both work simultaneously on these concepts and share notes. Or, you may want to explore activities that the art teacher has done in the past to support student learning in this particular area.

Project Notes

? **What is one of the most popular uses of polyhedra in games?**
- Polyhedra dice games are a popular way to explore mathematics. The following are examples of polyhedra dice.

? **What are the Archimedean Solids?**
- The Archimedean Solids are symmetric, semi-regular convex polyhedra. They are composed of two or more types of regular polygons meeting at identical vertices. Three are listed below. Visit *BigIdeasMath.com* to view all 13 Archimedean Solids.

Name	rhombicubocta-hedron	truncated cuboctahedron	rhombicosidodeca-hedron
Solid			
Net			
Faces	26	26	62
Faces (by type)	8 triangles; 18 squares	12 squares; 8 hexagons; 6 octagons	20 triangles; 30 squares; 12 pentagons
Edges	48	72	120

Closure

- **Rubric** An editable rubric for this project is available at *BigIdeasMath.com*.
- Students may present their reports to a parent panel or community members.

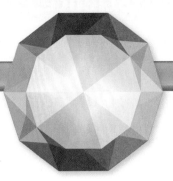

Faceted Cut Gem

2 Things to Include

- Explain why the platonic solids are sometimes referred to as the cosmic figures.

- Draw a net for an icosahedron or a dodecahedron. Cut out the net and fold it to form the polyhedron.

- Describe the 13 polyhedra that are called Archimedean solids. What is the definition of this category of polyhedra? Draw a net for one of them. Then cut out the net and fold it to form the polyhedron.

- Find examples of polyhedra in games and architecture.

Origami Polyhedron

3 Things to Remember

- Add your own illustrations or paper creations to your project.

- Organize your report in a folder, and think of a title for your report.

Concrete Tetrahedrons by Ocean

Bulatov Sculpture

A.4 Science Project

Our Solar System

STANDARDS OF LEARNING
8.1–17

1 Getting Started

Our solar system consists of four inner planets, four outer planets, dwarf planets such as Pluto, several moons, and many asteroids and comets.

Essential Question How do the characteristics of a planet influence whether or not it can sustain life?

Sample: The average temperatures of the eight planets in our solar system are shown in the graph.

The average temperature tends to drop as the distance between the Sun and the planet increases.

An exception to this rule is Venus. It has a higher average temperature than Mercury, even though Mercury is closer to the Sun.

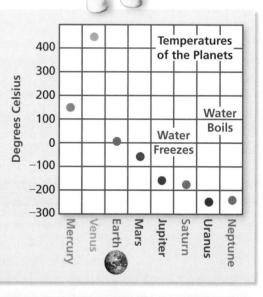

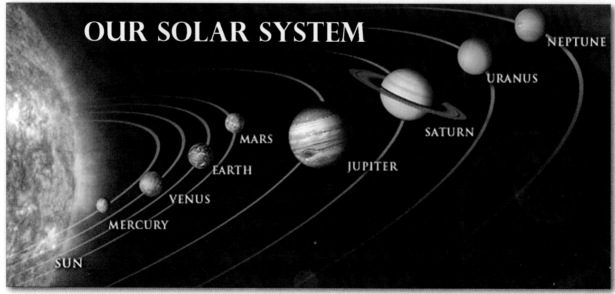

Project Notes

Standards of Learning
8.1–17

Introduction

For the Teacher
- **Goal:** Students will discover facts about objects in our solar system.
- **Management Tip:** Students can work in groups to create a report on our solar system.

Essential Question
- How do the characteristics of a planet influence whether or not it can sustain life?

References
Go to *BigIdeasMath.com* to access links related to this project.

Things to Think About

Inner System

	Mercury	Venus	Earth	Mars
Distance from the Sun	5.8×10^7 km	1.08×10^8 km	1.5×10^8 km	2.3×10^8 km
Diameter	4.8×10^3 km	1.2×10^4 km	1.27×10^4 km	6.7×10^3 km
Mass	3.3×10^{23} kg	4.9×10^{24} kg	6.0×10^{24} kg	6.4×10^{23} kg
Gravitational pull	38% of Earth	91% of Earth	100% of Earth	38% of Earth
Length of day	1407 hours, 30 minutes	5832 hours,	1 Earth Day	24 hours, 37 minutes
Length of year	88 days	225 days	365.25 days	687 days
Range or average temperature	−279°F to 801°F	864°F	45°F	−125°F to 23°F
Support human life?	No	No	Yes	No

❓ Have the planets been visited by humans?
- **Mercury** has been or will be visited by two spacecrafts; *Mariner 10* in 1974 and 1975 and *Messenger* which was launched by NASA in 2004. *Messenger* did several "flybys" in 2008 and is set to orbit Mercury beginning in 2011.

Cross-Curricular Instruction

Meet with a science teacher and review curriculum maps to identify whether students have covered or have yet to discuss the planets in our solar system. If the topic has been covered, you may want to discuss the work students have completed and review prior knowledge with them. If the science teacher has not discussed these concepts, perhaps you can both work simultaneously on these concepts and share notes. Or, you may want to explore activities that the science teacher has done in the past to support student learning in this particular area.

Project Notes

- **Venus** has been visited by at least 20 spacecrafts. *Mariner 2* was the first in 1962. Others have included *Pioneer Venus*, the Soviet's *Venera 7* and *Venera 9*, and ESA's *Venus Express*.
- **Mars** has been visited by several spacecrafts, the first being *Mariner 4* in 1965. Spacecrafts that have landed on Mars include: *Mars 2*, two *Viking* landers, *Mars Pathfinder*, and Mars Expedition Rovers *Spirit* and *Opportunity*.
- **Jupiter** has been visited by the spacecrafts *Pioneer 10*, *Pioneer 11*, *Voyager 1*, *Voyage 2*, *Ulysses*, and *Galileo*.
- **Saturn** has been visited by *Pioneer 11* in 1979, *Voyager 1*, *Voyager 2*, and *Cassini*.
- **Uranus** *Voyager 2* is the only spacecraft to have visited Uranus.
- **Neptune** *Voyager 2* is the only spacecraft to have visited Neptune.

Outer System

	Jupiter	Saturn	Uranus	Neptune
Distance from the Sun	7.7×10^8 km	1.4×10^9 km	2.8×10^9 km	4.5×10^9 km
Diameter	1.4×10^5 km	1.2×10^5 km	5.1×10^4 km	4.9×10^4 km
Mass	2.0×10^{27} kg	5.7×10^{26} kg	8.7×10^{25} kg	1.0×10^{26} kg
Gravitational pull	260% of Earth	117% of Earth	85% of Earth	120% of Earth
Length of day	9 hours, 56 minutes	10 hours, 39 minutes	17 hours, 5 minutes	16 hours, 7 minutes
Length of year	4331 days	10,759 days	30,687 days	60,190 days
Range or average temperature	−234°F	−288°F	−357°F	−353°F
Support human life?	No	No	No	No

Closure

- **Rubric** An editable rubric for this project is available at *BigIdeasMath.com*.
- Students may present their reports to the class or compare their report with other students' reports.

2   Things to Include

- Compare the masses of the planets.

- Compare the gravitational forces of the planets.

- How long is a "day" on each planet? Why?

- How long is a "year" on each planet? Why?

- Which planets or moons have humans explored?

- Which planets or moons could support human life? Explain your reasoning.

Mars Rover

3   Things to Remember

- Add your own drawings or photographs to your report. You can download photographs of the solar system and space travel at *NASA.gov*.

- Organize your report in a folder, and think of a title for your report.

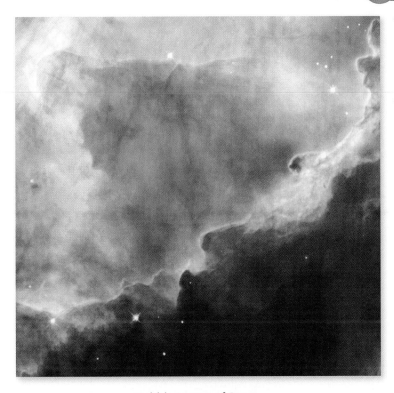

Hubble Image of Space

Hubble Spacecraft

Photo Credits

Selected Answers

Solving Simple Equations
(pages 7–9)

1. $+$ and $-$ are inverses. $\times$ and $\div$ are inverses.

3. $x - 3 = 6$; It is the only equation that does not have $x = 6$ as a solution.

5. $x = 57$　　　7. $x = -5$　　　9. $p = 21$　　　11. $x = 9\pi$　　　13. $d = \frac{1}{2}$　　　15. $n = -4.9$

17. **a.** $105 = x + 14$; $x = 91$

　　b. no; Because $82 + 9 = 91$, you did not knock down the last pin with the second ball of the frame.

19. $n = -5$　　　21. $m = 7.3\pi$　　　23. $k = 1\frac{2}{3}$　　　25. $p = -2\frac{1}{3}$

27. They should have added 1.5 to each side.

　　$-1.5 + k = 8.2$

　　　　$k = 8.2 + 1.5$

　　　　$k = 9.7$

29. $6.5x = 42.25$; \$6.50 per hour

31. $420 = \frac{7}{6}b$, $b = 360$; \$60

33. $h = -7$　　　35. $q = 3.2$　　　37. $x = -1\frac{4}{9}$

39. greater than; Because a negative number divided by a negative number is a positive number.

41. 3 mg　　　43. 8 in.　　　45. $7x - 4$　　　47. $\frac{25}{4}g - \frac{2}{3}$

Solving Multi-Step Equations
(pages 14 and 15)

1. $2 + 3x = 17$; $x = 5$　　　3. $k = 45$; $45°, 45°, 90°$　　　5. $b = 90$; $90°, 135°, 90°, 90°, 135°$

7. $c = 0.5$　　　9. $h = -9$　　　11. $x = -\frac{2}{9}$　　　13. 20 watches

15. $4(b + 3) = 24$; 3 in.

17. $\frac{2580 + 2920 + x}{3} = 3000$; 3500 people

19. $<$　　　21. $>$

Solving Equations with Variables on Both Sides
(pages 20 and 21)

1. no; When 3 is substituted for x, the left side simplifies to 4 and the right side simplifies to 3.

3. $x = 13.2$ in.　　　5. $x = 7.5$ in.　　　7. $k = -0.75$

9. $p = -48$　　　11. $n = -3.5$　　　13. $x = -4$

15. The 4 should have been added to the right side.

$$3x - 4 = 2x + 1$$
$$3x - 2x - 4 = 2x + 1 - 2x$$
$$x - 4 = 1$$
$$x - 4 + 4 = 1 + 4$$
$$x = 5$$

17. $15 + 0.5m = 25 + 0.25m$; 40 mi

19. 7.5 units

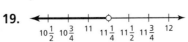
Hint

21. Remember that the box is with priority mail and the envelope is with express mail.

23. 10 mL

25. square: 12 units; triangle: 10 units, 19 units, 19 units

27. 54.6 in.^{3}

29. C

Section 1.4 — Rewriting Equations and Formulas
(pages 26 and 27)

1. no; The equation only contains one variable.

3. a. $A = \dfrac{1}{2}bh$ **b.** $b = \dfrac{2A}{h}$ **c.** $b = 12$ mm

5. $y = 4 - \dfrac{1}{3}x$

7. $y = \dfrac{2}{3} - \dfrac{4}{9}x$

9. $y = 3x - 1.5$

11. The y should have a negative sign in front of it.
$$2x - y = 5$$
$$-y = -2x + 5$$
$$y = 2x - 5$$

13. a. $t = \dfrac{I}{Pr}$

b. $t = 3$ yr

15. $m = \dfrac{e}{c^2}$

17. $\ell = \dfrac{A - \dfrac{1}{2}\pi w^2}{2w}$

19. $w = 6g - 40$

21. a. $F = 32 + \dfrac{9}{5}(K - 273.15)$

b. $32°F$

c. liquid nitrogen

23. $r^3 = \dfrac{3V}{4\pi}$; $r = 4.5$ in.

25. $6\dfrac{2}{5}$

27. $1\dfrac{1}{4}$

Section 1.5 — Writing and Graphing Inequalities
(pages 34 and 35)

1. An open circle would be used because 250 is not a solution.

3. no; $x \geq -9$ is all values of x greater than or equal to -9. $-9 \geq x$ is all values of x less than or equal to -9.

5. $x < -3$; all values of x less than -3

7. $y + 5.2 < 23$

9. $k - 8.3 > 48$

11. yes

13. yes

15. no

17.
```
 <-+--•--+--+--+--+--+->
  -7 -6 -5 -4 -3 -2 -1
```

19.
```
 <-+--+--+--o--+--+--+->
  10½ 10¾ 11 11¼ 11½ 11¾ 12
```

21. $x \geq 21$

23. yes

25. a. $a \geq 10$;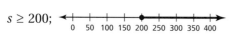

$s \geq 200$;

$t \geq 10$;

b. yes; You satisfy the swimming requirement of the course because $10(25) = 250$ and $250 \geq 200$.

27. a. $m < n; n \leq p$ **b.** $m < p$

c. no; Because n is no more than p and m is less than n, m cannot be equal to p.

29. $p = -1.7$

31. B

Section 1.6

Solving One-Step Inequalities
(pages 41–43)

1. *Sample answer:* Inequalities and equations represent a relationship between two expressions. In an equation, both expressions are equal. In an inequality, one expression is less than the other expression.

3. *Sample answer:* $x + 5 < -3$

5. *Sample answer:* $A = 350, C = 275, Y = 3105, T = 50, N = 2$

7. *Sample answer:* $A = 400, C = 380, Y = 6510, T = 83, N = 0$

9. $m < 10$;

11. $k \geq 4.4$;

13. $c > -\dfrac{1}{2}$;

15. $m < -7.6$;

17. When the solution was rewritten with the variable on the left side, the inequality symbol was not reversed. $x < -3.7$

19. $x + 12 \leq 22; \ x \leq 10$

21. $m > -9$;

23. $v \leq -30$;

25. $x < -\dfrac{6}{7}$;

27. $g > -20.4$;

29. $b \geq -3$;

31. $n > -20$;

33. $b > -18$;

35. $a \leq 5$;

37. $d \leq 6.8$;

39. $x \leq -3$;

41. a. $4.5x \geq 225; \ x \geq 50$; at least 50 sandwiches

b. If the price decreases, you will need to sell more than 50 to meet your goal. If the price increases, you can sell less than 50 to meet your goal.

43. $9x \geq 108$; $x \geq 12$ mm

45. always; The product of two positive numbers is positive.

47. never; The product of a negative number and a positive number is negative.

49. at least $1.25

51. no; *Sample answer:* $a = 3$, $b = 2$, $x = 8$, and $y = 1$; $a - x = -5$, $b - y = 1$; So, $a - x \not> b - y$.

53. no; *Sample answer:* $a = 4$, $b = 2$, $x = -2$, and $y = -4$; $\dfrac{a}{x} = -2$, $\dfrac{y}{b} = -2$; So $\dfrac{a}{x} \not> \dfrac{y}{b}$.

55. $m = 13$

57. B

Section 1.7 — Solving Two-Step Inequalities
(pages 48 and 49)

1. *Sample answer:* They use the same techniques, but when solving an inequality, you must be careful to reverse the inequality symbol when you multiply or divide by a negative number.

3. C

5. $b \geq 1$;

7. $m \geq -15$;

9. $p < -1$;

11. They did not perform the operations in proper order.

$$\frac{x}{4} + 6 \geq 3$$
$$\frac{x}{4} \geq -3$$
$$x \geq -12$$

13. $y \leq 13$;

15. $u < -17$;

17. $z > -0.9$;

19. $x \leq 6$;

21. $\dfrac{3}{16}x + 2 \leq 11$; $x \leq 48$; at most 48 lines

23. Remember that the whale needs to eat 140 pounds or more of fish each day.

25. $r \geq 8$ units

27. 625π in.^{2}

29. A

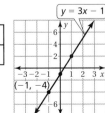

Section 2.1 — Graphing Linear Equations
(pages 66 and 67)

1. a line

3. *Sample answer:*

x	0	1
y = 3x − 1	−1	2

5.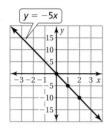

7.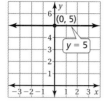

9.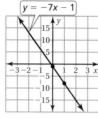

11.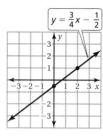

13.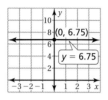

15.

17. $y = 3x + 1$

19. $y = 12x - 9$

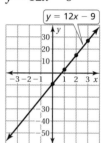

21. a. $y = 100 + 12.5x$

    b. 6 mo

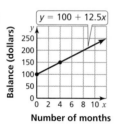

23. a. $y = 2x$

    b. *Sample answer:*
If you are 13 years old,
the sea level has risen
26 millimeters since
you were born.

25. $(5, 3)$

27. $(2, -2)$

29. B

1. a. B and C

    b. A

    c. no; All of the slopes are different.

3. The line is horizontal.

5.

The lines are parallel.

7. $\dfrac{3}{4}$

9. $-\dfrac{3}{5}$

11. 0

13. The 2 should be -2 because it goes down.

Slope $= -\dfrac{2}{3}$

15. 4

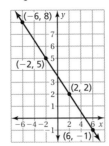

17. $-\dfrac{3}{4}$

19. $\dfrac{1}{3}$

21. red and green; They both have a slope of $\dfrac{4}{3}$.

23. no; Opposite sides have different slopes.

25. a. $\dfrac{3}{40}$

   b. The cost increases by $3 for every 40 miles you drive, or the cost increases by $0.075 for every mile you drive.

27. You can draw the slide in a coordinate plane and let the x-axis be the ground to find the slope.

29.

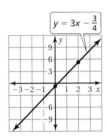

$y = 3x - \dfrac{3}{4}$

31. B

Section 2.3

Graphing Linear Equations in Slope-Intercept Form *(pages 80 and 81)*

1. Find the x-coordinate of the point where the graph crosses the x-axis.

3. *Sample answer:* The amount of gasoline y (in gallons) left in your tank after you travel x miles is $y = -\dfrac{1}{20}x + 20$. The slope of $-\dfrac{1}{20}$ means the car uses 1 gallon of gas for every 20 miles driven. The y-intercept of 20 means there is originally 20 gallons of gas in the tank.

5. A; slope: $\dfrac{1}{3}$; y-intercept: -2

7. slope: 4; y-intercept: -5

9. slope: $-\dfrac{4}{5}$; y-intercept: -2

11. slope: $\dfrac{4}{3}$; y-intercept: -1

13. slope: -2; y-intercept: 3.5

15. slope: 1.5; y-intercept: 11

17. a.

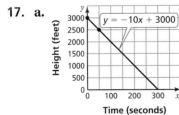

$y = -10x + 3000$

   b. The x-intercept of 300 means the skydiver lands on the ground after 300 seconds. The slope of -10 means that the skydiver falls to the ground at a rate of 10 feet per second.

Section 2.3

Graphing Linear Equations in Slope-Intercept Form *(continued)* *(pages 80 and 81)*

19.

x-intercept: $\dfrac{7}{6}$

21.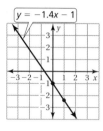

x-intercept: $-\dfrac{5}{7}$

23.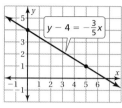

x-intercept: $\dfrac{20}{3}$

25. $y = 0.75x + 5$

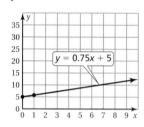

27. $y = 0.15x + 35$

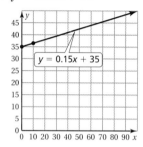

29. $y = 2x + 3$

31. $y = \dfrac{2}{3}x - 2$

33. B

Section 2.4

Graphing Linear Equations in Standard Form *(pages 86 and 87)*

1. no; The equation is in slope-intercept form.

3. $x =$ pounds of peaches

$y =$ pounds of apples

$y = -\dfrac{4}{3}x + 10$

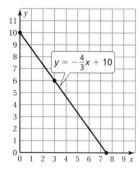

5. $y = -2x + 17$

7. $y = \dfrac{1}{2}x + 10$

11. *x*-intercept: -6

y-intercept: 3

13. *x*-intercept: none

y-intercept: -3

15. a. $-25x + y = 65$

b. $390

9.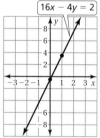

17.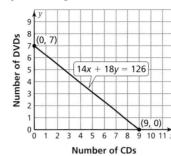

19. x-intercept: 9

y-intercept: 7

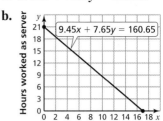

21. a. $9.45x + 7.65y = 160.65$

b.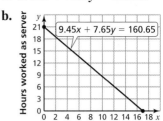

23. a. $y = 40x + 70$

b. x-intercept: $-\dfrac{7}{4}$; It will not be on the graph because you cannot have a negative time.

c.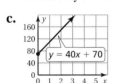

25.

x	-2	-1	0	1	2
$-5 - 3x$	1	-2	-5	-8	-11

Section 2.5

Writing Equations in Slope-Intercept Form
(pages 94 and 95)

1. *Sample answer:* Find the ratio of the rise to the run between the intercepts.

3. $y = 3x + 2$; $y = 3x - 10$; $y = 5$; $y = -1$

5. $y = x + 4$

7. $y = \dfrac{1}{4}x + 1$

9. $y = \dfrac{1}{3}x - 3$

11. The x-intercept was used instead of the y-intercept. $y = \dfrac{1}{2}x - 2$

13. $y = 5$

15. $y = -2$

17. **a–b.**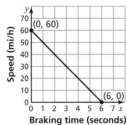

(0, 60) represents the speed of the automobile before braking. (6, 0) represents the amount of time it takes to stop. The line represents the speed y of the automobile after x seconds of braking.

c. $y = -10x + 60$

19. Be sure to check that your rate of growth will not lead to a 0-year-old tree with a negative height.

21 and 23.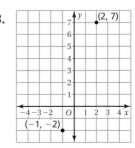

Section 2.6 — Writing Equations Using a Slope and a Point
(pages 100 and 101)

1. *Sample answer:* slope and a point

3. $y = \frac{1}{2}x + 1$

5. $y = -3x + 8$

7. $y = \frac{3}{4}x + 5$

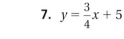

9. $y = -\frac{1}{7}x - 4$

11. $y = -2x - 6$

13. $V = \frac{2}{25}T + 22$

15. The rate of change is 0.25 degree per chirp.

17. **a.** $y = -0.03x + 2.9$

    b. 2 g/cm^2

    c. *Sample answer:* Eventually $y = 0$, which means the astronaut's bones will be very weak.

19. B

Section 2.7 — Writing Equations Using Two Points
(pages 106 and 107)

1. Plot both points and draw the line that passes through them. Use the graph to find the slope and y-intercept. Then write the equation in slope-intercept form.

3. slope $= -1$; y-intercept: 0; $y = -x$

5. slope $= \frac{1}{3}$; y-intercept: -2; $y = \frac{1}{3}x - 2$

7. $y = 2x$

9. $y = \frac{1}{4}x$

11. $y = x + 1$

13. $y = \frac{3}{2}x - 10$

15. They switched the slope and y-intercept in the equation. $y = 2x - 4$

17. **a.**

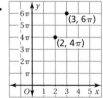

    b. $y = 2\pi x$; The equation is the formula for the circumference of a circle given the radius.

19. **a.** $y = -2000x + 21,000$

    b.

    c. $21,000; the original price of the car

21. **a.** $y = 14x - 108.5$

    b. 4 m

23. 175

25. D

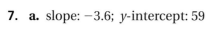

Section 2.8

Solving Real-Life Problems
(pages 112 and 113)

1. The *y*-intercept is -6 because the line crosses the *y*-axis at the point $(0, -6)$. The *x*-intercept is 2 because the line crosses the *x*-axis at the point $(2, 0)$. You can use these two points to find the slope.

$$\text{Slope} = \frac{\text{change in } y}{\text{change in } x} = \frac{6}{2} = 3$$

3. *Sample answer:* the rate at which something is happening

5. *Sample answer:* On a visit to Mexico, you spend 45 pesos every week. After 4 weeks, you have no pesos left.

7. a. slope: -3.6; *y*-intercept: 59 **b.** $y = -3.6x + 59$

    c. $59°F$

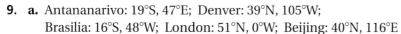

9. a. Antananarivo: 19°S, 47°E; Denver: 39°N, 105°W;
      Brasilia: 16°S, 48°W; London: 51°N, 0°W; Beijing: 40°N, 116°E

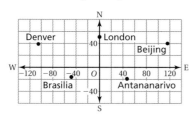

    b. $y = \dfrac{1}{221}x + \dfrac{8724}{221}$

    c. a place that is on the prime meridian

11. $x \le -1.3$

13. $m \le -7.2$

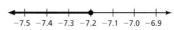

15. B

Section 3.1

Domain and Range of a Function
(pages 130 and 131)

1. *Sample answer:* An independent variable represents an input value, and a dependent variable represents an output value.

3. a. $y = 6 - 2x$ **b.** domain: 0, 1, 2, 3; range: 6, 4, 2, 0

    c. $x = 6$ is not in the domain because it would make *y* negative, and it is not possible to buy a negative number of headbands.

5. domain: $-2, -1, 0, 1, 2$; range: $-2, 0, 2$

7. The domain and range are switched. The domain is $-3, -1, 1$, and 3. The range is $-2, 0, 2$, and 4.

9.

x	−1	0	1	2
y	−4	2	8	14

domain: −1, 0, 1, 2

range: −4, 2, 8, 14

11.

x	−1	0	1	2
y	1.5	3	4.5	6

domain: −1, 0, 1, 2

range: 1.5, 3, 4.5, 6

13. Rewrite the percent as a fraction or decimal before writing an equation.

15.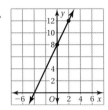

17.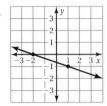

19. D

Section 3.2 **Discrete and Continuous Domains**
(pages 136 and 137)

1. A discrete domain consists of only certain numbers in an interval, whereas a continuous domain consists of all numbers in an interval.

3. domain: $x \geq 0$ and $x \leq 6$

range: $y \geq 0$ and $y \leq 6$;

continuous

5. 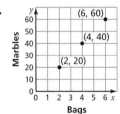 discrete

7. 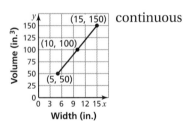 continuous

9. 2.5 is not in the domain because the domain is discrete, consisting only of 1, 2, 3, and 4.

11. The function with an input of length has a continuous domain because you can use any length, but you cannot have half a shirt.

13. 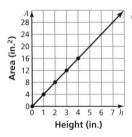 continuous

15. Before writing a function, draw one possible arrangement to understand the problem.

17. $-\dfrac{5}{2}$

19. C

Section 3.3 — Linear Function Patterns
(pages 144 and 145)

1. words, equation, table, graph

3. $y = \pi x$; x is the diameter; y is the circumference.

5. $y = \dfrac{4}{3}x + 2$

7. $y = 3$

9. $y = -\dfrac{1}{4}x$

11. **a.**

     discrete

     b. $y = 3x$ **c.** \$9

13. Substitute 8 for t in the equation.

15. $y = x$

17. $y = 1$

Section 3.4 — Comparing Linear and Nonlinear Functions
(pages 150 and 151)

1. A linear function has a constant rate of change. A nonlinear function does not have a constant rate of change.

3. linear

5. nonlinear

7. linear; The graph is a line.

9. linear; As x increases by 6, y increases by 4.

11. nonlinear; As x increases by 1, V increases by different amounts.

13. linear; The equation can be written in slope-intercept form.

15. Because you want the table to represent a linear function and 3 is half-way between 2 and 4, the missing value is half-way between 2.80 and 5.60.

17. nonlinear; x decreases by different amounts and y decreases by differesnt amounts.

19. linear; As the height increases by 1, the volume increases by 9π.

21. straight

23. right

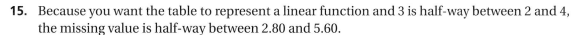

The Percent Equation
(pages 166 and 167)

1. A part of the whole is equal to a percent times the whole.

3. 55 is 20% of what number?; 275; 11

5. 37.5%
7. 84
9. 64

11. $45 = p \cdot 60$; 75%
13. $a = 0.32 \cdot 25$; 8
15. $12 = 0.005 \cdot w$; 2400
17. $102 = 1.2 \cdot w$; 85

19. 30 represents the part of the whole.

$30 = 0.6 \cdot w$

$50 = w$

21. $5400
23. 26 years old
25. 56 signers

27. If the percent is less than 100%, the percent of a number is less than the number. If the percent is equal to 100%, the percent of a number will equal the number. If the percent is greater than 100%, the percent of a number is greater than the number.

Hint

29. Remember when writing a proportion that either the units are the same on each side of the proportion, or the numerators have the same units and the denominators have the same units.

31. 92%
33. 0.88
35. 0.36

Percents of Increase and Decrease
(pages 172 and 173)

1. If the original amount decreases, the percent of change is a percent of decrease. If the original amount increases, the percent of change is a percent of increase.

3. The new amount is now 0.

5. decrease; 66.7%
7. increase; 225%
9. decrease; 12.5%
11. decrease; 37.5%

13. 10 m
15. 37 points
17. 153 students
19. 42.16 kg

21. They should have subtracted 10 in the last step because 25 is decreased by 40%.

40% of $25 = 0.4 \cdot 25 = 10$

So, $25 - 10 = 15$.

23. increase; 100%
25. increase; 133.3%

27. Increasing 20 to 40 is the same as increasing 20 by 20. So, it is a 100% increase. Decreasing 40 to 20 is the same as decreasing 40 by one-half of 40. So, it is a 50% decrease.

29. **a.** 100% increase **b.** 300% increase

31. less than; *Sample answer:* Let x represent the number. A 10% increase is equal to $x + 0.1x$, or $1.1x$. A 10% decrease of this new number is equal to $1.1x - 0.1(1.1x)$, or $0.99x$. Because $0.99x < x$, the result is less than the original number.

33. 10 girls
35. $39.2 = p \cdot 112$; 35%
37. $18 = 0.32 \cdot w$; 56.25

Section 4.3 — Discounts and Markups
(pages 180 and 181)

1. *Sample answer:* Multiply the original price by $100\% - 25\% = 75\%$ to find the sale price.

3. **a.** 6% tax on a discounted price; The discounted price is less, so the tax is less.

   b. 30% markup on a $30 shirt; 30% of $30 is less than $30.

5. $35.70   7. $76.16   9. $53.33   11. $450   13. $172.40   15. 20%

17. no; Only the amount of markup should be in the numerator, $\dfrac{105 - 60}{60} = 0.75$.
    So, the markup is 75%.

19. $36

21. "Multiply $45.85 by 0.1" and "Multiply $45.85 by 0.9, then subtract from $45.85." Both will give the sale price of $4.59. The first method is easier because it is only one step.

23. no; $31.08   25. $30   27. 180   29. C

Section 4.4 — Simple Interest
(pages 186 and 187)

1. I = simple interest, P = principal, r = annual interest rate (in decimal form), t = time (in years)

3. You have to change 6% to a decimal and 8 months to a fraction of a year.

5. **a.** $300   **b.** $1800   7. **a.** $292.50   **b.** $2092.50

9. **a.** $308.20   **b.** $1983.20   11. **a.** $1722.24   **b.** $6922.24

13. 3%   15. 4%   17. 2 yr   19. 1.5 yr   21. $1440   23. 2 yr

25. $2720   27. $6700.80   29. $8500   31. 5.25%   33. 4 yr

35. 12.5 yr; Substitute $2000 for P and I, 0.08 for r, and solve for t.

37. Year 1 = $520; Year 2 = $540.80; Year 3 = $562.43

39. 40, 25, 10

Section 5.1 — Classifying Angles
(pages 202 and 203)

1. The sum of the measures of two complementary angles is 90°. The sum of the measures of two supplementary angles is 180°.

3. sometimes; Either x or y may be obtuse.

5. never; Because x and y must both be less than 90° and greater than 0°.

7. complementary   9. supplementary   11. neither   13. vertical; 128

15. Vertical angles are congruent. The value of x is 35.

17. vertical; 75°, 75°

19. adjacent; 140°, 40°

21. a. $\angle CBD$ and $\angle DBE$; $\angle ABF$ and $\angle FBE$

    b. $\angle ABE$ and $\angle CBE$; $\angle ABD$ and $\angle CBD$; $\angle CBF$ and $\angle ABF$

23. Adjacent angles are not defined by their measure, so they can be complementary, supplementary, or neither.

25. Begin by drawing two intersecting lines and identifying the vertical angles.

27. 75

29. 35

Section 5.2

Angles and Sides of Triangles
(pages 208 and 209)

1. An equilateral triangle has three congruent sides. An isosceles triangle has at least two congruent sides. So, an equilateral triangle is a specific type of isosceles triangle.

3. right isosceles triangle

5. obtuse isosceles triangle

7. 94; obtuse scalene triangle

9. 67.5; acute isosceles triangle

11. 24; obtuse isosceles triangle

13. a. 70   **b.** acute isosceles triangle

15. no; 39.5°

17. yes

19. If two angle measures of a triangle were each greater than or equal to 90°, the sum of those two angle measures would be greater than or equal to 180°. The sum of the three angle measures would be greater than 180°, which is not possible.

21. $x + 9 + 12 = 28$; 7

23. $6x = 30$; 5

Section 5.3

Angles of Polygons
(pages 215–217)

1. *Sample answer:*

3. What is the measure of an angle of a regular pentagon?; 108°; 540°

5. 1260°

7. 1080°

9. 1800°

11. no; The angle measures given add up to 535°, but the sum of the angle measures of a pentagon is 540°.

13. 135

15. 140°

17. 140°

19. The sum of the angle measures should have been divided by the number of angles, 20. $3240° \div 20 = 162°$; The measure of each angle is 162°.

21. 24 sides

23. convex; No line segment connecting two vertices lies outside the polygon.

25. no; All of the angles would not be congruent.

27. 135°

29. 120°

31. You can determine if it is a linear function by writing an equation or by graphing the points.

33. 9

35. 3

37. D

Section 5.4 — Using Similar Triangles
(pages 224 and 225)

1. Write a proportion that uses the missing measurement because the ratios of corresponding side lengths are equal.

3. Student should draw a triangle with the same angle measures as the textbook. The ratio of the corresponding side lengths, $\dfrac{\text{student's triangle length}}{\text{book's triangle length}}$, should be greater than one.

5. yes; The triangles have the same angle measures, 107°, 39°, and 34°.

7. no; The triangles do not have the same angle measures.

9. The numerators of the fractions should be from the same triangle.
$$\frac{18}{16} = \frac{x}{8}$$
$$16x = 144$$
$$x = 9$$

11. 65

13. no; Each side increases by 50%, so each side is multiplied by a factor of $\dfrac{3}{2}$.

The area is $\dfrac{3}{2}\left(\dfrac{3}{2}\right) = \dfrac{9}{4}$ or 225% of the original area, which is a 125% increase.

15. When two triangles are similar, the ratios of corresponding sides are equal.

17. linear; The equation can be rewritten in slope-intercept form.

19. nonlinear; The equation cannot be rewritten in slope-intercept form.

Polygons and Transformations
(pages 231–233)

1. **a.** rotation   **b.** translation

   c. reflection   **d.** dilation

3. Anthony; yes; It is the same when rotated 180°.

5. $A'(-2, 9), B'(2, 9), C'(2, 2), D'(-1, 2)$ 7. $A'(0, 8), B'(-4, 8), C'(-4, 1), D'(-1, 1)$

9. $A'(8, 0), B'(8, -4), C'(1, -4), D'(1, -1)$ 11. $A'(0, 24), B'(12, 24), C'(12, 3), D'(3, 3)$

13. enlargement; reduction   15. *Sample answer:*

17. The vertices do not correspond for a translation. $A'B'C'D'$ is a 180° rotation of *ABCD*.

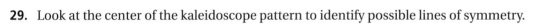

19. yes; The polygon and its image have the same size and shape.

21. no; The polygon and its image have the same shape but not the same size.

23. Quadrant II   25. Quadrant I   27. 2

29. Look at the center of the kaleidoscope pattern to identify possible lines of symmetry.

31. 270° counterclockwise; 270° clockwise

33. domain: $-1, 1, 3, 5$
    range: $0, 1, 2, 3$
     35. domain: $-5, -4, -3, -2$
    range: $-5, -3, -1, 1$

Perimeters of Composite Figures
(pages 238 and 239)

1. less than and equal to; The perimeter is *less than* when figures making up a composite figure share a common side (dashed line).

   The perimeter is *equal to* when the figures making up a composite figure share a common vertex.

3. 19.5 in.   5. 25.5 in.   7. 19 in.   9. 56 m

11. 30 cm   13. about 26.85 in.   15. about 36.84 ft

17. Remember to subtract the original garden side that you now cover up with the new portion of the flower garden when trying to add 15 feet to the perimeter.

19. Yes; *Sample answer:* By adding the triangle shown by the dashed line to the L-shaped figure, you *reduce* the perimeter.

21. 279.68   23. 205

Section 5.7
Areas of Composite Figures
(pages 244 and 245)

1. *Sample answer:* You could add the areas of an 8-inch × 4-inch rectangle and a triangle with a base of 6 inches and a height of 6 inches. Also you could add the area of a 2-inch × 4-inch rectangle to the area of a trapezoid with a height of 6 inches, and base lengths of 4 inches and 10 inches.

3. 28.5 in.^2 **5.** 25 in.^2 **7.** 25 in.^2 **9.** 132 cm^2

11. *Answer will include but is not limited to:* Tracings of a hand and foot on grid paper, estimates of the areas, and a statement of which is greater.

13. 23.5 in.^2 **15.** 24 m^2

17. Each envelope can be broken up into 5 smaller figures to find the area.

19. $y \div 6$ **21.** $7w$

Section 6.1
Drawing 3-Dimensional Figures
(pages 262 and 263)

1. Prisms and cylinders both have two parallel, identical bases. The bases of a cylinder are circles. The bases of a prism are polygons. A prism has lateral faces that are parallelograms or rectangles. A cylinder has one smooth, round lateral surface.

3. *Sample answer:* Prisms: A cereal box is a rectangular prism. A pup tent with parallel triangular bases at the front and back is a triangular prism.

Pyramids: The Egyptian pyramids are rectangular pyramids. A house roof forms a pyramid if it has lateral faces that are triangles that meet at a common vertex.

Cylinders: Some examples of cylinders are a soup can, a tuna fish can, and a new, unsharpened, round pencil.

Cones: Some examples of cones are a traffic cone, an ice cream sugar cone, a party hat, and the sharpened end of a pencil.

5. base: circle; solid: cylinder

7. front: side: top:

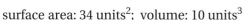

surface area: 34 units^2; volume: 10 units^3

9. front: side: top:

surface area: 38 units^2; volume: 9 units^3

11.   **13.**   **15.**

17. front:

side:

top:

19. front:

side:

top:

21. front: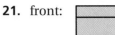

side:

top:

23. The Washington Monument is an *obelisk*. It consists of a pyramid sitting on top of a solid that tapers as it rises.

25.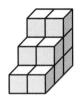

27. Use cubes to create solids that are possible.

29. 28 m^2

31. 15 ft^2

Section 6.2

Surface Areas of Prisms
(pages 268 and 269)

1. *Sample answer:* You want to paint a large toy chest in the form of a rectangular prism, and in order to know how much paint to buy, you need to know the surface area.

3. 18 cm^2

5. 108 cm^2

7. 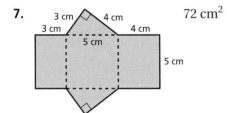 72 cm^2

9. 130 ft^2

11. 76 yd^2

13. 740 m^2

15. 448 in.^2; The surface area of the box is 448 square inches, so that is the least amount of paper needed to cover the box.

17. 156 in.^2

19. **a.** 83 ft^2

b. 332 ft^2

c. The amount of glass is 4 times greater.

21. $x = 4 \text{ in.}$

23. 25 units

25. 54 units

Section 6.3 — Surface Areas of Cylinders
(pages 274 and 275)

1. true

3. false; The area of the bases of a cylinder can be less than, equal to, or greater than its lateral surface area.

5. $44\pi \approx 138.2 \text{ yd}^2$ 7. $52.5\pi \approx 164.9 \text{ m}^2$ 9. $0.96\pi \approx 3.0 \text{ mm}^2$ 11. $306\pi \approx 960.8 \text{ cm}^2$

13. The dimensions of the red cylinder are 4 times greater than the dimensions of the blue cylinder. The surface area is 16 times greater.

15. **a.** $16\pi \approx 50.2 \text{ in.}^2$

   b. The lateral surface area triples.

17. **a.** 4 times greater; 9 times greater; 25 times greater; 100 times greater

   b. When both dimensions are increased by a factor of k, the surface area increases by a factor of k^2; 400 times greater

19. $y = 2x - 1$

Section 6.4 — Surface Areas of Pyramids
(pages 282 and 283)

1. the triangle and the hexagon

3. Knowing the slant height helps because it represents the height of the triangle that makes up each lateral face. So, the slant height helps you to find the area of each lateral face.

5. 178.3 mm^2 7. 144 ft^2 9. 170.1 yd^2

11. 1240.4 mm^2 13. 6 m

15. Determine how long the fabric needs to be so you can cut the fabric most efficiently.

17. 124 cm^2

19. $A \approx 452.16 \text{ units}^2$; $C \approx 75.36 \text{ units}$

21. $A \approx 572.265 \text{ units}^2$; $C \approx 84.78 \text{ units}$

Section 6.5 — Surface Areas of Cones
(pages 288 and 289)

1. no; The base of a cone is a circle. A circle is not a polygon.

3. $\ell > r$ 5. $36\pi \approx 113.0 \text{ m}^2$ 7. $119\pi \approx 373.7 \text{ ft}^2$

9. $64\pi \approx 201.0 \text{ yd}^2$ 11. 15 cm 13. $130\pi \approx 408.2 \text{ in.}^2$

15. $360\pi \approx 1130.4 \text{ in.}^2$; $2.5\pi \approx 7.85 \text{ ft}^2$ 17. $96\pi \approx 301.44 \text{ ft}^2$; $\dfrac{32}{3}\pi \approx 33.49\overline{3} \text{ yd}^2$

19. 12%   21. the lateral surface area

23. 45 in.^2 25. 16 ft^2

Section 6.6

Surface Areas of Composite Solids
(pages 294 and 295)

1. *Sample answer:*

3. three cylinders

5. rectangular prism, half of a cylinder

7. cones; $104\pi \approx 326.6 \text{ m}^2$

9. trapezoidal prism, rectangular prism; 152 cm² **11.** two rectangular prisms; 308 ft²

13. 63.4%   **15.** $144\pi \approx 452.2 \text{ in.}^2$ **17.** $806\pi \approx 2530.84 \text{ mm}^2$

19. 10 ft²   **21.** 47.5 in.²

Section 7.1

Volumes of Prisms
(pages 310 and 311)

1. cubic units

3. *Sample answers:* Volume because you want to make sure the product will fit inside the package. Surface area because of the cost of packaging.

5. 288 cm³   **7.** 160 yd³   **9.** 420 mm³   **11.** 645 mm³

13. The area of the base is wrong.

$$V = \frac{1}{2}(7)(5) \cdot 10$$
$$= 175 \text{ cm}^3$$

15. 225 in.³   **17.** 7200 ft³

19. 1728 in.³

$1 \times 1 \times 1 = 1 \text{ ft}^3$ $12 \times 12 \times 12 = 1728 \text{ in.}^3$

21. 20 cm

23. You can write the volume in cubic inches and use prime factorization to find the dimensions.

25. reflection   **27.** rotation

Section 7.2

Volumes of Cylinders
(pages 316 and 317)

1. Both formulas use the cylinder height and area of the base; In the formula for volume, the area of the base is multiplied by the height, but in the formula for surface area, the area of the base is doubled and added to the lateral surface area.

3. $50\pi \approx 157.0 \text{ m}^3$ **5.** $\pi \approx 3.1 \text{ mm}^3$ **7.** $112\pi \approx 351.7 \text{ yd}^3$

9. The area of the base should have a factor of π.

$$V = Bh$$
$$= \pi(3.5)^2(4)$$
$$= 49\pi \approx 153.9 \text{ yd}^3$$

11. The volume is 4 times greater.

13. Yes, the ratio of the volumes is a constant. No, depending on the values of r and h, the ratio of the surface areas may *not* be a constant.

15. One cup of water is equal to 8 fluid ounces. Use unit analysis when converting units of measure.

17. $x \geq 3$;

19. $y \leq -6\frac{1}{3}$;

Volumes of Pyramids
(pages 322 and 323)

1. The volume of a pyramid is $\frac{1}{3}$ times the area of the base times the height. The volume of a prism is the area of the base times the height.

3. 3 times

5. 20 mm^3

7. 80 in.^{3}

9. 252 mm^3

11. 700 mm^3

13. 30 in.^{2}

15. 7.5 ft

17. 12,000 in.^{3}; The volume of one paperweight is 12 cubic inches. So, 12 cubic inches of glass is needed to make one paperweight. So, it takes $12 \times 1000 = 12,000$ cubic inches to make 1000 paperweights.

19. *Sample answer:* 5 ft by 4 ft

21. 28

23. 60

25. B

Volumes of Cones
(pages 328 and 329)

1. The height of a cone is the distance from the vertex to the center of the base.

3. Divide by 3.

5. $9\pi \approx 28.3$ m^3

7. $\frac{2\pi}{3} \approx 2.1$ ft^3

9. $27\pi \approx 84.8$ yd^3

11. $\frac{125\pi}{6} \approx 65.4$ in.^{3}

13. The diameter was used instead of the radius.

$$V = \frac{1}{3}(\pi)(3)^2(8)$$

$$= 24\pi \, \text{m}^3$$

15. 1.5 ft

17. $\frac{40}{3\pi} \approx 4.2$ in.

19. 24.1 min

21. $3y$

23. 315 m^3

25. $152\pi \approx 477.28$ ft^3

Section 7.5 — Volumes of Composite Solids
(pages 336 and 337)

1. A composite solid is a solid that is made up of more than one solid.

3. In Example 2, you had to subtract the volume of the cylinder-shaped hole from the volume of the entire cylinder. In Example 1, you had to find the volumes of the square prism and the square pyramid and add them together.

5. $125 + 16\pi \approx 175.2$ in.^{3}

7. 220 cm^3

9. 173.3 ft^3

11. $216 - 24\pi \approx 140.6$ m^3

13. **a.** *Sample answer:* 80%

    b. *Sample answer:* $100\pi \approx 314$ in.^{3}

15. 13.875 in.^{3}; The volume of the hexagonal prism is $10.5(0.75)$ and the volume of the hexagonal pyramid is $\frac{1}{3}(6)(3)$.

17. $\dfrac{25}{9}$

19. B

Section 7.6 — Surface Areas and Volumes of Similar Solids
(pages 343–345)

1. Similar solids are solids of the same type that have proportional corresponding linear measures.

3. **a.** $\dfrac{4}{9}$ **b.** $\dfrac{8}{27}$

5. no

7. no

9. $b = 18$ m; $c = 19.5$ m; $h = 9$ m

11. 1012.5 in.^{2}

13. $13{,}564.8$ ft^3

15. 673.75 cm^2

17. **a.** yes; Because all circles are similar, the slant height and the circumference of the base of the cones are proportional.

    b. no; because the ratio of the volumes of similar solids is equal to the cube of the ratio of their corresponding linear measures

19. Choose two variables, one to represent the surface area of the smallest doll and one to represent the volume of the smallest doll. Use these variables to find the surface areas and volumes of the other dolls.

21. 1

23. C

Finding Square Roots
(pages 360 and 361)

1. no; There is no integer whose square is 26.

3. $\sqrt{256}$ represents the positive square root because there is not a − or a ± in front.

5. $s = 1.3$ km

7. 3 and −3

9. 2 and −2

11. 25

13. $\dfrac{1}{31}$ and $-\dfrac{1}{31}$

15. 2.2 and −2.2

17. The positive and negative square roots should have been given.
$$\pm\sqrt{\frac{1}{4}} = \frac{1}{2} \text{ and } -\frac{1}{2}$$

19. 9

21. 25

23. 40

25. because a negative radius does not make sense

27. =

29. 9 ft

31. 8 m/sec

33. 2.5 ft

35. 25

37. 144

39. B

The Pythagorean Theorem
(pages 366 and 367)

1. The hypotenuse is the longest side and the legs are the other two sides.

3. 24 cm

5. 9 in.

7. 12 ft

9. The length of the hypotenuse was substituted for the wrong variable.
$$\begin{aligned}
a^2 + b^2 &= c^2 \\
7^2 + b^2 &= 25^2 \\
49 + b^2 &= 625 \\
b^2 &= 576 \\
b &= 24
\end{aligned}$$

11. 16 cm

13. 10 ft

15. 8.4 cm

17. a. *Sample answer:* **b.** 45 ft

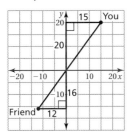

19. 6 and −6

21. 13

23. C

Section 8.3 — Approximating Square Roots
(pages 375–377)

1. A rational number can be written as the ratio of two integers. An irrational number cannot be written as the ratio of two integers.

3. all rational and irrational numbers; *Sample answer:* $-2, \dfrac{1}{8}, \sqrt{7}$

5. yes　　　　　　　　　　　　　7. no

9. whole, integer, rational　　　　11. integer, rational

13. natural, whole, integer, rational

15. 144 is a perfect square. So, $\sqrt{144}$ is rational.

17. **a.** If the last digit is 0, it is a whole number. Otherwise, it is a natural number.

　　b. irrational number　　**c.** irrational number

19. 26　　　　　　　　21. -10　　　　　　　　23. -13

25. 10; 10 is to the right of $\sqrt{20}$.　　　　27. $\sqrt{133}$; $\sqrt{133}$ is to the right of $10\dfrac{3}{4}$.

29. -0.25; -0.25 is to the right of $-\sqrt{0.25}$.

31. 8 ft　　　　　　　33. *Sample answer:* $a = 82, b = 97$

35. 1.1　　　　　　　37. 30.1 m/sec

39. Falling objects do not fall at a linear rate. Their speed increases with each second they are falling.

41. $-3x + 3y$

43. $40k - 9$

Section 8.4 — Simplifying Square Roots
(pages 382 and 383)

1. *Sample answer:* The square root is like a variable. So, you add or subtract the number in front to simplify.

3. about 1.62; yes　　　5. about 1.11; no　　　7. $\dfrac{\sqrt{7} + 1}{3}$

9. $6\sqrt{3}$　　　　　　　11. $2\sqrt{5}$　　　　　　13. $-7.7\sqrt{15}$

15. You do not add the radicands. $4\sqrt{5} + 3\sqrt{5} = 7\sqrt{5}$

17. $10\sqrt{2}$　　　19. $4\sqrt{3}$　　　21. $\dfrac{\sqrt{23}}{8}$　　　23. $\dfrac{\sqrt{17}}{7}$

25. $10\sqrt{2}$ in.　　　27. $6\sqrt{6}$　　　29. 210 ft^3

31. **a.** $88\sqrt{2}$ ft　　**b.** 680 ft^2

33. Remember to take the square root of each side when solving for r.

35. 24 in.

37. C

Section 8.5

Using the Pythagorean Theorem
(pages 388 and 389)

1. *Sample answer:* You can plot a point at the origin and then draw lengths that represent the legs. Then, you can use the Pythagorean Theorem to find the hypotenuse of the triangle.

3. 27.7 m   **5.** 11.3 yd   **7.** 7.2 units   **9.** 27.5 ft   **11.** 15.1 m

13. yes   **15.** no   **17.** yes   **19.** 12.8 ft

21. a. *Sample answer:* 5 in., 7 in., 3 in.

    b. *Sample answer:* $BC \approx 8.6$ in.; $AB \approx 9.1$ in.

    c. Check students' work.

23. mean: 13; median: 12.5; mode: 12   **25.** mean: 58; median: 59; mode: 59

Section 9.1

Scatter Plots and Lines of Best Fit
(pages 405–407)

1. They must be ordered pairs so there are equal amounts of *x*- and *y*-values.

3. a–b. 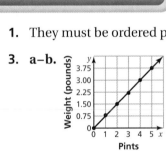   **c.** *Sample answer:* $y = 0.75x$

    d. *Sample answer:* 7.5 lb

    e. *Sample answer:* $16.88

5. a. 3.5 h   **b.** $85

    c. There is a positive relationship between hours worked and earnings.

7. positive relationship   **9.** negative relationship

11. a–b. 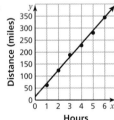   **c.** *Sample answer:* $y = 55x + 15$

    d. *Sample answer:* 400 mi

13. a. positive relationship

    b. The more time spent studying, the better the test score.

15. The slope of the line of best fit should be close to 1.

17. $-32, 64, -128$ **19.** B

Section 9.2 — Choosing a Data Display
(pages 413–415)

1. yes; Different displays may show different aspects of the data.

3. *Sample answer:*

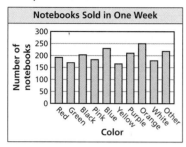

A bar graph shows the data in different color categories.

5. *Sample answer:* Line graph; shows changes over time.

7. *Sample answer:* Line graph; shows changes changes over time.

9. **a.** yes; The circle graph shows the data as parts of the whole.

   b. no; The bar graph shows the number of students, not the portion of students.

11. The pictures of the bikes are the largest on Monday and the smallest on Wednesday, which makes it seem like the distance is the same each day.

13. The intervals are not the same size.

15. *Sample answer:* bar graph; Each bar can represent a different vegetable.

17. *Sample answer:* line plot

19. Does one display better show the differences in digits?

21. $8x = 24$

Section 9.3 — Probability
(pages 423–425)

1. Perform an experiment several times. Count how often the event occurs and divide by the number of trials.

3. Experimental probability is based on actual results of an experiment, so it will not always equal the theoretical probability.

5. 1950

7. $\frac{1}{6}$, or about 16.7%

9. $\frac{1}{3}$, or about 33.3%

11. 0, or 0%

13. 30

15. 24

17. 0

19. $\frac{1}{6}$, or about 16.7%

21. $\frac{7}{40}$, or 17.5%

23. $\frac{9}{40}$, or 22.5%

25. The total number of trials, 40, should be in the denominator, not 28.

$$P(2) = \frac{12}{40} = \frac{3}{10}$$

27. 35

29. theoretical: $\frac{1}{5}$, or 20%; experimental: $\frac{39}{200}$, or 19.5%;

The experimental probability is close to the theoretical probability.

31. 2000

33. **a.** $\frac{5}{8}$, or 62.5%

b. 15

35. Rewrite the table listing the cards of each rank in a separate row.

37. 26 m

39. about 46.84 in.

Independent and Dependent Events
(pages 430 and 431)

1. Draw a tree diagram or multiply $P(A)$, $P(B)$, and $P(C)$.

3. independent; The marble from the first draw is replaced so it does not affect the outcome of the second draw.

5. dependent; There is one less marble to choose from on the second draw and two less marbles to choose from on the third draw.

7. independent; The outcome of one roll does not affect the outcome of the other rolls.

9. $\frac{5}{162}$, or about 3.1%

11. $\frac{4}{81}$, or about 4.9%

13. $\frac{2}{15}$, or about 13.3%

15. $\frac{1}{45}$, or about 2.2%

17. $\frac{4}{15}$, or about 26.7%

19. The two events are dependent, so the probability of the second event is $\frac{9}{14}$.

$P(\text{black and black}) = P(\text{black}) \cdot P(\text{black after black})$

$$= \frac{10}{15} \cdot \frac{9}{14}$$

$$= \frac{2}{3} \cdot \frac{9}{14} = \frac{3}{7}$$

21. The letters spell the city "Norfolk."

23. $-1.5\sqrt{11}$

25. D

Section 10.1 — Properties of Exponents
(pages 446 and 447)

1. power: 5^0, base: 5, exponent: 0; power: 2^{-8}, base: 2, exponent: -8

3. $\left(-\dfrac{1}{4}\right)^0 < 5^4$

5. 28,500 years old

7. 64

9. -8

11. 7.84

13. $\dfrac{1}{49}$

15. 1

17. $-\dfrac{1}{1000}$

19. The exponent should not be used as a factor.
$$5^{-2} = \frac{1}{5^2} = \frac{1}{25}$$

21. yes; no; The base is 7, not -7, so the middle step should be $-\dfrac{1}{(7)(7)(7)}$.

23. Use unit analysis when converting units of measures.

25. Multiply the denominator of $\dfrac{1}{729}$ by 3 to get $\dfrac{1}{2187}$.

27. yes

29. yes

Section 10.2 — Product of Powers Property
(pages 452 and 453)

1. when multiplying powers with the same base

3. 3^4

5. $(-4)^{12}$

7. h^7

9. $\left(-\dfrac{5}{7}\right)^{17}$

11. 5^{12}

13. 3.8^{12}

15. The bases should not be multiplied. $5^2 \cdot 5^9 = 5^{2+9} = 5^{11}$

17. $216g^3$

19. $\dfrac{1}{25}k^2$

21. $\dfrac{1}{r^6 t^6}$

23. no; $3^2 + 3^3 = 9 + 27 = 36$ and $3^5 = 243$

25. 496

27. 125

29. **a.** $16\pi \approx 50.24$ in.^{3}

b. $192\pi \approx 602.88$ in.^{3} Squaring each of the dimensions causes the volume to be 12 times larger.

31. Use the Commutative and Associative Properties of Multiplication to group the powers.

33. 4

35. 3

37. B

Section 10.3
Quotient of Powers Property
(pages 460 and 461)

1. *Sample answer:* To divide powers with the same base, write the power with the common base and the exponent found by subtracting the exponent in the denominator from the exponent in the numerator.

3. 6^6

5. $(-3)^3$

7. 5^6

9. $\dfrac{1}{(-17)^3}$

11. $(-6.4)^{14}$

13. $\dfrac{1}{b^{13}}$

15. You should subtract the exponents instead of dividing them. $\dfrac{6^{15}}{6^5} = 6^{15-5} = 6^{10}$

17. 2^9

19. $\dfrac{1}{\pi^{12}}$

21. $\dfrac{1}{k}$

23. $64x$

25. $125a^3b^2$

27. $\dfrac{x^7}{y^6}$

29. You are checking to see if there is a constant rate of change in the prices, not if it is a linear function.

Hint

31. 10^{13} galaxies

33. -9

35. 61

37. B

Section 10.4
Scientific Notation
(pages 467–469)

1. right; left

3. no; The factor is less than 1.

5. yes; The factor is greater than or equal to 1 and less than 10. The power of 10 has an integer exponent.

7. yes; The factor is greater than or equal to 1 and less than 10. The power of 10 has an integer exponent.

9. 7500

11. 0.000000389

13. 430,000

15. 0.000000000809

17. 96.54

19. 1.2×10^4

21. 2.7×10^{-1}

23. 2×10^{-3}

25. 1.75×10^6

27. 8.002×10^5

29. 0.000000275

31. The decimal point moved 7 places to the right, so the exponent should be negative.
$0.000000489 = 4.89 \times 10^{-7}$

33. 1.49×10^4, 1.09×10^4, 2.11×10^{-3}

35. 3.611×10^{-7}, 2.78×10^{-7}, 3.49×10^{-8}

37. 8×10^{10}

39. 1.5×10^0

41. 8.4×10^3

43. 5.612×10^{14} cm²

45. 3.78×10^4 cm²; 3.78 m²

47. 1.5×10^1 m; 1.5×10^3 cm

49. 3.1×10^{-2}, 0.03, $\dfrac{6}{205}$

51. 8922.1, 89×10^2, $\dfrac{2650}{3}$, 892%

Hmmm.

53. Begin by summarizing the information and writing the numbers in scientific notation.

55. discrete

57. B

Key Vocabulary Index

Mathematical terms are best understood when you see them used and defined *in context*. This index lists where you will find key vocabulary. A full glossary is available in your Record and Practice Journal and at *BigIdeasMath.com*.

Key Vocabulary Index

Student Index

This student-friendly index will help you find vocabulary, key ideas, and concepts. It is easily accessible and designed to be a reference for you whether you are looking for a definition, a real-life application, or help with avoiding common errors.

Student Index

Additional Answers

Chapter 1

Section 1.2
Record and Practice Journal

2. indigo: $45°, 45°, 90°$; violet: $60°, 60°, 60°$;
   orange: $75°, 65°, 40°$; yellow: $25°, 60°, 95°$;
   blue: $75°, 75°, 30°$; green: $15°, 135°, 30°$

Section 1.5
Practice and Problem Solving

25. **a.** $a \geq 10$;

$s \geq 200$;

$t \geq 10$;

  b. yes; You satisfy the swimming requirement of the course because $10(25) = 250$ and $250 \geq 200$.

Section 1.6
Practice and Problem Solving

8. $g > -3$;

9. $m < 10$;

10. $x \geq -7$;

11. $k \geq 4.4$;

12. $w \geq -2.2$;

13. $c > -\dfrac{1}{2}$;

14. $b \geq -\dfrac{7}{6}$ or $b \geq -1\dfrac{1}{6}$;

15. $m < -7.6$;

16. $x \leq \dfrac{28}{5}$ or $x \leq 5\dfrac{3}{5}$;

34. $p < -24$;

35. $a \leq 5$;

36. $u > 4.5$;

37. $d \leq 6.8$;

38. $h < -6$;

39. $x \leq -3$;

41. **a.** $4.5x \geq 225$; $x \geq 50$; at least 50 sandwiches

   b. If the price decreases, you will need to sell more than 50 to meet your goal. If the price increases, you can sell less than 50 to meet your goal.

50. yes; Given that $a > b$ and $x > y$, you know that $a + x > b + x$ and $b + x > b + y$ by the Addition Property of Inequality. So, $a + x > b + y$.

51. no; *Sample answer:* $a = 3$, $b = 2$, $x = 8$, and $y = 1$; $a - x = -5$, $b - y = 1$; So, $a - x \not> b - y$.

52. no; *Sample answer:* $a = 2$, $b = 1$, $x = -1$, and $y = -2$; $ax = -2$, $by = -2$; So, $ax \not> by$.

53. no; *Sample answer:* $a = 4$, $b = 2$, $x = -2$, and $y = -4$; $\dfrac{a}{x} = -2$, $\dfrac{y}{b} = -2$; So $\dfrac{a}{x} \not> \dfrac{y}{b}$.

Section 1.7
Practice and Problem Solving

13. $y \leq 13$;

14. $h \leq -3$;

15. $u < -17$;

16. $n < 4.7$;

17. $z > -0.9$;

18. $20x + 100 \leq 320$; $x \leq 11$; at most 11 \$20 bills

24. $3.5x + 350 \geq 500$; $x \geq 42\dfrac{6}{7}$; at least 43 more cars

25. $r \geq 8$ units

1.5–1.7 Quiz

14. a. $s \geq 100$;

$t \geq 5$;

$u \geq 10$;

b. yes; 100 yards is equal to 300 feet and $350 \geq 300$.

15. $6x + 20 \leq 50$; $x \leq 5$; at most 5 books

16. $5b < 35$; $b < 7$; less than 7 feet

Chapter 1 Test

12. $v \geq -2.1$;

13. $t > 1$;

Chapter 2

Section 2.1

On Your Own

1.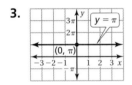

2.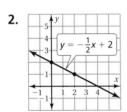

3.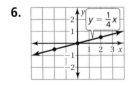

4.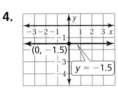

Practice and Problem Solving

6.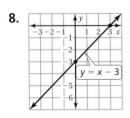

7.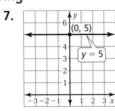

8.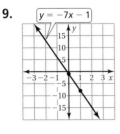

9.

10.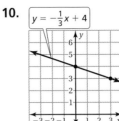

11.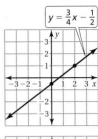

12.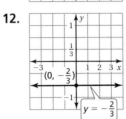

13.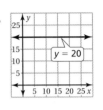

14. The equation $x = 4$ is graphed, not $y = 4$.

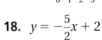

15.

16. a.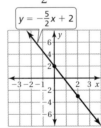

b. about \$5

c. \$5.25

18. $y = -\dfrac{5}{2}x + 2$

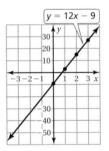

19. $y = 12x - 9$

20. $y = -2x + 3$

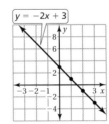

21. a. $y = 100 + 12.5x$ **b.** 6 mo

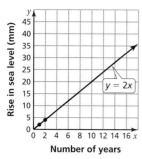

23. a. $y = 2x$

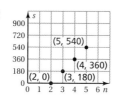

b. *Sample answer:* If you are 13 years old, the sea level has risen 26 millimeters since you were born.

24. *Sample answer:*

Yes, the points lie on a line.

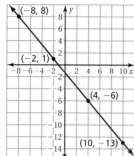

Section 2.2

Practice and Problem Solving

18. $-\dfrac{7}{6}$

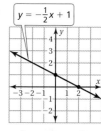

19. $\dfrac{1}{3}$

20. *Sample answer:*

a. Yes, it follows the guidelines.

b.

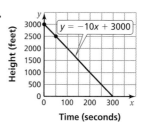

30 ft

2.5 ft

21. red and green; They both have a slope of $\dfrac{4}{3}$.

22. blue and red; They both have a slope of -3.

23. no; Opposite sides have different slopes.

24. yes; The opposite sides have equal slopes and lengths.

25. a. $\dfrac{3}{40}$

b. The cost increases by \$3 for every 40 miles you drive, or the cost increases by \$0.075 for every mile you drive.

26. The boat ramp, because it has a 16.67% grade.

Section 2.3

On Your Own

3.

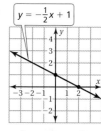

x-intercept: 4

4. $y = -\dfrac{1}{2}x + 1$

x-intercept: 2

5. The y-intercept means that the taxi has an initial fee of \$1.50. The slope means the taxi charges \$2 per mile.

Practice and Problem Solving

16. The y-intercept should be -3.
$y = 4x - 3$
The slope is 4 and the y-intercept is -3.

17. a.

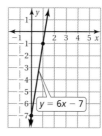

b. The x-intercept of 300 means the skydiver lands on the ground after 300 seconds. The slope of -10 means that the skydiver falls to the ground at a rate of 10 feet per second.

19.

x-intercept: $\dfrac{7}{6}$

20.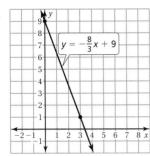

$y = -\frac{8}{3}x + 9$

x-intercept: $\frac{27}{8}$

21.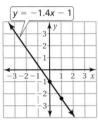

$y = -1.4x - 1$

x-intercept: $-\frac{5}{7}$

22.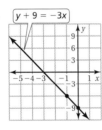

$y + 9 = -3x$

x-intercept: -3

23.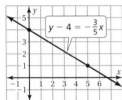

$y - 4 = -\frac{3}{5}x$

x-intercept: $\frac{20}{3}$

24. a.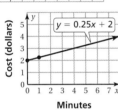

$y = 0.25x + 2$

b. The slope of 0.25 means that it costs $0.25 for each minute spent making a long distance call. The *y*-intercept of 2 means that there is an initial fee of $2.

25. $y = 0.75x + 5$

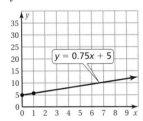

$y = 0.75x + 5$

26. $y = 5x - 40$

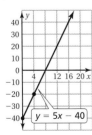

$y = 5x - 40$

27. $y = 0.15x + 35$

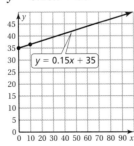

$y = 0.15x + 35$

Section 2.4

On Your Own

3.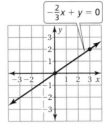

$-\frac{2}{3}x + y = 0$

4.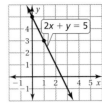

$2x + y = 5$

5.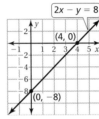

$2x - y = 8$

$(4, 0)$

$(0, -8)$

6.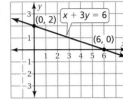

$x + 3y = 6$

$(0, 2)$

$(6, 0)$

7.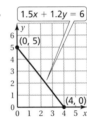

$1.5x + 1.2y = 6$

$(0, 5)$

$(4, 0)$

The *x*-intercept shows that you can buy 4 pounds of apples if you don't buy any oranges. The *y*-intercept shows that you can buy 5 pounds of oranges if you don't buy any apples.

Practice and Problem Solving

9.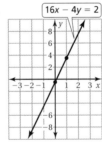

$16x - 4y = 2$

10.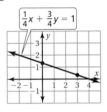

$\frac{1}{4}x + \frac{3}{4}y = 1$

11. *x*-intercept: -6
   y-intercept: 3

12. *x*-intercept: -4
   y-intercept: -5

13. *x*-intercept: none
   y-intercept: -3

14. They should have let $y = 0$, not $x = 0$.
$$-2x + 3y = 12$$
$$-2x + 3(0) = 12$$
$$-2x = 12$$
$$x = -6$$

15. a. $-25x + y = 65$

   b. $390

16.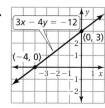

17.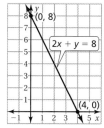

18.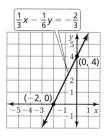

19. x-intercept: 9
y-intercept: 7

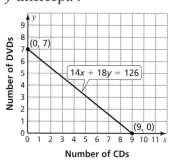

21. a. $9.45x + 7.65y = 160.65$

b.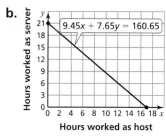

22. no; For example, $y = 5$ does not have an x-intercept, neither do any horizontal lines except $y = 0$.

23. a. $y = 40x + 70$

b. x-intercept: $-\dfrac{7}{4}$; It will not be on the graph because you cannot have a negative time.

c.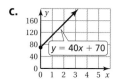

1.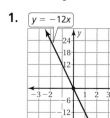

2.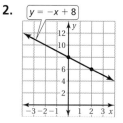

3.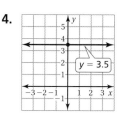

4.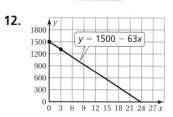

12.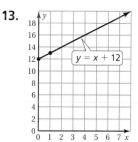

13.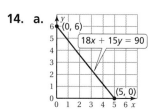

14. a.

b. The x-intercept, 5, shows that you can buy 5 gallons of blue paint if you do not buy any white paint. The y-intercept, 6, shows that you can buy 6 gallons of white paint if you do not buy any blue paint.

Section 2.5

Record and Practice Journal

1.

a. top line: slope: $\frac{1}{2}$; y-intercept: 4; $y = \frac{1}{2}x + 4$

middle line: slope: $\frac{1}{2}$; y-intercept: 1; $y = \frac{1}{2}x + 1$

bottom line: slope: $\frac{1}{2}$; y-intercept: -2;

$y = \frac{1}{2}x - 2$

The lines are parallel.

b. left line: slope: -2; y-intercept: -5;

$y = -2x - 5$

middle line: slope: -2; y-intercept: -1;

$y = -2x - 1$

right line: slope: -2; y-intercept: 3; $y = -2x + 3$

The lines are parallel.

c. line passing through $(3, 2)$: slope: $-\frac{1}{3}$;

y-intercept: 3; $y = -\frac{1}{3}x + 3$

line passing through $(3, 7)$: slope: $\frac{4}{3}$;

y-intercept: 3; $y = \frac{4}{3}x + 3$

line passing through $(6, 4)$: slope: $\frac{1}{6}$;

y-intercept: 3; $y = \frac{1}{6}x + 3$

The lines have the same y-intercept.

d. line passing through $(1, 2)$: slope: 2;

y-intercept: 0; $y = 2x$

line passing through $(1, -1)$: slope: -1;

y-intercept: 0; $y = -x$

line passing through $(3, 1)$: slope: $\frac{1}{3}$;

y-intercept: 0; $y = \frac{1}{3}x$

The lines have the same y-intercept.

2. a. $y = 4$ $y = -2x - 6$

$y = -2$

$y = -2x + 8$

b. $y = 5$ $y = x + 1$

$y = -2$

$y = x + 5$

Practice and Problem Solving

17. a–b.

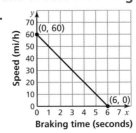

$(0, 60)$ represents the speed of the automobile before braking. $(6, 0)$ represents the amount of time it takes to stop. The line represents the speed y of the automobile after x seconds of braking.

c. $y = -10x + 60$

Section 2.7

Practice and Problem Solving

17. a.

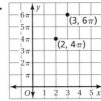

b. $y = 2\pi x$; The equation is the formula for the circumference of a circle given the radius.

19. a. $y = -2000x + 21,000$

b.

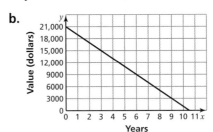

c. $\$21,000$; the original price of the car

Section 2.8

On Your Own

1. a.

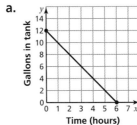

b. The x-intercept is 6. So, you can drive 6 hours before the tank is empty. The y-intercept is 12. So, there are 12 gallons in the tank before you start driving.

c. 3.5 or $3\frac{1}{2}$ h

Practice and Problem Solving

4. *Sample answer:* A gasoline tank initially has 16 gallons of gas. After 10 hours, the tank is empty.

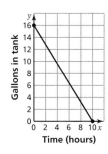

5. *Sample answer:* On a visit to Mexico, you spend 45 pesos every week. After 4 weeks, you have no pesos left.

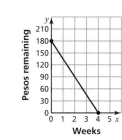

8. a. The *x*-intercept is 6. So, it takes 6 hours for your family to drive from Cincinnati to St. Louis. The *y*-intercept is 360. So, it is 360 miles from Cincinnati to St. Louis.

  b. -60; Your distance from St. Louis decreases at a rate of 60 miles per hour.

  c. $y = -60x + 360$; Both intercepts would be less and the slope would be the same.

Fair Game Review

11. $x \le -1.3$;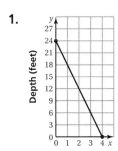

12. $k < -\dfrac{1}{2}$;

13. $m \le -7.2$;

14. $y > -8$;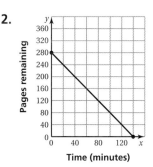

Record and Practice Journal Practice

1.

2.

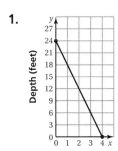
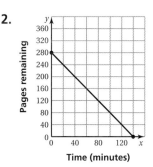

2.5–2.8 Quiz

8. a.

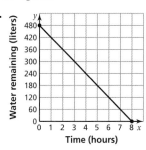

  b. The *x*-intercept is the number of hours it takes to drain the pond. The *y*-intercept represents the amount of water in the pond initially.

Chapter 2 Test

4. $\boxed{y = 2x + 4}$

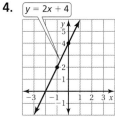

5. $\boxed{y = -\dfrac{1}{2}x - 5}$

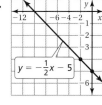

6. $\boxed{-3x + 6y = 12}$

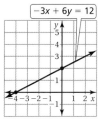

8. 3

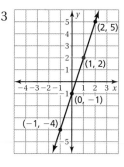

Chapter 3

Record and Practice Journal Fair Game Review

7. Input   Output

As the input increases by 1, the output increases by 3.

8. Input   Output

As the input increases by 2, the output decreases by 2.5.

9. Input   Output

As the input increases by 4, the output increases by 1.

10. Input   Output

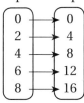

Section 3.1

Record and Practice Journal

4. b–c. women:

x (Domain)	$5\frac{1}{2}$	6	$6\frac{1}{2}$	7	$7\frac{1}{2}$	8	$8\frac{1}{2}$
y (Range)	8.8	9	9.2	9.3	9.5	9.7	9.8

x (Domain)	9	$9\frac{1}{2}$	10	$10\frac{1}{2}$	11	$11\frac{1}{2}$	12
y (Range)	10	10.2	10.3	10.5	10.7	10.8	11

4. b–c. men:

x (Domain)	$5\frac{1}{2}$	6	$6\frac{1}{2}$	7	$7\frac{1}{2}$	8	$8\frac{1}{2}$
y (Range)	9.1	9.3	9.5	9.6	9.8	10	10.1

x (Domain)	9	$9\frac{1}{2}$	10	$10\frac{1}{2}$	11	$11\frac{1}{2}$	12
y (Range)	10.3	10.5	10.6	10.8	11	11.1	11.3

On Your Own

3.

x	−1	0	1	2
y	−5	−3	−1	1

domain: −1, 0, 1, 2
range: −5, −3, −1, 1

4.

x	0	1	2	3
y	−3	−4	−5	−6

domain: 0, 1, 2, 3
range: −3, −4, −5, −6

Practice and Problem Solving

14. a. The domain is all real numbers because you can find the absolute value of any number. The range is all real numbers greater than or equal to 0 because the least an absolute value can be is 0.

b. The domain is all real numbers because you can find the absolute value of any number. The range is all real numbers less than or equal to 0 because the negative sign will make every y-value be 0 or negative.

c. The domain is all real numbers because you can find the absolute value of any number. The range is all real numbers greater than or equal to −6 because the least an absolute value can be is 0 and you subtract 6 from that.

d. The domain is all real numbers because you can find the absolute value of any number. The range is all real numbers less than or equal to 4 because the negative sign will make the greatest absolute value be 0 and you add 4 to that.

Fair Game Review

15.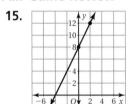

16.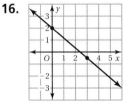

17.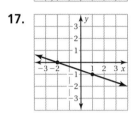

18.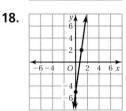

Record and Practice Journal Practice

5. b.

x	1	2	4	8	10
y	18,000	36,000	72,000	144,000	180,000

Section 3.2

On Your Own

2.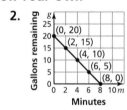

continuous

Practice and Problem Solving

6.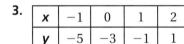

continuous

7.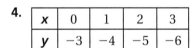

continuous

8.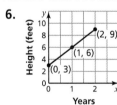

discrete

12.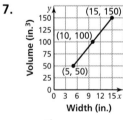

continuous

13.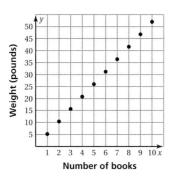

continuous

14. c.

3.1–3.2 Quiz

7.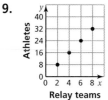

continuous

8.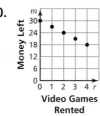

continuous

9.

discrete

10.

discrete

11. a. $y = 0.6x$; The independent variable is the body weight x and the dependent variable is the water weight y.

b.

x	100	120	140	160
y	60	72	84	96

Section 3.3

Practice and Problem Solving

14. a.

Temperature (°F), t	94	95	96	97	98
Heat Index (°F), H	122	126	130	134	138

b. $H = 4t - 254$

c. 146°F

Chapter 3 Test

3.

discrete

4.

continuous

Chapter 4

Section 4.2

Practice and Problem Solving

31. less than; *Sample answer:* Let x represent the number. A 10% increase is equal to $x + 0.1x$, or $1.1x$. A 10% decrease of this new number is equal to $1.1x - 0.1(1.1x)$, or $0.99x$. Because $0.99x < x$, the result is less than the original number.

Chapter 5

Section 5.1

Record and Practice Journal

1. a. linear; $y = 90 - x$; greater than 0 and less than 90.

b. linear; $y = 180 - x$; greater than 0 and less than 180.

3. b. $\angle A$ and $\angle ABE$; $\angle A$ and $\angle C$; $\angle A$ and $\angle BED$; $\angle A$ and $\angle BEF$; $\angle A$ and $\angle F$; $\angle ABE$ and $\angle C$; $\angle ABE$ and $\angle BED$; $\angle ABE$ and $\angle BEF$; $\angle ABE$ and $\angle F$; $\angle C$ and $\angle BED$; $\angle C$ and $\angle BEF$; $\angle C$ and $\angle F$; $\angle BED$ and $\angle BEF$; $\angle BED$ and $\angle F$; $\angle BEF$ and $\angle F$; $\angle A$ and $\angle CDE$; $\angle A$ and $\angle CBE$; $\angle ABE$ and $\angle CBE$; $\angle ABE$ and $\angle CDE$; $\angle BEF$ and $\angle CBE$; $\angle BEF$ and $\angle CDE$; $\angle F$ and $\angle CBE$; $\angle F$ and $\angle CDE$; $\angle CBE$ and $\angle C$; $\angle CBE$ and $\angle CDE$; $\angle CBE$ and $\angle BED$; $\angle C$ and $\angle CDE$; $\angle CDE$ and $\angle BED$

Section 5.2

Practice and Problem Solving

19. If two angle measures of a triangle were each greater than or equal to 90°, the sum of those two angle measures would be greater than or equal to 180°. The sum of the three angle measures would be greater than 180°, which is not possible.

Section 5.3

Practice and Problem Solving

26. *Sample answer:* rhombus

32. a. *Sample answer:*

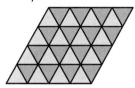

b. *Sample answer:* square, hexagon

c. *Sample answer:*

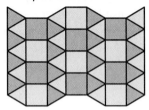

Section 5.4

Practice and Problem Solving

14. *Sample answer:* 10 ft

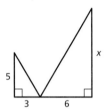

Section 5.5

Practice and Problem Solving

26. *Sample answers:*
Let the vertices of the red square be $A(0, 3)$, $B(3, 3)$, $C(3, 0)$, and $D(0, 0)$. The vertices of the blue square are:

Translation: $A'(0, 0)$, $B'(3, 0)$, $C'(3, -3)$, $D'(0, -3)$; The figure is translated 3 units down.

Reflection: $A'(0, -3)$, $B'(3, -3)$, $C'(3, 0)$, $D'(0, 0)$; The figure is reflected in the x-axis.

Rotation: $A'(3, 0)$, $B'(3, -3)$, $C'(0, -3)$, $D'(0, 0)$; The figure is rotated 90° clockwise about the origin.

Section 5.6

Practice and Problem Solving

18. The starting points are staggered so that each runner can run the same distance and use the same finish line. This is necessary because the circumference is different for each lane. The diagram shows this because the diameter is greater in the outer lanes.

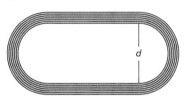

5.4–5.7 Quiz

11. Yes, if you have

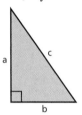

the perimeter is $a + b + c$, and the perimeter of

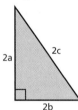

is $2a + 2b + 2c = 2(a + b + c)$.

Chapter 6

Section 6.1

Record and Practice Journal

1. b.

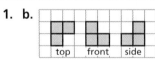

c.

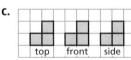

d.

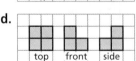

e.

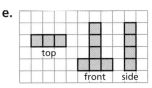

f.

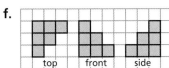

g.

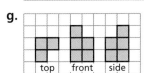

2. a.

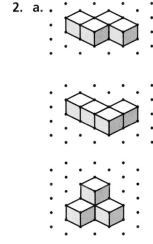

On Your Own

3. front:

  side:

  top:

4. front:

  side:

  top:

5. front: side: top: ○

Vocabulary and Concept Check

3. *Sample answer:* Prisms: A cereal box is a rectangular prism. A pup tent with parallel triangular bases at the front and back is a triangular prism.

Pyramids: The Egyptian pyramids are rectangular pyramids. A house roof forms a pyramid if it has lateral faces that are triangles that meet at a common vertex.
Cylinders: Some examples of cylinders are a soup can, a tuna fish can, and a new, unsharpened, round pencil.
Cones: Some examples of cones are a traffic cone, an ice cream sugar cone, a party hat, and the sharpened end of a pencil.

4. base: hexagon
solid: hexagonal pyramid

5. base: circle
solid: cylinder

6. base: pentagon
solid: pentagonal prism

Practice and Problem Solving

9. front: side:

  top: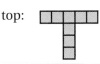

surface area: 38 units^2
volume: 9 units^3

10. 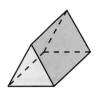 **11.**

12. 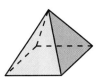 **13.**

14.   **15.**

16. front:

side:

top:

17. front:

side:

top:

18. front:

side:

top:

19. front:

side:

top:

20. front:

side:

top:

21. front:

side:

top:

22.

23. The Washington Monument is an *obelisk*. It consists of a pyramid sitting on top of a solid that tapers as it rises.

24.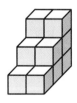

25.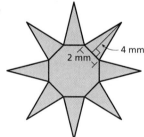

28. *Sample answer:*

a.

Triangular prism
6 vertices
9 edges

Square pyramid
5 vertices
8 edges

b. More than one solid can have the same number of faces, so knowing the number of edges and vertices can help you to draw the intended solid.

Section 6.3

Practice and Problem Solving

15. a. $16\pi \approx 50.2$ in.^{2}

b. The lateral surface area triples.

Record and Practice Journal Practice

3. The dimensions of the shaded cylinder are 2 times greater than the dimensions of the unshaded cylinder. The surface area is 4 times greater.

4. The dimensions of the shaded cylinder are 3 times greater than the dimensions of the unshaded cylinder. The surface area is 9 times greater.

Section 6.4

Record and Practice Journal

1. a. $S = 85,560$ m^2　　**b.** $S = 1404$ m^2

c. $S = 1960$ m^2　　**d.** $S = 1276$ m^2

2. b.

2 mm　4 mm

Section 6.5

Record and Practice Journal

2. Surface Area:

$$3\pi\left(\frac{5}{2}\right) + \left(\frac{5}{2}\right)^2 \pi \text{ in.}^2$$

$$3\pi\left(\frac{4}{2}\right) + \left(\frac{4}{2}\right)^2 \pi \text{ in.}^2$$

$$3\pi\left(\frac{3}{2}\right) + \left(\frac{3}{2}\right)^2 \pi \text{ in.}^2$$

$$3\pi\left(\frac{2}{2}\right) + \left(\frac{2}{2}\right)^2 \pi \text{ in.}^2$$

$$3\pi\left(\frac{1}{2}\right) + \left(\frac{1}{2}\right)^2 \pi \text{ in.}^2$$

Section 6.6

Record and Practice Journal

2.

Base of n Blocks	1	2	3	4	5
Surface Area	6	14	24	36	50

For each 1 unit increase of n, the increase in surface area is two square units greater than the last increase.

For 10 blocks, $S = 150$.

Chapter 7

Section 7.1

Record and Practice Journal

1. Because the three crowns were the same weight, Archimedes could compare the sizes of the crowns to determine if the jeweler used silver in the king's crown. Because the king's crown is larger than the 100% gold crown, it must have some silver in it.

Section 7.2

Practice and Problem Solving

16. a. The volume doubles. The surface area increases by an amount equal to the lateral surface area of the original cylinder.

b. The volume triples. The surface area increases by an amount equal to twice the lateral surface area of the original cylinder.

c. The volume is 8 times greater. The surface area is 4 times greater.

d. The volume is 27 times greater. The surface area is 9 times greater.

Fair Game Review

19. $y \leq -6\frac{1}{3}$;

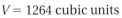

Section 7.6

Practice and Problem Solving

18. a. 9483 pounds; The ratio of the height of the original statue to the height of the small statue is 8.4 : 1. So, the ratio of the weights, or volumes is $\left(\frac{8.4}{1}\right)^3$.

b. 221,184 lb

Chapter 7 Test

11. *Sample answer:*

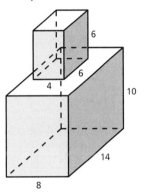

$V = 1264$ cubic units
$S = 784$ square units

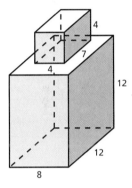

$V = 1264$ cubic units
$S = 760$ square units

Chapter 8

Section 8.5

Practice and Problem Solving

22. yes; *Sample answer:* Plot the points and connect to form a triangle. Then draw three right triangles outside the original triangle so that the hypotenuses are the side lengths of the original triangle. Then use the Pythagorean Theorem to find that the side lengths are $\sqrt{18}$, $\sqrt{50}$, and $\sqrt{68}$.

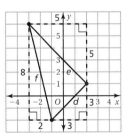

Chapter 9

Record and Practice Journal Fair Game Review

6.

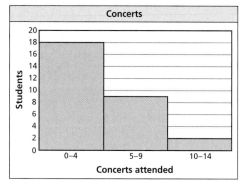

7.

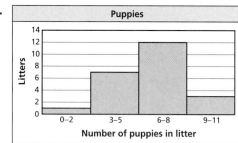

8.

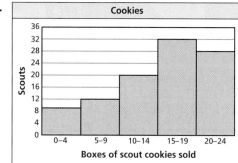

9.

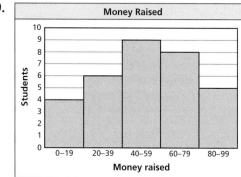

10.

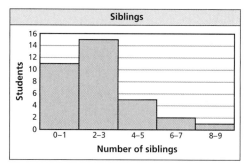

Section 9.1

On Your Own

2.

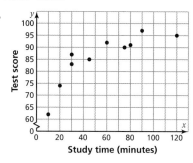

positive relationship

Practice and Problem Solving

16. **a.** (24.00, 40,000)

b. Because the outlier is below the other values, it will increase the steepness of the line of best fit.

c.

d. *Sample answer:* 41,000 people

Record and Practice Journal Practice

5. **b.**

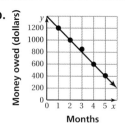

Section 9.2

Record and Practice Journal

1. c. *Sample answer:*

Raccoon Road Kill Weights

Stem	Leaf
9	4 5
10	
11	0
12	4 9
13	4 6 9
14	0 5 8 8
15	2 7
16	8
17	0 2 3 5
18	5 5 6 7
19	0 1 4
20	4
21	3 5 5 5
22	
23	
24	
25	4

Key: 9 | 4 = 9.4 pounds

The stem-and-leaf plot shows how the raccoon weights are distributed.

Record and Practice Journal Practice

4. Because the rain icon is larger than the sun icon, it makes it look as if there were equal amounts of sunny and rainy days when there was not.

9.1–9.2 Quiz

8. a–b.

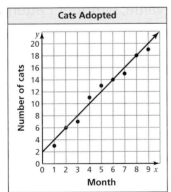

c. *Sample answer:* $y = 2x + 2$

d. *Sample answer:* 22 cats

Section 9.4

Practice and Problem Solving

19. The two events are dependent, so the probability of the second event is $\frac{9}{14}$.

P(black and black)

$= P$(black) $\cdot$ P(black after black)

$= \frac{10}{15} \cdot \frac{9}{14}$

$= \frac{2}{3} \cdot \frac{9}{14} = \frac{3}{7}$

20. The probability is greater if you replace the first straw;

With replacement,

P(purple and purple) $= \frac{12}{24} \cdot \frac{12}{24} = \frac{1}{4}$, or 25%.

Without replacement,

P(purple and purple) $= \frac{12}{24} \cdot \frac{11}{23} = \frac{11}{46}$,

or about 23.9%.

9.3–9.4 Quiz

15. $\frac{4}{11}$, or about 36.4%

16. 40

17. $\frac{3}{10}$, or 30%

Chapter 9 Test

9. a–b.

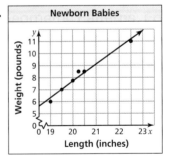

c. *Sample answer:* $y = 1.5x - 22.25$

d. *Sample answer:* 10.38 pounds